MW00396471

FISHER COLLEGE LIBRARY

5 20 5053 6 5

Facets® Movie Lovers Video Guide

Compiled and edited by
Catherine Foley and Milos Stehlik

Facets® Multi-Media/Academy Chicago Publishers

Cover and book design: Greiner Design

Typesetting and graphic production: MKS Composing

Copyright ©1998 Facets® Multi-Media, Inc.

No part of this book may be reproduced or transmitted in any form, electronic or mechanical, including photocopying, recording or any information storage and retrieval system now known or to be invented without written permission of Facets® Multi-Media, Inc. For information please contact Facets® Multi-Media, Inc., 1517 West Fullerton Avenue, Chicago, Illinois 60614.

ISBN #0-89733-451-5

Library of Congress Cataloging-in-Publication Data

Foley, Catherine, 1952–
    Facets movie lovers video guide / compiled and edited by Catherine Foley and Milos Stehlik.
        p.   cm.
    ISBN 0-89733-451-5 (pbk.)
    1. Motion pictures--Catalogs. 2. Video recordings--Catalogs.
I. Stehlik, Milos. II. Facets Multimedia (Chicago, Ill.)
III. Title.
PN1998.F63   1998
016.79143'75--dc21   98-19465
                                                                      CIP

Contents

Acknowledgements

The Facets® Movie Lovers Video Guide was compiled and edited by Catherine Foley and Milos Stehlik with the able assistance of Tracy Landecker, Shawn Brennan and Pamela Masco. Our gratitude to John Greiner for design, to Marty Bash for production, and to Anita and Jordan Miller and the staff of Chicago Academy Publishers for their continued support, ideas, resourcefulness and commitment.

viii

Upfront

Years later, we all try to remember how it was that our love affair with the movies began. A few have specific memories. For some that first experience was seeing de Sica's *Bicycle Thief,* for others *Dracula* or *The Beast from 20,000 Fathoms* or *Breathless* or *Red River.* For still others that first important experience with the movies is a distant and clouded memory.

It's kind of like romantic love. Not all first dates are memorable, and few first dates turn into the love stories of a lifetime. But once the affair—or call it eternal love—with the movies begins, it's hard to shake. Not many experiences surpass it. For true movie lovers, there is nothing better than a good film.

We've compiled and written this book for all those who dare carry on their passionate affair with the movies. Here you will find some 3,000 of the world's great movies, virtually all of them available for rental or purchase on video, laser disc or in DVD formats. We conceived of the **Facets® Movie Lovers Video Guide** as the ultimate book of lists of great films.

Some of the lists are the cumulative lists of winners at prestigious festivals like the Cannes International Film Festival, the Berlin International Film Festival or Sundance, or the recommended lists of cinematic treasures from the National Film Registry of the Library of Congress or the Vatican. Other lists in the **Facets® Movie Lovers Video Guide** are combinations of some of the most critically acclaimed, popular and sometimes rare films on video in special categories like foreign films, American classics, American independents or silents, or selections from film genres like science fiction or horror.

And then there are lists with which we just had a lot of fun—first with thinking up categories and then putting in the films. Lists like those of the worst-weather films or films on the themes of the three colors blue, white and red, or the best spaghetti westerns, and our general movie-related ruminations on some of the movies' all-time favorite themes of love, sex, money and death.

We put this book together by drawing on the enormous resources of the Facets® Video collection and by relying on the collective memories and free association of our staff of dedicated film lovers. We tried to emphasize those films which we consider to have the coolest title sequences, masterpieces of Technicolor, VistaVision and Cinemascope, great original screenplays, and most of all, the filmmaker's originality of vision. We know that you are bound to disagree with some of our choices, but that's what that passion of the movies is all about—discovery and disagreement. Most of all, we hope that you will be inspired to consider your own favorites and make up your own lists.

Film fanatics that we are, we hope that we've found each other and can share that passion for sitting in the dark and letting ourselves be taken over by flickering images of shadows and light. We hope that you will share some of your moments with us, even when we disagree. Write or visit us at www.facets.org

Where to Buy or Rent Tapes

You should be able to find most of the videos in this book in any good video store which ventures outside the hit-driven mentality and stocks foreign and independent features and documentaries.

If your video store is not one of these progressive outlets, you can purchase any video or laser disc in this book which is currently in print directly from Facets® Video. To order within the United States, call toll-free at 1-800-331-6197, e-mail to sales@facets.org or fax to 773-929-5437. Otherwise, call 773-281-9075 or write Facets® Video, 1517 West Fullerton Avenue, Chicago, IL 60614. The "S" and "LD" numbers at the end of each video description in this book refer to Facets® Video's sales order numbers.

Facets® Video also offers a rent-by-mail service within the continental United States, which includes rental of many now-out-of-print tapes. For rent-by-mail membership information call 1-800-5-FACETS (1-800-532-2387) or write Facets® Video Rentals, 1517 West Fullerton Avenue, Chicago, IL 60614.

Prices

The prices listed in this book were current at the time of publication. However, video and laser disc prices are volatile and do change at the drop of a hat. Fortunately, this most often means that they are substantially reduced.

Out of Print Tapes and Laser Discs

Much like the volatile price changes of home video and laser discs, tapes and discs do go in and out of print with increasing frequency. Licensing rights expire, video companies shift direction or go out of business. Many tapes which go out of print later reappear on another label, sometimes in a better version (newly mastered, restored, digitally enhanced or letterboxed). Video stores which purchased copies of the out-of-print tape before it went out of print continue to rent those tapes; or contact our Rare Video Department to check on availability of out-of-print tapes.

And now that you know how it all works, may we introduce you to our first list in the book? Here are some of our dear, life-long friends:

> the tough-talking gangster's moll
> the lady of easy virtue who hides a golden heart
> the shadowy figure who invokes a sense of dread
> the mustache-twirling villain with a penchant for attaching kicking females to railroad tracks
> the saintly mother trying to make ends meet, surrounded by half-dozen ragamuffins
> the freedom fighter who fights the good fight and listens to a higher cause
> the irresistable vamp who destroys the stalwart hero
> the innocent child who melts the jaded heart of the elderly curmudgeon
> the uptight, bespeckled librarian who, upon removing her glasses, is actually a gorgeous sexpot
> the nattily attired dandy with a roving eye and untrue heart
> the child who spends far too much time in a darkened movie theatre, watching film after film, enamored of each and every frame, bewitched by the magic up on the screen and never, ever wanting it to end...

So go ahead, cheer for the bad guy, have a good cry, sit on the edge of your seat.... We give you films that embrace the heart, that stimulate the mind, that inspire, touch, teach, and make us all film lovers for life.

33 Directors to Watch

Atom Egoyan

The Adjuster

Atom Egoyan's fourth feature deals with his recurrent themes of the omnipresence of video, voyeurism, fractured nuclear families and sexual control and domination. Three stories are intercut: Noah is an insurance adjuster who manipulates and controls the clients who've lost their property; his wife Hera is a government film censor who surreptitiously records the objectionable material on video; and an ex-football player and his twisted wife play out elaborate sexual games on the unsuspecting. With Elias Koteas, Arsinee Khanjian and Maury Chaykin.
VHS: S18458. $19.98.
Atom Egoyan, Canada, 1991, 102 mins.

Calendar

Atom Egoyan directs and appears as a photographer in this disturbingly funny film. The photographer is sent to Armenia to take pictures of historic churches. He takes his wife along as a translator but she is sidelined by the depth of her heritage and the charms of her handsome guide.
VHS: S25992. $24.95.
Atom Egoyan, Armenia/Canada, 1993, 75 mins.

Exotica

Atom Egoyan's most accessible film is also one of his best: an obsessive and dangerous love story set in a seedy Toronto night club. An exotic dancer meets a man strangely obsessed with her, especially when she wears a girl's school uniform. Egoyan's complicated plot reveals layer after layer of lust, perversion, sexual abuse and violence in an original vision of the darker side.
VHS: S26373. $19.95.
Laser: Letterboxed. **LD75077. $39.99.**
Atom Egoyan, Canada, 1995, 103 mins.

Family Viewing

Atom Egoyan's second feature observes a contemporary Canadian family in the crisis mode. Van is upset when he discovers that his childhood movie memories on videotape are being erased to make room for his father's bedroom activities. This prompts him to leave and kidnap his maternal grandmother from the old age home and set up housekeeping in an unused wing of a downtown hotel. A fascinating and very funny study of alienation in a high tech society. With David Hemblen, Aidan Tierney, Gabrielle Rose, Arsinee Khanjian and Selma Kekikian.
VHS: S13268. $19.98.
Atom Egoyan, Canada, 1987, 86 mins.

Next of Kin

Profoundly unhappy with his family life, a young man named Peter (Patrick Tierney) undergoes video therapy with his parents. One day, while at the hospital studying the tapes, he sees the videos of an Armenian family who feel guilty about surrendering their own son, while still an infant, to a foster home. Peter decides to present himself to this family as their long lost son, to finally act out a role different from the one assigned to him in his own life. Filled with haunting images of travel and displacement, *Next of Kin* reveals both a young WASP's response to working class Armenian culture and discourses on

the range of roles that life allows us to play.
VHS: S13587. $29.95.
Laser: LD70642. $24.98.
Atom Egoyan, Canada, 1984, 72 mins.

Speaking Parts

A brilliant cinematic jigsaw puzzle. A handsome hotel housekeeper is willing to do anything to advance his film career. Luckily for him, he bears a strong resemblance to a lonely screenwriter's dead brother. A chilly film of obsession, ambition and advances in video technology. With Michael McManus, Arsinee Khanjian.
VHS: S13269. $19.98.
Atom Egoyan, Canada, 1989, 92 mins.

Sally Potter

Orlando

Virginia Woolf's ground-breaking novel about a transsexual from the time of Renaissance England has been transformed into a beautiful film. Tilda Swinton stars with Billy Zane as her romantic American lover while Quentin Crisp reigns as Queen Elizabeth the First.
VHS: S20829. $19.95.
Laser: LD74471. $34.95.
Sally Potter, Great Britain, 1993, 93 mins.

Werner Herzog

Aguirre: The Wrath of God

"One of the great, mad, passionate, foolhardy masterpieces—as reckless and as brilliant as *Greed* or *Apocalypse Now*" (Roger Ebert). Shot on location in the Amazon, Klaus Kinski is Aguirre searching for El Dorado—the mythical City of Gold. German with English subtitles.
VHS: S00025. $29.95.
Werner Herzog, Germany, 1972, 94 mins.

Heart of Glass

Werner Herzog's brilliant, sensual, hypnotic film about the magical and desperate attempts of the people in a small village to learn the formula for making special glass, supplied by a wandering herdsman with extraordinary powers. An apocalyptic movie with stunning imagery (cinematography by Jorg Schmidt-Reitwin) that achieves a mystical, surreal power. With Josef Bierbichler, Stefan Guttler, Clemens Scheitz, and Sepp Muller. Music by Popol Vuh. German with English subtitles.
VHS: S17397. $29.95.
Werner Herzog, Germany, 1976, 94 mins.

Herdsmen of the Sun

Herzog's fascination with the natural world at its most enduringly strange led him to the southern Sahara for *Herdsmen of the Sun*, "a startling anthropological documentary about the nomadic members of the Wodaabe Tribe" (Janet Maslin).

Once a year, the men decorate themselves with beads and blue lipstick and festive hats to participate in what amounts to a beauty pageant. French, English and Peul with English subtitles.
VHS: S16054. $59.95.
Werner Herzog, Germany, 1988, 52 mins.

The Mystery of Kaspar Hauser
In 1828, a young man appeared in the town square of Nuremberg, his origins unknown, having apparently been kept in solitary confinement all his life; five years later he was murdered by an unidentified assailant. Kaspar's brief, enigmatic destiny becomes a powerful metaphor for life in Werner Herzog's vision of the extreme edges of existence. Former mental patient Bruno S. delivers a sympathetic and powerful performance. "Herzog achieves a visionary, overcast style" (Pauline Kael, *The New Yorker*). Also known as *Every Man for Himself and God against All*. With Walter Ladengast, Brigitte Mira, Hans Musaus and Willy Semmelrogge. German with English subtitles.
VHS: S20303. $29.95.
Werner Herzog, Germany, 1974, 110 mins.

Signs of Life
The breakthrough first feature from Werner Herzog. A young German soldier is stationed on a small Greek island, cut off from the larger traumatic events of the Second World War. The island's beauty tempts him with the promise of peace, but ultimately he cannot accept the potential of this enchanting place. German with English subtitles.
VHS: S26146. $69.95.
Werner Herzog, Germany, 1968, 90 mins.

Stroszek
The adventures of Herzog's alter-ego, Bruno S., continue as a former mental patient and Berlin street singer joins with a whore and an aging eccentric to emigrate to Wisconsin in search of the American dream. "Surprisingly positive, tragicomic, poetic narrative" (Leonard Maltin). With Eva Mattes and Clemens Scheitz. English and German with English subtitles.
VHS: S12826. $29.95.
Werner Herzog, Germany, 1977, 108 mins.

Where the Green Ants Dream
Two tribes of Aborigines, the Wororas and the Riratjingus, preserve their ancient legends, songs and laws of creation in the heart of Australia. They come into conflict with the laws of modern Australia when a large company tries to mine uranium in one of their holy places, the place where the "Green Ants Dream." With Bruce Spence, Wandjuk Marika, Roy Marika. English dialog.
VHS: S07103. $24.95.
Werner Herzog, Germany/Australia, 1985, 99 mins.

Woyzeck
Woyzeck represents one of the most extraordinary events in the history of literature. Written in 1836, just before its author's death at the age of 23, Buchner's drama anticipates by some 50 to 100 years the literary movements of the 20th century. Herzog's version of *Woyzeck* is a film without shadows. This caustic tragedy of an ordinary man's headlong plunge into madness and murder is filmed with a terrible clarity, punctuated by bursts of unexpected lyricism. In the title role, Klaus Kinski delivers a harrowing and unforgettable performance, as stark and unsentimental as the razor with which the hero carries out his chilling destiny. With Eva Mattes. German with English subtitles.
VHS: S12989. $59.95.
Werner Herzog, Germany, 1978, 82 mins.

Jim Jarmusch

Dead Man
Johnny Depp stars as a wounded man on the run from both bounty hunters and the law in this incredibly beautiful-looking film from American independent Jim Jarmusch. Through an odd chain of events, Depp becomes a hunted murder suspect as he sets out on life's final journey, meeting an interesting cast of characters along the way. Funny and unpredictable, Depp is supported by an amazing array of talent, including Robert Mitchum, Gabriel Byrne, John Hurt, Lance Henriksen and Crispin Glover. With bravura black-and-white cinematography by Robby Muller. "A masterpiece!" (*The Chicago Reader*).
VHS: S30457. $99.99.
Laser: LD76064. $39.99.
Jim Jarmusch, USA, 1996, 121 mins.

Down by Law
Jim Jarmusch's third feature following his immensely successful *Stranger Than Paradise* stars Tom Waits, John Lurie—and in a treasure of a performance, Roberto Benigni—as a group of escaped convicts in the swamps of Louisiana. A funny, original film featuring brilliant cinematography by the great Robby Muller.
VHS: S03022. $14.98.
Laser: LD76225. $39.98.
Jim Jarmusch, USA, 1986, 95 mins.

Mystery Train
"Jim Jarmusch makes bizarre, minimalist and simpatico road movies, with characters on the edge of pop culture discovering a poetically shabby America. We see the land through the eyes of foreigners, unspoiled but prejudiced by American myths." Three separate but interwoven episodes centered in a rundown Memphis hotel reveal the experiences of non-Americans in America. Two young Japanese lovers travel through town on a rock 'n roll pilgrimage, a newly widowed Italian woman waits for a flight back to Rome while she is visited by the ghost of Elvis, a British man makes some friends, gets drunk and commits murder. "There is no real mystery in *Mystery Train*. It makes it points on Elvis-worship, restlessness and race relations out front. But there is a mystery about its construction. The leisurely, distancing pace works beautifully" (Edwin Jahiel). 1990, 110 mins.
VHS: S12988. $19.98.
Jim Jarmusch, USA, 1989, 113 mins.

Night on Earth
Jim Jarmusch's film is structured episodically, with the narrative simultaneously unfolding in Los Angeles, New York, Paris, Rome and Helsinki, and concerns the relationship of cab drivers and their passengers. The ensemble cast includes Gena Rowlands, Winona Ryder, Rosie Perez, Giancarlo Esposito, Armin Mueller-Stahl, Beatrice Dalle, Isaach de Bankole, Roberto Benigni, Matti Pellonpaa and Kari Vaananen. Tom Waits composed the music and performs two numbers. Letterboxed.
VHS: S17625. $19.95.
Jim Jarmusch, USA, 1991, 125 mins.

Stranger Than Paradise
A wonderful film, a witty, new wave comedy about the Old World meeting the new, as Eddie's (Richard Edson) life is suddenly invaded by his friend Willie's (John Lurie) young Hungarian cousin, Eva. A totally unlikely series of very funny situations ensues.
VHS: Out of print. For rental only.
Laser: Letterboxed. LD75917. $49.95.
Jim Jarmusch, USA, 1985, 90 mins.

Arnaud Desplechin

My Sex Life (Or How to Get into an Argument)
Paul, a 29-year-old assistant professor, cannot complete his dissertation, breaks up with his girlfriend of 10 years, and learns his arch rival has just been promoted over him to full professor. To complicate matters, he finds himself involved in several simultaneous relationships, including one with his best friend's girlfriend. "Wildly romantic. One of the great French films of the decade" (*Village Voice*). French with English subtitles.
VHS: S33351. $89.98.
Arnaud Desplechin, France, 1997, 178 mins.

Mike Leigh

Abigail's Party
Mike Leigh's brilliant satire about middle-class English consumerism and appearances, with Alison Steadman's frightening performance as a frantic woman trying to orchestrate an important dinner party, which is interrupted by her husband's untimely heart attack. In this situation, the "unbearable and hopeless fuse to create an explosion of incredible hilarity."
VHS: $17604. $29.95.
Mike Leigh, Great Britain, 1977, 105 mins.

Bleak Moments
This breakthrough film from Leigh is the shrewdly observed and brilliantly understated portrait of London's offbeat residents and the fleeting but significant moments which define their lives. Sylvia (Anne Raitt), a clever but bored secretary, desperately seeks to escape from the bleak moments of her life, first in an awkward flirtation with a sexually repressed schoolteacher (Eric Allan), and then with the eccentric, guitar-playing hippie tenant living in her garage (Mike Bradwell).
VHS: $31636. $59.95.
Mike Leigh, Great Britain, 1971, 110 mins.

Career Girls
Mike Leigh's (*Secrets and Lies*) intelligent, poignant comedy about the reunion of two very different 30-ish women who were battling college roomates in London six years ago. Over the course of their brief reunion, Hannah and Annie (Katrin Cartlidge, *Naked* and *Breaking the Waves*, and Lynda Steadman, in stand-out performances) reveal the present while they talk about the past, in jittery flashbacks that match their emotions. As we watch these two progress from black leather to discreet beige, we also watch the growth that has carried them beyond the shared, angry turmoil of their college years.
VHS: $32797. $99.99.
Laser: LD76422. $39.98.
Mike Leigh, Great Britain, 1997, 87 mins.

Four Days in July
Mike Leigh's humanism is the hallmark of this BBC television film about the opposite fortunes of two couples in Northern Ireland, one Catholic and one Protestant, both of whom are expecting children. With Brid Brennan, Desmond McAleer, Charles Lawson and Paula Hamilton.
VHS: $17602. $29.95.
Mike Leigh, Great Britain, 1984, 99 mins.

Grown Ups
Mike Leigh's working class comedy about a recently wed couple who must deal with the wife's idiosyncratic sister and their next door neighbor, who was a high school instructor. With Philip Davis, Leslie Manville, Sam Kelly, Lindsay Duncan and Brenda Blethyn.
VHS: $19404. $29.95.
Mike Leigh, Great Britain, 1980, 95 mins.

Hard Labor
This emotionally horrific and yet oddly amusing film is a scathing indictment of classicism and sexism. The grinding daily abuse suffered by a poor elderly woman at the hands of her husband, her children and even her employer illustrate the nature of oppression. Ben Kingsley appears as a hairy but friendly cab driver.
VHS: $21507. $29.95.
Mike Leigh, Great Britain, 1973, 70 mins.

Home Sweet Home
This, the story of three not terribly jolly postmen, centers on Stan, a would-be ladies' man whose wife has left him. Insightful comedy results when Stan compensates for his loneliness by seducing his co-workers' wives. In this unusual film, England emerges as a land of bitter, isolated individuals unconsoled by marriage and pigeonholed by the state.
VHS: $21509. $29.95.
Mike Leigh, Great Britain, 1982, 90 mins.

Kiss of Death
Trevor is a quiet undertaker's assistant. His attempts at romance give shape to a plot characterized by whimsy and a puckish sense of humor. The courtship attempts of this strange misfit must rank among cinema's most funny and awkward expressions of tortured love.
VHS: $21508. $29.95.
Mike Leigh, Great Britain, 1977, 80 mins.

Life Is Sweet
Satirist Mike Leigh is at it again in the London south side with this decidedly bittersweet comedy about the members of a dysfunctional family and their oddball friends. It seems everyone in this film is striving for change. The family tries to balance their differences with alcoholic friends and their short fuses proves a challenge, but they don't forget to laugh a lot along the way.
VHS: $16628. $14.98.
Laser: LD71503. $29.98.
Mike Leigh, Great Britain, 1992, 103 mins.

Meantime
An early work by Mike Leigh, this wry and amusing working-class comedy is the story of Frank and his two unemployed deadbeat sons, Mark and Colin (Phil Daniels and Tim Roth), who live in a cramped apartment in London's East End. Wanting to escape the doldrums of his mediocre world, Colin starts hanging out with Coxy (Gary Oldman), a reckless skinhead. The new friendship sparks fear in Colin's family, whose overzealous attempts to direct Colin on a staight path prove futile.
VHS: $32361. $79.98.
Mike Leigh, Great Britain, 1983, 103 mins.

Naked
This film won in both the Best Film and Best Actor category at the Cannes Film Festival. David Thewlis stars in this funny, erotic and bizarre odyssey, set in the streets of London, that explores the seamy side of desire and longing of post-Thatcherite England.
VHS: $21119. $19.95.
Laser: Includes director's commentary, still photo gallery, trailers and short films. **LD74468. $69.95.**
Mike Leigh, Great Britain, 1993, 131 mins.

Nuts in May
British filmmaker Mike Leigh has a wonderful sense of rhythms and improvisational textures, and this film recounts the weird adventures of a fierce young couple trying to abide to their strict vegetarian diet, with dangerous repercussions. "Hilarious and appalling" (Vincent Canby). With Roger Sloman, Alison Steadman and Anthony O'Donnell.
VHS: $17603. $29.95.
Mike Leigh, Great Britain, 1976, 84 mins.

Secrets and Lies
Mike Leigh's heartwarming comedy of a young black woman (Marianne Jean-Baptiste) searching for her natural birth mother only to discover that her mom (the magnificent Brenda Blethyn) is white, makes for a film with "rare heart and soul" (Janet Maslin, *The New York Times*), from Britain's master of improvisational, working-class social comedies. With Timothy Spall. Winner of the Palm d'Or at Cannes Film Festival.
VHS: $31027. $103.99.
Laser: LD76141. $39.98.
Mike Leigh, Great Britain, 1996, 114 mins.

Who's Who
Set in a brokerage firm, the movie charts the greed and avarice of some ambitious young traders, each trying to step on top of the other. "In each of [Leigh's] films there comes a transforming moment when the unbearable and the hopeless fuse to create an explosion of recognition of high, incredible hilarity" (Vincent Canby). With Bridget Kane, Simon Chandler, Adam Norton, Philip Davis and Joolia Cappleman.
VHS: $19402. $29.95.
Mike Leigh, Great Britain, 1978, 75 mins.

John Greyson

Urinal
An innovative first feature, *Urinal* summons seven gay artists from 1937 and gives them an "Impossible Mission": they must research the policing of washroom sex in Ontario, and propose solutions.

Each night they convene to present a lecture, with every lecture adopting a different documentary convention. Using interviews with politicians, gay activists and men who have been charged with "gross indecency," hundreds of victims of police entrapment and video surveillance are revealed. A funny and disturbing film that probes into the roots of homosexual discrimination. From Canada's most controversial independent filmmaker.
VHS: $15808. $39.95.
John Greyson, Canada, 1988, 100 mins.

Zero Patience
An outrageous movie musical, this films depicts an imaginary love story between 19th-century Victorian writer and explorer Sir Richard Francis Burton and "Patient Zero", the Canadian flight attendant accused by the media of being the man who brought AIDS to North America.
VHS: $22669. $39.95.
John Greyson, Canada, 1993, 100 mins.

Lars von Trier

Breaking the Waves
In her incredible film debut, Emily Watson gives an Academy Award-nominated performance as Bess, a naive young woman who marries Jan, a handsome oil-rig worker. For the first time in her life, Bess experiences passion and physical pleasure she never imagined. But her marital bliss is cut short when an accident on the rig leaves Jan paralyzed. Believing she holds the key to his recovery, Bess will stop at nothing—even infidelity—in order to prolong Jan's life. "A powerhouse love story, a kind of miracle" (*Village Voice*). In English. Letterboxed.
VHS: $31256. $99.99.
  Laser: LD76284. $69.95.
Lars von Trier, Great Britain/Denmark, 1996, 152 mins.

The Element of Crime
Winner at the Cannes Film Festival, and a supremely stylish (and terrifying) thriller. Shot entirely in sepia tone, Michael Elphick plays the cop assigned the Lotto Murders—a diabolical slaughter of little girls. Elphick is a man traumatized by grotesque memories of post-nuke Europe, as in the futuristic nightmare *Blade Runner*, and in his ongoing madness, becomes obsessed with the criminal mind. In English.
VHS: $12279. $79.95.
Lars von Trier, Denmark, 1988, 104 mins.

The Kingdom
Lars von Trier's audacious and inspired soap opera is set in Copenhagen's Kingdom Hospital, which is ailing. Once a respected site of healing, it has become a carnival of horrors. A restless ghost haunts its corridors crying for redemption. Patients try seances while doctors turn to exorcism and voodoo. Despite these efforts, the terrible secret at the heart of *The Kingdom* remains and continues to ensnare the innocent. This film mixes a range of influences from the erotic to the sardonic in an unforgettable hybrid of comedy and terror. Danish with English subtitles.
VHS: $27595. $24.98.
  Laser: LD75556. $89.99.
Lars von Trier, Denmark, 1994, 265 mins.

Zentropa
Known in Europe as *Europa*, this stylistically daring work is set in a bleak, defeated Germany. A young American of German ancestry apprentices as a railway porter. He is seduced by a mysterious heiress whose father owns the line and becomes a pawn in a mysterious web of intrigue and deceit. With Jean Marc Barr, Barbara Sukowa and Eddie Constantine. Narrated by Max von Sydow. English and German with English subtitles.
VHS: $18368. $19.95.
Lars von Trier, Denmark/France/Sweden/ Germany, 1991, 112 mins.

Arturo Ripstein

Place Without Limits
From Arturo Ripstein, perhaps Mexico's most interesting filmmaker, a bittersweet dissection of machismo and homophobia in Latin America. La Manuela, a transvestite who lives in a brothel run by his daughter, "emerges as an all-out attack on machismo, suggesting that it can often mask in a man a highly insecure sense of masculinity" (*Los Angeles Times*). Spanish with English subtitles.
VHS: $31134. $79.95.
Arturo Ripstein, Mexico, 1977, 110 mins.

Emir Kusturica

Arizona Dream
Johnny Depp stars as a young drifter who meets a kindred spirit in Faye Dunaway and unexpectedly falls in love. Between their age differences and the reactions of their dysfunctional families, love is put on trial. Jerry Lewis is great as Depp's car dealership hmuckstering uncle.
VHS: $23859. $19.98.
Emir Kusturica, USA, 1994, 119 mins.

Do You Remember Dolly Bell?
Kusturica's beautifully modulated tale of a young man's entry into adulthood, his loss of virginity in the company of a B-movie stripper and prostitute. Set in the early 60s, Kusturica grafts the pathos of the Eastern European village movie into a complex tale of intrusive cultures, when Western influences such as fashion and rock and roll and the promise of European socialism threatened to roll over traditional customs, practiced rituals and Tito's political reign. With Slavo Stimac, Slobodan Aligrudic and Ljiljana Blagojevic. Serbo-Croatian with English subtitles.
VHS: $18457. $69.95.
Emir Kusturica, Yugoslavia, 1981, 106 mins.

Time of the Gypsies
A potent mix of comedy, drama and the supernatural, Kusturica's amazingly realistic drama set in the heart of the gypsy culture. Perhan, the hero, is telekinetic and is taken to Italy by the "sheik," where he gets a quick education in gypsy survival skills on the streets of Milan. Warm and affectionate, full of comic scenes, with a great gypsy music sound track. With Dvor Dujmovic and Bora Todorovic. Serbo-Croatian and Romany with English subtitles.
VHS: $12744. $19.95.
Emir Kusturica, Yugoslavia, 1990, 136 mins.

When Father Was Away on Business
Kusturica's Cannes-award winning film is a magical portrait of a boy's coming of age in 50's Yugoslavia. As little Malik takes up sleepwalking and experiences his first love, the family knows the real "business" that Father is conducting—in a labor camp for his unrepentant Stalinist leanings and his philandering. Serbo-Croatian with English subtitles.
VHS: $15547. $19.98.
  Laser: CAV. LD72198. $49.95.
Emir Kusturica, Yugoslavia, 1985, 144 mins.

Nanni Moretti

Caro Diario (Dear Diary)
This magical, virtually indescribable comedy by Nanni Moretti won the Best Director Prize at Cannes and follows the travails of a simple man (Moretti) in search of the true meaning of life. The film's three episodes confront, respectively, the changing character of Rome and of Moretti's generation, the possibility (and impossibility) of solitude, and the

nature of truth in medicine. Often hilarious, always original, to say that Moretti is the Italian Woody Allen is to underestimate the pathos which underlies the accuracy of his social observations, the incisiveness of his insights. Don't miss. Italian with English subtitles.
VHS: S23967. $19.98.
Nanni Moretti, Italy, 1994, 100 mins.

Palombella Rossa
Director Nanni Moretti's political comedy about the fate of Italian communism. The action follows a politician who is injured in a car crash and suffers from amnesia. He awakens to find himself about to play an important water polo match. While his teammates negotiate positions and devise strategies, he leaps out of the pool to interview a succession of bureaucrats, partyhacks and militants. "The scope of its concerns, and Moretti's ability to express these in visual terms, is ambitious and accomplished" (*Toronto Festival of Festivals*). Italian with English subtitles.
VHS: S19975. $19.98.
Nanni Moretti, Italy, 1989, 87 mins.

Alain Resnais

Hiroshima, Mon Amour
From the beginning, in which the love-making of a French actress (Emmanuelle Riva) and a Japanese architect (Eiji Okada) is intercut with newsreel footage of Hiroshima's atomic holocaust and its aftermath, to the couple's painful walk through the reconstructed city, Resnais' film recaptures both the pain and the richness of the war. French with English subtitles.
VHS: S00571. $29.95.
Alain Resnais, France, 1959, 91 mins.

La Guerre Est Finie
This great film by Alain Resnais, scripted by Jorge Semprun, stars Yves Montand, Genevieve Bujold, Ingrid Thulin and Michel Piccoli. Resnais shifts between reality and Montand's mental states in an incisive portrait of an aging Spanish revolutionary exile who is imprisoned by his past as he confronts the failure of his ideas. Resnais explores Montand's insecurities through his relationships with two very different women (Thulin and Bujold). French with English subtitles.
VHS: S23758. $29.95.
Alain Resnais, France, 1966, 120 mins.

Last Year at Marienbad
The strange geometry of a romantic triangle marks the beginning of this elegant, labyrinthine puzzle. Written by French New Wave novelist Alain Robbe-Grillet and from the director of *Hiroshima, Mon Amour, Last Year at Marienbad* is a film classic, the subject of myriad interpretations. Starring Delphine Seyrig, Giorgio Albertazzi, and Sacha Pitoeff. French with English subtitles. New presentation in videoscope.
VHS: S00730. $29.95.
Alain Resnais, France, 1961, 90 mins.

Mon Oncle d'Amerique
Three middle-class French drifters, each convinced they lack definition and excitement, dream about the imaginary and mythic "American Uncle," cross a behavioral scientist who instills in them a sense of wonder and excitement and the mystery of the unknown. The film is structured like a riddle, "one which proves that surrealism lives" (*Time Out*). With Gerard Depardieu, Nicole Garcia, Roger Pierre and Marie Dubois. French with English subtitles.
VHS: S02141. $29.95.
Alain Resnais, France, 1980, 126 mins.

Muriel
One of the most interesting films from Alain Resnais, a bold and beautiful film, in which Resnais takes an incident from provincial life, the reunion of a middle-aged woman and her old lover at Boulogne. Out of the trivia of everyday life and its anxieties, he creates a mosaic masterpiece that probes the themes of time and memory, and the relationship between personal conscience and public consciousness (the references

to the Algerian War). With Delphine Seyrig, Jean-Pierre Kerien, Nina Klein. Music by Hans Werner Henze. French with English subtitles.
VHS: S02079. $59.95.
Alain Resnais, France, 1963, 115 mins.

Night and Fog
A newly mastered version of what Francois Truffaut called "the greatest film of all time": Alain Resnais' incredibly powerful, searing, unforgettable film on Nazi concentration camps, truly a film for all time. Edited by Chris Marker. French with English subtitles.
VHS: S00930. $19.95.
Alain Resnais, France, 1955, 32 mins.

Stavisky
With *Stavisky*, director Alain Resnais has crafted an extraordinarily beautiful and sophisticated film that requires intense intense concentration but yields tremendous rewards. The story is that of a French swindler and conman extraordinaire, whose financial manipulations in the 30s brought on riots that helped to topple a government. With Jean-Paul Belmondo, Anny Duperey, Charles Boyer and Gerard Depardieu. Photographed by Sacha Vierny, with a musical score by Stephen Sondheim. French with English subtitles.
VHS: S14986. $59.95.
Alain Resnais, France, 1974, 117 mins.

Tran Anh Hung

Cyclo
Directed by Tran Anh Hung (*The Scent of Green Papaya*), this gritty tale of innocence lost in the urban jungle of Vietnam fuses the neorealist style of *The Bicycle Thief* with the kinetic energy of *Taxi Driver*. In the heart of Ho Chi Minh City, a young cyclo (pedicab driver) transports passengers through the streets, trying to eke out a meager living for his two sisters and elderly grandfather. When his bicycle is stolen by a local gang, he descends into a crime ring led by the charismatic Poet (Tony Leung), and his older sister turns to prostitution. Vietnamese with English subtitles.
VHS: S32014. $89.95.
Tran Anh Hung, Vietnam, 1996, 123 mins.

The Scent of Green Papaya
A moving and undeniably brilliant film by the talented Vietnamese-exile filmmaker Tran Anh Hung, set in 1951 and centered on a young woman who becomes a servant for a turbulent family. The film follows in exquisitely lyrical detail the quiet beauty and stoically accepted hardships of her life as, ten years later, she starts a love affair with her next employer. Shot entirely on a Paris soundstage, this, says critic Roger Ebert, "is a film to cherish." Vietnamese with English subtitles.
VHS: S23925. $19.95.
Laser: LD74799. $34.95.
Tran Anh Hung, Vietnam/France, 1993, 104 mins.

Mohsen Makhmalbaf

The Cyclist
A visually sophisticated film which deals with the themes of man's exploitation of man and the inequities between rich and poor. The cyclist is Nassim, an Afghan refugee in need of money to pay his wife's medical expenses. With work difficult to come by, a sleazy promoter suggests he undertake a bicycle marathon. Touting him as the Afghani superman, the huckster wagers that Nassim will circle a small area on the outskirts of town, day and night, for a week. Gamblers, bookies and food vendors gather to watch the desperate cyclist from the sidelines, turning his suffering to their own profit. Winner of the Best Film at the Riminicinema Film Festival. Farsi with English subtitles.
VHS: S27790. $29.95.
Mohsen Makhmalbaf, Iran, 1989, 75 mins.

The Peddler

Shockingly forthright in its view of the social and economic problems of the post-Shah era, *The Peddler* uses a different cameraman and different style for each of three short tales set among the poor of contemporary Tehran. The first episode follows a kindly but naive couple who want someone to adopt their newborn daughter. The second, an astonishing mix of absurdist comedy and the supernatural, concerns a mentally unstable man who lives with his mother in a ramshackle apartment. The final section draws on the American gangster film to show the last hours of a peddler suspected of betraying his friends. Farsi with English subtitles.
VHS: S27787. $29.95.
Mohsen Makhmalbaf, Iran, 1986, 95 mins.

Abbas Kiarostami

Life and Nothing More

The film investigates the aftermath of a devastating 1990 earthquake which killed some 50,000 people in northern Iran. This region provided the setting for Kiarostami's *Where Is the Friend's Home*. Kiarostami's search for the two young actors who played central roles in that film becomes the dramatic source of *Life and Nothing More*...as a father and son travel to Quoker, the hometown of the two boys, and along the way meet earthquake survivors who desperately and valiantly work to reconstruct their lives. "...in many ways the most beautiful and powerful Iranian film I've seen" (Jonathan Rosenbaum, *Chicago Reader*). Farsi with English subtitles.
VHS: S27792. $29.95.
Abbas Kiarostami, Iran, 1992, 91 mins.

Where Is the Friend's Home?

A lyrical tale about a traveller searching for his friend's home, who finds himself on an excursion through places and moments of great beauty and wonder. The friends are the schoolmates Ahmad and Mohammad Reza. Mohammad Reza's careless attitude towards his homework has drawn several reprimands from their stern teacher, culminating in the threat of expulsion if he does not do his work. When Ahmad prepares to do his own homework, he finds that he has accidentally picked up Mohammad Reza's notebook. Fearing that his friend will be expelled if he cannot submit his lesson the next day, Ahmad defies his parents and sets out to find his friend's home in the neighboring village. Winner of the Bronze Leopard at the Locarno Film Festival. Farsi with English subtitles.
VHS: S27791. $29.95.
Abbas Kiarostami, Iran, 1989, 90 mins.

Jean-Luc Godard

Alphaville

Eddie Constantine is Lemmy Caution, inter-galactic private eye, in this bravura mix of comic strip, science fiction and film noir in what is ultimately a new style of cinema in which form and content are identical. Lemmy sets out to dispose of diabolical scientist Leonard von Braun (a.k.a. Leonard Nosferatu) from Alphaville, the futuristic city run by an electronic brain, where love has been banished. A film in which poetry mixes freely with pulp to create a new dimension, a new cinematic reality. French with English subtitles.
VHS: S07702. $29.95.
Laser: LD75075. $49.95.
Jean-Luc Godard, France, 1965, 100 mins.

Band of Outsiders

Claude Brasseur, Sami Frey and Anna Karina plan to steal money hidden in a house where Karina works, but the robbery is messed up and murder is the result. Godard's thriller is set in the fringe world of *Breathless*—the world of outsiders. Most of the film

takes place in a suburb of Paris, and Godard has transformed it into a setting of beauty and poignancy. Godard's three characters are "trembling on the edge of crime...dancing on the edge of the volcano" (Richard Roud). French with English subtitles.
VHS: S00093. $29.95.
Jean-Luc Godard, France, 1964, 97 mins.

Breathless

The landmark French New Wave film by Godard features Jean-Paul Belmondo as a small-time hood on the run from the law, having an affair with an American girl in Paris (Jean Seberg). A film which owes much to American film noir and yet revolutionized the world of film. Remastered. French with English subtitles.
VHS: S08698. $24.95.
Laser: CLV. LD71507. $49.95.
Jean-Luc Godard, France, 1959, 89 mins.

Comment Ca Va? (How Is It Going?)

Co-directed by Anne-Marie Mieville, Jean-Luc Godard's work—combining video and film—is a fascinating dialectic on the dissemination and processing of information, both literary and visual. Two workers of a communist newspaper strike out to make a film and video about the newspaper and the printing plant. One of the workers, Odette (Mieville), has strange ideas about content and form and how the film should be made. *Comment ca va?* is a formally brilliant work about the transmission of ideas by the major media. French with English subtitles.
VHS: S19232. $59.95.
Jean-Luc Godard/Anne-Marie Mieville, France, 1976, 76 mins.

First Name: Carmen

An important recent film by Jean-Luc Godard; in this gun-crazy romance, Godard re-examines not only his own previous attitudes, but the entire *femme fatale* tradition of Western culture. Based freely on the novel by Prosper Merimee and the opera by Bizet, the film is a cool depiction of a sexually explicit romance between a policeman and a beautiful young woman who leads him into a life of crime and humiliation. With Myriem Roussel, Maruschka Detmers, Jacques Bonnaffre. French with English subtitles.
VHS: S09355. $29.95.
Jean-Luc Godard, France, 1983, 85 mins.

Godard/Truffaut Shorts

A short film by Jean-Luc Godard made prior to his release of *Breathless* entitled *All the Boys Are Called Patrick*, and a short film by Francois Truffaut, *Les Mistons*, a charming evocative film about the arousal of sexual feelings in a group of young boys on summer holiday. French with English subtitles.
VHS: S01777. $29.95.
Jean-Luc Godard/Francois Truffaut, France, 1957

Ici et Ailleurs (Here and Elsewhere)

Jean-Luc Godard initiated his radical video period with this startling film that combines videotape and film, enabling him to superimpose more than two images simultaneously. Made as part of the "Dziga Vertov group," with Jean-Pierre Gorin and Anne-Marie Mieville, the film was commissioned by the Palestinians and originally titled *Until Victory*. The film's original purpose was to examine life in the Palestinian camps. But following the defeat of the Palestine army in the Six Day War, *Ici et Ailleurs* was radically transformed, becoming a meditation on how cinema records history. Godard, Gorin and Mieville contrast a French family ("Here") with an impressionstic portrait of Palestine ("Elsewhere") reflected and transmitted by television, books and pictures. French with English subtitles.
VHS: S19231. $59.95.
Jean-Luc Godard, France/Switzerland, 1970/1976

JLG/JLG

In this autobiographical essay of confessional images, Godard speculates on the oppression of culture from the isolation of his home in Switzerland. Subtitled *A Self-Portrait in December*, Godard plays himself in an effort to explain what he has been doing for the past 30 years. In this unique cinematic self-portrait, Godard is self-absorbed and alone as he mumbles to himself or to his sexy young maid. In this cinematic self-portrait, sequestered from the world and bunkered in a safe and cozy haven with his books, his movie equipment and his eccentricities, he muses upon images of women, receives visits from various government officials and makes references to his past mistakes. French with English subtitles.
VHS: S30000. $89.95.
Jean-Luc Godard, France, 1994, 60 mins.

King Lear

Struggling to re-interpret his famous relative's tragic tale of passion and madness, the young William Shakespeare, Jr. the Fifth encounters a bewildering array of bizarre personalities and cryptic, ritualistic imagery. A surreal examination of The Bard's most powerful drama, from one of the avant-garde's most adventurous filmmakers. Featuring Burgess Meredith, Molly Ringwald, Woody Allen, Norman Mailer and Peter Sellars.
VHS: S16475. $24.95.
Jean-Luc Godard, France, 1987, 91 mins.

Le Gai Savoir

Two alien beings, brought together in an empty earth space, are exposed to our culture via its popular images—a compelling experiment that not only foreshadows the use of these images in Godard's later films but also explains precisely why these images are the building blocks of any film. As Godard explains at the end, "This film is not and cannot be an attempt to explain cinema or embody its object, but merely suggests effective ways to achieve it. This is not the film that should be made, but if a film is to be made it must follow some of the paths shown here." With Jean-Pierre Leaud and Juliet Berto. French with English subtitles.
VHS: S15378. $39.95.
Jean-Luc Godard, France, 1965, 96 mins.

Le Petit Soldat

The debut feature of Anna Karina, and Godard's second feature, this film was banned in France for its razor-sharp reflection of the Algerian war in a politically divided nation. Michel Subor is a French secret agent on an assassination mission. The film's depiction of brutality and torture, used by both sides in this bloody war, infuriated both the Left and the Right. French with English subtitles.
VHS: S08091. $29.95.
Jean-Luc Godard, France, 1960, 88 mins.

Les Carabiniers

One of the important early-period films from Jean-Luc Godard; a parable about the stupidity and ugliness of war. The story revolves around two gullible clodhoppers who set out to fight for their king in exchange for "all the treasures in the world." French with English subtitles.
VHS: S05327. $29.95.
Jean-Luc Godard, France, 1985, 107 mins.

A Married Woman

Godard managed to infuriate Charles de Gaulle with this frank document of a Parisian romantic triangle. Macha Meril is the young wife and mother in love with her husband and her lover. She doesn't want to decide between them because, quite frankly, she enjoys the attention of both. French with English subtitles.
VHS: S00829. $29.95.
Jean-Luc Godard, France, 1964, 94 mins.

Masculine Feminine

A film about the children of Marx and Coca Cola directed by the child of Brecht and Hollywood. Two young lovers attempt to communicate throughout 15 discontinuous, contrapuntal vignettes. Dancing between precision and improvisation, this is one of Godard's most complex films, representing both a search for tenderness and a disheartening foray into the Sex War. With Jean-Pierre Leaud, Chantal Goya, and Catherine-Isabelle Duport. French with English subtitles.
VHS: S00830. $29.95.
Jean-Luc Godard, France, 1966, 103 mins.

My Life to Live

This film in 12 episodes is "one of the most beautiful, touching and original films by Godard, an extremely complex blend of social document, theatricality and interior drama…" (Georges Sadoul). Anna Karina is a salesgirl in a record shop who can't pay her rent, is evicted by her landlady and becomes a prostitute. "It triumphs because it is intelligent, discreet, delicate to the touch. It both edifies and gives pleasure because it is about what is most important…the nature of our humanity" (Susan Sontag). French with English subtitles.
VHS: S00907. $29.95.
Laser: LD76282. $49.95.
Jean-Luc Godard, France, 1962, 85 mins.

Numero Deux

Jean-Luc Godard brilliantly mixes video and film, set in the director's Grenoble studio. The action unfolds on two television monitors. Godard secured the money for the film claiming the project was a remake of *Breathless*. The elusive plot essentially concerns the marital discord—set off by the wife's infidelity—between a young working-class couple (Sandrine Battistella and Pierre Oudry) who live in a claustrophobic, high rise apartment complex. The film, made in collaboration with Anne-Marie Mieville, is a dialectic on the relationship of sex and money. "I think it's something like a masterpiece. *Numero Deux* is among the most visually compelling films Godard has ever made. He uses his video monitors to invent a dozen new ways of splitting the screen or layering the image. Compared to it, every other movie in town is just a cavity on the screen" (J. Hoberman, *The Village Voice*). With Alexandre Rignault and Rachel Stefanopoli. French with English subtitles.
VHS: S19233. $59.95.
Jean-Luc Godard, France/Switzerland, 1976, 88 mins.

Oh Woe Is Me (Helas Pour Moi)

Gerard Depardieu meets Jean-Luc Godard in this gentle Godard fable in which divinity touches everyday life. Godard transposes to Switzerland the Greek myth in which Zeus inhabited Amphitryon's body to seduce a man's wife, with surprising results. Godardian touches like titles on the screen, townspeople who function as a theatrical chorus and music from Bach, Beethoven and Tchaikovsky make this a cerebral but passionate exploration of constancy and cinema. French with English subtitles.
VHS: S26336. $89.95.
Jean-Luc Godard, France, 1994, 84 mins.

Paris Vu Par (Six in Paris)

This omnibus film from the major figures of the French New Wave (Jean-Luc Godard, Claude Chabrol, Eric Rohmer, Jean Douchet, Jean Rouch and Jean-Daniel Pollet) offers a series of witty, wry vignettes about contemporary Paris. Godard's work, *Une Femme Est une Femme*, is about a young woman who dispatches letters to her two lovers and is concerned she mixed up the contents. With Joanna Shimkus, Nadine Ballot, Barbet Schroeder, Micheline Dax, Claude Melki, Chabrol and Stephane Audran. French with English subtitles. France, 1964, 98 mins.
VHS: S19543. $69.95.

Pierrot le Fo

One of the high points of 20th century cinema. Ravishing and moving, the story features Jean-Paul Belmondo as Ferdinand, who one evening leaves his wife with whom he was in love five years earlier, and who is involved with a gang of criminals. After Ferdinand finds a dead man in her room, they leave Paris for a deserted island. One of Godard's most poetic films, full of the anguish of love, aptly summarized in his own words over the first images of the film, "At the age of fifty, Velasquez no longer painted precise objects; he painted what lay between precise objects." The final murder-suicide sequence on the island is one of the most brilliant Godard has ever created. French with English subtitles.
VHS: S10739. $59.95.
Jean-Luc Godard, France, 1965, 110 mins.

Sympathy for the Devil

The Rolling Stones rehearse "Sympathy for the Devil" as a white revolutionary tries to commit suicide when her boyfriend switches to Black Power in this singular and daring film originally called *One Plus One*. The film, tackling the themes of growth and revolution, is envisioned as a collage which the viewer is challenged to "edit" himself. With The Rolling Stones, Anne Wiazemsky and Iain Quarrier.
VHS: S22456. $29.95.
Jean-Luc Godard, France, 1970, 92 mins.

Two or Three Things I Know About Her

Shot simultaneously with *Made in U.S.A.* (one was filmed mornings, the other in the evenings), this drama focuses on modern life in Paris. Vlady stars as a Parisian housewife who lives in a large housing estate and supplements her husband's income by working as a part-time prostitute. Against an aural backdrop of Beethoven, her life over a 24-hour period is detailed as it speaks about the sale of oneself in the pursuit of happiness. A barrage of words, images and philosophising, with whispering and narration by Godard, this highly inventive and energetic, early "mockumentary" set the standard for such works. French with English subtitles.
VHS: S29507. $89.95.
Jean-Luc Godard, France, 1966, 95 mins.

Weekend

"End of Cinema, end of world," read the titles at the conclusion of Godard's 1967 apocalyptic film *Weekend*. Godard himself described the work as both "a film found on the junk heap," and "a film lost in the cosmos." Presenting a dark, comic vision of the end of capitalist society, *Weekend* reflects the turmoil and chaos of the late sixties better than any Hollywood film from that era. It also stands as the climax to the first phase of Godard's filmmaking career, before he turned to the making of more experimental Marxist films after the social upheavals of 1968. With Mirielle Darc and Jean-Pierre Leaud. French with English subtitles.
VHS: $14572. $29.95.
Jean-Luc Godard, France, 1967, 105 mins.

A Woman Is a Woman

"I conceived this film within the framework of a neo-realist musical: *an absolute contradiction*, but that's the way I wanted to make the film," said Godard. Godard's closely-knit texture of small bistros, striptease joints, political suspicion and conjugal wavering is constantly violated in its naturalistic surface, not just by the comic turns of the plot, but by Godard's reminders not only that the film is a performance, but that the projected images are themselves illusory: "The film has a beauty that is brash and pathetic, like splintered colored glass, fragments that somehow compose a picture while refusing to hold together: musical, sad, uproarious, definitely frail" (Edgardo Cozarinsky). French with English subtitles.
VHS: $08090. $59.95.
Jean-Luc Godard, France, 1961, 85 mins.

David Cronenberg

Crash

Fasten your seatbelt (or not!) for Cronenberg's controversial, graphic and unconventional story of a man and woman who, after their cars collide, are lured into a mysterious world of sexually obsessed car crash enthusiasts. Winner of a special prize for originality and "audacity" at the Cannes Film Festival. With David Spader, Holly Hunter, Rosanna Arquette, Elias Koteas and Deborah Kara Unger. "Love it or hate it, David Cronenberg's *Crash* will be a film to live and contend with for a long time" (F.X. Feeney, *LA Weekly*).
VHS: $31676. $100.99.
Laser: Letterboxed. LD76336. $49.95.
David Cronenberg, Canada, 1996, 90 mins.

Dead Ringers

David Cronenberg does it again in this psychological horror film starring Jeremy Irons as a pair of disturbed, identical twin gynecologists. A technical and emotional masterpiece that subtly and quite creepily delves into what makes the Mantle brothers tick. With excellent supporting work by Genevieve Bujold. Based loosely on a true story.
VHS: $09841. $19.98.
Laser: LD75933. $124.95.
David Cronenberg, Canada, 1988, 113 mins.

The Dead Zone

Christopher Walken stars in this David Cronenberg film of a Stephen King novel about a man with the ability to read the thoughts of others. This gift is more a curse than a blessing. With Brooke Adams, Tom Skerritt, Herbert Lom and Martin Sheen as a very dangerous political candidate.
VHS: $06130. $19.95.
Laser: LD75359. $29.98.
David Cronenberg, USA, 1983, 104 mins.

The Fly

Cronenberg's *The Fly* is less a remake of the original film than a remake of the original short story about a brilliant scientist who develops a system to transport objects over space and reassemble the molecules in seconds. When an accident fuses his structure with that of a fly, the initial excitement turns to horror as the insect nature begins to exert itself. With an outstanding performance by Jeff Goldblum.
VHS: $02908. $29.98.
Laser: LD70984. $24.98.
David Cronenberg, USA, 1986, 96 mins.

M. Butterfly

Jeremy Irons stars as the French diplomatic functionary seduced by an illusionist from the Beijing Opera. Set in Maoist China and inspired by a true story of espionage, this tale of romance and reversal will surprise even the most jaded viewer. Previously a Broadway hit, the film convincingly portrays the unbelievable facts behind a startling and deceptive facade.
VHS: $20712. $19.98.
Laser: LD72383. $34.98.
David Cronenberg, USA, 1993, 101 mins.

Naked Lunch

David Cronenberg succeeds in filming what many considered unfilmable. He creates a bizarre, drug inspired world based on the once-banned 1959 underground novel by William Burroughs. Peter Weller couldn't be better as a Burroughs-like novelist/junkie who is sent to Interzone on a secret mission by a talking typewriter that transmutes to a roach. With Judy Davis, Julian Sands, Ian Holm and Roy Scheider as Dr. Benway. "A thrilling, astounding, devastating piece of work" (Dave Kehr, *Chicago Tribune*).
VHS: $16382. $94.98.
Laser: LD71581. $39.98.
David Cronenberg, USA, 1991, 117 mins.

Scanners

An explosive tale of mind control and the powers that exist to govern and observe its application. Patrick McGoohan (*The Prisoner*) is the manipulative head of a scientific corporate research facility. His character is called Dr. Ruth. With Stephen Lack and Michael Ironside as the telepathic scanners and Jennifer O'Neill as decoration.
VHS: $06189. $14.98.
Laser: LD72310. $39.99.
David Cronenberg, Canada, 1981, 104 mins.

Videodrome

Videodrome is a pulsating sci-fi nightmare from macabre master David Cronenberg (*Scanners*) about a world where video can control and alter human life. Featuring a wonderfully sleazy James Woods, and Deborah Harry as a kinky talk-show hostess.
VHS: $01414. $14.98.
David Cronenberg, Canada, 1982, 87 mins.

Michael Moore

Canadian Bacon

John Candy is joined by Dan Aykroyd, Rhea Perlman, Kevin Pollak and Bill Nunn in this outrageous comedy satire. Imagine that the U.S. is threatened by a very close, immense neighbor. The country would rally together to defeat the nefarious foe. This scenario is presented to the President of the United States and he decides that in order to ensure his re-election and get those wartime industries humming, he will invade that colossus of the North, Canada.
VHS: $26804. $19.95.
Laser: LD75407. $34.95.
Michael Moore, USA, 1994, 95 mins.

Roger & Me

The funniest movie you will ever see about thousands of people losing their jobs. Journalist Michael Moore turns a jaundiced eye on the closing of several General Motors plants in his hometown of Flint, Michigan. He also attempts to have a face-to-face confrontation with GM president Roger Smith. This non-fiction film uses humor and creative license to bring attention to a serious display of corporate indifference. With Anita Bryant, Pat Boone, Ronald Reagan and Flint native Bob Eubanks.
VHS: $12231. $19.98.
Laser: LD70667. $24.98.
Michael Moore, USA, 1989, 91 mins.

Benoit Jacquot

Jacques Lacan's Psychoanalysis Part One
A priceless document for anyone interested in contemporary thought and analysis. In interviews with Jacques-Alain Miller, Jacques Lacan, the famous French psychoanalyst called by many the French Freud, exposes with unexpected simplicity his most complex theories of the unconscious; the cure, the difference between psychoanalysis and psychotherapy, love and women. "For anyone hoping to understand the institutionalization of Freudian thought and the challenge Lacan represents, this is an essential work." French with English subtitles.
VHS: $18142. $69.95.
Benoit Jacquot, France, 1974, 60 mins.

A Single Girl
This intimate drama shows a day in the life of a young Parisian woman named Valerie, played by newcomer Virginie Ledoyen (*La Ceremonie*). Before her first day at work as a room service waitress at a four-star hotel, Valerie reveals to her boyfriend Remi (Benoit Magimentl), that she is four weeks pregnant. Shot in real time, we follow Valerie around as she meditates on the paths of human nature she crosses, sometimes comic, sometimes hostile, which lead her to make important decisions about her future. "Stunning...remarkable...exerts a hypnotic grip" (Michael Wilmington, *Chicago Tribune*). French with English subtitles.
VHS: $32169. $89.98.
Benoit Jacquot, France, 1996, 90 mins.

Daniel Reeves

Amida/A Mosaic for the Kali Yuga/Arches/Body Count/ Hey Joe
"Throughout all of Reeves' videotapes there is a pervasive sense of feeling of the artist's presence, psyche and spirit, of the artist using the medium as a means of understanding himself...the evolution of his work demonstrates...a refined and spare understanding of the relationship of poetry and image," wrote *Afterimage*. A collection of video work concerned with spiritual ideas, *Amida* explores reincarnation by depicting cycles of existence through images of natural beauty juxtaposed with symbols of death. *A Mosaic for the Kali Yuga* is a meditation on the acceleration, fragmentation and devaluation of truth. *Arches* constructs a poem using text, sound and image in an exploration of language and landscapes in the desert; *Body Count* is an emotionally searing work that ironically presents the fascination of youth with military glory. *Hey Joe* is a psychedelic video set to a Jimi Hendrix song.
VHS: $10417. $59.95.
Daniel Reeves, USA, 32 mins.

Sabda and Sombra a Sombra
The title *Sabda* refers to the *word*, the original sound of life. Using digital imaging techniques to produce ghostlike, transient figures passing through landscapes, "ancient words and drawn-out beautiful images construct a profound contemplation of human existence." "Reeves' lyrical video poem, a collaboration with some of the great Indian medieval poets. In it Reeves succeeds as few Westerners have in revealing the complex reality that is India" (Deirdre Boyle). *Sombra a Sombra* is an elegy of remembrance and meditation on the architecture of the abandoned as evoked in the writing of the Peruvian poet Cesar Vallejo. Recorded over a period of years in the Alpujanas and Pyrenian mountains of Spain, the tape explores the areas of the heart shaped by the departure of the people and things of this world.
VHS: $06303. $59.95.
Daniel Reeves, USA, 32 mins.

Smothering Dreams and Thousands Watch
It does in 23 minutes what *Apocalypse Now* and *Deer Hunter* tried to do in 3 hours...One of the most compelling, eloquently visual denunciations of war in any medium," wrote one critic of *Smothering Dreams*. Based on Reeves' own experiences, the tape is an autobiographical reflection on the Vietnam War, "a cathartic recollection, burning anti-war statement and searing analysis of the mass media's role in inculcating violence and aggression from childhood onward" (Deirdre Boyle). With dramatic re-enactments of the ambush of Reeves' platoon in 1969 and of childhood memories, *Smothering Dreams* is a collage of childhood dreams of battle and adult nightmares of the atrocities of war. *Thousands Watch* is an image-processed work that demystifies the suicidal nature of the use of nuclear weapons. Using 1936 newsreel footage cutting between images of war and domestic tranquility, *Thousands Watch* is a uniquely powerful poetic statement.
VHS: $01221. $59.95.
Daniel Reeves, USA, 40 mins.

David Fincher

Alien[3]
The third entry of the baroque horror/science fiction series finds Lt. Ripley (Sigourney Weaver) the sole survivor of the previous mission, marooned on a lice-ridden, deep-space penal colony inhabited entirely by men, and acutely aware of a regenerated alien's presence.
VHS: $17770. $19.98.
David Fincher, USA, 1992, 115 mins.

Seven
Morgan Freeman and Brad Pitt are two police officers set to work on a baffling, gruesome collection of serial killings. Pitt is new to the big city, while Freeman is getting ready to retire from his hellish occupation. As they track down the murderer they descend into an arena of moral mayhem where the ultimate victim is innocence. VHS letterboxed.
DVD: DV60096. $24.98.
VHS: $27256. $19.98.
Laser: LD75472. $124.95.
David Fincher, USA, 1995, 127 mins.

Wong Kar-Wai

Ashes of Time
This moody costume drama plays out almost entirely in close-up, with dialogue spoken at a whisper. The all-star cast includes Brigette Lin Ching-Hsia, Leslie Cheung Hok-Yau, Tony Leung Kar-Fai, Tony Leung Chiu-Wai, Carina Lau Kar-Ling, Maggie Cheung Man-Yu and Jacky Cheung Hok-Yau. Action directed by Sammo Hung with characters from Jin Yong's *Eagle-Shooting Heroes*. Two-tape set. Letterboxed. Cantonese/Mandarin with English subtitles.
VHS: $30525. $89.95.
Wong Kar-Wai, Hong Kong, 1992-94

Chungking Express
From one of the hottest filmmakers on the international film circuit, Wong Kar-Wai, a visually stunning, dream-like valentine to youth and hopeless love. Wong Kar-Wai juxtaposes two quirky, offbeat love stories with beautiful, mysterious women and colorful cops against a backdrop of a Chinese fast-food restaurant. An emotionally intense post-modern romantic comedy. Cantonese with English subtitles.
VHS: $30458. $99.99.
Laser: LD76065. $39.99.
Wong Kar-Wai, Hong Kong, 1996, 102 mins.

Days of Being Wild
A critical and commercial success, this award-winning tale binds together the lives of six young people in Hong Kong during the '60s. A sort of Cantonese *Rebel Without a Cause*, but with a more typically Chinese emphasis on the bonds between

people. With Maggie Cheung Man-Yu, Andy Lau Tak-Wah, Tony Leung Chiu-Wai, Carina Lau Kar-Ling and Jacky Cheung Hok-Yau. Cantonese/Mandarin with English subtitles.
VHS: $30325. $49.95.
Wong Kar-Wai, Hong Kong, 1990

Joel and Ethan Coen

Barton Fink
An inside look in the average life of a Hollywood screenwriter as interpreted by the brothers Coen. John Turturro and John Goodman star as fellow residents of the Hotel Earle, a very quiet California hotel where the most unusual things happen. Set in 1941, this truly bizarre and scathing period drama won three major awards at the Cannes Film Festival. With Judy Davis, Jon Polito, John Mahoney and Michael Lerner as studio boss Jack Lipnick. Have you got that Barton Fink feeling?
VHS: $15450. $19.98.
Laser: Letterboxed. **LD76152. $39.98.**
Joel Coen, USA, 1991, 116 minutes.

Blood Simple
The first film scripted by the talented Coen brothers. A critically acclaimed thriller set in rural Texas tells the old story of a man who hires a sleazy private eye to kill his wife and her boyfriend. Told in a very imaginative way, it combines chilling suspense with offbeat humor, with double and triple crosses building to a blood-curdling surprise climax. The most inventive and original thriller in years.
VHS: S00149. $14.98.
Laser: LD70016. $34.98.
Joel Coen, USA, 1983, 96 mins.

Fargo
Steve Buscemi, William Macy and Frances McDormand (in her Academy Award-winning role as a pregnant homicide detective) find thievery, treachery and murder out in the frozen upper Midwest. This seemingly straightforward morality tale is laced with wicked humor. The film's deadpan style mirrors the large, cold, empty spaces of the Minnesota landscape.
DVD: DV60003. $29.95.
VHS: S29808. $19.98.
Laser: LD75990. $34.95.
Joel Coen/Ethan Coen, USA, 1996, 98 mins.

Fargo Collectors Set
Pan-and-scan letterboxed edition of the Coen Brothers hit with behind-the-scenes footage and theatrical trailer, and limited edition, numbered *Fargo* snow globe. Steve Buscemi, William Macy and Frances McDormand in an Oscar-winning performance as a very pregnant homicide detective, find thievery, treachery and murder out in the frozen upper Midwest. This seemingly straightforward morality tale is laced with wicked humor. The film's deadpan style mirrors the large, cold, empty spaces of the Minnesota landscape.
VHS: $31156. $34.95.
Joel Coen/Ethan Coen, USA, 1996, 98 mins.

Hudsucker Proxy
The Coen Brothers' inventive, dazzling (and misunderstood) "comedy of invention" features dynamite performances from Tim Robbins as the fall guy and Jennifer Jason Leigh as the persuasive reporter who falls in love with him in this funny, stylish homage to the movies.
VHS: $21897. $19.98.
Laser: Widescreen. **LD74524. $34.98.**
Joel Coen, USA, 1993, 112 mins.

Miller's Crossing
A strikingly stylish gangster film. Set in 1929, *Miller's Crossing* is the story of the friendship between Leo (Albert Finney), the city's Irish political boss, and Tom (Gabriel Byrne), Leo's cool, brainy aide. Their friendship is severed when Leo and Tom both fall in love with Verna (Marcia Gay Harden). Tom joins ranks with Leo's foremost enemy and rival for political power, and a bloody gang war erupts. Also starring John Turturro and J.E. Freeman.
VHS: $13607. $19.98.
Laser: LD71228. $39.98.
Joel Coen, USA, 1990, 115 mins.

Raising Arizona
A comedy about parental expectations and criminal activity. Nicolas Cage and Holly Hunter are a childless couple who need a little bundle of joy to make their lives complete. So they borrow one of a group of quintuplets, but complications ensue in this wacky, live-action, road-runner-like farce.
VHS: S04626. $19.95.
Laser: LD71291. $39.98.
Joel Coen, USA, 1987, 94 mins.

Peter Greenaway

26 Bathrooms
The British structuralist Peter Greenaway (*Prospero's Books*) is best known for his pattern-obsessive, symmetrical, intellectual, playful and visually flamboyant features on the nature of the body and art. This short is a brief, comic essay on his larger themes, in short a work about bathrooms and the activities and people inhabiting them.
VHS: $18203. $19.95.
Peter Greenaway, Great Britain, 1993, 30 mins.

The Cook, The Thief, His Wife and Her Lover
Few contemporary filmmakers rival director Peter Greenaway's visual complexity and elaboration. In this style he creates a graphic and layered fable that casts a cynical eye on man's most primal urges: food, lust and violence. A brutal satire on capitalism set predominantly in an exclusive restaurant called "Le Hollandais".
VHS: $13017. $19.95.
Laser: LD75309. $39.98.
Peter Greenaway, Great Britain, 1990, 123 mins.

Death in the Seine
Peter Greenaway's fascinating essay on death and revolution is set in a period between April 1795 and September 1801, when over 300 bodies were pulled from the River Seine in Paris. Two mortuary attendants dutifully noted the condition of each body in great detail, including their clothing, possessions and wounds. This bounty of information is the basis for Greenaway's structuralist speculation on the lives of these corpses and their relationship to the French Revolution.
VHS: $27254. $29.95.
Peter Greenaway, Great Britain, 1994, 44 mins.

Drowning by Numbers
Three generations of women with the same name have rid themselves of their unwanted husbands in the same manner—they drown them. The local coroner, Madgett, agrees to declare the deaths accidental in return for sexual favors. But when things don't go exactly as planned, he devises a final game that could result in the undoing of them all. Another romp through the gutter with writer/director Peter Greenaway (*The Thief, The Cook, His Wife & Her Lover*), characterized by the same sterile beauty that can be found in nearly all of his work.
VHS: $15584. $19.98.
Peter Greenaway, Great Britain, 1991, 121 mins.

The Pillow Book
Peter Greenaway's bold, stylistic experiment has, as its theme, the "correspondence" between the daughter of a famous writer and a publisher, written on the bodies of their lovers. With a bravura use of video technology, this erotic, visually beautiful film is a powerful treatise on signs, silence, communication and desire. With Ewan McGregor, Vivian Yu, Ken Ogata, Yoshi Oida, Hideko Yoshida and Judy Ongg. Japanese and Mandarin with English subtitles.
VHS: $33013. $104.95.
Peter Greenaway, France/Great Britain/Netherlands, 1996, 126 mins.

Prospero's Books
Peter Greenaway's pattern-obsessed reworking of Shakespeare's *The Tempest* furthers his thematic obsession with numbers and order. Sir John Gielgud is Prospero, the former Duke of Milan who's banished onto a magical, isolated island, where he plots his revenge against the men who dethroned him, engages in magic and spectacle, and seeks solace in his collection of extravagantly illustrated books. With

Michael Clark, Isabelle Pasco, Erland Josephson and
Michael Gambon.
VHS: $17065. $19.95.
Peter Greenaway, Great Britain, 1991, 126 mins.

David Mamet

Homicide
David Mamet's third feature stars Joe Mantegna as a
hardened Baltimore detective whose investigation of
a cop-killing drug runner is accidentally interrupted
by an anti-Semitic slaying. Confronted by his Jewish
heritage, Montegna must choose between his oath to
the police force and his sudden affiliation with the
Jewish Mafia. A powerful film which links racism
toward Blacks and the still evident hatred of Jews.
VHS: $15928. $19.95.
David Mamet, USA, 1991, 102 mins.

Oleanna
David Mamet adapted his own provocative and
acclaimed stage play that brilliantly explores the
issues of sexual harassment. William H. Macy stars
as the college professor who is forced to confront the
moral and political implications of power, blackmail
and revenge on a contemporary college campus when
he is accused of sexual harassment.
VHS: $24825. $19.98.
Laser: LD74958. $39.99.
David Mamet, USA, 1994, 90 mins.

Things Change
A hilariously funny black comedy about the Mafia
and mistaken identity from David Mamet. Joe
Mantegna is assigned to deliver Mob witness Don
Ameche to court to take a phony rap for a bigshot
hoodlum. He decides to give the old man a weekend
vacation in Lake Tahoe for being such a stand-up guy.
Problems occur when Ameche is mistaken for a
bigshot hoodlum. With Robert Prosky. Great Fun.
VHS: S09834. $14.95.
David Mamet, USA, 1988, 114 mins.

Terence Davies

The Long Day Closes
Condensed childhood memories of 1940's England
are related through elegiac and anecdotal episodes.
Like the earlier *Distant Voices/Still Lives*, this film
employs similar techniques but focuses on the mother
instead of the father, resulting in a view infiltrated by
gentle humor.
VHS: $20710. $19.95.
Terence Davies, Great Britain, 1993, 84 mins.

The Neon Bible
Based on an early novel by John Kennedy Toole, the
posthumous Pulitzer Prize-winning author of *A
Confederacy of Dunces*, *The Neon Bible* is the
bittersweet story of David, a sensitive but conflicted
young man (Jacob Tierney) growing up in the
American South of the 1940s, who turns to his
flamboyant Aunt Mae (Gena Rowlands, *A Woman
Under the Influence*) for salvation from his troubled
home life with his brutal father (Denis Leary, *The
Ref*) and emotionally-fragile mother (Diana Scarwid,
Silkwood). From the acclaimed director of *The Long
Day Closes*.
VHS: $30048. $89.98.
Terence Davies, Great Britain/USA, 1996, 92 mins.

Terence Davies Trilogy
These magical films by Terence Davies, director of
The Long Day Closes and *The Neon Bible*, are set
against the background of industrial Liverpool and
follow the main character, Robert Tucker, from his
Catholic childhood to being bullied at school, dealing
with a violent and sick father at home and struggling
with his view of his own sexuality. The three films
include *Children*, *Madonna & Child* and *Death &
Transfiguration*.
VHS: $31107. $39.99.
Terence Davies, Great Britain, 1996, 101 mins.

Nick Gomez

Laws of Gravity
Nick Gomez's first feature was shot in 12 days and
made for $38,000. It's a daring excursion into male
bravado, the story of the small-time criminal
activities of two Bensonhurst hustlers and their
strong, determined girlfriends. The plot is motivated
by the reappearance of a neighborhood criminal, who
turns up with a bag full of handguns and an
unexplained source of money. The real star is
cinematographer Jean de Segonzac, who shot the
entire movie with a hand-held camera. With Peter
Greene, Edie Falco, Adam Trese and Arabella Field.
VHS: $18443. $89.95.
Laser: LD74455. $39.99.
Nick Gomez, USA, 1992, 100 mins.

New Jersey Drive
This tough urban tale follows a crew of homeys that
live for the thrill of stealing cars. They ride them and
sell them to chopshops for cash. A policeman takes a
personal interest in stopping their game and the chase
turns violent. The odds against survival are great but
there's a chance they can get out alive. Music by
Queen Latifah, Blak Panta, Heavy D, Naughty by
Nature and others.
VHS: $26345. $19.98.
Laser: LD75056. $34.98.
Nick Gomez, USA, 1995, 98 mins.

Agnieszka Holland

Angry Harvest
Agnieszka Holland's Academy-Award nominated
film is a powerful emotional drama set during the
German occupation of Poland. The raid on the ghetto,
in which a Christian farmer saves a young Jewish
woman on the run, and their resulting relationship
becomes one of inter-dependent love and ultimate
terror that ends in tragedy. A tour-de-force of acting
and directing, the film stars Armin Mueller-Stahl,
Elisabeth Trissenaar and Wojciech Pszoniak. German
with English subtitles.
VHS: $06013. $69.95.
Agnieszka Holland, Germany, 1986, 102 mins.

Europa Europa
The film which took America by storm: Agnieszka
Holland's powerful, moving story of a courageous
German-Jewish teenager who survived World War II
by concealing his identity and living as a Nazi during
seven harrowing years through three countries. Based
on a true story; a film which changes almost everyone
who sees it. "A pure, absurd miracle of history" (*New
Yorker Magazine*). Polish, German with English
subtitles.
VHS: $16327. $19.98.
**Agnieszka Holland, Poland/France, 1991,
100 mins.**

Fever
A gripping political thriller, set in 1905. A group of
anarchists plots to assassinate the Russian Tsar's
governor in Russian-partitioned Poland. A sensitive
script subtly probes the psychological motivations of
the anarchists as the bomb is passed among them.
Banned for many years by Poland's Communist
authorities despite its winning the Grand Prize at the
Gdansk Film Festival. With Jan Kanty Pawluskiewidz
and Barbara Grabowska. Polish with English
subtitles.
VHS: $11310. $49.95.
Agnieszka Holland, Poland, 1981, 115 mins.

A Lonely Woman
Agnieszka Holland's last film made in Poland prior
to her exile in France—a powerful portrait of a
woman raising her child in a small town. Deprived of
help and friendship, she is left to her own resources.
Will an encounter with a lonely man change her life?

Very powerful drama. Polish with English subtitles.
VHS: S11348. $49.95.
Agnieszka Holland, Poland, 1987, 94 mins.

Olivier Olivier
This very unusual story begins when the nine-year-old son of a provincial French family suddenly disappears. Six years later a young man turns up who claims to be the missing youngster, setting off a series of strange reactions from the people he claims as his family. Based, unimaginably, on a true story. With Brigitte Rouan, Jean-Francois Stevenin and Francois Cluzet. French with English subtitles.
VHS: S20708. $19.95.
Laser: LD72381. $34.95.
Agnieszka Holland, France, 1992, 110 mins.

Provincial Actors
This bold first feature is set in the microcosm of a group of actors working in the provinces. While the actors are staging an important Polish play, *Liberation*, ambition, jealousy and betrayal dominate their inter-personal relations. The leading actor longs for stardom but his dreams have placed his marriage into an impossible situation. Polish with English subtitles.
VHS: S25906. $79.95.
Agnieszka Holland, Poland, 1979, 104 mins.

The Secret Garden
Agnieszka Holland's haunting adaptation of Frances Hodgson Burnett's 1909 classic about an orphaned young girl (Kate Maberly) dispatched to her uncle's remote English estate. With the help of her painfully withdrawn cousin (Heydon Prowse) and a local boy (Andrew Knott), she discovers an enchanting garden. Holland beautifully captures the painful social isolation of childhood. Maggie Smith plays the tyrannical housekeeper.
VHS: S20217. $19.98.
Laser: LD72328. $34.98.
Agnieszka Holland, USA, 1993, 102 mins.

To Kill a Priest
Polish filmmaker-in-exile Agnieszka Holland tells the powerfully realistic story of an activist priest who endured the wrath of the secret police for his secular duties. French heartthrob Christopher Lambert is the political cleric in this story based on the true case of Father Jerzy Popieluszko; Ed Harris is the Communist cop out to get him. In English.
VHS: S11786. $89.95.
Agnieszka Holland, USA/France, 1988, 117 mins.

Total Eclipse
Leonardo Di Caprio and David Thewlis star in this film based on the affair between Arthur Rimbaud and Paul Verlaine. Rimbaud left a legacy of brilliant poetry and an example of extreme living that inspired contemporary stars like Jim Morrison. Verlaine, a highly regarded writer in his own right, was an older married man when he became infatuated with Rimbaud. This is a grand film about their passion for love and art, a passion finally doomed by madness. Christopher Hampton wrote the screenplay.
VHS: S27617. $19.98.
Laser: LD75553. $39.99.
Agnieszka Holland, Great Britain/France, 1995, 111 mins.

Chris Marker

La Jetee
Chris Marker's landmark film is set in postnuclear Paris. The story concerns an astronaut who travels back through time to realize a brief affair with a woman he once glimpsed. With the exception of a haunting shot of the woman blinking, the entire film is composed with still photographs and isolated shots. French with English subtitles.
VHS: S18956. $19.95.
Chris Marker, France, 1962, 29 mins.

La Jetee/ An Occurrence at Owl Creek Bridge
One of the most challenging films ever made, Chris Marker's neo-science fiction film is set in a ruined France after World War III, in which a man's vivid childhood experience allows him to travel forward

and backward in time. As a grown man, he meets the girl he had glimpsed as a child at the airport, falls in love with her, chooses to remain in the past, but is executed by those who hold power in the future. France, 1962, 29 mins. Also contains *An Occurrence at Owl Creek Bridge*, directed by Robert Enrico and based on a short story by Ambrose Bierce, which tells the tale of a man who is about to be hanged when the rope suddenly snaps and he is able to escape. Unfortunately, his newly found freedom is short-lived. USA, 1962, 27 mins.
VHS: S06274. $39.95.

Le Joli Mai
Chris Marker's great cinema-verite study of Paris in May, 1962, the month the Algerian War came to an end and France was at peace for the first time since 1939. The first part, "Prayer from the Top of the Eiffel Tower," is about personal happiness and ambition; the second, "The Return of Fantomas," concerned with social and political issues and the relationships of people to each other. A very moving, "personal, and ironic film aided by Pierre Lhomme's superb handling of the 'living camera' " (Georges Sadoul). French with English subtitles.
VHS: S05325. $29.95.
Chris Marker, France, 1962, 180 mins.

Sans Soleil
An audacious and remarkable work from the brilliant essayist and poet Chris Marker, *Sans Soleil* visually interprets a series of letters from a wandering cameraman, based on his travels and experiences from West Africa to Tokyo as he searches for purpose, identity and self-definition through his observations, rituals, speculations, passions and predicaments. "As entertaining as *Zelig*, as visionary as *Blade Runner*" (Jim Hoberman, *Village Voice*). In English.
VHS: S18422. $29.95.
Chris Marker, France, 1983, 100 mins.

Joe Berlinger and Bruce Sinofsky

Brother's Keeper
This riveting documentary by Joe Berlinger and Bruce Sinofsky is a reconstruction of the arrest and trial of Delbert Ward in the alleged suffocation and murder of his brother Bill. Set in a small town in upstate New York, Bill, Delbert and their two other brothers lived in a squalid farmhouse with no electricity or running water. *Brother's Keeper* is a powerful work about the nature of justice and community, and the grass-roots campaign to secure Delbert's freedom and exonerate him of the charges.
VHS: S18959. $19.98.
Laser: LD72274. $39.95.
Joe Berlinger/Bruce Sinofsky, USA, 1992, 105 mins.

Paradise Lost
Called "true crime reporting at its most bitterly revealing" by *The New York Times*, this gripping documentary from the makers of *Brother's Keeper* is the true story of the brutal slaying of three eight-year-old boys and the investigation that leads to the arrest and trial of three teenagers whose only crime seems to be that they dress in black and listen to heavy metal music. The families, the townspeople and the accused all clash in their efforts to see that justice is served.
VHS: S31169. $59.98.
Joe Berlinger/Bruce Sinofsky, USA, 1996, 150 mins.

Larry Fessenden

Experienced Movers
A video epic—the story of the robbery of an art museum in "Boraxville,"—*X-Movers* savors the interpersonal seaminess of a world of petty thugs and downwardly mobile youth. A story of love and

deception, from a play by Evan McHale.
VHS: S07115. $69.96.
Larry Fessenden, USA, 1985, 140 mins.

Hollow Venus: Diary of a Go-Go Dancer

This is the story of Coco Dupree, a young New York
performance artist who dances topless in a bar called
Paradise. There she meets a mob boss called God, a
thug named Richie, and a kept woman known as
Desiree. Heather Woodbury stars in this semi-
autobiographical glimpse of a netherworld where
porn and art mix.
VHS: S22505. $29.95.
Larry Fessenden, USA, 1989, 58 mins.

No Telling

When medical researcher Geoffrey (Stephen Ramsey)
receives a summer grant to study "chemo-electric
therapy," his artist wife Lillian (Miriam Healy-
Louie), worried about infertility, hopes that the
summer will offer a little romance in her faltering
marriage. Instead, Geoffrey locks himself in the
laboratory with his animal experiments. Completely
oblivious to the true nature of her husband's work,
Lillian paints and passes time with ecologist Alex
Vine (David van Tieghem). Her feelings of
loneliness, however, are nothing compared to her
reaction when she and Alex discover what Geoffrey's
really been up to all summer. "A smart, spare, skewed
update of the Frankenstein story" (Amy Taubin, *The
Village Voice*).
VHS: S32216. $79.95.
Larry Fessenden, USA, 1991, 93 mins.

Olivier Assayas

Irma Vep

Olivier Assayas' stylish take on the world of French
surrealist film serials stars Hong Kong action film
star Maggie Cheung, who, playing herself, is brought
to Paris to star in a modern version of the famous
silent Feuillade serial, *Les Vampires*. But Jean-Pierre
Leaud, who plays the director of the film, is at the
end of his emotional rope, and the production
becomes a series of emotional entanglements
between its protagonists. Assayas' witty, acute
observations of people and places touches on the
nature of creation in a film which is a favorite of film
festivals worldwide. English and French with English
subtitles.
VHS: S32984. $89.98.
Olivier Assayas, France, 1996, 97 mins.

Idrissa Ouedraogo

Tilai

One of the most highly acclaimed contemporary
African films. In this troubling drama, a young
African man is engaged to the woman he loves until
the man's father decides that he should marry this
woman himself. This fateful decision forces the
young lovers into an illicit affair. On the run, they
find tradition and the law will play a large role in
their fate. In More with English subtitles.
VHS: S26145. $79.95.
Idrissa Ouedraogo, Burkina Faso, 1990, 81 mins.

The Secret Garden

600 Best Foreign Films

The 400 Blows
One of the landmarks of cinema, which introduced the character of Antoine Doinel, played by Jean-Pierre Leaud, to the world, as the 12-year-old boy left to his own devices in an indifferent adult world. An uncompromising film, winner of innumerable awards. French with English subtitles.
VHS: S00006. $29.95.
Laser: LD70800. $59.95.
Francois Truffaut, France, 1959, 97 mins.

8½
Fellini's great autobiographical masterpiece, the loose portrayal of a film director during the course of making a film and finding himself trapped by his fears and insecurities. Continually inventive, with the performance of a lifetime from Marcello Mastroianni as Guido, the director, and from Claudia Cardinale, Anouk Aimee and Sandra Milo. Italian with English subtitles.
VHS: S07140. $59.95.
Laser: Widescreen. LD70806. $59.95.
Federico Fellini, Italy, 1963, 138 mins.

A Nous la Liberte
The inspiration for Chaplin's *Modern Times*, an imaginative social satire about a man who escapes from prison and builds a phonograph business with an assembly line every bit as repressive as the prison he escaped from. With elegantly futuristic sets, and a memorable score. French with English subtitles.
VHS: S19455. $29.98.
Rene Clair, France, 1931, 97 mins.

Adam's Rib
A contemporary Russian social comedy reminiscent of Chekhov. Set in a crowded flat, the great Irina Churikova plays the stressed-out post-Soviet woman taking care of mute, disabled (but opportunistic) Grandma and her own two daughters. She also tries to deal with her crazed ex-husband and to put a little love into her life, with devastating and hilarious results. A warm, wry comedy. Russian with English subtitles.
VHS: S20826. $19.98.
Vyacheslav Kristofovich, Russia, 1992, 77 mins.

Age of Gold
Bunuel's masterpiece extolls love and attacks religion and the social order in an amazing assemblage of images that remain no less provocative today than they were in 1930. Its central metaphor is a couple making love who are continually disturbed by the intrusions of officialdom, police and the Church. It remains one of the most unashamedly erotic films ever made, with a famous toe-sucking sequence. Financed by the Vicomte de Noailles, who gave Bunuel complete freedom and declared it "exquisite and delicious," the film immediately became the object of right-wing extremists and remained unseen for generations because of the Church's threat to excommunicate the Vicomte if the film were distributed. With Gaston Modot, Lya Lys, Max Ernst and Pierre Prevert. French with English subtitles.
VHS: S00024. $29.95.
Luis Bunuel, France, 1930, 62 mins.

Age of the Medici
With a script based on 15th century Florentine texts, this three-part film furthers Rossellini's exploration of the artistic, social, economic and political forces in our modern world. The key figures include Cosimo de Medici, son of an important banker, who saw that the major artistic visions should be allowed free rein as long as they operated under the sponsorship of the Medici. "*The Age of the Medici* is an epic representation of a particular time and space—the extensions of which are timeless and boundless"(Eric Sherman). The three parts are: *Cosimo de Medici*, *The Power of Cosimo*, and *Leon Battista Alberti: Humanism*. One of the major cinematic achievements ever. Available only as a complete, 252 minute set. In English.
VHS: S07384. $149.95.
Roberto Rossellini, Italy, 1973, 252 mins.

Aguirre: The Wrath of God
"One of the great, mad, passionate, foolhardy masterpieces—as reckless and as brilliant as *Greed* or *Apocalypse Now*" (Roger Ebert). Shot on location in the Amazon, Klaus Kinski is Aguirre searching for El Dorado—the mythical City of Gold. German with English subtitles.
VHS: S00025. $29.95.
Werner Herzog, Germany, 1972, 94 mins.

Alexander Nevsky
A newly re-mastered, beautiful print of Eisenstein's masterpiece arrives with the famous Prokofiev score newly recorded by the St. Petersburg Philharmonic Orchestra. Russian with English subtitles.
VHS: S24740. $24.98.
Laser: LD75363. $29.98.
Sergei Eisenstein, USSR, 1938, 110 mins.

Ali: Fear Eats the Soul
A major film by Fassbinder, *Ali* is the outrageous, touching story of the bumpy love affair between a sixtyish German floorwasher and an inarticulate Arab mechanic barely half her age. A moving romance, a perverse social comedy, a biting drama of racial prejudice, *Ali: Fear Eats the Soul* is all these things, although in Fassbinder's freewheeling vision it is not always easy to tell where one leaves off and another begins. Winner of the International Critics Prize, Cannes Film Festival. German with enhanced English subtitles.
VHS: S11590. $29.95.
Rainer W. Fassbinder, Germany, 1974, 94 mins.

Alias, La Gringa
This powerful political drama from Peru follows the adventures and escapades of La Gringa, a charismatic criminal who cannot be incarcerated by any jail. Helped by an imprisoned intellectual, he escapes. Determined to aid his accomplice, he returns to prison in disguise and is trapped by a riot and corruption beyond his grasp. Spanish with English subtitles.
VHS: S20383. $59.95.
Alberto Durant, Peru, 1991, 92 mins.

All the Mornings in the World
This film combines the fervor of passionate music making and young love in 17th century France in the story of cellist Marin Marais and his learning at the hands of teacher/composer Sainte-Colombe. Gerard Depardieu and his son Guillaume star as a musician in different stages of life, who must choose between his devotion to his instructor, his love for this instructor's daughter, and his art. French with English subtitles.
VHS: S20868. $19.95.
Laser: LD74487. $39.99.
Alain Corneau, France, 1992, 110 mins.

Alphaville
Eddie Constantine is Lemmy Caution, inter-galactic

private eye, in this bravura mix of comic strip, science fiction and film noir in what is ultimately a new style of cinema in which form and content are identical. Lemmy sets out to dispose of diabolical scientist Leonard von Braun (a.k.a. Leonard Nosferatu) from Alphaville, the futuristic city run by an electronic brain, where love has been banished. A film in which poetry mixes freely with pulp to create a new dimension, a new cinematic reality. French with English subtitles.
VHS: S07702. $29.95.
Laser: LD75075. $49.95.
Jean-Luc Godard, France, 1965, 100 mins.

Amarcord
A film which breathes freedom—a nostalgic, fantastic and funny reminiscence of growing up in Fellini's home town of Rimini—made, Fellini said, to finish with youth and tenderness. Against the comic background are sets of indelible characters and an omnipresent Fascist state. *Amarcord* breathlessly shifts between the melodramatic, the intimate and the burlesque in what is a deeply personal, shared vision. The images—a peacock flying through the snow, a child on his way to school who encounters cows that the early-morning fog has transformed into monsters—are like icons; unforgettable. Italian with English subtitles.
VHS: S00042. $39.95.
Laser: LD75072. $69.95.
Federico Fellini, Italy, 1974, 127 mins.

Three Colors:
Blue, White & Red

Blue (Kieslowski)
VHS: S21359. $19.95.
Laser: LD75022. $39.99.

Blue (Jarman)
VHS: S26598. $24.95.

The Blue Angel
VHS: S10872. $24.95.

Blue Collar
VHS: S04661. $69.95.

Blue in the Face
VHS: S27691. $19.95.
Laser: LD75572. $39.99.

Blue Jeans
VHS: S00158. $59.95.

The Blue Kite
VHS: S24377. $29.95.
Laser: LD75374. $49.98.

Blue Light
VHS: S00159. $29.95.

Blue Max
VHS: S12163. $19.98.

Blue Murder at St. Trinian's
VHS: S23782. $24.95.

Blue Sky
VHS: S24407. $14.98.
Laser: LD74918. $39.99.

Electra Glide in Blue
VHS: S06058. $14.95.
Laser: LD76364. $39.99.

The Moon Is Blue
VHS: S21166. $19.98.

Rhapsody in Blue
VHS: S14314. $19.98.
Laser: LD70199. $39.88.

The Thin Blue Line, Vol. 1
VHS: S31207. $19.95.

The Thin Blue Line, Vol. 2
VHS: S31208. $19.95.

Black God, White Devil
VHS: S07299. $79.95.

The Bride with White Hair
VHS: S29996. $39.95.
Laser: LD75499. $59.95.

In the White City
VHS: S16499. $79.95.

Man in the White Suit
VHS: S00812. $14.98.

Noir et Blanc
VHS: S23599. $79.95.

Only the Ball Was White
VHS: S20421. $19.98.

White
VHS: S23108. $19.95.
Laser: LD74805. $49.95.

White Cargo
VHS: S21020. $19.98.

White Heat
VHS: S09852. $19.95.

White Hell of Pitz Palu
VHS: S11450. $24.95.

White Nights
VHS: S13679. $59.95.

White Rose
VHS: S12151. $29.95.

White Sheik
VHS: S00135. $29.95.

The White Sister
VHS: S16110. $29.95.

White Zombie
VHS: S01454. $19.98.
Laser: LD75942. $39.95.

The Woman in White
VHS: S32040. $19.98.

The Big Red One
VHS: S03528. $19.98.

Raise the Red Lantern
VHS: S17881. $19.98.

Red
VHS: S25606. $19.95.
Laser: LD75015. $39.99.

The Red and the Black
VHS: S06438. $29.95.

Red Balloon
VHS: S01098. $14.95.

Red Desert
VHS: S02080. $29.95.

Red Earth
VHS: S18687. $59.95.

Red Firecracker Green Firecracker
VHS: S26694. $19.98.
Laser: LD75383. $49.98.

Red Headed Woman
VHS: S13648. $29.98.

Red House
VHS: S04065. $19.95.

Red Pony
VHS: S01100. $19.95.
Laser: LD72022. $39.98.

Red Riding Hood
VHS: S09815. $14.95.
Laser: CAV. LD70337. $99.95.
Laser: CLV. LD70338. $49.97.

Red River
VHS: S01101. $19.95.

Red Rock West
VHS: S23356. $19.95.

Red Shoes
VHS: S01655. $14.98.

Red Sorghum
VHS: S15392. $79.95.

Reds
VHS: S02566. $29.95.

Seeing Red
VHS: S19234. $29.95.

Stepping Razor Red X: The Peter Tosh Story
VHS: S23329. $29.95.

Red River

Andrei Rublev

The dazzling and harrowing tale of the 15th century icon painter who survives the cruelties of medieval Russia to create works of art. As bloody Tartar raids, religious brutality, and pagan rites work to quell Rublev's desires and needs, he undertakes a spiritual odyssey that affirms man's ability to transcend adversity. This restored director's cut is presented in letterbox format; Russian with English subtitles.
VHS: S16526. $19.98.
   Laser: Uncut, 205 mins. Contains behind-the-scenes production footage. **LD72435. $99.95.**
Andrei Tarkovsky, USSR, 1966, 185 mins.

Anna

Anna is a nun on the verge of taking her last vows, whose sinful life as a nightclub entertainer, passion for one man and drive to marry another haunt her. Her old feelings are renewed when her former fiancee is brought to the hospital where she now serves as a nurse after a serious accident. A first-rate performance by Silvana Mangano dominates this powerful drama about the conflict between the flesh and the spirit. With Vittorio Gassman and Raf Vallone. Italian with English subtitles.
VHS: S26387. $29.95.
Alberto Lattuada, Italy, 1952, 111 mins.

Antonia's Line

In this recasting in a woman's image of a story from the book of Genesis, an 88-year-old Dutchwoman recalls her past on the last day of her life, filled with colorful characters like a Russian midwife-undertaker, a Danish recluse, a mentally disabled girl, a village idiot and a mad Madonna who howls at the moon. An Academy Award winner for Best Foreign Language Film, the film also won Best Picture at the Toronto International Film Festival. Dutch with English subtitles.
VHS: S29956. $19.98.
   Laser: LD75969. $39.99.
Marleen Gorris, The Netherlands, 1995, 102 mins.

Aparajito

The second part of Satyajit Ray's *Apu* trilogy. *Aparajito* follows Apu (Smaran Ghosal) on his intellectual odyssey from the streets of Benares to the promise and optimism of Calcutta, as he begins his college studies. Music by Ravi Shankar. "It's transitional in structure, rather than dramatic, but it's full of insights and revelations" (Pauline Kael). With Pinaki Sen Gupta, Karuna and Kanu Banerji, and Ramani Sen Gupta. Newly remastered. Bengali with English subtitles.
VHS: S27703. $19.95.
Satyajit Ray, India, 1957, 108 mins.

Arabian Nights

Pasolini's final film of his Trilogy of Life, *Arabian Nights* is a carnal comic tale following the adventures of a slave girl, Pelligrini, as she rises to power. "Rich, romantic and magnificent! Its graphic sex scenes, which have a dreamy kind of beauty to them, are erotic without being pornographic" (Vincent Canby). Italian with English subtitles.
VHS: S07021. $79.95.
Pier Paolo Pasolini, Italy, 1974, 130 mins.

The Assault

The 1987 winner of the Oscar for Best Foreign Language Picture, Fons Rademakers' epic tale is of a young boy who witnesses the brutal massacre of his family in the final days of World War II. The only survivor, the nightmarish memory haunts him until he uncovers and faces the truth. English dubbed.
VHS: S03573. $79.95.
Fons Rademakers, The Netherlands, 1986, 126 mins.

Au Revoir les Enfants (Goodbye, Children)

Louis Malle returns to the days of German occupation during World War II to recount the story of the friendship between two schoolboys, one Jewish and the other Catholic. A winner of many awards including Best Picture in France. Familiar themes are explored. Subtitled.
VHS: S08496. $19.98.
Louis Malle, France, 1988, 104 mins.

An Autumn Afternoon

This profoundly simple and moving film examines changing familial relationships in an increasingly Americanized postwar Tokyo. With his unmistakable and inimitable style, Ozu has created a serenely beautiful film which tells the timeless, moving tale of a father giving up his only daughter in marriage. Both humorous and heartbreaking, *An Autumn Afternoon* was Ozu's 53rd and last film. Japanese with English subtitles.
VHS: S15393. $69.95.
Yasujiro Ozu, Japan, 1952, 112 mins.

Autumn Marathon

Andrei is a polite and educated man, an excellent translator of Dostoevsky, and at 45, an established man of letters and college professor. Alla, 25, is genuinely in love with him and Andrei feels perfectly at home in her flat. His official domicile, however, is with Nina, 40, attractive and charming, a good mother, excellent housewife, and in need of Andrei. So, you can see that life is hard for Andrei. This Soviet comedy, scripted by popular playwright Alexander Volodin, is one of the most interesting Soviet films of the last 20 years. Russian with English subtitles.
VHS: S12971. $59.96.
Georgi Daniela, USSR, 1979, 100 mins.

Autumn Sonata

Ingmar Bergman's intense chamber drama was Ingrid Bergman's first Swedish film in almost 40 years and also her last. She plays a famed international concert pianist whose reunion with her daughter quickly deteriorates from euphoria into recriminations over the past. Rivalry, longing and guilt threaten to destroy the bonds that join a mother and her daughter. With Erland Josephson and Gunnar Bjornstrand. Swedish with English subtitles.
VHS: S00078. $39.95.
   Laser: Subtitled. **LD70848. $49.95.**
Ingmar Bergman, Sweden, 1978, 97 mins.

Ay, Carmela

The always vivacious Carmen Maura, the star of so many films by Pedro Almodovar, plays the title role of an apolitical cabaret performer caught between the combatants of the Spanish Civil War. Maura performs several lively musical numbers in this historical drama directed by Carlos Saura (*Blood Wedding*). With Andres Pajares, Gabino Diego, Miguel Rellan and Maurizio De Razza as the Italian officer in charge of staging a musical revue for a very demanding Fascist audience. In Spanish with English subtitles.
VHS: S15353. $19.95.
Carlos Saura, Spain, 1990, 105 mins.

Babette's Feast

Stephane Audran is Babette, an exiled French cook-housekeeper for a pair of devoutly religious, elderly Danish sisters. When she wins a lottery she asks to prepare a Gallic feast for the women and their friends to show her appreciation. Based on the short story by Karen Blixen (Isak Dinesen). Winner of Academy Award. Danish with English subtitles.
VHS: S08497. $19.98.
   Laser: LD70850. $39.99.
Gabriel Axel, Denmark, 1987, 102 mins.

Baker's Wife

The earthy comedy to end all earthy comedies; a young wife leaves her husband for a handsome bread shepherd—but tragedy of all French tragedies—she happens to be the baker's wife. The baker, too heartsick to bake, throws the town into panic. And the townspeople organize to cajole, lure, or force the young lady in question away from her lover and back to her husband—so they can get back to their bread. French with English subtitles.
VHS: S00088. $59.95.
Marcel Pagnol, France, 1933, 101 mins.

Ballad of a Soldier

Grigori Chukrai's poetic and elegiac war story is one of the major works of post-war Russian cinema, detailing the odd, bemused moments of a soldier's earnest seduction of a country girl while visiting his mother. The film is also devastating at capturing the dread, pain and humiliation of war, and its effects on the people. "The picture flows in such a swift, poetic way that the tragedy of it is concealed by a gentle lyric quality" (*New York Times*). With Vladimir Ivashov and Shanna Prokhorenko. Russian with English subtitles.
VHS: S17516. $29.95.
Grigori Chukrai, Russia, 1959, 89 mins.

The Ballad of Narayama

Winner of the Grand Prize at the 1983 Cannes Film Festival, *The Ballad of Narayama* is based on one of the most astonishing of all Japanese legends. A century ago in a remote mountain village, local custom dictated that when a person reached 70 years

Belle Epoque

of age, he was taken to Mount Narayama to die. A brilliant film from director Imamura that delivers a vigorous and beautiful affirmation of family, life and death. "A masterpiece of Japanese Cinema to stand beside *Ugetsu, Tokyo Story*, or *The Seven Samurai*" (M. Wilmington *LA Weekly*). Japanese with English subtitles.
  VHS: $14498. $29.95.
Shohei Imamura, Japan, 1983, 129 mins.

Band of Outsiders
Claude Brasseur, Sami Frey and Anna Karina plan to steal money hidden in a house where Karina works, but the robbery is messed up and murder is the result. Godard's thriller is set in the fringe world of *Breathless*—the world of outsiders. Most of the film takes place in a suburb of Paris, and Godard has transformed it into a setting of beauty and poignancy. Godard's three characters are "trembling on the edge of crime...dancing on the edge of the volcano" (Richard Roud). French with English subtitles.
  VHS: $00093. $29.95.
Jean-Luc Godard, France, 1964, 97 mins.

Bandit Queen
Based on the true story of an Indian woman named Phoolan. Sold into marriage at age 11 to a man 20 years her senior, this remarkable woman broke free from convention and misery. She fell in with a group of bandits and inspired a country with her bravery and fearless originality. This Indian outlaw brought a government to its knees. Hindi with English subtitles.
  VHS: $27057. $19.98.
  Laser: LD75458. $39.95.
Sheekhar Kapur, India, 1994, 119 mins.

Baron Munchausen
Only the fourth color film made in Germany, *Munchausen* employs a wide range of sensational special effects which amaze and amuse in the recounting of the adventures of the legendary hero Baron von Munchausen. The action ranges from Venice to St. Petersburg to the moon and back, as the Baron (Hans Albers) travels by horse, balloon and cannonball. The film was recently reconstructed by the Friedrich Murnau Foundation. German with English subtitles.
  VHS: $00097. $69.95.
Josef von Baky, Germany, 1943, 110 mins.

Battle of Algiers
Internationally acclaimed, the staggering newsreel-like authenticity of the staged street riots and vital performances of the actors give *Battle of Algiers* a unique dramatic impact on this detailing of the Algerian revolt against the French. French/Algerian with English subtitles.
  VHS: $01976. $29.95.
Gillo Pontecorvo, Italy, 1967, 122 mins.

Beauty and the Beast
Jean Cocteau's superb adaptation of Marie Leprince de Beaumont's dark fairy tale is a ferociously inventive and stylized depiction of erotic obsession, about a young woman's discovery of a ravaged soul beneath a monstrous beast. With Jean Marais, Josette Day and Marcel Andre. Cinematography by Henri Alekan. "A sensuously fascinating film, the visual progression of the fable into a dream-world casts its unpredictable spell" (Bosley Crowther).
  VHS: $00110. $24.95.
  Laser: Cocteau, CAV. LD70865. $89.95.
Jean Cocteau, France, 1946, 93 mins.

Before the Rain
Three intertwined stories are joined in this haunting feature about individuals facing hard choices. Set in the former Yugoslavia and London, it combines ethical and moral quandaries with compelling situations and jarringly striking settings. Academy Award nominee for Best Foreign Language Picture. English and Macedonian with English subtitles.
  VHS: $25952. $19.95.
Milcho Manchevski, GB/Macedonia/Fr., 1994, 115 mins.

Belle de Jour
A masterpiece from Luis Bunuel in which the cool Catherine Deneuve sparkles as a respectable middle-class wife with a very contented husband, who finds a day job in a brothel that gives her an outlet for deeper, darker passions. "Bunuel constructs both a clear portrait of the bourgeoisie as degenerate, dishonest and directionless, and an unhysterical depiction of Deneuve's inner fantasy life where she entertains dreams of humiliations galore" (Geoff Andrew). French with English subtitles.
  VHS: $26707. $19.98.
  Laser: LD75380. $49.98.
Luis Bunuel, France, 1967, 100 mins.

Belle Epoque
This film won an Oscar as the Best Foreign Language Film in 1994. In this charming romantic comedy, a handsome young soldier flees the Spanish Revolution only to inspire his own sexual revolution. Finding

succor in the house of an artist who has four daughters, he proceeds to seduce them all, or is it the other way around? Spanish with English subtitles.
VHS: S22768. $19.95.
Laser: LD74619. $34.95.
Fernando Trueba, Spain, 1992, 109 mins.

The Best Intentions
Danish filmmaker Bille August (*Pelle the Conquerer*) directs Ingmar Bergman's autobiographical screenplay about the early courtship, marriage and discord of Bergman's parents. Set between 1909 and 1918, *The Best Intentions* follows Henrik Bergman (Samuel Froler), an emotionally neutral Lutheran pastor, and the vivacious Anna Akerblom (Pernilla August). August and Bergman beautifully delineate the conflicts that arise between Henrik's spartan lifestyle and Anna's demands for possessions. Winner of the 1992 Palme d'Or at the Cannes Film festival. Pernilla August won the Best Actress award. Cinematography by Jorgen Persson. With Max von Sydow, Ghita Norby and Lennart Hjulstrom. Swedish with English subtitles.
VHS: S19019. $29.98.
Bille August, Sweden/Denmark, 1992, 182 mins.

Betty
Claude Chabrol's masterful tale of alienation stars Stephane Audran as a mysterious woman living in an elegant Versailles hotel, who takes in Marie Trintignant, a wife running away from an emotionless middle class marriage. Set in a world of casual affairs and ice-cold betrayals, *Betty* is a suspenseful, moving psychological study. French with English subtitles.
VHS: S21503. $89.95.
Claude Chabrol, France, 1993, 103 mins.

Beware of a Holy Whore

Beware of a Holy Whore
Hanna Schygulla and Rainer Werner Fassbinder are both featured in this film about a doomed film production unit. Both the crew and cast are besieged by every conceivable problem in a luxurious seaside hotel. As they wait for the director to show up and the producer scrambles to procure more cash, they are forced to confront themselves and each other. German with English subtitles.
VHS: S24950. $19.98.
Rainer W. Fassbinder, Germany, 1970, 103 mins.

The Bicycle Thief
Perhaps the single most important and moving film of Italian neo-realism, *Bicycle Thief* tells the deceptively simple story of an unemployed man finding work to paste up signs, work requiring a bicycle, which is then stolen. A landmark of cinema. Italian with English subtitles.
VHS: S00128. $69.95.
Laser: Original Italian dialog with English subtitles; analog track contains the English dubbed soundtrack. Includes theatrical trailer and the English dubbed version. **LD70881. $39.95.**
Vittorio de Sica, Italy, 1948, 90 mins.

Bitter Rice
In the dreary rice fields of the Po Valley, a thief on the run meets a hard-working, beautiful girl. Silvana Mangano portrays the seductive rice worker who betrays her comrades in order to steal the thief's loot, a role which rocketed her to international stardom. With Vittorio Gassman, Raf Vallone, Doris Dowling and Lia Corelli. Italian with English subtitles.
VHS: S16185. $29.95.
Giuseppe de Santis, Italy, 1949, 96 mins.

The Bitter Tears of Petra Von Kant
"A tragi-comic love story disguised as a lesbian slumber party in high-camp drag" (Molly Haskell), the film makes us a witness to the struggles for domination among three lesbians: a successful and "liberated" fashion designer, her contented and silent slave girl, and a sultry but cruel model who ends up making the master her slave. The dynamics of their interrelationships are played out in this claustrophobic, self-contained little world, accompanied only by the music of The Platters and Giuseppe Verdi. A riveting chamber drama of style. With Margit Carstensen, Hanna Schygulla, Eva Mattes and Irm Hermann. German with English subtitles.
VHS: S13914. $29.95.
Rainer W. Fassbinder, Germany, 1972, 124 mins.

Black God, White Devil
A quintessential film from Brazil's Cinema Novo, this film of immense power from Glauber Rocha is set in the impoverished Northeastern Brazil, and focuses on a poor peasant as he changes from a fanatical preacher into an honorable bandit. A violent yet lyrical portrait of Brazilian society. Portuguese with English subtitles.
VHS: S07299. $79.95.
Glauber Rocha, Brazil, 1964, 102 mins.

Black Orpheus
Marcel Camus' quintessential love story based on the Greek myth of Orpheus and Eurydice is set against the vivid backdrop of carnival in Rio de Janeiro. Orpheus, the streetcar conductor, falls hopelessly in love with Eurydice; winner of the Grand Prize at Cannes as well as an Oscar for Best Foreign Film. Portuguese with English subtitles.
VHS: S00138. $29.95.
Laser: LD70346. $79.95.
Marcel Camus, Brazil, 1958, 103 mins.

Black Rain
A somber, restrained, and very moving story detailing ten years in the life of a family which survived the nuclear bombing of Hiroshima—and the ways in which their bodies and souls were poisoned by the fallout. Filled with haunting images. Japanese with English subtitles. Letterbox format.
VHS: S14068. $19.98.
Shohei Imamura, Japan, 1988, 123 mins.

Black River
Absolute power corrupts absolutely in the Amazonian jungles of Rio Negro. First, a new governor and his ambitious wife (Angela Molina) successfully confront the brutal local chief, but the era they usher in is one of gambling, prostitution and economic exploitation. Frank Ramirez plays the head of security, who grabs control only to initiate a regime of austerity and restriction as madness buries good intentions. Spanish with English subtitles.
VHS: S27737. $59.95.
Atahualpa Lichy, Venezuela/Spain, 1990, 116 mins.

Blaise Pascal
Generally considered the finest of Rossellini's series of history films, this finely detailed portrait of life in seventeenth century France was described by Rossellini as "the drama of a man who develops scientific thought which is in conflict with the dogmatism of his deep religious faith." Rossellini's portrait of the philosopher/scientist is also a speculation on the nature of knowledge, cultural development, substance, space and time. French with English subtitles.
VHS: S06031. $79.95.
Roberto Rossellini, Italy/France, 1971, 131 mins.

Blind Chance
The film presents three different biographies of a man's life, using the "what if" formula. Depicted are the possible careers he could have chosen at the turning point in his life, including that of a physician, a political dissident and a party activist. A brave, probing film. Polish with English subtitles.
VHS: S11308. $49.95.
Krzysztof Kieslowski, Poland, 1982, 122 mins.

Blood of a Poet

The first work of the significant poet, playwright and surrealist Jean Cocteau is one of the most important contributions to early avant-garde cinema—a stunning, primal and powerful work that uses jagged, poetic, harsh and highly personal images, dreams and symbols to reflect an artist's inner life. The work is composed in four illogical, timeless sequences. French with English subtitles.
VHS: S17880. $29.95.
Laser: LD75381. $49.98.
Jean Cocteau, France, 1930, 54 mins.

Blood Wedding

A flamenco ballet version of Federico Garcia Lorca's classic, from the director of *Carmen*. The climax of this dramatic story is a duel to the death between the bridegroom and the bride's former lover. Featuring choreographer Antonio Gades, former director of the National Ballet of Spain. Music by Emilio de Diego. Spanish with English subtitles.
VHS: S00150. $24.95.
Carlos Saura, Spain, 1981, 71 mins.

Blue

Juliette Binoche stars in this provocative thriller, a role for which she won the Cesar Award and the Venice Film Festival Award as best actress. She becomes entangled in a mysterious web of passion and lies after she digs into the past life of her recently and unexpectedly deceased husband. Part One of Kieslowski's acclaimed trilogy, *Three Colors*.
VHS: S21359. $19.95.
Laser: LD75022. $39.99.
Krzysztof Kieslowski, France, 1993, 98 mins.

The Blue Angel

Josef von Sternberg's adaptation of Heinrich Mann's novel about a repressed school teacher (Emil Jannings) who is seduced and destroyed by his demonic obsession for nightclub singer Lola Lola (Marlene Dietrich). "The film is striking for its creative use of sound and its impressive recreation of the sleazy atmosphere of cabaret life" (David Cook, *The History of Narrative Film*). With Kurt Gerron, Hans Albers and Eduard von Winterstein. German with English subtitles.
VHS: S10872. $24.95.
Josef von Sternberg, Germany, 1930, 108 mins.

The Blue Kite

Banned by the Chinese government, *The Blue Kite* provides a unique window into contemporary Chinese life and politics. During the Cultural Revolution in China, a man called Teitou, his family and his friends all experienced the political and social upheavals that shook a continent. This scathing indictment of life under Chairman Mao was banned along with the filmmaker. Mandarin with English subtitles.
VHS: S24377. $29.95.
Laser: Widescreen. LD75374. $49.98.
Tian Zhuangzhuang, China, 1993, 138 mins.

Bob le Flambeur

An amazing film noir thriller and a film which anticipates the French New Wave with its gritty locations, free-wheeling camera, jump cuts and a musical jazz score. Roger Duchesne plays petty hood and small-time gambler Bob who, newly released from prison, immediately plots to rob the casino at Deauville. Shot between dusk and dawn in Pigalle, this is the quintessential "city at night" film with Bob the kind of a gangster who still has a moral code. Great cinematography by Henri Decae. French with English subtitles.
VHS: S20741. $59.95.
Jean-Pierre Melville, France, 1955, 97 mins.

Boudu Saved from Drowning

A light comedy as well as a satire on bourgeois lifestyle in France. Michel Simon is Boudu, a scruffy tramp who is saved from his suicide attempt by a bookseller. Boudu insists his rescuer is now responsible for him, and creates chaos in his new home. French with English subtitles.
VHS: S17512. $59.95.
Laser: LD75419. $39.99.
Jean Renoir, France, 1932, 87 mins.

Bread and Chocolate

Nino Manfredi stars as an Italian immigrant struggling to make a life in the difficult Teutonic world of Switzerland. This comic Everyman finds himself forced into ever more degrading situations, but he never gives up. The result is a comedy with an intense feeling of pathos. With Anna Karina. Italian

with English subtitles.
VHS: S27409. $59.95.
Franco Brusati, Italy, 1974, 109 mins.

Breathless

The landmark French New Wave film by Godard features Jean-Paul Belmondo as a small-time hood on the run from the law, having an affair with an American girl in Paris (Jean Seberg). A film which owes much to American film noir and yet revolutionized the world of film. Remastered. French with English subtitles.
VHS: S08698. $24.95.
Laser: CLV. LD71507. $49.95.
Jean-Luc Godard, France, 1959, 89 mins.

The Bridge (Die Brucke)

A powerful, deeply moving classic of German cinema. Set in 1945, seven German boys defend an insignificant bridge from an American attack. Based on the autobiographical novel of Manfred Gregor, this searing film was nominated for an Oscar and won a Golden Globe award. Its depiction of futile valor and wasted youth touched audiences the world over. German with English subtitles.
VHS: S26597. $39.95.
Bernhard Wicki, Germany, 1959, 102 mins.

Buccaneer Soul

One of Brazil's Cinema Novo's guiding spirits, Carlos Reichenbach, directs this fascinating look at Brazilian love through literature, cinema and music in the story of two friends living through the chaotic 1960s. "One of the most interesting and creative Brazilian filmmakers" (Jonathan Rosenbaum, *Chicago Reader*). Portuguese with English subtitles.
VHS: S27735. $59.95.
Carlos Reichenbach, Brazil, 1993, 116 mins.

Burnt by the Sun

This Academy Award-winning feature (Best Foreign Language Film) is a wonderfully intimate, Chekhovian idyll set in Stalinist Russia which, at its conclusion, packs an explosive political climax. Director Nikita Mikhalkov plays a legendary revolutionary hero living in a dacha outside Moscow with family and friends. Most of the film's complex relationships are seen through the innocent eyes of Mikhalkov's (and the hero's) beautiful daughter in a film that gently reveals the tragedy of living under Stalinism. Russian with English subtitles.
VHS: S26809. $19.98.
Laser: LD75391. $39.95.
Nikita Mikhalkov, Russia, 1994, 134 mins.

Butterfly Wings

This unusual drama about a dysfunctional family registers alternately as sad, horrifying and somber. Carmen hopes her unborn child is a son in order to carry on her husband's name. Guilt and fear prevent her from telling her sensitive and shy six-year-old daughter. The birth of the child triggers a series of nightmarish events. Winner of the Best Picture at the San Sebastian Film Festival. Spanish with English subtitles.
VHS: S20382. $59.95.
Juanma Bajo Ulloa, Spain, 1991, 105 mins.

Bye Bye Brazil

A small-time travelling sideshow plays over 9,000 miles of backwards Brazil, a mixture of primitivism and progress. One of the most original and entertaining films of recent years, *Bye Bye Brazil* is exotic and exuberant, and often very moving. Portuguese with English subtitles.
VHS: S00198. $19.98.
Carlos Diegues, Brazil, 1980, 110 mins.

Cabeza de Vaca

A visually spellbinding biography of the Spanish explorer Nunez Cabeza de Vaca, the sole survivor of a 16th-century Spanish shipwreck off the coast of Florida. Cabeza de Vaca discovers the Iguase, a traditional Indian tribe, which allows Cabeza into their tribe. Over the next eight years, he learns about their mysterious culture and becomes a leader of the group. But his former identity catches up with him when a team of Spanish conquistadors return to colonize the Indians. "Bold and imaginative, the film has ambition, freshness, imagination, mystery and exhilarating reach. It has greatness in it" (Jay Carr, *Boston Globe*). With Juan Diego, Daniel Gimenez Cacho and Roberto Sosa. Spanish and Indian with English subtitles.
VHS: S19356. $29.95.
Nicolas Echevarria, Mexico/Spain, 1991, 109 mins.

Cabinet of Dr. Caligari

The great Expressionist classic with Werner Krauss as Caligari, the fairground showman who hypnotizes his servant (Conrad Veidt) into committing murder at night. Famous for its distorted painted sets, its grotesque camera angles and its atmospheric horror, this cinematic landmark is now newly mastered from a 35mm archive print with an orchestral score. English intertitles.
DVD: DV60034. $29.95.
VHS: S10765. $29.95.
Laser: LD75516. $49.99.
Robert Wiene, Germany, 1919, 52 mins.

Cafe au Lait

In this audacious comedy from Mathieu Kassovitz, director of *La Haine* (*Hate*), an interracial romantic trio comes to grips with joint parenthood. A beautiful, pregnant young West Indian woman has two lovers, an African Muslim law student and a Jewish bicycle messenger, who hate one another. When she refuses to reveal which of them is the father of her expected child, they are forced to get along. French with English subtitles.
VHS: S28397. $89.95.
Mathieu Kassovitz, France, 1994, 94 mins.

Camera Buff (Amator)

In Communist Poland, a young father with a movie camera begins to pose a threat when his initial interest in filmmaking is superceded. He intended to photograph his newborn daughter, but suddenly, this newly formed shutterbug is filming everything in sight, including things the authorities would rather not have exposed. One of the key works of modern Polish cinema. Polish with English subtitles.
VHS: S21197. $79.95.
Krzysztof Kieslowski, Poland, 1979, 112 mins.

Camila

A young Catholic socialite from Buenos Aires falls in love and runs away with a young Jesuit priest. The two find temporary happiness in a small provincial village, but eventually they are recognized and ultimately condemned to death without a trial. Spanish with English subtitles.
VHS: S00209. $59.95.
Maria-Luisa Bemberg, Argentina, 1984, 90 mins.

Camille Claudel

Intense performances by Isabelle Adjani and Gerard Depardieu add fire to this adaptation of the family-"authorized" biography of overlooked sculptress Camille Claudel. After years of living with master sculptor Auguste Rodin (Depardieu) as pupil and lover, Claudel fell into a paranoid depression when he left her. Her disapproving family had her committed to a mental institution, where she wasted away for the remaining 30 years of her life. Adjani won a Cesar for her performance in this tragic story. French with English subtitles.
VHS: S12987. $19.98.
Laser: LD70900. $49.95.
Bruno Nuytten, France, 1990, 149 mins.

The Canterbury Tales

A film which fits within the context of Pasolini's explorations of bawdy, historical classics (together with *Arabian Nights* and *Decameron*), Pasolini once again seeks out the exotic and controversial aspect of Chaucer's classic. In English.
VHS: S07821. $79.95.
Pier Paolo Pasolini, Italy, 1971, 109 mins.

Captain from Koepenick

A big success, this German comedy about a cobbler, who in order to free himself from the dehumanizing effects of petty bureaucracy on the common man impersonates an army officer, is a funny social satire. German with English subtitles.
VHS: S06442. $39.95.
Helmut Kautner, Germany, 1957, 88 mins.

Caro Diario (Dear Diary)

This magical, virtually indescribable comedy by Nanni Moretti won the Best Director Prize at Cannes and follows the travails of a simple man (Moretti) in search of the true meaning of life. The film's three episodes confront, respectively, the changing character of Rome and of Moretti's generation, the possibility (and impossibility) of solitude, and the nature of truth in medicine. Often hilarious, always original, it's to say that Moretti is the Italian Woody Allen is to underestimate the pathos which underlies the accuracy of his social observations, the incisiveness of his insights. Don't miss. Italian with

English subtitles.
VHS: S23967. $19.98.
Nanni Moretti, Italy, 1994, 100 mins.

Cartouche

An 18th century cooper's son (Jean-Paul Belmondo) becomes a quick-witted and gallant thief in this hilarious spoof of swashbucklers from Philippe de Broca (*King of Hearts*). He and his friends take over the crime syndicate in Paris, and eventually dedicate themselves to avenging the death of their co-leader, Venus. With Claudia Cardinale, Odile Versois and Philippe Lemaire. French with English subtitles.
VHS: S16186. $29.95.
Philippe de Broca, France/Italy, 1964, 115 mins.

Celestial Clockwork

With her only dress on her back and a poster of her idol under her arm, a young woman dives into a modern-day fairy tale where dreams really do come true. Pursing her longtime dream in Paris, Ana's adventure is filled with distractions and obstacles, including a gay clairvoyant, an eccentric psychoanalyst, a Puerto Rican witch doctor and a jealous roommate determined to bring her down. But when all is said and done, she will become the belle of the ball. French and Spanish with English subtitles. "Outrageous, funny and a visual delight" (*Siskel & Ebert*).
VHS: S30751. $99.99.
Laser: LD76109. $39.99.
Fina Torres, Venezuela, 1996, 83 mins.

Celine and Julie Go Boating

A most wonderful film from Jacques Rivette, a multi-layered, exuberant lark about two hyperimaginative young ladies (Dominique Labourier and Juliet Berto) involved in a haunted house mystery. Considered by many critics to be the seminal movie of the '70s; a dazzling jack-in-the-box. "The most radical and delightful narrative film since *Citizen Kane*! The experience of a lifetime" (David Thomson, *Soho Weekly*). French with English subtitles.
VHS: S31131. $89.95.
Jacques Rivette, France, 1974, 193 mins.

Chapayev

A stirring account of a beloved hero of the Russian Revolution, an illiterate Russian who served in Czar's army; after the Revolution, formed his own forces and went on the Red Side, fighting the Whites. Full of incredible images, the film was made from personal experience of the filmmakers. Russian with English subtitles.
VHS: S00231. $49.95.
S. & G. Vassiliev, USSR, 1934, 100 mins.

Charuga

The spectacular, true story of a Croatian 1920s Robin Hood, a fanatic ex-soldier and Bolshevik who tried to bring the Revolution to Yugoslavia. A visually complex, engrossing, sensual and unsettling action-adventure movie which is also a serious political drama, Charuga began by robbing from the rich and giving to the poor. But as with many self-styled revolutionaries, he soon robs from everyone and keeps it all for himself. Croatian with English subtitles.
VHS: S27795. $29.95.
Rajko Grlic, Croatia, 1991, 108 mins.

Charulata (The Lonely Wife)

Ray considered this film, structured like a musical rondo, to be his best work. Set in 1879 during the social reform movement in Calcutta, it tells of Charulata (Madhabi Mukherjee, in an exquisitely graceful performance), the bored and neglected upper-class wife of the reformer Bhupati Dutta (Sailen Mukherjee). Wrapped up in the politics of the times, Bhupati is oblivious to his wife's loneliness. When his young cousin Amal (Soumitra Chatterji) arrives, Bhupati hopes that he will encourage Charulata in her reading of literature; instead, she falls in love with the young man. "Gets nearer to the heart of the 'woman's dilemma' than films which see the problem in terms of career possibilities. In so doing, [Ray] has made a film that is extraordinarily contemporary" (Molly Haskell). Fully restored. Bengali with English subtitles.
VHS: S32165. $19.95.
Satyajit Ray, India, 1964, 124 mins.

The Chekist

In 1917, secret police from the KGB forerunner, C.H.E.K.A., unleashed a reign of terror on all those considered enemies of the revolution. A Cheka officer interrogates, judges and then executes a wide

variety of people who cannot fit into the new Soviet system, from Christians and Jews to former aristocrats. Russian with English subtitles.
VHS: S29476. $89.95.
Alexandr Rogozhkin, Russia, 1992, 90 mins.

The Chess Players (Shatranj Ke Khiladi)
Ray's so-called Hindi debut film (it is actually in Urdu with English), although featuring major Hindi stars, was refused a commercial release by local distributors because of Ray's Calcutta art-house reputation. This is a colorful period drama about colonialism and indigenous culture set in 1856 at the court of Wajid Ali Shah in Lucknow. Beginning with an animated cartoon about the British annexation policy (featuring the voice of Amitabh Bachchan), this film features two narratives: the first is based on Premchand's short story about two hookah-smoking zamindars playing interminable games of chess; the second dramatizes the conflict between Wajid and General Charles Outram. Stars Sanjeev Kumar, Saeed Jaffrey, Amjad Khan, Richard Attenborough and Shabana Azmi. Urdu with English subtitles.
VHS: S30069. $29.95.
Satyajit Ray, India, 1977

Chicago Latino Cinema Collection: I
The best of contemporary Latin American cinema in six recent feature films as curated in the Chicago Latino Film Festival. The six features in this special collection, each available on a single cassette, are: *Confessing to Laura* (Jaime Osorio Gomez, Colombia); *Tango: Our Dance* (Jorge Zanada, Argentina); *Shoot to Kill* (Carlos Azpurua, Venezuela); *Butterfly Wings* (Juanma Bajo Ulloa, Spain); *Alias, La Gringa* (Alberto Durant, Peru) and *Savage Capitalism* (Andre Klotzel, Brazil). Six-volume set.
VHS: S20598. $299.99.

Chicago Latino Cinema Collection: II
Eight recent Latin American films, including the work of the legendary Argentine director Leopoldo Torre Nilsson and his son, make up this unique retrospective of award-winning contemporary films. The eight feature films in this second collection of Latin American cinema include *Buccaneer Soul* (Carlos Reichenbach, Brazil); *The Love of Silent Movies* (Pablo Torre, Argentina); *Black River* (Atahualpa Lichy, Venezuela/Spain); *We're All Stars* (Felipe Degregori, Peru); *The Day You Love Me* (Sergio Dow, Colombia); *Martin Fierro* (Loepoldo Torre Nilsson, Argentina); *Painted Lips (Boquitas Pintadas)* (Leopoldo Torre Nilsson, Argentina) and *The Seven Madmen* (*Los Siete Locos*) (Loepoldo Torre Nilsson, Argentina). Eight-volume set.
VHS: S27831. $349.99.

Chikamatsu Monogatari (Crucified Lovers)
One of the masterworks of Kenji Mizoguchi: in 17th century Japan, the illicit love between a merchant's wife and her servant leads to tragedy. Based on a story by Chikamatsu and derived from a Bunraku play, "it is perhaps Mizoguchi's most intense and concentrated study of social mores in feudal Japan and among his most visually sensuous films" (Georges Sadoul). Japanese with English subtitles.
VHS: S09097. $69.95.
Kenji Mizoguchi, Japan, 1954, 110 mins.

The Children Are Watching Us
With his fifth film, Vittorio de Sica surprised everyone by turning into a vicious critic of society. The film, set among the bourgeoisie, focuses on a marital triangle. The mother of a four-year-old boy leaves her husband for another man; the husband, unable to stand the humiliation, commits suicide. The boy, lonely and unwanted, is sent to an orphanage. The script was written by six scenarists, including Cesare Zavattini, who, through the film, emerged as a driving force in Italian cinema for many years to come. B&W. Italian with English subtitles.
VHS: S02077. $29.95.
Vittorio de Sica, Italy, 1944, 92 mins.

Children of Nature
Academy Award nominee for Best Foreign Film, *Children of Nature* is an enchanting love story about an elderly farmer, now in an old-age home, who is reunited with his childhood sweetheart. Together, they rekindle the passion of their youth and set off on an incredible adventure. Icelandic with English subtitles.
VHS: S20574. $19.98.
Fridrik Thor Fridriksson, Iceland, 1993, 85 mins.

Children of Paradise
Set in the 1840's, when pantomime and melodrama were at their height on Paris' famed theater street, the Boulevard du Crime, Marcel Carne's delicate yet elaborate portrait of the actors and thieves who made the Boulevard their home has all the passion, intelligence and authority of a truly great work of art. "The *Gone with the Wind* of art films" (Andrew Sarris).
VHS: S14499. $39.95.
Laser: CAV/CLV. Includes interview with Carne, treatment and photos. **LD70124. $89.95.**
Marcel Carne, France, 1943-45, 188 mins.

China, My Sorrow
An awestruck 13-year-old boy is arrested by Mao's cultural police for propagating obscene records during the Cultural Revolution. (He composed a love song for a 13-year-old girl.) Isolated in mountain corridors, the young boy befriends another teenage "terrorist" and an elderly Buddhist monk. He imparts on them his need to preserve their family structures and create a greater sense of self. "A deft and oddly lighthearted tribute to the traditions and the spirit of freedom that survived the Cultural Revolution" (Caryn James, *The New York Times*). With Guo Liang Yi and Tieu Quan Nghieu. Mandarin and Shanghaiese with English subtitles.
VHS: S19065. $79.95.
Dai Sijie, China, 1989, 86 mins.

A Chinese Ghost Story
An entertaining and atmospheric supernatural love story with knock-out special effects. In ancient China, a young scholar takes shelter from the rain in a haunted temple where he falls for a beautiful ghost. With the aid of a Taoist monk, the young couple battle a variety of foes (including a giant tongue which gives new meaning to the expression "I've been slimed") and even storm the gates of Hell. With Leslie Cheung, Wong Tsu Hsien, and Wu Ma.

12 Sword & Sandal Epics

Alexander the Great
VHS: S20769. $19.98.
Laser: LD71648. $39.98.

Ali Baba and the Forty Thieves
VHS: S20758. $59.95.

Ben-Hur
VHS: S02517. $29.98.
Laser: LD70524. $49.98.

Cleopatra (Colbert/De Mille)
VHS: S02669. $39.95.

Cleopatra (Taylor/Mankiewicz)
VHS: S04586. $29.95.

Fall of the Roman Empire
VHS: S09309. $29.95.
Laser: LD76007. $59.95.

Hercules
VHS: S08040. $19.98.

I, Claudius
VHS: S14130. $129.98.

Jason and the Argonauts
VHS: S08522. $14.95.
Laser: LD71557. $99.95.

Quo Vadis
VHS: S02564. $24.98.
Laser: LD70161. $39.98.

Samson and Delilah
VHS: S04340. $29.95.

Spartacus
VHS: S15075. $19.95.
Laser: LD70082. $124.95.

Cantonese with English subtitles.
VHS: $13480. $49.95.
Ching Siu Tung, Hong Kong, 1987, 93 mins.

A Chinese Ghost Story Part II
A romance story between a couple who grew up as neighbors in 1960s Hong Kong, separated, and met again while filming the movie *Everlasting*, narrated by friends of the couple and the couple's daughter, 20 years after the affair. With Andy Lau and Wu Jin Ling. Cantonese with English subtitles.
VHS: $30609. $49.95.
Cheng Xiaodong, Hong Kong, 1990, 103 mins.

Chocolat
Claire Denis takes the viewer on an emotional and strikingly visual memory trip back to the colonial Africa of her youth. In her directorial debut, she spins an engaging tale of a small white girl growing up in Cameroon on the isolated compound of her French official father and her lonely gorgeous mother. With Guilia Boschi, Issach de Bankole, Francois Cluzet and Cecile Ducasse. French with English subtitles.
VHS: $11534. $19.98.
Claire Denis, France, 1988, 105 mins.

Chungking Express
From one of the hottest filmmakers on the international film circuit, Wong Kar-Wai, a visually stunning, dream-like valentine to youth and hopeless love. Kar-Wai juxtaposes two quirky, offbeat love stories with beautiful, mysterious women and colorful cops against a backdrop of a Chinese fast-food restaurant. An emotionally intense post-modern romantic comedy. Cantonese with English subtitles.
VHS: $30458. $99.99.
Laser: LD76065. $39.99.
Wong Kar-Wai, Hong Kong, 1996, 102 mins.

Ciao, Professore
This brilliant comedy details the outrageous clash between a strict, no-nonsense teacher and his class of rambunctious, street-smart children. Ultimately it's the teacher who ends up learning more about life from his charges than the other way round. Italian with English subtitles.
VHS: $23107. $19.95.
Laser: Letterboxed. LD74806. $39.99.
Lina Wertmuller, Italy, 1993, 91 mins.

Cinema Paradiso
An affectionate salute to the magic of the movies and the individuals who spend their lives in the projection booth. This Italian film received an Oscar for Best Foreign Language Film. Philippe Noiret stars as Alfredo, the projectionist for a small Sicilian village movie palace, who opens up new worlds for one very inquisitive child. With Jaques Perrin, Salvatore Cascio, Pupella Maggio and Marco Leonardi. Italian with English subtitles.
VHS: $12603. $19.98.
Giuseppe Tornatore, Italy, 1989, 125 mins.

Circus
Grigori Alexandrov's daring attempt to import the American musical comedy form into the Soviet Union was conceived by its director as "an eccentric comedy...a real side-splitter."Its star is an American circus artiste who has a black baby—a daring conceit for 1936! The only way she can find happiness is among the Soviet people. Lyubov Orlova is the star in this rare comedy. Russian with English subtitles.
VHS: $27216. $29.95.
Grigori Alexandrov, USSR, 1936, 89 mins.

The City of Lost Children
This cross between a children's fairy tale and a hellish sci-fi nightmare questions the very nature of dreams, fantasy and the hope of a collective social fabric. Though heavy with ambition, the fantastic sets and backdrops, together with superb effects, animate a truly engrossing cast of characters. These range from a villainous pair of Siamese twins to hitmen fleas. Amidst the tumult, children struggle in a world dominated by crime and perverse ambitions. Jean-Paul Gaultier did the costumes. French with English subtitles.
VHS: $28392. $99.99.
Laser: Letterboxed. LD75826. $34.95.
Marc Caro/Jean-Pierre Jeunet, France, 1995, 112 mins.

The City of the Dogs
(La Ciudad de los Perros)
A terrific film adaptation of the great South American novel by Mario Vargas Llosa, *The City of Dogs* is the powerful story of a young man's upbringing in the military academy, and eventual disillusionment with both the military structures, the power which they represent, and the system which they enforce. The original title of Llosa's novel was "Time of the Hero". Spanish with English subtitles.
VHS: $04611. $39.95.
Francisco J. Lombardi Pery, 1985, 135 mins.

City of Women
Federico Fellini's imaginative voyage into the world of women—or, more accurately, into the world of male fantasies about women, set adrift in the threatening seas of middle-age and feminism. Part apocalyptic joyride, part funhouse, part dream, part vaudeville, *City of Women* stars Marcello Mastroianni in an outlandish work of fantasy and humor. Italian with enhanced English subtitles.
VHS: $11591. $79.95.
Federico Fellini, Italy, 1980, 138 mins.

Cleo from 5 to 7
Ninety minutes, exactly, in the life of the singer Corinne Marchand, as she waits for the results of a medical test for cancer, and meets a young soldier about to leave for the Algerian war. Because of the anticipation, every trivial incident takes on a new significance. "Produced mainly in the streets of Paris, this is a moving poem of love and death" (Georges Sadoul). With Antoine Bourseiller. French with English subtitles.
VHS: $03510. $29.95.
Agnes Varda, France/Italy, 1961, 90 mins.

The Clockmaker
Tavernier's debut film, in which Philippe Noiret is the clockmaker whose existence is shattered by the news that his son has been accused of a political murder. Tavernier invests the film with details from the cultural to the personal and domestic. French with English subtitles.
VHS: $00250. $59.95.
Bertrand Tavernier, France, 1975, 105 mins.

Close to Eden
Also known as *Urga*, Nikita Mikhalkov's film is set in the vast rolling steppes of inner Mongolia. The young Mongolian shepherd Gombo, his wife Pagma and family live a simple, 19th century existence. Their lives are interrupted a Russian truck driver named Sergei who insinuates himself into their protected lives. Sergei alters the family's traditional perspective when he takes Gombo on a revealing and hilarious trek into the city. Cinematography by Villenn Kaluta. With Badema, Bayaerty, Vladimir Gostukhin and Babushka. Russian and Mongolian with English subtitles.
VHS: $19262. $94.95.
Nikita Mikhalkov, Mongolia/USSR/France, 1991, 118 mins.

Closely Watched Trains
An ironic, funny film about a young man on his first job in a small town railroad station, trying to get sexually initiated (in hilarious scenes) who, unwittingly, becomes a tragic hero. Offbeat but tender, *Closely Watched Trains* is a comedy about frustration, eroticism and adventure. Academy Award winner for Best Foreign Picture. With Vaclav Neckar and Jitka Bendova. Czech with English subtitles.
VHS: $00252. $19.98.
Jiri Menzel, Czechoslovakia, 1966, 89 mins.

Cold Days
One of the most important Hungarian films of the 1960's, Andras Kovacs' *Cold Days* was an extremely courageous theme to tackle at the time, in view of the silence which had, until then, shrouded the Hungarian role in World War II. The film is based on the massacre of several thousand Jewish and Serbian people of Novi Sad in 1942. "The film is structured round the memories and self-justifications of four men involved in the massacre as they await trial in 1946. Each, of course, denies his complicity or responsibility...Many of the images in the film remain unforgettable." Hungarian with English subtitles.
VHS: $13338. $59.95.
Andras Kovacs, Hungary, 1966, 102 mins.

Colonel Chabert
Gerard Depardieu stars as the returning war hero who is not supposed to return. Now he faces another battle at home to claim that which is rightfully his. Honore de Balzac's novel is treated to a lush production. Also features Fanny Ardant, Fabrice Luchini and Andre Dussollier. French with English subtitles.
VHS: $24953. $14.95.
Yves Angelo, France, 1992, 111 mins.

Cries and Whispers

The Color of Pomegranates
Paradjanov's sublime mosaic on the life, art and spiritual odyssey of the 18th-century Armenian poet Sayat Nova. The film is a collection of images and tableaux that interweave landscapes, villages, costumes, props and music to form a metaphorical history of the Armenian nation. The film "achieves a sort of visionary para-surrealism through the most economical means of gesture, props and texture…A sublime and heartbreaking film" (J. Hoberman, *The Village Voice*). This director's cut repositions the shots and images and restores censored footage. With Sofico Chiaureli, M. Aleksanian and V. Galstian. Armenian with English subtitles. On the same program is *Hagop Hovnatanian*, Paradjanov's 12-minute short on the Armenian artist.
  VHS: $19064. $29.95.
Sergei Paradjanov, USSR, 1969, 78 mins.

Come and See
This towering, cathartic experience, described as "142 minutes of raw emotion," won top prizes at the Moscow and Venice film festivals. The story is based on writer Alex Adamovich's WWII memoirs of SS reprisals against partisans. Set in occupied Byelorussia in 1943, the film follows a raw teenager into the swamps and forests of the border provinces, where he undergoes a hell of atrocities, becoming a middle-aged wreck as he tries to survive the carnage. Remarkable acting, camera work, crowd scenes and direction raise the film far beyond anything comparable as director Elem Klimov manages both a savage beauty and an impassioned elegy in this anti-war film. Russian with English subtitles.
  VHS: $12963. $59.95.
Elem Klimov, USSR, 1985, 142 mins.

Comment Ca Va? (How Is It Going?)
Co-directed by Anne-Marie Mieville, Jean-Luc Godard's work—combining video and film—is a fascinating dialectic on the dissemination and processing of information, both literary and visual. Two workers of a communist newspaper strike out to make a film and video about the newspaper and the printing plant. One of the workers, Odette (Mieville), has strange ideas about content and form and how the film should be made. *Comment ca va?* is a formally brilliant work about the transmission of ideas by the

major media. French with English subtitles.
  VHS: $19232. $59.95.
Jean-Luc Godard/Anne-Marie Mieville, France, 1976, 76 mins.

Commissar
One of the most celebrated Soviet films. In 1967, a Soviet filmmaker told a tale of Jewish life, suffering, bravery and fatalism in a movie about a Red Army commissar who finds herself living with a small-town Jewish family while civil war rages around them. The film, an indictment of anti-Semitism, was Askoldov's first and last feature film. Shortly after its completion, Askoldov was fired and the film locked away. Now finally released, the film's "artistic and emotional impact is formidable…Askoldov has mastered a poetic style" (*Sight and Sound*). Russian with English subtitles.
  VHS: $12962. $59.95.
Alexander Askoldov, USSR, 1967-87, 110 mins.

Confessing to Laura
A gut-wrenching drama from Colombia which is set during a raging civil war in the aftermath of the assassination of liberal leader Jorge Elieser Gaitain in 1948. Three people are trapped in Laura's home during a riot, setting the stage for an intense, unforgettable night. Spanish with English subtitles.
  VHS: $20379. $59.95.
Jaime Osorio Gomez, Colombia, 1990, 90 mins.

The Cow
A brilliant achievement from Czech filmmaker Karel Kachyna: the parable about a simple man on a remote mountain top who cares for his ailing mother until he is forced to sell their single cow in order to buy her morphine. The mother dies anyway, but is replaced by a house maid, who in turn is replaced by another woman. This enigmatic fable-like film evokes a sense of hope amidst the most mundane events of an ordinary life in an extraordinary achievement of post-Velvet Revolution Czech cinema. Czech with English subtitles.
  VHS: $26411. $89.95.
Karel Kachyna, Czech Republic, 1994, 86 mins.

The Cranes Are Flying
A film that marked a radical opening for Soviet

Dark Side of the Heart

cinema; the lighthearted, romantic, lyrical story of a beautiful young girl (Tatiana Samoilova) caught up in the horrors of war. When her fiance (Alexei Batalov) goes off to war, she marries a man whom she does not love and who raped her, is evacuated to Siberia, and after the war, learns of her fiance's death. But she refuses to believe it and waits for his return. A great international success which won the Grand Prix at Cannes. Russian with English subtitles.
VHS: S17517. $59.95.
Mikhail Kalatozov, USSR, 1957, 94 mins.

Cries and Whispers
Ingmar Bergman's anguished, searing examination of the lust, envy, betrayal, love and self-mutilation that passes between four women—three sisters and a family provider—in this sculpted, metaphysical drama. "Bergman uses the women as metaphors for humanity, representing how we respond to anxiety, death, and the visitations of what appears to be a wrathful rather than benevolent God" (James Monaco). With Harriet Andersson, Ingrid Thulin and Liv Ullmann. Cinematography by Sven Nykvist. Swedish with English subtitles.
VHS: S00282. $39.95.
Ingmar Bergman, Sweden, 1972, 91 mins.

Crime and Punishment
Lev Kulijanov's supremely authentic translation of Dostoevsky's great novel to the screen, with Innokenti Smoktunovsky playing the Police Inspector Porfiry, and Georgi Taratorkin as the impoverished student-murderer Raskolnikov. Perhaps the best performance, however, belongs to Tatyana Bedova as Sonia, the beautiful woman with the power of redemption. Cinemascope. Russian with English subtitles.
VHS: S10718. $29.95.
Lev Kulijanov, USSR, 1970, 220 mins.

Crime of Monsieur Lange
Based on a scenario of Jacques Prevert, and one of the great films of Jean Renoir, the film sprang from Renoir's belief that the common man, by united action, could overcome tyranny. The head of a small printing press disappears with all the firm's capital. The employees band together, collect some money, and go into business as publishers of the popular novelettes of their neighbor, Monsieur Lange. "The world's greatest...director is Jean Renoir...life is always spilling over a Renoir frame as if the screen were not big enough to encompass all the humanity" (Andrew Sarris, *The Village Voice*). French with English subtitles.
VHS: S05324. $59.95.
Jean Renoir, France, 1936, 90 mins.

The Criminal Life of Archibaldo de la Cruz
Archibaldo believes a musical box he owned as a youth had the power to kill. He still believes he can kill women and, in fact, confesses to several murders. Bunuel delivers a hilarious portrait of a frustrated sadist who "is an artist...His crimes are his very conscious, aesthetic attempts to revive a delicious sensation" (Raymond Durgnat). With Ernesto Alonso, Miroslava and Rita Macedo. Spanish with English subtitles.
VHS: S18118. $29.95.
Luis Bunuel, Mexico, 1955, 91 mins.

The Crucible
Arthur Miller's dramatic masterpiece; the screenplay and dialogue were written by Jean-Paul Sartre and this French film stars Simone Signoret, Yves Montand and Mylene Demongeot. Set in Salem, Massachusetts, in 1692, the film dramatizes the persecution of witches and serves as a powerful allegory for the anti-communist hysteria of America in the 1950s. French with English subtitles.
VHS: S23571. $39.95.
Raymond Rouleau, France, 1957, 108 mins.

The Cyclist
A visually sophisticated film which deals with the themes of man's exploitation of man and the inequities between rich and poor. The cyclist is Nassim, an Afghan refugee in need of money to pay his wife's medical expenses. With work difficult to come by, a sleazy promoter suggests he undertake a bicycle marathon. Touting him as the Afghani superman, the huckster wagers that Nassim will circle a small area on the outskirts of town, day and night, for a week. Gamblers, bookies and food vendors gather to watch the desperate cyclist from the sidelines, turning his suffering to their own profit. Winner of the Best Film at the Riminicinema Film Festival. Farsi with English subtitles.
VHS: S27790. $29.95.
Mohsen Makhmalbaf, Iran, 1989, 75 mins.

Cyclo
Directed by Tran Anh Hung (*The Scent of Green Papaya*), this gritty tale of innocence lost in the urban jungle of Vietnam fuses the neorealist style of *The Bicycle Thief* with the kinetic energy of *Taxi Driver*. In the heart of Ho Chi Minh City, a young cyclo (pedicab driver) transports passengers through the streets, trying to eke out a meager living for his two sisters and elderly grandfather. When his bicycle is stolen by a local gang, he descends into a crime ring led by the charismatic Poet (Tony Leung), and his older sister turns to prostitution. Vietnamese with English subtitles.
VHS: S32014. $89.95.
Tran Anh Hung, Vietnam, 1996, 123 mins.

Cyrano de Bergerac
Gerard Depardieu is magnificent as the poetic soldier with the prominent proboscis. Based on the classic play by Rostand in which a 17th century swordsman proves inarticulate only when it comes to expressing his love for his cousin Roxanne face to face. Packed with pageantry, poetry and robust performances. With Anne Brochet, Jacques Weber, and some 2000 extras. French with English subtitles.
VHS: S14784. $19.98.
Laser: LD72215. $49.95.
Jean-Paul Rappeneau, France, 1989, 135 mins.

Danzon
This sensual, exuberant work by the gifted Mexican director Maria Novaro tells the story of Julia (Maria Rojo), a 40-year-old telephone operator and single mother whose emotional life consists of ballroom dancing. When her dancing partner disappears, Julia undertakes a grueling odyssey to locate him. Her search takes her on an extraordinary inner voyage. "One of the most enchanting surprises of the season" (Andrew Sarris). With Carmen Salinas, Blanca Guerra and Tito Vasconcelos. Spanish with English subtitles.
VHS: S19334. $19.95.
Maria Novaro, Mexico, 1991, 96 mins.

Dark Habits
An outrageous comedy from Pedro Almodovar, set in a convent that's falling apart. Mother Superior is feeling low, the youngest nun has been eaten by cannibals, and the convent hasn't saved a soul in years. But a night club singer on the run has taken refuge in the convent, and the nuns throw their wildest party yet. "Hilarious, irreverent fun," wrote *The Village Voice*, "Part Luis Bunuel, part John Waters camp. Lots of laughs." Spanish with English subtitles.
VHS: S08103. $79.95.
Pedro Almodovar, Spain, 1984, 116 mins.

Dark Side of the Heart
From the director of *Man Facing Southeast* comes this parable about a narcissistic poet in search of the perfect woman. Claiming he will not "tolerate a woman who cannot fly," young Oliverio rejects potential lovers. When he meets a prostitute named Ana who can actually fly, she prefers to keep their relationship a business arrangement. Tormented and lovelorn, Oliverio must face the consequences of pursuing his dream. An original work of magical realism by Argentina's talented Subiela. With Dario Grandineti, Sandra Ballesteros and Nacha Guevara. "Intoxicatingly lush and sensual" (*Los Angeles Times*). Spanish with English subtitles.
VHS: S32657. $89.95.
Eliseo Subiela, Argentina/Canada, 1992, 127 mins.

Das Boot: The Director's Cut
Wolfgang Petersen's riveting, claustrophobic, German U-Boat warfare drama is presented in its original widescreen theatrical release ratio. This version also includes a newly redesigned digital soundtrack. With Juergen Prochnow, Herbert Gruenemeyer and Klaus Wennemann. Presented on two cassettes. German with English subtitles.
VHS: S14834. $24.95.
Laser: 3 sides. **LD72444. $39.95.**
Wolfgang Petersen, Germany, 1981, 209 mins.

Daughters of Darkness: Director's Cut
This classic, cult vampire favorite, originally cut by more than 12 minutes, is restored to the full film that director Harry Kumel intended. A pair of newlyweds stop at a posh French hotel and encounter the Scarlet Countess (Delphine Seyrig), a stunning and seductive woman who, according to the hotel owner, hasn't aged a day in 40 years. Before long, the couple's innocent intrigue leads them into a sexually charged game of cat and mouse as the mysterious countess turns deadly. "Subtle, stately, stunningly colored and exquisitely directed.... The most artistic vampire shocker since *Blood and Roses*" (*The New York Times*). With Andrea Rau, Danielle Ouimet and John Karlen. In English.
VHS: S31446. $14.98.
Laser: Letterboxed. **LD76337. $49.95.**
Harry Kumel, Belgium/France/Germany, 1971, 100 mins.

Day for Night
Truffaut's love poem to the movies and movie-making features Truffaut playing a director who struggles to complete a film while at the same time handling the emotional problems of staff and crew. Funny and bittersweet, *Day for Night* provides insights into the movie process. Oscar winner for Best Foreign Picture, with Jean-Pierre Leaud, Jacqueline Bisset. English dubbed.
VHS: S00308. $59.95.
Francois Truffaut, France, 1973, 116 mins.

Day in the Country
Based on a story by Guy de Maupassant: "An innocent girl comes of age in Jean Renoir's short film. This lyrical tragedy rates with Renoir's greatest... Visually it recaptures the impressionist period" (Pauline Kael). French with English subtitles.
VHS: S19931. $39.95.
Jean Renoir, France, 1935, 40 mins.

The Day You Love Me
Winner of the Casa de las Americas award for Best Latin American feature, this humorous period film recaptures 1935, the year of Juan Vicente Gomez' dictatorship when Venezuela played host to the great tango singer Carlos Gardel as he presented his film *The Day You Love Me*. Romance and politics clash, exposing the lies, hopes and false dreams of an era on the eve of change as a small city meets, for the first time, the King of the Tango. Spanish with English subtitles.
VHS: S27739. $59.95.
Sergio Dow, Colombia, 1986, 80 mins.

De Mayerling a Sarajevo (Mayerling to Sarajevo)
The assassination in Sarajevo of the Archduke Franz-Ferdinand and his wife, the Countess Sophie, is the spark that starts World War I. This historical event energizes Max Ophuls' classic tale of romance, power and greed. Casting an ironic eye on the extravagance and absurdity of the ruling class and portraying a bittersweet romance against the background of operas, balls and rides through the woods, Ophuls is at his masterful best. French with English subtitles.
VHS: S30613. $29.95.
Max Ophuls, France, 1940, 89 mins.

Death in Venice
Visconti's adaptation of the classic Thomas Mann novella was a tremendous triumph; Dirk Bogarde plays the aging artist who, in Venice, becomes obsessed with the ideal beauty of a young boy. With stunning cinematography and Visconti's elegant, operatic touch. English dubbed.
VHS: S00316. $59.95.
Luchino Visconti, Italy, 1971, 130 mins.

Death of a Bureaucrat
With *Death of a Bureaucrat*, Alea pays homage to the history of film comedy—from the anarchic tradition of Bunuel and Vigo, to the satire of Billy Wilder and the physical comedy of silent greats Harold Lloyd and Buster Keaton. The story of a young man's attempt to fight the system is an entertaining and hilarious account of galloping bureaucracy and the tyranny of red tape. An adventurous mix of slapstick farce and paranoid nightmare make this comedy a rich and enjoyable frenzy of laughter. Spanish with English subtitles.
VHS: S13916. $59.95.
Tomas Gutierrez Alea, Cuba, 1966, 87 mins.

Decameron
The first part of Pasolini's great trilogy, based on the ribald tales of Boccaccio, which deal with human sensuality and artistic creation. Pasolini has re-fashioned the 100 tales into a collection of 11 sketches that is at the same time erotic, political, humorous and autobiographical. Pasolini himself appears in the role of the painter Giotto, and continues to use non-professional actors because, he said, he was fed up with the traditional cinema's "false language of realism." Italian with English subtitles.
VHS: S08260. $79.95.
Pier Paolo Pasolini, Italy, 1970, 111 mins.

Delicatessen
Imagine the Coen brothers remaking Terry Gilliam's *Brazil* on speed and you get the idea of this film, set in a vaguely post-nuclear Paris. The action unfolds in a decaying building, where a war breaks out between a group of innocents, cannibals and militant vegetarians. French with English subtitles. With Dominique Pinon (*Diva*), Laure Dougnac and Claude Dreyfus.
VHS: S18069. $89.98.
Laser: LD75125. $39.95.
Jean-Marie Jeunet/Marc Caro, France, 1991, 95 mins.

Dersu Uzala
Kurosawa's remarkable personal tale of the friendship between a wise old man and a young, Soviet explorer, filmed in the beautiful expanse of Siberia, is a unique story of man's unity with nature, and a powerful testament to faith. Russian dialog with English subtitles.
VHS: S01809. $39.95.
Laser: Widescreen. **LD75028. $69.95.**
Akira Kurosawa, Japan, 1975, 124 mins.

Devil in the Flesh
Although the theme has been done many times, Marco Bellocchio managed to shock the international festival circuit with his notoriously explicit oral sex scene between Maruschka Detmers and Federico Pitzalis. *Devil in the Flesh*, wrote *Variety*, is "paradoxically one of the funniest, lightest works Bellocchio has come up with in some time. Yes, eroticism is a key theme, and thanks to an electrifying performance by Detmers, sparks fly in all directions." Andrea is quietly studying in his last year in high school when Giulia (Detmers) comes into his life.
VHS: S09594. $19.98.
Marco Bellocchio, Italy, 1986, 110 mins.

The Devil, Probably
Predating the "after the revolution" disillusionment of recent Generation-X films, this film from French new wave master Robert Bresson follows Charles, a modern-day fallen angel, and his quartet of friends, who are all in revolt against the pollution of an industrialized consumer society. Unable to find redemption in revolution, the church, psychoanalysis or even love, Charles makes a desperate bargain with a junkie friend. Originally banned in France for its daring portrait of alienated youth, *The Devil, Probably* "expresses the malaise of our time more profoundly and more magnificently than any work of art in any medium" (Andrew Sarris, *Village Voice*). "A masterpiece! A voluptuous film!" (Francois Truffaut). French with English subtitles.
VHS: S30824. $89.95.
Robert Bresson, France, 1977, 95 mins.

Diabolique
The sadistic headmaster of a boys school is murdered by his tremulous wife and vengeful mistress in this classic French thriller. They dump the body, but suddenly the deceased appears in a recent school photograph. The suspense builds to an explosive climax. With Simone Signoret, Vera Clouzot, Paul Meurisse and Charles Vanel. French with English subtitles.
VHS: S00335. $29.95.
Laser: LD70749. $49.95.
Henri-Georges Clouzot, France, 1955, 116 mins.

Diamonds of the Night
One of the breakthrough films of the Czech New Wave; based on a short story by Arnost Lustig, and brilliantly directed by Jan Nemec, it is the story of two boys who escape from a Nazi transport train, told in a visual, surrealistic style. On the same tape is Nemec/Lustig's short film *A Loaf of Bread*. Czech with English subtitles. B.&W.
VHS: S04737. $59.95.
Jan Nemec, Czechoslovakia, 1964, 71 mins.

Diary of a Country Priest
The story of an ailing priest who believes he has failed. Pauline Kael said: "*Diary of a Country Priest* is one of the most profound emotional experiences in the history of the cinema." French with English subtitles.
VHS: S19932. $59.95.
Robert Bresson, France, 1951, 116 mins.

The Discreet Charm of the Bourgeoisie
Six characters are forever trying to sit down for a meal, but bizarre events—dreams, fantasies, guests, terrorists—interfere. Bunuel's brilliant satire lampoons the church, diplomats, wealthy socialites and radical terrorists and is a pure joy to watch. With Fernando Rey, Delphine Seyrig, Stephane Audran, Bulle Ogier, Jean-Pierre Cassel and Michel Piccoli. French with English subtitles.
VHS: S00345. $24.95.
Luis Bunuel, France, 1972, 100 mins.

Diva
A breathtaking series of visual images in this stylish romantic thriller; at the heart of the film is an opera-intoxicated 18-year-old mail carrier who becomes unwittingly entangled in a web of murder, intrigue and passion. French dialog with English subtitles.
DVD: DV60128. $29.98.
VHS: S00348. $29.95.
Laser: Widescreen. LD75998. $69.95.
Jean-Jacques Beineix, France, 1982, 123 mins.

Dodes'ka-den
Unforgettable: Kurosawa's blending of fantasy and reality in the story of a group of Tokyo slum dwellers who, cheated by life, survive on illusion and imagination. A passionate affirmation of life, beautifully photographed. The title of the film comes from the sound of the trolleys. Japanese with English subtitles.
VHS: S00351. $29.95.
Laser: LD75389. $69.99.
Akira Kurosawa, Japan, 1976, 140 mins.

Don Quixote
A masterful adaptation of Cervantes' great novel features Nikolai Cherkassov as Quixote, who becomes so impressed with tales of chivalry that he becomes a knight errant, and takes up arms to defend the poor and oppressed. Kozintsev brings to the adaptation a great sense of color, spectacle and comedy, but preserves Don Quixote's dignity. Russian with English subtitles.
VHS: S01551. $59.95.
Grigori Kozintsev, USSR, 1957, 110 mins.

Dona Barbara
Based on the 1929 novel by Romulo Gallegos, *Dona Barbara* tells of a dramatic confrontation over land and civil rights, notable for its passionate characterizations.
VHS: S04610. $39.95.
Fernando de Fuentes, Mexico, 1943, 138 mins.

The Double Life of Veronique
Two remarkably similar women, in Warsaw and Paris, are acutely aware of each other's existence in this film about the linkage of souls. Veronika is a Polish music student with a beautiful voice and a heart condition. Veronique is a French school teacher paralyzed by doubt. Both roles are played by the beautiful Irene Jacob. Slawomir Idziak's cinematography and Zbigniew Preisner's score are alternately haunting and unforgettable. Polish and French with English subtitles.
VHS: S16928. $89.95.
Laser: LD75182. $34.98.
Krzysztof Kieslowski, Poland/France, 1991, 92 mins.

Dragon Chow
A beautiful and moving film, *Dragon Chow* tells the story of Asian political refugees living on the edge of deportation in the land of economic miracles, West Germany. The film's hero, Shezad, a gentle but resourceful Pakistani, lands a job in a second-rate

Chinese restaurant, where he befriends an Oriental waiter named Xiao (Ric Young of *The Last Emperor*). Together they attempt to storm the citadel of Western capitalism by opening a restaurant of their own. German, Urdu and Mandarin with English subtitles.
VHS: S12468. $69.95.
Jan Schutte, Germany, 1987, 75 mins.

Dreams
From master director Akira Kurosawa (*Rashomon, Kagemusha, Ran*) comes perhaps his most personal film. Eight fascinating episodes dealing with war, childhood fears, the nuclear power question and man's never-ending need to harmonize with nature. Featuring breathtaking visual sequences and Martin Scorsese as Vincent Van Gogh. Japanese with English subtitles.
VHS: S13489. $92.95.
Akira Kurosawa, Japan, 1990, 120 mins.

Early Summer
Director Ozu gracefully portrays the conflicts between three generations in this classic story of a 28-year-old woman who lives with her brother, sister-in-law, nephews and aging parents and must endure their pressure to marry the man of their choice. With Setsuko Hara, Kuniko Miyake and Chishu Ryu. "A sensitively rendered film about basic human emotions made by a master filmmaker" (Leonard Maltin).
VHS: S06459. $29.95.
Laser: LD76190. $69.95.
Yasujiro Ozu, Japan, 1951, 135 mins.

Eclipse (Antonioni)
The third of Antonioni's great trilogy, with Monica Vitti the alienated woman among the upper bourgeoisie. A brilliant film, with its stupefying climax of silence, comprised of 58 shots lasting 7 minutes. Italian with English subtitles.
VHS: S00393. $29.95.
Michelangelo Antonioni, Italy, 1966, 123 mins.

Eclipse (Podeswa)
Directed by Jeremy Podeswa, the producer for Canadian icon Atom Egoyan, this offbeat feature is set the week before a total solar eclipse which will plunge the city into total darkness. As the countdown continues, people come together in love, desire and need.
VHS: S31106. $39.99.
Jeremy Podeswa, Canada/Germany, 1994, 96 mins.

Edvard Munch
This biographical dramatization of Norway's most famous artist reveals the tumultuous events of his life as recorded in Munch's own memoirs. With stuffy 19th-century Oslo as the background, the creative process of one the world's foremost expressionist painters emerges. Norwegian and German with English subtitles.
VHS: S20594. $29.95.
Peter Watkins, Norway/Sweden, 1973, 167 mins.

Effi Briest
Fassbinder's masterpiece is the German *Madame Bovary*. Hanna Schygulla plays the inexperienced, beautiful and naive woman who marries a much older Prussian diplomat, falls prey to a charming, shrewd womanizer, and suffers the consequences of an unforgiving society. Beautifully shot in black and white with elegant framing, the film is both a very accurate adaptation of the novel by Theodor Fontane, and a critical re-analysis. With Wolfgang Schenck and Ulli Lommel. German with English subtitles.
VHS: S17620. $59.95.
Rainer W. Fassbinder, Germany, 1974, 140 mins.

El (This Strange Passion)
The psychological study of a man obsessed. A wealthy, middle-aged man marries a young woman and then develops a paranoid obsession with her supposed infidelity. One of the great films from Bunuel's Mexican period, the black humor of *El* failed to be appreciated by critics at the time of its release. It is now considered one of the most representative of Bunuel's personal mythology. Spanish with English subtitles.
VHS: S13680. $24.95.
Luis Bunuel, Mexico, 1952, 88 mins.

El Super
A hilarious comedy set in New York, but made by two Cuban exiles. Roberto, a Cuban, has been a building superintendent in New York City for ten years but, from his basement-level point of view, he has eyes only for Cuba or Miami, where it doesn't

snow. With humor, compassion and accuracy, the film describes Roberto's dream of returning to his crime-free, snow-free homeland. Spanish with English subtitles.
VHS: $11592. $79.95.
L. Ichaso/O. Jimenez-Leal, USA, 1979, 90 mins.

Enjo
A superb adaptation of Mishima's novel *Temple of the Golden Pavillion*, this beautifully photographed, disturbing portrait of a man pushed to extremes is the story of innocence betrayed. The young man (played by Ichikawa) comes to post-war Kyoto to become a monk at a cherished Japanese temple. His miserably poor background and his innocence do not prepare him for the pervasive corruption of the urban world, and in a final desperate and violent act, he makes a plea for a fiery purity by setting fire to the holy temple. Japanese with English subtitles.
VHS: $23756. $79.95.
Kon Ichikawa, Japan, 1958, 98 mins.

Ermo
In this delightful comedy about men and what women want, a humble noodle-maker in a remote Chinese province feels that she is being taken for granted by family and friends. To impress them, she decides to bring home the biggest, most expensive TV she can find—no matter how many noodles she has to peddle to buy it. "A delicious comedy…a terrific surprise" (*New York Times*). Chinese with English subtitles.
VHS: $30577. $99.95.
Laser: LD76170. $39.98.
Zhou Xiaowen, China, 1995, 95 mins.

Ernesto
A lushly mounted, sensitively directed, complex depiction of homosexuality with Martin Halm as the boy who cooly tries anything and Michele Placido as the older, seducing man. "Genuinely erotic…*Ernesto* reconciles the legacies of Pasolini and Fassbinder." Italian with English subtitles.
VHS: $00416. $49.95.
Salvatore Samperi, Italy, 1983, 98 mins.

The Errors of Youth (Wild Oats)
Deemed "too close to 'real' life in the former Soviet Union" and thus banned in 1979, *The Errors of Youth* is the story of Dmitri (Stanislav Zhdanko), a former conscript in the Red Army (now a highly-paid construction worker in Siberia), who finds his love affair disintegrating over the question of children. Disillusioned, he moves to Leningrad, falls into a life

of black marketeers, and enters into a marriage of expediency. Director Boris Frumin left the unfinished film behind and emigrated to the United States, and in a historic gesture on Russia's part, was invited back to Leningrad 11 years later to complete the film. With Stanislav Zhdanko, Marina Neyelova and Natalia Varley. Russian with English subtitles.
VHS: $26332. $59.95.
Boris Frumin, USSR, 1978-1989, 87 mins.

Europa Europa
The film which took America by storm: Agnieszka Holland's powerful, moving story of a courageous German-Jewish teenager who survived World War II by concealing his identity and living as a Nazi during seven harrowing years through three countries. Based on a true story; a film which changes almost everyone who sees it. "A pure, absurd miracle of history" (*New Yorker Magazine*). Polish, German with English subtitles.
VHS: $16327. $19.98.
Agnieszka Holland, Poland/France, 1991, 100 mins.

The Exterminating Angel
A metaphorically rich and comic film, *Exterminating Angel* is the story of guests invited to an elegant dinner party who find they are unable to leave at the end of the evening. A mysterious force compels them to stay…and stay…and stay. After several days, their well-heeled social facades collapse as hunger, thirst, fear, and boredom send them into a frenzy. Bunuel stated that this film is "a metaphor, a deeply felt, disturbing reflection of the life of modern man, a witness to the fundamental preoccupations of our time." It is certainly one of Bunuel's greatest achievements. Spanish with English subtitles.
VHS: $00422. $24.95.
Luis Bunuel, Mexico, 1962, 95 mins.

Extramuros
Carmen Maura, famed for her riveting portrayals in *Women on the Verge of a Nervous Breakdown* and *Law of Desire*, plays a nun who is challenged by her irrepressible lesbian desires. Set in a convent during the Spanish Inquisition, the film is not only a depiction of repressed passion, but a sharply critical look at the relationship between the Church and political power as the convent vies for fame and money through the faked visions and stigmata of the lesbian sisters. Spanish with English subtitles.
VHS: $24033. $39.95.
Miguel Picazo, Spain, 1985, 120 mins.

The Exterminating Angel

45 Out-of-Mind Adventures

12 Monkeys
VHS: S28391. $19.98.
Laser: LD75702. $49.95.

Aguirre: The Wrath of God
VHS: S00025. $29.95.

Arsenic and Old Lace
VHS: S02351. $19.95.
Laser: LD70340. $39.95.

Camille Claudel
VHS: S12987. $19.98.
Laser: LD70900. $49.95.

Clean, Shaven
VHS: S26938. $19.98.

Dead of Night
VHS: S00314. $14.95.

Devi
VHS: S16955. $19.95.

Don't Look Now
VHS: S00358. $49.95.

Dr. Jekyll and Mr. Hyde
VHS: S05382. $29.95.

El (This Strange Passion)
VHS: S13680. $24.95.

The Fisher King
VHS: S15711. $19.95.
Laser: LD71180. $99.95.

Frances
VHS: S04335. $19.95.

From the Life of the Marionettes
VHS: S00472. $29.95.

Heavenly Creatures
VHS: S24774. $19.95.
Laser: LD74976. $39.99.

Housekeeping
VHS: S06998. $79.95.

Icy Breasts
VHS: S04246. $59.95.

King of Hearts
VHS: S00680. $19.95.
Laser: LD71078. $49.95.

Leave Her to Heaven
VHS: S23757. $19.98.
Laser: LD74915. $39.99.

Lilith
VHS: S04662. $59.95.

Marat/Sade (The Persecution and Assassination of Jean-Paul Marat as Performed by the Inmates of the Asylum of Charenton Under the Direction of Marquis de Sade)
VHS: S09855. $29.95.
Laser: LD70264. $39.95.

Mother Kusters Goes to Heaven
VHS: S16695. $29.95.

Nuts
VHS: S06813. $19.98.

One Flew Over the Cuckoo's Nest
DVD: DV60091. $24.98.
VHS: S18973. $19.98.

Play Misty for Me
VHS: S06818. $19.95.

Psycho
VHS: S01068. $19.95.
Laser: LD70068. $34.98.

Repulsion
VHS: S01106. $39.95.
Laser: LD75387. $99.95.

The Ruling Class
VHS: S01137. $39.95.

Seance on a Wet Afternoon
VHS: S01764. $29.95.

Shine
DVD: DV60098. $24.98.
VHS: S31545. $19.98.
Laser: LD76252. $39.99.

Shock Corridor
VHS: S18328. $29.95.
Laser: LD70458. $49.95.

Sling Blade
VHS: S31532. $103.99.
Laser: LD76306. $59.95.

Snake Pit
VHS: S18103. $19.98.
Laser: LD72113. $49.98.

Spellbound
VHS: S01238. $19.98.

Story of Adele H.
VHS: S01259. $19.99.
Laser: LD71510. $34.98.

Sweetie
VHS: S12478. $14.98.

The Tenant
VHS: S01308. $49.95.

The Testament of Dr. Mabuse
VHS: S04915. $24.95.

They Might Be Giants
VHS: S04966. $59.95.

The Three Faces of Eve
VHS: S18098. $19.98.
Laser: LD72339. $59.98.

What About Bob?
VHS: S27888. $19.95.

A Woman Under the Influence
VHS: S17304. $19.95.

The Eye of Vichy
Claude Chabrol strips the mask off a forbidden chapter of French history, the Vichy regime, in this controversial documentary which touches the sensitive subject of French complicity and collaboration with the Nazis during World War II. French with English subtitles.
VHS: S27610. $59.95.
Claude Chabrol, France, 1993, 110 mins.

Faraway, So Close
Otto Sander, Nastassia Kinski, Willem Dafoe and Peter Falk are joined by Lou Reed as himself and a Mikhail Gorbachev look-alike for another angel's view of Berlin. When an angel loses his wings, the temptations of earthly life inevitably tempt Satan and lead to bad memories and gangster inspired violence. English and German with English subtitles.
VHS: S21353. $94.95.
Laser: LD74473. $39.95.
Wim Wenders, Germany, 1993, 146 mins.

Farewell My Concubine
This complex story of passion and political intrigue won the Best Film Award at Cannes and is an ambitious historical epic of China in the 20th century. It follows the enduring friendship between two opera stars in old Beijing. As they prosper, the political upheavals of war and revolution take their toll. When a young prostitute threatens their professional and personal union, it becomes just one of many trials which test the enduring strength of art and love that bind these two men.
VHS: S20736. $19.95.
Laser: LD74457. $39.99.
Chen Kaige, China, 1993, 157 mins.

Farinelli
Farinelli, an 18th-century castrato, was one of Europe's most acclaimed singers. This lavishly designed, brilliantly costumed film focuses on his troubled artistic and personal life as he conquers the opera world and has women faint in his presence, yet needs his brother to consummate his sexual conquests. Corbiau ingeniously recreates the unique castrato sound by electronically blending a male and female voice; Jeroen Krabbe appears as Friedrich Handel. French with English subtitles.
VHS: S26396. $19.95.
Laser: LD75080. $34.95.
Gerard Corbiau, France/Belgium/Italy, 1995, 115 mins.

Faust
Murnau's last German production before going to Hollywood is a lavish one, inspired by Romantic painters like Caspar David Friedrich. Gosta Ekman is the elderly professor who sells his soul to the devil, Emil Jannings plays Mephistopholes and Camilla Horn is Marguerite. This version is mastered from a restored print. Silent with music track, English intertitles.
VHS: S00437. $29.95.
Friedrich W. Murnau, Germany, 1926, 117 mins.

Fellini Satyricon
Federico Fellini freely adapts the work of Petronius Arbiter in this sexual odyssey through ancient Rome. With an emphasis on spectacle and the grotesque, we follow two young Romans in their pursuit of pleasure and personal survival. With Martin Potter, Hiram Keller, Capucine and Luigi Montefiori as the

Minotaur. Letterboxed. Italian with English subtitles.
VHS: S06318. $19.98.
Laser: Widescreen. LD70979. $124.95.
Federico Fellini, Italy, 1969, 138 mins.

The Fire Within
Louis Malle's painful and devastating portrait of dissolution and self-destruction, capturing the final two days of a wealthy French writer visiting his friends, following his release from a mental asylum. Brilliantly scored by Erik Satie, the film has a harsh, bleak beauty and despair. With Maurice Ronet, Lena Skerla, Yvonne Clech and Hubert Deschamps. French with English subtitles.
VHS: S17697. $29.95.
Louis Malle, France, 1963, 108 mins.

Firemen's Ball
One of the hallmarks of the Czech New Wave, Milos Forman's anarchic and freewheeling black comedy is a wry and devastating parable about Stalinist authoritarianism. The inventive story concerns the rituals surrounding a small town's celebration of a retiring fire chief and a bizarre beauty pageant as a trenchant commentary about the social and political order. Screenplay by Ivan Passer and Jaroslav Papousek. Cinematography by Miroslav Ondricek. Forman's last Czech film. Czech with English subtitles.
VHS: S00443. $39.95.
Milos Forman, Czechoslovakia, 1967, 73 mins.

Fitzcarraldo
Herzog's saga of an impressario's obsession to bring his own opera boat up the Amazon River and over a mountain into Peru where he will have Caruso sing features Klaus Kinski, Claudia Cardinale, in a legendary production made against impossible odds. English dialog.
VHS: S00446. $69.95.
Werner Herzog, Germany, 1982, 157 mins.

The Flower of My Secret
Almodovar's fun story of a romance writer, fresh out of inspiration, who goes looking for a real-life love of her own. Starring Marisa Paredes, Juan Echanove, Carmen Elias, Rossy de Palma and Chus Lampreave. "Delicious! Funny! Almodovar returns to the comedy of his earlier, best work" (Caryn James, *The New York Times*). Spanish with English subtitles.
VHS: S30148. $19.95.
Laser: LD75995. $39.95.
Pedro Almodovar, Spain, 1996, 101 mins.

Forbidden Games
Rene Clement's beautiful allegory is the story of two children orphaned by the war who build a secret cemetery for animals and steal crosses from the church yard to mark the graves. Wonderfully natural performances from Georges Pojouly, whom Clement discovered in a camp, and Brigitte Fossey create a moving film about the effects of war on children. Winner at the Venice Film Festival and Best Foreign Film Oscar. French with English subtitles.
VHS: S00457. $29.95.
Laser: LD70988. $39.95.
Rene Clement, France, 1952, 90 mins.

Fort Saganne
This lavish recreation of the Foreign Legion genre stars Gerard Depardieu and Catherine Deneuve in one of the most expensive French films ever made. The epic film follows the story of an extraordinary leader denied the fruits of his labor because of his peasant background. He somehow manages to rise to a position of prominence. Just when he can rightly enjoy the benefits of his rank, the murderous Algerian revolt of 1914 occurs. French with English subtitles.
VHS: S21510. $89.95.
Alain Corneau, France, 1984, 180 mins.

Fortunata y Jacinta
Based on the best-known novel by the great 19th century novelist Benito Perez Galdos, who has been often compared to the Latin equivalent of Flaubert, *Fortunata y Jacinta* is a detailed, keenly observed story of two women who are in love with the same man. Spanish with English subtitles.
VHS: S04609. $39.95.
Angelino Fons, Spain, 1969, 108 mins.

Four Adventures of Reinette and Mirabelle
In many ways, Rohmer's most offbeat film since 1978's *Perceval*. The film centers on the relationship between two young women: Reinette, a naive but talented painter from the provinces, and Mirabelle, a

worldly Parisian student who meets Reinette during summer vacation and invites her to share an apartment during the upcoming school year. The narrative is partitioned into the four segments of the title, each one yielding a graceful epiphany and playing upon a central theme of the perils of idealism. A delightful comedy enhanced by Rohmer's customary richness of characterization. French with English subtitles.
VHS: S13577. $29.95.
Eric Rohmer, France, 1989, 95 mins.

Freedom Is Paradise
With his mother dead and a missing father that he has never met, 13-year-old Sasha finds himself the unwilling resident of a grim reform school. When Sasha accidentally learns of his father's whereabouts, he sets off on a 1,000 mile odyssey to a gulag-style high security prison. Russian with English subtitles.
VHS: S16260. $69.95.
Sergei Bodrov, USSR, 1989, 75 mins.

Freeze, Die, Come to Life
A brilliant Soviet film about the brutal conditions of life in and around Stalinist labor camps as seen through the eyes of two remarkable children. This first feature by Vitaly Kanevski, who also wrote the screenplay and co-produced the film, is based on some of his own experiences during the eight years he spent growing up outside such a camp. With Pavel Nazarov, Dinara Drukarova, Yelena Popova. Awarded the Camera D'Or for best first film at Cannes. Russian with English subtitles.
VHS: S15941. $19.98.
Vitaly Kanevski, USSR, 1991, 105 mins.

French Twist
Loli (Victoria Abril) thought she had the perfect marriage until she realized her husband (Alain Chabat) had been cheating on her for years. When Loli takes a mistress herself (Josiane Balasko, the film's director), her philandering husband must pour on the charm to become his own wife's lover again. Also stars Miguel Bose, Catherine Hiegel and many actors from the esteemed Comedie Francaise. French with English subtitles.
VHS: S29824. $99.99.
Laser: LD75966. $39.99.
Josiane Balasko, France, 1996, 100 mins.

Friends
A brilliant debut feature, this is the story of three South African women who find their friendship put to the test by extreme political circumstances. One of the three, a black activist, is involved in a deadly bomb incident. This sets in motion passionate and blinding forces that threaten to destroy the ideals that originally joined them. With Kerry Fox (*An Angel at My Table*). "Fascinating and bold...has a blazing urgency and passion...boasts a thrilling performance by one of the world's great young actresses, New Zealander Kerry Fox" (Michael Wilmington, *Chicago Tribune*).
VHS: S26870. $59.95.
Elaine Proctor, South Africa, 1994, 109 mins.

The Garcia Marquez Collection
A compilation of six feature films based on the stories, chronicles and novels written by Nobel Prize winner Gabriel Garcia Marquez, author of *Love in the Time of Cholera*. Includes *Miracle in Rome, Letters from the Park, Fable of the Beautiful Pigeon Fancier, The Summer of Miss Forbes, I'm the One You're Looking For* and *A Very Old Man with Enormous Wings*. All titles are in Spanish with English subtitles.
VHS: S14457. $119.88.

The Garden of the Finzi-Continis
Vittorio de Sica's (*The Bicycle Thief, Miracle in Milan*) Academy Award-winning masterpiece is visually restored and remastered in Dolby stereo. Dominique Sanda plays the daughter of a cultured Italian Jewish family of immense wealth, languishing in aristocratic privilege on their estate, oblivious, until the end, to the danger that Fascism poses for their precious world. Italian with English subtitles.
VHS: S00480. $99.99.
Laser: LD71000. $49.95.
Vittorio de Sica, Italy, 1971, 94 mins.

Germany in Autumn
Eleven leading filmmakers collaborated on this protest against Fascist tendencies in West Germany by reflecting on the tragic events of Autumn, 1977, when public official Hanns Martin Schleyer was kidnapped and murdered by the Baader-Meinhof group, whose members mysteriously died in prison.

The film's contents range from an elegiac sequence of the burial of the prisoners to newsreel clips of Rommel's cortege and a fictitious argument among TV executives about a controversial production of *Antigone*. In the amazing Fassbinder sequence, he interviews his mother, who first endorses the dictatorship and then physically abuses her boyfriend. The contradictions in the film "belong to one nation: only if all the country's contradictions are together, can you accept this history and understand it" (Alexander Kluge). Screenplay by Heinrich Boll and Peter Steinbach. Directed by Alf Brusellin, Bernhard Sinkel, Rainer W. Fassbinder, Alexander Kluge, Beate Mainka-Jellinghaus, Maximiliane Mainka, Peter Schubert, Edgar Reitz, Katja Rupe, Hans Peter Cloos and Volker Schloendorff. Germany, 1978, 134 mins.
VHS: S20729. $29.95.
Werner Fassbinder, et al., Germany, 1978, 134 mins.

Germany Year Zero
The original edition of Roberto Rossellini's great film—in its German language subtitled version. "The actors were all nonprofessionals. Made in the neo-realist style...his lyrical view of Germany in the immediate postwar period has some magnificent scenes.... Among the memorable...are the voice of Hitler on a phonograph among the ruins of the Chancellery, and the death of the hero in a gutted building" (Georges Sadoul).
VHS: S02952. $79.95.
Roberto Rossellini, Germany/Italy, 1947, 75 mins.

Germinal
Gerard Depardieu stars in this sweeping film based on Emile Zola's masterful novel. A simple but honest and charismatic miner takes on a heroic quest for justice that leads him and his entire community to a fateful end. This tale of unforgivable wrongs stirs the soul. French with English subtitles.
VHS: S22537. $19.95.
Laser: LD74612. $39.95.
Claude Berri, France, 1993, 158 mins.

Get Out Your Handkerchiefs
Raoul is a doting husband who thinks the best way to pick up his wife's spirits is with an affair. But a menage-a-trois with a bewildered stranger doesn't work, and finally hope arrives with a precocious 13-year-old Christian who achieves the seemingly impossible. An Academy Award winner for "Best Foreign Film". With Gerard Depardieu, Patrick Dewaere, Carole Laure and Michel Serrault. French with English subtitles.
VHS: S00494. $59.95.
Bertrand Blier, France, 1978, 109 mins.

Glasnost Film Festival
This remarkable 12-volume set is a unique opportunity to witness first-hand the contemporary achievements of Soviet filmmakers as they examine a broad range of topics and issues affecting their society.
VHS: S11678. $399.99.

God Is My Witness (Khuda Gawah)
Veteran Indian film actor Amitabh Bachchan stars as the noble Badshah Khan in his 85th film role. Khan meets the lovely Benazir (Sridevi) over a game of Buzkashi in Afghanistan, but before he can marry her, he must go to India and avenge Benazir's father's death. "A three-hour opus about love, prison and a man's word of honor...Spectacular!" (Anon Berger, *LA Weekly*). Winner of nine Indian Academy Awards, including Best Director, Best Cinematography and Best Supporting Actor. Featuring Nagarjun and Shilpa Shirodka. Hindi with English subtitles.
VHS: S25883. $79.95.

Gods of the Plague
Fassbinder's third feature, about a petty criminal who plans to rob a supermarket, only to be betrayed by the two women who love him. "Fassbinder's gangster film doesn't happen on the level of black limousines, bursts of machine-gun fire, blinking blondes and detective brilliance; it uses more lower-class people and shoplifters; 'little' girls who do all that for love of the great glamour" (*Goethe Institute*). With Hanna Schygulla, Harry Baer and Margarethe von Trotta. German with English subtitles.
VHS: S11149. $29.95.
Rainer W. Fassbinder, Germany, 1969, 92 mins.

The Golem
Based on the ancient Jewish legend of the clay figure created by Rabbi Loew in the 16th century to defend the Jews in the Prague ghetto against pogrom. In this great classic famous for its extraordinary crowd scenes and painted sets, the Golem falls in love with the Rabbi's daughter, terrorizes the emperor's court and is subdued by an innocent child. "The alternately terrified and exultant crowd at times recalls the flamboyant outlines and disjointed movement of a painting by El Greco" (Lotte Eisner). With Paul Wegener, Albert Steinbruck and Lyda Salmonova. Silent with music track, English titles.
VHS: S00514. $29.95.
Paul Wegener/Carl Boese, Germany, 1920, 118 mins.

Good Morning (Ohayo)
In this biting comedy, Yasujiro Ozu exposes the hypocrisy of the adult world. When a father (Chishu Ryu, *Tokyo Story*) refuses to buy a television set for his sons, the two small boys take a vow of silence, refusing to say "good morning" to a neighbor. Soon the gossipy apartment complex where they live is in an uproar—the boys' mother must be holding a grudge against her neighbors. Written by Ozu and longtime collaborator Kogo Noda, this witty film makes keen observations about communication and familial relationships. The charming performances of the young leads and a cast of Ozu regulars make it "an all-around pleasure" (*The Faber Companion to Foreign Films*). Japanese with English subtitles.
VHS: S30740. $29.95.
Yasujiro Ozu, Japan, 1959, 93 mins.

The Gorky Trilogy
The renowned Russian film series by director Mark Donskoi, which is based on the autobiography of Maxim Gorky. Here Donskoi re-creates the tone and mood of Gorky's autobiographical stories with an astounding intensity of feeling. "These dramas still retain their vast humanity and optimism, and they remain the best loved of all Soviet films" (David Robinson). Russian with English subtitles. 100 mins. each.
Part 1: My Childhood. The first and most famous part of the trilogy depicts Gorky's early life in the 1870's. At the age of four Gorky is placed in the care of his cruel grandfather and loving grandmother. After experiencing the misery of abuse and poverty with his new family, he is forced into the streets and becomes a wandering beggar. 1938.
VHS: S15372. $39.95.
Part 2: My Apprenticeship. In the second part of the trilogy, Gorky begins earning his living at the age of eight. Becoming an apprentice to a bourgeois family that falsely promises him an education, he secretly learns to read on his own and sets off on a series of land and sea voyages. During these excursions Gorky sees that the poverty and misery he has continually suffered are facts of everyday life for most of the Russian people. With this recognition he encounters the seeds of the coming revolution. 1939.
VHS: S15373. $39.95.
Mark Donskoi, USSR, 1938-40

The Gospel According to St. Matthew
Non-actors, rugged Southern Italian landscapes and towns, cinema-verite techniques, expressive close-ups are some of the elements of Pasolini's moving sacred and mythic epic. His Christ is anguished, determined, a peripatetic preacher against the afflictions of social injustice, whose miracles are matter-of-fact. Italian with English subtitles.
VHS: S18168. $29.95.
Pier Paolo Pasolini, Italy, 1964, 136 mins.

Grand Illusion
A beautifully mastered version of Jean Renoir's great masterpiece, a classic comment on war's fading glory. Set in WW I, the film tells of two French officers captured by German forces. Interred in a prison camp, the two officers encounter Von Rauffenstein, an aristocratic career officer played by von Stroheim. With Jean Gabin, Pierre Fresnay and von Stroheim.French with English subtitles.
VHS: S12469. $29.95.
Laser: LD70373. $89.95.
Jean Renoir, France, 1937, 111 mins.

The Great Madcap (El Gran Calavera)
Bunuel's hilarious portrait of the hypocrisy of the middle class centers on the disastrous results of a wealthy man's spendthrift habits and womanizing on his family. An elegant satire on class, sex, advertising and the reverse exploitation of the ruling elite. Spanish with English subtitles.
VHS: S18117. $29.95.
Luis Bunuel, Mexico, 1949, 90 mins.

The Green Wall

A breakthrough film from South America, *The Green Wall* is based on Armando Robles Godoy's own experiences of homesteading in the Peruvian jungle. *The Green Wall* is "a bitter and beautiful movie," in which "Godoy translates his experience into film poetry rather than flat reportage and uses the physical environment (exquisitely photographed by his cameraman brother, Mario) as a great natural mystery, idyllic but cruel, rich but unyielding to the will of a handsome young settler (Mexican star Julio Aleman, in a vibrant performance) who is determined to survive there with his family." The idyll is broken both by the bureaucracy in far-off Lima, and at the film's end: "The blow comes from the rain forest near their house, where father and son have constructed a mock city of clay as a symbol of the civilized stupidity they sought to escape. The film's final sequence, an almost wordless funeral, is masterful movie making, a haunting glimpse of humanity that lingers in the mind" (Pauline Kael, *The New Yorker*). "A masterpiece!" (Roger Ebert). Spanish with English subtitles.
VHS: $11250. $79.95.
Armando Robles Godoy, Peru, 1970, 110 mins.

Harikiri

This grim and exquisite film explores the honor in death and the death of honor venerated by the 17th-century samurai. After an unemployed samurai is forced to commit ritual suicide before a feudal lord, his father-in-law returns to the scene, seemingly to commit the same act. Instead this warrior acts out against the cruelly rigid society that enforces such harsh discipline. Japanese with English subtitles.
VHS: $22459. $39.95.
Masaki Kobayashi, Japan, 1962, 135 mins.

Hate (La Haine)

Winner of Best Director at the Cannes Film Festival 1995, Mathieu Kassovitz's harsh black-and-white drama of dispossessed urban youth is an unremitting look at the violence, unemployment and racial hatred that divide the young of contemporary France. Set in a Paris suburb over the course of 24 hours, the film is remarkable for the verve of its authentic performances and its gritty, realistic feel. French with English subtitles. Letterboxed.
VHS: $29387. $19.95.
Mathieu Kassovitz, France, 1995, 91 mins.

Heart of Glass

Werner Herzog's brilliant, sensual, hypnotic film about the magical and desperate attempts of the people in a small village to learn the formula for making special glass, supplied by a wandering herdsman with extraordinary powers. An apocalyptic movie with stunning imagery (cinematography by Jorg Schmidt-Reitwin) that achieves a mystical, surreal power. With Josef Bierbichler, Stefan Guttler, Clemens Scheitz, and Sepp Muller. Music by Popol

Vuh. German with English subtitles.
VHS: $17397. $29.95.
Werner Herzog, Germany, 1976, 94 mins.

Heimat

While America watched *Roots*, Germany watched *Heimat* with the same mixture of pride and shame that held a nation spellbound. The riveting 16-hour film, presented as a 9-tape boxed set, was the sensation of the Munich, London and Venice Film Festivals and a huge hit in France and Germany. It is the incredible interlocking saga of a German family from the end of World War I to 1982. Ambitious, grand, yet very intimate, *Heimat* is an incredible motion picture chronicle—an immersion in the lives, loves and tragedies of the extended Simon family. Shot over two years, the film features 28 leading performers, 140 speaking roles and a cast of 5,000 non-professional actors. German with English subtitles.
VHS: $27403. $149.95.
Edgar Reitz, Germany, 1984, 924 mins.

Heimat II

"Staggeringly rich....*The Second Heimat*, which runs 25½ hours, forms, with its predecessor, a magnificent, nearly unprecedented 'film novel': a portrait of Germany in the 20th century with few equals in either film or literature...outlandishly ambitious...an often dazzling success. That [Edgar] Reitz is able to sustain growth and tension, inexorable flow and translucent clarity through the entire vast length, and hold audiences rapt...seems something of a miracle. The story is of Maria's son, Herrmann Simon, and his life in Munich from 1960 to 1970. There, a brilliant young modernist musician and composer, he falls in with an incandescent circle of young students, artists, rebels and lovers—all brought shatteringly to life by Reitz and a splendid cast of actors and musicians...*The Second Heimat* may be the screen's finest portrayal of youth in the '60s" (Michael Wilmington, *Chicago Tribune*). German with clear English subtitles.
VHS: $27808. $249.95.
Edgar Reitz, Germany, 1994, 1416 mins.

Heimat Set

Includes *Heimat* and *The Second Heimat*.
VHS: $30170. $349.95.
Edgar Reitz, Germany, 1984/1994, 2340 mins.

The Hidden Fortress

Set during Japan's feudal wars, this restored version of Akira Kurosawa's drama concerns a gilded princess and her loyal general who undertake a dangerous journey to their homeland, assisted only by a pair of misfits and pursued by warriors and bandits attempting to loot their gold and valuable possessions. Beautifully photographed in widescreen by Ichio Yamazaki. Letterboxed. With Toshiro Mifune, Misa Uehara and Minoru Chiaki. Japanese with English subtitles. With 13 minutes of added

Hate

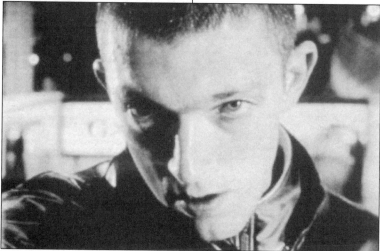

footage.
VHS: S00566. $39.95.
Laser: LD71042. $89.95.
Akira Kurosawa, Japan, 1958, 139 mins.

High Heels

Part revenge comedy, thriller and sexual farce, Pedro Almodovar's *High Heels* is a Sirkian melodrama about the bizarre relationship between an aging Spanish movie star and singer (Marisa Paredes) and her daughter, a prominent local television anchor woman (Victoria Abril). Almodovar throws in an acrobatic sex scene, a prison dance number, an on-camera confession, a buried family secret and a final reconciliation. Spanish with English subtitles.
VHS: S16919. $89.95.
Pedro Almodovar, Spain, 1990, 115 mins.

Hiroshima, Mon Amour

From the beginning, in which the love-making of a French actress (Emmanuelle Riva) and a Japanese architect (Eiji Okada) is intercut with newsreel footage of Hiroshima's atomic holocaust and its aftermath, to the couple's painful walk through the reconstructed city, Resnais' film recaptures both the pain and the richness of the war. French with English subtitles.
VHS: S00571. $29.95.
Alain Resnais, France, 1959, 91 mins.

Hour of the Wolf

Max von Sydow portrays an artist living with his wife (Liv Ullmann) on a remote island, haunted by darkness, demons and his imagination, in this effective study of the creative process. Bergman brilliantly uses the eerie landscape to show von Sydow's descent into madness as he is haunted by images of the death of a child. Swedish with English subtitles.
VHS: S17862. $39.95.
Ingmar Bergman, Sweden, 1968, 88 mins.

How Tasty Was My Little Frenchman

One of the high points of Brazil's Cinema Novo, this wicked black comedy inspired a furor at Cannes. A French explorer is captured by an Amazon tribe and tries desperately to be accepted by his captors. The tribe feeds him well—only at the end does the Frenchman realize why. A brilliant satire on the Colonialist mentality. French and Tupi with English subtitles.
VHS: S25905. $79.95.
Nelson Pereira dos Santos, Brazil, 1971, 80 mins.

The Hunt

Made under the repressive regime of Franco's Spain, this brilliant allegory deals with four men rabbit-hunting in the country outside Madrid. As the day passes, the sun gets hotter and petty jealousies spark memories and guilt about the Spanish Civil War. The day ends in violence and a shocking climax as the men's seething anger and hatreds are stripped bare. Spanish with English subtitles.
VHS: S20836. $59.95.
Carlos Saura, Spain, 1965, 87 mins.

Hyenas

Based on Friedrich Durrenmatt's play *The Visit of the Old Woman*, *Hyenas* is the story of Linguere Ramatou (Ami Diakhate), a woman who returns to the village she was banished from 30 years before. She left poor, unmarried and pregnant, and now returns wealthy, free—and vengeful. Linguere promises the people of the village of Colobane her entire fortune in exchange for the life of Dramaan Drameh (Mansour Diouf), the man who betrayed her and sent her into exile. A brilliant metaphor for post-colonial Africa. "A crowd pleaser...a wicked tale told with wit and irony" (Georgia Brown, *The Village Voice*). In Wolof with English subtitles.
VHS: S31624. $79.95.
Djibril Diop Mambety, Senegal, 1992, 113 mins.

Hypothesis of the Stolen Painting

One of the most important films of the seventies, *The Hypothesis of the Stolen Painting* began as a documentary on writer Pierre Klossowski but soon became, in Ruiz's words, "a fiction about theory." A pompous art collector offers a new history of western art through a guided tour of a fantastic gallery of "living images," all created by the "forgotten" artist, Tonnerr. As our guide drones away about aspects of his collection, the human figures begin to smirk and fidget, emphasizing their play-acting and introducing a new level of spectating into the narrative. Structured as a kind of never-ending detective thriller, Ruiz's film is a daring, fascinating meditation

on the relationship between words and images, between works of art and their description or interpretation. Photographed by Sacha Vierny. French with English subtitles.
VHS: S15343. $59.95.
Raul Ruiz, France, 1978, 67 mins.

I Am Cuba

The Cuban revolution is at the center of Mikhail Kalatazov's strange, poetic film from 1964 which unites four stories. Originally controversial because of a uniquely Russian view of Cuba, it was not widely seen. Now the film, which features a poem by Yevgeni Yevtushenko, has been re-released to critical acclaim. It offers a uniquely earthy view of Cuba in the early 1960s. Spanish with English subtitles.
VHS: S27339. $79.95.
Laser: LD75464. $69.95.
Mikhail Kalatazov, Cuba/Russia, 1964, 141 mins.

I Can't Sleep

Paralleling such recent jigsaw narratives as *Red* and *Pulp Fiction*, Claire Denis weaves together disparate fragments which gradually reveal the underlying connections between a group of disconnected characters: a tall Lithuanian blonde arrives in Paris looking for work as an actress; a West Indian musician pressures his wife to move back to Martinique; the police hunt a serial killer and a beautiful black queen performs in drag at a local nightclub. In a major atmospheric study of contemporary alienation, Denis beautifully captures the psychological undercurrents that haunt the modern urban world. French with English subtitles.
VHS: S28632. $89.95.
Claire Denis, France, 1995, 110 mins.

I the Worst of All

Based on the book *Traps of Faith* by Nobel Prize winner Octavio Paz, this is the last film completed by Maria Luisa Bemberg (*Camilla, I Don't Want to Talk About It*) before her death in 1995. The film tells the story of real-life poet and writer Sister Juana Ines de la Cruz (Assumpta Serna, *Matador*), a target of the Spanish Inquisition, and her passionate relationship with a Viceroy's wife (Dominique Sanda, *The Conformist*), who protects the nun so that she may continue her work. As the Sister's status begins to grow among the peasants, the Church attempts to silence the nun. Considered radical for her time, Sister Juana is now recognized as one of Spain's greatest poets. Spanish with English subtitles.
VHS: S27733. $29.95.
Maria Luisa Bemberg, Argentina, 1993, 100 mins.

I Vitelloni

The young, restless men in a small town on the Adriatic are, each in his own way, discontent. They spend their time pursuing diversion and girls, vaguely dreaming impossible pipe dreams. This brilliant, acid-sharp look at a generation nevertheless reveals Fellini's affection for his characters. The film "is the story of adolescents who cannot see anything more in life than satisfying their animal desires, sleeping, eating, fornication. I was trying to say there is something more, there is always more. Life must have a meaning beyond the animal" (Fellini). Italian with English subtitles.
VHS: S00601. $59.95.
Federico Fellini, Italy, 1953, 104 mins.

Ici et Ailleurs (Here and Elsewhere)

Jean-Luc Godard initiated his radical video period with this startling film that combines videotape and film, enabling him to superimpose more than two images simultaneously. Made as part of the "Dziga Vertov group," with Jean-Pierre Gorin and Anne-Marie Mieville, the film was commissioned by the Palestinians and originally titled *Until Victory*. The film's original purpose was to examine life in the Palestinian camps. But following the defeat of the Palestine army in the Six Day War, *Ici et Ailleurs* was radically transformed, becoming a meditation on how cinema records history. Godard, Gorin and Mieville contrast a French family ("Here") with an impressionstic portrait of Palestine ("Elsewhere") reflected and transmitted by television, books and pictures. French with English subtitles.
VHS: S19231. $59.95.
Jean-Luc Godard, France/Switzerland, 1970/1976

The Idiot

Drawing from Fyodor Dostoyevsky, Kurosawa transposes this bitter story to postwar Japan. Kameda, a war criminal sentenced to be shot, has been pardoned at the last moment. The shock makes him into an idiot and prone to epileptic fits. Upon release,

he is befriended by the strong and tenacious Akama. When they both fall for the beautiful Takeo Nasu, madness becomes a common denominator in this grossly tragic and haunting film. Japanese with English subtitles.
VHS: S15681. $79.95.
Akira Kurosawa, Japan, 1951, 166 mins.

Ikiru
Akira Kurosawa moved outside his usual stylistic preoccupations to make this poetic and emotionally powerful work about a gravely ill, quiet and dignified civil servant who vows to find grace and purpose in his final months, through the building of a public park. It's a thoughtful, contemplative, lyrical work centered by Takashi Shimura's virtuoso performance. With Nobuo Kaneko, Kyoko Seki and Miki Odagiri. Japanese with English subtitles.
VHS: S00608. $39.95.
Laser: LD70383. $59.95.
Akira Kurosawa, Japan, 1952, 143 mins.

Il Bell'Antonio
Marcello Mastroianni and Claudia Cardinale star in this passionate story of love and sex which was written by Pier Paolo Pasolini and Gino Visentini. Mastroianni plays the dashing Antonio Magnano, who finally relinquishes his bachelorhood and faces the loss of his libido in this ribald satire of marriage, Catholicism and machismo. Italian with English subtitles.
VHS: S20570. $24.95.
Mauro Bolognini, Italy, 1960, 115 mins.

Il Bidone
Three small-time crooks run scams on the poor by disguising themselves as priests, in this film that begins as a comedy and turns tragic. When one of them tries to double-cross the others, they beat him up and leave him to die on a stony hillside. In a powerful final sequence, he finds salvation before he dies. With Broderick Crawford, Franco Fabrizi, Giulietta Masina and Richard Basehart. English title: *The Swindle*. Italian with English subtitles.
VHS: S10873. $69.95.
Federico Fellini, Italy, 1955, 92 mins.

Il Postino (The Postman)
Massimo Troisi stars as a humble postman in a small but beautiful Italian village, whose life is transformed by the simple powers of poetry. Pablo Neruda is poet-living-in-exile who gives this bumbling mailman the right words to seduce the woman of his dreams. Troisi died abruptly after completing this role, turning this touching and deeply felt film into a highly apt but wholly unexpected memorial to his skills as a comic actor. With Maria Grazia Cucinotta and Philippe Noiret. Based on the novel *Burning Patience*, by Antonia Skarmenta. Italian with English subtitles.
VHS: S27378. $19.95.
Laser: LD75509. $39.99.
Michael Radford, Italy, 1995, 108 mins.

In a Year of Thirteen Moons
One of Fassbinder's most unusual and daring films, *In a Year of Thirteen Moons* stars Erwin Spengler as a man desperately in love with his business partner. He decides to have a sex change operation, becomes Elvira, but this fails to attract the love of his beloved. Instead, the new "she" finds a series of damaging relationships and betrayals. Fassbinder uses harsh color, asymmetrical sets, a dissonant sound track and alternating narrative techniques to evoke the pain of Erwin/Elvira in a film that stretches the boundaries of conventional storytelling. German with English subtitles.
VHS: S23998. $29.95.
Rainer W. Fassbinder, Germany, 1979, 129 mins.

In Custody
Based on the novel by Anita Desai, this comedy has all the delightful details one expects from a Merchant/Ivory production. Surrounded by wine, women and song, a great poet lives his final days in comic self-indulgence. Then an earnest professor changes everything by interviewing him. Winner, National Film of India, Best Picture and Best Actor—Shashi Kapoor. Hindi with English subtitles.
VHS: S23428. $29.95.
Ismail Merchant, India, 1993, 123 mins.

In the Jaws of Life
At the heart of this disarmingly funny and sexy comedy is a middle-aged woman filmmaker, a bit on the chubby side, with a rather confused personal life, who is making a soap opera titled *The Jaws of Life*.

Il Postino

The TV soap opera follows the life of a chubby office clerk not unlike the filmmaker. The two stories unfold side by side until the stories begin to converge. "This sex farce is as rueful as it is funny, as earthy as it is politically astute, as cleverly structured as it is unexpected" (*Village Voice*). Croatian with English subtitles.
VHS: S27796. $29.95.
Rajko Grlic, Yugoslavia, 1984, 95 mins.

In the Realm of the Senses
A scandal when it was seized by the New York customs and refused entry into the United States, and the sensation of the New York Film Festival, *In the Realm of the Senses* is, in the words of the *Los Angeles Times*, "probably the most thoughtful work of and on eroticism ever created." Explicit in its depiction of sex, and a film about the literally consuming passions of two people, the film is most infamous for its final castration sequence. Japanese with English subtitles.
VHS: S12222. $19.98.
Nagisa Oshima, Japan, 1971, 100 mins.

Indochine
Regis Wargnier's epic is set during the French occupation of Southeast Asia in the 1930s. Catherine Deneuve plays a plantation owner who searches for her adopted Vietnamese daughter Camille (Linh Dan Pham) after the young woman falls in love and becomes a communist revolutionary. "This intimate and tautly scripted work interweaves layers of deep affection with stirring historical details of 30s French Indochina, maintaining throughout an unshakable tension of a world about to change" (*Toronto Festival of Festivals*). Winner of the 1992 Academy Award for Best Foreign Language Film. French with English subtitles.
VHS: S20220. $19.95.
Laser: LD72330. $39.95.
Regis Wargnier, France, 1992, 160 mins.

The Innocent
An elegant, visually beautiful exploration of the constraints of marriage and its disintegration. Featuring a remarkably sensuous performance by Laura Antonelli, and an equally strong performance from Giancarlo Giannini. "*The Innocent* is one of

Visconti's most beautiful films" (Vincent Canby). Italian with English subtitles.
VHS: $00625. $29.95.
Luchino Visconti, Italy, 1976, 125 mins.

Inspector General
Gogol's famous play, performed by members of the Moscow Art Theatre, filmed by Vladimir Petrov. Gogol's work is a satire of provincial corruption in Czarist Russia. An entire town mistakes an illiterate worker for the Czar's Inspector General, and the corrupt officials panic as they believe the man has come to check up on them. Russian with English subtitles.
VHS: $00628. $49.95.
Vladimir Petrov, USSR, 1954, 128 mins.

Interrogation
The 1990 Cannes Film Festival awarded its Best Actress Award to Krystyna Janda for her performance in this intense drama of a woman victimized by a Stalinist government. The film details the horrible abuse of a cabaret singer in 1950's Warsaw who is arrested after a one night stand with a military officer. Originally banned by the Polish government, *Interrogation* is one of the most powerful films to come out of Poland in the last several decades. Polish with English subtitles.
VHS: $14066. $79.95.
Ryszard Bugajski, Poland, 1982, 118 mins.

Intervista
Fellini's movie combines the film-within-a-film, the essay memoir, a playful recollection of previous works and an eerie conflating of the past and present in this surreal and imaginative distillation of a man's life and work. As Fellini prepares to adapt Kafka's *Amerika*, his every move and gesture is captured by a Japanese documentary crew. The structure allows Fellini to delve into his past, with visits from Marcello Mastroianni and Anita Ekberg and profound remembrances of *La Dolce Vita*. "An enchanting work, a magical mixture of recollection, parody, memoir, satire, self-examination, and joyous fantasy with Fellini himself as the master of ceremonies" (Vincent Canby, *New York Times*). Italian with English subtitles.
VHS: $18583. $89.95.
Federico Fellini, Italy, 1987, 109 mins.

Invisible Adversaries
"A winning combination of sexual frankness and visual wit," wrote J. Hoberman in *The Village Voice*, "Funny, violent, sexual…It makes you reconsider what you and everyone else is doing in art,"said Amy Taubin in *Soho Weekly News*. Set in contemporary Vienna, Valie Export's controversial feature has been called a feminist *Invasion of the Body Snatchers*. Anna (Susanne Widl), a Viennese photographer, discovers that extra-terrestrial beings are colonizing the minds of her fellow citizens by raising the human aggression quotient. The outer world immediately becomes disjointed, but the inner world does too, as Anna and her love (Peter Weibel) try to hang onto their deteriorating relationship. A unique and totally original work by Austria's foremost filmmaker, *Invisible Adversaries* is at once philosophical and funny, psychologically revealing and sexually frank—"a witty and visually brilliant essay on gender and experience, culture and environment" (National Film Theatre, London). German with English subtitles.
VHS: $10414. $59.95.
Valie Export, Austria, 1977, 112 mins.

The Invitation
Claude Goretta (*The Lacemaker*) takes viewers to a garden party that begins respectfully and falls to pieces as the sun and alcohol take their toll. Removed from their office surroundings, the guests let down their reserve until the butler restores the party and people to their proper order. Both charming and insightful, the film wryly observes the impact that time and space have on ordinary people. "One of the most impressive works to come out of Switzerland" (James Monaco, *The Movie Guide*). Digitally mastered with new electronic subtitles. French with English subtitles.
VHS: $30144. $29.95.
Claude Goretta, Switzerland/France, 1973, 100 mins.

Irma Vep
Olivier Assayas' stylish take on the world of French surrealist film serials stars Hong Kong action film star Maggie Cheung, who, playing herself, is brought to Paris to star in a modern version of the famous silent Feuilliade serial, *Les Vampires*. But Jean-Pierre Leaud, who plays the director of the film, is at the end of his emotional rope, and the production becomes a series of emotional entanglements between its protagonists. Assayas' witty, acute observations of people and places touches on the nature of creation in a film which is a favorite of film festivals worldwide. English and French with English subtitles.
VHS: $32984. $89.98.
Olivier Assayas, France, 1996, 97 mins.

Ivan and Abraham
Winner at the Cannes Film Festival, this powerful film is the story of the friendship of Abraham, a volatile Jewish boy, and Ivan, an older Christian boy, who flee 1930s Poland, where political tensions are mounting, to the vast and perilous countryside. The runaways are followed by Aaron, a young Communist outlaw, and Abraham's teenage sister, Rachel, whose love for Aaron has estranged her from her family. Expertly interweaving personal drama and and historical perspective, the film centers on these four outcasts as they try to detach themselves from a world hurtling into chaos and violence. "Dazzling in its beauty, its audacity, its intelligence, its subtlety, its freedom" (Claude Lanzmann, director of *Shoah*). Yiddish, Polish, Russian and Gypsy dialog with English subtitles. Letterboxed.
VHS: $31191. $89.95.
Yolande Zauberman, France, 1993, 105 mins.

Ivan the Terrible, Part I
Huge close-ups, rich decor and Prokofiev's choral music help make this film one of the great achievements of Russian cinema. In part one, Ivan Grozny is proclaimed Czar of all Russia, but faces treachery within his own family. Russian with English subtitles.
VHS: $00645. $29.95.
Sergei Eisenstein, USSR, 1944, 94 mins.

Ivan the Terrible, Part II
After the great success of *Ivan the Terrible, Part I*, Eisenstein rushed to complete *Part II* of what was to be a trilogy. Eisenstein used color in two sequences to signify psychological meaning. Part II details Ivan's revenge on friends who had denounced him. Russian with English subtitles.
VHS: $00646. $29.95.
Sergei Eisenstein, USSR, 1946, 90 mins.

J'Accuse
One of the great films by Abel Gance (*Napoleon*) and a powerful statement against war. A strange man, obsessed with the horrors of war, calls upon the millions of dead soldiers from World War I to rise from their graves and march upon the cities of the world. With Victor Francen, Jean Max. French with English subtitles.
VHS: $12329. $29.95.
Abel Gance, France, 1938, 127 mins.

Jamon, Jamon
This winner of the Silver Lion at the Venice Film Festival combines outrageous humor and steamy sex in a quirky movie of mismatched love affairs. Anna Galiena, Stefania Sandrelli, Javier Bardem and Penelope Cruz are all featured in this tale of erotic passions.
VHS: $21097. $19.98.
Bigas Luna, Spain, 1993, 95 mins.

Jana Aranya (The Middleman)
When Somnath, a young Calcuttan college graduate, fails to get a job in spite of his qualifications, he breaks with Brahmin tradition and goes into business as a middleman, which, he discovers, imposes a painful choice between morality and survival. Eventually the trafficking of goods becomes the trafficking of human beings as he begins supplying call girls to his clients. With Pradip Mukherjee, Satya Bannerfi, Dipankar Dey, Lily Chakravarti and Aparna Sen. Fully restored. "Under Ray's piercing yet compassionate glance, his characters darken with loss of innocence. The quiet urgency and emotional intensity of the film transcend its context; this is not only a film about India" (New York Film Festival note). Bengali with English subtitles.
VHS: $32168. $19.95.
Satyajit Ray, India, 1975, 131 mins.

Jazz Comedy (Jolly Fellows)
Grigori Alexandrov's first musical comedy is the rags-to-fame story of a shepherd boy who reaches lofty heights as a jazz-orchestra conductor. The film belongs to its heroine—Lyubov Orlova—who

established herself as the first recognized star of Soviet cinema. *Jazz Comedy* is also remarkable for the clever camera work of Vladimir Nilsen, who introduced Western camera tricks to Soviet cinema. Russian with English subtitles.
VHS: S27215. $29.95.
Grigori Alexandrov, USSR, 1934, 98 mins.

Jean de Florette
A marvelous tale of greed and intolerance from the novel by Pagnol about a city hunchback who inherits a valuable piece of property in rural France only to have his efforts thwarted by the villainy of his venal neighbor. With Gerard Depardieu, Yves Montand, Daniel Auteuil, Elisabeth Depardieu and Ernestine Mazurownas as little Manon. French with English subtitles. 122 mins.
VHS: S07522. $19.98.
Claude Berri, France, 1987, 122 mins.

Jesus of Montreal
A charismatic actor is hired to punch up the annual Montreal Passion play and discovers he is beginning to take his work far more seriously than he intended. Lothaire Bluteau is truly inspirational in the title role of this award-winning film by Denys Arcand. With Catherine Wilkening, Johanne-Marie Tremblay, Remy Girard and Yves Jacques. French with English subtitles.
VHS: S13674. $19.98.
Denys Arcand, Canada/France, 1989, 118 mins.

The Jew
Set during the Spanish Inquisition, this provocative, unusual Portuguese film is based on the true story of Antonio da Silva, a talented playwright and writer in 18th-century Portugal who is accused of heresy: still secretly being a Jew, even after converting to Catholicism. He must stand up to a ferocious Church hierarchy at odds with a decadent monarchy. "Even more hair-raising than *The Crucible*.... An incongruously beautiful period film" (Michael Wilmington, *Chicago Tribune*). Portuguese with English subtitles.
VHS: S32684. $79.95.
Jom Tob Azuley, Portugal/Brazil, 1995, 85 mins.

JLG/JLG
In this autobiographical essay of confessional images, Godard speculates on the oppression of culture from the isolation of his home in Switzerland. Subtitled *A Self-Portrait in December*, Godard plays himself in an effort to explain what he has been doing for the past 30 years. In this unique cinematic self-portrait, Godard is self-absorbed and alone as he mumbles to himself or to his sexy young maid. In this cinematic self-portrait, sequestered from the world and bunkered in a safe and cozy haven with his books, his movie equipment and his eccentricities, he muses upon images of women, receives visits from various government officials and makes references to his past mistakes. French with English subtitles.
VHS: S30000. $89.95.
Jean-Luc Godard, France, 1994, 60 mins.

Jonah Who Will Be 25 in the Year 2000
Alain Tanner's masterpiece; a sensitive, literate and engaging comedy follows eight individuals affected by the political events of 1968. Tanner describes the film as "a dramatic tragi-comedy in political science fiction." Stars Myriam Boyer, Jean-Luc Bideau, Roger Jendly, Jacques Denis and Miou-Miou as a lovely supermarket clerk with no qualms about liberating groceries. French with English subtitles.
VHS: S16679. $29.95.
Alain Tanner, Switzerland, 1976, 115 mins.

Journey of Hope
A naive Kurdish family of refugees from Turkey travel to the Swiss border and are forced to cross the Alps at night during the winter. A grueling tale based on fact, it was awarded an Oscar for Best Foreign Language Film. Turkish, Kurdish and German with English subtitles.
VHS: S15418. $19.98.
Laser: LD75210. $34.98.
Xavier Koller, Switzerland, 1990, 111 minutes.

Juliet of te Spirits
"Within a simple, naively romantic narrative frame concerning a wife's desperation over her husband's philanderings, director Federico Fellini has put together an imperial-size fantasy of a physical opulence to make the old Vincente Minnelli musicals look like Army training films," wrote Vincent Canby. Newly mastered from a beautiful print. Italian with

Ivan and Abraham

English subtitles.
VHS: S11178. $29.95.
Federico Fellini, Italy, 1965, 146 mins.

Kagemusha
A masterpiece. Set in 1531 Japan torn by civil strife, *Kagemusha* deals with a mighty Japanese warlord and his commoner look-alike who, after the warlord's death, is used to keep his clan together. Tatsuya Nakadai is superb in the dual role of the war lord and his double, both caught up in the swirl of history as the mighty powers clash in fierce battles and political intrigue. Winner of the Grand Prize at Cannes. Japanese with English subtitles.
VHS: S00668. $29.98.
Laser: CLV. LD72114. $69.98.
Akira Kurosawa, Japan, 1980, 159 mins.

Kaspar Hauser
One of the greatest mysteries of his age: a 16-year-old youth was found abandoned in Nuremberg, Germany, unable to walk, write or speak. He became renowned as "a wild child," and as the object of scientific study. The case inspired over 2,000 books as well as the acclaimed film by Werner Herzog, *Every Man for Himself and God Against All.* Now filmmaker Peter Sehr makes a compelling film which looks at Kaspar Hauser in a social and historical context: as the crown prince of Baden, abducted as a child in the name of political intrigue, and raised in a dungeon. "A tour de force of wit, originality and poignancy" (Kevin Thomas, *Los Angeles Times*). German with English subtitles.
VHS: S31105. $79.95.
Peter Sehr, Germany, 1994, 137 mins.

The Key
Humor, pathos and suspense fill this story of a four-year-old and an infant left home alone while their mother runs out to do some shopping. Young Amir Mohammad has his own ideas about what he wants to do—and watching his baby brother and the meal cooking in the kitchen are not among them. Minor crisis piles on crisis, culminating in the threat of disaster when the cooking pot boils over, dousing the flame on the gas range. As frantic neighbors yell advice to the resourceful youngster, tension mounts. Winner of the award for Best Children's Film at the Berlin Film Festival. Screenplay by Abbas Kiarostami. Farsi with English subtitles.
VHS: S27789. $29.95.
Ebrahim Forouzesh, Iran, 1986, 76 mins.

Kika
Pedro Almodovar's offbeat sex farce is the story of Kika, a make-up artist who lives with her lover Ramon, a photographer specializing in women's lingerie. Their maid, Juanita, is madly in love with Kika, while Ramon's stepfather likes to seduce her from time to time. That's only the beginning of the preposterous goings on which really heat up when Pablo, Juanita's brother, an on-the-lam ex-porno star, enters the picture. Spanish with English subtitles.
VHS: S23572. $14.98.
Laser: LD75489. $39.99.
Pedro Almodovar, Spain, 1994, 109 mins.

The Kingdom
Lars von Trier's audacious and inspired soap opera is set in Copenhagen's Kingdom Hospital, which is ailing. Once a respected site of healing, it has become a carnival of horrors. A restless ghost haunts its corridors crying for redemption. Patients try seances while doctors turn to exorcism and voodoo. Despite these efforts, the terrible secret at the heart of *The Kingdom* remains and continues to ensnare the

innocent. This film mixes a range of influences from the erotic to the sardonic in an unforgettable hybrid of comedy and terror. Danish with English subtitles.
VHS: S27595. $24.98.
Laser: LD75556. $89.99.
Lars von Trier, Denmark, 1994, 265 mins.

Kolya
A charmer of a movie, due, in no small part, to the wonderful performances of Zdenek Sverak as the confirmed, set-in-his-ways bachelor and Andrej Chalimon as the six-year-old Russian boy stranded in Prague by his mother, who first turns Sverak's life upside down and ultimately wins over his heart. An Oscar- and Golden Globe-winner for Best Foreign Film, this "gem of a film" (*New York Times*) also features political overtones in its whimsical look at a musician reduced to playing at funerals because of his outspokenness and the fact that his brother has emigrated. Czech with English subtitles.
VHS: S31824. $103.99.
Laser: LD76332. $39.99.
Jan Sverak, Czech Republic, 1996, 105 mins.

Krik? Krak! Tales of a Nightmare
An innovative feature set in Haiti which blends documentary and fiction scenes to delve into the tormented history of the Black world: Haiti, the terrible experience under Papa Doc Duvalier, and the work of his infamous paramilitary force, the Tontons Macoutes. "Remarkably insightful, original, compassionate picture of the eternal Haiti" (Graham Greene). "Unflinching. Passionate. Creativity and daring in shooting, editing and music are matched by the depth of feeling for the Haitian people" (Jonathan Demme).
VHS: S27807. $29.95.
Vanyoska Gert/Jac Avila, Haiti/USA, 78 mins.

L'Argent
The subject of *L'Argent* is materialism, specifically the consequences of the passing of a counterfeit 500-franc note which initiates a chain reaction of corruption and moral error leading to a truly terrifying climax. *L'Argent* is one of Bresson's most perfect works; its subject and form are inseparable; every action leaves a trace, nothing is superfluous. With Christian Patey, Sylvie Van Den Elsen, Michel Briquet and Caroline Lang. French with English subtitles.
VHS: S20302. $59.95.
Robert Bresson, France/Switzerland, 1983, 82 mins.

L'Atalante
The high water mark of French poetic realism, set on a barge plying the Seine. A young barge captain and his bride live on a barge with the eccentric Pere Jules (Michel Simon). With Boris Kauffman's cinematography, which evokes Paris and the Seine

with the luminosity of Atget or Cartier-Bresson, and everyday life full of magical moments like Pere Jules' "museum" of exotic marvels and the husband's underwater vision of his lost bride. "May be the greatest film ever made" (Georgia Brown, *The Village Voice*). Initially cut by seven minutes, this version is the fully restored, 89-minute cut. With Dita Parlo, Jean Daste and Michel Simon. French with English subtitles.
VHS: S17696. $59.95.
Jean Vigo, France, 1934, 89 mins.

L'Avventura
A film about the fragility of human relationships which established Antonioni as a major talent. A party of rich Italians land on an uninhabited island, and one young woman disappears. "Our drama is non-communication," said Antonioni, "and it is this feeling that dominates the characters in my film." With Monica Vitti. Winner of the Special Jury Award at Cannes. Italian with English subtitles.
VHS: S00696. $29.95.
Laser: LD70342. $124.95.
Michelangelo Antonioni, Italy, 1960, 145 mins.

L'Enfer
Claude Chabrol is in top form in this top-notch thriller—the study of deranged jealousy—based on a script by Henri-Georges (*Diabolique*) Clouzot. Paul Cluzet plays the owner of a small hotel who has everything—a beautiful wife, a new son, and a successful business located on a serene lake. But then he hears voices and begins to question his wife's fidelity, which begins a downward spiral into madness. With Emmanuelle Beart. French with English subtitles.
VHS: S25816. $19.98.
Claude Chabrol, France, 1994, 100 mins.

L'Homme Blesse (The Wounded Man)
The sensitive story of a French teenager and his discovery of his own homosexuality, this film directed by Patrice Chereau received the French Cesar. Henri, the teenager, tries to stop an attack on a man in a public toilet, is given a sexy kiss by the attacker, and discovers that he is strongly attracted to men. French with English subtitles.
VHS: S06588. $79.95.
Patrice Chereau, France, 1984, 90 mins.

La Belle Noiseuse
Jacques Rivette's ambitious masterpiece explores the artistic process in terms of both its transcendent power and its potential for exploitation and destructivness. The core of the film is the confrontation between Frenhofer, a renowned but inactive painter, and a model (played by Emmanuelle Beart). It begins in wary hostility, escalates into a pitched battle of wills, and ends as a true collaboration, with each driving the other to

L'Avventura

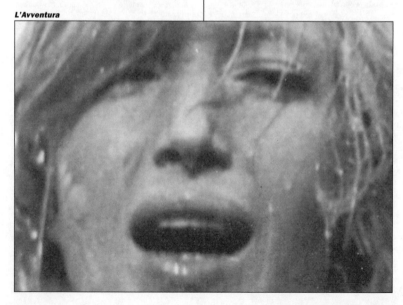

dangerous limits. "One of the finest films ever made about art" (Gene Siskel, *Chicago Tribune*). Winner of the Grand Jury Prize at the Cannes Film Festival. Cinematography by William Lubtchansky. With Michel Piccoli and Bernard Dufour. French with English subtitles.
VHS: S20304. $89.95.
Jacques Rivette, France/Switzerland, 1990, 240 mins.

La Bete Humaine
A psychological drama of murder, revenge, conscience and the eternal triangle, based on a story by Emile Zola. Renoir fills the film with hauntingly beautiful symbolism. French with English subtitles.
VHS: S00700. $39.95.
Jean Renoir, France, 1938, 101 mins.

La Boca del Lobo
Hailed by Judy Stone of the *San Francisco Chronicle* as "a powerful drama" and considered by many to be one of the finest films to emerge from Latin and South America in recent years, *La Boca del Lobo* is the study of a bloody encounter between the Peruvian Army and the Maoist Shining Path. Winner of the Grand Prize at the San Sebastian Film Festival. Spanish with English subtitles.
VHS: S12363. $79.95.
Miguel Pereira, Peru, 1989, 100 mins.

La Ceremonie
Claude Chabrol returns in great form with this gripping suspense thriller. Sophie (Sandrine Bonnaire, *Monsieur Hire*) is a quiet, eccentric maid, hired by the Lelievres, a fashionable, bourgeoise French family living in a Brittany country estate. When Sophie befriends Jeanne (Isabelle Huppert), a boisterous postal worker who hates the Lelievres, the two misfits form a destructive bond, secured on a similar secret past. French with English subtitles.
VHS: S31550. $89.95.
Claude Chabrol, France, 1996, 111 mins.

La Chevre (The Goat)
The comedy team of Gerard Depardieu and Pierre Richard, who were so successful in *Les Comperes*, bring to the screen another great French farce. Their travels range from the board rooms of a huge multinational conglomerate to the tropics of Mexico, in search of the chairman of the board's missing accident-prone daughter. French with English subtitles.
VHS: S05209. $69.95.
Francis Veber, France, 1985, 91 mins.

La Collectionneuse
This is the third in a series of six films from "The Moral Tales," a group of films by the consummate master of comic French drama. A handsome man onvacation in St. Tropez is unnerved by the sybaritic presence of a fellow guest who is staying at the same pension. He confronts her erotic threat by a renewed commitment to moral turpitude. French with English subtitles.
VHS: S28995. $19.98.
Eric Rohmer, France, 1966, 88 mins.

La Dolce Vita
"A landmark of cinematic social comment," wrote one critic about Fellini's journey through a decadent Rome. Banned by the Church in many countries, the sensationalism of the film often obscured its serious intent. *La Dolce Vita* follows a society journalist (Marcello Mastroianni) through a nightmarish world in which emotions have been destroyed by surface realities, moral conventions and unresolved guilt. With Anita Ekberg, Anouk Aimee, Alain Cuny and Nadia Gray. Italian with English subtitles.
VHS: S00705. $24.95.
Federico Fellini, Italy, 1961, 174 mins.

La Femme Nikita
A stylish punk thriller from director Luc Besson (*Subway, The Big Blue*) in which a French street junkie (played by the beautiful Anne Parillaud) is arrested and threatened with life imprisonment. She is then allowed to leave if she agrees to go to work for the French secret police as an assassin. This suspenseful film is highlighted by Besson's stylishly decorous visual compositions and innate sense of dramatic pacing. Also starring Tcheky Karyo and Jeanne Moreau. French with English subtitles.
VHS: S14530. $19.95.
Laser: Widescreen. LD75217. $34.98.
Luc Besson, France, 1991, 117 mins.

La Grande Bouffe (The Great Feed)
Marcello Mastroianni, Philippe Noiret, Ugo Tognazzi and Michel Piccoli star in this strange, depraved comedy which was a 1970's worldwide sensation. The four men—victims of their appetites—retire to a Parisian villa, where they fill their systems with an overload of carnal pleasures until they die in a blow-out of orgiastic over-indulgence. French with English subtitles.
VHS: S26480. $79.95.
Marco Ferreri, France/Italy, 1973, 125 mins.

La Grande Vadrouille
In 1943, three allied parachutists land behind enemy lines and end up creating chaos for the conductor and decorator who find them. The only way for this pair to regain their peaceable existence lies in the return of this troublesome trio to a free zone. French with English subtitles.
VHS: S20756. $29.95.
Gerard Oury, France, 1966, 122 mins.

La Guerre Est Finie
This great film by Alain Resnais, scripted by Jorge Semprun, stars Yves Montand, Genevieve Bujold, Ingrid Thulin and Michel Piccoli. Resnais shifts between reality and Montand's mental states in an incisive portrait of an aging Spanish revolutionary exile who is imprisoned by his past as he confronts the failure of his ideas. Resnais explores Montand's insecurities through his relationships with two very different women (Thulin and Bujold). French with English subtitles.
VHS: S23758. $29.95.
Alain Resnais, France, 1966, 120 mins.

La Jetee
Chris Marker's landmark film is set in postnuclear Paris. The story concerns an astronaut who travels back through time to realize a brief affair with a woman he once glimpsed. With the exception of a haunting shot of the woman blinking, the entire film is composed with still photographs and isolated shots. French with English subtitles.
VHS: S18956. $19.95.
Chris Marker, France, 1962, 29 mins.

La Marseillaise
Renoir's remarkable ability to recreate the mood of the past was never more evident than in *La Marseillaise*. A classic tribute to the glory of the French Revolution, the film captures the human values of the struggle as well as the historical perspective. French with English subtitles.
VHS: S17513. $39.95.
Jean Renoir, France, 1938, 131 mins.

La Memoria del Agua
The story of Joseph Fruferman, whose memories of his childhood in Russia and his adult life in France take up the last moments of his life. Images of his mother, late wife and daughter frame these poignant memories in a haunting black-and-white film in which the narrative is interspliced with documentary fragments. The film centers on the love that makes the impossible possible through its overwhelming power and survives physical death and separation just as water retains its memory even after its molecules separate. Spanish and Russian dialog with English subtitles.
VHS: S27799. $29.95.
Hector Faver, Spain, 1991, 82 mins.

La Notte
The second installment of Italian director Michelangelo Antonioni's trilogy. Jeanne Moreau plays a bored, dissatisfied woman who abandons her simple minded husband (Marcello Mastroianni), who in turn attempts to seduce a beautiful, vacant woman (Monica Vitti). Moody, introverted and beautiful, brilliantly photographed by Gianni Di Venanzo. Italian with English subtitles.
VHS: S14850. $39.95.
Michelangelo Antonioni, Italy, 1961, 122 mins.

La Paz
A respected Bolivian heart surgeon returns to his native Bolivia during the summer of 1980, just as a coup has threatened the lives of thousands. He finds himself trapped by a curfew in the very classroom where a mentoring teacher once helped him. As he ponders the now dead teacher, a committed woman journalist appears. Spanish with English subtitles.
VHS: S29878. $14.98.
Jose Sanchez, Bolivia, 1994, 25 mins.

La Roue (Wheel of Fate)

In its time, this film had such an impact on French filmmakers that Jean Cocteau supposedly began referring to "a cinema before and after *La Roue*." It is the tragic tale of Sisif (Severin Mars), an engine driver, who saves a girl from a train crash and adopts her, then falls in love with her as she grows up into a beautiful young woman (Ivy Close). He marries her off to a rich railway administrator in an effort to rid himself of temptation and guilt but his torment does not cease. "No film since De Mille's *The Cheat*, not even L'Herbier's *El Dorado*, had so stunned the French filmmakers, critics and cinephiles" (Richard Abel, *French Cinema*). Silent with French titles.
VHS: $30195. $24.95.
Abel Gance, France, 1921, 130 mins.

La Silence de la Mer
(The Silence of the Sea)

An old man and his beautiful niece are forced to endure the presence of a Nazi officer during the German occupation of their small French village. Vowing never to speak to the invader, the couple listen in silence as the officer pours out his ideas and feelings about music, war and his love of France. Just as the officer overcomes their enmity and at the same time discovers the realities of Nazism in France, he is ordered to the eastern front. French with English subtitles.
VHS: $30612. $29.95.
Jean-Pierre Melville, France, 1947, 86 mins.

La Strada

Fellini's masterpiece. Giulietta Masina plays Gelsomina, a tragic waif sold to play clown to travelling show strongman Zampano (Anthony Quinn). "Simplicity itself, *La Strada* is a magical tale and an unbearably painful account of loneliness which will always be associated with the sublimely Chaplinesque Masina…but Quinn, too, is superb, particularly in the final revelation of his own heartbreak and isolation." With Richard Basehart and Aldo Silvani. Italian with English subtitles.
VHS: S00712. $29.95.
Laser: LD71088. $49.95.
Federico Fellini, Italy, 1954, 107 mins.

La Symphonie Pastorale

Based on Andre Gide's introspective short story. Set in a mountain village, the story follows the spiritual growth and decline of a well-meaning pastor (Pierre Blanchar) and Gertrude (Michele Morgan), a blind orphan he takes into his home. Initially, the minister is guided by Christian principles to raise Gertrude

loves, and sing his favorite song ("La Vie Est Belle") on national television. French with English subtitles.
VHS: $27561. $59.95.
Ngangura Mweze/Benoit Lamy, Zaire/Belgium, 1987, 85 mins.

Labyrinth of Passion

Pedro Almodovar's second feature film features nymphomaniacs, incest victims, transvestites, rock musicians and Iranian fundamentalists living in Madrid. In other words, something for everyone who thinks this filmmaker is the kinkiest and most entertaining modern artist to emerge from the Iberian peninsula since Salvador Dali. Cast includes Cecilia Roth, Helga Line, Marta Fernandez-Mura, Fernando Vivanco and Ruze Neiro as the uncomfortable heir to the Arabian throne. Spanish with English subtitles.
VHS: $12364. $79.95.
Pedro Almodovar, Spain, 1982, 100 mins.

The Lacemaker

Isabelle Huppert shot from minor actress to international star with a mesmerizing performance as a young woman incapable of escaping anonymity. This acclaimed and beautiful film by Swiss director Claude Goretta is a sad twist on the Cinderella story as Huppert is swept away by Francois, a rich, handsome young student. At first, he is captivated by her graceful movements and enticed by her virginity. But their romance is short-lived; he soon breaks with her and brings about her mental collapse. French with English subtitles.
VHS: $12953. $29.95.
Claude Goretta, Switzerland/France, 1977, 107 mins.

The Ladies of the Bois de Boulogne
(Les Dames du Bois de Boulogne)

This rarely-seen second feature by Bresson was co-scripted by Jean Cocteau based on an anecdote in a novel by Diderot. Two sophisticated lovers, Helene and Jean, agree to remain friends even when their ardor for one another has died. Helene good naturedly introduces her ex-lover Jean to a new woman and everything seems fine as a new romance begins. But this woman harbors a mysterious past that threatens to unsettle everything. Maria Casares stars in a rigorous, intense film remarkable for Cocteau's layered dialog. French with English subtitles.
VHS: $24045. $59.95.
Robert Bresson, France, 1944, 83 mins.

Lamerica

Called "one of the great films of the past decade" (Michael Wilmington, *Chicago Tribune*), Gianni

9 People Who Like to Watch

The Tenant

Apartment Zero
VHS: S11690. $19.98.

Body Double
VHS: S02862. $14.95.
Laser: LD74477. $34.95.

The Conversation
VHS: S00267. $19.95.
Laser: LD75356. $29.98.

In the Realm of the Senses
VHS: S12222. $19.98.

The Key
VHS: S27789. $29.95.

Monsieur Hire
VHS: S13672. $19.98.

Peeping Tom
VHS: S01006. $29.95.
Laser: LD72275. $49.95.

Rear Window
VHS: S01095. $19.95.

The Tenant
VHS: S01308. $49.95.

with fatherly love, but as she grows into a beautiful woman, he is driven by a passion that destroys the happiness of his wife and son. Digitally mastered with new electronic subtitles. French with English subtitles.
VHS: $30143. $29.95.
Jean Delannoy, France, 1976, 105 mins.

La Vie Est Belle (Life Is Rosy)

A farce infused with the Zairian sense of belief in Systeme-D or debrouillardise (the art of hustling for survival), this film explores the rich musical world of Kinshasha. It follows a young man who uses wit and guile to trick his greedy boss, attain the woman he

Amelio's elaborate fresco-of-a-film is set in Albania. Fiore, an unscrupulous Italian businessman, arrives to grab the spoils of the post-Communist turmoil. He appoints a half-crazy old Albanian man as his patsy to serve as chairman of his fraudulent company. When this puppet slips away from his manipulators, Fiore's cocky assistant Gino is dispatched to track him down. The film takes the form of an odyssey that is also a moral awakening. With Enrico Lo Verso, Michele Placido and Carmelo Di Mazzarelli. Italian with English subtitles.
VHS: $30257. $89.95.
Gianni Amelio, Italy, 1995, 120 mins.

Lancelot of the Lake

Robert Bresson's masterpiece is set in the last days of the age of chivalry. As the Knights return to King Arthur's Court after a doomed quest for the Holy Grail, they are torn apart by jealousies and rivalries, at the center of which is Lancelot and his relationship with Guinevere. Told in Bresson's austere style, with rich colors and stark images, the film becomes a hypnotic study in the loss of faith, in which reality stands in sharp relief to the spiritual. With Luc Simon, Laura Duc Condominas and Humbert Balsan. French with English subtitles.
VHS: $23284. $79.95.
Robert Bresson, France/Italy, 1975, 80 mins.

Land of Promise

Based on the novel by Nobel Prize-winner Wladyslav Reymont, Andrzej Wajda's epic film examines the relationships among three industrialists who own a textile factory in Lodz at the turn of the century. The film is an epic about complex class structures; each man represents a different ethnic group: a Pole (Daniel Olbrychski), a German (Andrzej Seweryn) and a Jew (Wojciech Pszoniak). The drama builds to a climax when the overworked, underpaid workers threaten to revolt. With Anna Nehrebecka. Polish with English subtitles.
VHS: $19397. $79.95.
Andrzej Wajda, Poland, 1974, 178 mins.

Landscape in the Mist

Theo Angelopoulos' moving portrait of two sad-eyed children who traverse Greece in search of their father is a portrayal of loneliness, disillusionment and betrayal and the vision of a world that is both impersonal and unfeeling. The children's painful odyssey is fraught with terrifying figures, allegorical visions (a hand rising from the sea, a dead white horse outlined in the snow) and self-delusion. With Michalis Zeke, Tania Palaiologou, Eva Kotamanidou and Alika Georgouli. Greek with English subtitles.
VHS: $19542. $59.95.
Theo Angelopoulos, Greece/France/Italy, 1988, 125 mins.

Last Metro

Truffaut's poignant, compelling drama, set in Nazi-occupied Paris, unfolds in the Theatre Montmartre, as a group of actors rehearse. But everyone harbors a secret. Catherine Deneuve visits her exiled Jewish husband; the leading man is a member of the Resistance. Touching and tense.
VHS: $00724. $29.95.
Laser: LD71522. $69.95.
Francois Truffaut, France, 1980, 135 mins.

The Last Supper

A celebrated film from Cuba, photographed with a lush palette, this startlingly beautiful masterpiece is based on an incident from 18th century Cuban history. The film is also a dazzling moral tale of a pious slaveholder who decides to improve his soul and instruct his slaves in the glories of Christianity by inviting 12 of them to participate in a reenactment of the Last Supper. Spanish with English subtitles.
VHS: $12466. $69.95.
Tomas Gutierrez Alea, Cuba, 1976, 101 mins.

Last Year at Marienbad

The strange geometry of a romantic triangle marks the beginning of this elegant, labyrinthine puzzle. Written by French New Wave novelist Alain Robbe-Grillet and from the director of *Hiroshima, Mon Amour, Last Year at Marienbad* is a film classic, the subject of myriad interpretations. Starring Delphine Seyrig, Giorgio Albertazzi, and Sacha Pitoeff. French with English subtitles. New presentation in videoscope.
VHS: $00730. $29.95.
Alain Resnais, France, 1961, 90 mins.

Latcho Drom (Safe Journey)

In Romany, "Latcho Drom" means "safe journey." This haunting, vibrant, seamless, award-winning film is neither a documentary nor a fiction film but a musical that tells the story of the historic odyssey of the Gypsies from India to Egypt and the pain and joy of being in an outsider culture. With gypsy musicians from India, Egypt, Turkey, Romania, Hungary, Slovakia, France and Spain. Winner of the Prix Gervais at the Cannes Film Festival. Romany with English subtitles. "Remarkable...exuberant, passionate...at times ecstatic" (Michael Wilmington, *Chicago Tribune*).
VHS: $29702. $89.95.
Tony Gatlif, France, 1992/93, 103 mins.

Late Spring

In *Late Spring*, a father feels he is keeping his daughter from marriage; when she is erroneously told that her father is thinking of re-marrying, she agrees to an offer. *Late Spring*, wrote Donald Richie, is "one of the most perfect, most complete, and most successful studies of character ever achieved in the Japanese cinema." With Setsuko Hara, Chishu Ryu. Japanese with English subtitles.
VHS: $21502. $69.95.
Yasujiro Ozu, Japan, 1949, 107 mins.

Lazarillo

This morality tale is set in 17th-century Castile. A fatherless boy is abandoned by his mother and subsequently finds work with a strange succession of employers. A blind beggar, a miserly sacristan, a fake nobleman and even a traveling band of performers all teach him valuable lessons in vanity, cunning, deception and, ultimately, survival. Spanish with English subtitles.
VHS: $21606. $24.95.
Cesar Ardavin, Spain, 1959, 109 mins.

Le Beau Serge

Claude Chabrol's first, great film—one of the landmarks of the French New Wave. Produced on a miniscule budget in the natural setting in Sardent, Francois (Jean-Claude Brialy) is convalescing in his native village to find his childhood friend (Gerard Blain) a drunkard in a bad marriage, and after an affair with Bernadette Lafont, interferes in Serge's life only to finally accept reality and understand. French with English subtitles.
VHS: $03509. $29.95.
Claude Chabrol, France, 1958, 97 mins.

Le Bonheur

A beautiful, elegant, romantic film that explores the issue of a man who is trying to love two women. Jean-Claude Drouot plays a happily married carpenter who wants his wife to accept that he can love his mistress at the same time. Controversial because of its exploration of morality and because Drouot's real-life family play his wife and children. Agnes Varda's daring is to explore the nature of relationship from a woman's point of view. French with English subtitles.
VHS: $16188. $29.95.
Agnes Varda, France, 1965, 87 mins.

Le Boucher

A first rate psychological thriller from Claude Chabrol about the evolving relationship of a beautiful school teacher and a serial murderer. "In Chabrol's films, the relationships are plotted with a mathematical precision that does not rule out surprising developments" (Roy Armes). With Stephane Audran, Antonio Passallia, Mario Beccaria and Pasquale Ferone. French with English subtitles.
VHS: $16929. $24.95.
Laser: CLV. LD72051. $39.95.
Claude Chabrol, France/Italy, 1969, 90 mins.

Le Doulos

A complicated thriller of double and triple crosses, beautiful women and a dark vision of a world in a masterful film noir. Set in the Paris underworld, at the center of which is Jean-Paul Belmondo, a professional informer who maintains his relationship with a police inspector and a burglar just out of jail and afraid he can't hack the criminal life anymore. Famous for its 9½ minute single take—brilliant camerawork from Nicolas Hayer—and terrific performances. With Serge Reggiani, Jean Desailly and Michel Piccoli. French with English subtitles.
VHS: $09905. $59.95.
Jean-Pierre Melville, France, 1962, 108 mins.

Le Gai Savoir

Two alien beings, brought together in an empty earth space, are exposed to our culture via its popular images—a compelling experiment that not only foreshadows the use of these images in Godard's later films but also explains precisely why these images are the building blocks of any film. As Godard explains at the end, "This film is not and cannot be an attempt to explain cinema or embody its object, but merely suggests effective ways to achieve it. This is not the film that should be made, but if a film is to be made it must follow some of the paths shown here." With Jean-Pierre Leaud and Juliet Berto. French with English subtitles.
VHS: $15378. $39.95.
Jean-Luc Godard, France, 1965, 96 mins.

Le Gendarme de St. Tropez

This is the first of a highly popular series featuring

the comic antics of gendarme Ludovic Cruchot. His ambitions are at odds with the laid-back atmosphere of the resort St. Tropez, and his hopes are finally dashed when his daughter has just a little too much fun on the beach. French with English subtitles.
VHS: $20770. $29.95.
Jean Girault, France, 1965, 95 mins.

Le Jaguar
Part fiction, part documentary and part social commentary, *Jaguar* is the story of three young men from the savannah of Niger who leave their homeland to seek wealth and adventure on the coast and in the cities of Ghana. Filmed in the 1950s when no portable synchronized sound equipment was available, Jean Rouch had the main characters of the film improvise a narrative while they viewed the footage which in itself was improvised. The resulting soundtrack consists of remembered dialog, joking and exclamations, and questions and explanations about the action on screen. The three young men, a herdsman, a fisherman and their friend, travel for a month to the coast of Ghana and eventually part to take jobs in the cities. Successful but homesick, they return to Niger; they have become *jaguars* with a knowledge of life in the modern city. English narration.
VHS: $10730. $350.00.
Jean Rouch, France/Niger, 1954, 96 mins.

Le Joli Mai
Chris Marker's great cinema-verite study of Paris in May, 1962, the month the Algerian War came to an end and France was at peace for the first time since 1939. The first part, "Prayer from the Top of the Eiffel Tower," is about personal happiness and ambition; the second, "The Return of Fantomas," concerned with social and political issues and the relationships of people to each other. A very moving, "personal, and ironic film aided by Pierre Lhomme's superb handling of the 'living camera' " (Georges Sadoul). French with English subtitles.
VHS: S05325. $29.95.
Chris Marker, France, 1962, 180 mins.

Le Samourai
Melville's classic film noir masterpiece stars Alain Delon as a cool and mysterious contract killer who lives by a personal code of *bushido*, moving in and out of shadows in the Parisian rain wearing a trenchcoat and a fedora hiding his eyes. A mythical revenge story with Cathy Rosier as a jazz piano player who witnesses one of his hits but doesn't tell the police. With Nathalie Delon. "The closest thing to a perfect movie that I have ever seen" (John Woo).
VHS: $32197. $89.95.
Jean-Pierre Melville, France, 1967, 95 mins.

Les Enfants Terribles
A lyrical treatment of Jean Cocteau's perverse tribute to rebellious adolescence. Made in 1949, even today it is one of the most electrifying confrontations of normality by abnormality in the cinema. Paul (Edouard Dermithe) and Elisabeth (Nicole Stephane) are born into such extreme wealth that they are immune to the confines and limits of the real world. Their innocence leads them to self-destruction and to crime. Jean Cocteau's claustrophobic drama is brought to the screen by the great Jean-Pierre Melville in this perverse story of love, death and incest. French with English subtitles.
VHS: S01663. $29.95.
Jean-Pierre Melville, France, 1949, 105 mins.

Les Maitres Fous
Jean Rouch's quintessential film documents the ceremony of a West African religious movement, the Hauku, which was widespread in Niger and Ghana from the 20s to the 50s. In 1954, Rouch was asked by a small group in Ghana to film their annual ceremony in which the participants would enter into a trance and become possessed by a variety of spirits associated with the western colonial powers. Today, *Les Maitres Fous* remains as one of the great works of ethnographic cinema. English narration.
VHS: $10728. $200.00.
Jean Rouch, France/Ghana, 1955, 35 mins.

Les Miserables
Jean-Paul Belmondo stars as a retired fighter inspired by the Victor Hugo novel. This illiterate boxer does everything he can, at great risk to his own life, to save a desperate Jewish family during the Nazi domination of France. It won a Golden Globe for its grand sweep and epic proportions. French with

English subtitles.
VHS: $27648. $29.98.
Laser: LD75557. $39.98.
Claude Lelouch, France, 1995, 175 mins.

Lessons at the End of Spring
A young boy's loss of innocence within a pre-perestroika Russian prison is the Kafkaesque premise of this harrowing film. The impressive feature debut of writer-director Oleg Kavun, *Lessons at the End of Spring* immediately places him at the forefront of Russia's groundbreaking new wave of angry young filmmakers. A landmark in the evolution of Soviet cinema. Mature themes and extensive male nudity. Russian with English subtitles.
VHS: $15495. $69.95.
Olag Kavun, USSR, 1989, 75 mins.

Letters from the Park
The enchanting story of two young people too shy to pursue the intimacy they both seek. They independently enlist the help of the local poet to write love letters to each other. The poet writes the letters to make some extra money but also to unburden himself of the unbounded love he feels but for which he has no outlet. When the young woman of the couple becomes the object of his affection, he is confused and faced with a moral and emotional dilemma in this surprising and sweet romance. Based on an original story by Gabriel Garcia Marquez, who also co-wrote the screenplay. Spanish with English subtitles.
VHS: $13510. $19.98.
Tomas Gutierrez Alea, Spain, 1988, 85 mins.

Life and Nothing But
Bertrand Tavernier once again explores the awful legacy of war. Set in 1920, this powerful drama unfolds in post World War I France—a country devastated both physically and spiritually. It tells the story of two women of differing backgrounds who are looking for the missing men they love. Along the way they encounter two French officers, one detailed to identify the dead and the other assigned to choose a body to be honored as France's unknown soldier. Tavernier turns his film into an incredibly moving journey through the postwar landscape of France, touching on the deep psychological scars which the conflict has left behind. With Philippe Noiret, Sabine Azema and Pascale Vidal. French with English subtitles.
VHS: $14787. $19.98.
Bertrand Tavernier, France, 1989, 135 mins.

Life and Nothing More
The film investigates the aftermath of a devastating 1990 earthquake which killed some 50,000 people in northern Iran. This region provided the setting for Kiarostami's *Where Is the Friend's Home*. Kiarostami's search for the two young actors who played central roles in that film becomes the dramatic source of *Life and Nothing More*…as a father and son travel to Quoker, the hometown of the two boys, and along the way meet earthquake survivors who desperately and valiantly work to reconstruct their lives. "…in many ways the most beautiful and powerful Iranian film I've seen" (Jonathan Rosenbaum, *Chicago Reader*). Farsi with English subtitles.
VHS: $27792. $29.95.
Abbas Kiarostami, Iran, 1992, 91 mins.

Life Is a Long Quiet River
An understated social comedy about a nurse who takes revenge on her indifferent lover, a married doctor, by switching two newborn babies. The narrative picks up 12 years later, as the two radically different families adjust to the severe changes when the children are returned to their rightful parents. Chatiliez dissects the mores of the two families, the upper middle class Le Quesnoys and the nefarious, criminal Groseilles. With Benoit Magimel, Helene Vincent and Daniel Gelin. French with English subtitles.
VHS: $18931. $79.95.
Etience Chatiliez, France, 1987, 90 mins.

Life of Oharu
An enduring masterpiece of world cinema, from the director of *Ugetsu. Life of Oharu* is a poignant, exquisitely filmed portrait of a woman victimized by the brutal strictures of 17th-century feudal Japan. Mizoguchi shows remarkable insight into the psychology of his female protagonist, and photographs her with slow, graceful, hauntingly beautiful camera movements. Japanese with English

subtitles.
VHS: S00753. $29.95.
Laser: LD76169. $69.95.
Kenji Mizoguchi, Japan, 1952, 136 mins.

Like Water for Chocolate

Immensely popular, magical story of a young girl
whose cooking is infused with her emotions as she
prepares her meals. Unrequited passions, changing
political situations and madness emerge in this highly
entertaining, sensual and funny story. Written by
Laura Esquivel and directed by her husband. Spanish
with English subtitles.
VHS: S21358. $19.95.
Laser: Letterboxed. LD74638. $39.99.
Alfonso Arau, Mexico, 1992, 105 mins.

Lisbon Story

Wenders' elegiac docudrama is a declaration of love
for the city of Lisbon and an elegant play with the
camera. Rudiger Volger is Phillip Winter, a soundman
who travels to Lisbon at the request of a friend, the
elusive and mysterious filmmaker Friedrich Monroe
(Patrick Bauchau). When he arrives at Friedrich's
flat, he discovers his friend has vanished but left
behind some silent footage from a film the two were
working on. Phillip strikes up a relationship with a
group of Portuguese children and starts to rove the
streets of Lisbon to record sound for his friend's
images. With an appearance by Manuel de Oliveira.
English, German and Portuguese with English
subtitles.
VHS: S32681. $89.95.
**Wim Wenders, Germany/Portugal, 1994,
100 mins.**

Lone Wolf and Cub—
Baby Cart at the River Styx

More Samurai graphic violence and sex in this
journey of terror along a river of blood! The Yagyu
clan has murdered Ogami Itto's wife and stripped him
of his position of Official Shogunate Second. Now
Ogami Itto and his son Daigoro wander the
countryside as the hired assassins known as Lone
Wolf and Cub, bent on the desire for revenge upon
the Yagyu. Japanese with English subtitles.
VHS: S30767. $29.95.
Misumi Kenji, Japan, 81 mins.

Los Olvidados

A milestone of filmmaking; Bunuel's great film looks
at the lives of young people growing up in the slums
of Mexico, and in particular, at the desperately
inevitable process by which an older, more corrupt
gang leader, Jacob, hounds and destroys the younger,
more innocent Pedro, before being destroyed himself.
Spanish with English subtitles.
VHS: S09000. $59.95.
Luis Bunuel, Mexico, 1950, 81 mins.

Los Placeres Ocultos

A closeted banker, middle-aged and successful, falls
madly in love with a poor but handsome 18-year-old
student—with devastating consequences for the
young man. Carefully crafted and insightfully
scripted, *Los Placeres Ocultos* was the first openly
gay film to emerge from Spain following the death of
Franco. Virtually unknown to American audiences,
this complex updating of *Death in Venice* is among
the most powerful affirmations of gay life ever
depicted on film. Spanish with English subtitles.
VHS: S11636. $79.95.
Eloy de la Iglesia, Spain, 1977, 97 mins.

Love in the City

One of the key omnibus films, which brought
together the best Italian filmmakers of the 50's. The
episodes are: *The Spectator*, by Dino Risi; *When Love
Fails*, by Antonioni; *Love Cheerfully Arranged* (also
known as *The Matrimonial Agency*), by Fellini; *Paid
Love*, by Carlo Lizzani; *The Love of a Mother*, by
Zavattini and Maselli and *Italy Turns Around*, by
Alberto Lattuada. The inspiration for the film is said
to have been Zavattini; particularly notable are the
Antonioni episode, in which unsuccessful suicides
tell why they blame disappointment in love for trying
to end their lives, and the very funny Fellini episode,
in which a client (played by Fellini) at a matrimonial
agency pretends that he is searching for a wife for a
friend who thinks he is a werewolf. 90 mins. Italian
with English subtitles.
VHS: S01969. $39.95.

Ludwig

Luchino Visconti's legendary epic of (mad) King
Ludwig of Bavaria. Visconti focuses on Ludwig's
fears and fantasies and his relationship with

M

composer Richard Wagner to create a portrait of a
"homosexual recluse whose passions are opera, fairytale castles, and exquisite young men. Nothing is
more sumptuous than Helmut Berger's performance
in the lead, the brooding mad scenes, the deliberately
contrived hysterical outbursts" (Tony Rayns). With
Romy Schneider, Trevor Howard and Silvana
Mangano. This version is longer than the original
American theatrical release version by 47 minutes.
Italian with English subtitles.
VHS: S32982. $79.95.
**Luchino Visconti, France/Italy/Germany, 1972,
231 mins.**

Luna Park

A gang of young, tough skinheads make their mark in
the chaotic turmoil of post-Communist Russia, where
right-wing extremists of all sorts abound. This iron-
pumping gang, led by its crazed leader, knows no
limits in its terrifying effort to purify the nation. It's a
rollercoaster ride of an action film in the tradition of
Mad Max. Russian with English subtitles.
VHS: S21196. $29.95.
Pavel Lounguine, Russia, 1992, 107 mins.

Lysistrata

Aristophanes' ancient Greek play is brought to life in
this new adaptation starring Jenny Karezi and Costas
Kazakos. Lysistrata is the Athenian woman disgusted
by the way men have ruined the country with their
endless war. Rallying other women, she proposes that
they impose an embargo on sexual relations with men
as long as the war lasts. The film liberates the action
from the stage, places it on location in the acropolis,
and renders Aristophanes' plea in a forceful manner.
Contains nudity and strong language. Greek with
English subtitles.
VHS: S11718. $39.95.
Yiannis Negrepontis, Greece, 1987, 97 mins.

M

A series of schoolgirls are murdered by a psychopath
who terrorizes a large city and is hunted by the police
through a network of beggars. Inspired by the real-
life "vampire of Dusseldorf," Fritz Lang's great film
is one of the key films of German Expressionism.
Peter Lorre's performance as the murderer is one of
the great screen performances of all time. German
with English subtitles.
VHS: S00787. $19.95.
Laser: LD76405. $49.95.
Fritz Lang, Germany, 1931, 95 mins.

Madame Bovary

The classic 19th century novel by Gustave Flaubert
has been masterfully adapted to the screen by veteran
filmmaker Claude Chabrol. Isabelle Huppert occupies
the erotic title role of Emma Bovary, the unhappily
married woman who wants more out of life. With
Christophe Malavoy, Jean Yanne, Lucas Belvaux and
Christiane Minazolli. French with English subtitles.
VHS: S16504. $14.98.
Laser: LD71454. $39.98.
Claude Chabrol, France, 1991, 130 mins.

Madame Butterfly

This award-winning film from the popular Puccini

opera is the heart-wrenching story of a beautiful young geisha who forsakes her family, and ultimately her life, for her American husband. With an international cast of opera stars, including Ying Huang, Richard Troxell of the New York City Opera, Ning Liang and Richard Cowan. Italian with English subtitles.
VHS: $31204. $24.95.
Frederic Mitterand, France, 1995, 129 mins.

Madame Rosa
Simone Signoret stars in the role of a Holocaust survivor forced into prostitution who befriends and shelters the children of the dispossessed, the prostitutes, Jews and Arabs who can no longer provide or care for their children. With Ben Youb, Claude Dauphin and filmmaker Costa-Gavras. French with English subtitles.
VHS: $00794. $24.95.
Moshe Mizrahi, France, 1977, 104 mins.

The Magic Flute
Quite possibly the best opera adaptation ever put on film, Ingmar Bergman's magical, delightful, enchanting version of Mozart's playful opera, sung in Swedish by a remarkably terrific cast. Bergman and Mozart meeting centuries later, in different mediums, is still a meeting of minds. Swedish with English subtitles.
VHS: $00797. $29.95.
Laser: LD75386. $99.95.
Ingmar Bergman, Sweden, 1973, 134 mins.

The Mahabharata
Adapted from the sacred 2000-year-old Sanskrit poem *The Great Story of Mankind*, this full-length film adaptation of the milestone theatre piece by an international company directed by Peter Brook captures the epic sweep of an entire world view. 318 mins.
VHS: $13333. $99.95.
Peter Brook, France/Great Britain, 1992, 318 mins.

Mahanagar (The Big City)
Madhabi Mukherjee gives a beautiful performance as Arati, a housewife who, upon the urging of her bank clerk husband, takes a job selling knitting machines door to door to help support her family and her husband's extended family. Although the families disapprove of the idea, Arati is successful and finds her strength in the work. Focusing in particular on the role of women in this metaphorphosis, Ray tells a story that is both particular to Calcutta and universally recognizable. Fully restored. "Few directors can match Ray's facility for observation or his perceptiveness in registering those tiny moments of conflict when a casual nuance can drop like a bomb" (David Wilson, *Monthly Film Bulletin*). With Anil Chatterjee, Haradhan Benerjee and Haren Chatterjee. Bengali with English subtitles.
VHS: $32167. $19.95.
Satyajit Ray, India, 1963, 131 mins.

Mamma Roma
Anna Magnani gives a terrific performance in the title role of this key film. It was Pasolini's second feature but it is rarely seen. The story revolves around a former prostitute, played by Magnani, who gets a new chance for a different life. She does her best to help her son, Ettore, get ahead. He is mesmerized, however, by the evils of the big city, so she makes one last desperate attempt to get him a respectable job. Italian with English subtitles.
VHS: $26664. $79.95.
Pier Paolo Pasolini, Italy, 1963, 110 mins.

A Man Escaped
A perfect film, based on the true story of a French Resistance fighter's escape from a Gestapo prison. In Bresson's hands, the narrative of the prison escape just hours before he is executed becomes a transcendental meditation on the meaning of freedom and existence told in light and shadows. "I would like to show this miracle: an invisible hand over the prison, directing what happens…the film is a mystery…The Spirit breathes where it will," said Bresson. Struck from a beautiful, newly mastered print. French with English subtitles.
VHS: $06464. $29.95.
Robert Bresson, France, 1956, 102 mins.

Man Facing Southeast
In this critically-acclaimed Argentine film a man named Rantes suddenly appears in a Buenos Aires hospital, expertly playing the organ. But who is he— this man with no recorded identity? Doctor Denis

dismisses Rantes' claim of being an alien visitor as a simple case of paranoid delusion. Beatriz, his only visitor, sees him as an intimate and knowing companion. The other patients, intrigued by his mysterious intelligence, see him as their only source of hope. Dubbed.
VHS: $05214. $19.95.
Eliseo Subiela, Argentina, 1986, 105 mins.

Man of Marble
Thirteen years in the making, Wajda's film caused packed houses to rise and sing the Polish national anthem when it finally premiered in Poland in 1977. Denied entrance at Cannes by Polish authorities, it played nonetheless at a commercial theatre there and won the International Critics' Prize. Hailed as "a milestone in Polish cinema" by *Variety, Man of Marble* is the story of a young filmmaker trying to reconstruct a truthful picture of the Stalinist past, a past obscured by 20 years of shifting propaganda. Polish with English subtitles.
VHS: $12828. $29.95.
Andrzej Wajda, Poland, 1977, 160 mins.

Man on the Roof
Based on the bestselling novel *The Abominable Man*, this unconventional and influential thriller opens with the murder of a sadistic police officer in a Stockholm hospital. Homicide investigator Martin Beck (Carl Gustav Lindstedt) tracks a killer bent on taking revenge against the police. Director Bo Widerberg used hand-held cameras and other photojournalistic techniques rarely employed in detective films of the time in this visually stunning film. With Sven Wollter and Thomas Hellberg. "A first-rate thriller with an almost unbearably tense climax" (*The Hollywood Reporter*). Swedish with English subtitles.
VHS: $32656. $89.95.
Bo Widerberg, Sweden, 1976, 110 mins.

Manon of the Spring
Emmanuelle Beart is the grown-up, revenge-seeking daughter of the kindly hunchback who was destroyed by the greed of his neighbors. Yves Montand and his nephew Daniel Auteuil learn the awful truth of their villainy in the conclusion of a classic tale of misinformation and retribution. From the novel by Pagnol. French with English subtitles. 123 mins.
VHS: $07523. $19.98.
Claude Berri, France, 1987, 113 mins.

Marianela
Based on the novel by Benito Perez Galdos, Marianela is the story of a disfigured orphan girl whose only solace is to serve as a guide to a young and handsome blind man, Pablo. When Pablo recovers his eyesight, Marianela's fragile world is shattered. Spanish with English subtitles.
VHS: $03197. $39.95.
Angelino Fons, Spain, 1972, 105 mins.

Marianne and Juliane
Barbara Sukowa, Jutta Lampe and Rudiger Vogler star in this drama which chronicles the story of two sisters. One is a left-wing editor, while the other became a communist terrorist who ends up in prison. This film offers a chilling personal account that illustrates the political turmoil that afflicted West Germany in the 1970s. German with English subtitles.
VHS: $21504. $59.95.
Margarethe von Trotta, Germany, 1980, 106 mins.

The Marriage of Maria Braun
Hanna Schygulla stars in Fassbinder's spectacular weaving of soap opera, comedy, history, politics and social satire into a lucid whole. Maria marries Hermann Braun the night before he is called to the front in WWII Germany. Soon he's believed to be dead, and Maria starts working her way up through the bedrooms of the social elite. When her husband suddenly returns, a fight ensues and she ends up clobbering her lover to death. At the American war trial, Hermann accepts blame and prison sentence, while Maria is left to deal with her uncertain pregnancy and promiscuous nature in this darkly humorous metaphor for the German post-war national spirit. German with English subtitles.
VHS: $01909. $29.95.
Rainer W. Fassbinder, Germany, 1979, 120 mins.

Martin Fierro
This riveting film by Leopoldo Torre Nilsson deals with the life of Martin Fierro. Drafted into military service, he is assigned to work for the commander. When he returns home, his wife and family are gone. As he descends into depression, he kills a black man

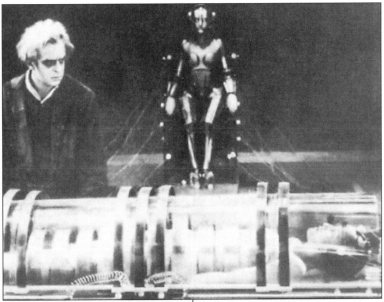

Metropolis

during a drunken fight, and is forced to flee. Together with his friend Cruz, he lives in an Indian encampment in relative safety. Spanish with English subtitles.
VHS: S27740. $59.95.
Leopoldo Torre Nilsson, Argentina, 1968, 135 mins.

Masala
Srinivas Krishna's colorful, independent feature is set in the East Indian community in Toronto. Krishna (played by the director) is traumatized by his parents' deaths and believes he won't live long. "A brash and sprightly Canadian comedy about Indian emigres in Toronto, with musical numbers, erotic dream sequences, exploding airplanes, a blue-skinned Hindu deity who exists mainly on video, a fair amount of farce, and a great deal of satire" (Jonathan Rosenbaum, *Chicago Reader*). With Saeed Jaffrey, Zohra Segal, Sakina Jaffrey and Heri Johal.
VHS: S19728. $19.98.
Srinivas Krishna, Canada, 1991, 105 mins.

Masculine Feminine
A film about the children of Marx and Coca Cola directed by the child of Brecht and Hollywood. Two young lovers attempt to communicate throughout 15 discontinuous, contrapuntal vignettes. Dancing between precision and improvisation, this is one of Godard's most complex films, representing both a search for tenderness and a disheartening foray into the Sex War. With Jean-Pierre Leaud, Chantal Goya, and Catherine-Isabelle Duport. French with English subtitles.
VHS: S00830. $29.95.
Jean-Luc Godard, France, 1966, 103 mins.

Matador
From Pedro Almodovar, another excursion into the bizarre and offbeat. A retired bullfighter and a female defense attorney find they share similar interests, which happen to be sex and death. His darkest film yet, but filled with madcap characters and wry humor. With Assumpta Serna, Antonio Banderas, Nacho Martinez, Eva Cobo, Chus Lampreave and Carmen Maura. In Spanish with English subtitles.
VHS: S10733. $79.95.
Pedro Almodovar, Spain, 1986, 115 mins.

Mayerling
The romantic, sumptuous film that established Charles Boyer as a screen idol. Set in Vienna in 1883, Boyer plays the Archduke Rudolf, who is madly in love with Maria Vetsera, played by Danielle Darrieux. An opulent romance with a sharp portrait

of the Hapsburg court. French with English subtitles.
VHS: S00837. $29.95.
Anatole Litvak, France, 1936, 91 mins.

Medea
Soprano Maria Callas in a dramatic, non-musical interpretation of Euripides' tragedy. "Under Pasolini's direction, Callas becomes a fascinating cinematic presence, brilliant and brutal" (*NY Times*). Italian with English subtitles.
VHS: S00841. $49.95.
Pier Paolo Pasolini, Italy, 1970, 100 mins.

Mediterraneo
Winner of the 1991 Best Foreign Language Academy Award. A small, eight-man battalion is ordered to secure a strategically unimportant Greek island. They are cut off from their superiors and encounter a liberated, magical community of beautiful women, sad-hearted prostitutes, a sympathetic priest and no resistance. With Diego Abatantuono, Claudio Bigagli and Giuseppe Cederna. Italian with English subtitles.
VHS: S18159. $19.98.
Gabriele Salvatores, Italy, 1991, 99 mins.

Melody Haunts My Reverie (You Only Love Once)
Voted the third best Yugoslav film ever made, and an Official Selection at Cannes, this daring film is the story of an idealistic, young, partisan war hero who becomes a leader in the emerging socialist society of a small Croat village, and finds adjustment to the "new Yugoslavia" extremely difficult. He meets and falls in love with a middle-class ballerina, becomes involved with her bourgeois family and is eventually imprisoned. "A highly sensual romance…as passionate as it is politically catastrophic" (*L.A. Times*). Croatian with English subtitles.
VHS: S27797. $29.95.
Rajko Grlic, Yugoslavia, 1981, 103 mins.

Memories of Underdevelopment
A breakthrough Cuban film, the first Cuban film to be released in the U.S. Set in the 1960s, the film centers on a Europeanized Cuban intellectual, too idealistic (or lazy) to leave for Miami, but too decadent to fit into the new Cuban society. The film is a remarkable demonstration that artistic subtlety, political commitment, and superior entertainment need not be incompatible. Spanish with English subtitles.
VHS: S11593. $59.95.
Tomas Gutierrez Alea, Cuba, 1968, 97 mins.

Men
Doris Dorrie's runaway hit of a screwball comedy

7 Top Spaghetti Westerns

A Fistful of Dynamite
VHS: S03672. $19.98.
Laser: LD75542. $49.98.

For a Few Dollars More
VHS: S02525. $19.98.
Laser: LD71883. $39.98.

**The Good, the Bad
and the Ugly**
VHS: S11553. $24.98.
Laser: LD70587. $39.98.

The Grand Duel
VHS: S32592. $24.95.

**Gunfight at Red Sands
(Gringo)**
VHS: S32590. $24.95.

The Last Tomahawk
VHS: S32594. $24.95.

Once Upon a Time in the West
VHS: S00962. $29.95.

The Good, the Bad and the Ugly

---

about a businessman (Heiner Lauterbach) who discovers his wife is having an affair with a Bohemian artist. Disguised as the artist's roommate, Lauterbach watches, waits, and plots a strange reversal on the unsuspecting couple. German with English subtitles.
VHS: S20591. $29.95.
Doris Dorrie, Germany, 1985, 99 mins.

Merchant of Four Seasons
A climax in the prolific career of Rainer Werner Fassbinder. The story, that of a fruit peddler who watches his unexceptional life disintegrate, sounds like a slice-of-life melodrama gone slightly amok, but the treatment is everything; a virtuoso balance of soap opera, social comedy, irony, politics, farce and brilliant ensemble acting. German with English subtitles. With Irm Hermann, Hanna Schygulla.
VHS: S12467. $29.95.
Rainer W. Fassbinder, Germany, 1972, 88 mins.

Metropolis
A newly mastered version of Fritz Lang's great masterpiece, the first classic of the science fiction genre. His depiction of a giant city controlled by an authoritarian industrialist who lives in a paradise-like garden while the workers live and struggle in subterranean sections of the city was as important for its vision of man in the service of those who control technology as for its implicit and moving social message. "A brilliant piece of expressionist design...with moments of almost incredible beauty and power" (Pauline Kael). Silent with music score.
VHS: S10764. $29.95.
Fritz Lang, Germany, 1926, 90 mins.

Mexican Bus Ride
Bunuel, in a relaxed, populist mood, presents this story of a young peasant who is forced to leave his bride on their wedding night to travel to the city to finalize his dying mother's will. On his bus journey he encounters a diverse group of passengers in a picaresque adventure which is not without its anarchic and surreal overtones. Spanish with English subtitles.
VHS: S02664. $29.95.
Luis Bunuel, Mexico, 1951, 85 mins.

Mina Tannenbaum
Mousy, introspective Mina and overweight, outgoing Ethel meet at the age of seven, and for the next 25 years their lives are intertwined. They survive adolescence—the humiliations of an ugly duckling childhood, their guilt-happy Jewish mothers—and emerge, Mina as a star of the Paris art world and Ethel as a self-determined woman. Romane Bohringer and Elsa Zylberstein deliver remarkable performances in a powerful, emotional work called the "best foreign film of the year" by the Boston Society of Film Critics. French with English subtitles.
VHS: S28615. $89.95.
Martine Dugowson, France, 1993, 128 mins.

Minbo—Or the Gentle Art of Japanese Extortion
Juzo Itami turns his acid humor to Japan's infamous institution—the Yakuza gangs—in this film about a courageous attorney who rallies all of the employees at a hotel in an effort to resist the Yakuza blackmail. After the film was completed, thugs viciously attacked the director, forcing him to go into hiding. A brilliant, satirical look at the underbelly of Japanese modern life. Japanese with English subtitles.
VHS: S26090. $29.95.
Juzo Itami, Japan, 1994, 123 mins.

Miracle in Rome
Called "a small miracle itself" by the *New York Times, Miracle in Rome* tells the story of Margarito Duarte, a man whose seven-year-old daughter dies suddenly. Upon visiting her grave 12 years later, Margarito finds his daughter's body just as he had left it. His fellow townspeople call the event a miracle, but the town bishop wants the girl reburied. Based on an original story by Gabriel Garcia Marquez, who also co-wrote the screenplay. Spanish with English subtitles.
VHS: S13511. $19.98.
Lisandro Duque Naranjo, Spain, 1988, 76 mins.

Miracle of Marcelino
The classic, immensely popular film of the 50's, set in a rural area of Spain, an emotionally moving story of a young boy discovering faith. Spanish with English subtitles.
VHS: S06478. $59.95.
Ladislao Vajda, Spain, 1956, 88 mins.

The Mirror
Tarkovsky's looking glass is not merely cracked but shattered and we see the jagged, jumbled reflections of its shards, images of the director's childhood mixed with fragments of his adult life...a child's wartime exile, a mother's experience with political terror, the breakup of a marriage, life in a country home; all intermingled with slow motion dream sequences and stark newsreel. An essential film whose puzzles provide the key to this intense filmmaker's other works. Russian with English subtitles.
VHS: S13009. $59.95.
Andrei Tarkovsky, USSR, 1985, 101 mins.

Miss Julie
The definitive version of August Strindberg's riveting play concerning social and sexual domination. Miss Julie is a noblewoman who allows her butler to seduce her after her engagement is broken. With Anita Bjork and Anders Henrikson. Swedish with English subtitles.
VHS: S01720. $29.95.
Alf Sjoberg, Sweden, 1950, 90 mins.

Misty Wharf (Quai des Brumes)

A deserter, Jean Gabin, arrives at the port looking for a ship in which to escape from the police. He has committed a murder during a fit of temper, and while still searching for a likely ship he falls in love with Michele Morgan and her nostalgic beauty. French with English subtitles.
VHS: $21756. $39.95.
Marcel Carne, France, 1938, 90 mins.

Mon Oncle

A masterpiece by the great French comic Jacques Tati which concentrates on young Gerard Arpel and his Uncle Hulot (Jacques Tati) in a house where gadgets overpower everything. Sound effects, minimal dialog contribute to Tati's wry humor. French with English subtitles.
VHS: $00870. $29.95.
Laser: LD71234. $49.95.
Jacques Tati, France, 1958, 114 mins.

Mon Oncle d'Amerique

Three middle-class French drifters, each convinced they lack definition and excitement, dream about the imaginary and mythic "American Uncle," cross a behavioral scientist who instills in them a sense of wonder and excitement and the mystery of the unknown. The film is structured like a riddle, "one which proves that surrealism lives" (*Time Out*). With Gerard Depardieu, Nicole Garcia, Roger Pierre and Marie Dubois. French with English subtitles.
VHS: $02141. $29.95.
Alain Resnais, France, 1980, 126 mins.

Moscow Does Not Believe in Tears

Vladimir Menshov's melodrama about the cruel anonymity of city life is structured in two parts. The first half is set in 1958, as Menshov charts the interlocking romantic fates of three Russian girls shunned to a workers' dormitory. Tonya (Raisa Ryazanova) finds grace and happiness; Ludmila (Irina Muraveva) is trapped in an unhealthy and oppressive marriage; Katerina (Vera Alentova) is cruelly abandoned when her lover discovers she's pregnant. The second half resumes their stories and lives 20 years later. Winner of the 1980 Academy Award for Best Foreign Film. With Alexei Batalov, Alexander Fatiushin and Boris Smorchkov. Russian with English subtitles.
VHS: $19053. $59.95.
Vladimir Menshov, Russia, 1980, 148 mins.

Mother India (Bharat Mata)

This massively successful, award-winning film epic has acquired the status of an Indian *Gone with the Wind*. A color remake of Mehboob's own *Aurat*, the film stars Nargis as an old woman remembering her past and her happy married life with three sons in a rural village. Also stars Raj Kumar, Sunil Dutt and Rajendra Kumar. Hindi with English subtitles.
VHS: $30067. $29.95.
Mehboob Khan, India, 1957

Mother Joan of the Angels

One of the landmarks of modern Polish cinema, this gripping adaptation of Aldous Huxley's *The Devils of Loudun* (like Ken Russell's *The Devils*), transposes the action to a 17th-century French convent, where a priest investigates demonic possession among nuns. But the exorcist finds himself involved in an unavoidable mutual attraction with the Mother Superior. Full of brilliant symbolism, Kawalerowicz weaves a powerful allegory of good vs. evil, chastity vs. eroticism. Polish with English subtitles.
VHS: $22598. $59.95.
Jerzy Kawalerowicz, Poland, 1960, 108 mins.

Mother Kusters Goes to Heaven

A major Fassbinder film. Mother Kusters finds herself suddenly widowed. Her husband was a factory worker who one day goes berserk, killing the boss' son and throwing himself into the machinery. Her daughter, a would-be chanteuse, moves in with a muckraking journalist to further her career. Soon the dead man's life is distorted throughout pages of a cheap tabloid. Fassbinder paints a world where the honest and the good fall prey to a system of corrupt media and politics, a world where only small kindnesses carry relief to overwhelming suffering. German with English subtitles.
VHS: $16695. $29.95.
Rainer W. Fassbinder, Germany, 1975, 108 mins.

Mouchette

"Bresson constructs a drama of extraordinary tension and adventure," wrote *The New York Times*. "The adventure leads to escape from life, to a moment when nature and the supernatural meet in a fleeting intimation of grace so powerful that even an awareness of what the camera cannot show us is happiness enough." A 14-year-old friendless schoolgirl, Mouchette, lives with her alcoholic bootleg father, and her mother is dying. She is more sensitive than anyone around her and thus, paradoxically, less able to communicate. Based on the novel *La Nouvelle Histoire de Mouchette* by Georges Bernanos, Mouchette, says Bresson, "is found everywhere: wars, concentration camps, tortures, assassinations." French with English subtitles.
VHS: $06465. $59.95.
Robert Bresson, France, 1960, 80 mins.

Mr. Hulot's Holiday

Jacques Tati's second film introduces M. Hulot (Tati), a genial, eccentric, middle-class French everyman whose vacation at a seaside French resort in Brittany produces one minor catastrophe after another. Tati's intricate juxtaposition of mime and slapstick is so refined, pure and expressive, there's an extraordinary pain, passion and tenderness that produces laughter and heartbreak. With Nathalie Pascaud, Michele Rolla and Louis Perrault. French with English subtitles.
VHS: $00891. $24.95.
Laser: LD71241. $59.95.
Jacques Tati, France, 1952, 91 mins.

Mr. Klein

Set in France during the 1942 occupation, Joseph Losey's French film stars Alain Delon as a cultivated and ruthless art dealer who discovers that someone is using his identity to cover their anti-Nazi resistance activities. As Mr. Klein becomes obsessed with the search for his imposter, he meets an elegant society lady (Jeanne Moreau), who leads him further into the trap. This existential period thriller was hailed by the *New York Times* as "seductive, splendidly visual, witty, cool, and elegant." French with English subtitles.
VHS: $32685. $59.95.
Joseph Losey, France/Italy, 1976, 123 mins.

Murderers Are Among Us

A woman returns from her internment in a concentration camp only to find her Berlin apartment occupied by a young doctor. Both end up living there, leading to a complicated series of attachments. The doctor is especially problematic. He is traumatized by his wartime experiences and decides to seek revenge against a former superior. Stars Hildegard Knef and Ernst Wilhelm Borchert. German with English subtitles.
VHS: $29869. $39.95.
Wolfgang Staudte, Germany, 1946, 84 mins.

Muriel

One of the most interesting films from Alain Resnais, a bold and beautiful film, in which Resnais takes an incident from provincial life, the reunion of a middle-aged woman and her old lover at Boulogne. Out of the trivia of everyday life and its anxieties, he creates a mosaic masterpiece that probes the themes of time and memory, and the relationship between personal conscience and public consciousness (the references to the Algerian War). With Delphine Seyrig, Jean-Pierre Kerien, Nina Klein. Music by Hans Werner Henze. French with English subtitles.
VHS: $02079. $59.95.
Alain Resnais, France, 1963, 115 mins.

My Father Is Coming

An adventurous German woman receives word from her Bavarian father of his intentions to visit her in New York, where she must pull off an elaborate facade of being married and successful. Her gay roommate poses as her husband but complications ensue when a string of bizarre circumstances result in her father's transformation into an underground sexual icon. With Shelly Kastner, Alfred Edel and Annie Sprinkle.
VHS: $18412. $29.95.
Monika Treut, USA/Germany, 1991, 83 mins.

My Father's Glory

An 11-year-old boy spends an enchanting summer in the rugged French countryside with his family. The experience becomes a turning point in his young life and cements his relationship with his father. From the novel by Marcel Pagnol, a gorgeous film starring Philippe Caubere and Nathalie Roussel. French with English subtitles.
VHS: $16035. $19.98.
Yves Robert, France, 1991, 103 mins.

Open City

My Favorite Season (Ma Saison Preferee)

Techine's fascinating, dark and somber story of a middle-aged brother and sister (Catherine Deneuve and Daniel Auteuil), a provincial lawyer and a skilled surgeon, respectively, who begin to come to terms with what they have become professionally and personally when their aging mother (Marthe Villalonge) begins to disintegrate after a stroke. Techine himself describes *Ma Saison Preferee* as a film "about individuality and the frigity of the modern world." French with English subtitles.
VHS: S32613. $89.98.
Andre Techine, France, 1993, 124 mins.

My Life as a Dog

More than just a movie, a phenomenon that has captured the hearts of America. A bright, funny, touching tale of one boy's special growing-up year. Bundled off to a rural village while his ill mother recuperates, young Ingermar finds unexpected adventure with the town's warmhearted eccentrics. Swedish with English subtitles.
VHS: S06240. $19.98.
Laser: Subtitled. LD75232. $34.98.
Lasse Hallstrom, Sweden, 1987, 101 mins.

My Life to Live

"One of the most beautiful, touching and original films by Godard, an extremely complex blend of social document, theatricality and interior drama…" (Georges Sadoul). A film in 12 episodes, with Anna Karina the salesgirl in a record shop, who can't pay her rent, is evicted by her landlady and becomes a prostitute. "It triumphs because it is intelligent, discreet, delicate to the touch. It both edifies and gives pleasure because it is about what is most important…the nature of our humanity" (Susan Sontag). French with English subtitles.
VHS: S00907. $29.95.
Laser: LD76282. $49.95.
Jean-Luc Godard, France, 1962, 85 mins.

My Mother's Castle

In the companion film to *My Father's Glory*, a boy continues his love affair with the wild country of southern France. Through frequent family visits to their summer home, he learns to love and understand his mother's true nature. The heartfelt conclusion to the story by Marcel Pagnol. French with English subtitles.
VHS: S16036. $19.98.
Yves Robert, France, 1991, 117 mins.

My Sweet Little Village

The overbearing Pavek threatens to replace his sidekick, the simple-minded Otik, but he never does. Instead the two continue to work together in this carefully observed portrait of life in a funny little village. Around this Laurel and Hardy-like pair are a group of eccentrics, all bemusedly following their own quirky obsessions. Czech with English subtitles.
VHS: S26207. $24.95.
Jiri Menzel, Czech Republic, 1986, 100 mins.

The Mystery of Kaspar Hauser

In 1828, a young man appeared in the town square of Nuremberg, his origins unknown, having apparently been kept in solitary confinement all his life; five years later he was murdered by an unidentified assailant. Kaspar's brief, enigmatic destiny becomes a powerful metaphor for life in Werner Herzog's vision of the extreme edges of existence. Former mental patient Bruno S. delivers a sympathetic and powerful performance. "Herzog achieves a visionary, overcast style" (Pauline Kael, *The New Yorker*). Also known as *Every Man for Himself and God against All*. With Walter Ladengast, Brigitte Mira, Hans Musaus and Willy Semmelrogge. German with English subtitles.
VHS: S20303. $29.95.
Werner Herzog, Germany, 1974, 110 mins.

The Mystery of Rampo

A famous mystery writer continually pushes the bounds of taste with his fiction in this atmospheric thriller from Japan which is filled with eroticism and suspense. As one of the writer's characters suddenly comes to life, he is pushed into ever more surreal and dangerous situations. Japanese with English subtitles.
VHS: S26861. $19.98.
Laser: LD75415. $39.99.
Kazuyoshi Okuyama, Japan, 1994, 101 mins.

Napoleon

Orson Welles, Maria Schell, Yves Montand, and Erich von Stroheim star in Sacha Guitry's classic biography of Napoleon, from his youth as a soldier in the French Army until his exile to the Island of Elba. A monumental production with a cast of thousands, originally shot in Technicolor. English dialog.
VHS: S00918. $59.95.
Laser: LD70061. $89.98.
Sacha Guitry, France, 1955, 115 mins.

The Nasty Girl

When Sonja investigates the secret past of her home town, she uncovers more than she expected—and more than the townsfolk want revealed. Before she knows it, she is nicknamed "the nasty girl" and her trouble really begins. This provocative comedy about secrets and surprises features a fabulous performance by Lena Stolze and is based on a true story. "One of the best films of the year!" (*Los Angeles Daily News*). German with yellow English subtitles. Presented in letterbox format.
VHS: S15354. $19.95.
Michael Verhoeven, Germany, 1991, 94 mins.

The Need

"One of those rare works in which the perfect rendering of simple elements produces a small, unforgettable masterpiece. The film's two main characters are boys poised between childhood and manhood. Both are poor. The boy through whose eyes we experience the drama has lost his father in the war and seems to have only the bleakest of prospects, until a relative finds him a choice apprentice's position in a print shop. But there is a catch; another boy coveting the spot has also been taken on, with the better of the two getting the permanent job after a trial period. Thus begins a fierce if somewhat covert rivalry that results in workplace sabotage, fighting and then, very surprisingly, friendship" (Godfrey Cheshire, *Film Comment*). Farsi with English subtitles.
VHS: S27788. $29.95.
Alireza Davudneshad, Iran, 1991, 81 mins.

Nelly and Monsieur Arnaud

In this engaging romance of longing and denial reminiscent of Kieslowski's *Red*, Emmanuelle Beart plays Nelly, who is introduced to the wealthy Arnaud (Michel Serrault) and agrees to transcribe his memoirs. The unlikely couple develop a playful flirtation, which is complicated by Nelly's involvement with Arnaud's charming editor (Jean-Hugues Anglade). What follows is a devastating succession of near-misses and might-have-beens that frame the hesitations and sudden pleasures of unexpected love. "A winning romance! Exceptionally touching and astonishing" (Gary Arnold, *Washington Times*). French with English subtitles.
VHS: S30936. $89.95.
Claude Sautet, France, 1996, 103 mins.

A Night of Love

Alfred Molina, Eric Stoltz, Gabrielle Anwar and Camilla Soeberg star in Dusan Makavejev's inventive adaptation of a story by Emile Zola. Originally titled *Manifesto*, the film is full of gentle, erotic irony as a guard (Molina) must protect a king on a visit to his subjects in a small town. A number of revolutionaries will stop at nothing to get the king. Seduction,

misguided faith and sheer incompetence combine to produce a wicked, sexy comedy.
VHS: S26402. $19.98.
Dusan Makavejev, Yugoslavia/USA, 1988, 97 mins.

Night of the Shooting Stars
This magical film by the Taviani Brothers is set on the night of the Feast of St. Lawrence during the last days of World War II. A woman recalls her beloved and a night years ago when, on another such night, a group of peasants fled through the Tuscan countryside amid exploding shells lighting up the sky instead of stars. The film is a beautiful tapestry of fact, myth and wartime memory, romantic and intense. Italian with English subtitles.
VHS: S00933. $19.98.
Paolo & Vittorio Taviani, Italy, 1982, 106 mins.

Nights of Cabiria
The third of Fellini's trilogy of solitude, *Nights of Cabiria* features Giuletta Masina as an impoverished prostitute living on the outskirts of Rome, who is betrayed by her faith in human nature. Winner of the Academy Award for Best Foreign Film, Masina's performance is one of the great performances on film. Italian with English subtitles.
VHS: S18582. $39.95.
Federico Fellini, Italy, 1957, 110 mins.

No Regrets for Our Youth
An unusual feminist epic saga which focuses on a charming, talented and self-absorbed Japanese woman, Yukie, who is preparing herself for the role of a spoiled, cultured wife. She flirts with two suitors, one a disaffected leftist, the other a right-wing careerist, though she has no personal interest in politics. The earliest personal and first great film by Kurosawa, with a commanding performance by Setsuko Hara as the complex woman whose life unfolds against the backdrop of Japanese militarist society. Japanese with English subtitles.
VHS: S11176. $29.95.
Akira Kurosawa, Japan, 1946, 110 mins.

Nosferatu
One of Murnau's best known films, *Nosferatu*'s eerie telling of the Dracula story was filmed on location in the mountains, towns, and castles of Bavaria. This German Expressionist symphony of horror is brilliantly infused with the subtle tones of nature: both pure and fresh, as well as twisted and sinister. Newly restored and color tinted, this version was remastered from a 35mm negative and includes recently discovered scenes and inter-titles freshly translated from the original German script. At 84 minutes, it is the most complete version available on home video.
DVD: DV60031. $29.95.
VHS: S15038. $29.95.
Friedrich W. Murnau, Germany, 1922, 84 mins.

Nueba Yol
This charming film about disappointment, triumph and the American dream broke all box office records in the Dominican Republic. When Balbuena (Luisito Marti) moves from Santo Domingo to New York ("Nueba Yol" in Dominican slang) hoping to make a fortune, he is in for a harsh disappointment, but finds the inner resources to succeed and find love in this land of crime, betrayal and strict labor laws. "*Nueba Yol*'s well-placed plot and endearing characters provide a solid foundation for the deeper, more thought-provoking issues it raises. The film addresses not only immigration and crime but also the more universal themes of dreams, disappointment and triumph" (Mary Ann Farley, *Video Business*). Spanish with English subtitles.
VHS: S30285. $19.95.
Angel Muniz, Dominican Republic, 1996, 105 mins.

Numero Deux
Jean-Luc Godard brilliantly mixes video and film, set in the director's Grenoble studio. The action unfolds on two television monitors. Godard secured the money for the film claiming the project was a remake of *Breathless*. The elusive plot essentially concerns the marital discord—set off by the wife's infidelity—between a young working-class couple (Sandrine Battistella and Pierre Oudry) who live in a claustrophobic, high rise apartment complex. The film, made in collaboration with Anne-Marie Mieville, is a dialectic on the relationship of sex and money. "I think it's something like a masterpiece. *Numero Deux* is among the most visually compelling films Godard has ever made. He uses his video monitors to invent a dozen new ways of splitting the screen or layering the image. Compared to it, every other movie in town is just a cavity on the screen" (J. Hoberman, *The Village Voice*). With Alexandre Rignault and Rachel Stefanopoli. French with English subtitles.
VHS: S19233. $59.95.
Jean-Luc Godard, France/Switzerland, 1976, 88 mins.

Oblomov
A beautiful adaptation of the famous Ivan Goncharov novel by Nikita (*Dark Eyes, Slave of Love*) Mikhalkov. Oblomov owns 350 serfs he's never met, and just lies on his back in a St. Petersburg apartment, sleeping, eating, sleeping some more, watching his finances dwindle and whining at his servant for not being sensitive enough. A detailed, beautifully photographed film. Russian with English subtitles.
VHS: S12969. $59.95.
Nikita Mikhalkov, USSR, 1980, 120 mins.

The Official Story
Winner of the Academy Award for Best Foreign Language Film in 1985, this powerful Argentinean feature is the true story of a comfortable middle-class couple and their adopted daughter. As the film progresses, the couple gradually begin to suspect that their daughter may be one of the many Argentinean children separated from their parents as they are detained or tortured and given away. The wife's journey of self-discovery reveals the horrors of the military dictatorship in Argentina. Directed by Luis Puenzo. With great performances from Hector Alterio and Norma Aleandro. Spanish with English subtitles.
VHS: S00949. $19.98.
Luis Puenzo, Argentina, 1985, 112 mins.

Oh Woe Is Me (Helas Pour Moi)
Gerard Depardieu meets Jean-Luc Godard in this gentle Godard fable in which divinity touches everyday life. Godard transposes to Switzerland the Greek myth in which Zeus inhabited Amphitryon's body to seduce a man's wife, with surprising results. Godardian touches like titles on the screen, townspeople who function as a theatrical chorus and music from Bach, Beethoven and Tchaikovsky make this a cerebral but passionate exploration of constancy and cinema. French with English subtitles.
VHS: S26336. $89.95.
Jean-Luc Godard, France, 1994, 84 mins.

One Deadly Summer
Psychological thriller features Isabelle Adjani as a mysterious woman who returns to her mother's village to seek revenge on three men who had beaten and raped her mother years before. French with English subtitles.
VHS: S03313. $59.95.
Jean Becker, France, 1983, 134 mins.

Open City
A beautiful video master, transferred from a new negative, of this key film of Italian Neo-Realism, shot largely during the Nazi occupation of Rome. Two resistance leaders, one a Communist, the other a priest, work toward weakening the German occupation. The cumulative power of Rossellini's feeling for his subject was translated into a visual intensity that makes the picture sometimes almost impossible to watch. With a great performance by Anna Magnani. Italian with English subtitles.
VHS: S13591. $24.95.
Laser: LD75058. $49.95.
Roberto Rossellini, Italy, 1945, 103 mins.

Oriane
A taut, Gothic, Latin American romance, winner of the Camera d'Or at the Cannes Film Festival. Marie returns to a rundown Venezuelan house in the jungle where she spent summers as a child. Her return ignites memories of a summer when her adolescent sexual curiosity led to a surprising encounter. "An exotic *Jane Eyre* set in a jungle-choked hacienda" (*Seattle Weekly*). With Doris Wells and Daniela Silverio. Spanish with English subtitles.
VHS: S27801. $29.95.
Fina Torres, Venezuela, 1991, 92 mins.

Orlova Three-Pack
Includes three films starring Lyubov Orlova, the first recognized star of Soviet cinema: *Volga-Volga, Jazz Comedy* (*Jolly Fellows*) and *Circus*. Russian with English subtitles.
VHS: S27217. $79.95.
Grigori Alexandrov, USSR, 1934-37, 277 mins.

Orpheus

Cocteau's famous retelling of the Greek myth, with Jean Marais as Orphee, the successful poet envied and despised, who pushes himself beyond mortality, and Maria Casares as the dark, troubled, passionate Death. A great film. French with English subtitles.
VHS: S00977. $29.95.
Jean Cocteau, France, 1949, 95 mins.

Ossessione

One of the great revelations of the cinema: Luchino Visconti's adaptation of James M. Cain's *The Postman Always Rings Twice*, about the tragic love between a wanderer and the wife of an innkeeper, who murder the husband. For long never shown in the U.S., the film had a profound influence on the course of the cinema, beginning the era that would become Italian neo-realism. A masterpiece. Italian with English subtitles.
VHS: S05922. $29.95.
Luchino Visconti, Italy, 1942, 135 mins.

The Oyster Princess

This witty satire on the American businessman and the Prussian aristocracy tells the story of Ossi (Ossi Oswalda), whose American "Oyster King" father promises to buy her a prince to marry. The victim recommended by their marriage broker is Prince Nucki, who lives in a run-down apartment with his friend Josef. What follows is one of the most lavish weddings ever filmed, but the wedding night is not at all what the "princess" had in mind. With Harry Liedtke, Viktor Janson, Julius Falkenstein and Curt Bois. Silent with English intertitles. "A summoning up of everything Lubitsch had learned about the art of comedy" (Herman G. Weinberg, in *The Lubitsch Touch*).
VHS: S30211. $29.95.
Ernst Lubitsch, Germany, 1919, 70 mins.

Painted Lips (Boquitas Pintadas)

This feature about obsessive love deals with a romantically handsome young man in the later stages of tuberculosis who is furiously fought over by four women. The film tells the story as it is recalled after his death by one of the women, who dies 30 years later, finally "cured" of romance. With Alfredo Alcon, Martha Gonzalez and Luisina Brando. Spanish with English subtitles.
VHS: S27741. $59.95.
Leopoldo Torre Nilsson, Argentina, 1975, 120 mins.

Pandora's Box

G.W. Pabst's baroque interpretation of Wedekind's *Lulu* plays is an eerie depiction of erotic obsession and sexual abandon. The action moves between Berlin and London, as Lulu (Louise Brooks), a beautiful, charismatic chorus girl, orchestrates a succession of casual affairs until her fateful encounter with Jack the Ripper. With Fritz Kortner, Franz Lederer and Carl Goetz. Silent with music track. English titles.
VHS: S00990. $24.95.
G.W. Pabst, Germany, 1928, 110 mins.

Paris Belongs to Us

Shot on weekends, with no money and no sets, with actors donating their time and Chabrol providing left-over film stock, this film concerns a group of amateurs who come together in Paris to stage a performance of Shakespeare's *Pericles*. But sexual and political tensions develop, their composer dies, the producer kills himself and a fascist conspiracy seems to be lurking in the background. The result of Rivette's two-year struggle is a work of total originality and inventiveness, of amazing depth and independence of vision. French with English subtitles.
VHS: S07472. $59.95.
Jacques Rivette, France, 1958-60, 124 mins.

Paris Vu Par (Six in Paris)

This omnibus film from the major figures of the French New Wave (Jean-Luc Godard, Claude Chabrol, Eric Rohmer, Jean Douchet, Jean Rouch and Jean-Daniel Pollet) offers a series of witty, wry vignettes about contemporary Paris. Godard's work, *Une Femme Est une Femme*, is about a young woman who dispatches letters to her two lovers and is concerned she mixed up the contents. With Joanna Shimkus, Nadine Ballot, Barbet Schroeder, Micheline Dax, Claude Melki, Chabrol and Stephane Audran. French with English subtitles. France, 1964, 98 mins.
VHS: S19543. $69.95.

Passion of Joan of Arc

One of the most poignant, terrifying and unrelenting emotional historical documents ever filmed. Called an austere masterpiece in reference to the stark sets and extreme close-up photography, *Joan of Arc* is brilliantly portrayed by Maria Falconetti. Silent.
VHS: S00998. $29.95.
Carl Theodor Dreyer, France, 1928, 114 mins.

Pather Panchali

The opening entry of Satyajit Ray's extraordinary *Apu* trilogy, adapted from the epic novel of Bengali writer B.B. Bandapaddhay, is a fiercely naturalistic, devastating portrait of poverty and despair. Ray uses his considerable storytelling powers of detail, incident and observation to interpret the relationship of a young Bengali boy and his family. The film has an emotional rhythm and a fluid, precise lyricism. Winner of the Jury Prize at the 1956 Cannes Film festival. Music composed and performed by Ravi Shankar. With Kanu Banerji, Karuna Banerji, Uma Da Gupta and Chunibala Devi. Newly remastered. Bengali with English subtitles.
VHS: S27702. $19.95.
Satyajit Ray, India, 1955, 112 mins.

The Peddler

Shockingly forthright in its view of the social and economic problems of the post-Shah era, *The Peddler* uses a different cameraman and different style for each of three short tales set among the poor of contemporary Tehran. The first episode follows a kindly but naive couple who want someone to adopt their newborn daughter. The second, an astonishing mix of absurdist comedy and the supernatural, concerns a mentally unstable man who lives with his mother in a ramshackle apartment. The final section draws on the American gangster film to show the last hours of a peddler suspected of betraying his friends. Farsi with English subtitles.
VHS: S27787. $29.95.
Mohsen Makhmalbaf, Iran, 1986, 95 mins.

Pepe le Moko

A gem of French cinema with an unbelievable performance by Jean Gabin as Pepe le Moko, a Parisian gangster hiding out in the Algerian Casbah. A menacing atmosphere full of shadows contributes to the image of Pepe as the outsider/hero who falls in love with a Parisian woman, tries to escape with her and finds his path blocked by the police. The spine-tingling ending is classic. With Mireille Balin and Line Noro. French with English subtitles.
VHS: S01007. $29.95.
Julien Duvivier, France, 1936, 95 mins.

Peppermint Soda

Diane Kurys' autobiographical first feature charts the adventures of two carefree sisters, Anne (Elenore Klarwein), a shy misfit, and Frederique (Odile Michel), a free-spirited extrovert, during the socially turbulent Paris of the early '60s. Living with their divorced Jewish mother, the girls shuttle between a rigid, claustrophobic school and awkward holidays with their father. "The film is a harsh, unsentimental look at adolescence, with the '60s setting serving primarily to define the social and political context of the girls' rites of passage" (*Time Out*). With Anouk Ferjac, Michel Puterflam, Yves Renier and Robert Rimbaud. French with English subtitles.
VHS: S19416. $29.95.
Diane Kurys, France, 1977, 97 mins.

Perfumed Nightmare

Called "one of the year's best films" by J. Hoberman in *The Village Voice*, an enchanting, poignant, and totally original fable by young Philippino filmmaker Kidlat Tahimik, about his awakening to and reaction against American cultural colonialism. Born in 1942 during the Occupation, Tahimik spent the "next 33 typhoon seasons in a cocoon of American dreams." This is his perfumed nightmare: the lotus-land of American technological promise. In his primitive village he worshiped the heroism of the Machine, the sleek beauty of rockets, the efficiency of industrialism. He is the president of his own Werner Von Braun fan club. A bizarre, hallucinatory movie full of dazzling images and outlandish ideas, shot on super 8 for less than $10,000. Winner of the International Critics Award, Berlin Film Festival. English and Tagalog with English subtitles.
VHS: S09300. $59.95.
Kidlat Tahimik, Philippines, 1983, 91 mins.

Persona

Ingmar Bergman's great achievement, a study of madness, breakdown and transference of identity. The

story concerns a brilliant actress who unaccountably loses her will to speak and her shifting, intricate and elaborate relationship with the nurse assigned to her rehabilitation. Liv Ullmann is the actress, Harriet Andersson is the nurse. Cinematography by Sven Nykvist. Swedish with English subtitles.
VHS: S17865. $19.98.
Laser: Digital Transfer. **LD74926. $34.98.**
Ingmar Bergman, Sweden, 1967, 81 mins.

Phantom of Liberty
One of Bunuel's masterpieces of surrealism, this loosely structured series of anecdotes deals with the concept of freedom. A daisy-chain of characters move through this cinema of dreams and absurdity, demonstrating the cosmic comedy of humans who constantly enslave themselves in order to be free. The lightest and liveliest of Bunuel's films filled with riddles, jokes and outrageous associations ridiculing the power to reason. French with English subtitles.
VHS: S04869. $24.95.
Luis Bunuel, France, 1974, 102 mins.

Pierrot le Fou
One of the high points of 20th century cinema. Ravishing and moving, the story features Jean-Paul Belmondo as Ferdinand, who one evening leaves his wife in the middle of a boring party. He meets a girl with whom he was in love five years earlier, and who is involved with a gang of criminals. After Ferdinand finds a dead man in her room, they leave Paris for a deserted island. One of Godard's most poetic films, full of the anguish of love, aptly summarized in his own words over the first images of the film, "At the age of fifty, Velasquez no longer painted precise objects; he painted what lay between precise objects." The final murder-suicide sequence on the island is one of the most brilliant Godard has ever created.

French with English subtitles.
VHS: S10739. $59.95.
Jean-Luc Godard, France, 1965, 110 mins.

Pixote
This acclaimed feature by Hector Babenco has been out of release for years. Nothing in recent cinema comes close to the devastating account of brutalization and exploitation offered in Babenco's film about a 12-year-old boy who somehow survives the vicious oppression of reform school to escape and find his way into dope-dealing, prostitution and murder on the streets of Sao Paolo, Brazil. Portuguese with English subtitles.
VHS: S30982. $89.95.
Hector Babenco, Brazil, 1981, 127 mins.

Playtime
Called one of the funniest men in the world by the *New York Times*, Jacques Tati's *Playtime* is an hilarious comedy and satire on coping with the modern world. For Tati's now-legendary character, M. Hulot, everything seems to be against him—a glass-fronted airport, a new restaurant, even a supermarket. Full of visual gags and inventive use of sound, *Playtime* is one of the most imaginative and funniest films ever. Digitally remastered and letterboxed. English dialog.
VHS: S01038. $39.95.
Jacques Tati, France, 1967, 108 mins.

Portrait of Teresa
One of the key Cuban films shot in a fluid style, the film focuses on the stubborn survival of deeply ingrained traditions of machismo and sexism in post-revolutionary society. Teresa, a housewife, incurs the displeasure of her husband because of her involvement in political and cultural groups. Perhaps the most controversial Cuban film to be released in

Pixote

U.S. Spanish with English subtitles.
VHS: $12197. $69.95.
Pastor Vega, Cuba, 1979, 115 mins.

Pretty Boy

In this unflinching and harshly poetic film, the chronicle of a young runaway boy unfolds on the streets of Copenhagen. There he becomes a street hustler. Before the camera, innocence is plundered and finally lost in this compelling exploration of desire. Danish with English subtitles.
VHS: $23290. $69.95.
Carsten Sonder, Denmark, 1993, 87 mins.

Princess Yang Kwei Fei

Kenji Mizoguchi's film about a young servant girl who is transformed into a princess and then destroyed by the shifting loyalties, betrayal and revenge around her. Mizoguchi's use of color, decor and diagonal compositions is fluid and baroque and perfectly reflects the characters' emotional conditions. "One of the most beautiful films ever to treat beauty as a subject" (*Andrew Sarris*). With Masayuki Mori, Machiko Kyo and So Yamamura. Japanese with English subtitles.
VHS: $18421. $29.95.
Kenji Mizoguchi, Japan, 1955, 125 mins.

The Promise

In this love story the Berlin wall separates two young lovers. They first fall for each other in their teens and their passion stretches over 28 years until the wall no longer presents an obstacle to their joint happiness. It's an epic story about the endurance of love. German with English subtitles.
VHS: $27255. $19.98.
Laser: LD75471. $39.99.
Margarethe von Trotta, Germany, 1995, 115 mins.

Pubis Angelical

Based on a novel by Manuel (*Kiss of the Spider Woman*) Puig—the poignant story of a dying woman reflecting on her life, intertwining dreams and fantasies of political events with her frustration with the men who stifled her. With Graciella Borges, Alfredo Alcon. Spanish with English subtitles.
VHS: $07740. $39.95.
Raul de la Torre, Argentina, 1983, 117 mins.

Purple Noon (Plein Soleil)

Rene Clement's psychological thriller, with the young Alain Delon as a morally bankrupt individual who is stricken with envy of his best friend. He murders him and then takes over his identity, even becoming the lover of his friend's girlfriend. Based on Patricia Highsmith's novel *The Talented Mr. Ripley*, *Purple Noon* is a startling and disturbing film that elicits audience fascination with a cunning "anti-hero." Stunningly photographed by Henri Decae against the backgrounds of southern Italy. French with English subtitles.
VHS: $30639. $103.99.
Laser: Widescreen. LD76093. $49.98.
Rene Clement, France/Italy, 1959, 118 mins.

Que Viva Mexico

Eisenstein's long-lost diamond-in-the-rough, shot by the great Eduard Tisse, and financed by Upton Sinclair. Reconstructed in 1979 by Grigori Alexandrov, the last surviving member of Eisenstein's Mexican team, *Que Viva Mexico* is a silent film narrated in Russian and subtitled in English. Divided into segments: a wedding, a bullfight, a fiesta, a dramatized abortive uprising by peons against feudal masters at the turn of the century. Anyone who has seen the lyrical, ravishing images of Eduard Tisse's *Que Viva Mexico* will revel in the priceless beauty of Eisenstein's incomplete master-work. Russian with English subtitles.
VHS: $12976. $59.95.
Eisenstein/Alexandrov, USSR, 1931, 90 mins.

Queen Margot

Winner of five Cesar Awards, Patrice Chereau's stylish, realistic adaptation Alexander Dumas' tale is set during the Catholic-Protestant wars of 16th-century France. Isabelle Adjani plays Margot, the unwilling daughter of Catherine de Medici (Virna Lisi in a Cannes Festival-winning role), who is married to Protestant leader King Henry of Navarre (Daniel Auteuil). In the film Chereau creates a non-stop series of betrayals, intrigues, plots, poisonings, love affairs and executions as Margot falls for a common soldier (Vincent Perez). French with English subtitles.
VHS: $25051. $19.98.
Laser: LD74955. $39.99.
Patrice Chereau, France, 1994, 144 mins.

Quilombo

From Carlos Diegues, the director of *Bye Bye Brazil* and *Xica*, comes a handsome tale of revolution and conflict set in the mid-1600s. Disgruntled slaves in northeastern Brazil leave their plantations and form Quilombo de Palmares—their own democratic nation in the jungle. But this doesn't sit well with the Portuguese landowners, who send in their troops to restore control. A sequel of sorts to *Ganga Zumba*, this historical saga is a stirring fusion of folklore, political impact and dynamic storytelling, realized in vibrant tropical colors and set to the pulsing beat of Gilberto Gil's musical score. With Antonio Pompeu, Toni Tornado, and the dazzling Zeze Motta as Dandara the temptress. Portuguese with English subtitles.
VHS: $14573. $29.95.
Carlos Diegues, Brazil, 1984, 114 mins.

Raise the Red Lantern

The third feature of Zhang Yimou stars the beautiful Gong Li as a 20-year-old college student who leaves school to become the fourth wife of a wealthy, powerful aristocrat. Her presence occasions a series of bitter jealousies and disputes with the three other wives. A fascinating work about sex, oppression and patriarchy. Mandarin with English subtitles.
VHS: $17881. $19.98.
Zhang Yimou, China/Taiwan, 1991, 125 mins.

Rashomon

A cinematic landmark, a brilliant study of the nature of truth. Set in the 12th century. A samurai and his wife are traveling through the woods near Kyoto. They are attacked by a bandit, the wife raped and the husband killed. Four different versions of the incident are told by the participants and a woodcutter who was a witness. Japanese with English subtitles.
VHS: $01092. $29.95.
Laser: LD70440. $49.95.
Akira Kurosawa, Japan, 1951, 89 mins.

The Raven (Le Corbeau)

An ingenious, suspenseful thriller, made in wartime occupied France and based on a true story. A small French town is torn asunder by poison pen letters which breed tensions and suicides. The suspects are a doctor, a crippled girl and a sick woman. Ultimately, it is discovered that the criminal is a revered old man. With brilliant performances from Ginette Leclerc and Pierre Fresnay. As the old man says in the film, "You think that goodness is light and darkness is evil. But where is the darkness? Where the light?" French with English subtitles.
VHS: $16563. $59.95.
Henri-Georges Clouzot, France, 1943, 92 mins.

Record of a Tenement Gentleman

One of Ozu's most wonderful films, a bittersweet comedy about an abandoned child who manages to create a new surrogate family in an unlikely setting from a very unlikely candidate. The surprise ending only reinforces how carefully this film depicts human emotions. Japanese with English subtitles.
VHS: $25907. $69.95.
Yasujiro Ozu, Japan, 1947, 73 mins.

Red

Kieslowski's striking conclusion of his Three Colors trilogy stars Irene Jacob as a model, separated from her lover, who is brought by accident into the life of the aging Jean-Louis Trintignant, retired judge and electronic peeping Tom. As Irene slowly uncovers her lover's secret life, she discovers that her own past is inevitably linked to her destiny. With Jean-Pierre Lorit and Frederique Feder.
VHS: $25606. $19.95.
Laser: Letterboxed. LD75015. $39.99.
Krzysztof Kieslowski, Switzerland, 1994, 99 mins.

The Red and the Black

Gerard Philipe stars in this adaptation of the famous novel by Stendhal, cast in the role of the opportunist Julien Sorel; Danielle Darrieux is Madame de Renal. French with English subtitles.
VHS: $06438. $29.95.
Claude Autant-Lara, France, 1953, 140 mins.

The Red and the White

One of the most original of films, a haunting work about the absurdity and evil of war. Set in Central Russia during the Civil War of 1918, the story details the constant shifting of power between the White guards and the Red soldiers, first at an abandoned monastery, and later, at a field hospital. Using the wide-screen technique consisting of very long takes and a ceaselessly tracking camera movement, Miklos

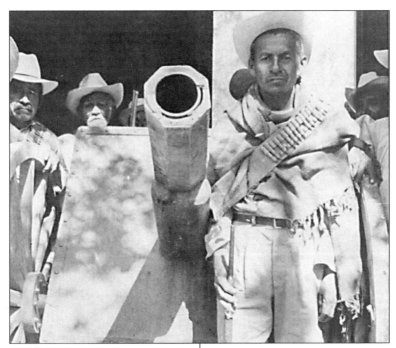

Reed: Mexico Insurgente

Jancso has fashioned a brilliant visual style which is truly unique in the history of cinema. Hungarian with English subtitles.
VHS: S08940. $79.95.
Miklos Jancso, Hungary, 1968, 92 mins.

Red Desert
Antonioni's masterpiece, with the great Monica Vitti playing the neurotic young woman married to an engineer in the industrial wasteland of northern Italy, searching in vain for meaning in life. Antonioni's first film in color—and what color! One of the most important films of the last half of the century. Italian with English subtitles.
VHS: S02080. $29.95.
Michelangelo Antonioni, Italy, 1964 , 116 mins.

Red Sorghum
A visually spectacular film which is a sweeping modern-day fable. The first part tells of a nervous young bride's arrival at a remote provincial winery and her takeover of the family business when her older husband is mysteriously murdered. The second half is a heroic and harrowing drama focused on the brutality of the Japanese during their occupation of China, and on partisan resistance. "The film's exoticism is palpable, almost intoxicating" (David Edelstein, *The Village Voice*). Mandarin with yellow English subtitles.
VHS: S15392. $79.95.
Zhang Yimou, China, 1987, 91 mins.

The Red Squirrel
Jota, a rock musician deserted by his girlfriend, is contemplating suicide when he rushes to the aid of a young woman after her motorcycle crashes. When he discovers she has lost her memory as a result of the accident, he pretends to be her lover and creates a fictitious life for her. *The Daily Telegraph* called this modern-day version of Alfred Hitchcock's masterpiece, *Vertigo*, "as taut and intricate as anything by Hitchcock." Winner of Director's Fortnight at Cannes and Best Young Picture at European Felix Awards. Spanish with English subtitles.
VHS: S30041. $89.95.
Julio Medem, Spain, 1993, 104 mins.

Reed: Mexico Insurgente
Paul Leduc's (*Frida Naturelaza Vida*) brilliant first feature focuses on John Reed's experience as an American journalist who covered the Mexican Revolution of 1914. The film shows the Revolution as both mundane and disorganized and poses the question of whether a journalist—surrounded by suffering—can remain an impartial observer. An important milestone in the history of contemporary Latin American cinema, and a powerful, intelligent film. Spanish with English subtitles.
VHS: S25733. $59.95.
Paul Leduc, Mexico, 1971, 106 mins.

Rendevous in Paris
Through the picturesque cafes and parks of Paris in the springtime, New Wave master Eric Rohmer displays his unique take on the follies and treacheries of the human heart in this witty, enchanting comedy which follows three young couples as they face the vanities, cruelties and deceptions of their romantic entanglements. "The perfect little gift for lovers of film, of Paris and of love!" (Richard Corliss, *Time*). French with English subtitles.
VHS: S31412. $89.95.
Eric Rohmer, France, 1996, 100 mins.

A Report on the Party and the Guests
A miracle of the Czech New Wave, distinguished with being "banned forever" shortly after it was completed. Voted one of the best films of the year by *The New York Times*, it is "an extraordinary allegory...evocative of Kafka or Dostoevsky" (*International Film Guide*). A group of picnickers are led to an elegant banquet, where the "guests" quickly turn collaborators in this brilliant analysis of society and the individual. Czech with English subtitles.
VHS: S05654. $59.95.
Jan Nemec, Czechoslovakia, 1966, 71 mins.

Return of Martin Guerre
Dramatization of an extraordinary imposture that took place in the 16th century and became a legend; the husband leaves his family and years later, returns. He re-integrates himself into the family and community, but then serious doubts spring up about his identity—is he the real Martin Guerre? With Gerard Depardieu, Nathalie Baye. French with English subtitles.
VHS: S01107. $29.98.
Laser: Widescreen. **LD76003. $69.95.**
Daniel Vigne, France, 1983, 123 mins.

Ridicule

Ridicule
The Oscar-nominated satire of 18th-century French court manners in the reign of Louis XVI directed by Patrice Leconte (*Monsieur Hire*) and written by first-time screenwriter Remi Waterhouse. A young man, in a noble quest to save his hometown, becomes torn between two beautiful women in a triangle of love and deceipt. A beautifully detailed study of court life, manners and wit, directed with a sense of controlled elegance. French with English subtitles.
VHS: S31277. $103.99.
Laser: LD76255. $39.99.
Patrice Leconte, France, 1996, 103 mins.

Rififi
Jules Dassin's classic tale, one of the most famous French gangster films ever made, is the story of a gangster who, when sprung from jail, finds his wife living with another man. He returns to his old racket, jewel thievery, and there follows an aftermath of murder, kidnapping and retribution. Steeped in the details of the sleazy Montmartre neighborhood, the film builds incredible suspense, and is particularly famous for its 30-minute, silent bank heist in which the audience is drawn in as participants. This is the complete, 117-minute version, which includes several scenes cut from the film because of sexual or violent content. French with English subtitles.
VHS: S15387. $24.95.
Jules Dassin, France, 1955, 117 mins.

Rikyu
Teshigahara presents a poignant film exploring the struggle between art and power. Drinking tea was once a casual ritual around which social and diplomatic relationships were practiced. In the 16th Century, Sen-no Rikyu refined the art of the tea ceremony to aesthetic and spiritual heights. His revolutionary ideas brought him to the forefront of Japanese politics when war lord Hideyoshi Toyotomi confided in him as Tea Master, and together they sought what to each was most high: for Rikyu it was beauty, for Hideyoshi, power. Thoughtful performances from Rentaro Mikune, Tsutomu Yamazaki and Yoshiko Mita bring this historical allegory to its tragic close. Japanese with English subtitles.
VHS: S15684. $79.95.
Laser: CLV. LD71490. $39.95.
Hiroshi Teshigahara, Japan, 1990, 116 mins.

The Rise of Louis XIV
Italian master Roberto Rossellini works in a documentary-like naturalism to showcase the peculiar antics, mystery and bizarre nature of the extremely unconventional aristocratic French leader. With Jean-Marie Patte, Raymond Jourdan, Silvagni and Katharina Renn. Produced for French television. French with English subtitles.
VHS: S17845. $59.95.
Roberto Rossellini, France, 1966, 100 mins.

Road to Life
Orphaned youths collect into gangs following the turmoil caused by Russia's Revolutionary and Civil wars. Mustafa leads one band sent to be reformed in an experimental program. Despite a caring teacher, change is complicated by new trades and their inescapable criminal pasts. Russian with English subtitles.
VHS: S22473. $39.95.
Nicolai Ekk, Russia, 1931, 100 mins.

Rocco and His Brothers
Luchino Visconti's brilliant work concentrates on the dramatic clash between two differing value systems—an intellectual belief in the cause of progress and emotional nostalgia for a decaying past. The struggle is played out by two sons, Rocco (Alain Delon), a gentle boy, who is in conflict with Simone (Renato Salvatori), a loutish boxer. Both are in love with Nadia (Annie Girardot), a prostitute, and are bound by old traditions that neither can escape. Considered by many critics to be Visconti's greatest film. Italian with English subtitles.
VHS: S07471. $79.95.
Luchino Visconti, Italy, 1960, 134 mins.

Rodrigo D: No Future
A truly powerful film about growing up on the streets in the drug capital of Medelin, Colombia. Shot in quasi-documentary style, many of the young people who appeared in the film are now dead or in jail. In the tradition of *Los Olvidados* and *Pixote*, we meet a variety of young people who will never have to worry about growing old. Spanish with English subtitles.
VHS: S14744. $79.95.
Victor Gaviria, Colombia, 1990, 93 mins.

Rogopag
The title reflects four brilliant European directors who contributed short films to this collection: Roberto Rossellini, Jean-Luc Godard, Pier Paolo Pasolini and Ugo Gregoretti. *Virginity*, by Rossellini, is a comic essay on the distinctions between illusion and reality. Orson Welles stars in Pasolini's *La Ricotta*, a satire about the debasement of religion. This film caused Pasolini to be charged and sentenced to prison for "insulting the religion of [Italy]." *The New World*, by Godard, offers a chilling view of Paris after a nuclear war. And in Gregoretti's *The Range Grown Chicken*, a family suffers the ravages of brain-washing consumerism. France/Italy, 1962, 122 mins. French and Italian with English subtitles.
VHS: S23995. $24.95.

Rosa Luxemburg
Rosa Luxemburg's amazing life as a political radical and fiercely independent woman is brought to life in this sweeping biography starring the acclaimed actress Barbara Sukowa. From war and revolution to Luxemburg's tempestuous personal life, including her love affairs and numerous jail sentences, this charismatic figure stayed true to her ideals. German with English subtitles.
VHS: S20595. $29.95.
Margarethe von Trotta, Germany, 1985, 122 mins.

Rouge
The popular singers/actors Anita Mui and Leslie Cheung are paired in this supernatural love story which alternates between the brothels, theaters and opium dens of Hong Kong in the Thirties, and the cool, detached world of the present day. The ghost of a courtesan appeals to a young journalist to help her find her lost lover who recovered from their joint suicide attempt and thus failed to join her in the spirit world. Cantonese with English subtitles.
VHS: S13465. $49.95.
Stanley Kwan, Hong Kong, 1987, 99 mins.

Rules of the Game
One of the great films of all time, a satirical anatomy of polite society, with a mixture of farce and bitterness. Set at a weekend party at the chateau of the rich Marquis de la Chayniest, the story concerns complicated love intrigues. French with English subtitles.
VHS: S04456. $29.95.
Laser: LD70446. $89.95.
Jean Renoir, France, 1939, 90 mins.

Ruy Blas
Jean Marais plays two roles in Jean Cocteau's adaptation of the Victor Hugo novel. Danielle Darrieux portrays the Queen of Spain in this story of mistaken identity set in the court of Charles II. Revenge and love are the driving forces that set this

court aflame with intrigues and romance. French with English subtitles.
VHS: S22034. $59.95.
Pierre Billon, France, 1948, 90 mins.

Salo: 120 Days of Sodom
An extremely controversial film, the last work by Pier Paolo Pasolini. Loosely based on the book by the Marquis de Sade, Pasolini transplanted the setting to Mussolini's post-Nazi-fascist state of Salo. Pasolini creates a symbolic place where sexual joy and normality are punished while perversion is rewarded. The plot concerns eight fascists who round up 16 teenage boys and girls and, in a secluded villa, submit their hostages to various sadistic ordeals including rape, mutilation and murder. "Pasolini has intended the film to work on many different levels: an illustration of the moral anarchy of absolute power; the debasement of sexuality through violence; an exploration of victims as victimizers. The result is, alternately, surreal, harrowing, depressing, repulsive, and fascinating…a hellish journey through a sick soul." Contains nudity, explicit sexual situations and extreme graphic violence; for mature audiences only. Italian with English subtitles.
VHS: S11717. $89.95.
Laser: CLV. LD72111. $49.95.
Pier Paolo Pasolini, Italy, 1975, 115 mins.

Sanjuro
The hero of Kurosawa's *Yojimbo* returns to help a group of very earnest, very green, very young samurai get their clan rid of corruption. As in *Yojimbo*, much of the comic effect comes from imaginative composition and incongruous movement. With Toshiro Mifune. Japanese with English subtitles.
VHS: S01157. $29.95.
Laser: LD72345. $49.95.
Akira Kurosawa, Japan, 1962, 92 mins.

Sans Soleil
An audacious and remarkable work from the brilliant essayist and poet Chris Marker, *Sans Soleil* visually interprets a series of letters from a wandering cameraman, based on his travels and experiences from West Africa to Tokyo as he searches for purpose, identity and self-definition through his observations, rituals, speculations, passions and predicaments. "As entertaining as *Zelig*, as visionary as *Blade Runner*" (Jim Hoberman, *Village Voice*). In English.
VHS: S18422. $29.95.
Chris Marker, France, 1983, 100 mins.

The Saragossa Manuscript
A cult classic, one of the most interesting films to emerge from Eastern Europe, based on the novel *Sanatorium under the Hourglass* by Bruno Schultz, this romantic, fantastic and witty tale chronicles the adventures of a Walloon guard under the King of Spain. Something of a Don Juan, this colorful 19th-century character must pass numerous tests to prove his courage, honesty and honor in order to become a member of the powerful Maurentantian family. Polish with English subtitles.
VHS: S22596. $59.95.
Wojciech J. Has, Poland, 1965, 174 mins.

Satyajit Ray's Apu Trilogy
Lifetime Achievement Award winner Satyajit Ray's three-part masterpiece of a Bengali boy's life from birth through manhood is collected here for the first time for home viewing. *Pather Panchali* (1955, 113 mins.), *Aparajito* (1956, 113 mins.) and *The World of Apu* (1959, 106 mins.), voted Best Foreign Film by the National Board of Review, have all been fully restored to their original beauty and clarity and feature new subtitles for easier viewing, as well as a digitally remixed and remastered soundtrack of Ravi Shankar's original scores. Three-volume box set. Bengali with English subtitles.
VHS: S27701. $59.95.
Satyajit Ray, India, 1995, 332 min.

Scarecrow
Called the Soviet *Lord of the Flies*, *Scarecrow* is a haunting and touching film about a little girl who is ostracized by her cruel classmates. She learns about mob psychology the hard way, registering her bitter comprehension with a luminously expressive face. Russian with English subtitles. With Christula Crbakaita, Yuri Nukulin.
VHS: S12964. $59.95.
Rolan Bykov, USSR, 1985, 101 mins.

Scenes from a Marriage
Liv Ullmann stars in this exploration of the relationship between two people over a 20-year period. "Never before has this extraordinary director and writer explored relationships between the sexes with such compassion and humor. *Scenes from a Marriage* seems to be the simplest, most lucid, most spare film that Bergman has ever made," wrote Vincent Canby in *The New York Times*. Roger Ebert calls it "one of the truest, most luminous love stories ever made, an almost heart-breaking masterpiece." With Erland Josephson.
VHS: S26300. $39.95.
Laser: Widescreen. LD75409. $69.95.
Ingmar Bergman, Sweden, 1974, 168 mins.

Scent of a Woman (Profumo di Donna)
The original, award-winning Italian version of the comedy-drama was directed by Dino Risi and stars Vittorio Gassman in a tour-de-force performance as a blind and embittered army captain who undertakes a tour of Italy acccompanied by his young aide (Alessandro Momo). At first his adventures seem innocent and amusing, but as the two men travel through Genoa and Rome, a darker purpose is revealed. With Agostina Belli. Italian with English subtitles.
VHS: S08780. $89.95.
Dino Risi, Italy, 1974, 103 mins.

The Scent of Green Papaya
A moving and undeniably brilliant film by the talented Vietnamese-exile filmmaker Tran Anh Hung, set in 1951 and centered on a young woman who becomes a servant for a turbulent family. The film follows in exquisitely lyrical detail the quiet beauty and stoically accepted hardships of her life as, ten years later, she starts a love affair with her next employer. Shot entirely on a Paris soundstage, this, says critic Roger Ebert, "is a film to cherish." Vietnamese with English subtitles.
VHS: S23925. $19.95.
Laser: LD74799. $34.95.
Tran Anh Hung, Vietnam/France, 1993, 104 mins.

Seagull
A sensitive, exquisitely acted version of Chekhov's great play, set in provincial Russia, a penetrating study of the languid melancholia of the residents of an isolated country estate. With Alla Demidova, Lyudmila Savelyeva, Yuri Yakovlev. Russian with English subtitles.
VHS: S01170. $29.95.
Yuri Karasik, USSR, 1971, 99 mins.

The Seducer's Diary (Le Journal du Seducteur)
Chiara Mastroianni is Claire, a young psychology student who falls under the spell of Gregoire (Melvil Poupard) a troubled philosophy student who successfully seduces women by giving them a copy of Kierkegaard's *Diary of a Seducer*. The Parisian cast of characters also includes Claire's amnesiac shrink (Hubert Saint Macary), an androgynous slacker (Mathieu Amalric) who cons his way into Claire's house and her mother's bed, Gregoire's paranoid grandmother (Micheline Presle), his baby literature professor, Mr. Icon (Jean-Pierre Leaud), and a dead body in the refrigerator. "Dubroux has a light touch, a slow-burning sense of humor and a dark admiration for Cocteau" (Barbara Shulgasser,*San Francisco Examiner*).
VHS: S32680. $89.95.
Daniele Dubroux, France, 1995, 95 mins.

Senso
One of Luchino Visconti's greatest films—luscious, operatic, and an extraordinary portrait of a decadent and corrupt aristocracy. Set in Venice of 1866, Alida Valli plays an Italian countess who falls in love with an Austrian officer (Farley Granger). When war breaks out, she is torn between her patriotism and her emotional obsession with the officer. Visconti portrays a milieu in which "Livia's seduction and treachery and Franz's cowardice and deceit are an inevitable result of their environment." Italian with English subtitles.
VHS: S09353. $29.95.
Luchino Visconti, Italy, 1955, 115 mins.

The Seven Madmen (Los Siete Locos)
A daring political thriller set in South America in the 1930s. A failed idealist links up with a strangely assorted group which intends to overthrow the government and install a new regime. But the plan ultimately fails when a military coup beats it to the revolution. With Alfredo Alcon, Norma Aleandro and

Thelma Biral. Spanish with English subtitles.
VHS: S27742. $59.95.
Leopoldo Torre Nilsson, Argentina, 1973, 121 mins.

Seven Samurai

Set in medieval Japan, Kurosawa's epic centers on a group of impoverished peasants who enlist the protection of seven unemployed samurai to defend their property and harvest from the brutal bandits who terrorize their village. The film is groundbreaking for its visual intensity, stylistic command of movement, space and action, and its expressive emotional range and social criticism. The battle sequences are frightening, devastating and eerie. Cinematography by Asaichi Nakai. With Takashi Shimura, Yoshio Inaba and Toshiro Mifune. Japanese with English subtitles.
VHS: S01182. $34.95.
Laser: CLV, widescreen. LD70452. $59.95.
Akira Kurosawa, Japan, 1954, 208 mins.

Seventh Seal

Bergman's powerful allegory of man's search for meaning in life is stunningly visualized. A knight, upon return from the Crusades, plays chess with Death while the Plague ravages medieval Europe. With Max von Sydow, Gunnar Bjornstrand, Bibi Andersson. Swedish with English subtitles.
VHS: S01185. $29.95.
Laser: CAV. LD70453. $79.95.
Laser: CLV. LD70454. $49.95.
Ingmar Bergman, Sweden, 1956, 96 mins.

A Shadow You Soon Will Be

Based on the novel by Osvaldo Soriano and directed by Hector Olivera (*Funny Dirty Little War*), this road movie about a group of wandering misfits on their way to nowhere is an allegory of contemporary Argentine society. "A modern-day *Don Quixote* as imagined by Luis Bunuel" (Stephen Holden, *The New York Times*). Spanish with English subtitles.
VHS: S30042. $89.95.
Hector Olivera, Argentina , 1994, 105 mins.

Shadows of Forgotten Ancestors

Sergei Paradjanov's masterpiece, a brilliant, epic story of starcrossed lovers set against the ethnographic panorama of the Carpathian Mountains. The film is a visual tour-de-force of symbols, metaphor, lyrical photography and active camera as it interweaves myth and narrative into an elliptical, seamless work of art. Its images "become superimposed on the mind, and will emerge later with a new and more profound meaning, a meaning that escapes logical analysis, that cannot be grasped intellectually, but which calls upon us to respond with feeling" (Robert Walke). With Ivan Nikolaichuk and Larisa Kadochnikova. Ukrainian with English subtitles.
VHS: S07576. $29.95.
Sergei Paradjanov, USSR, 1964, 99 mins.

The Shame

A brilliant young couple, both violinists, attempt to evade a long-raging civil war and retreat to an island off the coast. The war follows them and they're charged with collaborating with the enemy. A visually spare, emotionally powerful work about hopelessness, betrayal and human weakness. With Liv Ullmann, Max Von Sydow and Gunnar Bjornstrand. Cinematography by Sven Nykvist. Swedish with English subtitles.
VHS: S17863. $39.95.
Ingmar Bergman, Sweden, 1968, 103 mins.

Shanghai Triad

Gong Li is once again the star of a lavish period piece from China's most celebrated director. Li becomes enmeshed in a struggle between vicious, feuding warlords. As the mistress of Shanghai's chief gangster, she doesn't have much say in the matter. Beautiful cinematography, for which this film was nominated for an Academy Award, makes it simply spellbinding. The cause of controversy in China, it offers an unparalleled look at China's enduring power politics. Mandarin with English subtitles.
VHS: S28035. $19.95.
Laser: LD75605. $34.95.
Zhang Yimou, China, 1995, 107 mins.

Shoeshine

One of the great films of Italian neo-realism; in Nazi-occupied Rome, two young shoeshine boys get involved in a black market deal in order to raise money for a horse, are caught and sent to prison, and one of them betrays the other. A collaboration

between de Sica and the father of neo-realism, Cesare Zavattini, a work of incredible emotion and power. Italian with English subtitles.
VHS: S05869. $79.95.
Vittorio de Sica, Italy, 1947, 90 mins.

Shoot the Piano Player

Charles Aznavour is the skilled concert pianist whose role in his wife's suicide has made him hide from life by playing in a bistro. But life and love refuse to pass him by, and inevitably he is drawn back into feeling once again. The film includes many touches of light humor, including Truffaut's homage to American gangster films. French with English subtitles.
VHS: S01192. $29.95.
Laser: LD70461. $49.95.
Francois Truffaut, France, 1960, 80 mins.

Shoot to Kill

A mother seeks to clear the damaged reputation of her son when he is murdered during a routine police round-up and condemned as a criminal. She launches a campaign for justice and vindication for her son. "An ambitious suspense thriller which current events in Venezuela make particularly relevant" (*Variety*). Spanish with English subtitles.
VHS: S20381. $59.95.
Carlos Azpurua, Venezuela, 1990, 90 mins.

The Shop on Main Street

A haunting work about the intersecting of the political and personal, developed through the strange yet touching relationship of an elderly Jewish shop owner and a passive carpenter whom the Nazis appoint as her "Aryan controller." Winner of the 1965 Best Foreign Film. With Ida Kaminska and Josef Kroner. "It manages to translate the apocalyptic tragedy of our century into human terms and to do so with laughter and tears, with scorn and passion" (Judith Crist). Slovak with English subtitles.
VHS: S01195. $24.95.
Jan Kadar, Czechoslovakia, 1965, 128 mins.

Siberiade

Russian history over six decades is revealed through the eyes of two opposing families in this epic film. One proletarian family, the Ustyuzhanins, yearns for change, while the aristocratic Solomins desperately cling to their privileged past. These opposing views finally climax in a battle over oil in Siberia. Winner of the 1979 Jury Prize at Cannes. Russian with English subtitles.
VHS: S21541. $79.95.
Andrei Konchalovsky, Russia, 1979, 190 mins.

Sideburns

Yuri Mamin's bitter, dark satire about the rise of fascism and reactionary elements in Russia concerns The Pushkin Club, a right-wing movement, enlisted by the Party to orchestrate "a social cleaning service," charged with eliminating "the scum of Western influence." The film's goal is "to make people laugh at reality before they die of horror," Mamin says. Russian with English subtitles.
VHS: S16737. $59.95.
Yuri Mamin, Russia, 1991, 110 mins.

The Silence of Neto

Mixing magic-realism and historical events, this "fine, richly entertaining film" (Michael Wilmington, *Chicago Tribune*) is the first film produced entirely in Guatemala. Filmed in the colonial city of Antigua, it tells the politically charged story of a young boy striving to follow his dreams while his country struggles to preserve democracy amidst CIA cold-war propaganda. Through the eyes of young Neto, we are given an authentic insider's look at the diverse people of Guatemala and the historical events that have shaped their destiny. Spanish with English subtitles.
VHS: S32224. $49.95.
Luis Argueta, Guatemala, 1994, 106 mins.

Silences of the Palace

This "exquisite, compelling" (Kevin Thomas, *Los Angeles Times*) film is a rare work by a woman filmmaker working in an Arab country, as well as an emotionally powerful look at the role of women in a changing world. Set in Tunisia in the 1950s, Tlatli tells the personal story of servant women living through the last days of French colonial rule, virtual prisoners in the palace of "the beys." Winner of the Camera d'Or at Cannes Film Festival. "A universal coming-of-age story with a feminist twist, a tale that translates effortlessly" (Caryn James, *New York Times*). Arabic and French with English subtitles.
VHS: S31118. $79.95.
Moufida Tlatli, Tunisia, 1996, 127 mins.

A Simple Story

Romy Schneider, in her French Academy Award-winning performance, plays a successful industrial designer disturbed by intangible doubts brought on with the approach of middle age. At the crossroads of her life she must balance her career, a teenage son, an ex-husband, a boyfriend and her peers. French with English subtitles.
VHS: S01205. $29.95.
Claude Sautet, France, 1978, 100 mins.

Sisters of Gion

Often considered to be the best pre-war Japanese film, and Mizoguchi's masterpiece, *Sisters of Gion* is set in the red-light district of Kyoto. The film tells of two sisters—the older trained as a geisha in the old tradition, the younger an apprentice devoted to the more progressive ideas. This conflict between the old and the new, wrote Donald Richie in *The Japanese Film*, has become "the protest symbol of modern Japan."
VHS: S03517. $29.95.
Kenji Mizoguchi, Japan, 1936, 69 mins.

Skyline

Fernando Colombo's unconventional drama about cultural dislocation. The film details the comical day-to-day activities of a resettled Spanish photographer, Gustavo (Antonio Resines), as he attempts to establish his reputation and earn a living in New York. The film has a documentary-style naturalism as Gustavo endures small and private struggles heightened by his unfamiliarity with the language through his determination for self-sufficiency and respect. With Beatriz Perez-Porro, Patricia Cisarano and Jaime Nos. Spanish with English subtitles.
VHS: S01211. $39.95.
Laser: LD71328. $49.95.
Fernando Colombo, Spain, 1983, 90 mins.

Small Change

Small Change presents the viewer with ten boys and girls whose adventures illustrate the different stages of passage from early childhood to adolescence. Some episodes are funny, some serious, some sheer fantasy. Together they animate the notion that childhood is often perilous but also full of grace. French with English subtitles.
VHS: S01216. $19.99.
Laser: LD72156. $34.98.
Francois Truffaut, France, 1976, 106 mins.

Smiles of a Summer Night

Ingmar Bergman's liveliest work concerns the sexual and romantic roundelay of four couples invited to a country mansion for a summer weekend. "The film is erotic and lyrical, full of blithe spirits brilliantly evoked" (James Monaco). With Gunnar Bjornstrand, Eva Dahlbeck, Ulla Jacobsson and Harriet Andersson. Swedish with English subtitles.
VHS: S01219. $29.95.
Laser: LD70465. $49.95.
Ingmar Bergman, Sweden, 1955, 108 mins.

Snow Country

Directed by Shiro Toyoda, *Snow Country* focuses on the conflict between Komako, a woman living in the region of northwest Honshu known as the snow country, and Shimamura, a painter in the Nihonga style who feels out of place in Tokyo and wants to escape from the capital, where he only feels alienation. Based on the novel by the same name, *Snow Country* features Ryo Ikebe and Keoko Kishi. Japanese with English subtitles.
VHS: S08518. $29.95.
Shiro Toyoda, Japan, 1967, 144 mins.

Solaris

The release of this remarkable science fiction film marked a milestone in Soviet cinema. *Solaris,* adapted from the science fiction novel by respected Polish writer Stanislav Lem, is one of those rare screen works which improves upon and deepens its literary source. The story deals with a series of expeditions to the planet Solaris—closely examining the ways the various earth scientists there interact among themselves and, more importantly, the ways in which they interact with each other's memories. "I find it one of the most original, most poetic, most beautifully paced science-fiction movies I've ever seen" (Jonas Mekas, *The Village Voice*). Presented in letterboxed format. Russian with English subtitles.
VHS: S14289. $19.98.
Andrei Tarkovsky, USSR, 1972, 167 mins.

Son of the Shark

This highly acclaimed French film won the International Critics Prize at the Venice Film Festival. It is based on a true story, and follows a pair of inseparable young brothers. Abandoned by their parents, they terrorize their hometown with acts of desperate violence. Yet some mystical bond keeps this shocking pair oddly in sync. A brilliant feature

Solaris

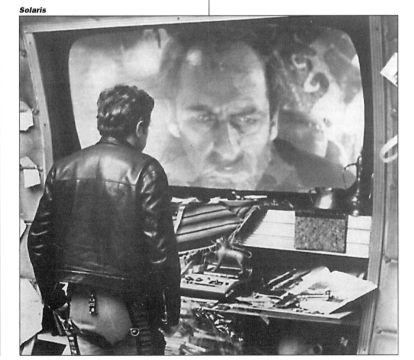

Tale of Winter

from one of France's hottest young director-stars. French with English subtitles.
VHS: $26279. $19.98.
Agnes Merlet, France, 1994, 85 mins.

Spices

Spices is a spirited, feminist fable from India, where women have few rights and little power. This story of oppression and rebellion was shot in rural Gujarat with both actual villagers and India's top name stars. It explores a community's reaction to a woman's plight as an impoverished beauty named Sonbai spurns the amorous advances of a local tax collector (called sudebars) and takes refuge in a pepper factory. Few of the villagers have the courage to defend her, least of all its men, who are blind to injustice against women. Sonbai's eventual victory is not simply over the villainous sudebar, but over tyranny itself and the subservience that sustains it. The fiery Sonbai was Smita Patil's (two-time winner of India's National Best Actress Award) last role. Originally titled *Mirch Masala*. Hindi with English subtitles.
VHS: $13652. $29.95.
Ketan Mehta, India, 1986, 98 mins.

Spirit of the Beehive

A landmark Spanish film by Victor Erice, featuring the remarkable Ana Torrent in the story of two little girls growing up after the Spanish Civil War in the countryside. The hypnotic, spellbinding nature of the film is a rare achievement in cinema, as Erice evokes a deep poetry of childhood in a portrait of isolation. Spanish with English subtitles.
VHS: $08104. $29.95.
Victor Erice, Spain, 1973, 95 mins.

Spirits of the Dead

Jane and Peter Fonda, Alain Delon, Brigitte Bardot and Terence Stamp are among the stars cast in this adaptation of three Edgar Allan Poe tales. The three episodes are *Metzerngerstein*, directed by Roger Vadim; *William Wilson*, directed by Louis Malle; and Fellini's brilliant *Toby Dammit*. In the first, the Fonda siblings are involved in a macabre tale built around incestuous desire. The middle work concerns a sadistic fiend (Delon) who, among other things, whips the then-wildly famous Bardot. Finally, Stamp plays a movie star who loses his head and makes a bet with the devil, whom Fellini portrays, in a brilliant master stroke, as a beautiful little girl in a white dress. French with English subtitles.
VHS: $27647. $59.95.
Laser: Letterboxed. **LD76043. $39.98.**
Roger Vadim/Louis Malle/Federico Fellini, France/Italy, 1968, 117 mins.

Stalingrad

From the same production team that brought the world *Das Boot*, this film brings the bloodiest battle in the history of warfare to the screen: the legendary battle of Stalingrad. With German forces following Hitler's orders to neither retreat nor surrender, over two million Russians and Germans lost their lives in what came to be a turning point in the defeat of Germany in the Second World War. One of the most unflinchingly realistic war films ever made, *Stalingrad* stands alone in its searing, unforgettable imagery, "powerfully underscoring the adage that war is hell" (*The New York Times*). German with English subtitles.
VHS: $30467. $29.95.
Joseph Vilsmaier, Germany, 1996, 150 mins.

Stalker

In this eerie, hypnotic and highly symbolic work, shot in painterly images that seamlessly move from black and white to color, a fallen meteorite produces the Zone, a blistered wasteland that's only penetrated by special guides called "Stalkers." Tarkovsky's film concerns a three-man expedition into this surreal, frightening region. A powerful, extraordinary cinematic experience that anticipates the dread of Chernobyl. With Alexander Kaidanovsky, Nikolai Grinko, and Anatoli Solonitsin. Russian with English subtitles.
VHS: $16984. $19.98.
Andrei Tarkovsky, Russia, 1979, 161 mins.

The Stationmaster's Wife

Elisabeth Trissenaar is the bored wife whose flamboyant affairs epitomize the fake bourgeois morality and buried social and political resentments within German society. Her pleasant, attentive husband (Kurt Raab) is no match for the succession of oppressive lovers she falls prey to. Fassbinder dramatizes this through a Sirkian deployment of bold, ironic colors, brisk melodrama and tight framing. With Bernard Helfrich, Karl Heinz-von Hassel and Udo Kier. German with English subtitles.
VHS: $18933. $29.95.
Rainer W. Fassbinder, Germany, 1977, 113 mins.

Stavisky

With *Stavisky*, director Alain Resnais has crafted an extraordinarily beautiful and sophisticated film that requires intense concentration and yields tremendous rewards. The story is that of a French swindler and conman extraordinaire, whose financial manipulations in the 30s brought on riots that helped to topple a government. With Jean-Paul Belmondo,

Anny Duperey, Charles Boyer and Gerard Depardieu. Photographed by Sacha Vierny, with a musical score by Stephen Sondheim. French with English subtitles.
VHS: $14986. $59.95.
Alain Resnais, France, 1974, 117 mins.

The Story of Qiu Ju
In this comedy a woman seeks justice for a simple slight against her husband. Along the way, she encounters a welter of bureaucracy and politesse in this well-observed portrait of contemporary Chinese life. Chinese with English subtitles.
VHS: $20709. $19.95.
Laser: LD72382. $34.95.
Zhang Yimou, China, 1993, 100 mins.

Story of the Last Chrysanthemum
Kenji Mizoguchi's chronicle of a Kabuki actor. As the son of a prominent Kabuki family, the young man would be assured eventual fame, but he runs afoul of his father by falling in love with a servant girl, and sets out to make it himself on his own. Contains some of Mizoguchi's most ethereal imagery, as well as some fascinating use of compositions suggestive of Cinemascope before the widescreen process was invented. Japanese with English subtitles.
VHS: $03516. $29.95.
Kenji Mizoguchi, Japan, 1939, 115 mins.

Story of Women
An almost perfect film; Claude Chabrol bases his Venice Film Festival award-winning film on the true story of the last woman to be guillotined in France, at the onset of WWII. Isabelle Huppert delivers a stunning, riveting performance as the wife-abortionist who, despite the compromises she makes for the sake of a "better" life, is redeemed as a true individual at the end. A brilliant film from the hands of a true master. French with English subtitles.
VHS: $12990. $29.95.
Claude Chabrol, France, 1988, 112 mins.

The Stranger (Agantuk)
Ray's last great masterpiece is the provocative tale of Manmohan, a world traveler who returns to Calcutta after 35 years to visit his niece, Anila. Anila's suspicious husband believes the long-lost uncle to be an imposter who has come to claim an inheritance. As Manmohan's identity is slowly revealed, Anila and her husband must examine their own identities in relation to traditional values and modern civilization. Bengali with English subtitles. "A tour-de-force as the film maestro fathoms his characters psychologically and intellectually…the camera is wielded like a conductor's baton as *Agantuk* strikes chords deep in the mind…a dream of a performance!" (*The Times*).
VHS: $30611. $59.95.
Satyajit Ray, India, 1991, 120 mins.

Stray Dog
A first-rate thriller in which Kurosawa has acknowledged his debt to Georges Simenon. Toshiro Mifune plays rookie Detective Murakami, who loses his gun only to discover that it has fallen into the hands of a killer. Terrified of losing his job, his search takes him into the Tokyo underworld, full of postwar shortages, "divinely hellish under Kurosawa's odd-angled lensing and staccato editing…*Stray Dog* is a Dostoevskian saga of guilt, and expiation, by association" (*Pacific Film Archive*). Japanese with English subtitles.
VHS: $06462. $24.95.
Akira Kurosawa, Japan, 1949, 122 mins.

Stroszek
The adventures of Herzog's alter-ego, Bruno S., continue as a former mental patient and Berlin street singer joins with a whore and an aging eccentric to emigrate to Wisconsin in search of the American dream. "Surprisingly positive, tragicomic, poetic narrative" (Leonard Maltin). With Eva Mattes and Clemens Scheitz. English and German with English subtitles.
VHS: $12826. $29.95.
Werner Herzog, Germany, 1977, 108 mins.

The Student of Prague
One of the earliest, most important films in the history of silent German cinema, the film incorporates the myths of the Doppelganger, the Faust legend and the shattered mirror image; often considered the first film to incorporate Expressionist means. Silent with English subtitles.
VHS: $01274. $29.95.
Stellan Rye, Germany, 1913, 45 mins.

Sugar Cane Alley
Euzhan Palcy's lyrical village drama set in French-occupied 1930s Martinique. The story examines the relationship of a determined, impoverished 11-year-old and his equally difficult and shrewd grandmother, who sacrifices everything for the boy's happiness. With Darling Legitimus, Garry Cadenat, Routa Seck and Joby Bernabe. French with English subtitles.
VHS: $01278. $29.95.
Euzhan Palcy, France, 1984, 107 mins.

The Summer of Aviya
The story of one summer in the life of Aviya, a ten-year-old girl the daughter of a Holocaust survivor, during the first years of Israel's independence. Aviya's mother had been a partisan fighter during the war and walked the thin line between sanity and madness; Aviya lived in orphanages most of her life. This was the summer she would return home. Based on the life of Gila Almagor, writer/producer and star of the film. Winner of the Silver Bear, Berlin Film Festival and three silver Menorah awards, Israel. "The emotionally powerful story…reveals the scars, both mental and physical, that Holocaust survivors brought with them to Israel" (American Historical Review). Hebrew with English subtitles.
VHS: $30527. $79.95.
Eli Cohen, Israel, 1989, 96 mins.

The Summer of Miss Forbes
Written by Nobel prize-winning author Gabriel Garcia Marquez, *The Summer of Miss Forbes* is a wickedly funny black comedy about two children plotting to kill their authoritarian nanny. A biting comedy reminiscent of the work of legendary filmmaker Luis Bunuel, *The Summer of Miss Forbes* was directed by Jaime Humberto Hermosillo, one of Mexico's premier filmmakers. Spanish with English subtitles.
VHS: $13693. $19.98.
Jaime H. Hermosillo, Mex./Spain, 1988, 85 min.

The Sun's Burial
Oshima's most blatantly amoral and extravagantly violent version of the juvenile delinquency drama, set in a world of rival teenage gangs, pimps and prostitutes. Set in a hellish Osaka where an exquisitely cruel femme fatale vies for control of the area's most profitable business with the gangs. Japanese with English subtitles.
VHS: $20596. $29.95.
Nagisa Oshima, Japan, 1960, 87 mins.

Sundays and Cybele
Winner of multiple awards including an Oscar, the moving, intelligently-told account of shell-shocked Hardy Kruger, who finds a source of communication with the outside world through his friendship with the orphaned girl Patricia Gozzi. French with English subtitles.
VHS: $01284. $29.95.
Serge Bourguignon, France, 1962, 110 mins.

Sweet Movie
The modern cult classic, a hilarious comedy with elements of thriller and horror, "an experience to defy criticism…one of the most challenging, shocking and provocative films of recent years" (Roger Ebert). This daring and totally original film skillfully blends two independent stories with often shocking newsreel footage into a "movie we can't be passive about." The beautiful Carole Laure, winner of the Miss Virginity World contest, is married to Mr. Kapital, a Texas oil billionaire who, instead of consummating their marriage, sterilizes her body with rubbing alcohol. Barely escaping with her life, in Paris Carole has a sexual encounter with El Macho, a rock star at the Eiffel Tower, and ends up in a radical therapy commune. The second story features Anna Prucnal, survivor of The Revolution, now the captain of a boat floating the canals of Amsterdam, whose joyous sexual meeting with a sailor (Pierre Clementi) from the Battleship Potemkin ends up in his murder in a vat of sugar. Pure, unadulterated brilliance, "an audacious attempt…filled with images impossible to forget" (Roger Ebert). English and other languages with English subtitles.
VHS: $10575. $79.95.
Dusan Makavejev, Canada/France, 1975, 97 min.

Swept Away
Raffaella, a rich, beautiful, acid-tongued Milanese who has chartered a yacht, and Gennarino, a swarthy Sicilian deckhand, are marooned on an isolated island in the Mediterranean. She is a capitalist for whom the system has paid off, he is a dedicated Communist. *Swept Away* is the story of their tumultuous courtship,

in what one critic described as a "fierce battle of the sexes as witty as it is wise." Letterboxed. Italian with , English subtitles.
DVD: DV60125. $29.98.
VHS: S01290. $29.98.
Laser: LD75999. $49.95.
Lina Wertmuller, Italy, 1975, 116 mins.

Tale of Winter
Charlotte Very, Michel Voletti, Herve Furic, and Frederic Van Dren Dreissche are cast in this bubbling romantic comedy from Eric Rohmer. Very plays a woman unhappy with her two current lovers. In the pursuit of simplicity, she begins a torrid affair with an old flame. French with English subtitles.
VHS: S26144. $89.95.
Eric Rohmer, France, 1994, 114 mins.

Tall Blond Man with One Black Shoe
A beautifully mastered print of the original French version of Yves Robert's international comedy hit. Rival factions within French intelligence try to pass off a randomly selected dupe as a "superagent." Frizzy-haired Pierre Richard, France's reigning king of comedy, is the concert-violinist turned patsy in love with a very pretty but very married harpist. French with English subtitles.
VHS: S13282. $29.95.
Laser: LD71628. $39.95.
Pierre Richard, France, 1972, 90 mins.

Tartuffe
In his first directorial effort, Gerard Depardieu (*Green Card, Cyrano*) breathes new life into Moliere's classic stage masterpiece about religious and sexual hypocrisy. The dazzling cast includes Depardieu, his wife Elizabeth, and renowned classical actor Francois Perier. Based on a stage production directed by Jacques Lasalle of the Theatre National de Strasbourg. "The best production of *Tartuffe* I've seen" (Stanley Kauffmann). French with English subtitles.
VHS: S13590. $79.95.
Gerard Depardieu, France, 1984, 140 mins.

Taxi Blues
Pavel Lounguine's first feature is a critique of contemporary Soviet society, captured through the bleak and paternalistic relationship of a hard-drinking, fascist, anti-Semitic taxi driver and a dependent, alcoholic Jewish saxophonist. A French/Soviet co-production with excellent lead performances of Piotr Mamonov and Piotr Zaitchenko. Russian with English subtitles.
VHS: S17398. $29.95.
Pavel Lounguine, Russia/France, 1990, 110 mins.

A Taxing Woman's Return
In this rousing follow-up to his 1987 hit, *A Taxing Woman*, Juzo Itami brings back his resourceful and charming heroine, tax inspector Ryoko Itakura (described by Vincent Canby of *The New York Times* as "a far more endearing crime buster than Batman") for another battle of wits against the fat cats and swindlers who thrive in Japan's booming economy. Japanese with English subtitles.
VHS: S12195. $29.95.
Juzo Itami, Japan, 1989, 127 mins.

Ten Days That Shook the World
Also known as *October*, Eisenstein's famous recreation of the October Revolution during which the Bolsheviks overthrew the Kerensky government. Like his previous work, the film continues Eisenstein's experimental methods. Silent.
VHS: S01306. $29.95.
Sergei Eisenstein, USSR, 1927, 95 mins.

Teorema
Pier Paolo Pasolini's breakthrough film, predicated on the theorem that "anything done by the bourgeoisie, however sincere and profound, and noble, is on the wrong track." Into the home of a classic bourgeois family walks in Terence Stamp, a stranger. Each one of the family—mother, father, son, daughter, maid—seeks and finds in the stranger a catalyst for the fulfillment of desire denied within the confines of the family structure. "Liberated thus by a moment of authenticity, each is left, on the visitor's departure, with a personal kind of madness, stripped naked in a symbolic desert." Italian with English subtitles.
VHS: S18193. $29.95.
Pier Paolo Pasolini, Italy, 1968, 93 mins.

Terra em Transe
The brief story of this important film by Glauber Rocha is the story of a young poet and journalist who is persuaded by his lover to become involved in the politics of his country…"*Terra em Transe* is perhaps Rocha's most personal film and the most politically committed and polemical film of the Brazilian *cinema novo*. In Brazil it was attacked as fascist by the academic left and hailed by the extreme left as a revolutionary film …full of extremely moving and provocative images—including footage from a Rocha documentary, *Maranhao*" (Georges Sadoul). "For me, my most important film…a more profound expression of my life" (Rocha). Portuguese with English subtitles.
VHS: S08783. $69.95.
Glauber Rocha, Brazil, 1966, 112 mins.

The Theme
Glen Panfilov's daring work was banned by Soviet authorities for eight years. Esenin (Mikhail Ulyanov), a government-approved playwright and functionary, visits his native village for some artistic rejuvenation and falls for a dynamic and brilliant but uncompromising young artist, Sasa (Inna Churikova), who rejects his overtures. Winner of the 1987 Golden Bear winner at the Berlin Film Festival. With Stanislav Lyubshin, Evgeny Vesnik and Sergei Nikonenko. Russian with English subtitles.
VHS: S19054. $59.95.
Gleb Panfilov, Russia, 1979, 98 mins.

Thieves
Andre Techine's crime thriller, told from multiple, overlapping points of view, features strong, subtle performances from Daniel Auteuil as tormented Lyon policeman Alex Noel, Didier Bezace as his shady older brother Ivan, and a dazzling Catherine Deneuve as Marie, a lesbian philosophy professor and author. "Techine takes the stuff of slick French cinema and deepens it with every frame" (*New City*). French with English subtitles.
VHS: S31788. $98.99.
Laser: LD76307. $39.95.
Andre Techine, France, 1996, 116 mins.

Thirty-Two Short Films About Glenn Gould
In this inventive film, the unique genius of musician Glenn Gould is revealed in a series of dramatic re-enactments, archival footage and film interviews. It rises above the usual biographic movie formulas to capture intimate and revealing details about its elusive subject, who avoided public scrutiny by playing largely in his studio. Colm Feore stars.
VHS: S23677. $19.95.
Laser: LD74759. $34.95.
Francois Girard, Canada, 1993, 94 mins.

Three Men and a Cradle
One of the funniest French films in recent years, an unlikely story of three confirmed bachelors who receive a six-month-old roommate. This little bundle of joy can turn into a big bundle of trouble, and chaos of a hilarious kind ensues. French with English subtitles.
VHS: S02266. $14.98.
Coline Serreau, France, 1985, 100 mins.

The Threepenny Opera
Lotte Lenya plays Jenny in this famous adaptation of Bertolt Brecht/Kurt Weill's play, freely based on John Gay's *Beggar's Opera*. In London at the turn of the century the best friend of a police chief, the bandit Mack the Knife, marries Polly without the knowledge of her father, Peachum, the king of the beggars, and thus starts a conflict between the beggars and the thieves. A newly remastered version. German with English subtitles.
VHS: S21186. $39.95.
Laser: LD70797. $39.95.
G.W. Pabst, Germany, 1931, 114 mins.

Throne of Blood
Kurosawa's brilliant interpretation of Shakespeare's *Macbeth* shifts the action to 16th century feudal Japan, where a samurai is motivated by his ambitious wife and spirit to kill his friend. The movie balances stylized action and movement of the Noh theater with the intensity of the American western. Kurosawa and cinematographer Asaichi Nakai create a foreboding atmosphere in the castles and landscape. With Toshiro Mifune, Isuzu Yamada and Minoru Chiaki. Japanese with English subtitles.
VHS: S01338. $39.95.
Laser: CAV. LD70726. $89.95.
Akira Kurosawa, Japan, 1957, 110 mins.

Through a Glass Darkly

Powerful psychological study of a young woman's descent into madness. Harriet Andersson plays Karin, who has read that she is an incurable schizophrenic and plunges into a visionary world where God is a spider. With Gunnar Bjornstrand and Max von Sydow. Swedish with English subtitles.
VHS: S01339. $29.95.
Laser: Digital transfer. **LD74974. $49.95.**
Ingmar Bergman, Sweden, 1961, 91 mins.

Tie Me Up, Tie Me Down

The controversial hit by Pedro Almodovar about Ricki, who falls in love with Marina, an ex-porn movie star, and proceeds to capture her and tie her up at her own apartment. She is torn between trying to escape and falling in love with him. "Almodovar's theme is not the domination of women, but the strangeness of love and possessiveness. The performances are outstanding. Antonio Banderas is psychopathic and vulnerable, Victoria Abril is fierce and funny" (*Sight and Sound*). Spanish with English subtitles (only R version available).
VHS: S12994. $19.95.
Pedro Almodovar, Spain, 1990, 103 mins.

Tilai

One of the most highly acclaimed contemporary African films. In this troubling drama, a young African man is engaged to the woman he loves until the man's father decides that he should marry this woman himself. This fateful decision forces the young lovers into an illicit affair. On the run, they find tradition and the law will play a large role in their fate. In More with English subtitles.
VHS: S26145. $79.95.
Idrissa Ouedraogo, Burkina Faso, 1990, 81 mins.

Time of the Gypsies

A potent mix of comedy, drama and the supernatural, Kusturica's amazingly realistic drama set in the heart of the gypsy culture. Perhan, the hero, is telekinetic and is taken to Italy by the "sheik," where he gets a quick education in gypsy survival skills on the streets of Milan. Warm and affectionate, full of comic scenes, with a great gypsy music sound track. With Dvor Dujmovic and Bora Todorovic. Serbo-Croatian and Romany with English subtitles.
VHS: S12744. $19.95.
Emir Kusturica, Yugoslavia, 1990, 136 mins.

The Tin Drum

The 1979 Academy Award winner for Best Foreign Film. *The Tin Drum* is a masterpiece of dazzling exuberance and originality adapted from the novel by Gunter Grass. The film is a stunning parable of modern society in violent transition narrated by a unique hero for our times—Oskar, a boy who decides at three not to grow any older. Letterboxed. German with English subtitles.
VHS: S01349. $39.95.
Laser: LD76415. $69.99.
Volker Schlondorff, Germany, 1979, 142 min.

To Live

Winner of the 1994 Cannes Palme d'Or, Zhang Yimou's daring political tale of modern China landed him in major difficulties with the Chinese authorities. *To Live* follows a contemporary family across the turbulent face of modern China, from the Japanese invasion through Mao's Great Leap Forward and the Cultural Revolution. The powerful drama is made all the more potent by strong performances from Gong Li. Mandarin Chinese with English subtitles.
VHS: S25900. $19.98.
Zhang Yimou, China, 1994, 132 mins.

Tokyo Decadence

Japanese novelist and filmmaker Ryu Murakami adapts his novel *Topaz*, about a prostitute's (Miho Nikaido) search for redemption. Ai falls under the spell of a charismatic dominatrix and tries desperately to reverse her slide into cocaine dependency and sexual slavery. "Murakami adeptly throws us off balance, with deadpan black humor and a complex politic involving the notion of 'wealth without pride' " (Toronto Film Festival). With Sayoko Amano, Tenmei Kanou and Masahiko Shimada. Japanese with English subtitles.
VHS: S19176. $29.95.
Ryu Murakami, Japan, 1991, 112 mins.

Tokyo Story

One of the legendary classics of humanist cinema, *Tokyo Story* tells the simple, sad story of an elderly couple who travel to Tokyo to visit their two married children, only to find themselves politely ushered off to a hot springs resort. "Ozu's technique, as spare and concentrated as a haiku master's verse, transforms the very banalities of the subject into moments of intimacy and beauty seldom captured on film. As always, the themes go beyond the obvious and are conveyed so gently that only afterwards are many

To Live

apparent." Japanese with English subtitles. With new electronic subtitles.
  VHS: S10919. $69.95.
Yasujiro Ozu, Japan, 1953, 139 mins.

Torment
The budding love between two students, Jan-Erik and Bertha, is threatened by a sadistic Latin teacher nicknamed "Caligula" who torments Jan-Erik in class. When Jan-Erik finds Bertha dead in her room and Caligula hiding in a closet, he accuses him of causing her death. Based on the (first) script by Ingmar Bergman, the character of Caligula was seen as a symbol of Nazism. The film is remarkable for its expressive style and a powerful performance by Mai Zetterling as Bertha. With Alf Kjellin and Stig Olin. Swedish with English subtitles.
  VHS: S04913. $29.95.
Alf Sjoberg, Sweden, 1944, 90 mins.

Toto the Hero
Winner of the Camera d'Or at the 1991 Cannes Film Festival, this witty and audacious debut film by Belgian director Jaco Van Dormael concerns Thomas, who is convinced he was exchanged at birth with his neighbor Alfred and subsequently condemned to lead an anonymous, insignificant life. Appearing as 'Toto le Heros', the invented secret agent of his adolescence, Thomas undergoes a fantastic odyssey to track Alfred down and uncover his true identity. With Michel Bouquet, Mireille Perrier and Jo de Backer. French with English subtitles.
  VHS: S18544. $94.95.
  Laser: LD75277. $34.98.
Jaco Van Dormael, Belgium/France/Germany, 1991, 90 mins.

Traffic Jam
A young Tokyo couple are at the center of this dark, comic satire. They take their children to visit the husband's faraway parents, but the long road trip proves to be filled with disastrous incidents. Their journey becomes a metaphor for the gap between young Japanese people and their ancestral roots. Japanese with English subtitles.
  VHS: S24731. $79.95.
Mitsuo Kurotsuchi, Japan, 1991, 108 mins.

Tree of the Wooden Clogs
A passionate, moving film, an epic celebration of an Italian family's indomitable spirit, winner of the Grand Prize at the 1978 Cannes Film Festival. The subject of the film is peasant life in northern Italy at the turn of the century, focusing on about a year in the life of three families living on a feudal estate. "A quiet masterpiece" (Newsweek). "The movie, which runs slightly more than three hours, is an accumulation of dozens of experiences of children, adults, old people, village idiots, of harvest times and plantings, of moments of boredom and jealousy, celebrations, fatigue, brief pleasures and mysterious ones. It moves so effortlessly, often with great humor and always with compassion, it seems much shorter than most 90-minute films" (Vincent Canby, New York Times). Italian with English subtitles.
  VHS: S12946. $19.98.
Ermanno Olmi, Italy, 1978, 185 mins.

Tristana
The stunning Catherine Deneuve is Tristana, a victim of her own captivating beauty who is desired by two men. The first is her lecherous guardian (played by the great Fernando Rey) who, after raising her from a teenager, takes her as his mistress. The other is a young artist (Franco Nero) who wants to marry her but lacks the courage to free her from the corrupt relationship with her guardian. Set in 1920's Spain, Tristana is a scathing examination of moral decay viewed through Bunuel's typically dispassionate and ironic eyes. Spanish with English subtitles. Letterboxed.
  VHS: S15344. $24.95.
  Laser: LD75490. $49.95.
Luis Bunuel, Spain, 1970, 98 mins.

Triumph of the Will
Enormously controversial film record of a Nazi party solidarity rally at Nuremberg in 1934, crafted by Riefenstahl in her second directorial assignment. A fascinating lesson in the methods used by the Nazis to inspire national support. German with English subtitles.
  VHS: S18194. $29.95.
Leni Riefenstahl, Germany, 1936, 80 mins.

Two or Three Things I Know About Her
Shot simultaneously with Made in U.S.A. (one was

filmed mornings, the other in the evenings), this drama focuses on modern life in Paris. Vlady stars as a Parisian housewife who lives in a large housing estate and supplements her husband's income by working as a part-time prostitute. Against an aural backdrop of Beethoven, her life over a 24-hour period is detailed as it speaks about the sale of oneself in the pursuit of happiness. A barrage of words, images and philosophising, with whispering and narration by Godard, this inventive and energetic, early "mockumentary" set the standard for such works. French with English subtitles.
  VHS: $29507. $89.95.
Jean-Luc Godard, France, 1966, 95 mins.

Ugetsu
Kenji Mizoguchi's poetic film is set in feudal, war-ravaged, 16th-century Japan and focuses on the opposite fortunes of two peasants who abandon their families to accumulate wealth and prestige and find emptiness and despair. The film is remarkable for its expressive photography, diagonal compositions and uninterrupted takes. With Machiko Kyo and Masayuki Mori. "Scenes of everyday life alternate with those of a dreamlike, erotic intensity. At the end it is difficult to remember where reality stops and hallucination begins" (Newsweek). Japanese with English subtitles. Newly remastered, translated and subtitled print. Presented in original aspect ratio.
  VHS: S01390. $24.95.
  Laser: LD75412. $49.95.
Kenji Mizoguchi, Japan, 1953, 96 mins.

Umberto D
One of the masterpieces of Italian Neo-Realist cinema— the Italian postwar Renaissance. The story centers on a retired civil servant, living only on his pension, whose best friend is his dog. Unable to survive on his meager income, he sacrifices a part of his pension for his dog, and is evicted by his landlord for non-payment of rent. Italian with English subtitles.
  VHS: S01393. $29.95.
  Laser: LD70483. $49.95.
Vittorio de Sica, Italy, 1952, 89 mins.

Umbrella for Three
(Paraguas Para Tres)
Daniel and Maria are two recently divorced professionals living in modern Spain who happen to run into each other an awful lot. This is a romantic comedy after all, and though it takes a while for it to dawn on them, they are fated to fall in love. Only after a series of comic misadventures do they come to understand the mysteries of chance and love. In Spanish with English subtitles.
  VHS: S26277. $59.95.
Felipe Vega, Spain, 1992, 93 mins.

The Umbrellas of Cherbourg
Catherine Deneuve stars in this sumptuously photographed romantic musical of two lovers who are split up by the Algerian war. The girl marries another when she discovers she is pregnant. He also marries; yet they meet again. All dialog is sung; with haunting music by Michel LeGrand and lyrics by Demy, including the song, "I Will Wait for You." "A masterpiece! More beautiful and more startling than ever!" (New York Daily News). "The kind of movie that audiences will remember all their lives" (Chicago Tribune).
  DVD: DV60126. $29.98.
  VHS: S30735. $29.95.
  Laser: Widescreen. LD76164. $49.98.
Jacques Demy, France/Germany, 1964, 92 mins.

Un Chien Andalou/Land Without Bread
Two great early films by Luis Bunuel: Un Chien Andalou continues to shock audiences today as it did

Un Chien Andalou

in 1928; *Land Without Bread* is a horrifying account of one of Spain's most desolate regions, a documentary masterpiece made all the more harrowing for its travelogue style.
VHS: S12462. $29.95.
Luis Bunuel, Spain, 1928/32, 42 mins.

Un Coeur en Hiver
Claude Sautet's 13th feature is loosely based on Lermontov's novel *A Hero of Our Time*. Two violin makers (Daniel Auteuil and Andre Dussollier) are affected when a beautiful violinist (Emmanuelle Beart) enters their lives. The film addresses the question of whether Auteuil is able to reconcile his cold, rigid nature with his deep, emotional attraction to Beart. With Elizabeth Bourgine, Myriam Boyer, Brigitte Catillon, and Maurice Garrel as a brilliant music teacher. French with English subtitles.
VHS: S20208. $19.98.
Claude Sautet, France, 1991, 100 mins.

Under the Domim Tree
Based on the autobiographical memoir by Gila Almagor (*The Summer of Aviya*), this "gentle, loving film about confronting the past" (*Los Angeles Times*) is the poignant and harrowing story of a group of teenagers living in a youth village for orphans who survived the Nazi concentration camps and other troubled Israeli youths in the 1950s. When life becomes unbearable, the teens find refuge under the beautiful Domim Tree, the only place where they feel at peace. "One of the most beautiful movies of the past 20 years, maybe longer" (*The Record*). Hebrew with English subtitles.
VHS: S30736. $89.98.
Eli Cohen, Israel, 1996, 102 mins.

Under the Sun of Satan
A work of great subtlety and tremendous assurance, the film stars Depardieu in his perhaps most astonishing performance, as a tortured country priest who feels unworthy of God's love. Depardieu's priest encounters the young and beautiful Mouchette, played by Sandrine Bonnaire, who lives in the same town and is a murderess who unwittingly shapes the priest's life. A brilliant new film from one of France's most uncompromising directors. French with English subtitles.
VHS: S10868. $29.95.
Maurice Pialat, France, 1987, 101 mins.

Une Femme Douce (A Gentle Woman)
Bresson's first film in color, which introduced 20-year-old Dominique Sanda to the world in a haunting transposition of Dostoevsky's story *A Gentle Creature*. Sanda plays the role of a young woman who marries a pawn broker (Guy Frangin) but finds she cannot bring herself to adapt her life to his, and so leaps to her death from a Paris balcony. We—like the husband—don't really know the reason why. As the young woman, Sanda delivers a star-making performance, perhaps the most erotic and natural of all of Bresson's heroines. French with English subtitles.
VHS: S26462. $29.95.
Robert Bresson, France, 1969, 87 mins.

An Unfinished Piece for a Mechanical Piano
A bittersweet, humorous tapestry of human folly and lost dreams, loosely based on Chekhov's play *Platonov*. The course of the film takes place during a summer day at a decaying summer dacha. The hero had a spoilt love affair and now meets his old girlfriend, married to another. All his passions and frustrations burst out in the open. The film's leisurely atmosphere belies the intensity of the emotional content underneath, with Mikhalkov revealing profound moments of truth. With Alexander Kalyagin, Yelena Solovieva and Yevgey Glushenko. Russian with English subtitles.
VHS: S18694. $29.95.
Nikita Mikhalkov, USSR, 1977, 100 mins.

An Unforgettable Summer
An unconventional love story from Lucian Pintilie (*The Oak*), featuring a first-rate performance from Kristin Scott-Thomas (*Bitter Moon, Four Weddings and a Funeral*). A recently married army officer and his bride are sent to an army outpost in a backwoods area. The wife tries to establish a genteel, civilized presence there, but conflicts between the couple and both army personnel and the locals of the remote region cause her efforts to be in vain. French, Romanian and Bulgarian with English subtitles.
VHS: S27200. $89.95.
Lucian Pintilie, Romania, 1994, 82 mins.

Until the End of the World
Wim Wenders filmed this epic, futuristic drama in fifteen cities in eight countries around the world. The year is 1999. Solveig Dommartin, the enchanting trapeze artist from *Wings of Desire*, pursues William Hurt, who helped himself to stolen money she was guarding for some very nice criminals. She also just might be in love with the mysterious Hurt who is on a secret mission for Max Von Sydow, his even more mysterious father who lives in an underground laboratory in the middle of Australia. Also along for the global chase are boyfriend Sam Neill, and detectives Rudiger Vogler and Ernie Dingo. This ambitious work explores the potential end of the world and the incredible power of our dreams. The tape is presented in a letter-boxed format with Surround Sound and employs state-of-the-art High-Definition video technology.
VHS: S16633. $19.98.
Laser: LD71505. $34.98.
Wim Wenders, France/Germany/Australia, 1991, 178 min.

Up to a Certain Point
This sly social comedy stars Oscar Alvarez, Mirta Ibarra and Omar Valdes. A married, middle-aged screenwriter is researching the problem of machismo in Cuban society and suddenly falls under the spell of Lina, a strong, self-supporting, young dockworker. Spanish with English subtitles.
VHS: S23285. $79.95.
Tomas Gutierrez Alea, Cuba, 1985, 72 mins.

Utamaro and His Five Women
Mizoguchi's exquisite portrait of the artistic life of Tokyo of the 18th century is a portrait of Edo artist Utamaro (Minnosuke Bando) and his relationship to women. Utamaro stands at the center of the lives of five women who compete for his attention in a film which is remarkably modern for its attitude toward the rights of women. The scenarist, Yoshikata Yoda, stated that the film was an unconscious portrait of Mizoguchi himself. With Kinuyo Tanaka, Kotaro Bando and Hiroko Kawasaki. Japanese with English subtitles.
VHS: S19418. $69.95.
Kenji Mizoguchi, Japan, 1946, 89 mins.

Vagabond
Agnes Varda's extraordinarily bleak account of a young woman's death and life. In a breathtaking performance, Sandrine Bonnaire (*A Nos Amours*) is Mona, a waif who drops out of Parisian society to wander the southwest French countryside, exploring the open spaces and implicit freedom absent in her life. In the opening scene, her body is discovered frozen. Varda expertly recounts her life, carefully dissecting French society. French with English subtitles.
VHS: S02982. $24.95.
Agnes Varda, France, 1986, 105 mins.

A Very Old Man with Enormous Wings
Magical realism and comic confusion blend in a startling film about visions and expectations. Amid the debris of a Columbian cyclone lands an old man with enormous wings, whose seemingly miraculous anatomy attracts the curious and devout from around the world. Silent and disheveled, this fantastical "creature" is housed in a chicken coop as his hosts and the onlookers wait for his heavenly message—which turns out to be a very mixed blessing. Original story by Gabriel Garcia Marquez, who also co-wrote the screenplay. Spanish with English subtitles.
VHS: S13841. $19.98.
Fernando Birri, Cuba/Spain, 1988, 90 mins.

The Virgin Spring
Max von Sydow stars in this exploration of a father's revenge for the rape and murder of his daughter. Highly contrasting black and white images evoke an imaginative, medieval world created by cinematographer Sven Nykvist. A stunning work. Swedish with English subtitles.
VHS: S01418. $29.95.
Laser: LD75073. $49.95.
Ingmar Bergman, Sweden, 1960, 88 mins.

Viridiana
Bunuel's outrageous and devastating attack on religion and society. Viridiana, about to take her vows as a nun, takes to the pure Christian life by organizing a haven for a blind man, leper, cripple and beggar. Full of Freudian symbolism, the film ends in a famous orgy of destruction, containing Bunuel's blasphemous scene of the Last Supper. The film that got Bunuel kicked out of Spain. Spanish with English

subtitles.
VHS: S01419. $29.95.
Luis Bunuel, Spain, 1961, 90 mins.

The Visitors
The biggest-grossing French film comedy in a long time, Alain Terzian's *The Visitors* (*Les Visiteurs*) is a wacky comedy about two time-travelling medieval knights who get stuck in the 20th century with some nutty results. "Uproarious...a truly hilarious farce" (*Wall Street Journal*). With Christian Claver, Jean Reno and Valerie LeMercier. French with English subtitles.
VHS: S31025. $103.99.
Laser: LD76158. $39.98.
Jean-Marie Poire, France, 1993, 107 mins.

Vive L'Amour
Considered by critics as reminiscent of the best of Michelangelo Antonioni (*Blow Up*), this "wonderfully evocative" (*New York Times*) film stars Yan Kuei-Mei and Chen Chao-Jung (both from the hit comedy *Eat Drink Man Woman*) as May, a chic and seductive real estate agent, and Ah-jong, a street merchant, and their encounters in one of the thousands of vacant, anonymous apartments that fill Taipei, Taiwan. After a chance meeting, the couple use the apartment for their impulsive sexual liaisons, while a shy young gay man hides in the same apartment and spies on the couple, creating a bizarre love triangle. Taiwanese with English subtitles. "A tour de force...tender, stylish" (Amy Taubin, *The Village Voice*).
VHS: S30884. $89.98.
Tsai Ming-Liang, Taiwan, 1996, 118 mins.

Volga-Volga
An unseen miracle of 1930's Soviet cinema, *Volga Volga* is a revelation—a classic musical comedy that catapulted Lyubov Orlova into a Russian mega star. The setting is a giant steamboat making its way up the Volga River. On board is a motley collection of amateur singers and dancers travelling to Moscow to take part in a musical contest. At their center is Lyubov Orlova, featured alongside veteran Meyerhold comedian Igor Ilinsky. A triumphant success upon its release, it remains one of the most important and best-loved films produced by the Soviet regime. Russian with English subtitles.
VHS: S27214. $29.95.
Grigori Alexandrov, USSR, 1937, 90 mins.

Vukovar
Filmed in 1933 in the bombed-out city of Vukovar, Yugoslavia, while the war was still raging, *Vukovar* is the award-winning story of two childhood friends— one Croat, the other Serb—who marry, only to be torn apart by a war which ravages their native Yugoslavia. A grim testament to the inexorable effects of war, *Vukovar* was recommended for a White House screening and blocked by the Croatian government from a United Nations screening. Serbo-Croatian with English subtitles.
VHS: S31628. $89.95.
Boro Draskovic, Yugoslavia, 1994, 95 mins.

The Wages of Fear
An exercise in terror and suspense, this uncut version stars Yves Montand and Charles Vanel as uncertain comrades—trapped in a South American village— who identify because they are both French and both penniless. Desperate for a job, they agree to drive two trucks filled with nitroglycerine 300 miles over treacherous roads. Basil Wright called this film "the greatest suspense thriller of all time; it is the suspense not of mystery but of Damocles' sword." French with English subtitles.
VHS: S16210. $29.95.
Laser: LD70766. $59.95.
Henri-Georges Clouzot, France, 1953, 148 mins.

Walkabout
Nicolas Roeg's solo directorial debut, based on the novel by James Vance Marshall, is the story of two British children lost in the Australian desert and rescued by an Aborigine boy. It is also a mystical, lyrical story of three children enjoying life in a free, uncomplicated, unspoiled, primitive world. With Jenny Agutter, Lucien John, David Gumpilil and John Meillon. "A movie that celebrates life—full of lovely things" (Vincent Canby, *The New York Times*).
VHS: S28614. $79.95.
Laser: Letterboxed. LD76326. $49.95.
Nicolas Roeg, Australia, 1970, 100 mins.

The Wanderer
Alain Fournier's classic novel, *Le Grand Meaulnes*,

is interpreted by Albiococco with fantastic imagery and stunning color—in a remarkable recreation of a child's memories and examination of his transition from romantic, idealistic youth to clear-eyed adult. With Jean Blaise and Brigitte Fossey. "Heartbreaking...Romantic" (*L.A. Times*). French with English subtitles.
VHS: S15273. $29.95.
Jean-Gabriel Albicocco, France, 1967, 108 mins.

War and Peace
The definitive version of Sergei Bondarchuk's epic adaptation of Tolstoy's novel. The story concerns how Napoleon's 1912 Russian invasion affected two upper class families. Winner of the 1968 Best Foreign Language Academy award, the film was shot over five years, with a cast of 10,000 soldiers, nearly 300 sets, 2,000 costumes and production design and art direction culled from more than 40 Russian museums. The film is notable for its gritty authenticity and naturalism and its panoramic social and political portraits, especially the battle of Borodino. Three cassettes. With Ludmila Savelyeva, Vyacheslav Tikhonov and Bondarchuk.
Dubbed in English.
VHS: S07683. $99.95.
Russian with English Subtitles.
VHS: S18466. $99.95.
Sergei Bondarchuk, Russia, 1968, 403 mins.

We're All Stars
This wacky comedy of errors takes off when the members of the Huambachano family get a chance to win fame and fortune and to appear as the "family of the week" on the popular TV game show, *We're All Stars*. The only catch: the television needs the "perfect" family, so the Huambachanos are forced to cover up the family divorce. Winner of Best Picture awards at three international film festivals. Spanish with English subtitles.
VHS: S27738. $59.95.
Felipe Degregori, Peru, 1993, 80 mins.

Wedding in Galilee
An intimate and multi-layered portrait of a Palestinian village under Israeli occupation. The mukhtar of the village wants to hold a traditional wedding for his son, and invites the Israeli military governor as a guest of honor. Beautifully filmed and acted by a cast of non-professionals, the story moves between the alienated grandfather, an angry group of young males prone to violence, an impotent groom and a resourceful bride. Arabic and Hebrew with English subtitles.
VHS: S08938. $24.95.
Michel Kleifi, Israel/Belgium, 1986, 113 mins.

Weekend
"End of Cinema, end of world," read the titles at the conclusion of Godard's 1967 apocalyptic film *Weekend*. Godard himself described the work as both "a film found on the junk heap," and "a film lost in the cosmos." Presenting a dark, comic vision of the end of capitalist society, *Weekend* reflects the turmoil and chaos of the late sixties better than any Hollywood film from that era. It also stands as the climax to the first phase of Godard's filmmaking career, before he turned to the making of more experimental Marxist films after the social upheavals of 1968. With Mirielle Darc and Jean-Pierre Leaud. French with English subtitles.
VHS: S14572. $29.95.
Jean-Luc Godard, France, 1967, 105 mins.

What Have I Done to Deserve This?
Carmen Maura stars as a housewife and cleaning woman hooked on no-doz who ends up selling one of her sons to a dentist and killing her husband with a ham bone. "An absolutely wonderful black comedy. A small masterpiece," wrote *The New York Times*. Spanish with English subtitles.
VHS: S08102. $79.95.
Pedro Almodovar, Spain, 1985, 100 mins.

When Father Was Away on Business
Kusturica's Cannes-award winning film is a magical portrait of a boy's coming of age in 50's Yugoslavia. As little Malik takes up sleepwalking and experiences his first love, the family knows the real "business" Father is conducting—in a labor camp for his unrepentant Stalinist leanings and his philandering. Serbo-Croatian with English subtitles.
VHS: S15547. $19.98.
Laser: CAV. LD72198. $49.95.
Emir Kusturica, Yugoslavia, 1985, 144 mins.

When the Cat's Away

The missing cat of a beautiful, young French fashion stylist (Garance Clavel) serves to re-unite a Parisian neighborhood in this intimate drama which features the actual residents of the Bastille section of Paris. The film has an emotional authenticity and "effortlessness that is a rare thing in our time" (*New City*). French with English subtitles.
VHS: S32798. $98.99.
Cedric Klapisch, France, 1997, 91 mins.

Where Is the Friend's Home?

A lyrical tale about a traveller searching for his friend's home, who finds himself on an excursion through places and moments of great beauty and wonder. The friends are the schoolmates Ahmad and Mohammad Reza. Mohammad Reza's careless attitude towards his homework has drawn several reprimands from their stern teacher, culminating in the threat of expulsion if he does not do his work. When Ahmad prepares to do his own homework, he finds that he has accidentally picked up Mohammad Reza's notebook. Fearing that his friend will be expelled if he cannot submit his lesson the next day, Ahmad defies his parents and sets out to find his friend's home in the neighboring village. Winner of the Bronze Leopard at the Locarno Film Festival. Farsi with English subtitles.
VHS: S27791. $29.95.
Abbas Kiarostami, Iran, 1989, 90 mins.

Where the Green Ants Dream

Two tribes of Aborigines, the Wororas and the Riratjingus, preserve their ancient legends, songs and laws of creation in the heart of Australia. They come into conflict with the laws of modern Australia when a large company tries to mine uranium in one of their holy places, the place where the "Green Ants Dream." With Bruce Spence, Wandjuk Marika, Roy Marika. English dialog.
VHS: S07103. $24.95.
Werner Herzog, Germany/Australia, 1985, 99 mins.

White

The second part of Kieslowski's Blue-White-Red trilogy, based on the concepts of the French tri-colour flag. A Polish man's life disintegrates when his new French bride deserts him after only six months. Forced to begin anew, he returns to Poland and plans a clever scheme of revenge against her. Julie Delpy is great as the young wife. French and Polish with English subtitles.
VHS: S23108. $19.95.
Laser: Letterboxed. **LD74805. $49.95.**
Krzysztof Kieslowski, France/Poland, 1993, 92 mins.

White Balloon

Winner of the Camera d'Or and co-winner of the International Critic's Prize at the 1995 Cannes Film Festival, this Iranian breakthrough feature tells the story of a young girl's desire for a pretty goldfish to start her New Year's holiday. Snake charmers, a distracted dry cleaner tailor, a lonely and talkative soldier and other assorted adults get in the way of her goal. With a script by Abbas Kiarostami (*Life and Nothing But...*). "A miracle! Profound!" (Lloyd Sachs, *Chicago Sun-Times*). Farsi with English subtitles.
VHS: S30428. $19.95.
Laser: LD76061. $39.98.
Jafar Panahi, Iran, 1996, 85 mins.

White Nights

Mario, a shy young man, meets a mysterious girl, Natalie, weeping as she stands on a canal bridge. She tells him that she loves a sailor who left on a long journey and promised to return in one year; a year has passed and he still hasn't arrived. Gradually, Mario falls in love with the girl and struggles to persuade her that the sailor will never return. Just when he seems to have convinced her, the man from her past does in fact appear. Based on a story by Fyodor Dostoyevsky. With Marcello Mastroianni, Maria Schell and Jean Marais. Italian with English subtitles.
VHS: S13679. $59.95.
Luchino Visconti, Italy, 1957, 107 mins.

Walkabout

White Sheik

When a provincial couple go to Rome for their honeymoon, the bride sneaks off to the movie set where her idol, the White Sheik, is making a film. "Perhaps the freshest and the most tender and naturalistic of Fellini's films" (Pauline Kael). Italian with English subtitles.

VHS: S00135. $29.95.
Federico Fellini, Italy, 1952, 86 mins.

Why Does Herr R. Run Amok?

Herr R., a likable office worker with a family, calmly picks up an ornate lamp one evening and bludgeons to death his wife, child and neighbor. One of Fassbinder's most notorious films, full of brilliant insights into the loneliness of existence, the terrors and anxieties of middle-class life. With Lilith Ungerer, Amadeus Fengler, Franz Maron and Hanna Schygulla. German with English subtitles.

VHS: S20306. $59.95.
Rainer W. Fassbinder, Germany, 1969, 87 mins.

Why Has Bodhi-Dharma Left for the East?

An aged monk, his young apprentice and an orphan inhabit a remote monastery. This fascinating Korean film by Bae Yong-kyun focuses on their interaction and, in the process, provokes a contemplation on life, death and enlightenment. A solo effort, the film took ten years to complete. Korean with English subtitles.

VHS: S27338. $79.95.
Laser: LD75463. $69.95.
Bae Yong-kyun, Korea, 1989, 135 mins.

The Wild Child

The Wild Child is based on a remarkable journal, the 1806 memoirs of a French physician, a certain Jean Itard. The record begins in 1798, when a child is found living in the forest like an animal. Dr. Itard sets for himself the task of educating this child who is totally alien to civilization. Shot in austere black and white, the film achieves a depth of vision treating anew love, freedom, the nature of childhood and childhood's end. French with English subtitles.

VHS: S14810. $19.99.
Laser: LD75540. $39.98.
Francois Truffaut, France, 1970, 85 mins.

Wild Reeds

In 1962, a group of teenagers confront emotional, sexual and political turmoil provoked by both their own personal lives and the larger social framework of a small provincial town affected by the French-Algerian War. This engaging, elegaic film captures both the fleeting nature of youth and the profound turmoil of this intriguing stage of life. French with English subtitles.

VHS: S29407. $29.98.
Andre Techine, France, 1995, 110 mins.

Wild Strawberries

One of the great films of Bergman, with Victor Sjostrom as the aged Stockholm professor who recollects his past experiences and becomes aware, for the first time, of his failings and shortcomings. With Bibi Andersson, Ingrid Thulin, Gunnar Bjornstrand. Swedish with English subtitles.

VHS: S01462. $29.95.
Laser: LD70487. $49.95.
Ingmar Bergman, Sweden, 1957, 95 mins.

Window to Paris

This wonderfully inventive, wildly hilarious comedy from Yuri Mamin starts in St. Petersburg, where an impoverished music teacher finds that the closet door of his new one-room apartment opens onto a window on the other side of which lies…Paris! Soon the denizens of the Russian flat are busy transporting themselves (and all the goods they can find) over the Paris rooftops into their St. Petersburg apartment. *Window to Paris* is a sharp, witty and totally original satire. Russian with English subtitles.

VHS: S27083. $96.99.
Laser: LD75447. $34.95.
Yuri Mamin, Russia, 1994, 92 mins.

Wings of Desire

"The first time I saw the film I thought it was a knockout; on second viewing it already seemed a classic," wrote J. Hoberman of Wim Wenders' re-examination of the divided city of Berlin. Damiel, played by Bruno Ganz, is the angel who has grown tired and frustrated at his inability to affect people's lives. When he falls in love with a beautiful trapeze artist, he decides to leave the heavens and enter the mortal world. With incredible cinematography by Henri Alekan, *Wings of Desire* is one of the rare movies of the past decade that actually stretch, break and re-form the boundaries of the medium" (David Denby, *New York Magazine*). German with yellow English subtitles.

VHS: S09593. $19.98.
Wim Wenders, Germany, 1988, 110 mins.

Woman in the Dunes

A woman, confined to a deep pit in the sand dunes, where she is fed by neighbors and forced to clear her house of the threatening sands, is joined by a passing photographer whom the villagers have trapped into sharing her work and bed—forever. This is the situation of Teshigahara's great symbolic and sensual adaptation of Kobo Abe's novel, in which he "builds up the erotic tension…with extreme close-ups that transform the human body into landscape…" (*Oxford Companion to Film*). With Eiji Okada and Kyoko Kishida. Japanese with English subtitles.

VHS: S13589. $19.95.
Hiroshi Teshigahara, Japan, 1964, 123 mins.

A Woman Is a Woman

"I conceived this film within the framework of a neo-realist musical: *an absolute contradiction*, but that's the way I wanted to make the film," said Godard. Godard's closely-knit texture of small bistros, striptease joints, political suspicion and conjugal wavering is constantly violated in its naturalistic surface, not just by the comic turns of the plot, but by Godard's reminders not only that the film is a performance, but that the projected images are themselves illusory: "The film has a beauty that is brash and pathetic, like splintered colored glass, fragments that somehow compose a picture while refusing to hold together: musical, sad, uproarious, definitely frail" (Edgardo Cozarinsky). French with English subtitles.

VHS: S08090. $59.95.
Jean-Luc Godard, France, 1961, 85 mins.

Women from the Lake of Scented Souls

At the center of this moving intergenerational family drama is an old legend about two girls. They drowned themselves in a local lake and were said to have flown away as beautiful birds. A contemporary entrepreneur succeeds in business despite her drunken, abusive husband. Now she faces the chore of putting another woman into an unhappy arranged marriage because her mentally ill son desires a wife. Can this older, wiser woman prevent another drowning? Co-winner of the Golden Bear at the 1993 Berlin Film Festival. Mandarin with English subtitles.

VHS: S25832. $89.95.
Xie Fei, China, 1993, 106 mins.

Women on the Verge of a Nervous Breakdown

The latest wacky comedy from Pedro Almodovar once again stars Carmen Maura, his perennial leading lady. She plays a popular Spanish actress driven to distraction when her lover leaves for another woman. She knows she can talk him out of leaving if only she can talk directly to him and not deal with the answering machine. A comedy of errors ensues that involve a drugged pitcher of gazpacho, Shiite terrorists and a mental patient who left the asylum too soon. Spanish with English subtitles.

VHS: S10757. $19.98.
Pedro Almodovar, Spain, 1988, 98 mins.

The World of Apu

The final part of Satyajit Ray's *Apu* trilogy, adapted from Bengali writer B.B. Bandopaddhay's epic novel, is a poignant summing up of the earlier films' themes and stylistic preoccupations. Its story traces Apu's leap into adulthood, the consequences of his marriage and birth of his first child. Ray's painterly use of landscape finds a poetry in the incidental, loose textures of daily life. Music by Ravi Shankar. With Soumitra Chatterjee (as Apu), Sharmila Tagore, Alok Chakravarty, and Swapan Mukherji. Newly remastered. Bengali with English subtitles.

VHS: S27704. $19.95.
Satyajit Ray, India, 1959, 105 mins.

WR: Mysteries of the Organism

Called "an outrageous, exuberant, marvelous work," by Amos Vogel in *Film Comment* and "a weird and hilarious fantasy…witty and exuberant" by *The New York Times*, *WR: Mysteries of the Organism* is a unique blend of fact and fiction, and Makavejev's landmark film. It deftly juxtaposes the story of the sexual encounter between the beautiful, liberated Milena and a repressed Soviet figure-skating

champion with an exploration of the life and theories of psychoanalyst Wilhelm Reich. The "WR" in the film's title stands for either "Wilhelm Reich" or "World Revolution." Makavejev describes it as "a black comedy, political circus, a fantasy on the fascism and communism of human bodies, the political life of human genitals, a proclamation of the pornographic essence of any system of authority and power over others....If you watch for more than five minutes, you become my accomplice." With Dravic, Jagoda Kaloper, Tuli Kupferberg, Jackie Curtis. English and Serbian with English subtitles.
VHS: S11290. $79.95.
Dusan Makavejev, Yugoslavia/USA, 1971, 84 min.

Xica
Carlos Diegues' comedy concerns Xica (Zeze Motta), a beautiful black slave who uses her sexual charm and savvy to benefit from Brazil's economic emergence. The film is set in the 18th century, when the fantastic wealth produced from the diamond trade transformed Brazil into a decadent hothouse. Xica ascends to the role of unofficial Empress, gleefully mocking her former masters while stockpiling newly found assets and power. "The film marks Diegues as one of Brazil's most innovative directors, who speaks his piece with exuberance, wit and style" (*San Francisco Chronicle*). With Walmor Chagas, Jose Wilker, Marcus Vinicius and Altair Lima. Portuguese with English subtitles.
VHS: S19417. $79.95.
Carlos Diegues, Brazil, 1976, 109 mins.

Yellow Earth
A striking collaboration between two Fifth Generation Chinese filmmakers, director Chen Kaige (*Farewell My Concubine*) and Zhang Yimou (*Raise the Red Lantern*), who photographed the film in deep, stylized colors. Set in spring, 1939, a young soldier researching folk songs enters a small community and gets emotionally entangled with an old man, his 14-year-old daughter and his younger son. The film's conflict is set up by the young woman's attraction to the soldier. With Xue Bai, Wang Xueqi, Tan Tuo and Liu Qiang. Mandarin with English subtitles.
VHS: S19445. $19.98.
Chen Kaige, China, 1984, 89 mins.

Yesterday, Today and Tomorrow
Sophia Loren and Marcello Mastroianni star in this Oscar-winning film that contains three different comic stories. Loren is great as the skilled temptress who uses sex to get what she wants, and her striptease remains a steamy, unforgettable film achievement.
VHS: S21220. $29.99.
Vittorio de Sica, Italy, 1964, 119 mins.

Yidl with a Fiddle (Yidl mitn Fidl)
The classic Yiddish language musical comedy. Molly Picon plays a shtetl girl who, disguised as a boy, goes off with her father and a band of traveling musicians into the Polish countryside. Made in pre-war Poland, the film provides a warm rendering of Eastern European Jewish life, made all the more fun and wonderful by Molly Picon's unequaled ability to amuse and entertain. Newly mastered and restored. Yiddish with English subtitles.
VHS: S10258. $72.00.
Joseph Green, Poland, 1936, 92 mins.

Yojimbo
Kurosawa's first full-length comedy. Toshiro Mifune is the unemployed samurai warrior who comes to a small village torn apart by two warring factions where he is hired first by one side, then by the other. "Explosively comic and exhilarating," said Pauline Kael. Japanese with English subtitles.
VHS: S01489. $29.95.
Laser: LD70489. $49.95.
Akira Kurosawa, Japan, 1961, 110 mins.

You Are Not Alone
This Danish film honestly explores the boundaries between friendship and love in a boys' school in a film which is full of nuance, gentleness and humor, reminiscent of the early films of Truffaut. Danish with English subtitles.
VHS: S01491. $79.95.
Nielsen & Johansen, Denmark, 1982, 90 mins.

Zazie dans le Metro
Called "an exceedingly funny picture...funny in a bold, delicate, freakish, vulgar, outrageous, and occasionally nightmarish way...From start to finish, the picture is crammed with sight gags and preposterous photographic stunts. *Zazie* is a film like

Alice in Wonderland; Zazie is a foul-mouthed little cynic, age 11, who comes to Paris for a weekend with her uncle (Philippe Noiret), a female impersonator, and nobody and nothing are quite what they seem" (Pauline Kael). From Louis Malle, the director of *Murmur of the Heart*. French with English subtitles.
VHS: S12991. $29.95.
Louis Malle, France, 1960, 85 mins.

Zentropa
Known in Europe as *Europa*, this stylistically daring work is set in a bleak, defeated Germany. A young American of German ancestry apprentices as a railway porter. He is seduced by a mysterious heiress whose father owns the line and becomes a pawn in a mysterious web of intrigue and deceit. With Jean Marc Barr, Barbara Sukowa and Eddie Constantine. Narrated by Max von Sydow. English and German with English subtitles.
VHS: S18368. $19.95.
Lars von Trier, Denmark/France/Sweden/Germany, 1991, 112 mins.

Zero for Conduct
Based on Vigo's personal childhood experiences, a poetic yet revolutionary portrait of a revolt at a boarding school. Vigo creates a claustrophobic world in which the petty tyrannies of the school regime stand in sharp relief to the tender delirium of the children. Filled with deep psychological insights, this cinematic landmark was banned in France until 1946 on the grounds that it maliciously attacked the French educational system. Music by Maurice Jaubert, photography by Boris Kaufman. With Jean Daste and Louis Lefebvre. French with English subtitles.
VHS: S01500. $29.95.
Jean Vigo, France, 1933, 44 mins.

Zuppa di Pesce (Fish Soup)
Set between the 1950s and late '70s against the beauty of the Tuscany seaside, *Fish Soup* offers small sketches of family behavior and psychology, from gatherings to complicated relationships. Narrating with a rare balance of frankness, naturalness and tenderness, Infascelli reveals a Chekhovian understanding of family relationships as we follow the development of Isabella (Chiara Caselli) and her relationship with her father (Philippe Noiret) and family. With Macha Meril, Andrea Prodan, Renzo Montagnani and Fausto Fiorentini. "A family-size *Amarcord* set of recollections" (*L'Avvenire*). Italian with English subtitles.
VHS: S32622. $29.95.
Fiorella Infascelli, Italy/France, 1991, 107 mins.

Window to Paris

7 Films from Iran

Where Is the Friend's Home?

The Cyclist

A visually sophisticated film which deals with the themes of man's exploitation of man and the inequities between rich and poor. The cyclist is Nassim, an Afghan refugee in need of money to pay his wife's medical expenses. With work difficult to come by, a sleazy promoter suggests he undertake a bicycle marathon. Touting him as the Afghani superman, the huckster wagers that Nassim will circle a small area on the outskirts of town, day and night, for a week. Gamblers, bookies and food vendors gather to watch the desperate cyclist from the sidelines, turning his suffering to their own profit. Winner of the Best Film at the Riminicinema Film Festival. Farsi with English subtitles.
   VHS: $27790. $29.95.
Mohsen Makhmalbaf, Iran, 1989, 75 mins.

The Key

Humor, pathos and suspense fill this story of a four-year-old and an infant left home alone while their mother runs out to do some shopping. Young Amir Mohammad has his own ideas about what he wants to do—and watching his baby brother and the meal cooking in the kitchen are not among them. Minor crisis piles on crisis, culminating in the threat of disaster when the cooking pot boils over, dousing the flame on the gas range. As frantic neighbors yell advice to the resourceful youngster, tension mounts. Winner of the award for Best Children's Film at the Berlin Film Festival. Screenplay by Abbas Kiarostami. Farsi with English subtitles.
   VHS: $27789. $29.95.
Ebrahim Forouzesh, Iran, 1986, 76 mins.

Life and Nothing More

The film investigates the aftermath of a devastating 1990 earthquake which killed some 50,000 people in northern Iran. This region provided the setting for Kiarostami's *Where Is the Friend's Home.* Kiarostami's search for the two young actors who played central roles in that film becomes the dramatic source of *Life and Nothing More*…as a father and son travel to Quoker, the hometown of the two boys, and along the way meet earthquake survivors who desperately and valiantly work to reconstruct their lives. "…in many ways the most beautiful and powerful Iranian film I've seen" (Jonathan Rosenbaum, *Chicago Reader*). Farsi with English subtitles.
   VHS: $27792. $29.95.
Abbas Kiarostami, Iran, 1992, 91 mins.

The Need

"One of those rare works in which the perfect rendering of simple elements produces a small, unforgettable masterpiece. The film's two main characters are boys poised between childhood and manhood. Both are poor. The boy through whose eyes we experience the drama has lost his father in the war and seems to have only the bleakest of prospects, until a relative finds him a choice apprentice's position in a print shop. But there is a catch; another boy coveting the spot has also been taken on, with the better of the two getting the permanent job after a trial period. Thus begins a fierce if somewhat covert rivalry that results in workplace sabotage, fighting and then, very surprisingly, friendship" (Godfrey Cheshire, *Film Comment*). Farsi with English subtitles.
   VHS: $27788. $29.95.
Alireza Davudneshad, Iran, 1991, 81 mins.

The Peddler

Shockingly forthright in its view of the social and economic problems of the post-Shah era, *The Peddler* uses a different cameraman and different style for each of three short tales set among the poor of contemporary Tehran. The first episode follows a kindly but naive couple who want someone to adopt their newborn daughter. The second, an astonishing mix of absurdist comedy and the supernatural, concerns a mentally unstable man who lives with his mother in a ramshackle apartment. The final section draws on the American gangster film to show the last hours of a peddler suspected of betraying his friends. Farsi with English subtitles.
   VHS: $27787. $29.95.
Mohsen Makhmalbaf, Iran, 1986, 95 mins.

Where Is the Friend's Home?

A lyrical tale about a traveller searching for his friend's home, who finds himself on an excursion through places and moments of great beauty and wonder. The friends are the schoolmates Ahmad and Mohammad Reza. Mohammad Reza's careless attitude towards his homework has drawn several reprimands from their stern teacher, culminating in the threat of expulsion if he does not do his work. When Ahmad prepares to do his own homework, he finds that he has accidentally picked up Mohammad Reza's notebook. Fearing that his friend will be expelled if he cannot submit his lesson the next day, Ahmad defies his parents and sets out to find his friend's home in the neighboring village. Winner of the Bronze Leopard at the Locarno Film Festival. Farsi with English subtitles.
   VHS: $27791. $29.95.
Abbas Kiarostami, Iran, 1989, 90 mins.

White Balloon

Winner of the Camera d'Or and co-winner of the International Critic's Prize at the 1995 Cannes Film Festival, this Iranian breakthrough feature tells the story of a young girl's desire for a pretty goldfish to start her New Year's holiday. Snake charmers, a distracted dry cleaner tailor, a lonely and talkative soldier and other assorted adults get in the way of her goal. With a script by Abbas Kiarostami (*Life and Nothing But*…). "A miracle! Profound!" (Lloyd Sachs, *Chicago Sun-Times*). Farsi with English subtitles.
   VHS: $30428. $19.95.
   Laser: LD76061. $39.98.
Jafar Panahi, Iran, 1996, 85 mins.

10 African Features

Faces of Women
Eugenie Cisse Roland, Sidiki Bakaba and Albertine N'Guessan star in this vibrant, adventurous film about contemporary Africa. Two women try to balance the demands of tradition and modern life in their changing world. It's a sensual, joyous combination of raucous comedy and pulsating African music. In indigenous languages and French with English subtitles.
VHS: S22444. $79.95.
Desire Ecare, Ivory Coast, 1985, 105 mins.

Harvest: 3,000 Years
Haile Gerima (*Sankofa*) returned to his native Ethiopia to make this realistic drama set in contemporary Africa. A peasant family struggles to survive under conditions that remain tied to a feudal past, fighting against the demands of a wealthy and uncaring landowner. Gerima's realism puts the story into the broader historical context of the colonialist African legacy. In Amharic with English subtitles.
VHS: S25565. $59.95.
Haile Gerima, Ethiopia, 1976, 150 mins.

Hyenas
Based on Friedrich Durrenmatt's play *The Visit of the Old Woman*, *Hyenas* is the story of Linguere Ramatou (Ami Diakhate), a woman who returns to the village she left banished from 30 years before. She left poor, unmarried and pregnant, and now returns wealthy, free—and vengeful. Linguere promises the people of the village of Colobane her entire fortune in exchange for the life of Dramaan Drameh (Mansour Diouf), the man who betrayed her and sent her into exile. A brilliant metaphor for post-colonial Africa. "A crowd pleaser...a wicked tale told with wit and irony" (Georgia Brown, *The Village Voice*). In Wolof with English subtitles.
VHS: S31624. $79.95.
Djibril Diop Mambety, Senegal, 1992, 113 mins.

Jit
An old-fashioned romantic comedy from Zimbabwe which features the irresistible beat of African jit-jive in the story of UK, determined to win the heart of Sofi, who is closely guarded by her gangster boyfriend. UK's efforts to win Sofi's heart are hilariously hindered by an ancestral spirit. English language.
VHS: S21893. $29.95.
Michael Raeburn, Zimbabwe, 1993, 98 mins.

Kasarmu Ce: This Land Is Ours
A taut West African thriller that draws on Hausa and western storytelling, centering on the efforts of a young man to avenge the murder of his grandfather by a brutal land baron attempting to seize control of the iron-rich village lands. A politically potent and culturally interesting film, *Kasarmu Ce* is a "penetrating, poetic, joyously contemplative thriller set in a rural backdrop" (*West African Magazine*). Hausa with English subtitles.
VHS: S18889. $19.95.
Saddik Balewa, Nigeria, 1991, 84 mins.

La Vie Est Belle (Life Is Rosy)
A farce infused with the Zairian sense of belief in Systeme-D or debrouillardise (the art of hustling for survival), this film explores the rich musical world of Kinshasha. It follows a young man who uses wit and guile to trick his greedy boss, attain the woman he loves, and sing his favorite song ("La Vie Est Belle") on national television. French with English subtitles.
VHS: S27561. $59.95.
Ngangura Mweze/Benoit Lamy, Zaire/Belgium, 1987, 85 mins.

Quartier Mozart
Winner of the *Prix Afrique en Creation* at Cannes in 1992, this humorous and magical tale is filled with the sexual antics that enliven a working class neighborhood in Yaounde. A girl takes on the body of a man and learns the true sexual politics of the men around her. In addition, the woman who helps her achieve this transformation metamorphoses herself into Panka, a comic figure who can make a man's penis disappear with a handshake. French with English subtitles.
VHS: S27559. $59.95.
Jean-Pierre Bekolo, Cameroon, 1992, 80 mins.

Tilai
One of the most highly acclaimed contemporary African films. In this troubling drama, a young African man is engaged to the woman he loves until the man's father decides that he should marry this woman himself. This fateful decision forces the young lovers into an illicit affair. On the run, they find tradition and the law will play a large role in their fate. In More with English subtitles.
VHS: S26145. $79.95.
Idrissa Ouedraogo, Burkina Faso, 1990, 81 mins.

Touki Bouki (Journey of the Hyena)
Mory and his girlfriend Anta imagine an escape from the difficult life they share in Dakar. Paris is their destination, and like the heroes of French New Wave films, they are utterly alienated from their surroundings. A series of adventures ensues as they plot ways to raise money for their trip, but only one can face up to the reality that awaits them. Wolof with English subtitles.
VHS: S27558. $59.95.
Djibril Diop Mambety, Senegal, 1973, 85 mins.

Wend Kuuni (God's Gift)
The measured rhythms and formal compositions of African oral traditions give shape to this metaphoric film about Mossi values. A young mute boy, orphaned when his mother refuses to marry, is found and adopted by a village, which names him "Wend Kuuni," or "God's Gift." This remarkable film won a Cesar and numerous other international awards. More with English subtitles.
VHS: S27560. $59.95.
Gaston Kabore, Burkina Faso, 1982, 70 mins.

Quartier Mozart

What it's about

Love Affair
Love After Love
Love and Anarchy
Love and Death
Love and the Frenchwoman
Love and Other Catastrophes
Love & Other Sorrows
Love & Sex Among the Ruins
Love at Large
Love Bites
Love Crazy
Love Crimes
Love Dolls Superstars
Love 'em and Leave 'em
Love Eternal
Love Finds Andy Hardy
Love Flower
Love for Lydia
Love from a Stranger
Love God?
Love Goddesses
Love in Bloom
Love Into Waste
Love Jones
Love Happy
Love Has Many Faces
Love in the City
Love in Germany
Love in the Afternnoon
Love is a Many Splendored Thing
Love is Better than Ever
Love Letter to Edy
Love Letters
Love Me or Leave Me
Love Me Tender
Love of Destiny
Love of Sunya
Love Nest
Love Never Dies
Love of Jeanne Ney
Love of Three Queens
Love on the Dole
Love on the Run
Love Play
Love Serenade
Love Skills
Love Songs
Love Story
Love Trap
Love! Valour! Compassion!
Love with the Proper Stranger
Love Without Pity
Love Your Mama
Loved One
Loveless

Geriatric Love

Love Among the Ruins
Roman Spring of Mrs. Stone
Coccoon
La Cage aux Folles
On Golden Pond

Mommy Dearest

Murmur of the Heart
Get Out Your Handkerchiefs
Spanking the Monkey
Summer of '42

Obsessive Love

Niagara
Fatal Attraction
Play Misty for Me
L'enfer
Blue Angel
Lolita
Shanghai Gesture
A Place in the Sun
Possessed
Women on the Verge
 of a Nervous Breakdown

Oil tycoon and part-time Hollywood investor **John Smith**, in a grand but fatal attempt to prove his LOVE AND DEVOTION to a 14 year old girl, plummets to his death while attempting to cross Niagara Falls in a barrel.

"There were two great loves in Johnny Gray's life: his engine and his girl."

The opening title card in Buster Keaton's The General.

> ## "Love is blind - and your cane is pink."
>
> *Serge Gainsbourg*

"I never loved another person the way I loved myself."

Mae West, *Playboy*

self - love
Quentin Tarantino
Oliver Stone
Barbra Streisand
Spike Lee

Love for Sale
Sunset Boulevard
Irma la Deuce
Taxi Driver
American Gigolo
Butterfield 8
Klute
Yesterday, Today and Tomorrow
Leaving Las Vegas
Belle de Jour
Crimes of Passion
Blush

Puppy Love
Les Mistons
Say Anything
A Little Romance
Welcome to the Dollhouse
My Own Private Idaho
Sixteen Candles

LOVE

L'enfer

50 Years of Oscar-Winning Foreign-Language Films

The Best Foreign Language Film has been awarded for 50 of the Academy Awards' 70-year history. Films released in any language other than English are eligible for the Academy's consideration. Facets salutes the 50 Foreign-Language Film Oscar winners to date:

Sciuscia (*Shoeshine*) - Italy, 1947

Directed by Vittorio De Sica, screenplay by Sergio Amidei, Adolfo Franci, C.G. Viola, and Cesare Zavattini. Considered one of the great films of Italian neo-realism, *Shoeshine* compellingly confronts social themes with unabashed emotional directness as it wistfully observes the loss of childhood and the ascension into adulthood. It is an emotionally charged portrait of war-torn, poverty-ridden Italy as seen through the eyes of Giuseppe and the older Pasquale (played believably by nonprofessional actors Rinaldo Smordoni and Franco Interlenghi), two young shoeshine boys struggling to make a living during the early days of the American occupation of Rome after World War II. The two get involved in a black market deal in order to raise money to buy a horse, they get caught and are sent to a prison-like reform school where they are separated. Pasquale is deceived into unwittingly betraying Giuseppe, and the corruption of the prison causes the two close friends to become enemies, whose mutual vengeance leads to deadly consequences. A powerful and emotional collaboration between De Sica and the father of neo-realism, Cesare Zavattini. **S05869. $79.95.**

Monsieur Vincent - France, 1948

Directed by Maurice Cloche, based on a scenario by Jean Anouilh, cinematography by Claude Renoir. Pierre Fresnay offers an extraordinarily human, emotional portrayal of St. Vincent de Paul, the 17th-century French priest, as he struggles to carry on his charitable work against all obstacles and bring about peace and harmony among the peasants and nobles during the Black Death in Europe. An inspirational true story. **S00874. $29.95.**

Ladri di biciclette (*The Bicycle Thief*) - Italy, 1949

Directed by Vittorio De Sica, screenplay by Cesare

Zavattini. Perhaps the single most important and moving film of Italian neo-realism, *The Bicycle Thief* tells the deceptively simple story of Antonio Ricci, a poor, unemployed married man who finds work pasting up signs in the outskirts of Rome, work that requires a bicycle. When the tool of Antonio's livelihood is stolen, we share the gamut of his emotions—frustration, anger and humiliation—as he tries to recover the stolen bicycle with the help of his son, Bruno, and eventually succumbs to the corruption of society and becomes a thief himself. In the irony of the situation we learn a great deal about the hopes and frustrations of a human being in an indifferent world. De Sica got wonderfully real and moving performances from his three lead nonprofessional actors: Lamberto Maggio (Antonio), a factory worker, Lianella Carell (Maria), a journalist who interviewed De Sica, and Enzo Staiola (Bruno), whom De Sica spotted in a crowd of onlookers while working on a scene. **S00128. $69.95. LD70881. $39.95.**

Au-delà des grilles (*Walls of Malapaga*) - France/Italy, 1950

Directed by Rene Clement, screenplay by Jean Aurenche, Suso Cecchi D'Amico, Alfredo Guarini, Cesare Zavattini, and Pierre Bost. In this unusual Franco-Italian production combining the romantic, melodramic pre-war French style with the harsh, poetic post-war Italian style, Jean Gabin is a Frenchman on the run for killing his mistress. Safely stowed away on a ship, a sudden toothache sends him searching for succor in Genoa. There he meets and spends a few days with a lonely, troubled waitress (Isa Miranda) and her impressionable young daughter (Vera Talchi). The fugitive and the waitress fall in love, but in this simple tale of desperation and loneliness it may be too late for these sad figures. Clement's "'sensitivity' is like a glue holding the picture together" (Pauline Kael, *5001 Nights at the Movies*). **S21607. $24.95.**

Rashomon - Japan, 1951

Written and directed
by Akira Kurosawa.
The most famous
Japanese film of all
time, this cinematic
landmark is a
brilliant study of the
ungraspable nature
of truth. Set in the
12th-century feudal
Japan, *Rashomon*
cleverly uses a
flashback within a
flashback technique

to recount the story
of a samurai and his wife, who, while traveling
through the woods near Kyoto, are attacked by a
bandit (brilliantly played by Toshiro Mifune), the
wife raped and the husband violently murdered. Four
versions of the incident are told by the participants
and a woodcutter who was a witness—each version
self-serving and incompatible, yet curiously and in
their own way true. The first Japanese film to receive
international acclaim, *Rashomon* is grand
entertainment, brimming with action, mystery and
suspense. With Machiko Kyo, Masayuki Mori, and
Takashi Shimura. S01092. $29.95. **LD70440. $49.95.**

Jeux interdits (Forbidden Games) - France, 1952

Directed by Rene
Clement, screenplay
and dialogue by
Clement, Jean
Aurenche and Pierre
Bost, based on a
story by Francois
Boyer. Rene
Clement's allegory is
the story of Paulette,
a little orphaned
French girl, who is
taken in by a peasant

family and plays with their young son, Michel.
Imitating the adult life that surrounds them, the
children build a secret cemetery for animals and steal
crosses from the churchyard to mark the graves. Their
games end in tragedy when the police arrive at the
peasant home to recover the missing church crosses
and the children are separated when Paulette is taken
to a refugee center. Wonderfully natural performances
from Georges Pojouly, whom Clement discovered in
a camp, and Brigitte Fossey. A moving anti-war film
about the effects of war on children that does not deal
with warfare. S00457. $29.95. LD70988. $39.95.

1953 [not awarded]

Jigokumon (Gate of Hell) - Japan, 1954

Directed by
Teinosuke Kinugasa,
screenplay by
Kinugasa, Kan
Kikuchi, and
Masaichi Nagata.
Based on *Rape of
Lucrece*, detailing a
crime that took place
in 1159, Kinusago's
exquisitely stylized
tragedy is set during
the civil wars of
12th-century Japan.

It tells of a samurai
who falls in love with a married noblewoman. When
the samurai threatens to kill the woman's husband
unless she yields to the samurai, the woman, in a
brave move to preserve honor, takes the place of the
husband and is stabbed to death. In atonement of this
heinous crime the samurai becomes a monk. Told in
exotic color, photographed by gifted painter
SanzoWada, with wonderfully choreographed battle
scenes, incredible textures and composition. With
Kazuo Hasegawa, Machiko Kyo, and Isao Yamaata.
S00483. $24.95.

Samurai I: Musashi Miyamomo - Japan, 1955

Directed by Hiroshi Inagaki, screenplay by Inagaki,
Hideji Hojo, Tokuhei Wakao, and Eiji Yoshikawa.
The first part of Hiroshi Inagaki's trilogy about
Japan's most notorious 17th-century swordfighter,
Musashi Miyamoto (Toshiro Mifune), details his
odyssey from ronin farmer to bandit to full-fledged
samurai. Having fought on the losing side during the
civil war at Sekigahara, Musashi returns as a manic
outlaw caught between his feelings for a beautiful
village girl and a sympathetic Buddhist priest, who
forces Musashi to learn zen. ''The beauty of wooded
sequences, several mass battle scenes and other
settings is extraordinary" (*Variety*). With Rentaro
Mikuni, Karuo Yashigusa and Koji Tsurato. S18905.
$29.95.

La Strada (The Road) - Italy, 1956

Directed by Federico
Fellini, screenplay by
Fellini, Ennio
Flaiano, and Tullio
Pinelli. Fellini's
masterpiece,
considered one of the
landmark films of all
time, marks Fellini's
departure from the
neo-realist tradition.
The sublimely
Chaplinesque
Giuletta Masina

offers a tour-de-force
performance as Gelsomina, a tragic waif sold to play
clown to travelling show strongman Zampano
(Anthony Quinn in a superb performance). Despite
his brutishness, she falls in love with him, until they
meet a gentle acrobat who changes their fate (Richard
Basehart). A simple and magical tale; an unbearably
painful account of loneliness, heartbreak and
isolation. With Aldo Silvani. S00712. $29.95.
LD71088. $49.95.

Le Notti di Cabiria (Nights of Cabiria) - Italy, 1957

Directed by Federico
Fellini, screenplay by
Fellini, Ennio
Flaiano, Pier Paolo
Pasolini, and Tullio
Pinelli. The third of
Fellini's trilogy of
solitude, *Nights of
Cabiria* features
Giuletta Masina (in
one of the great
performances on
film) as an

impoverished and naive prostitute living on the
outskirts of Rome, who thinks she's fallen in love,
but is betrayed by her faith in human nature. Based
on the musical *Sweet Charity*. S18582. $39.95.

Mon Oncle (My Uncle) - France, 1958

Directed by Jacques Tati, written by Tati and Jean
L'Hote. A masterpiece by and starring the great
French comic Jacques Tati satirizing the tedium and
depersonalization of modern life. The story focuses
on Monsier Hulot (Tati) who lives in a fully
automated house where modern gadgets overpower
everything, including his young nephew Gerard
Arpel. Monsieur Hulot's brother-in-law, the manager
of a plastics manufacturing factory, gets Hulot a job
in his factory to take away Hulot's influence on
Gerard. Sound effects, minimal dialog contribute to
Tati's wry humor. With Jean-Pierre Zola, Lucien
Fregis and Alain Becourt. S00870. $29.95. LD71234.
$49.95.

Orfeo Negro (Black Orpheus) - Brazil, 1959

Directed by Marcel
Camus, screenplay
by Marcel Camus,
Vinicius De Moraes,
and Jacques Viot.
Enhanced by some of
the most magnificent
music and color
photography ever put
on film, Marcel
Camus'
quintessential love
story is considered

one of the most beautiful films ever made. Based on
the Greek myth of Orpheus and Eurydice and the play
by Brazilian poet Vinicius De Moraes, *Black Orpheus*
is set against the vivid backdrop of carnival in the
black section of modern-day Rio de Janeiro. Orpheus,
the streetcar conductor and the most talented of the
Mardi Gras singers and dancers, is involved with a
headstrong and jealous woman, but falls hopelessly in
love with the lovely Eurydice, an innocent country
girl fleeing from a man sworn to kill her. With music

by Antonio Carlos Jobim and cinematography by Jean Bourgoin. "Fills the ears and eyes...it is the music, the movement, the storm of color" (*The New York Times*). **S00138. $29.95. LD70346. $79.95.**

Jungfrukällan (*The Virgin Spring*) - Sweden, 1960

Directed by Ingmar Berman, screenplay by Ulla Isaksson. In this "violently beautiful miracle play" (*Time Magazine*), Max von Sydow stars as Herre Tore, who has two daughters: the blonde, beautiful and virtuous Karin (Birgitta Pettersson), and her dark, pregnant, and envious stepsister, Ingeri (Gunnel Lindblom). Karin is raped and murdered by herdsmen on her way to church because of a prank Ingeri played on her. Herr Tore reaps revenge by killing each herdsman one by one, as well as a child, and vows to build a cathedral on the spot where Karin's naked, dead body lay. In answer, a spring is suddenly born on the spot. Highly contrasting black-and-white images evoke and imaginative, medieval world created by cinematographer Sven Nykvist. **S01418. $29.95. LD75073. $49.95.**

Såsomienspegel (*Through a Glass Darkly*) - Sweden, 1961

Written and directed by Ingmar Berman. This first film in Bergman's religious trilogy chronicles 24 hours in the life of a family on an isolated island and the pathetic collapse of a young woman into madness. Gunnar Bjornstrand portrays the father, a writer who has neglected his family for his art. He has a son, a son-in-law, and a schizophrenic daughter, Karin (Harriet Andersson). The father has discovered that Karin is incurable and has been observing her with the detached eye of a novelist, recording her illness in his diary. Karin finds the diary and is accelerated towards madness, plunging through a series of compulsive acts into a hallucinatory world where she imagines God is a spider emerging from the walls. Through the daughter's tragedy, the father is able to make some contact with his son. With technical accuracy Bergman charts the moving, powerful, personal, and psychological drama of a descent into insanity. With Max von Sydow. **S01339. $29.95. LD74974. $49.95.**

Les Dimanches de Ville d'Arvay (*Sundays and Cybele*) - France, 1962

Directed by Serge Bourguignon. An old, shell-shocked war veteran (Hardy Kruger) and a young orphan girl (Patricia Gozzi) become friends and emotional support for each other in this touching story. The relationship is looked down upon by the local townspeople. Musical score by the competent Maurice Jarre. **S01284. $29.95.**

8½ - Italy, 1963

Directed by Federico Fellini, written by Fellini, Ennio Flaiano, Tullio Pinelli, and Brunello Rondi. Fellini's great autobiographical masterpiece, the loose portrayal of a film director during the course of making a film and finding himself trapped by his fears and insecurities. Marcello Mastroianni, in the performance of a lifetime, stars as Italian director Guido Anselmi, who is trying to relax after his last big hit and lost all inspiration for his upcoming film. Meanwhile, his mistress, his wife, his producer, crew, and all the rest of his friends, are pressuring him

about one thing or another. Retreating into his dreams, Guido recalls major happenings in his life and the women he has loved and left, and finds inspiration to make his new film and face the world. With Claudia Cardinale, Anouk Aimee and Sandra Milo. **S07140. $59.95. LD70806. $59.95.**

Ieri, Oggi E Domani (*Yesterday, Today and Tomorrow*) - Italy, 1964

Directed by Vittorio De Sica, screenplay by Eduardo de Filippo, Bella Bella and Cesare Zavattini. Four-time Oscar-winner and master of the film style known as Italian neorealism, De Sica changes gears and tries his hand at light comedy with this trio of short films starring a voluptuous Sophia Loren and an amusing Marcello Mastroianni. Loren plays, by turn, a black marketeer (*Adelina of Naples*) who must remain pregnant in order to avoid a prison sentence, a rich society matron (*Anna of Milan*) bored with the high life and ready for passion, and a prostitute (*Mara of Rome*) who, much to the chagrin of his grandmother, attracts the attention of a young seminarian. The film is primarily notable for the first pairing of Loren and Mastroianni and for the famous striptease Sophia performs for Marcello, which manages to be both sexy and funny at the same time. **S21220. $29.99.**

Obchod na Korze (*Shop on Main Street*) - Czechoslovakia, 1965

Shop on Main Street, directed by Jan Kadar and Elmar Klos, screenplay by Ladislav Grossman, Klos and Kadar. The first Oscar to be awarded to a film from Eastern Europe, *Shop on Main Street*, set in a small town in Slovakia during WWII, is a poignant telling of an individual's responsibility to fight prejudice and oppression. A law prohibiting Jews from owning businesses provides the opportunity for a hapless carpenter (Tono) to take possession of a button shop formerly run by an elderly, deaf Jewish woman (famed Polish actress Ida Kaminska). Their relationship grows from one of begrudging tolerance to a gentle, protective love. Ultimately, Tono, faced with a complex moral dilemma, must decide whether to save himself by sacrificing her. Beginning with comic, almost farcical overtones, the film's mood becomes darker and more somber as the fascist presence looms stronger and more threatening. The film ends in an imaginative, slow-motion dream sequence with the principals dancing in a brilliantly lit, happier world. The emphasis on serious moral, ethical and social concerns, the juxtaposition of comedy with tragedy, the utilization of fantastic or surreal elements are the cinematic trademarks of the film movement known as the Czech New Wave. *Shop on Main Street* is a cornerstone of that movement. **S01195. $24.95.**

Un Homme et Un Femme (*A Man and a Woman*) - France, 1966

Directed and written by Claude Lelouch. This enormous international success tells the overtly sentimental story of two widowers (ably played by Anouk Aimee and Jean-Louis Trintignant) who meet at their children's boarding school and fall in love. When the woman cannot emotionally detach from the romanticized memory of her dead husband, the couple separate but are reunited in one of the most famous images in contemporary film. Rushing into each other's arms at a train station, the camera whirls around them in a 360-degree pan shot.Considered by many to be more of a technician than a true cine artiste, Lelouch uses camera tricks, filters, hot-shot editing, and a confusing employment of both color and black-and-white photography, a characteristic that seems more economical than stylistic. The film features a memorable score by Francis Lai, the theme song of which became a popular hit in the U.S. **S02322. $19.98.**

Ostre Sledovane Vlaky (*Closely Watched Trains*) - Czechoslovakia, 1967

Directed and written by Jiri Menzel, based on a book by Czech author Bohumil Hrabal. During the Second World War, a young train dispatcher's mind is preoccupied with sex and finding a way to lose his virginity. The film, also known as *Closely Observed Trains,* was made during the height of the Czech New Wave (1963-1968), a period of intense creative output for Czechoslovak filmmakers. The style of this movement is identified by its concern for moral, ethical and social issues, a perception of life as both tragic and humorous, and an occasional use of fantasy or surrealism. Director Menzel deftly handles this wry and charming comedy, blending a droll sensibility with moments of great seriousness, including a casual view of a very real suicide attempt by the affable lead and an offhand treatment of his death, who is shot while blowing up a Nazi train carrying ammunition. **S00252. $19.98.**

War and Peace - Russia, 1968

Directed by Sergei Bondarchuk, screenplay by Vasili Solovyev and Sergei Bondarchuk. Epic adaptation of Tolstoy's novel of the effects of Napoleon's invasion of Russia on two aristocratic families. This massive undertaking took over five years and $100 million to create, building 300-plus sets, 2,000 costumes and production design borrowed from more than 40 Russian museums.The film is necessarily lengthy (running over seven hours), but worthwhile, particularly for its fantastic battle scenes. The battle of Borodino is executed on a mammoth scale, employing over 10,000 extras as soldiers, and that panoramic spectacle alone should be seen. The cinematography (by Anatoli Petritsky), balancing light and shadow, rises to its monumental task, utilizing every resource known to the camera, including widescreen, split screen, irises, fades, dissolves, wipes, superimpositions, filters, color, tints, and moving the camera with long, tracking, crane and helicopter shots. All of this serves to draw the audience into the sweeping, monumental production and appreciate the effort that clearly went in to such a project. **S18466. $99.95.**

Z - France, 1969

Directed by Costa-Gavras, screenplay by Jorge Semprun and Costa-Gavras from the novel by Vassili Vassilikos. This stylish political thriller, based on the true-life assassination of Gregorios Lambrakis, a liberal deputy in the national assembly, is told in a gripping narrative with a pounding score by Theodorakis. An investigator (Jean-Louis Trintignant), looking into the death of a medical professor and pacifist politician (Yves Montand), uncovers massive police corruption and governmental obstruction of justice.The suspense is palpable; the famous sequence where a co-worker of the slain deputy is chased down by a speeding car is heightened by wild sense of urgency through rapid editing, the use of a hand-held camera, tracking shots and rousing musical score. Due to the political climate in Greece, the film was shot in Algiers and France.This influential film, whose politics extended far beyond Greece, won the Jury Prize at the Cannes Film Festival. **S01496. $29.98.**

Indagine su un cittadino al di sopra di ogni sospeto (*Investigation of a Citizen Above Suspicion*) - Italy, 1970

Directed by Elio Petri, screenplay by Ugo Pirro. Prime example of the Italian political cinema of the 1960s and 1970s, of which Pirro was one of the most skilled political and social scriptwriters. An egomanical, power-hungry police inspector, skillfully portrayed by Gian Maria Volonte, murders his mistress as an exercise in testing police procedures, leaking clues and setting traps in motion for his dim-witted subordinates, playing out a cerebral cat-and-mouse game of his own devision. Petri is most interested in the mechanics and misuse of power and to what extent position and power can protect the guilty. A political allegory treated with Kafkaesque realism, *Investigation* bears homage to Hitchcock (and particularly to *Psycho)* with its Bernard Herrmannesque score (by the great Ennio Moricone), receding stairway, and blood spiralling down the shower floor. Never released on video.

Il giardino dei Finzi-Contini (*The Garden of the Finzi-Continis*) - Italy, 1971

Directed by Vittorio De Sica, screenplay by Cesare Zavattini. After a series of lackluster feature films, De Sica returns in strong form with this story of unrequited love set against a backdrop of impending doom. In 1938, an upper-class Jewish family segregate themselves at their palatial estate as Fascism takes hold of the small town of Ferrara, Italy. Fine performances from Dominique Sanda, Helmut Berger and Lino Capolicchio and lush cinematography by Ennio Guarnieri create a visually rich and powerful drama as this dream-like world inside the garden wall is threatened by the outside Nazi storm. As human rights are systematically stripped away from Jews living in the town, color is used to reflect the rising persecution, opening with brilliant tennis whites and evening gowns of ecru and eventually going to black once the family's fate is sealed. Music is by De Sica's son, Manuel. **S00480. $99.99.**

Le charme discret de la bourgeoisie (*The Discreet Charm of the Bourgeoisie*) - France, 1972

Directed by Luis Buñuel, screenplay by Buñuel and Jean-Claude Carriere. Buñuel's brilliant satire lampoons the church, diplomats, wealthy socialites and radical terrorists and is a pure joy to watch. In this acerbic comedy of manners, six decadent ruling class characters are forever trying to sit down for a meal, but bizarre events—dreams, fantasies, guests, terrorists—interfere. Alternately amusing and repulsive, they get away with murder, dope smuggling and other corruptions in seeming immunity. The protagonists are repeatedly waking, up, revealing preceding scenes to have been dreams. ''The movie is a tease, but Buñuel lets the audience in on the joke'' (Robert Mundy). With Fernando Rey, Delphine Seyrig, Stephance Audran, Bulle Ogier, Jean-Pierre Cassel and Michel Piccoli. **S00345. $24.95.**

La Nuit Americaine (Day for Night) - France, 1973

Directed by Francois Truffaut, screenplay by Truffaut, Jean-Louis Richard and Suzanne Schiffman. French New Wave director Truffaut's undying love for film—and filmmaking—is never more evident than in this story of a film company  (actors, technicians, director) at work. The film-within-a-film framework (which stars Jacqueline Bisset and Truffaut regular Jean-Pierre Leaud) provides many cinematic in-jokes for fans of both Truffaut and movies, in general. The title comes from the process of shooting night time scenes during the day using a special filter. The nonsensical plot of the interior film is really just an excuse to reveal the inner workings of filmmaking: the juggling of egos of temperamental stars, dealing with technical problems, revealing trade "secrets" and various on- and off-screen romances. With music provided by the fabulous Georges Delerue, what *Day for Night* finally presents us with is a giant Valentine to the biggest love affair of Truffaut's life: the movies. **S00308. $59.95.**

Amarcord - Italy, 1974

Directed by Federico Fellini, screenplay by Federico Fellini and Tonino Guerra. Semi-autobiographical reminiscences ("Amarcord" translates to "I Remember") of a small town in Italy in the 1930s gorgeously shot by Giuseppe Rotunno and beautifully scored by  Nino Rota. A visual feast for the eyes, Fellini's dream-like imagery is never better served than in this memoir of his childhood in Rimini at the onset of Fascism. Fellini's observations on school days, politics, family, sex—that is, life itself—are all explored in a series of little stories and episodes and great exaggerated characters. Reality and fantasy blend to create a joyous, exuberant and funny film that touches the youth in us all. **S00042. $39.95. LD75072. $69.95.**

Dersu Uzala - Japan, 1975

Directed by Akira Kurosawa. A group of Russian soldiers, studying the Siberian terrain for the making of topography maps, meet a fiesty Goldi hunter in the forest, who consents to be their guide.This gentle story of the growing friendship and respect between the commanding  officer from the city and the wise but cantankerous hunter, at one with nature, is beautifully told through small gestures and the breathtaking cinematography of their respective worlds. Outstanding performances from both principals, Maksim Munzuk and Yuri Solomon make this simple story one with profound and universal implications. **S01809. $39.95. LD75028. $69.95.**

La Victoire en Chantant (Black and White in Color) - France, 1976

Directed by Jean-Jacques Annaud, screenplay by George Conchon and Jean-Jacques Annaud. Shot and set in Africa's Ivory Coast in 1915, this liberal satire focuses on a small group of French settlers and soldiers, who, upon hearing of the outbreak of World War I, rally the local natives and launch an attack on a nearby German outpost. Colonialism and racism are broadly lampooned in this benign feature. Currently unavailable for sale; available through Facets' rental department only.

La Vie Devant Soi (Madame Rosa) - France, 1977

Directed by Moshe Mizrahi, adapted from the novel by Emile Ajar. Simone Signoret stars as a Holocaust survivor forced into prostitution who befriends and helps raise destitute children of prostitutes, Jews and Arabs, who can no longer provide or care for their children. This conceit serves as an allegory for the Israeli/Arab conflict; a tearjerker with a contrived and sentimental ending that wraps up with the sweet-faced central child being adopted by a fashionable, affluent young couple. **S00794. $24.95.**

Preparez Vos Mouchoirs (Get Out Your Handkerchiefs) - France, 1978

Directed and written by Bertrand Blier. A young and good-looking Gerard Depardieu stars in this amusing sex comedy. When Depardieu's wife (Carole Laure) loses interest in life, he enlists the aid of a stranger (Patrick Dewaere) to seduce her and cure her of her ennui. When she  meets a precocious 13-year-old boy, she becomes his entry into the world of sex and both blossom under her tutelage. **S00494. $59.95.**

Die Blechtrommel (The Tin Drum) - Germany, 1979

Directed by Volker Schlondorff, written by Schlondorff, Jean Claude Carriere, Gunter Grass and Franz Seitz. A hypnotic masterpiece of dazzling exuberance and originality adapted from the 1959 novel by Gunter Grass. The  film is a surreal study of the origins of the German nightmare and the rise of Nazism in violent transition, narrated by a unique hero for our times: Oskar Matzerath (remarkably played by 12-year-old David Bennent), a boy who, disgusted with the hypocritical behavior of adults, decides at three not to grow any more. Though he continues to become older, he remains the same size physically, beating on his favorite toy tin drum in protest and shrieking loud enough to shatter glass and pierce illusions. Recently banned in Oklahoma, the film—like Oskar—hasn't aged a bit and still packs a whallop after almost 20 years. With Angela Winkler as Oskar's mother Angela, Mario Adorf as Oskar's father, Daniel Olbrychski as Oskar's uncle—and possibly his birth father—and French singer Charles Aznavour (*Shoot the Piano Player*) in a moving performance as a Jewish shopkeeper concerned about the welfare of Oskar and his mother. **S01349. $39.95.**

Moskva slezam ne verit (Moscow Does Not Believe in Tears) - Russia, 1980

Directed by Vladimir Menshov, screenplay by Valentin Chernykh. Vladimir Menshov's melodrama about the cruel anonymity of city life is structured in two parts. The first half is set in 1958, as Menshov charts the interlocking romantic fates of  three Russian girls shunned to a workers' dormitory. Tonya (Raisa Ryazanova) finds grace and happiness; Ludmil (Irina Muraveva) tries to conquer the town and fails; Katerina (Vera Alentova) is crudely abandoned when her lover discovers she's pregnant. The second half resumes their stories and lives 20 years later as Tonya is fulfilled in marriage and motherhood; Ludmil winds up trapped in an unhealthy and oppressive marriage; and Katerina graduates from an Institute and becomes director of a large chemical products plant. As a successful career woman, Katerina has earned the respect of her daughter Alexandra, but is unlucky in her private life, until she meets Gosha, a mature man different from the men she has known. Katerina and Gosha's disparate personalities clash constantly, yet the two are permanently attracted to one another, and this is how Katerina eventually finds true happiness. With Alexei Batalov, Alexander Fatiushin and Boris Smorchkov. **S19053. $59.95.**

Mephisto - Hungary, 1981

Directed by Istvan Szabo, screenplay by Peter Dobai, adapted from the novel by Klaus Mann. An actor in Fascist Germany, exuberantly played by Klaus Maria Brandauer, sells out to the Nazis in exchange for the further propellment of his career, including an eventual post as director of the National Theatre. The film is notable for the subtlety and pacing by which Szabo slowly reveals the inner disintegration of the lead character, beginning with his performance of radical theatrical works and avant-garde interpretations to acting and endorsing Aryan or party approved art. His fall includes the betrayal of both Jewish colleagues, dissident friends, and his black mistress and longtime love. Visually often fantastic, particularly so in the grand finale in a dark and empty stadium, as blue-white lights seek out Mephisto and where he will clearly get his due. **S00848. $19.98.**

Volver a Empezar (To Begin Again) - Spain, 1982

Directed by Jose Luis Garci, screenplay by Garci and Angel Llorente. After winning a Nobel Prize, an expatriate author, suffering from a terminal illness, returns to his home town and rekindles an old romance. With deft performances by Antonio Ferrandis and Encarna Paso. Not currently available on video.

Fanny och Alexander (Fanny and Alexander) - Sweden, 1983

Written and directed by Ingmar Berman. A kind of Swedish *Amarcord, Fanny and Alexander* is a nostalgic tribute to the highlights of Bergman's childhood and to a bygone world. Part comedy, part ghost story, this magical film is set in a rural Swedish university town in 1907 and tells the story of a year in the lives of the colorful theatrical upper-middle-class family, the Eckdahls: the widowed matriarch, Helena (Gunn Wallgren), her three sons and their wives, and two of the grandchildren, Fanny and Alexander (Bertil Guve and Pernilla Allwin). When young Fanny and Alexander's father dies, their mother, Emilie (Ewa Froling), marries the town bishop (Jan Malmsjo) in the hope that his ascetic piety will provide a firm foundation for her and her children. But the bishop and his relatives turn out to be monsters who create a nightmare for Emilie and her children. Reminiscent of Shakespeare's *Hamlet* and *The Tempest, Fanny and Alexander* is a fervent recommitment to art itself; a lush, sprawling, glowing work, running over three hours—every minute a cinematic gem. Not currently available on video.

La Diagonale du fou (Dangerous Moves) - Switzerland, 1984

Written and directed by Richard Dembo. In his absorbing first feature, Dembo captures the obsession of two world chess champions: Akiva Liebskind (Michel Piccoli), an aging Jewish master with heart trouble, representing the Soviet Union, and his former student, a young, hot-headed defector to the West, Pavius Fromm (Alexander Arbatt, a real-life defector himself), as they prepare for and compete in a world chess match in Geneva. Suggested by real-life tournaments between champion Anatoly Karpov

and Soviet defector Viktor Korchnoi, it's a classic sports confrontation, reminiscent of *The Hustler* and *The Cincinnati Kid*, brimming with tension, emotion, and political intrigue. With Leslie Caron as Liebskind's long-suffering, zealously loyal wife, and a scene-stealing performance by the ageless Liv Ullmann as Fromm's estranged wife and former prisoner in a Russian mental hospital. Not currently available on video.

La Historia Oficial (The Official Story) - Argentina, 1985

Directed by Luis Puenzo, screenplay by Puenzo and Aida Bortnik. Puenzo's powerful Argentinean first feature caused a stir in many countries after its international premiere at Cannes, with its grim theme of political repression and execution. Set in Argentina in 1983 after the country's defeat in the Falklands, it is the true story of Alicia, a high school history teacher, her husband, Roberto, a successful entrepreneur (portrayed beautifully by Norma Aleandro and Hector Alterio) and their daughter, Gaby (Analia Castro), whom the couple adopted as an infant five years earlier. When Alicia is reunited with her friend Ana (Chunchuna Villafane), who has just returned from political exile, her friend's depiction of her 36 days in prison causes Alicia to suspect that Gaby may be a *desaparecido*, one of the many Argentinean children separated from their parents as they are detained or tortured and given away. Alicia's obsessive search for the child's true identity becomes a journey of self-discovery revealing the horrors of the military dictatorship in Argentina. **S00949. $19.98.**

De Aanslag (The Assault) - Netherlands, 1986

Directed by Fons Rademakers, screenplay by Gerard Soeteman, based on the novel by Harry Mulisch. In the final days of World War II in Nazi-occupied Holland, a Dutch collaborator is killed in the street by partisans. Shadowy figures drag the body in front of the house where 12-year-old Anton Steenwijk (Derek de Lint) lives. The house is then set on fire, and Anton's father, mother and brother are then taken away by Nazis and killed, leaving young Anton the only survivor. Anton goes on with his life, attends college, marries, has a child, and becomes successful in his profession, but the memory of that terrible night haunts him until he uncovers and faces the truth about what really happened. Like a fictional footnote to *Shoah, The Assault* is also like Kurosawa's *Rashomon* in its ability to look at the same crime from many different viewpoints and discover different versions of the truth. **S03573. $79.95.**

Babettes gæstebud (Babette's Feast) - Denmark, 1987

Written and directed by Gabriel Axel, based on the short story by Karen Blixen (Isak Dinesen). A metaphoric fable of haute cuisine as art. Set in a desolate, 19th-century village on a Danish coast, this visual and epicurean feast stars Stephane Audran as Babette, an exiled French cook-housekeeper employed—without wages—for a pair of elderly, devoutly religious, yet obliviously self-serving, Danish sisters. When Babette wins a lottery, she asks to prepare a Gallic feast for the women on the 100th birthday of the town's long-dead minister. She then produces a staggering spread of sybarite proportions, yet the two pious sisters and their guests will not admit the sensual pleasure of the meal, fearing they have sinned. And so they admit nothing of what they feel, without as usual, a word of praise to Babette. Babette, however, is fulfilled in her art, and the sisters too, are spiritually renewed. **S08497. $19.98.**

Pelle Erobreren (Pelle the Conqueror) - Denmark, 1988

Directed by Bille August, screenplay by Bille August. *Pelle the Conqueror* is the epic telling of an aging and ineffectual Swedish widower (in a wonderful performance by Max Von Sydow) and his young son, Pelle, who emigrate to Denmark to find a better life. Upon arrival, they are put to work as stable hands on a farm governed by a sadistic manager and cruel trainer and owned by a philandering husband and his sad, alcoholic wife. In a triumph of the human spirit, Pelle survives the belittling, beatings and under-nourishment and sets out on his own for America to "conquer the world." Beautifully shot by veteran cinematographer Jorgen Persson (*Elvira Madigan*), the soft, pastoral look of the film, making beautiful the grey and icy white Danish winters and luminous spring, is a visual feast and serves as a contrast to the unblinking, bleak reality of their Dickensian lives. Winner of the Palme d'Or at Cannes. Currently unavailable for sale; available through Facets' rental department only.

Cinema Paradiso - Italy, 1989

Directed by Giuseppe Tornatore, screenplay by Tornatore and Peter Fernandea. An affectionate salute to the magic of the movies and the individuals who spend their lives in the projection booth. Philippe Noiret stars as Alfredo, the projectionist for a small Sicilian village movie palace, who opens up new worlds for Toto (amazingly portrayed by non-professional Salvatore Cascio), an inquisitive child who divides his spare time between the church as an altar boy and the cinema. But it is really the projection booth that fascinates Toto, and its magician, the surly but gentle Alfredo. Although Alfredo tries to chase the child away from the dangerous booth, Toto never leaves his side. When the theater catches fire, Alfredo loses his sight in the accident. As Toto grows older he becomes the only projectionist of the new cinema, and it is Alfredo who is now at his side, guiding and endouraging the younger projectionist. With Jaques Perrin, Pupella Maggio and Marco Leonardi. **S12609. $19.98.**

Reise der Hoffnung (Journey of Hope) - Switzerland, 1990

Directed by Xavier Koller, screenplay by Oller and Feride Cicekoglu. The story of a poor Kurdish family who travel from Turkey by every means possible (train, boat, car, van, and lastly on foot through freezing conditions across the Alps) to arrive at a better life in Switzerland. Selling off their goods, leaving all but one child behind, the mother and father pay every last cent to exploitive Turks ready to make the fast buck. They are apprehended at the border as illegal immigrants, losing more than just money and illusions along the way. Ably acted with a winning performance by Emin Sivas as Mehmet Ali, the six-year-old son with the big eyes and bigger heart. Award-winning cinematographer Elemer Ragalyi does a capable job with the camera work, including capturing the deadly, dark cold faced by the straggly, ill-prepared Turks as they hide half-caught in the icy, snow-blown cliffs. Within their line of view, as they sit huddled tightly to ward off the freeze, they can see and almost feel, so near, the inviting warmth of the border office and the certain arrest that that sanctuary holds. **S15418. $19.98. LD75210. $34.98.**

Mediterraneo - Italy, 1991

Directed by Gabriele Salvatores, screenplay by Enzo Monteleone, a small group of eight Italian soldiers, sent to garrison a Greek island during WWII, find themselves progressively less enchanted with fulfilling their patriotic duty and more interested in revelling in the joys of life on this idyllic island. With their boat out of commission and their radio broken, they settle into a pleasant life of painting, dancing,

eating, enjoying women and warm weather. A bittersweet commentary on war and peace with an emphasis on making time during this life for the things that matter, the film charms with colorful, quirky characters, spectacularly beautiful views of the Mediterranean, and a contagious joie de vivre. Stressing the commonalities between the Greeks and the Italians ("one race, one face"), and therefore, all humanity, the film is sweetly dedicated to "all who wish to run away." **S18159. $19.98.**

Indochine - France, 1992

Directed by Regis Wargnier, screenplay by Catherine Cohen, Louis Gardel, Erik Orsenna and Wargnier. Regis Wargnier's stylish epic spans the history of the French occupation of Southeast Asia from the early stirrings of revolution in the 1930s to the loss of the colony in 1954. The story revolves around the relationship between the cooly imperial, proudly passionate Eliane (in an Oscar-nominated fire-and-ice performance by Catherine Deneuve), a French rubber plantation owner, and Camille (Linh Dan Pham) her adopted Vietnamese daughter. The close bond between mother and daughter is tested at first by their passion for the same dashing French naval officer (Vincent Perez), then by the forces of history, as Camille, swept up in the revolution, endures a perilous trek across her war-torn nation and becomes a folk heroine to the Communist insurgents. The film shrewdly balances traditional romance and action with enhanced historical accuracy and updated political attitudes, punctuated by a series of stunningly photographed set pieces. **S20220. $19.95. LD72330. $39.95.**

Belle Epoque (The Age of Beauty) - Spain, 1993

Directed by Fernando Trueba, screenplay by Rafael Azcona. Cute, romantic story of a young army deserter's coming-of-age in 1930s Spain. When he is invited to hide at a farmhouse of an artist, he is delighted to find it comes equipped with four daughters, each more beautiful than the next . In a turn-about in the game of the sexes, he is seduced by each girl, falling in love with them all. This charming fantasy also features lovely scenery, top-notch acting from all of the principals and a delightful cameo by Carmen Ramirez as the beloved matriarch with a penchant for operatic singing and a besotted, compliant lover. **S22768. $19.95. LD74619. $34.95.**

Outomilonnye Solntsem (Burnt by the Sun) - Russia, 1994

Directed by Nikita Mikhalkov, screenplay by Nikita Mikhalkov and Rustam Ibragimbekov. With humor and beauty, Mikhalkov tells the story of a Bolshevic Revolution hero named Sergei (Mikhalkov), his wife and charming seven-year-old daughter (Mikhalkov's real-life daughter) who spend their lives in an idyllic countryside home surrounded by friends and extended family. This bucolic, pastoral setting is disrupted with the arrival of an old friend and, as it turns out, lover) of the wife. Now working for Stalin's secret police, it becomes clear that he is a threat both emotionally and physically, and that under his cheery, innocent veneer lies a plan to destroy the charismatic leader and consequently, the family. Winner of the Grand Jury Prize at Cannes, this lyrical film is cinematically lovely with consistently good performances throughout, not the least of which is by Mikhalkov's delightful young daughter, Nadya. **S26809. $19.98. LD75391. $39.95.**

Antonia (Antonia's Line) - Netherlands, 1995

Directed and written by Marleen Gorris. *Antonia's Line* tells its story through the remembrances of an old lady who, now ready to die, looks back on her colorful and eventful life. Beginning with her return to her home town following WWII, it is a chronicle of birth, life, and death. The family lineage referred to is four generations of fiercely independent

women, including Antonia herself, her daughter, granddaughter and finally, great granddaughter. Called a feminist film (only in the sense that all of the women are strong and self-reliant), it is certainly told from a feminine perspective, with Antonia providing an open environment on her farm for the misfits and misbegotten of the neighboring village. The women are allowed to live as they wish, breaking out of traditional roles as mothers or wives for their own fulfillment and for the enrichment of all the lives they touch. **S29956. $19.98. LD75969. $39.99.**

Kolya - Czech Republic, 1996

Directed by Jan Sverak, written by Zdenak Sverak and Pavel Taussig. In this charmer of a film, Zdenek Sverak stars as Frantisek Louka, a confirmed, set-in-his-ways, womanizing middle-aged bachelor, who has lost his job with the highly regarded Czech Philharmonic Orchestra because of his outspokenness, and is now reduced to playing at funerals. Louka's life is turned upside down when he reluctantly agrees to marry a young Russian woman (for a price) so she can get her Czech papers and leave the the Soviet Union. The woman leaves Louka for her lover in Germany, abandoning her six-year-old son, Kolya (Andrej Chalimon) in Prague. Louka is trapped and tries to dump the tiny Russian invader, but slowly becomes attached to Kolya as he comes to realize the boy fills a void in his life he never knew existed. A ''gem of a film'' (*The New York Times*) as heartwarming as it is political. **S31824. $103.99.**

Karakter (*Character*) - Netherlands, 1997

Directed by Mike van Diem, written by van Diem, Ferdinand Bordewijk, Laurens Geels, and Ruud van Megen. Based on the novel by Ferdinand Bordewijk, *Character* is a raw and robust movie about the struggle between father and son and impossible love. J.W. Katadreuffe (Fedja van Huet) is the son of Joba Katadreuffe, the housekeeper (Betty Schuurman) of his father, bailiff A.B. Dreverhaven (Jan Decleir). Though the stubborn and prideful Joba ignores Dreverhaven's marriage proposals and completely neglects Katadreuffe, Dreverhaven ensures the successfull career of his son. At 30, Katadreuffe becomes a lawyer and tells his father that he doesn't want to have anything to do with him. When Katadreuffe gets in financial trouble, the creditor happens to be his father, who tries to strangle his son financially. When the police find the body of Dreverhaven after a fight between the father and son,in bits and pieces Katadreuffe tells the history of their volatile relationship. Not currently available on video.

Kolya

Cannes Film Festival Palme d'Or Winners

1997

Taste of the Cherry (tie)
Currently unavailable on video.
Abbas Kiarostami, Iran, 1997

The Eel (tie)
Currently unavailable on video.
Shohei Imamura, Japan, 1997

1996

Secrets and Lies
Mike Leigh's heartwarming comedy of a young black woman (Marianne Jean-Baptiste) searching for her natural birth mother only to discover that her mom (the magnificent Brenda Blethyn) is white, makes for a film with "rare heart and soul" (Janet Maslin, *The New York Times*), from Britain's master of improvisational, working-class social comedies. With Timothy Spall. Winner of the Palm d'Or at Cannes Film Festival.
   VHS: S31027. $103.99.
   Laser: LD76141. $39.98.
Mike Leigh, Great Britain, 1996, 114 mins.

1995

Underground
Kusturica's controversial, Cannes Film Festival Award-winning, unreleased feature; a mythical history of the former Yugoslavia. Serbian with English subtitles. Coming soon to video.
Emir Kusturica, France/Germany/Hungary, 1995, 192 mins.

1994

Pulp Fiction
John Travolta, Uma Thurman, Samuel Jackson, Bruce Willis, Harvey Keitel and Rosanna Arquette are all part of the stellar cast of this highly acclaimed film. Two hit men encounter a bizarre series of adventures in a seamy L.A. world of criminals and kooks. The Academy Award-winning screenplay by Quentin Tarantino can't be beat. Letterboxed.
   VHS: S26211. $19.95.
   Laser: CLV, THX. LD75062. $39.99.
Quentin Tarantino, USA, 1994, 154 mins.

1993

Farewell My Concubine (tie)
This complex story of passion and political intrigue won the Best Film Award at Cannes and is an ambitious historical epic of China in the 20th century. It follows the enduring friendship between two opera stars in old Beijing. As they prosper, the political upheavals of war and revolution take their toll. When a young prostitute threatens their professional and personal union, it becomes just one of many trials which test the enduring strength of art and love that bind these two men.
   VHS: S20736. $19.95.
   Laser: LD74457. $39.99.
Chen Kaige, China, 1993, 157 mins.

The Piano (tie)
Holly Hunter's Oscar-winning performance as a mute woman dedicated to her music takes center stage in this lush drama set in 19th century New Zealand. Harvey Keitel co-stars as the brutish but sensitive man who gives her back what seemed irrevocably lost. A young Anna Paquin more than holds her own with a performance that garnered this new star an Oscar for Best Supporting Actress.
   VHS: S20871. $19.98.
Jane Campion, Australia/New Zealand, 1993, 121 mins.

1992

The Best Intentions
Danish filmmaker Bille August (*Pelle the Conquerer*) directs Ingmar Bergman's autobiographical screenplay about the early courtship, marriage and discord of Bergman's parents. Set between 1909 and 1918, *The Best Intentions* follows Henrik Bergman (Samuel Froler), an emotionally neutral Lutheran pastor, and the vivacious Anna Akerblom (Pernilla August). August and Bergman beautifully delineate the conflicts that arise between Henrik's spartan lifestyle and Anna's demands for possessions. Winner of the 1992 Palme d'Or at the Cannes Film festival. Pernilla August won the Best Actress award. Cinematography by Jorgen Persson. With Max von Sydow, Ghita Norby and Lennart Hjulstrom. Swedish with English subtitles.
   VHS: S19019. $29.98.
Bille August, Sweden/Denmark, 1992, 182 mins.

1991

Barton Fink
An inside look in the average life of a Hollywood screenwriter as interpreted by the brothers Coen. John Turturro and John Goodman star as fellow residents of the Hotel Earle, a very quiet California hotel where the most unusual things happen. Set in 1941, this truly bizarre and scathing period drama won three major awards at the Cannes Film Festival. With Judy Davis, Jon Polito, John Mahoney and Michael Lerner as studio boss Jack Lipnick. Have you got that Barton Fink feeling?
   VHS: S15450. $19.98.
   Laser: Letterboxed. LD76152. $39.98.
Joel Coen, USA, 1991, 116 minutes.

1990

Wild at Heart
Based on Barry Gifford's novel about two southern lovers on the run, this film is director David Lynch's (*Blue Velvet, Eraserhead*) campiest feature to date. Despite the loopy subtext of references (mostly to Elvis and *The Wizard of Oz*), Lynch manages to present some powerful visual compositions here and gets all-out performances from stars Nicolas Cage and Laura Dern. Also starring Willem Dafoe, Crispin Glover, Diane Ladd, Isabella Rossellini and Harry Dean Stanton. Winner of the Cannes Film Festival's 1990 Palme d'Or.
VHS: S13515. $19.98.
Laser: LD71210. $49.95.
David Lynch, USA, 1990, 125 mins.

1989

sex, lies and videotape
When an old college buddy drops into the lives of a Louisiana yuppie couple, the bonds of matrimony begin to fray. Steve Soderbergh's accomplished feature film debut scored a big win at Cannes and really annoyed Spike Lee. James Spader also won a Best Actor Award at Cannes for his role as the soft-spoken, sensitive visitor. With Peter Gallagher and Andie MacDowell as the former perfect couple and Laura San Giacomo as the lusty sister-in-law.
VHS: S11693. $19.95.
Laser: CAV. LD70456. $124.95.
Laser: CLV. LD70457. $134.98.
Steven Soderbergh, USA, 1989, 100 mins.

1988

Pelle the Conqueror
Winner of the Cannes Festival Palme d'Or and the Academy Award for Best Foreign Picture, Bille August's moving film features a remarkable performance by Max von Sydow as the Swedish father who takes his son Pelle to Denmark in search of a new life. In the harsh milieu of the Danish farm, Pelle is inspired by the dreams of those around him, but realising that his father cannot help him fulfill his dream, Pelle sets off for a life of adventure—to conquer the world. Danish with English subtitles. Currently unavailable on video.
VHS: S09289.
Bille August, Denmark, 1988, 138 mins.

1987

Under the Sun of Satan
A work of great subtlety and tremendous assurance, the film stars Depardieu in his perhaps most astonishing performance, as a tortured country priest who feels unworthy of God's love. Depardieu's priest encounters the young and beautiful Mouchette, played by Sandrine Bonnaire, who lives in the same town and is a murderess who unwittingly shapes the priest's life. A brilliant new film from one of France's most uncompromising directors. French with English subtitles.
VHS: S10868. $29.95.
Maurice Pialat, France, 1987, 101 mins.

1986

Mission
Two renegade Jesuit priests force the ruling European landowners to climb up a very tall mountain and massacre innocent South American indians. Robert De Niro and Jeremy Irons star in this beautifully photographed, historical drama. With Aidan Quinn.
VHS: S04306. $19.98.
Laser: Letterboxed. LD71201. $39.98.
Roland Joffe, USA, 1986, 126 mins.

1985

When Father Was Away on Business
Kusturica's Cannes award-winning film is a magical portrait of a boy's coming of age in '50s Yugoslavia. As little Malik takes up sleepwalking and experiences his first love, the family knows the real "business" Father is conducting—in a labor camp for his unrepentant Stalinist leanings and his philandering. Serbo-Croatian with English subtitles.
VHS: S15547. $19.98.
Laser: CAV. LD72198. $49.95.
Emir Kusturica, Yugoslavia, 1985, 144 mins.

1984

Paris, Texas
A film by German director Wim Wenders, written by Sam Shepard, photography by Robby Muller, music by Ry Cooder and starring Harry Dean Stanton and Nastassia Kinski! A contemporary story of a man's journey, actual and psychological, to recover his past.
VHS: S00993. $19.98.
Wim Wenders, USA, 1984, 145 mins.

1983

The Ballad of Narayama
Winner of the Grand Prize at the 1983 Cannes Film Festival, *The Ballad of Narayama* is based on one of the most astonishing of all Japanese legends. A century ago in a remote mountain village, local custom dictated that when a person reached 70 years of age, he was taken to Mount Narayama to die. A brilliant film from director Imamura that delivers a vigorous and beautiful affirmation of family, life and death. "A masterpiece of Japanese Cinema to stand beside *Ugetsu, Tokyo Story*, or *The Seven Samurai*" (M. Wilmington *LA Weekly*). Japanese with English subtitles.
VHS: S14498. $29.95.
Shohei Imamura, Japan, 1983, 129 mins.

1982

Missing (tie)
Jack Lemmon, Sissy Spacek and John Shea star in Costa-Gavras' political thriller based on the true story of Charles Horman, an American writer who disappears and is killed during the overthrow of Allende's government in Chile. Lemmon is the concerned father whose attempts to learn the truth are stonewalled by bureaucracy and cover-up. English dialog.
VHS: S00862. $24.95.
Costa-Gavras, USA, 1983, 122 mins.

Yol (tie)
Winner at the Cannes Film Festival, a powerful film about five Kurdish prisoners given a week's leave to visit their villages; *Yol* is based on personal experiences of the filmmaker, and is a film about political, religious and sexual oppression. Turkish with English subtitles.
VHS: S01490. $19.95.
Yilmaz Guney, Turkey, 1983, 115 mins.

1981

Man of Iron
Made in the center of political events surrounding it, Andrzej Wajda's *Man of Iron* is a powerful sequel to *Man of Marble*. The film merges documentary footage of the Solidarity strike into a fictionalized drama of a disillusioned radio producer (Marian Opania) who is ordered to Gdansk to undermine the reputation of one of the leaders of the worker revolt. "An urgent, nervy narrative conveys all the exhilaration and bewilderment of finding oneself on the very crestline of crucial historical change" (*Time Out*). With Jerzy Radziwilowicz, Krystyna Janda, Irena Byrska and Wieslawa Kosmalska. Winner of the

Palme d'Or, 1981 Cannes Film festival. Polish with
English subtitles.
VHS: S20403. $19.98.
Laser: LD76328. $49.95.
Andrzej Wajda, Poland, 1981, 152 mins.

1980

All That Jazz (tie)
Bob Fosse casts Roy Scheider as basically himself in
this semi-autobiographical musical extravaganza.
He's a talented director-choreographer who loves
show business, cigarettes and too many other women
to keep his marriage intact. With Ann Reinking, Ben
Vereen, Leland Palmer and Jessica Lange as the
Angel of Death. A prophetic and dazzling film.
VHS: S07558. $19.98.
Bob Fosse, USA, 1979, 123 mins.

Kagemusha (tie)
A masterpiece. Set in 1531 Japan torn by civil strife,
Kagemusha deals with a mighty Japanese warlord and
his commoner look-alike who, after the warlord's
death, is used to keep his clan together. Tatsuya
Nakadai is superb in the dual role of the war lord and
his double, both caught up in the swirl of history as
the mighty powers clash in fierce battles and political
intrigue. Winner of the Grand Prize at Cannes.
Japanese with English subtitles.
VHS: S00668. $29.98.
Laser: CLV. LD72114. $69.98.
Akira Kurosawa, Japan, 1980, 159 mins.

1979

Apocalypse Now (tie)
Francis Ford Coppola's Vietnam War epic conveys a
madness with parallels to Joseph Conrad's *Heart of
Darkness*. Lieutenant Willard receives orders to seek
out a renegade military outpost led by errant officer
Colonel Kurtz, and to "terminate his command with
extreme prejudice." This newly enhanced version
features a remastered soundtrack in Dolby surround
stereo.
VHS: S00066. $29.95.
Francis F. Coppola, USA, 1979, 153 mins.

The Tin Drum (tie)
The 1979 Academy Award winner for Best Foreign
Film. *The Tin Drum* is a masterpiece of dazzling
exuberance and originality adapted from the novel by
Gunter Grass. The film is a stunning parable of
modern society in violent transition narrated by a
unique hero for our times—Oskar, a boy who decides
at three not to grow any older. Letterboxed. German
with English subtitles.
VHS: S01349. $39.95.
Laser: LD76415. $69.99.
Volker Schlondorff, Germany, 1979, 142 min.

1978

Tree of the Wooden Clogs
A passionate, moving film, an epic celebration of an
Italian family's indomitable spirit, winner of the
Grand Prize at the 1978 Cannes Film Festival. The
subject of the film is peasant life in northern Italy at
the turn of the century, focusing on about a year in
the life of three families living on a feudal estate. "A
quiet masterpiece" (*Newsweek*). The movie, which
runs slightly more than three hours, is an
accumulation of dozens of experiences of children,
adults, old people, village idiots, of harvest times and
plantings, of moments of boredom and jealousy,
celebrations, fatigue, brief pleasures and mysterious
ones. It moves so effortlessly, often with great humor
and always with compassion, it seems much shorter
than most 90-minute films" (Vincent Canby, *New
York Times*). Italian with English subtitles.
VHS: S12946. $19.98.
Ermanno Olmi, Italy, 1978, 185 mins.

1977

Padre Padrone
A shepherd boy from the backwaters of Sardinia
molds himself into a linguistic scholar. This simple
tale forms the foundation of one of the most
important recent Italian films—a major statement on
the third-world cycle of poverty. Using non-actors for
its cast, the film won universal acclaim and the Grand
Prize at the Cannes Film Festival. Italian with
English subtitles.
VHS: S00986. $59.95.
**Paolo Taviani/Vittorio Taviani, Italy, 1977, 117
mins.**

1976

Taxi Driver
Scorsese's now-classic film with Robert De Niro as
the psychotic cabbie driven to violence in an attempt
to "rescue" a teenage prostitute (Jodie Foster). With
Albert Brooks, Harvey Keitel, Leonard Harris, Peter
Boyle and Cybill Shepherd.
DVD: DV60027. $24.95.
VHS: S01303. $14.95.
Laser: CAV, widescreen. LD70470. $99.95.
Laser: CLV, widescreen. LD70471. $49.95.
Martin Scorsese, USA, 1976, 114 mins.

1975

Chronicle of the Burning Years
Currently unavailable on video.
Mohammed Hamina, Algeria, 1975

1974

The Conversation
Gene Hackman is brilliant as Harry Caul, the
surveillance man who becomes the object of
surveillance himself. Coppola's great achievement is
in evoking an obsessive sense of paranoia as
Hackman struggles to free himself from the maze of
secrecy and murder. With Cindy Williams, Harrison
Ford, Frederic Forrest.
VHS: S00267. $19.95.
Laser: LD75356. $29.98.
Francis F. Coppola, USA, 1974, 113 mins.

1973

The Hireling (tie)
Currently unavailable on video.
Alan Bridges, Great Britain, 1973

Scarecrow (tie)
Gene Hackman and Al Pacino star as a pair of drifters
on the run from impossible dreams and ex-wives.
From the director of *Panic in Needle Park*, Jerry
Schatzberg, this is an oddball drama about friendship
and survival. With Eileen Brennan, Ann Wedgeworth,
Dorothy Tristan and Richard Lynch as a prison bully.
Terrific photography by Vilmos Zsigmond.
VHS: S08720. $19.98.
Jerry Schatzberg, USA, 1973, 115 mins.

1972

The Mattei Affair (tie)
Currently unavailable on video.
Francesco Rosi, Italy, 1972

The Working Class Goes to Heaven (tie)
Currently unavailable on video.
Elio Petri, Italy, 1972

1971

The Go-Between
Joseph Losey's tense, sexual class drama based on a
brilliant script by Harold Pinter. Julie Christie is the
upper-class beauty whose passionate, illicit affair
with the groundskeeper (Alan Bates) is orchestrated
through notes carried by a young boy, the go-
between. The film, told largely in flashback through
the boy's eyes, is full of nuance and innuendo; a
brilliant dissection of sex and class.
VHS: S27183. $19.95.
Joseph Losey, Great Britain, 1971, 118 mins.

1970

M*A*S*H
Donald Sutherland, Elliott Gould and Robert Duvall in the original, superb, classic dark comedy directed with verve by Robert Altman, juxtaposing the horrors of war with the resiliency of the human spirit. Written by Ring Lardner, Jr.
VHS: S02643. $14.98.
Laser: Letterboxed. LD76743. $24.98.
Robert Altman, USA, 1970, 116 mins.

1969

If...
A sometimes shocking portrait of life in a repressive English boarding school. Three non-conforming senior schoolboys revolt against practically everything. Anderson skillfully employs both professional and non-professional actors in building to a shattering, violent climax.
VHS: S00606. $49.95.
Laser: LD75354. $29.98.
Lindsay Anderson, Great Britain, 1969, 111 mins.

1968

Festival interrompu à cause de l'actualité politique

1967

Blow-Up
The classic film questioning the relationship between image and reality; David Hemmings plays a fashion photographer who photographs a woman (Vanessa Redgrave) in a park and later comes to believe that he has actually photographed a murder. Through the photograph, Hemmings is lured out of his life to search for the truth. English dialog.
VHS: S00152. $19.98.
Laser: CAV, widescreen, 2 discs, Criterion. LD70351. $79.95.
Laser: Extended play, chapter search, MGM. LD70528. $34.98.
Michelangelo Antonioni, Great Britain, 1966, 111 mins.

1966

The Birds, The Bees and the Italians (tie)
Currently unavailable on video.
Pietro Germi, Italy, 1966

A Man and a Woman (tie)
The 1966 Academy Award winner, a legendary love story starring Jean-Louis Trintignant as a race car driver who falls in love with Anouk Aimee. Stylish, well-acted and visually dynamic. Available only in a dubbed version.
VHS: S02322. $19.98.
Claude Lelouch, France, 1966, 103 mins.

1965

The Knack...and How to Get It
Richard Lester's chic film set in swinging 60s London about three men (Michael Crawford, Ray Brooks and Donal Donnelly) who occupy the same London house, and a beautiful country girl (Rita Tushingham) who moves in with them. Sexual hijinks abound as the three angle to seduce women, with the charismatic Brooks in the lead as a master of killer charm.
VHS: S20400. $19.98.
Laser: LD76359. $39.99.
Richard Lester, Great Britain, 1965, 84 mins.

1964

The Umbrellas of Cherbourg
Catherine Deneuve stars in this sumptuously photographed romantic musical of two lovers who are split up by the Algerian war. The girl marries another when she discovers she is pregnant. He also marries; yet they meet again. All dialog is sung; with haunting music by Michel LeGrand and lyrics by Demy, including the song, "I Will Wait for You." "A masterpiece! More beautiful and more startling than ever!" (*New York Daily News*). "The kind of movie that audiences will remember all their lives" (*Chicago Tribune*).
DVD: DV60126. $29.98.
VHS: S30735. $29.95.
Laser: Widescreen. LD76164. $49.98.
Jacques Demy, France/Germany, 1964, 92 mins.

1963

The Leopard (Il Gattopardo)
Currently unavailable on video.
Luchino Visconti, Italy, 1963

1962

The Given Word
Currently unavailable on video.
Anselmo Duarte, Brazil, 1962

1961

Such a Long Absence (tie)
Currently unavailable on video.
Henri Copli, France, 1961

Viridiana (tie)
Bunuel's outrageous and devastating attack on religion and society. Viridiana, about to take her vows as a nun, takes to the pure Christian life by organizing a haven for a blind man, leper, cripple and beggar. Full of Freudian symbolism, the film ends in a famous orgy of destruction, containing Bunuel's blasphemous scene of the Last Supper. The film that got Bunuel kicked out of Spain. Spanish with English subtitles.
VHS: S01419. $29.95.
Luis Bunuel, Spain, 1961, 90 mins.

1960

La Dolce Vita
"A landmark of cinematic social comment," wrote one critic about Fellini's journey through a decadent Rome. Banned by the Church in many countries, the sensationalism of the film often obscured its serious intent. *La Dolce Vita* follows a society journalist (Marcello Mastroianni) through a nightmarish world in which emotions have been destroyed by surface realities, moral conventions and unresolved guilt. With Anita Ekberg, Anouk Aimee, Alain Cuny and Nadia Gray. Italian with English subtitles.
VHS: S00705. $24.95.
Federico Fellini, Italy, 1960, 174 mins.

1959

Black Orpheus
Marcel Camus' quintessential love story based on the Greek myth of Orpheus and Eurydice is set against the vivid backdrop of carnival in Rio de Janeiro. Orpheus, the streetcar conductor, falls hopelessly in love with Eurydice; winner of the Grand Prize at Cannes as well as an Oscar for Best Foreign Film. Portuguese with English subtitles.
VHS: S00138. $29.95.
Laser: LD70346. $79.95.
Marcel Camus, Brazil, 1958, 103 mins.

1958

The Cranes Are Flying

A film that marked a radical opening for Soviet cinema; the lighthearted, romantic, lyrical story of a beautiful young girl (Tatiana Samoilova) caught up in the horrors of war. When her fiance (Alexei Batalov) goes off to war, she marries a man whom she does not love and who raped her, is evacuated to Siberia, and after the war, learns of her fiance's death. But she refuses to believe it and waits for his return. A great international success which won the Grand Prix at Cannes. Russian with English subtitles.
VHS: S17517. $59.95.
Mikhail Kalatozov, USSR, 1957, 94 mins.

1957

Friendly Persuasion

Gary Cooper and Dorothy McGuire are Quakers buffeted by the American Civil War. Their son's decision to fight leads to a religious crisis that tests their individual faith, courage and belief. Currently unavailable on video.
VHS: S03538.
William Wyler, USA, 1956, 138 mins.

1956

The Silent World

Currently unavailable on video.
Louis Malle/Jacques Cousteau, France, 1956

1955

Marty

Ernest Borgnine won a well-deserved Oscar for Best Actor as the shy Bronx butcher who finds love. Academy Awards also went for direction, screenplay and Best Picture. With Betsy Blair, Joe De Santis and Esther Minciotti. From the teleplay by Paddy Chayefsky.
Laser: Chapter Search. Includes original theatrical trailer. **LD71670. $34.98.**
Delbert Mann, USA, 1955, 91 mins.

1954

Gate of Hell

An exquisitely stylized tragedy of a warrior's desire for a married noblewoman told in exotic color. Wonderfully choreographed battle scenes, incredible textures and composition. Story is set in 12th century Japan and based on *Rape of Lucrece*. Japanese with English subtitles.
VHS: S00483. $24.95.
Teinosuke Kinugasa, Japan, 1954

1953

The Wages of Fear

An exercise in terror and suspense, this uncut version stars Yves Montand and Charles Vanel as uncertain comrades—trapped in a South American village—who identify because they are both French and both penniless. Desperate for a job, they agree to drive two trucks filled with nitroglycerine 300 miles over treacherous roads. Basil Wright called this film "the greatest suspense thriller of all time; it is the suspense not of mystery but of Damocles' sword." French with English subtitles.
VHS: S16210. $29.95.
Laser: LD70766. $59.95.
Henri-Georges Clouzot, France, 1953, 148 mins.

1952

Othello (tie)

Orson Welles' 1952 film is one of the most important of his career. Shot over four years and made on the run, the images literally composed inside the director's head, Welles' virtuoso *Othello* unfolds in flashbacks, detailing the Moor's shifting relationships with Iago (Michael MacLiammoir) and his beautiful young wife, Desdemona (Suzanne Cloutier). With Robert Coote, Fay Compton and Michael Laurence. Art direction by Alexander Trauner. The film has undergone a significant restoration, cleaning up the images and digitally re-recording the soundtrack in stereo, with members of the Chicago Symphony Orchestra and Lyric Opera of Chicago. The voices were electronically isolated to improve the fidelity of the soundtrack.
Laser: LD72284. $99.95.
Orson Welles, Italy/France/USA, 1952, 93 mins.

Two Cents Worth of Hope (tie)

Currently unavailable on video.
Renato Castellani, Italy, 1952

1951

Miracle in Milan (tie)

A masterpiece, a key work of Italian neo-realist cinema, a wonderfully inventive and comic film that effectively condemns the inequities that existed for millions of displaced Europeans after World War II. "The rich vein of sly, compassionate humor that Chaplin and Rene Clair used has been tapped by de Sica; the great director has brought up purest gold" (*New York Times*). Grand Award, Cannes Film Festival. Italian with English subtitles.
VHS: S12957. $29.95.
Laser: LD70419. $49.95.
Vittorio de Sica, Italy, 1951, 96 mins.

Miss Julie (tie)

The definitive version of August Strindberg's riveting play concerning social and sexual domination. Miss Julie is a noblewoman who allows her butler to seduce her after her engagement is broken. With Anita Bjork and Anders Henrikson. Swedish with English subtitles. Currently unavailable on video.
VHS: S01720.
Alf Sjoberg, Sweden, 1950, 90 mins.

1950

Pas de festival

1949

The Third Man

Graham Greene wrote the script for Carol Reed's film about an American pulp fiction writer's search for the mysterious and enigmatic war profiteer Harry Lime (a wonderful Orson Welles) in post-war Vienna. The film welds German expressionism, British classicism and American B-movie energy and motion. Anton Karas's haunting zither score is nearly as well known as Welles's extraordinary entrance. With Joseph Cotton, Trevor Howard and Bernard Lee. Awardwinning cinematography by Robert Krasker.
VHS: S01327. $24.95.
Laser: LD71366. $39.95.
Carol Reed, Great Britain, 1949, 104 mins.

Sidewalk Cafe at Cannes

Berlin International Film Festival Golden Bear Awards

1998

Central Station
Never Released on Video

1997

The People vs. Larry Flynt
Based on the true story of the controversial *Hustler* magazine publisher, who was sued by the Religious Right and paralyzed by an unknown assassin's bullet, Forman's film focuses on Flynt's (Woody Harrelson) inadvertent crusade for freedom of the press and on his unconventional marriage to an ex-stripper (Courtney Love, in an award-winning performance). With Edward Norton.
  DVD: DV60137. $24.95.
  VHS: S31292. $19.95.
  Laser: LD76206. $39.95.

Milos Forman, USA, 1996, 130 mins.

1996

Sense and Sensibility
Emma Thompson and Hugh Grant are terrific as the central couple in this Oscar-winning adaptation of the Jane Austen classic. Two sisters fall in love, and their engaging romances play out in completely opposite ways. The settings and costumes are perfect without being overpowering. This film may well be the best adaptation of an Austen novel ever made. VHS letterboxed.
  VHS: S27828. $19.95.
  Laser: LD75582. $39.99.
Ang Lee, Great Britain, 1995, 136 mins.

1995

Fresh Bait
Never Released on Video

1994

In the Name of the Father
Over seven Academy Award nominations testify to the power of this film. Accused of an act of terrorism, a young man finds that not only his whole life is destroyed, but also the lives of those he loves most. From the streets of Belfast to the most hellish British prisons, this film recounts the true story of a man caught in the struggle for Irish independence. With Daniel Day-Lewis and Emma Thompson.
  VHS: S21158. $19.98.
  Laser: LD72420. $39.98.
Jim Sheridan, Great Britain, 1993, 133 mins.

1993

The Wedding Banquet
Ang Lee's surprise hit is a poignant and funny story of the gay Taiwanese yuppie (Winston Chao) who lives with his American lover (Mitchell Lichtenstein) and tries to end his family's endless matchmaking attempts by announcing that he's engaged. His parents unexpectedly fly in to see the bride and turn their son's deception into a complicated affair.
  VHS: S21895. $94.98.
  Laser: LD74593. $39.98.
Ang Lee, USA/Taiwan, 1994, 105 mins.

Women from the Lake of Scented Souls
At the center of this moving intergenerational family drama is an old legend about two girls. They drowned themselves in a local lake and were said to have flown away as beautiful birds. A contemporary entrepreneur succeeds in business despite her drunken, abusive husband. Now she faces the chore of putting another woman into an unhappy arranged marriage because her mentally ill son desires a wife. Can this older, wiser woman prevent another drowning? Co-winner of the Golden Bear at the 1993 Berlin Film Festival. Mandarin with English subtitles.
  VHS: S25832. $89.95.
Xie Fei, China, 1993, 106 mins.

1992

Grand Canyon

Lawrence Kasdan looks at the problems of living in Los Angeles in the '90s and offers a variety of possible alternatives to urban angst. Among them, an uplifting trip to the Grand Canyon. The all-star cast includes Danny Glover, Kevin Kline, Steve Martin, Mary McDonnell, Mary-Louise Parker and Alfre Woodard.
VHS: S16330. $19.98.
Lawrence Kasdan, USA, 1991, 134 mins.

1991

House of Smiles (Italy)

Never Released on Video

1990

Music Box

Winner of the Golden Bear at the Berlin Film Festival, Costa-Gavras' political thriller stars Jessica Lange as a Chicago attorney defending a Hungarian immigrant (Armin Mueller-Stahl) accused of heinous war crimes more than 50 years ago.
VHS: S12213. $19.95.
Costa-Gavras, USA, 1989, 126 mins.

Larks on a String

From director Jiri Menzel (*Closely Watched Trains*) comes a buoyant and lyrical romantic comedy that was banned in Czechoslovakia until the melt-down of the iron curtain in Europe. While serving time for desertion, and taking steps toward re-education, a rag-tag group of workers unite as a young couple in the camp decides to marry. We soon find that even the prison guards can't resist the unlikely romance, as the wedding and on-site honeymoon unfold in a series of hilarious plot twists. With Vaclav Neckar and Jityka Zelenohorska. Czech with yellow English subtitles.
VHS: S15169. $19.98.
Jiri Menzel, Czechoslovakia, 1969, 96 mins.

1989

Rain Man

Four Oscars including Best Picture went to this road movie about two brothers who didn't know the other existed until fate tosses them together. The plot may be very similar to the movie comedy *Twins* starring Danny DeVito and Arnold Schwarzenegger but Tom Cruise and Dustin Hoffman look spiffier in their matching outfits. A sensitive and strongly performed film. VHS letterboxed.
DVD: DV60095. $24.98.
VHS: S09575. $19.98.
Laser: LD70662. $29.98.
Barry Levinson, USA, 1988, 120 mins.

1988

Red Sorghum

A visually spectacular film which is a sweeping modern-day fable. The first part tells of a nervous young bride's arrival at a remote provincial winery and her takeover of the family business when her older husband is mysteriously murdered. The second half is a heroic and harrowing drama focused on the brutality of the Japanese during their occupation of China, and on partisan resistance. "The film's exoticism is palpable, almost intoxicating" (David Edelstein, *The Village Voice*). Mandarin with yellow English subtitles.
VHS: S15392. $79.95.
Zhang Yimou, China, 1987, 91 mins.*

1987

The Theme

Glen Panfilov's daring work was banned by Soviet authorities for eight years. Esenin (Mikhail Ulyanov), a government-approved playwright and functionary, visits his native village for some artistic rejuvenation and falls for a dynamic and brilliant but uncompromising young artist, Sasa (Inna Churikova), who rejects his overtures. Winner of the 1987 Golden Bear winner at the Berlin Film Festival. With Stanislav Lyubshin, Evgeny Vesnik and Sergei Nikonenko. Russian with English subtitles.
VHS: S19054. $59.95.
Gleb Panfilov, Russia, 1979, 98 mins.

1986

Stammheim (Germany)

Never Released on Video

1985

Wetherby

Written and directed by the brilliant playwright David Hare (*Plenty, Pravda*), Vanessa Redgrave stars as a repressed, middle class English professor whose idyllic existence is shattered by the violent and brutal suicide of an uninvited guest. Hare shrewdly and brilliantly uses Redgrave as a metaphor for the psychological and physical tormenting that threatens Britain's national psyche. A powerful work of erotic dislocation, social analysis and character development. With first rate performances from Ian Holm and Judi Dench. No longer available; for rental only.
David Hare, Great Britain, 1985, 118 mins.

Die Frau und der Fremde (Germany)

Never Released on Video

1984

Love Streams

John Cassavetes directs and stars with his wife, Gena Rowlands, in this off-beat story of a brother and sister who attempt to find sanctuary during a difficult period in their lives. An examination of contemporary life in the fast lane. No longer available; for rental only.
John Cassavetes, USA, 1984, 122 mins.

1983

Ascendancy (Great Britain)

Never Released on Video

The Beehive (Spain)

Never Released on Video

1982

Veronika Voss

Inspired by the life story of the popular actress Sybille Schmitz, "the German Greta Garbo," who made movies between 1929 and 1953, was mostly wasted in potboilers, became depressed, turned to drugs, and killed herself in 1955 at the age of 46. An ominous and lurid melodrama, *Veronika Voss* is constructed as a complex compendium of film styles and filmic references, not spelled out in anthological form but integrated, blended, interwoven with the dramatic content. A hauntingly original work. German with English subtitles. No longer available; for rental only.
Rainer W. Fassbinder, Germany, 1982, 105 mins.

1981

Deprisa! Deprisa! (Spain)

Never Released on Video

1980

Heartland

One of the most acclaimed American independent films of recent years, *Heartland* is set in Wyoming

during the 1910's, and is the story of one woman's life—and courage of spirit—on the frontier. Conchata Ferrell and Rip Torn bring powerful, arresting performances to their roles. No longer available; for rental only.
Annick Smith, USA, 1981, 95 mins.

Palermo oder Wolsburg (Germany)
Never Released on Video

1979

David
Awarded the Best Film prize at the Berlin Film Festival, the moving story of a Jewish boy and his family trying to survive in and escape Nazi Germany. German with English subtitles. No longer available; for rental only.
Peter Lilienthal, West Germany, 1979, 101 mins.

1978

The Trout, Max's Words, Ascensor (Spain)
Never Released on Video

1977

The Ascent (USSR)
Never Released on Video

1976

Buffalo Bill and the Indians or Sitting Bull's History Lesson (award declined)
From director Robert Altman comes this uproarious, high-spirited look at "Buffalo Bill" Cody (Paul Newman), the legendary Western adventurer. Although Bill has fought Indians and Civil War battles, nothing can prepare him for his newest challenge: show business. His popular "Wild West Show" features stunt-riders, battle recreations and Annie Oakley (Geraldine Chaplin), the beautiful sharpshooter. But when Bill signs Chief Sitting Bull for a featured role in the show, a hilarious clash of cultures ensues. With Burt Lancaster, Harvey Keitel, Joel Grey and Shelley Duvall.
VHS: S31367. $19.95.
Laser: LD76130. $49.98.
Robert Altman, USA, 1976, 123 mins.

1975

Adoption
The breakthrough film for Marta Meszaros (*Diary for All My Children*, a unique mixture of documentary and fictional techniques in the story of Mary, a middle-aged woman, who befriends the younger Julia, who insists on having her child live with her. A film of considerable psychological insight. Hungarian with English subtitles.
VHS: S04726. $69.95.
Marta Meszaros, Hungary, 1975, 89 mins.

1974

The Apprenticeship of Duddy Kravitz
Richard Dreyfuss stars as an ambitious Canadian Jew determined to become a success at any price. Based on Mordecai Richler's novel, this powerful comic-drama features an equally able supporting cast. With Jack Warden, Denholm Elliott, Joe Silver, Joseph Wiseman and Micheline Lanctot.
VHS: S06341. $19.95.
Ted Kotcheff, Canada, 1974, 121 mins.

1973

Distant Thunder
A moving dramatization of the effects of famine in India during World War II when the government controlled the food supply in order to feed troops, letting common people starve. The film follows the lives of several individuals including a doctor who humbles himself to survive. Bengali with English subtitles.
VHS: S01547. $44.95.
Satyajit Ray, India, 1974, 92 mins.

1972

The Canterbury Tales
A film which fits within the context of Pasolini's explorations of bawdy, historical classics (together with *Arabian Nights* and *Decameron*), Pasolini once again seeks out the exotic and controversial aspect of Chaucer's classic. In English.
VHS: S07821. $79.95.
Pier Paolo Pasolini, Italy, 1971, 109 mins.

1971

The Garden of the Finzi-Continis
Vittorio de Sica's (*The Bicycle Thief, Miracle in Milan*) Academy Award-winning masterpiece is visually restored and remastered in Dolby stereo. Dominique Sanda plays the daughter of a cultured Italian Jewish family of immense wealth, languishing in aristocratic privilege on their estate, oblivious, until the end, to the danger that Fascism poses for their precious world. Italian with English subtitles.
VHS: S00480. $99.99.
Laser: LD71000. $49.95.
Vittorio de Sica, Italy, 1971, 94 mins.

1970

Festival cancelled due to controversy surrounding West German Michael Verhoeven's *O.K.*, which was loosely based on an actual incident involving American servicemen who kidnapped, raped and murdered a South Vietnamese girl.

1969

Early Years (Yugoslavia)
Never Released on Video

1968

Old Dole Dorf (Sweden)
Never Released on Video

1967

Le Depart (Belgium)
Never Released on Video

1966

Cul de Sac
Two failed and wounded gangsters invade the lives of middle-aged milquetoast Donald Pleasance and his nubile young wife (Francoise Dorleac) in Roman Polanski's black comedy. Holding the odd couple hostage, the gangsters become increasingly irrational, and Pleasance is constantly challenged by his wife to take violent action in protest. With superb performances from Jack MacGowran, Lionel Stander, and Jacqueline Bisset. No longer available; for rental only.
Roman Polanski, Great Britain, 1966, 111 mins.

1965

Alphaville
Eddie Constantine is Lemmy Caution, inter-galactic private eye, in this bravura mix of comic strip, science fiction and film noir in what is ultimately a new style of cinema in which form and content are identical. Lemmy sets out to dispose of diabolical scientist Leonard von Braun (a.k.a. Leonard Nosferatu) from Alphaville, the futuristic city run by

an electronic brain, where love has been banished. A film in which poetry mixes freely with pulp to create a new dimension, a new cinematic reality. French with English subtitles.
VHS: S07702. $29.95.
Laser: LD75075. $49.95.
Jean-Luc Godard, France, 1965, 100 mins.

1964

Dry Summer
Never Released on Video

1963

Bushido: Samurai Saga (Japan)
Never Released on Video

1962

A Kind of Loving (Great Britain)
Never Released on Video

1961

La Notte
The second installment of Italian director Michelangelo Antonioni's trilogy. Jeanne Moreau plays a bored, dissatisfied woman who abandons her simple minded husband (Marcello Mastroianni), who in turn attempts to seduce a beautiful, vacant woman (Monica Vitti). Moody, introverted and beautiful, brilliantly photographed by Gianni Di Venanzo. Italian with English subtitles.
VHS: S14850. $39.95.
Michelangelo Antonioni, Italy, 1961, 122 mins.

1960

Lazarillo
This morality tale is set in 17th-century Castile. A fatherless boy is abandoned by his mother and subsequently finds work with a strange succession of employers. A blind beggar, a miserly sacristan, a fake nobleman and even a traveling band of performers all teach him valuable lessons in vanity, cunning, deception and, ultimately, survival. Spanish with English subtitles.
VHS: S21606. $24.95.
Cesar Ardavin, Spain, 1959, 109 mins.

1959

Les Cousins
One of the great Chabrol early films; Charles (Gerard Blain), a student from the provinces, comes to Paris to live with his sophisticated, bullying cousin Paul, falls in love with Florence, but she becomes Paul's mistress. During their examinations, Paul passes effortlessly while Charles fails, and Charles accidentally kills Paul after trying to kill him. An ingenious, brilliant portrayal of student life in Paris, with great cinematography by Henri Decae. French with English subtitles.
VHS: S04906. $79.95.
Claude Chabrol, France, 1958, 110 mins.

1958

Wild Strawberries
One of the great films of Bergman, with Victor Sjostrom as the aged Stockholm professor who recollects his past experiences and becomes aware, for the first time, of his failings and shortcomings. With Bibi Andersson, Ingrid Thulin, Gunnar Bjornstrand. Swedish with English subtitles.
VHS: S01462. $29.95.
Laser: LD70487. $49.95.
Ingmar Bergman, Sweden, 1957, 95 mins.

1957

Twelve Angry Men
A teenage boy is accused of killing his father, and between him and capital punishment stands just one man. A vivid, shocking courtroom drama with a powerful cast including Henry Fonda, Lee J. Cobb, E.G. Marshall and Jack Warden.
VHS: S11432. $29.95.
Laser: LD70478. $39.95.
Sidney Lumet, USA, 1957, 96 mins.

1956

Invitation to the Dance
Gene Kelly wrote, directed, choreographed and performed in this three-part tribute to his fascination with movies and movement. "Circus", "Ring around the Rosy" and "Sinbad the Sailor" each incorporate Kelly's love of dance. "Sinbad" is partially animated by the Hanna-Barbera studios. With Claire Sombert, Carol Haney, Tamara Toumanova and Igor Youskevitch.
VHS: S06169. $19.98.
Gene Kelly, USA, 1956, 93 mins.

1955

The Rats (Germany)
Never Released on Video

1954

Hobson's Choice
Charles Laughton stars in this comedy as a boot shop owner whose despotic manner is challenged when his hot tempered daughter (Brenda de Banzie) decides to marry a meek boot maker played by John Mills. David Lean adapted this farce from one of Britain's most popular plays.
VHS: S02032. $29.95.
Laser: LD75382. $49.98.
David Lean, Great Britain, 1953, 107 mins.

1953

The Wages of Fear
An exercise in terror and suspense, this uncut version stars Yves Montand and Charles Vanel as uncertain comrades—trapped in a South American village—who identify because they are both French and both penniless. Desperate for a job, they agree to drive two trucks filled with nitroglycerine 300 miles over treacherous roads. Basil Wright called this film "the greatest suspense thriller of all time; it is the suspense not of mystery but of Damocles' sword." French with English subtitles.
VHS: S16210. $29.95.
Laser: LD70766. $59.95.
Henri-Georges Clouzot, France, 1953, 148 mins.

1952

One Summer of Happiness (Sweden)
Never Released on Video

1951

Four in a Jeep
Viveca Lindfors, Ralph Meeker and Michael Medwin star in this Berlin Film Festival winner. Vienna is divided among the allied powers, thereby forcing soldiers from the four powers to patrol the streets together. Soon the Russian and American in the group are at odds over a young Austrian woman whose husband has just escaped from a Russian camp.
VHS: S24003. $24.95.
Leopold Lindtberg, Switzerland, 1951, 81 mins.

Heaven Sent

The Vatican has selected films of special artistic or religious merit to help mark the 100th anniversary of cinema. The list comes from a board called the Pontifical Council for Social Communications, who were advised by an international committee on the basis of "the informed personal taste of experts, on opinion polls and also on plain evidence." They have selected 15 films under each of three categories: religion, values and art.

Religion

Andrei Rublev

The dazzling and harrowing tale of the 15th century icon painter who survives the cruelties of medieval Russia to create works of art. As bloody Tartar raids, religious brutality, and pagan rites work to quell Rublev's desires and needs, he undertakes a spiritual odyssey that affirms man's ability to transcend adversity. This restored director's cut is presented in letterbox format; Russian with English subtitles.
VHS: S16526. $19.98.
Laser: Uncut, 205 mins. Contains behind-the-scenes production footage. **LD72435. $99.95.**
Andrei Tarkovsky, USSR, 1966, 185 mins.

Babette's Feast

Stephane Audran is Babette, an exiled French cook-housekeeper for a pair of devoutly religious, elderly Danish sisters. When she wins a lottery she asks to prepare a Gallic feast for the women and their friends to show her appreciation. Based on the short story by Karen Blixen (Isak Dinesen). Winner of Academy Award. Danish with English subtitles.
VHS: S08497. $19.98.
Laser: LD70850. $39.99.
Gabriel Axel, Denmark, 1987, 102 mins.

Ben-Hur (35th Anniversary Edition)

Celebrating the timelessness of this multi-academy award-winning film, this new Deluxe Collector's Edition of the classic starring Charlton Heston also includes the documentary *Ben Hur: The Making of*

an Epic, narrated by Christopher Plummer, and the original theatrical trailer. VHS letterboxed.
VHS: S20641. $39.98.
Laser: 5-disc CAV boxed set. **LD72371. $99.98.**
William Wyler, 1959, USA, 204 mins.

Flowers of St. Francis

Rossellini's continuing investigation of the nature of history and myth in the re-telling of the story of St. Francis of Assisi and his band of friars, as they attain perfect harmony with nature. This is the British release version, identical to the original Italian release, 10-15 mins. longer than the original U.S. release. Italian with English subtitles.
VHS: S02076. $29.98.
Roberto Rossellini, Italy, 1950, 75 mins.

Francis

Directed by Liliana Cavani. Not available on video.

The Gospel According to St. Matthew

Non-actors, rugged Southern Italian landscapes and towns, cinema-verite techniques, expressive close-ups are some of the elements of Pasolini's moving sacred and mythic epic. His Christ is anguished, determined, a peripatetic preacher against the afflictions of social injustice, whose miracles are matter-of-fact. Italian with English subtitles.
VHS: S18168. $29.95.
Pier Paolo Pasolini, Italy, 1964, 136 mins.

La Passion Pathe

Not available on video.

A Man for All Seasons

Literate, penetrating treatment of the conflict between Thomas More (Paul Scofield) and King Henry VIII (Robert Shaw). Director Zinnemann concentrates on characterization rather than spectacle with superior results. With Orson Welles, Susannah York and Vanessa Redgrave.
VHS: S02639. $19.95.
Laser: Widescreen. **LD75496. $44.95.**
Fred Zinnemann, Great Britain, 1966, 120 mins.

The Mission

Two renegade Jesuit priests force the ruling European landowners to climb up a very tall mountain and massacre innocent South American indians. Robert De Niro and Jeremy Irons star in this beautifully photographed, historical drama. With Aidan Quinn.
VHS: S04306. $19.98.
Laser: Letterboxed. **LD71201. $39.98.**
Roland Joffe, USA, 1986, 126 mins.

Monsieur Vincent

Winner of an Academy Award as Best Foreign Film, Pierre Fresnay gives the characterization of Vincent de Paul an extraordinarily human, emotional portrayal. Based on a scenario by Jean Anouilh, cinematography by Claude Renoir. French with English subtitles.
VHS: S00874. $39.95.
Maurice Cloche, France, 1948

Nazarin

A simple priest tries to live by Christian precepts in one of Luis Bunuel's best—and most unjustly neglected—films. "I am very much attached to Nazarin," said Bunuel. "He is a priest. He could as well be a hairdresser or a waiter. What interests me about him is that he stands by his ideas, that these ideas are unacceptable to society at large, and that after his adventures with prostitutes, thieves and so forth, they lead him to being irrevocably damned by the prevailing social order." With Francisco Rabal, Marga Lopez and Rita Macedo. Spanish with English subtitles.
VHS: S08695. $69.95.
Luis Bunuel, Mexico, 1958, 92 mins.

Ordet

From the director of *Passion of Joan of Arc*, *Ordet* is the story of a theology student who loses his memory and believes he is Christ. Based on a play by Kaj Munk, *Ordet* is Dreyer's portrayal of the conflict between organized religion and personal belief. Danish with English subtitles.
VHS: S00969. $29.95.
Carl Theodor Dreyer, Denmark, 1955, 126 mins.

Passion of Joan of Arc

One of the most poignant, terrifying and unrelenting emotional historical documents ever filmed. Called an austere masterpiece in reference to the stark sets and extreme close-up photography, *Joan of Arc* is brilliantly portrayed by Maria Falconetti. Silent.
VHS: S00998. $29.95.
Carl Theodor Dreyer, France, 1928, 114 mins.

The Sacrifice

Andrei Tarkovsky's epitaph, a dark and complex film about redemption and nuclear holocaust, filmed in exile from his native Russia in Sweden, and starring Erland Josephson. With cinematography by Sven Nykvist, one of the most daring films of the decade. Swedish with English subtitles.
VHS: S03568. $29.95.
Andrei Tarkovsky, Sweden, 1986, 145 mins.

Therese

Alain Cavalier's acclaimed film follows Therese, a 15-year-old girl from provincial France, as she becomes a Carmelite nun and battles with doubts of her faith in the convent. Based on the journal of Therese, published as *Story of a Soul*. The actual Therese was canonized in 1925 and became known as "The Little Flower of Jesus". French with English subtitles. Currently unavailable on video.
Alain Cavalier, France, 1986, 100 mins.

Values

Au Revoir les Enfants (Goodbye, Children)

Louis Malle returns to the days of German occupation during World War II to recount the story of the friendship between two schoolboys, one Jewish and the other Catholic. A winner of many awards including Best Picture in France. Familiar themes are explored. Subtitled.
VHS: S08496. $19.98.
Louis Malle, France, 1988, 104 mins.

The Bicycle Thief

Perhaps the single most important and moving film of Italian neo-realism, *Bicycle Thief* tells the deceptively simple story of an unemployed man finding work to paste up signs, work requiring a bicycle, which is then stolen. A landmark of cinema. Italian with English subtitles.
VHS: S00128. $69.95.
Laser: Original Italian dialog with English subtitles; analog track contains the English dubbed soundtrack. Includes theatrical trailer and the English dubbed version. **LD70881. $39.95.**
Vittorio de Sica, Italy, 1948, 90 mins.

The Burmese Harp

A Japanese army private in Burma is so revolted by the carnage of war that he refuses to return home. Dressed as a Buddhist monk, he remains to bury the dead. The first Japanese film to stress pacifism, *Burmese Harp* is remarkable for its pulsating black and white images and its humanist fervor. Japanese with English subtitles.
VHS: S00545. $29.95.
Laser: LD72321. $49.95.
Kon Ichikawa, Japan, 1956, 116 mins.

Chariots of Fire

Drama based on a true story of two young men who run in the 1924 Olympics—a Jewish student from Cambridge and a Scottish missionary. Winner of Oscar for Best Picture, as well as Best Musical Score

by Vangelis.
DVD: DV60085. $24.98.
VHS: S00228. $19.98.
Laser: LD70542. $34.98.
Hugh Hudson, Great Britain, 1981, 123 mins.

Dersu Uzala

Kurosawa's remarkable personal tale of the friendship between a wise old man and a young, Soviet explorer, filmed in the beautiful expanse of Siberia, is a unique story of man's unity with nature, and a powerful testament to faith. Russian dialog with English subtitles.
VHS: S01809. $39.95.
Laser: Widescreen. LD75028. $69.95.
Akira Kurosawa, Japan, 1975, 124 mins.

Gandhi

Richard Attenborough's dream project realized in epic style with Ben Kingsley as Gandhi in an Oscar winning performance, and a cast including Candice Bergen, Martin Sheen and John Gielgud.
VHS: S02022. $29.95.
Laser: LD72202. $49.95.
Richard Attenborough, Great Britain, 1982, 187 mins.

Il Decalago

Directed by Krzysztof Kieslowski. Not available on video.

Intolerance

Four separate stories are interwoven: the fall of Babylon, the death of Christ, the massacre of the Hugenots, and a modern drama—all cross-cut and building with enormous energy to a thrilling chase and finale. Far ahead of its time, Griffith created a spectacle which audiences of the day did not accept but which has become a classic of world cinema. This specially packaged double cassette edition of *Intolerance* has been remastered using variable speed projection and color tints to match the original release prints, making it the best version available anywhere. Tinted with organ score.
VHS: S13048. $29.95.
Laser: CAV. LD71052. $69.95.
D.W. Griffith, USA, 1919, 190 min.

It's a Wonderful Life

James Stewart is George Bailey, trapped in Bedford Falls, until his faith in life is restored by his Guardian Angel in Frank Capra's delightful comedy, nominated for multiple Academy Awards. Donna Reed, Lionel Barrymore, Thomas Mitchell and Beulah Bondi also star.
VHS: S15106. $19.98.
Laser: CAV. LD70387. $89.95.
Laser: CLV. LD71996. $59.98.
Frank Capra, USA, 1946, 160 mins.

On the Waterfront

Marlon Brando stars in the archetypal role as ex-fighter Terry Malloy, working for Boss Johnny Friendly (Lee J. Cobb) on the gang-ridden waterfront. The classic American movie of redemption, with a

great script by Budd Schulberg.
VHS: S00960. $19.95.
Laser: LD72070. $34.95.
Elia Kazan, USA, 1954, 108 mins.

Open City

A beautiful video master, transferred from a new negative, of this key film of Italian Neo-Realism, shot largely during the Nazi occupation of Rome. Two resistance leaders, one a Communist, the other a priest, work toward weakening the German occupation. The cumulative power of Rossellini's feeling for his subject was translated into a visual intensity that makes the picture sometimes almost impossible to watch. With a great performance by Anna Magnani. Italian with English subtitles.
VHS: S13591. $24.95.
Laser: LD75058. $49.95.
Roberto Rossellini, Italy, 1945, 103 mins.

Schindler's List

This Academy Award-winning film tells the story of Oskar Schindler, who saved hundreds of Jews from certain death in Nazi-dominated Europe. Adapted from Thomas Keneally's novel and starring Ben Kingsley, Liam Neeson and Ralph Fiennes. The Collector's Edition includes the novel, a compact disc of the Academy Award-winning score by John Williams and a booklet with an introduction by Steven Spielberg. Letterboxed.
Standard Edition.
VHS: S21539. $29.95.
Laser: LD74525. $49.98.
Steven Spielberg, USA, 1993, 197 mins.

Seventh Seal

Bergman's powerful allegory of man's search for meaning in life is stunningly visualized. A knight, upon return from the Crusades, plays chess with Death while the Plague ravages medieval Europe. With Max von Sydow, Gunnar Bjornstrand, Bibi Andersson. Swedish with English subtitles.
VHS: S01185. $29.95.
Laser: CAV. LD70453. $79.95.
Laser: CLV. LD70454. $49.95.
Ingmar Bergman, Sweden, 1956, 96 mins.

The Tree of Wooden Clogs

A passionate, moving film, an epic celebration of an

Italian family's indomitable spirit, winner of the Grand Prize at the 1978 Cannes Film Festival. The subject of the film is peasant life in northern Italy at the turn of the century, focusing on about a year in the life of three families living on a feudal estate. "A quiet masterpiece" (*Newsweek*). "The movie, which runs slightly more than three hours, is an accumulation of dozens of experiences of children, adults, old people, village idiots, of harvest times and plantings, of moments of boredom and jealousy, celebrations, fatigue, brief pleasures and mysterious ones. It moves so effortlessly, often with great humor and always with compassion, it seems much shorter than most 90-minute films" (Vincent Canby, *New York Times*). Italian with English subtitles.
VHS: $12946. $19.98.
Ermanno Olmi, Italy, 1978, 185 mins.

Wild Strawberries
One of the great films of Bergman, with Victor Sjostrom as the aged Stockholm professor who recollects his past experiences and becomes aware, for the first time, of his failings and shortcomings. With Bibi Andersson, Ingrid Thulin, Gunnar Bjornstrand. Swedish with English subtitles.
VHS: S01462. $29.95.
Laser: LD70487. $49.95.
Ingmar Bergman, Sweden, 1957, 95 mins.

Art

2001: A Space Odyssey (25th Anniversary Edition)
Stanley Kubrick's landmark film traces the three stages of man, from evolutionary, predatory animals to futuristic space travelers, astronauts on a mission to Jupiter sabotaged by a malfunctioning computer known as HAL. "A uniquely poetic piece of science fiction that's hypnotically entertaining" (*The New Yorker*). Adapted from Arthur C. Clarke's story *The Sentinel*. With Keir Dullea, Gary Lockwood and William Sylvester. Special visual effects by Douglas Trumbull. Letterboxed.
VHS: S18674. $19.98.
Laser: CAV, 3 discs, with 4-page insert. LD71876. $69.98.
Laser: CLV, 2 discs. LD71877. $39.98.
Stanley Kubrick, USA, 1968, 141 mins.

8½
Fellini's great autobiographical masterpiece, the loose portrayal of a film director during the course of making a film and finding himself trapped by his fears and insecurities. Continually inventive, with the performance of a lifetime from Marcello Mastroianni as Guido, the director, and from Claudia Cardinale, Anouk Aimee and Sandra Milo. Italian with English subtitles.
VHS: S07140. $59.95.
Laser: Widescreen. LD70806. $59.95.
Federico Fellini, Italy, 1963, 138 mins.

Citizen Kane (50th Anniversary Edition)

One of the greatest films ever made is now available in a version painstakingly restored to its original brilliance in honor of the film's 50th anniversary. With Orson Welles, Dorothy Comingore, Everett Sloane, Paul Stewart. Cinematography by Gregg Toland, script by Welles and Herman Mankiewicz.
VHS: $14599. $19.98.
Laser: CAV. LD70745. $124.95.
Laser: CLV. LD70356. $39.95.
Laser: CLV. LD70746. $39.95.
Orson Welles, USA, 1941, 119 mins.

Fantasia
The magic of Disney animation is gloriously blended with the music of eight classical pieces conducted by Leopold Stokowski. Relive those memorable moments with dancing mushrooms and hippos, dinosaurs, demons, abstract shapes, centaurs, and a certain sorcerer's apprentice who Walt felt needed a career boost. Currently unavailable on video.
Walt Disney, USA, 1940, 116 mins.

Grand Illusion

A beautifully mastered version of Jean Renoir's great masterpiece, a classic comment on war's fading glory. Set in WW I, the film tells of two French officers captured by German forces. Interred in a prison camp, the two officers encounter Von Rauffenstein, an aristocratic career officer played by von Stroheim. With Jean Gabin, Pierre Fresnay and von Stroheim. French with English subtitles.
VHS: $12469. $29.95.
Laser: LD70373. $89.95.
Jean Renoir, France, 1937, 111 mins.

Il Gattopardo (The Leopard)

Directed by Luchino Visconti, Italy, 1963. Not available on video.

La Strada

Fellini's masterpiece. Giulietta Masina plays Gelsomina, a tragic waif sold to play clown to travelling show strongman Zampano (Anthony Quinn). "Simplicity itself, *La Strada* is a magical tale and an unbearably painful account of loneliness which will always be associated with the sublimely Chaplinesque Masina…but Quinn, too, is superb, particularly in the final revelation of his own heartbreak and isolation." With Richard Basehart and Aldo Silvani. Italian with English subtitles.
VHS: S00712. $29.95.
Laser: LD71088. $49.95.
Federico Fellini, Italy, 1954, 107 mins.

The Lavender Hill Mob

Alec Guinness in one of his most memorable roles, as a shy bank clerk who conspires to steal a million pounds in gold bars from the Bank of England. His plan is to melt down the gold and mold it in the shape of tiny Eiffel Tower souvenirs for resale. Things appear to go well until... Zany, witty and very British, a beloved and classic British comedy.
VHS: S00732. $14.98.
Charles Crichton, Great Britain, 1951, 78 mins.

Little Women

"Endless pleasure no matter how many times you've seen it" (Leonard Maltin). The Louisa May Alcott novel is portrayed on film featuring Katharine Hepburn, Joan Bennett, Frances Dee and Paul Lukas.
VHS: S03008. $19.95.
Laser: LD70137. $34.98.
George Cukor, USA, 1933, 116 mins.

Metropolis

A newly mastered version of Fritz Lang's great masterpiece, the first classic of the science fiction genre. His depiction of a giant city controlled by an authoritarian industrialist who lives in a paradise-like garden while the workers live and struggle in subterranean sections of the city was as important for its vision of man in the service of those who control technology as for its implicit and moving social message. "A brilliant piece of expressionist design...with moments of almost incredible beauty and power" (Pauline Kael). Silent with music score.
VHS: S10764. $29.95.
Fritz Lang, Germany, 1926, 90 mins.

Modern Times

Charlie Chaplin's silent homage to the human spirit, in which Chaplin is the victim of industrial boom. He plays the factory worker gone looney by the assembly line who falls in love with a down-and-out young lady and tries through various and eccentric means to find a bit of financial peace. A great comedy, and a great film.
VHS: S00866. $19.98.
Charles Chaplin, USA, 1936, 89 mins.

Napoleon

A masterpiece of world cinema, employing a variety

of new techniques, including triple screen and mobile use of the camera by strapping it to a galloping horse. Long thought to be lost, the film has been reconstructed and is presented with a sound track composed by Carmine Coppola.
VHS: S00917. $79.95.
Abel Gance, France, 1927, 235 mins.

Nosferatu

One of Murnau's best known films, *Nosferatu*'s eerie telling of the Dracula story was filmed on location in the mountains, towns, and castles of Bavaria. This German Expressionist symphony of horror is brilliantly infused with the subtle tones of nature: both pure and fresh, as well as twisted and sinister. Newly restored and color tinted, this version was remastered from a 35mm negative and includes recently discovered scenes and inter-titles freshly translated from the original German script. At 84 minutes, it is the most complete version available on home video.
DVD: DV60031. $29.95.
VHS: S15038. $29.95.
Friedrich W. Murnau, Germany, 1922, 84 mins.

Stagecoach

John Ford at his greatest in a story of nine passengers on a Cheyenne-bound stagecoach, each with a singular reason for the journey, determined to live through the dangerous trip. With John Wayne, Claire Trevor, John Carradine, Andy Devine.
VHS: S01247. $19.98.
Laser: LD74715. $34.98.
John Ford, USA, 1939, 96 mins.

The Wizard of Oz

Judy Garland, Ray Bolger, Jack Haley, Bert Lahr, Frank Morgan, Margaret Hamilton, Billie Burke and Toto in the land of Oz, in MGM's great, Technicolor fantasy where Judy follows the Yellow Brick Road.
DVD: DV60104. $24.98.
VHS: S09609. $19.95.
Laser: CLV, MGM. **LD70709. $24.98.**
Laser: CAV, Criterion. **LD71215. $99.95.**
Victor Fleming, USA, 1939, 101 mins.

100 Top American Independent Features

All the Vermeers in New York
From the tenacious American independent Jon Jost, this visually ravishing, precise and emotionally fluid piece tracks the romantic obsession, emotional desperation, individual expression and tension of a disparate group of New York artists and businessmen. Largely about the conflicts produced between commerce and art, the movie is less a narrative than a collection of vignettes about the textures and off-center rhythms of urban culture. Shot in widescreen, with some wonderfully executed tracking shots, Jost conceived, wrote, photographed and edited this audacious work. With Stephen Lack, French actress Emmanuelle Chaulet and Katherine Bean.
VHS: $17499. $24.98.
Jon Jost, USA, 1990, 87 mins.

Amateur
Hal Hartley directed this offbeat comedy, which stars Martin Donovan, Isabelle Huppert and Elina Lowensohn as three individuals joined in a love triangle and trapped in a fight for survival. How can an amnesiac, a porn star and a nymphomaniac ex-nun escape ruthless, single-minded corporate killers? That's where the comedy of this stylish film comes in.
VHS: $26700. $96.99.
Laser: LD75112. $39.95.
Hal Hartley, USA/Great Britain/France, 1994, 105 mins.

Ashes and Embers
This award-winning film is the story of a Vietnam veteran who, nearly a decade later, begins to come to terms with his role in the war and his role as a Black person in America. His transformation from an embittered ex-soldier to a strong and confident man is provoked and encouraged by the love and chastisement of his grandmother and friends.
VHS: $13411. $59.95.
Haile Gerima, USA, 1983, 120 mins.

Basquiat
The critically acclaimed film about the rise and fall of controversial 1980s Haitian-Puerto Rican graffiti artist-turned-Soho-supernova Jean-Michel Basquiat, who died of a heroin overdose in 1988. Starring Dennis Hopper, Gary Oldman, David Bowie as Andy Warhol, and Tony Award-winner Jeffrey Wright (*Angels in America*) as Basquiat. With Willem Dafoe, Courtney Love, Parker Posey and Tatum O'Neal and music by David Bowie, Van Morrison and Tom Waits. "One of the year's best" (*Siskel & Ebert*).
VHS: $30822. $103.99.
Laser: LD76102. $39.99.
Julian Schnabel, USA, 1996, 111 mins.

Bastard Out of Carolina
Anjelica Huston's directorial debut, produced by the Turner Network and then banned when Ted Turner saw it, has been controversial from the start because of its graphic depiction of a rape scene. Jennifer Jason Leigh delivers a very strong performance in this true story of a dysfunctional South Carolina family, which ends with tragedy. With Ron Eldard, Glenne Headly, Lyle Lovett, Diana Scarwid and Christina Ricci. "Directed…with a fine eye and a strong will" (*The New York Times*).
VHS: $31061. $19.95.
Laser: LD76202. $39.98.
Anjelica Huston, USA, 1996, 97 mins.

Blood Simple
The first film scripted by the talented Coen brothers. A critically acclaimed thriller set in rural Texas tells the old story of a man who hires a sleazy private eye to kill his wife and her boyfriend. Told in a very imaginative way, it combines chilling suspense with offbeat humor, with double and triple crosses building to a blood-curdling surprise climax. The most inventive and original thriller in years.
VHS: $00149. $14.98.
Laser: LD70016. $34.98.
Joel Coen, USA, 1983, 96 mins.

The Bloody Child
Maverick American independent filmmaker Nina Menkes' film was inspired by the true story of a young U.S. marine, just back from the Gulf War, who was arrested while digging a grave in the middle of the Mojave Desert for his murdered wife, whose bloodied body lay in the backseat of his car. Menkes turns the mundane realism of the marine's arrest into a haunting, hallucinatory journey, a jagged look back at the nature of violence. The filmmaker's sister and collaborator, Tinka Menkes, portrays a marine captain; all other cast members are actual Desert Storm veterans.
VHS: $32371. $79.95.
Nina Menkes, USA, 1996, 85 mins.

Born in Flames
A landmark in the independent film movement, Lizzie Borden's sci-fi/feminist/adventure story is set in America ten years after the Second American Revolution, a socialist rebellion that has redefined the roles of women and minorities. When Adelaide Norris, the black lesbian founder of the Woman's Army, is mysteriously killed, a coalition of women across all lines of race, class, and sexual preference emerges to blow the system apart. "Funny, gutsy and inspiring" (*Ms. Magazine*).
VHS: $31350. $29.95.
Lizzie Borden, USA, 1984, 90 mins.

Bound

Pulp prince James M. Cain meets lesbian sexpert Susie Bright in this "sultry slice of noir gamesmanship that boasts clever twists, crackling flirtations, smart, assertive camerawork, and a believable, sensual, sexual relationship between two women" (*Chicago Reader*) by the Wachowski Brothers. A mobster (Joe Pantoliano), his mistress (Jennifer Tilly) and a tough, female ex-con (Tina Gershon) are caught in a dangerous plot starting with $2 million of the Mob's money and ending in seduction and betrayal. "Sleek!" (Janet Maslin, *New York Times*).

VHS: S30825. $14.95.
Laser: LD76078. $34.98.
Andy Wachowski/Larry Wachowski, USA, 1996, 108 mins.

Boyz N The Hood

John Singleton made Oscar history as the first African-American to be nominated as best director. He also became, at age 23, the youngest filmmaker to be so honored for this powerful drama about responsibility and survival. Cuba Gooding Jr. delivers a fine performance as Tre Styles, a young man trying to make the right decisions while dealing with the dangers of living in South Central L.A. With excellent work by rapper Ice Cube, Morris Chestnut and Larry Fishburne as Tre's discerning father.

VHS: S15671. $19.95.
Laser: LD71181. $49.95.
John Singleton, USA, 1991, 107 mins.

The Brothers McMullen

In this romantic comedy, the Best Picture at the 1995 Sundance Festival, three brothers from Long Island confront the unknown territory of love and marriage. After their father dies, their mother returns to Ireland to be with the man she really loves. The three Irish Catholic brothers are left to deal with varying stages of love and marriage, ranging from initial attraction to engagement to the prospect of an extramarital affair. With Edward Burns, Jack Mulcahy, Mike McGlone and Connie Britton.

VHS: S27210. $19.95.
Laser: LD75482. $39.98.
Edward Burns, USA, 1995, 98 mins.

Bush Mama

This landmark of African-American cinema reveals the powerful drama of a black woman living on welfare in the Los Angeles ghetto, trying to care for her daughter after being stranded alone by her man's imprisonment for a crime he didn't commit. Though scripted and professionally acted, the film succeeds in capturing the rich style of ghetto language and humor. Its street scenes, where outbursts of violence assume a fantasy-like power, alternate with fantasy scenes, which gain in reality from the juxtaposition. The narrative is loosely structured, flowing readily from real time to flashback, real life to nightmare. A daring film in concept and execution.

VHS: S15644. $59.95.
Haile Gerima, USA, 1976, 100 mins.

Chain Letters

Rappaport's "most deliciously lush and Byzantine work" (Ray Carney, Boston University) is one where strange puzzles, symmetries and coincidences abound and doppelgangers lurk around every corner. Can we connect the dots to unlock the mysteries of life, or, as one character in the film believes, is all of life a plot orchestrated by a vast government bureaucracy? "Vintage Rappaport. Original, eccentric and highly amusing" (*American Film*).

VHS: S31137. $29.99.
Mark Rappaport, USA, 1985, 96 mins.

Chappaqua

A controversial, startling and hypnotic mix of music and visuals in Conrad Rooks' (*Siddhartha*) semi-autobiographical drama following his journey from addiction to health. Rooks, a young, well-to-do alcoholic and junkie, heads for Switzerland for the "Swiss Sleeping Cure," where he enters a psychedelic, explosive and delusional world of the mind. With William S. Burroughs, Allen Ginsberg, Jean-Louis Barrault and Ornette Coleman; music by Ravi Shankar, Philip Glass and The Fugs. "Exceptionally interesting…a superb feat of imagination" (*The New Yorker*).

VHS: S31116. $59.98.
Conrad Rooks, USA, 1966, 82 mins.

The Bloody Child

Charles Bukowski Tapes
"It's a gem...an outrageously stimulating and
unnerving all-night drinking session with a gutter
eloquent barroom philosopher who has made his soul
your own...One of the most intimate, revelatory and
unsparing glimpses any film or video has ever given
us of a writer's life and personality," raved Michael
Wilmington in *The Los Angeles Times*. Directed by
Barbet Schroeder (*Barfly*), a 4-hour video portrait of
the renegade poet of contemporary literature.
VHS: S08117. $100.00.
Barbet Schroeder, USA/France, 1987, 240 mins.

Clean, Shaven
Peter Greene stars as a man desperately hoping to
find his lost daughter. Schizophrenic hallucinations
and a rabid policeman complicate this overwhelming
task. Detective McNally won't let up because he
suspects this strange character is actually a serial
killer stalking children. Winner of Best First Feature
award at the 1993 Chicago International Film
Festival.
VHS: S26938. $19.98.
Lodge Kerrigan, USA, 1993, 80 mins.

becomes a hunted murder suspect as he sets out on
life's final journey, meeting an interesting cast of
characters along the way. Funny and unpredictable,
Depp is supported by an amazing array of talent,
including Robert Mitchum, Gabriel Byrne, John Hurt,
Lance Henriksen and Crispin Glover. With bravura
black-and-white cinematography by Robby Muller.
"A masterpiece!" (*The Chicago Reader*).
VHS: S30457. $99.99.
Laser: LD76064. $39.99.
Jim Jarmusch, USA, 1996, 121 mins.

Desert Hearts
Wonderful love story between a repressed English
professor who is waiting for a divorce at a dude ranch
for women, and a beautiful casino worker in Reno
who lives at the ranch with her mother. Adapted from
the novel *Desert of the Heart*, by Jane Rule, with a
fabulous soundtrack!
VHS: S01919. $19.98.
Laser: LD75919. $39.99.
Donna Deitch, USA, 1985, 96 mins.

Do The Right Thing
Spike Lee's powerful, gritty film set in Brooklyn's

Flower Children

200 Motels VHS: S06227. $19.95. Laser: LD76153. $39.98.	**Easy Rider** VHS: S01821. $19.95. Laser: LD75091. $59.95.	**Monterey Pop** VHS: S00876. $19.98. Laser: LD70422. $49.95.
Alice's Restaurant VHS: S06228. $14.95.	**Grateful Dead Movie** VHS: S04787. $39.95.	**Running on Empty** VHS: S09840. $19.98. Laser: LD74697. $24.98.
Berkeley in the Sixties VHS: S18146. $29.95.	**Hair** VHS: S03486. $19.98. Laser: LD71163. $39.98.	**Who'll Stop the Rain** VHS: S06992. $14.95. Laser: LD76367. $49.98.
Born on the 4th of July VHS: S12464. $19.95. Laser: LD70017. $39.98.	**Head** VHS: S02531. $19.95.	**Woodstock** DVD: DV60119. $24.98. VHS: S06044. $24.98. Laser: LD70712. $49.98.
Coming Home VHS: S04718. $19.98. Laser: LD71636. $39.98.	**I Love You, Alice B. Toklas** VHS: S14569. $19.98. Laser: LD71474. $34.98.	

Clerks
For the slacker generation life seems to be just a
series of dead-end jobs where catering to jerks is the
only way to pay the bills. This great, independently-
made comedy follows a parade of annoying shoppers
helped by two friends. One works at a convenience
store and the other at a video shop next door.
VHS: S24576. $19.95.
Laser: Letterboxed. LD74977. $39.99.
Kevin Smith, USA, 1994, 92 mins.

The Connection
The Living Theatre's production of the play by Jack
Gelber: a quintessential work of theatre of the 60's, a
harrowing depiction of the dope peddling milieu, as
the characters wait for the arrival of Cowboy with the
heroin. Critics Prize, Cannes.
VHS: S00265. $29.95.
Shirley Clarke, USA, 1961, 105 mins.

Daughters of the Dust
This remarkable first feature by Julie Dash follows
three generations of African-American women at the
turn of the century, structured around the family's
migration from the Sea Island to the mainland.
Beautifully shot by Arthur Jaffa, the film is a poetic
series of pastoral images, landscapes, sound, ritual,
music, colors and voice. The film is steeped in the
highly distinctive, traditional oral black storytelling,
told through a highly unusual narrative device,
related by an unborn child. The images sing. With
Cora Lee Day, Alva Rogers, Barbara-O, Turla
Hoosier and Kaycee Moore.
VHS: S16913. $24.95.
Julie Dash, USA, 1991, 113 mins.

Dead Man
Johnny Depp stars as a wounded man on the run from
both bounty hunters and the law in this incredibly
beautiful-looking film from American independent
Jim Jarmusch. Through an odd chain of events, Depp

Bedford Stuyvesant community, called "a great film"
by Roger Ebert. Danny Aiello stars as the pizza parlor
owner, Spike Lee himself as the delivery boy. Notable
for its uncanny depiction of the community, its focus
on the moral issues of racism and non-violence—a
gripping experience. With Ossie Davis, Ruby Dee,
Richard Edson.
VHS: S11445. $19.95.
Laser: LD70023. $39.98.
Spike Lee, USA, 1989, 120 mins.

Down by Law
Jim Jarmusch's third feature following his immensely
successful *Stranger Than Paradise* stars Tom Waits,
John Lurie—and in a treasure of a performance,
Roberto Benigni—as a group of escaped convicts in
the swamps of Louisiana. A funny, original film
featuring brilliant cinematography by the great Robby
Muller.
VHS: S03022. $14.98.
Laser: LD76225. $39.98.
Jim Jarmusch, USA, 1986, 95 mins.

Dracula
Warhol's version of the Dracula story finds the Count
touring Italy for a marriageable virgin, and there are
few to be found. With Joe Dallesandro as a class-
conscious estate hand.
VHS: S02301. $14.98.
Paul Morrissey, USA, 1974, 106 mins.

Drugstore Cowboy
Matt Dillon gives the performance of his career as the
drug-addicted criminal who masterminds a series of
robberies in the Pacific Northwest. A harsh and
decidedly unsentimental look at life on the fringe that
deals honestly with the world of controlled
substances. A top notch cast includes Kelly Lynch,
James LeGros, Heather Graham, James Remar and
William Burroughs as Father Tom, the junkie priest.

Don't say "no" to this drug movie.
VHS: $11724. $14.98.
Laser: LD70955. $39.95.
Gus Van Sant, USA, 1989, 100 mins.

Eat a Bowl of Tea
Chinese-American filmmaker Wayne Wang spins a tale of returning soldiers in search of brides and old men in need of grandchildren. Set in post-WWII New York, he exposes the shoddy treatment of Chinese immigrants and the notorious exclusion laws that kept families apart for much of this century. An entertaining and invigorating film based on the 1961 novel by Louis Chu. Cast includes Russell Wong, Victor Wong, Eric Tsang Chi Wai and Cora Miao, the director's wife, as the bashful bride from the old country who grows up fast.
VHS: $11484. $19.95.
Wayne Wang, USA, 1988, 102 mins.

Eat Drink Man Woman
Ang Lee's (*The Wedding Banquet*) winning blockbuster of a movie about food, sex and independence. Master Chef Chu is Taipei's legendary chef whose extraordinary culinary creations are the center piece of the film. His three beautiful daughters are both sexy and rebellious, but Master Chu holds the family together with his Sunday ritual dinners. But as the generations clash, and Master Chu retires, it's the experienced generation that has the final word in a film that's original, funny, surprising—and delectable. Chinese with English subtitles.
VHS: $24824. $19.98.
Laser: LD74957. $39.99.
Ang Lee, Taiwan/USA , 1994, 104 mins.

El Mariachi
This film by 24-year-old director Robert Rodriquez was made for the unbelievable sum of $7,000. Rodriguez playfully evokes Peckinpah, noir westerns and Hitchcock. A maverick loner and mariachi player (Carlos Gallardo) enters a Mexican border town and is instantly confused with a stark, brutally efficient assassin (Reinol Martinez). Spanish with English subtitles.
VHS: $19057. $16.95.
Laser: Special Collector's Edition. **LD71892. $49.95.**
Richard Rodriguez, USA, 1992, 80 mins.

Faces
One of the foundation stones of independent American cinema, *Faces* features Gena Rowlands, John Marley, Lynn Carlin and Seymour Cassel in a riveting account of the events leading to the breakdown of a marriage. The performances are extraordinary in a film which is a legend.
VHS: $26961. $19.95.
John Cassavetes, USA, 1968, 130 mins.

Fairgrounds
David Wells' film debut is an excellent example of contemporary American cinema. Shot in beautiful black and white, over 11 days, the low-budget feature concerns two partners in a circus sideshow junk-eating act who start to go their separate ways as the apprentice strives to replace the master, and the master becomes distracted by a strange yet compelling woman with a bizarre definition of romance. The wonderful screenplay, which Wells adapted from his award-winning play of the same name, contains some of the wittiest dialogue in recent memory. As a friend of the filmmaker said, "If Jim Jarmusch and Samuel Beckett went to the carnival and ate a bad corndog, you would get *Fairgrounds*."
VHS: $30440. $39.95.
David Wells, USA, 1996, 90 mins.

Female Misbehavior
Monika Treut's kinky exploration of nonconformist women combines two older short films, *Bondage* (1983), about a sadomasochistic lesbian, and *Annie* (1989), a portrait of former porno star Annie Sprinkle, with two recent documentaries, *Dr. Paglia* and *Max*. The former is a witty send-up of controversial academic Camille Paglia; the latter, a look at a lesbianNative American that shows her transsexual change from woman to man. "Treut is a sexual-political provocateur who in her explorations of the sexual fringe takes us where few filmmakers visit" (*New York Post*).
VHS: $19558. $29.95.
Monika Treut, Germany/USA, 1992, 80 mins.

Fireworks
A collection which includes *Fireworks* (a dissatisfied dreamer awakes, goes out in the night seeking a

light…), *Rabbit's Moon* (a fable of the unattainable, combining elements of Commedia dell'Arte with Japanese myth), and *Eaux d'Artifice* (a costumed figure moves through Tivoli gardens…), by perhaps the most important American experimental filmmaker of the post-war years. *Eaux d'Artifice* is included in the National Film Registry.
VHS: $00800. $29.95.
Kenneth Anger, USA, 1947-55, 34 mins.

Flirt
One script, three different stories. Ruminating on whether place and culture can affect the course of desire and trouble, Hartley employs different characters, actors, settings and situations, using the same dialog in three different cities: New York, Tokyo and Berlin. With Bill Sage, Martin Donovan, Parker Posey, Hal Hartley and Miho Nikaidoh. "The quintessential Hartley movie, a gorgeously mounted bauble, a post-Godardian sketchbook" (Ray Pride, *New City*).
VHS: $31269. $98.99.
Hal Hartley, USA, 1996, 85 mins.

Flirting with Disaster
"Hang on and prepare to laugh" (*USA Today*) with this all-star comedy voted one of the year's ten best by *Time Magazine*. Mel Coplin (Ben Stiller) and his wife Nancy (Patricia Arquette) are led by a wacky adoption counselor (Tea Leone) on a wild cross-country search to find his birth parents (Alan Alda and Lily Tomlin). Hilarious and unpredictable situations complicate the trip as Mel searches for his roots. By the time Mel's adoptive parents (Mary Tyler Moore and George Segal) show up to crash the reunion, everyone seems to be "flirting with disaster."
VHS: $30829. $103.99.
Laser: LD76100. $39.99.
David O. Russell, USA, 1996, 92 mins.

Frisk
Based on the novel by Dennis Cooper, this controversial, sensual and suggestive work is about fantasy, sexuality and how violence and pornography shape the human psyche. Punctuated with strobe flashes of layered S & M images, it unfolds in an elliptical style. Stars Michael Gunther, Craig Chester, Parker Posey, Alexis Arquette, Raoul O'Connell, Jaie Laplante, James Lyons and Michael Stock. "…a serious and discreet work of considerable dark impact—and no little humor" (Kevin Thomas, *Los Angeles Times*).
VHS: $30136. $59.99.
Todd Verow, USA, 1996, 84 mins.

The Funeral
Abel Ferrara's (*Bad Lieutenant*) "hot-blooded, broodingly well-acted" (*New York Times*) film of underworld betrayal and explosive retribution set in 1930s New York stars Christopher Walken, Chris Penn, Isabella Rossellini and Annabella Sciorra. A powerful crime family's three street-hardened brothers and the women they love are about to be plunged into a deadly confrontation with their enemies, with each other and with their own dark heritage of violence, madness and murder.
VHS: $31109. $101.99.
Laser: LD76198. $39.98.
Abel Ferrara, USA, 1996, 101 mins.

Get on the Bus
Spike Lee makes cinematic history when he combines the comedy of the classic road movie with the controversy of the Million Man March. Twenty very different men travel from L.A. to Washington, DC, as strangers, but return as blood brothers, destined to ride into history together. With Ossie Davis, Charles S. Dutton, Andre Braugher and Richard Belzer.
VHS: $31206. $19.95.
Laser: LD76180. $39.95.
Spike Lee, USA, 1996, 121 mins.

Grief
Alexis Arquette and Craig Chester are featured in this quirky comedy about behind the scenes intrigues set in the offices of an over-the-top soap opera. Camp humor, unfulfilled longing, male homoeroticism and even that standby of television daytime drama, overnight success, are thrown into this crazy mixed-up world of Hollywood's second string producers.
VHS: $22062. $39.99.
Richard Glatzer, USA, 1994, 87 mins.

Grind
In this slice of blue-collar life, Billy Crudup (*Inventing the Abbotts*) is Eddie, a handsome 20-something who has just been released from prison.

Broke, Eddie shows up on the doorstep of his older brother Terry (Paul Shulze, *Laws of Gravity*) and his wife, Janey (Adrienne Shelly, *Trust*), where he is taken into their family. When Eddie switches to the night shift at the treadmill factory, he finds himself spending his days with Janey. They discover that they yearn for something other than the monotony that characterizes their lives, and the three find themselves in a final, shattering confrontation. With Frank Vincent. "A true sense of the blue-collar soul" (*Newsday*).
VHS: $31801. $89.98.
Chris Kentis, USA, 1996, 96 mins.

Highway Patrolman

Hangin' with the Homeboys
Four friends from the South Bronx, two black and two Puerto Rican, spend an eventful Friday night in Manhattan. This fresh and funny film, written and directed by Joseph B. Vasquez, has heart and soul and a streetsmart sensibility. With John Leguizamo, Mario Joyner, Doug E. Doug and Nestor Serrano.
VHS: $15822. $19.95.
Joseph B. Vasquez, USA, 1991, 88 mins.

Highway Patrolman
Part road movie, part western, this "gringo valentine" (J. Hoberman, *Village Voice*) by Alex Cox (*Repo Man*) is the gripping story of Pedro and Anibal, their coming of age, and their loves. When police academy grad Pedro gets a job working as a highway patrolman in Matimi, Durango, his wife complains about the low wages, leading him into a life of corruption. "Vibrantly alive...*Highway Patrolman*...recalls the westerns of John Ford and John Huston" (Kevin Thomas, *Los Angeles Times*). Spanish with English subtitles.
VHS: $31627. $89.95.
Alex Cox, Mexico/USA, 1992, 104 mins.

I Shot Andy Warhol
Lili Taylor is Valerie Solanas, the eccentric writer of a play called *Up Your Ass* and the founder and sole member of the revolutionary group the Society for Cutting Up Men. This film shows Warhol's Factory through its heyday, until it all was radically changed by a furious, gun-toting Solanas. Her revenge against Warhol for refusing to produce her play sent shockwaves through the art world. Stephen Dorff is Candy Darling and Jared Harris is Warhol.
VHS: $29783. $19.98.
Laser: LD76039. $39.98.
Mary Harron, USA, 1996, 100 mins.

Imposters
This "insolent, high-camp comedy about magic, obsession, role-playing and love" (David Denby, *New York*) is "one of the wildest and wittiest American movies of the decade. A hysterically convoluted, elegantly mounted tale of wisecracks and woe" (Jonathan Rosenbaum, *Chicago Reader*). With avant-garde theater pioneer Charles Ludlam.
VHS: $31138. $29.99.
Mark Rappaport, USA, 1980, 110 mins.

Inauguration of the Pleasure Dome
"A convocation of magicians assume the identity of gods and goddesses in a Dionysian revel....Dedicated to the few and to Aleister Crowley, and the crowned and conquering child" (Anger). One of the key works of American experimental cinema.
VHS: $00801. $29.95.
Kenneth Anger, USA, 1954, 38 mins.

Just Another Girl on the I.R.T.
Leslie Harris' debut film is a vivid portrait of the panache of a 17-year-old Brooklyn African-American

woman. Ambitious and colorful, she is played by astonishing newcomer named Ariyan Johnson, who portrays a street-tough woman with plans to attend college and study medicine. Harris documents life in the projects, from the unique perspective of a young black woman. With Kevin Thigpen, Jerard Washington and Ebony Jerido.
VHS: $19024. $14.98.
Laser: LD75214. $34.98.
Leslie Harris, USA, 1992, 90 mins.

Kafka
Steven Soderbergh's follow-up to *sex, lies and videotape* is set in a baroque, sinister Prague. Jeremy Irons plays an insurance underwriter who, following a friend's disappearance, gets entangled with a shadowy anarchist group and an unbalanced doctor performing perverse scientific experiments. The cast includes Theresa Russell, Joel Grey, Ian Holm, Jeroen Krabbe, Armin Mueller-Stahl and Alec Guinness.
VHS: $17789. $92.95.
Steven Soderbergh, USA/France/Great Britain, 1991, 100 mins.

Kids
Famed photographer Larry Clark makes his directorial debut with this sensational story of teenage life in Manhattan. Ignoring the challenge posed by AIDS, these kids pursue sex and drugs with no regard for the future in a world as violent as it is hopeless. Justifiably controversial, *Kids* was hailed as "very, very powerful" (Roger Ebert) and denounced as manipulative and exploitative. "The confident visual style and flat, elliptical, near plotless storytelling are tremendously accomplished, yet the same elements...could be seen as a celebration of amorality, as a contrived, romanticized celebration of the death wish" (Ray Pride, *New City*).
VHS: $26956. $14.95.
Larry Clark, USA, 1995, 91 mins.

The Killing Floor
A very powerful, raw film produced for American Playhouse. Shot in Chicago and set against the backdrop of the Chicago stock yards, the film focuses on Frank, recently returned from World War I, who wants a better life and becomes involved in the labor movement. But the pressures of the recession mount, and the stock yards become filled with racial tension. Finally, bloodshed erupts on the streets with the Chicago race riot of 1919. The film has a remarkable documentary feel, and features strong performances from Damien Leake, Alfre Woodard, Moses Gunn, Clarence Felder and Bill Bremer.
VHS: $10894. $29.95.
Bill Duke, USA, 1984, 118 mins.

Koyaanisqatsi
With no dialog, only the music of Phillip Glass, and no characters other than the entire human race and the five elements, this years-in-the making film is a symphony of sound and image, fast-paced, dazzling, hypnotic.
VHS: $00692. $14.95.
Godfrey Reggio, USA, 1983, 87 mins.

Laws of Gravity
Nick Gomez's first feature was shot in 12 days and made for $38,000. It's a daring excursion into male bravado, the story of the small-time criminal activities of two Bensonhurst hustlers and their strong, determined girlfriends. The plot is motivated by the reappearance of a neighborhood criminal, who turns up with a bag full of handguns and an unexplained source of money. The real star is cinematographer Jean de Segonzac, who shot the entire movie with a hand-held camera. With Peter Greene, Edie Falco, Adam Trese and Arabella Field.
VHS: $18443. $89.95.
Laser: LD74455. $39.99.
Nick Gomez, USA, 1992, 100 mins.

Living in Oblivion
Steve Buscemi heads up an exciting cast featuring James LeGros, Catherine Keener and Dermot Mulroney. This wrenching but comic look at independent filmmaking shows a young filmmaker forced to ponder the inevitable question: Can anything be worth going through the hell of making a low-budget feature film? Winner of the Screenwriting Award at the 1995 Sundance Film Festival.
VHS: $27006. $96.99.
Laser: LD75441. $34.95.
Tom DiCillo, USA, 1995, 92 mins.

Lone Star
The discovery of a human skull and a sheriff's badge

buried on the outskirts of a small west Texas border town reveals a 40-year-old mystery that touches the past of nearly everyone in town—including the current sheriff. As the clues to solving the puzzle are discovered, past wounds are re-opened, old flames are reignited and secrets long-hidden are revealed, in this gripping, suspenseful tale. With Kris Kristofferson, Matthew McConaughey, Chris Cooper, Elizabeth Pena and Frances McDormand. "Sayles' best film so far…quietly stunning" (Janet Maslin, *New York Times*).
VHS: S30944. $19.95.
Laser: LD76135. $39.95.
John Sayles, USA, 1996, 138 mins.

Lost Highway
Lynch's sexy, eerie thriller is a blend of horrifying violence and dark mysterious characters in which a man's (Bill Pullman) feelings for his wife (Patricia Arquette) lead him to the edge of madness. A romantic tragedy fantasy nightmare in true Lynchian tradition. With Robert Loggia, Gary Busey, Robert Blake and Richard Pryor. "Transfixing, seriously spooky" (*The New York Times*). VHS letterboxed.
VHS: S31739. $101.99.
Laser: LD76298. $49.99.
David Lynch, USA, 1997, 135 mins.

love jones
In this hip *When Harry Met Sally*, a beautiful photographer (Nia Long, *Boyz 'N the Hood*) and a struggling writer (Larenz Tate, *Menace II Society*) are two star-crossed lovers caught in the ups and downs of modern-day romance. "Glamorous, romantic fun" (*Los Angeles Times*).
VHS: S31729. $19.98.
Laser: LD76296. $39.99.
Theodore Witcher, USA, 1996, 110 mins.

Lucifer Rising
Invocation of My Demon Brother (a conjuration of pagan forces), and Anger's most recent, *Lucifer Rising*, "a film about the love generation, the birthday party of the Aquarian Age, showing actual ceremonies to make Lucifer rise."
VHS: S00802. $29.95.
Kenneth Anger, USA, 1969, 39 mins.

Matewan
Writer-director John Sayles recreates the life and labor conditions that led to the infamous West Virginia shoot-out known as the Matewan Massacre. In a coal mining town in the 1920's union organizers come up against strong opposition from the mine owners and violence flares. With Chris Cooper, Mary McDonnell and James Earl Jones.
VHS: S06028. $14.98.
John Sayles, USA, 1987, 132 mins.

Mi Vida Loca: My Crazy Life
Allison Anders' vibrant feature is set in Echo Park, Los Angeles, where best friends Sad Girl and Mousie are now enemies as they have both become pregnant by the same man, Ernesto, a local drug dealer. A gritty slice of life.
VHS: S23484. $19.95.
Laser: LD75229. $34.98.
Allison Anders, USA, 1994, 94 mins.

Mikey and Nicky
On the run from the mob, Nicky (John Cassavetes) turns to his old friend Mikey (Peter Falk) for help. Throughout the night they roam the streets of Philadelphia, hiding out and reminiscing about old times, as their stormy past comes to light and the mob closes in. With Ned Beatty. "A gangster film like no other" (Michael Ventura, *LA Weekly*).
VHS: S31557. $29.95.
Elaine May, USA, 1976, 106 mins.

Miller's Crossing
A strikingly stylish gangster film. Set in 1929, *Miller's Crossing* is the story of the friendship between Leo (Albert Finney), the city's Irish political boss, and Tom (Gabriel Byrne), Leo's cool, brainy aide. Their friendship is severed when Leo and Tom both fall in love with Verna (Marcia Gay Harden). Tom joins ranks with Leo's foremost enemy and rival for political power, and a bloody gang war erupts. Also starring John Turturro and J.E. Freeman.
VHS: S13607. $19.98.
Laser: LD71228. $39.98.
Joel Coen, USA, 1990, 115 mins.

My Own Private Idaho
In this modern restructuring of the '60s road movie, River Phoenix and Keanu Reeves hustle their way

through Seattle, Portland, Idaho and Rome on a quest for River's missing mother. With a meticulous, lyric style, the film combines sprawling landscapes, scenes of passionless sexuality and allusions to Orson Welles' *Chimes at Midnight* as it addresses issues of love, family, politics and homosexuality. A work of great complexity and beauty from the director of *Mala Noche* and *Drugstore Cowboy*.
VHS: S15927. $19.95.
Gus Van Sant, USA, 1991, 102 mins.

Mystery Train
"Jim Jarmusch makes bizarre, minimalist and simpatico road movies, with characters on the edge of pop culture discovering a poetically shabby America. We see the land through the eyes of foreigners, unspoiled but prejudiced by American myths." Three separate but interwoven episodes centered in a rundown Memphis hotel reveal the experiences of non-Americans in America. Two young Japanese lovers travel through town on a rock 'n roll pilgrimage, a newly widowed Italian woman waits for a flight back to Rome while she is visited by the ghost of Elvis, a British man makes some friends, gets drunk and commits murder. "There is no real mystery in *Mystery Train*. It makes it points on Elvis-worship, restlessness and race relations out front. But there is a mystery about its construction. The leisurely, distancing pace works beautifully" (Edwin Jahiel). 1990, 110 mins.
VHS: S12988. $19.98.
Jim Jarmusch, USA, 1989, 113 mins.

Nadja
In this stylish, supernatural thriller, a pair of twin brother and sister vampires haunt contemporary New York. Their father is killed by the meddling Dr. Van Helsing, but they resolve to fight back. On the prowl amidst New York's extensive nightlife, they attempt to seduce Van Helsing's beloved niece and nephew. Featuring Peter Fonda, Elina Lowensohn, Martin Donovan, Suzy Amis and Galaxy Craze. B&W.
VHS: S27056. $14.98.
Laser: LD75457. $39.95.
Michael Almereyda, USA, 1995, 92 mins.

Nice Girls…Films by and About Women
This compilation of award-winning short films is a sometimes challenging, always entertaining look into the lives, and through the lenses, of women today. Whatever you do, don't miss *Nice Girls Don't Do It*—an explicit, celebratory analysis of female ejaculation. This collection includes *Emergence of Eunice*, *You Take Care Now*, *Urban Steal*, *Constant State of Departure*, *Broken Heart*, *Social Experiment*, *New Shoes*, *A Still Life of Postcards*, *Another Great Day!*, *Giving Away* and, of course, *Nice Girls Don't Do It*. USA, 90 mins.
VHS: S15541. $19.95.

Night on Earth
Jim Jarmusch's film is structured episodically, with the narrative simultaneously unfolding in Los Angeles, New York, Paris, Rome and Helsinki, and concerns the relationship of cab drivers and their passengers. The ensemble cast includes Gena Rowlands, Winona Ryder, Rosie Perez, Giancarlo Esposito, Armin Mueller-Stahl, Beatrice Dalle, Isaach de Bankole, Roberto Benigni, Matti Pellonpaa and Kari Vaananen. Tom Waits composed the music and performs two numbers. Letterboxed.
VHS: S17625. $19.95.
Jim Jarmusch, USA, 1991, 125 mins.

Palookaville
A comical story about a trio of bumbling down-and-out buddies who make a hilariously inept foray into the world of crime. William Forsythe and Frances McDormand star in this story of two New Jersey chums whose accomplishments include chiseling their way into a bakery when they try to rob a jewelry store. Winner of the Best Film Award at the 1995 Venice Film Festival. With Vincent Gallo and Adam Trese.
VHS: S31108. $99.99.
Laser: LD76199. $39.98.
Alan Taylor, USA, 1995, 92 mins.

Peter Thompson Films
Three extremely moving documentaries: *Two Portraits*, a diptych film about the filmmaker's father and mother; *Universal Hotel* records the filmmaker's search for historical graphic evidence on medical experiments in deep cold by Nazi doctors; and *Universal Citizen* records an encounter with a former

inmate at Dachau, now a smuggler in the Guatemalan jungle.
VHS: S05650. $59.95.
Peter Thompson, USA, 63 mins.

Picture Bride
Tamlyn Tomita stars in this gripping drama based on one woman's journey to a new life spawned by a photograph. Tomita's character travels to Hawaii in order to marry a man whom she has never met, with only a picture to help her find him. Once there, the tropical splendor of Hawaii inspires her toward a passionate romance. Winner of Best Picture Award at Sundance Film Festival.
VHS: S26398. $99.99.
Laser: LD75082. $39.99.
Kayo Hatta, USA, 1995, 95 mins.

Poison
An interwoven trilogy, the film uses three distinct stylistic conventions to explore the writings of Jean Genet, arriving at a profound realization of poison in the human mind, body and soul: A gritty prison drama reveals a homosexual's despair at being constantly confronted by forbidden passions; a campy '50s horror film send-up portrays a scientist's search for the essence of sexuality, and draws a compelling parallel to the HIV crisis when things go awry; and a tabloid mystery criticizes religious sentimentality as it reveals the circumstances surrounding the murder of a wife-beater by his own child, who then flew out the window toward heaven. Winner of the Grand Jury Prize at the Sundance Film Festival.
VHS: S15839. $19.98.
Laser: LD72226. $34.95.
Todd Haynes, USA, 1991, 85 mins.

Portrait of an Artist as a Young Man
This beautiful adaptation of Joyce's autobiographical novel is a faithful portrait of the young author and his coming of age. It portrays Stephen Daedalus and his Irish Catholic upbringing—his confrontation with the tyranny of the church, his sexual guilt and frustration—which start him on the path of rebellion. "Packed with great passages of the Joycean language, and the cast is superb." With Bosco Hogan, T.P. McKenna, John Gielgud.
VHS: S09553. $29.95.
Joseph Strick, USA, 1977, 93 mins.

Powwow Highway
Philbert Bono (Gary Farmer) is a political renegade; Buddy Red Bows (A. Martinez) is a mammoth Cheyenne. With nothing in common but their Indian heritage and a beat-up '64 Buick Wildcat, the two set out on a cross-country adventure filled with comedic and dramatic detours and discover the lingering spirit of their people despite government injustice. With Amanda Wyss and songs by Robbie Robertson, John Fogarty and Rachel Sweet.
VHS: S30826. $14.98.
Jonathan Wacks, USA, 1989, 91 mins.

Puppets & Demons:
Films by Patrick McGuinn
This anthology of ten award-winning short films by the director of *Suroh: Alien Hitchhiker* and *Desert Spirits* blends folkloric icons and modern dilemmas to tell humorous, fresh and unique stories. The collection includes *Terrance Baum: Intergalactic Assassin*, about one night in the life of an "intergalactic parasite terminator" who must save innocent Doris from an oozing being from the Planet Saliva; *Stella!*, *Gran'ma* and *Say Thankyou, Please*, starring Vincent, an id-like puppet doppelganger; *Agnes Keedan's Secret Plan*, a Hansel and Gretal tale of a lonely suburban witch; *Evolution*, the claymation comedy about the food chain; *Satan's Game*; *When the Owling Has Come*, *The Resurrectors* and *So Many People*. "If Jim Henson and David Lynch were genetically melded...these films might be the result" (*GO! Magazine*).
VHS: S31139. $19.95.
Patrick McGuinn, USA, 1997, 60 mins.

Pushing Hands
A loving comedy from the director of *Eat Drink Man Woman*, *The Wedding Banquet* and *Sense and Sensibility*. Mr. Chu is a widowed tai-chi master who leaves Beijing to live with his only son in a New York suburb. The result of this incongruous meeting of differing cultures is a warm comedy. Though his daughter-in-law has no use for him and everything seems to change too quickly, Mr. Chu responds the way he knows best, with the traditional tai-chi exercise of Pushing Hands. English and Mandarin

with English subtitles.
VHS: S27008. $92.99.
Laser: LD75459. $39.95.
Ang Lee, USA, 1995, 100 mins.

Queen of Diamonds
Nina Menkes' audacious feature is set in contemporary Las Vegas. Menkes' style suggests an American Chantal Akerman, with her painterly, evocative depiction of real time characterized by long takes, natural light and a documentary-style naturalism. Tinka Menkes plays a Vegas blackjack dealer abandoned by her husband. Her life is irrevocably altered by her friendship and caring for a dying old man. "Within this arid emotional landscape the protagonist stands, able to dish out what she receives—anger, boredom, contempt—but threatening to vanish if she is not soon loved. *Queen of Diamonds* is a powerful film which spurns resolution, daring its viewers instead to tune into the psychic frequencies of American alienation" (Jon Stout, Los Angeles Film Forum).
VHS: S18685. $59.95.
Nina Menkes, USA, 1991, 77 mins.

Safe
Todd Haynes (*Poison*) directs this unusual, stylish film which stars Julianne Moore (*Vanya on 42nd Street*) as a California suburban housewife who suffers from an insidious modern dilemma. Everything she is surrounded by becomes toxic to her; she is made ill by the poisoned, chemically-laden environment. She seeks refuge in a holistic center in Albuquerque only to discover that the center's magnetic leader has his own personal agenda.
VHS: S26860. $96.99.
Laser: LD75396. $39.95.
Todd Haynes, USA, 1995, 119 mins.

Sankofa
This remarkable, independently-made film by African-American filmmaker Haile Gerima (*Bush Mama*, *Harvest: 3000 Years*) has become a quiet boxoffice sensation entirely by word-of-mouth. *Sankofa* is a Ghanaian word that means returning to the past in order to go forward. Gerima uses this concept to transport a fashion model who is possessed by lingering spirits in the Cape Coast Castle to a sugar plantation where she suffers constant abuse as a slave. *Sankofa* is an attempt to heal the psychic legacy of slavery and to address those in the African Diaspora who neglect their own history. "Engrossing and provocative." (*New York Times*).
VHS: S25625. $64.95.
Haile Gerima, USA/Ghana, 1993, 125 mins.

Shadows
One of the foundation stones of independent American cinema, John Cassavetes' first film features two brothers and a sister who move jerkily through their lives as Cassavetes' free-wheeling camera, naturalistic dialog and jump cuts capture their arguments, sexual encounters and parties. With Lelia Goldoni, Ben Carruthers and Hugh Hurd.
VHS: S26962. $19.95.
John Cassavetes, USA, 1959, 87 mins.

She's Gotta Have It
A brazenly comic foray into sexual politics. Tracy Camila Johns stars as Nola Darling—a beautiful, free-spirited artist who simultaneously shares three men for her pleasure, dominance and one-upmanship. Lee's acute comic perception, innovative cutting and hilarious use of montage aesthetics—where Nola's suitors slay her with opening lines and come-ons—are evidence of a stream-of-consciousness talent and film school sensibility. His father, Bill Lee, composed the music.
VHS: S02777. $14.98.
Laser: LD74463. $49.95.
Spike Lee, USA, 1986, 84 mins.

Slacker
A true sleeper. Richard Linklater's first feature film is a wickedly funny social satire on a new American sub-culture that's inventive, quite bizarre and refreshingly offbeat. Filmed entirely in Austin, Texas, with a cast of hundreds of local residents. The film is a human chain letter: you meet one person and through that person you meet another person, and another ...The local characters voice their opinions on a variety of subjects including Madonna's pap smear, the sniper Charles Whitman, and the JFK assassination.
VHS: S16328. $19.98.
Richard Linklater, USA, 1991, 101 mins.

Sling Blade
Billy Bob Thornton stars in his Academy Award-winning screenplay as Karl, a quiet and simple man who is released from prison 25 years after killing his mother and her lover, and returns to the small Arkansas town of his youth. After he befriends a young boy (Lucas Black), his mother (Natalie Canerday) and her boss (John Ritter), Karl's new life is shattered when he finds himself in conflict with the woman's violent lover (Dwight Yokum), as he confronts his past. With J.T. Walsh, Robert Duvall, and a cameo by Jim Jarmusch.
VHS: S31532. $103.99.
Laser: LD76306. $59.95.
Billy Bob Thornton, USA, 1996, 135 mins.

Smoke
Harvey Keitel, William Hurt, Forest Whitaker, Stockard Channing and Ashley Judd star in this offbeat comedy set in a New York cigar shop. Sparks fly when the manager, played by Keitel, gets involved in the intertwining lives of his colorful customers. A gentle love letter to Brooklyn.
VHS: S26708. $99.99.
Laser: LD75322. $39.98.
Wayne Wang, USA, 1995, 112 mins.

Strong Medicine
Internationally acclaimed theater director Richard Foreman's complex, surreal and alternately funny and frightening first feature is the Alice-in-Wonderland-like adventure of Rhoda, whose husband gives her a gift of a vacation for her birthday, hoping to get her out of his life. Stars American avant-garde theater legends Kate Manheim and David Warrilow, with cameos by Wallace Shawn, Carol Kane, Buck Henry and Raul Julia. "Richard Foreman's work gives resonance and a disturbance not felt from any other company. A pioneer in end-of-millennium controlled chaos" (David Bowie).
VHS: S30250. $34.95.
Richard Foreman, USA, 1980, 95 mins.

SubUrbia
Richard Linklater (*Dazed and Confused*) directed and Eric Bogosian (*Talk Radio*) wrote the screenplay for this "*American Graffiti* for the *Dazed and Confused* set" (Bob Healy, *Satellite News Network*) about a successful rock star who returns home to find his old high school friends doing the same old high school thing—hanging out in the parking lot of a local convenience store. With Jayce Bartok, Parker Posey, Giovanni Ribisi, Steve Zahn, Nicky Katt and Dina Spybey.
VHS: S31720. $19.95.
Richard Linklater, USA, 1997, 121 mins.

Sweet Sweetback's Baadasssss Song
Melvin Van Peebles wrote, directed, produced, scored and starred in this critically acclaimed, reverse racist blaxploitation movie that has Van Peebles on the run from the police after he kills two cops who were beating up on a black man. With John Amos, Simon Chuckster and Rhetta Hughes. X-rated when first released.
VHS: S06195. $59.95.
Laser: LD76004. $49.95.
Melvin Van Peebles, USA, 1971, 90 mins.

Three Short Films (Mark Rappaport)
Three films from the filmmaker who's been called "more hilarious than the Coen brothers, weirder than Hal Hartley, deeper than Woody Allen, and more deadpan than Stephen Wright" (Ray Carney, Boston University). Includes *Mark Rappaport: The TV Spinoff* (1980; 28 mins.), which the *Chicago Reader* called "the best possible introduction to Rappaport's film work;" the "deliciously ironic...amusing, biting" (*Los Angeles Times*) *Postcards* (1990; 26 mins.), a love story told through 1960s postcards; and "the inventive, gorgeous" (*LA Weekly*) *Exterior Night* (1993; 36 mins.). "Mark Rappaport makes movies that look, sound and feel like nobody else's movies. He's an original" (Roger Ebert, *Chicago Sun-Times*).
VHS: S31125. $29.99.
Mark Rappaport, USA, 1980/1990/1993, 90 mins.

Times of Harvey Milk
Academy Award-winning, powerful documentary about the powerful, charismatic, compassionate, gay San Francisco city official Harvey Milk, who was suddenly assassinated. Winner of numerous awards; a powerful document.
VHS: S01348. $39.95.
Epstein & Schmeichen, USA, 1984, 90 mins.

To Die For
Nicole Kidman stars as Suzanne Stone, a beautiful but vacuous weather girl whose real talents lie in manipulation, treachery, and self-promotion. Matt Dillon plays the unsuspecting husband who becomes the target of her murder plot. She doesn't plan to do it alone but rather enlists a love-struck teen-ager to act as assassin. It's the perfect scenario for launching her career as a celebrity. With Joaquin Phoenix and Illeana Douglas.
VHS: S27526. $19.95.
Laser: LD75525. $34.95.
Gus Van Sant, USA, 1995, 107 mins.

To Sleep with Anger
Danny Glover stars as Harry Mention, a mysterious and magnetic visitor from the Deep South who comes to stay with an old friend, named Gideon (Paul Butler), in South-Central Los Angeles. Harry's effect on Gideon and his assimilated black middle-class family is both immediate and profound. He spins tales full of folklore, lucky charms and bad magic that seem exotic and ominous to these urban up-and-comers who have lost touch with the rural tradition.
VHS: S13817. $19.95.
Charles Burnett, USA, 1990, 105 mins.

Trees Lounge
Written, directed and starring actor Steve Buscemi, *Trees Lounge* is the humorous, semi-autobiographical story of Tommy Basilio, a 31-year-old barfly and unemployed auto mechanic with a quick wit and a

Swingin' Sixties

Alfie
VHS: S00028. $14.95.
Laser: LD76037. $39.98.

The Alley Cats
VHS: S32677. $29.95.

Austin Powers: International Man of Mystery
VHS: S32236. $104.99.

Barbarella
VHS: S00095. $19.95.
Laser: LD75155. $34.98.

Blow-Up
VHS: S00152. $19.98.
Laser: Criterion Collection. LD70351. $79.95.
Laser: LD70528. $34.98.

Bye Bye Birdie
VHS: S05338. $19.95.

Casino Royale
VHS: S00217. $14.95.
Laser: LD74615. $39.95.

Georgy Girl
VHS: S03299. $19.95.

Goldfinger
VHS: S00513. $14.95.
Laser: LD70584. $98.99.

Hairspray
VHS: S07303. $14.98.
Laser: LD76261. $39.99.

In Like Flint
VHS: S11264. $19.98.

The Knack...and How to Get It
VHS: S20400. $19.98.
Laser: LD76359. $39.99.

La Dolce Vita
VHS: S00705. $24.95.

The Love God
VHS: S29994. $14.98.

The Party
VHS: S11734. $19.98.
Laser: LD71166. $34.98.

Robin and the 7 Hoods
VHS: S26865. $14.95.

Valley of the Dolls
VHS: S18598. $14.98.
Laser: LD76739. $39.98.

What's New Pussycat
VHS: S13217. $19.95.
Laser: LD72134. $34.98.

chip on his shoulder who spends most nights at his favorite bar, Trees Lounge, in the pursuit of one-night stands. When he loses his pregnant girlfriend (Elizabeth Bracco) to his best friend and former boss (Anthony LaPaglia), he makes an attempt to put his life back together. He finds temporary salvation driving his deceased uncle's ice cream truck, but gets dangerously close to his 17-year-old helper, Debbie (Chloe Sevigny, *Kids*). Tommy discovers a disturbing truth about himself in the last place he expected. "*Trees Lounge* is a winner!" (*People Magazine*).
VHS: $30614. $96.99.
Steve Buscemi, USA, 1996, 94 mins.

Two Small Bodies
Fred Ward and Suzi Amis star in this psychosexual battle of the sexes. Ward is Lieutenant Brown, a detective who believes Eileen (Amis) has murdered her children. Repulsion and attraction send them spinning in orbit around each other until the boundary between truth and illusion is dissolved.
VHS: $21790. $19.98.
Beth B, USA/Germany, 1994, 85 mins.

The Underneath
In this thriller, a handsome drifter (Peter Gallagher) named Michael Chambers goes home. There he finds that the good looks and the good luck he relied on while traveling may not be worth much. His mother wants to start a new life while his brother is consumed by jealous rage. Chambers hopes to reignite an old flame, but there is a complication there as well. Soon he is transfixed in a treacherous game of emotional turmoil, joining sex, desire and violence.
VHS: $26991. $19.98.
Laser: LD75430. $34.98.
Steven Soderbergh, USA, 1994, 100 mins.

Unhook the Stars
In this "self-assured, sweet surprise" (*New City*) about the value of growing up around a variety of women, Nick Cassavetes directs mom, Gena Rowlands, as a widow coping with loneliness, whose life is complicated by her young next door neighbor (Marisa Tomei) when she asks her to take care of her young son for a few hours. Delightful performances by both Rowlands and Tomei; with Gerard Depardieu and Moira Kelly.
VHS: $31285. $103.99.
Laser: LD76214. $39.99.
Nick Cassavetes, USA, 1996, 105 mins.

Union City
Deborah Harry stars in this tale of murder and paranoia set in a large industrial city. With a guest appearance by Pat Benatar, music composed by Blondie's Chris Stein.
VHS: S01766. $19.98.
Mark Reichert, USA, 1981, 82 mins.

Waiting for Guffman
A sort of *Spinal Tap* for community theater, this hilarious mockumentary stars *Tap* alumnus Christopher Guest as Corky St. Clair, a flamboyant and desperate Broadway wannabe who directs an ambitious, hapless and unintentinally hilarious musical celebrating Blaine, Missouri's 150th anniversary. Fred Willard, Parker Posey, Bob Balaban and *SCTV* alumni Eugene Levy and Catherine O'Hara costar as stage-struck residents hoping to be discovered when they hear reports that big-time talent scout Mort Guffman will be in the audience.
VHS: $31683. $96.99.
Christopher Guest, USA, 1997, 84 mins.

Walking and Talking
This "wildly funny" (CBS Radio, Los Angeles) comedy for everyone who wants to get married and stay single at the same time follows the antics of four friends as they search for true love, from bad dates to long-distance phone sex. With Anne Heche, Todd Field, Liev Schreiber and Catherine Keener.
VHS: $30830. $103.99.
Laser: LD76101. $39.99.
Nicole Holofcener, USA, 1996, 85 mins.

The Wedding Banquet
Ang Lee's surprise hit is a poignant and funny story of the gay Taiwanese yuppie (Winston Chao) who lives with his American lover (Mitchell Lichtenstein) and tries to end his family's endless matchmaking attempts by announcing that he's engaged. His parents unexpectedly fly in to see the bride and turn

Waiting for Guffman

their son's deception into a complicated affair.
VHS: $21895. $94.98.
Laser: LD74593. $39.98.
Ang Lee, USA/Taiwan, 1994, 105 mins.

Welcome to the Dollhouse
Winner of the Grand Jury Prize at the 1996 Sundance Film Festival, a dark and very funny look at adolescence told through the eyes of an angry, young, geeky girl. The usual teen stuff is covered—school, grades, puppy love, sex and rock 'n' roll—but with an original and highly amusing take which "never loses its sense of compassion and respect for the underdog" (*New York Daily News*). With Heather Matarazzo, Matthew Faber, Angela Pietropinto and Eric Mabius (*I Shot Andy Warhol*).
VHS: $30422. $19.95.
Laser: LD76028. $39.95.
Todd Solondz, USA, 1996, 88 mins.

What About Me
Filmed in black and white on location in Tompkins Square Park and the Lower East Side, this gritty film portrays the gradual deterioration of Lisa Napolitano (Rachel Amodeo), a young woman forced to exist on the streets, intermingling with the outcasts of society. Along the way she encounters a shell-shocked Vietnam veteran, Nick (Richard Edson), a nihilistic East Villager, Tom (Nick Zed), and a sympathetic good samaritan, Paul (Richard Hell). With Gregory Corso, Judy Carne, Johnny Thunders, Jerry Nolan and Dee Dee Ramone. Music by Johnny Thunders. "Rachel Amodeo keeps the spirit of Lower East Side filmmaking alive with *What About Me*" (Jim Jarmusch).
VHS: $30744. $29.98.
Rachel Amodeo, USA, 1993, 87 mins.

The Wife
In this "new age *Who's Afraid of Virginia Woolf*" (Amy Taubin, *Village Voice*), actor/writer/director Tom Noonan (*What Happened Was...*) and Julie Hagerty (*Airplane*) star as Jack and Rita, a couple trapped in a fragile marriage who share their lives and professions as psychotherapists in a remote Vermont farmhouse. When Jack's patient Cosmo (Wallace Shawn, *My Dinner with Andre*) drops in for an unexpected visit with his uninhibited wife Arlie (Karen Young, *9½ Weeks*), both couples are in for a delirious night of heavy drinking, pill popping, sexual flirtations, verbal assaults—and shattering revelations. "One of the most strangely funny films of the last few years" (Mick LaSalle, *San Francisco Chronicle*).
VHS: $30738. $19.95.
Tom Noonan, USA, 1996, 101 mins.

A Woman Under the Influence
John Cassavetes' masterpiece centers on a dysfunctional Los Angeles family; in an astounding performance, Gena Rowlands stars as a tightly-wound woman who loves her children too much, withholds her affection from her husband (Peter Falk), and goes slowly insane by her unrealized expectations. A brilliant, uncompromising work, with strong secondary work by Katherine Cassavetes, Lady Rowlands and Fred Draper.
VHS: S17304. $19.95.
John Cassavetes, USA, 1974, 155 mins.

25 Experimental Works on Video

8×8 (A Chess Sonata in 8 Movements)
A masterpiece of experimental film and a projection of the surrealist vision into cinema by its outstanding artists. Described by Richter as "part Freud, part Lewis Carroll," it is a fairy tale for the subconscious based on the game of chess. This chess-sonata is played by a host of artists including Paul Bowles, Jean Cocteau, Julian Levy, Jacqueline Matisse, Jose Sert, Yves Tanguy, Marcel Duchamp, Max Ernst and Alexander Calder. "What interested me is…the poetry of images, the melody and rhythm of forms and colors" (Hans Richter).
VHS: S04359. $59.95.
Hans Richter, USA, 1957, 81 mins.

Avant Garde & Experimental Film
Five early experimental films: Bunuel and Dali's *Un Chien Andalou*, Joris Ivens and Mannus Franken's *Rain*, Erno Metzner's *Uberfall*, Orson Welles' 1934 *Hearts of Age* and Fernand Leger's *Ballet Mecanique*. Silent, with English subtitles. 74 mins.
VHS: S00079. $29.95.

Avant Garde Program #2
Three early silent German and French experimental works: Eggeling's *Symphonie Diagonale*, Man Ray's *L'Etoile de Mer*, and Rene Clair's *Entr'Acte*, starring Man Ray and Marcel Duchamp. 42 mins.
VHS: S00080. $24.95.

Avant Garde Program #11
Features David Lynch's cult-early-classic *Alphabet* (1970, 4 mins), in which the director of *Eraserhead* uses a stunning combination of media to move at breakneck speed through Lynch's vision of the ABC's; Jean Mitry's *Pacific 231*, a film poem which Mitry photographed and cut to fit a twelve-tone musical divertisement which was written by Arthur Honegger some 14 years earlier when Honegger had been aboard the famous train; Marcel Duchamp's *Anemic Cinema* (1926, 5 mins), a series of verbal and visual puns with nonsense phrases.
VHS: S07696. $39.95.

Avant Garde Program #12
Features Germaine Dulac's *Seashell and the Clergyman*, Chris Marker's famous *La Jetee*—both of these are individually available and separately described in the catalog—and Robert Florey/Slavko Vorkapich's *Life and Death of 9413, A Hollywood Extra* , made in 1928, the first important American experimental film, influenced by German Expressionist cinema, a fantasy about an aspiring movie star.
VHS: S07170. $39.95.

Avant Garde Program #14
Three films by the great photographer/artist/filmmaker Man Ray: *Retour a la Raison* (1923, 3 mins) was produced to aggravate audiences at the last great Dada soiree, without the use of a camera, by sprinkling the raw film stock and exposing it light; *Émak Bakia* (1927, 19 mins) is a famous surrealist short in which Man Ray throws the camera into the air; *Les Mysteres du Chateau du De* (1929, 21 mins) features a modern villa designed by Mallet-Stevens as the setting for an unsolved mystery.
VHS: S07169. $39.95.
Man Ray, France, 1921-27, 43 mins.

Experimental Avant Garde Series Volume 19 (Very Serious Fun)
Five short films featuring Hitler, Godzilla, Bambi, JFK and the Grim Reaper: *Bambi Meets Godzilla*—Marv Neuland's wry look at what might happen if these two entertainment legends ever got together. *Lambeth Walk Nazi Style*—Len Lye takes newsreel footage of Hitler and his troops and using freeze frames, jump cuts, repeat action and other techniques, pieces it all together and sets it to a popular British jig. *Loves of Franistan*—a funny take-off of big budget film spectaculars. *The Dove*—a wicked takeoff of Ingmar Bergman films; in one scene Death plays badminton instead of chess. *The JFK Workout*—an offbeat training film made in the 60's to promote JFK's physical fitness; includes a discourse on the inferiority of females. This is not necessarily an avant garde work, but it is so weird and silly we just couldn't leave it out. 60 mins.
VHS: S13504. $39.95.

Experimental Avant Garde Series Volume 20 (The Secret Lives of Inanimate Objects)
Four short films: *Ghosts before Breakfast*—Hans Richter's lively absurdist piece featuring juxtapositions of everyday objects taking on new roles in most unusual settings. *Rhythmus 21*—Richter returns to explore the extremely complex form of the simple square. *H2O*—Ralph Steiner's visually delightful study on water. *The Vanished World of Gloves*—Unusual film by Czechoslovakian Jiri Barta that uses live action and animation to tell this story of some gloves that have come to life. 55 mins.
VHS: S13505. $39.95.

Experimental Avant Garde Series Volume 21 (An Attack on Social, Sexual, and Political Order)
Two short films: *Lot in Sodom*—Watson and Webber's famed filming of the Old Testament story complete with homosexual orgies, sensuous sexual dances and a pillar of salt. *L'Historie du Soldat Inconnu*—Henri Storck uses the signing of the Kellogg-Briand pact to launch his hyperbolic attack on everything including, but not limited to, the bourgeoisie, democracy, religion and capitalism. 45 mins.
VHS: S13506. $29.95.

Experimental Avant Garde Series Volume 22
Knights on Bikes, featuring jousting motorcycle drivers, and *Peepshow* are two of famed director Ken Russell's earliest works. *Happy Anniversary*, by Pierre Etaix and Jean-Claude Carriere, stages a number of gags around the celebration of marital bliss. Finally, director Bert Haanstra exposes the nasty truth about the *The Zoo* in this collection of absurd and serious films. 50 mins.
VHS: S22468. $29.95.

Films of Charles and Ray Eames
Charles and Ray Eames are among the most influential American designers of this century. Best known for their ground-breaking contributions to architecture, furniture design, industrial design and photography, their legacy also includes over 75 innovative short films. The finest of these programs is in a new series, introduced in a narration by Gregory Peck.
Films of Charles and Ray Eames, Volume 1. Powers of Ten, the film that revolutionized the way we view our world, takes us on a breathtaking voyage from the interior of an atom to the furthest reaches of the universe. Starting with the closeup of a man's hand, and increasing the distance from the starting point ten times every ten seconds, this startling adventure in magnitudes illustrates as few films ever have the concepts of space and time. 21 mins.
VHS: S13218. $39.95.
Laser: LD70774. $49.95.
Films of Charles and Ray Eames, Volume 2. The second volume in the series consists of seven short films of dazzling impact and variety. From *Toccata for Toy Trains*, a magical look at antique toy trains, to *The Black Ships*, a subtle view of Admiral Perry's opening of Asia as seen through the Japanese art of the time, this collection illustrates the Eames' remarkable warmth, diversity and intelligence. 62 mins.
VHS: S13219. $39.95.
Laser: LD70775. $49.95.
Films of Charles and Ray Eames, Volume 3. The lives of Benjamin Franklin and Thomas Jefferson spanned 120 years and shaped the course of American history. This film, produced and directed by the famous design team of Charles and Ray Eames, is a masterful tribute to the two founding

fathers of American independence. Franklin and Jefferson's philosophies and contributions are viewed against the background of the literary, scientific and artistic developments of their time. Using a visual timeline constructed of portraits, documents and other historical artifacts, the interlocking chapters of each man's story are brought to life. Narrated by Orson Welles and Nina Foch, with original music by Elmer Bernstein. USA, 35 mins.
VHS: $15395. $39.95.

Films of Charles and Ray Eames, Volume 4. This design workshop by Charles Eames features *Design Q & A*, one of the most concise and witty statements about design on film. *Goods*, a discussion of the "new convertables" and one of Eames legendary 3-screen slide shows are also included, as well as *IBM Math Peep Shows, SX-70, Polychris Hapus, The Fiberglass Chairs* and *Copernicus*. 59 mins.
VHS: $21522. $39.95.

The Films of Scott Bartlett

Visionary—one of America's most celebrated experimental filmmakers. Pioneer—Bartlett's landmark films *Offon* and *Moon 1969* are acknowledged as the earliest expressions of electronic cinema.
Volume 1: The Birth of the Counter Culture. Three landmark films: *Offon*, a classic of experimental film, "a perfect, magical fusion of non-verbal communication and advanced technological filmmaking" (Amos Vogel); *Moon 1969*, "a beautiful, eerie, haunting film, all the more wonderful for the fact that we do not once see the moon—only the manifestations of its powers here on earth" (*L.A. Times*); *1970*, a dramatic autobiographical film that is a multiplexed portrait of the San Francisco sub-culture of the 1960's, "a lasting testament to a time we will never forget" (L.A. Film Festival). 55 mins.
VHS: S05621. $59.95.
Volume 2: The Future of Human Mythology. The serpent embodies the primal chaotic life force in mythic symbology. *Serpent* uses natural and electronic imagery to convey this elusive force in what is "an outstanding piece of art. Striking, kinetic. A beautiful combination of pure visual poetry and ideas about man and the world" (American Film Festival). Also contains *Medina*, an extraordinary, lucid and lyrical documentary of Morocco, "the richest, boldest, most subtly disciplined evocation of a place that I have ever seen on film" (*New York Times*). Also included are *Sound of One*, the unique melding of T'ai Chi Ch'uan and filmmaking, and *Heavy Metal*, which employs elaborate optical techniques to create an instant audio-visual trip back to 1929. 52 mins.
VHS: S05644. $59.95.
Volume 3: The Process of Creation. In the summer of 1967, Scott Bartlett's film loops and Glen McKay's light show liquids were mixed through a video effects bank and the results were filmed by Mike MacNamee. The finished film was called *Offon*. In 1980, Bartlett recreated the event in a video production class at UCLA. The result is *Making Offon*, a video primer. Wipes, keying and feedback are first illustrated and named, then woven into a sound and picture puzzle of the 60's. In *Making Serpent*, Bartlett narrates and describes the creative process behind *Serpent*, his award-winning film. *Making Serpent* is a step-by-step teaching device that explores film techniques such as how to structure a non-verbal narrative, how to shoot film for special editing techniques, how to isolate universal images in nature, and how to make exciting visuals inexpensively. "Eisenstein's *Film Form* continued on film" (Bruce Baillie). 50 mins.
VHS: S05643. $59.95.
Scott Bartlett, USA, 1968-1980

Flaming Creatures

Jack Smith's groundbreaking, lyrical queer film is being released in a special limited-edition series to raise funds that will help restore and preserve his other works. This classic may seem tame by current standards, but its great camp style stands the test of time.
VHS: S27242. $195.00.

Hans Richter: Early Avant-Garde Films

Richter on Film (1972, 14 mins.) is an interview with Hans Richter at age 83 in his Connecticut home, talking about his early experimental films and their relationship to his paintings, scrolls and collages. The pioneer work *Rhythm 21* (*Rhythmus 21*, 1921-4) orchestrates the squares and rectangles of the film screen, while *Rhythm 23* (*Rhythmus 23*, 1923, 3 mins., silent) features criss-cross patterns, negative

reversals, intercut stringed forms and further variations of the rectangle and square. *Film Study* (*Filmstudie*, 1926, 4 mins.) integrates abstract images with their recognizable counterparts. *Ghosts Before Breakfast* (*Vormittagespuk*, 1927-8, 7 mins.) is Richter's witty, cinegenic mini-classic on the universal theme of the object's revolt and an excellent introduction to avant-garde film for all audiences. *Inflation* (*Inflation*, 1926-9) and *Everything Turns, Everything Revolves* (*Alles Dreht Sich, Alles Bewegt Sich*, 1926-9, 9 mins.) are two cinema essays reflecting life in pre-Nazi Germany, using inventive documentary and avant-garde techniques. *Race Symphony* (*Rennsymphonie*, 1928-9) is an excerpt from Richter's study of a day at the races in pre-Nazi Germany. *Two-Penny Magic* (1928-9, 10 mins.) is an essay in rhyming images, made to advertise a picture magazine.
VHS: S30215. $100.00.
Hans Richter, 1921-29, 42 mins.

Man Ray Video

Films by the important experimental filmmaker, photographer and surrealist, Man Ray. *Emak Bakia* was described by Man Ray as a "cine poem," (1927, 18 mins.); *L'Etoile de Mer* (1928, 15 mins.) is based on a poem by Robert Desnos and juxtaposes still lives, masked faces, a woman, a starfish and Paris; *Le Retour a la Raison* (1923) weaves abstract and concrete images; *Les Mysteres du Chateau du De* (1929), filmed at the chateau of the Comte de Noailles, explores the structure and dramatic light effects of the forms of the villa.
VHS: S09050. $24.95.
Man Ray, France, 1927-29

Maya Deren Experimental Films

A newly re-mastered, top quality reproduction of the leading female experimental filmmaker in cinematic history. Maya Deren's six chamber films included here are: *Meshes of the Afternoon, At Land, A Study in Choreography for Camera, Ritual in Transfigured Time, Meditation on Violence* and *The Very Eye of Night*. Silent.
VHS: S00836. $29.95.
Maya Deren, USA, 1943-49, 76 mins.

Nam Jun Paik

Profile of avant-garde composer/performance artist Nam Jun Paik. Includes excerpts from video experiments. 1975, 28 mins.
VHS: S31599. $59.95.

Stan Brakhage Selected Films: Vol. 1

Includes six Brakhage short films from 1954-57: *Desistfilm* (1954, 7 mins.), *Reflections on Black* (1955, 12 mins.), *The Wonder Ring* (1955, 4 mins.), *Flesh of Morning* (1956, 25 mins.), *Loving* (1956, 6 mins.) and *Daybreak & Whiteye* (1957, 8 mins.).
VHS: S30216. $100.00.
Stan Brakhage, USA, 1954-1957, 62 mins.

Hans Richter: Early Avant-Garde Films

Stan Brakhage Selected Films: Vol. 2

Includes six Brakhage short films from 1959-62: *Cat's Cradle* (1959, 5 mins.), *Window Water Baby Moving* (1959, 12 mins.), *Sirius Remembered* (1959, 12 mins.), *The Dead* (1960, 11 mins.), *Thigh Line Lyre Triangular* (1961, 5 mins.), *Blue Moses* (1962, 11 mins.) and *Mothlight* (1963, 4 mins.).
VHS: S30218. $100.00.
Stan Brakhage, USA, 1959-1962, 60 mins.

Sundance Film Festival Winners

1997

Grand Jury Prize, Dramatic

Sunday
Unavailable on video.
Jonathan Nossiter

Grand Jury Prize, Documentary

Girls Like Us
Unavailable on video.
Jane C. Wagner/Tina DeFeliciantonia

Filmmakers Trophy, Dramatic

In the Company of Men
One of the most talked about films of the year: the
controversial story of two young businessmen who
seek revenge on the female gender through a young,
deaf secretary. A brilliant black comedy with stellar
performances by all the leads.
  VHS: S33318. $105.99.
Neil LaBute

Filmmakers Trophy, Documentary

Licensed to Kill
Unavailable on video.
Arthur Dong

Directing Award, Dramatic

Hurricane
Unavailable on video.
Morgan J. Freeman

Directing Award, Documentary

Licensed to Kill

Audience Awards, Dramatic

Hurricane

love jones
In this hip *When Harry Met Sally*, a beautiful
photographer (Nia Long, *Boyz 'N the Hood*) and a
struggling writer (Larenz Tate, *Menace II Society*)
are two star-crossed lovers caught in the ups and
downs of modern-day romance. "Glamorous,
romantic fun" (*Los Angeles Times*).
  VHS: S31729. $19.98.
  Laser: LD76296. $39.99.
Theodore Witcher, USA, 1996, 110 mins.

Audience Award, Documentary

**Paul Monette:
The Brink of Summer's End**
Unavailable on video.
Monte Bramer

Cinematography Award, Dramatic

Hurricane
Cinematographer: Enrique Chediak

Cinematography Award, Documentary

**My America...or Honk
If You Love Buddha**
Unavailable on video.
Cinematographer: Christine Choy

Waldo Salt Screenwriting Award

Sunday
Screenwriters: James Lasdun and Jonathan
Nossiter

Freedom of Expression Awards

**Fear and Learning at
Hoover Elementary**
Unavailable on video.
Laura Angelica Simon
Family Name
Unavailable on video.
Macky Alston

Latin-American Cinema Award

Landscapes of Memory
Unavailable on video.
Jose Araujo

Honorable Mention in Latin-American Cinema

Deep Crimson
Unavailable on video.
Arturo Ripstein

Short Filmmaking Award

Man About Town
Unavailable on video.
Kris Isacsson

Color of a Brisk and Leaping Day

Syphon Gun
Unavailable on video.
KC Amos

Birdhouse
Unavailable on video.
Richard C. Zimmerman

Special Recognition

Sick: The Life and Death of Bob Flanagan
Unavailable on video.
Kirby Dick

Special Recognition for Acting

Parker Posey in
The House of Yes
Existing "somewhere between *Long Day's Journey into Night* and *The Addams Family*" (Roger Ebert, *Chicago Sun-Times*), *The House of Yes* is an offbeat comedy about Marty Pascal (Josh Hamilton), who brings his fiance, Lesly (Tori Spelling), home for Thanksgiving in 1983 to meet his dysfunctional family. It soon becomes clear that Marty's jealous twin sister (Parker Posey)—who calls herself Jackie-O—is a little too close to her twin. But Jackie isn't the only family member with problems, in this house where the word "no" is never heard. With Freddie Prinze, Jr., and Genevieve Bujold.
VHS: S33697. $103.99.
Laser: LD76814. $39.99.
Mark Waters, USA, 1997, 87 mins.

Special Recognition for Production Design

Therese DePrez for
Going All the Way
Unavailable on video.

1996

Grand Jury Prize, Dramatic

Welcome to the Dollhouse
A dark and very funny look at adolescence told through the eyes of an angry, young, geeky girl. The usual teen stuff is covered—school, grades, puppy love, sex and rock 'n' roll—but with an original and highly amusing take which "never loses its sense of compassion and respect for the underdog" (*New York Daily News*). With Heather Matarazzo, Matthew Faber, Angela Pietropinto and Eric Mabius (*I Shot Andy Warhol*).
VHS: S30422. $19.95.
Laser: LD76028. $39.95.
Todd Solondz, USA, 1996, 88 mins.

Grand Jury Prize, Documentary

Troublesome Creek: A Midwestern
The absorbing, award-winning documentary of an Iowa family's struggle against debt, flawed government policies and a dispassionate local banker to save their family farm, which has been turning out crops by the Jordan family since the 1860s, as told by the youngest daughter of the Jordan family and her filmmaker husband. "A story about loss, about how a time and a place that meant so much to us is being bulldozed under" (John Petrakis, *Chicago Tribune*).
VHS: S31727. $59.99.
Jeanne Jordan/Steven Ascher, USA, 1997, 88 mins.

Filmmakers Trophy, Dramatic

Girls Town
Lili Taylor (*I Shot Andy Warhol*) heads an impressive ensemble cast in this gritty coming-of-age tale of four tough inner-city high school friends and the unexpected forces that tear them apart. Only weeks from graduation, an unforseen tragedy shatters their already fragile world, forcing them into a soul-wrenching struggle over loyalty, love, betrayal and

identity in this funny, raw, exciting slice of real life.
VHS: S30581. $19.98.
Jim McKay, USA, 1996, 90 mins.

Filmmakers Trophy, Documentary

Cutting Loose
Unavailable on video.
Susan Todd/Andrew Young

Audience Award, Dramatic

Care of the Spitfire Grill
After her release from prison, the mysterious Percy
(Alison Elliot, *The Underneath*) arrives in the small
town of Gilead, Maine, on the run from her past.
Working as a waitress at the Spitfire Grill, run by
cantankerous Hannah (Ellen Burstyn) and Shelby
(Marcia Gay Harden), Percy comes face-to-face with
her future. "One of the year's most compelling,
haunting and beautifully acted films" (CBS Radio
Los Angeles).
VHS: S30965. $19.95.
Laser: LD76137. $39.95.
Lee David Zlotoff, USA, 1996, 111 mins.

Audience Award, Documentary

Troublesome Creek: A Midwestern

Cinematography Award, Dramatic

Color of a Brisk and Leaping Day
Unavailable on video.
Rob Sweeney

Cinematography Award, Documentary

Cutting Loose
Susan Todd/Andrew Young

Waldo Salt Screenwriting Award

Big Night
This charmer of a movie—a big winner with
audiences, and a treat for movie and food lovers—is
the story of two Italian brothers whose restaurant
teeters on the brink of bankruptcy. With Minnie
Driver, Ian Holm, Isabella Rossellini, Campbell
Scott, Tony Shalhoub and Stanley Tucci. "A feast of a
film" (Peter Travers, *Newsday*).
VHS: S31122. $19.95.
Laser: LD76173. $34.99.
Stanley Tucci, USA, 1996, 109 mins.

Freedom of Expression Award

The Celluloid Closet
Lily Tomlin, Shirley MacLaine, Tony Curtis, Susan
Sarandon, Tom Hanks, Whoopi Goldberg and others
provide the commentary to entertaining clips from
over 120 films as we learn all the secrets and hear all
the stories in this compilation of the history of
homosexuality in Hollywood movies. A fun romp
with some amazing pre-Breen-code early footage.
"An indispensable addition to the history of
Hollywood, with the popular appeal of *That's
Entertainment*" (Janet Maslin, *New York Times*).
VHS: S30403. $19.95.
Laser: LD76027. $39.95.
**Rob Epstein/Jeffrey Friedman, USA, 1996, 102
mins.**

Special Jury Recognition

When We Were Kings
Leon Cast's Academy Award-winning documentary is
a knockout 20-year labor of love chronicling the
famous 1974 "Rumble in the Jungle" heavyweight
championship fight between 32-year-old Muhammad
Ali and George Foreman in Zaire. Capturing the wit,
charisma, intelligence and determination of "the
Greatest," Cast's film is a lasting legacy of Ali the
boxer, provocateur and political instigator. With
interviews with Norman Mailer, George Plimpton and
Spike Lee.
DVD: DV60129. $29.95.
VHS: S31675. $19.95.
Laser: Letterboxed. LD76286. $39.99.
Leon Cast, USA, 1997, 90 mins.

Girls Town
I Shot Andy Warhol
Lili Taylor is Valerie Solanas, the eccentric writer of
a play called *Up Your Ass* and the founder and sole
member of the revolutionary group the Society for
Cutting Up Men. This film shows Warhol's Factory
through its heyday, until it all was radically changed
by a furious, gun-toting Solanas. Her revenge against
Warhol for refusing to produce her play sent
shockwaves through the art world. Stephen Dorff is
Candy Darling and Jared Harris is Warhol.
VHS: S29783. $19.98.
Laser: LD76039. $39.98.
Mary Harron, USA, 1996, 100 mins.

Special Recognition in Latin-American Cinema

Madagascar
Unavailable on video.
Fernando Perez

Special Mentions in Latin-American Cinema

Guantanamera
Unavailable on video.
Tomas Gutierez Alea/Juan Carlos Tabio

Wild Horses
When an elderly pensioner (Hector Alterio) resorts to
bank robbery to recover his $15,000 nest egg, a
young employee (Leonard Sbaraglia) gives him
$500,000 and volunteers to be his hostage. The
unlikely duo escapes and hits the road to Patagonia.
During their flight, Jose and Pedro send videotaped
messages to the press detailing the money's illegal
origins and their own good intentions. Ordinary
citizens soon come to their aid, and Jose and Pedro
find themselves in the limelight. With Cecilia
Dopazo. "Cut from the same cloth as *Butch Cassidy
and the Sundance Kid* and *Thelma and Louise* with a
touch of Tarantino thrown in" (*Box Office Magazine*).
Spanish with English subtitles.
VHS: S32962. $89.95.
Marcelo Pineyro, Argentina, 1995, 122 mins.

Special Recognition in Short Filmmaking

A Small Domain
Unavailable on video.
Britta Sjogren

Honorable Mentions in Short Filmmaking

Pig!
Unavailable on video.
Francine McDougall

Dry Mount
Unavailable on video.
Nichol Simmons

1995

Grand Jury Prize, Dramatic

The Brothers McMullen
In this romantic comedy, three brothers from Long Island confront the unknown territory of love and marriage. After their father dies, their mother returns to Ireland to be with the man she really loves. The three Irish Catholic brothers are left to deal with varying stages of love and marriage, ranging from initial attraction to engagement to the prospect of an extramarital affair. With Edward Burns, Jack Mulcahy, Mike McGlone and Connie Britton.
VHS: $27210. $19.95.
Laser: LD75482. $39.98.
Edward Burns, USA, 1995, 98 mins.

Grand Jury Prize, Documentary

Crumb
Robert Crumb, the multi-talented underground comic book artist, is profiled in this unique, in-depth documentary portrait. Emerging from a dysfunctional family, it's a wonder that Crumb managed to channel his peculiar take on the world into a relatively socially acceptable form. Part of the great fascination of this film is the revelation that his brothers, both also quite gifted, were not as lucky.
VHS: $27253. $19.95.
Laser: LD75491. $39.95.
Terry Zwigoff, USA, 1995, 119 mins.

Filmmakers Trophy, Dramatic

Angela
Unavailable on video.
Rebecca Miller

Filmmakers Trophy, Documentary

Black Is...Black Ain't
Unavailable on video.
Marlon T. Riggs

Audience Award, Dramatic

Picture Bride
Tamlyn Tomita stars in this gripping drama based on one woman's journey to a new life spawned by a photograph. Tomita's character travels to Hawaii in order to marry a man whom she has never met, with only a picture to help her find him. Once there, the tropical splendor of Hawaii inspires her toward a passionate romance.
VHS: $26398. $99.99.
Laser: LD75082. $39.99.
Kayo Hatta, USA, 1995, 95 mins.

Audience Awards, Documentary

Ballot Measure 9
Follows the fight around Oregon's Ballot Measure 9. Essentially, the initiative would have denied lesbians and gay men civil rights protection. Though defeated, it was the center of acrimonious debate and tense standoffs. This documentary captures the heroic spirits of the people who stood up against bigotry, even under threat of physical harm.
VHS: $27476. $29.98.
Heather MacDonald, USA, 1995, 72 mins.

Unzipped
Isaac Mizrahi, the New York-based fashion designer, is the central subject of this frothy and humorous documentary. This surprisingly intimate film was directed by Mizrahi's former boyfriend. (They broke up during the editing.) It begins with a depressed Mizrahi contemplating his poorly received Spring 1994 collection and ends with the creation of his Fall collection. Along with supermodels Kate Moss, Cindy Crawford, Linda Evangelista and Naomi Campbell, Mizrahi provides witty insights into the world of fashion and artifice.
VHS: $26999. $99.99.
Laser: LD75453. $39.95.
Douglas Keeve, USA, 1995, 73 mins.

Cinematography Award, Dramatic

Angela
Ellen Kuras

Cinematography Award, Documentary

Crumb

Waldo Salt Screenwriting Award

Living in Oblivion
Steve Buscemi heads up an exciting cast featuring James LeGros, Catherine Keener and Dermot Mulroney. This wrenching but comic look at independent filmmaking shows a young filmmaker forced to ponder the inevitable question: Can anything be worth going through the hell of making a low-budget feature film?
VHS: $27066. $96.99.
Laser: LD75441. $34.95.
Tom DiCillo, USA, 1995, 92 mins.

Freedom of Expression Award

When Billy Broke His Head...and Other Tales of Wonder
Unavailable on video.
Billy Golfus/David E. Simpson

Special Jury Recognition

Jupiter's Wife
Maggie is a beguiling homeless woman who lives in Central Park and claims to be the daughter of Robert Ryan and the wife of the god Jupiter. This documentary gets around her enchanting view of the world to discover the real-life mystery behind this cryptic personality.
VHS: $29867. $24.95.
Michel Negroponte, USA, 1994, 78 mins.

Special Recognition for Directing

Heavy
The life of an overweight pizza chef (Pruitt Taylor Vince) changes dramatically when his mother (Shelley Winters) dies and a beautiful and kind waitress (Liv Tyler) opens his heart to love. With Deborah Harry (Blondie) and Evan Dando (The Lemonheads) and music by Sonic Youth's Thurston Moore. "Quietly earthshaking...eloquent, purposeful" (Janet Maslin, *New York Times*).
VHS: $31197. $98.99.
James Mangold, USA, 1995, 104 mins.

Rhythm Thief
In this "lower East Side *Breathless*" (Jay Carr, *Boston Globe*), Simon (Jason Andrews) is a New York City bootlegger who sells stolen music on the Lower East Side, in between trysts with Cyd, a Ludlow Street chick (Kimberly Flynn), and Marty, a former lover (Eddie Daniels). Simon's bootleg activity kickstarts an all-out war with a militant all-girl punk band. Driven out of town to Far Rockaway, Simon and his buddy Fuller (Kevin Corrigan, *Walking and Talking*) are drawn into a classic showdown under the 105th Street boardwalk. "Inventive, exciting, original"

(Martin Scorsese).
VHS: S32682. $39.99.
Matthew Harrison, USA, 1994, 88 mins.

Special Recognition in Latin-American Cinema

Eagles Don't Hunt Flies
Unavailable on video.
Sergio Cabrera

Special Mention in Latin-American Cinema

Strawberry & Chocolate
A sensation from Cuba in which a chance encounter over ice cream between a middle-aged gay man and a young, fervent believer in contemporary Cuban Marxism sets the stage for a funny but serious film about difference and acceptance. Their friendship develops despite official intolerance of homosexuality and it soon withstands that short-sighted policy. This film broke box office attendance records in Cuba and achieved world-wide acclaim. Spanish with English subtitles.
VHS: S26613. $19.95.
Laser: LD75320. $39.98.
Tomas Gutierrez Alea, Cuba, 1994, 104 mins.

Ballot Measure 9

Special Recognition in Short Filmmaking Awards

The Salesman and Other Adventures
Unavailable on video.
Hannah Weyer

Tom's Flesh
Unavailable on video.
Jane Wagner/Tom diMaria

Honorable Mentions in Short Filmmaking

Trevor
Unavailable on video.
Peggy Rajski

Nonnie and Alex
Unavailable on video.
Todd Field

1994

Grand Jury Prize, Dramatic

What Happened Was...
Dating is often an unnerving, albeit exciting and sexy, prospect. Two young office workers venture into the unknown territory of their dreams and desires, which results in a number of startling revelations. The journey into the uncharted territory of erotic fantasies and private thoughts makes for one highly unpredictable romantic encounter. With Karen Sillas.
VHS: S27257. $14.98.
Laser: LD75473. $39.99.
Tom Noonan, USA, 1994, 90 mins.

Grand Jury Prize, Documentary

Freedom on My Mind
Unavailable on video.
Connie Field/Marilyn Mulford

Filmmakers Trophies, Dramatic

Clerks
For the slacker generation life seems to be just a series of dead-end jobs where catering to jerks is the only way to pay the bills. This great, independently made comedy follows a parade of annoying shoppers helped by two friends. One works at a convenience store and the other at a video shop next door.
VHS: S24576. $19.95.
Laser: LD74977. $39.99.
Kevin Smith, USA, 1994, 92 mins.

Fresh
An electrifying feature about a 12-year-old boy (Sean Nelson) who walks a fine line between attending school and carrying drugs in his drug-infested Brooklyn environment. After witnessing a murder, he must fight for his own survival. A film that's at once powerful and riveting, and one that refuses to make a judgment call on its young protagonist. With Samuel L. Jackson.
VHS: S23480. $96.98.
Laser: Letterboxed. LD74939. $39.99.
Boaz Yakin, USA, 1994, 114 mins.

Filmmakers Trophy, Documentary

Theremin: An Electronic Odyssey
A cross between Albert Einstein and Ed Wood, Leon Theremin pioneered the electronic music revolution four decades before the rise of Electronic Rock. His invention, the Theremin, produced an eerie, warbling sound, and was used on many Hollywood sound tracks, including *Spellbound*, *The Day the Earth Stood Still* and *The Lost Weekend*, and by rock legends Brian Wilson and Todd Rundgren. At the height of his popularity, Theremin was kidnapped by Soviet agents and forced to develop spy technology for Stalin's KGB. Janet Maslin (*The New York Times*) calls it "fascinating," and it is. Winner at the Sundance and San Francisco Film Festivals.
VHS: S27436. $19.98.
Laser: LD75505. $39.99.
Steven M. Martin, USA/Great Britain, 1995, 84 mins.

Audience Award, Dramatic

Spanking the Monkey
Jeremy Davies stars as a young man on his way to a prestigious summer internship in Washington, D.C., after finishing his first year of pre-med. He returns to his home town for a weekend visit, to find his mother confined to her bed with a broken leg and his father unwilling and unable to care for her. Forced to delay his internship, he attempts to deal with his incestuous relationship with his mother and the absenteeism of

his controlling father.
VHS: $22891. $19.95.
David O. Russell, USA, 1994, 99 mins.

Hoop Dreams

The groundbreaking documentary about the dream
that inspires young men throughout the country: the
dream of playing professional basketball for the
NBA. Seven years in the making, *Hoop Dreams* is an
innovative work that closely focuses on the maze of
high school sports, agents and the system as well as
on the dreams of escaping the inner city. A
remarkable, heartrending piece of history that says a
lot about basketball, and about the life we all choose
to live. Produced by Kartemquin Films.
VHS: $24386. $19.98.
Laser: Widescreen. LD74943. $49.99.
Steve James/Fred Marx/Peter Gilbert, USA, 1994,
176 mins.

Suture

Dennis Haybert, Mel Harris and Michael Harris star
in this tense thriller which mixes treachery, passion
and mistaken identity. An homage to Hitchcock, the
central characters are two brothers. When one brother
is set up to be mistaken for the other all the worst of
one's deeds come back to haunt them both. "Daringly
original! A mind-blowing journey to the outer limits"
(*New York Post*).
VHS: $25099. $19.98.
Laser: LD75021. $39.99.
Scott McGehee/David Siegel, USA, 1994, 96 mins.

Colorado Cowboy: The Bruce Ford Story

Bruce Ford is a legend in rodeo. No man has won
more championships in the same event. This film
explores the roots and horizons of a man pursuing his
own dream, a tradition of pride inherited from his
father, a legacy of grace. It's a documentary that
traces the line between championship and despair in
the Western sport of bareback riding.
VHS: $23286. $24.95.
Arthur Elgort, USA, 1993, 78 mins.

What Happened Was...

Dialogues with Madwomen

Unavailable on video.
Allie Light

Heart of the Matter

Unavailable on video.
Gini Reticker/Amber Hollibaugh

Coming Out Under Fire

Tells the story of nine lesbians and gay male veterans
of the U.S. military. Based on Alan Berube's book of
the same name, this film fleshes out this often
misunderstood case of grave social injustice, using
declassified documents, rare archival footage,
interviews, photographs and more, and touches on the
World War II origins of the current "don't ask, don't
tell" policy. B&W.
VHS: $26966. $29.98.
Arthur Dong, USA, 1994, 71 mins.

Sean Nelson in
Fresh

Alicia Witt and Renee Humphrey in
Fun
In this "dazzling and disturbing" (*New Musical
Express*) psychological thriller, two suburban
teenaged girls meet and quickly become best friends.
In the span of a single afternoon they share their most
guarded secrets, and, in a rising frenzy, murder an
elderly woman for "fun." A kind of *Heavenly
Creatures* from Hell. With Alicia Witt and Renee
Humphrey.
VHS: $32154. $94.95.
Rafael Zelinsky, USA, 1994, 95 mins.

1993

Ruby in Paradise

This film, starring the beautiful and accomplished
Ashley Judd, charts the progress of a woman toward
her own personal paradise. Visually stunning
cinematography shows the Florida locations to great
advantage in this story of one woman's quest for
meaning.
VHS: $20711. $19.95.
Victor Nunez, USA, 1993, 115 mins.

Public Access

Unavailable on video.
Bryan Singer

Children of Fate

Unavailable on video.
Andrew Young/Susan Todd

Silverlake Life: The View from Here

This highly acclaimed documentary was shown on
PBS's *Point of View* series. It follows the slow
demise of a longtime film and video maker, Tom
Joslin, who is dying of AIDS. This unvarnished self-
portrait of a man (Mark Massi), his family
and his friends offers an unparalleled look into the
heart of the AIDS crises.
VHS: $21880. $19.95.
Laser: CLV. LD74626. $39.95.
Tom Joslin/Peter Friedman, USA, 1993, 89 mins.

Fly by Night

Unavailable on video.
Steve Gomer

Something Within Me

Unavailable on video.
Jerret Engle/Emma Joan Morris

El Mariachi

This film by 24-year-old director Robert Rodriquez
was made for the unbelievable sum of $7,000.
Rodriguez playfully evokes Peckinpah, noir westerns
and Hitchcock. A maverick loner and mariachi player
(Carlos Gallardo) enters a Mexican border town and
is instantly confused with a stark, brutally efficient
assassin (Reinol Martinez). Spanish with English

subtitles.
VHS: S19057. $19.95.
Laser: Special Collector's Edition. **LD71892.**
$49.95.
Robert Rodriguez, USA, 1992, 80 mins.

Audience Award, Documentary

Something Within Me

Cinematography Award, Dramatic

An Ambush of Ghosts
Unavailable on video.
Jody Irola

Cinematography Award, Documentary

Children of Fate

Waldo Salt Screenwriting Award

Combination Platter
The story of an undocumented Chinese waiter in a gritty, remarkably powerful, independent feature by Tony Chan. In the pressure laden world he inhabits, a green card holds the greatest promise for a better life. He finds himself contemplating an American wife, only to reject the chosen woman. But he hadn't counted on a visit from immigration.
VHS: S21747. $89.95.
Tony Chan, USA, 1991, 85 mins.

Freedom of Expression Award

Silverlake Life: The View from Here

Special Jury Prize for a First Feature

Just Another Girl on the I.R.T.
Leslie Harris' debut film is a vivid portrait of the panache of a 17-year-old Brooklyn African-American

Swoon

woman. Ambitious and colorful, she is played by astonishing newcomer named Ariyan Johnson, who portrays a street-tough woman with plans to attend college and study medicine. Harris documents life in the projects, from the unique perspective of a young black woman. With Kevin Thigpen, Jerard Washington and Ebony Jerido.
VHS: S19024. $14.98.
Laser: LD75214. $34.98.
Leslie Harris, USA, 1992, 90 mins.

Special Jury Prize for Distinction

Lillian
Unavailable on video.
David Williams

Special Jury Prize for Superb Technical Achievement

Earth and the American Dream
Unavailable on video.
Bill Couterie

Special Jury Prize for Merit

Something Within Me

1992

Grand Jury Prize, Dramatic

In the Soup
Alexandre Rockwell's film features Seymour Cassel as a mid-level New York mobster entangled with a struggling Lower East Side filmmaker (Steve Buscemi) who's trying to finance production on his 500-page script. Jennifer Beals is a waitress and the object of Buscemi's affection. With Will Patton, Steve Randazzo, Frank Messina and cameos by Jim Jarmusch and Carol Kane.
VHS: S18854. $19.95.
Alexandre Rockwell, USA, 1992, 96 mins.

A Brief History of Time

Errol Morris' documentary about the English physicist Stephen Hawking takes its title from Hawking's best seller. The film explores Hawking's groundbreaking work in quantum physics and the study of the origins of the universe, despite his debilitating physical state, brought about by amyotrophic lateral sclerosis. Morris interweaves anecdotes, family dynamics and Hawking's background into a kaleidoscope of images, movements and sound. Music by Philip Glass.
VHS: $18370. $19.95.
Errol Morris, USA/Great Britain, 1991, 84 mins.

Finding Christa

Unavailable on video.
Camille Bishops/James Hatch

Filmmakers Trophy, Dramatic

Zebrahead

Anthony Drazan's feature debut is a poetic reworking of *Romeo and Juliet*. The film depicts an unlikely romance between battle-scarred, high school teens: Zack (Michael Rappaport), a tough Jewish kid who falls for Nikki (N'Bushe Wright), an independent black woman. With De Shon Castle, Ron Johnson and Ray Sharkey. Cinematography by Maryse Albert. Music by Taj Mahal.
VHS: $18871. $19.95.
Anthony Drazan, USA, 1991, 100 mins.

Filmmakers Trophy, Documentary

A Brief History of Time

Audience Award, Dramatic

The Waterdance

This autobiographical work by Neal Jimenez (*River's Edge*) is a tragicomedy about the recovery of a talented young novelist (Eric Stoltz) paralyzed in a mountain climbing accident, and his time in a paraplegic ward at a local hospital. With Wesley Snipes and William Forsythe as two embittered antagonists, Elizabeth Pena, and Helen Hunt as Stoltz's married lover.
VHS: $18116. $92.95.
Laser: LD71843. $34.95.
Neal Jimenez/Michael Steinberg, USA, 1991, 110 mins.

Audience Award, Documentary

Brother's Keeper

This riveting documentary by Joe Berlinger and Bruce Sinofsky is a reconstruction of the arrest and trial of Delbert Ward in the alleged suffocation and murder of his brother Bill. Set in a small town in upstate New York, Bill, Delbert and their two other brothers lived in a squalid farmhouse with no electricity or running water. *Brother's Keeper* is a powerful work about the nature of justice and community, and the grass-roots campaign to secure Delbert's freedom and exonerate him of the charges.
VHS: $18959. $19.98.
Laser: CLV. LD74472. $39.95.
Joe Berlinger/Bruce Sinofsky, USA, 1992, 105 mins.

Award for Excellence in Cinematography, Dramatic

Swoon

A highly stylized black-and-white reconsideration of the Leopold and Loeb case, in which two University of Chicago students attempt the perfect crime: the kidnapping of a 12-year-old boy, that resulted in his death. This film provides a historical and sexual context for the crime, finding its roots in homoerotic fixation. With Daniel Schlachet, Craig Chester and Ron Vawter.
VHS: $18518. $19.95.
Tom Kalin, USA, 1991, 92 mins.

Award for Excellence in Cinematography, Documentary

Shoot for the Contents

Unavailable on video.
Trinh T. Minh-ha/Kathleen Beeler

Waldo Salt Screenwriting Award

The Waterdance

Special Jury Recognition

The Hours and Times

Christopher Munch's feature debut focuses on the circumstances and possible sexual relationship that existed between John Lennon and the Beatles' manager Brian Epstein during a four-day holiday in Barcelona in Spring 1963. A work of delicacy and heartbreak, the film delves into the inner world of each man, depicting Epstein's erotic obsession and Lennon's confusion and pain as an emerging rock-and-roll icon. With David Angus, Ian Hart and Stephanie Pack.
VHS: $18741. $19.98.
Christopher Munch, USA, 1991, 60 mins.

Mi Vida Loca: My Crazy Life

Allison Anders' vibrant feature is set in Echo Park, Los Angeles, where best friends Sad Girl and Mousie are now enemies as they have both become pregnant by the same man, Ernesto, a local drug dealer. A gritty slice of life.
VHS: $23484. $19.95.
Laser: LD75229. $34.98.
Allison Anders, USA, 1994, 94 mins.

Special Jury Recognition for Performance

Seymour Cassel in
In the Soup

1991

Grand Jury Prize, Dramatic

Poison

An interwoven trilogy, the film uses three distinct stylistic conventions to explore the writings of Jean Genet, arriving at a profound realization of poison in the human mind, body and soul: A gritty prison drama reveals a homosexual's despair at being constantly confronted by forbidden passions; a campy '50s horror film send-up portrays a scientist's search for the essence of sexuality, and draws a compelling parallel to the HIV crisis when things go awry; and a tabloid mystery criticizes religious sentimentality as it reveals the circumstances surrounding the murder of a wife-beater by his own child, who then flew out the window toward heaven.
VHS: $15839. $19.98.
Laser: LD72226. $34.95.
Todd Haynes, USA, 1991, 85 mins.

Grand Jury Prizes, Documentary

American Dream

The winner of the 1990 Academy award for best documentary, forceful account of the labor strike and

political discord in a small, closely knit Minnesota town, at the Hormel Meat Packing plant. Kopple brilliantly covers the issues, background, social and economic context and the key players. The fight literally pitted brother against brother, after some workers crossed the picket line. Kopple strips away the layers of deception and anger to present a startling portrait of Reagan/Bush era greed and the frightening repercussions and break up of a community. Kopple worked on the film for more than seven years.
VHS: $17633. $19.98.
Barbara Kopple, USA, 1990, 90 mins.

Paris Is Burning
The title of this lively New York-based documentary is taken from the name of a drag ball. Filmmaker Jenny Livingston spent several years interviewing members of the black and Hispanic gay community and attending their lavish social functions. These costume balls, in a search for expanding the concept of "realness," have gone beyond simple female impersonation to include such categories as butch queens, military attire, executive looks and fierce vogueing competitions. With the participation of such legends as Dorian Corey, Pepper Lebeija, Venus Xtravaganza, Octavia St. Laurent and Willi Ninja.
VHS: $16701. $19.98.
Jennie Livingston, USA, 1990, 71 mins.

Filmmakers Trophy, Dramatic

Privilege
Unavailable on vodeo.
Yvonne Rainer

Filmmakers Trophy, Documentary

American Dream

Audience Award, Dramatic

One Cup of Coffee
Unavailable on video.
Robin B. Armstrong

Audience Award, Documentary

American Dream

Cinematography Award

Daughters of the Dust
This remarkable first feature by Julie Dash follows three generations of African-American women at the turn of the century, structured around the family's migration from Sea Island to the mainland. Beautifully shot by Arthur Jaffa, the film is a poetic series of pastoral images, landscapes, sound, ritual, music, colors and voice. The film is steeped in the highly distinctive, traditional oral black storytelling, told through a highly unusual narrative device, related by an unborrn child. The images sing. With Cora Lee Day, Alva Rogers, Barbara-O, Turla

Powwow Highway

Hoosier and Kaycee Moore.
VHS: $16913. $24.95.
Julie Dash, USA, 1991, 113 mins.

Cinematography Award, Documentary

Christo in Paris
Since the days of King Henry IV, Paris' Pont Neuf has inspired artists. Here it is the focus of environmental sculptor Christo Javacheff and his wife, Jeanne-Claude, and the millions of Parisians who watch them create an astounding architectural poem. Rich in political intrigue and artistic debate, this "love story" from the Maysles brothers tracks Christo's escape from Bulgaria, his early years as a struggling artist, his romance with Jeanne-Claude and the fulfillment of a ten-year obsession begun in 1975: the wrapping of the Pont Neuf. "*Christo* is another gem from the Maysles, the superstars of cinema verite" (Desson Howe, *Washington Post*). English and French with English subtitles. Cinematography by Deborah Dickson and Susan Fromke.
VHS: $33770. $39.95.
David Maysles/Albert Maysles/Deborah Dickson/Susan Fromke

Special Jury Recognition

Straight Out of Brooklyn
Dennis Brown has been raised in the projects of Brooklyn—entrapped in a world of desperation, drugs and danger. His parents tell him to study hard, go to college and be patient, but Dennis can't wait any longer. He plans a robbery that'll take them out of Brooklyn forever, only now the neighborhood threatens to close in on him before he can escape. An astonishing tale of struggle and achievement from 19-year-old director Matty Rich. "A strong film…honest and effective…the truth is there and it echoes long after the film is over" (Roger Ebert).
VHS: $15274. $19.98.
Laser: LD75134. $24.98.
Matty Rich, USA, 1991, 83 mins.

1990

Grand Jury Prize, Dramatic

Chameleon Street
This debut work by director/writer Wendell B. Harris Jr. is a brilliant portrait of William Douglas Street, a self-educated, high school drop out from Detroit who pulled a series of complicated hoaxes, at various times impersonating a journalist, surgeon, student and lawyer before he was imprisoned. "Harris is an original and eccentric talent" (*New York Times*). With Paula McGee, Anthony Ennis and Daven Kiley.
VHS: $17244. $19.98.
Wendell B. Harris Jr., USA, 1989, 95 mins.

Grand Jury Prizes, Documentary

H-2 Worker
Unavailable on video.
Stephanie Black

Water and Power
Unavailable on video.
Pat O'Neill

Filmmakers Trophy, Dramatic

House Party
One night in East St. Louis, Illinois—the "Blackest city in America"—two teens named Kid and Play decide to take advantage of vacationing parents by throwing a bash, a blow out, a house party. Peppered with hip rap music by these real-life musicians, this is the story of that fateful night and the misadventures of the teens and their friends. A def, Black version of

Paris Is Burning

Risky Business.
VHS: $12749. $19.98.
Reginald Hudlin, USA, 1990, 100 mins.

**Filmmakers Trophy,
Documentary**

Metamorphosis: Man into Woman
Unavailable on video.
Lisa Leeman

Audience Award, Dramatic

Longtime Companion
The impact of AIDS on the gay community is the
subject of this well-received and honestly acted
drama. Bruce Davison stands out in a distinguished
ensemble cast as a man facing the loss of his life
partner. With Stephen Caffrey, Patrick Cassidy, Brian
Cousins, John Dosett, Mark Lamos, Dermot
Mulroney, Mary-Louise Parker.
VHS: $13301. $19.95.
Norman Rene, USA, 1990, 100 mins.

Audience Award, Documentary

Berkeley in the Sixties
A moving documentary about the 1960s social,
political and sexual revolution at the University of
California at Berkeley. The documentary traces the
anti-war protest movement, the free speech
movement, civil rights protests and the formation of
the women's movement. Director Mark Kitchell
interweaves archival footage with interviews with
key leaders of the movement. The soundtrack
includes Joan Baez, Mario Savio, Country Joe and
the Fish, The Band, Jimi Hendrix and The Grateful
Dead. "Probably the best documentary on the sixties
to date" (*Village Voice*).
VHS: $18146. $29.95.
Mark Kitchell, USA, 1990, 117 mins.

**Cinematography Award,
Dramatic**

House Party

**Cinematography Award,
Documentary**

H-2 Worker

**Special Jury Recognition,
Dramatic**

To Sleep with Anger
Danny Glover stars as Harry Mention, a mysterious
and magnetic visitor from the Deep South who comes
to stay with an old friend, named Gideon (Paul
Butler), in South-Central Los Angeles. Harry's effect
on Gideon and his assimilated black middle-class
family is both immediate and profound. He spins
tales full of folklore, lucky charms and bad magic
that seem exotic and ominous to these urban up-and-
comers who have lost touch with the rural tradition.
VHS: $13817. $19.95.
Charles Burnett, USA, 1990, 105 mins.

**Special Jury Recognition,
Documentary**

**Samsara: Death and Rebirth in
Cambodia**
Unavailable on video.
Ellen Bruno

1989

Grand Jury Prize, Dramatic

True Love
Unavailable on video.
Nancy Savoca

Grand Jury Prize, Documentary

For All Mankind
From 1968 to 1972, 24 astronauts traveled to the moon. This is their story, told in their words, in their voices, using the images of their experiences.
Laser: CLV. **LD70986. $39.95.**
Laser: CAV. **LD70987. $99.95.**

Filmmakers Trophy, Dramatic

Powwow Highway
Philbert Bono (Gary Farmer) is a political renegade; Buddy Red Bows (A. Martinez) is a mammoth Cheyenne. With nothing in common but their Indian heritage and a beat-up '64 Buick Wildcat, the two set out on a cross-country adventure filled with comedic and dramatic detours and discover the lingering spirit of their people despite government injustice. With Amanda Wyss and songs by Robbie Robertson, John Fogarty and Rachel Sweet.
VHS: S30826. $14.98.
Jonathan Wacks, USA, 1989, 91 mins.

Filmmakers Trophy, Documentary

John Huston
Unavailable on video.
Frank Martin

Audience Award, Dramatic

sex, lies and videotape
When an old college buddy drops into the lives of a Louisiana yuppie couple, the bonds of matrimony begin to fray. Soderbergh's accomplished feature film debut scored a big win at Cannes and really annoyed Spike Lee. James Spader also won a Best Actor Award at Cannes for his role as the soft-spoken, sensitive visitor. With Peter Gallagher and Andie MacDowell as the former perfect couple and Laura San Giacomo as the lusty sister-in-law.
VHS: S11693. $19.95.
Laser: CAV. **LD70456. $124.95.**
Laser: CLV. **LD70457. $134.98.**
Steven Soderbergh, USA, 1989, 100 mins.

Audience Award, Documentary

For All Mankind

1988

Grand Jury Prize, Dramatic

Heat and Sunlight
Jealousy and obsession overwhelm a photographer during the final 16 hours of his love affair with a dancer. This independent American film is an intense look at the darker side of human relationships. "Narratively wild and aesthetically risky, it's an emotionally gritty and raucously tender film, a remarkable feat" (*Hollywood Reporter*). B&W.
VHS: S12822. $29.95.
Rob Nilsson, USA, 1987, 98 mins.

Grand Jury Prize, Documentary

Beirut: The Last Home Movie
This award-winning documentary chronicles three months in the life of a Lebanese family living in Beirut's heavily bombed and all-but-deserted neighborhood Christian Ashrafia. The Bustros family has chosen to remain in their family home—a 200-year-old palace reminiscent of the Ottoman Empire. They must endure fire, snipers, bombings, sieges—the constant threat of death. Why, then, do they choose to stay? *Beirut: The Last Home Movie* captures the visceral, subjective experience of a family living in one of the most chaotic wars in modern history. "Best Documentary of the Year" (*Writers Guild*, France); "Golden Gate Award" (*San Francisco Film Festival*, USA). Currently out of print.
Jennifer Fox, USA, 1988, 90 mins.

1987

Grand Jury Prizes, Dramatic

Waiting for the Moon
Jill Godmilow's meditation on Gertrude Stein and Alice B. Toklas. Linda Hunt plays Alice B. Toklas and Linda Bassett is Gertrude Stein, in a personal drama about the two remarkable women who were the focal point of Paris expatriate culture and society. Currently out of print.
Jill Godmilow, USA, 1986, 101 mins.

Trouble with Dick
Unavailable on video.
Gary Walkow

Grand Jury Prize, Documentary

Sherman's March
Consistently named on ten best lists all over the country: "uproarious…it'll put you in a pleased delirium and leave you with a happy daze" (*San Francisco Examiner*). The subtitle of the film promises "A Documentary Meditation upon the Possibilities of Romantic Love in the South during an Era of Nuclear Weapons Proliferation," and director Ross McElwee delivers an engaging nonfiction journey through the South in a picaresque tour of contemporary relationships. "If Woody Allen made *Gone with the Wind*, it might resemble *Sherman's March!*" (*People Magazine*).
VHS: S10929. $29.95.
Ross McElwee, USA, 1985, 155 mins.

1986

Grand Jury Prize, Dramatic

Smooth Talk
An adaptation of Joyce Carol Oates' short story *Where Are You Going, Where Have You Been?*, about a 15-year-old girl's stormy coming of age. With Treat Williams and Laura Dern. Currently out of print.
Joyce Chopra, Canada, 1985, 92 mins.

Grand Jury Prize, Documentary

Private Conversations/
On the Set of Death of a Salesman
A first-rate documentary produced with PBS that views the collaborative involvement in the highly praised CBS theatrical play *Death of a Salesman*, starring Dustin Hoffman and John Malkovich. The film features interviews with playwright Arthur Miller, director Volker Schlondorff and Malkovich that buttress its cinema verite authenticity—a deep

focus view on the celebration of the theatre's naturalism. Currently out of print.
Christian Blackwood, USA, 1986, 82 mins.

1985

Grand Jury Prize, Dramatic

Blood Simple
The first film scripted by the talented Coen brothers. A critically acclaimed thriller set in rural Texas tells the old story of a man who hires a sleazy private eye

to kill his wife and her boyfriend. Told in a very imaginative way, it combines chilling suspense with offbeat humor, with double- and triple-crosses building to a blood-curdling surprise climax. The most inventive and original thriller in years.
VHS: S00149. $14.98.
Laser: LD70016. $34.98.
Joel Coen, USA, 1983, 96 mins.

Grand Jury Prize, Documentary

Seventeen
Unavailable on video.
Joel DeMott/Jeff Kreines

Daughters of the Dust

Independent Spirit Award Winners

Organized in 1985, with 345 members, the IFP (Independent Film Project) was formed to honor independent filmmakers and to provide some coverage for films which otherwise might be overlooked by the public, either because the films were only shown in big cities, or got very limited exposure. "Independents" were often misconceived as "obscure foreign films with hard-to-read subtitles or non-linear narratives." What follows are the award-winners to date:

1998

Best Feature

The Apostle
Producer: Rob Carliner

Best First Feature

Eve's Bayou
This assured film debut by Kasi Lemmons explores the secrets of a Louisiana family through the eyes of a 10-year-old girl. "In the way it examines a family's emotional life, it reminded me of the family dramas of Ingmar Bergman" (Roger Ebert, *Chicago Sun-Times*). With Samuel Jackson, Lynn Whitfield and Debbi Morgan.
VHS: $33312. $105.99.
Kasi Lemmons, USA, 1997, 109 mins.

Best Director

Robert Duvall, *The Apostle*

Best Female Lead

Julie Christie, *Afterglow*
Afterglow
Rudolph's "doozy of digression and tonal shifts" (Ray Pride, *New City*) about four characters in four different emotional time zones. A fable about two married couples whose lives intersect in contemporary Montreal, *Afterglow* stars Nick Nolte as Dicky Mann, a Mr. Fix-It who knows most of the married women on his side of town, and Julie Christie, in an Oscar-nominated performance, as his former B-actress wife, who mourns the past as she watches old tapes of herself. With Lara Flynn Boyle and Sonny Lee Miller.
VHS: $34140. $104.99.
Alan Rudolph, USA, 1997, 114 mins.

Best Supporting Female

Debbi Morgan, *Eve's Bayou*

Best Male Lead

Robert Duvall, *The Apostle*

Best Supporting Male

Jason Lee, *Chasing Amy*
Chasing Amy
From the talented young writer and director of *Clerks* comes this wickedly witty and insightful story of hip young comics artist Holden (Ben Affleck), who, against the advice of his jealous collaborator Banky (Jason Lee), falls for Alyssa, a funny and sexy fellow comics artist—who happens to be a lesbian. "Ripe with Smith's trademark virtuosic verbosity, raunchy sexual discussions, intense dramatic confrontations" (*New City*).
VHS: $32660. $103.99.
Laser: LD76438. $49.95.
Kevin Smith, USA, 1997, 105 mins.

Best Debut Performance

Aaron Eckhart, *In the Company of Men*
In the Company of Men
Neil LaBute's disturbing, controversial, intelligent film about the male prerogative—two executives who compete for the same woman, a pretty, deaf clerk, in a callous sexist game. With stunning performances by Aaron Eckhart, Stacy Edwards and Matt Malloy. "The kind of bold, uncompromising film that insists on being thought about afterward" (Roger Ebert, *Chicago Sun-Times*).
VHS: $33318. $105.99.
Neil LaBute, Canada, 1997, 97 mins.

Best Screenplay

Kevin Smith, *Chasing Amy*

Sling Blade

Best First Screenplay

Neil LaBute, *In the Company of Men*

Best Cinematography

Declan Quinn, *Kama Sutra*
Kama Sutra
A seductive tale of love and betrayal in which a
king's courtesan is forbidden to embrace her one true
love. Trained in the art of pleasure, Maya (Indira
Varma), the beautiful servant girl, becomes defiant,
rebelling against ancient tradition. As passion takes
over, the conflict brings consequences that no one
ever envisioned. With Naveen Andrews, Sarita
Choudury and Ramon Tiikaram. In English.
VHS: $31738. $99.99.
Mira Nair, India, 1996, 113 mins.

Best Foreign Film

The Sweet Hereafter
Following a tragic schoolbus accident, high-profile
lawyer Mitchel Stephens (Ian Holm) descends upon a
small town, with promises of retribution and a class-
action lawsuit filed on behalf of the community. But
as his investigation into the quiet town begins,
Stephens uncovers a tangled web of lies, deceit and
forbidden desires that mirrors his own troubled
personal life. Gradually, we learn that Stephens has
his own agenda, and that everyone has secrets to
keep.
VHS: $34412. $100.99.
Atom Egoyan, Canada, 1997, 112 mins.

Truer Than Fiction Award

(Presented to the director of a nonfiction feature film
of outstanding artistic and dramatic achievement. The
award's purpose is to foster wider appreciation and
theatrical distribution of nonfiction, feature-length
motion pictures—films that by their very nature are
independent. The $20,000 award is funded by The
Independent Film Channel and Landmark Theaters.)
Danielle Gardner for *Soul in the Hole*

Errol Morris for *Fast, Cheap & Out of Control*
Fast, Cheap & Out of Control
Documentary master Errol Morris' magical portrait
of the weird and wonderful worlds of an elderly
topiary gardener, a retired lion tamer, an expert on
mole rats and a cutting-edge robotics designer. Morris
interplays, overlaps and interrelates the lives of these
four men who tread the thin line between genius and
madness, in order to study humanity, as he raises
questions about the future of mankind.
VHS: $34294. $98.99.
Errol Morris, USA, 1997, 82 mins.

Swatch Someone to Watch Award

(A $20,000 grant created to honor a filmmaker with
exceptional talent and unique vision, and to help that
individual in pursuit of his or her craft.)
Scott Saunders

Ralph Lauren Producers Award

(This award was created to bring attention to a
producer(s) who demonstrates the exceptional
creativity, tenacity and vision required to produce
quality independent films despite highly limited
resources.)
Scott Macaulay
Robin O'Hara

Findie ("Friends of Independents") Award

(A special honor given each year to an individual or
organization who has made influential contributions
to the independent filmmaking community.)
Robert H. Harvey
Panavision

1997

Best Feature

Fargo
Steve Buscemi, William Macy and Frances
McDormand (in her Academy Award-winning role as
a pregnant homicide detective) find thievery,
treachery and murder out in the frozen upper
Midwest. This seemingly straightforward morality
tale is laced with wicked humor. The film's deadpan
style mirrors the large, cold, empty spaces of the
Minnesota landscape.
DVD: DV60003. $29.95.
VHS: $29808. $19.98.
Laser: LD75990. $34.95.
Joel and Ethan Coen, USA, 1996, 98 mins.
Producer: Ethan Coen

Best First Feature

Sling Blade
Billy Bob Thornton stars in his Academy Award-
winning screenplay as Karl, a quiet and simple man
who is released from prison 25 years after killing his
mother and her lover, and returns to the small
Arkansas town of his youth. After he befriends a
young boy (Lucas Black), his mother (Natalie
Canerday) and her boss (John Ritter), Karl's new life
is shattered when he finds himself in conflict with the
woman's violent lover (Dwight Yokum), as he
confronts his past. With J.T. Walsh, Robert Duvall,
and a cameo by Jim Jarmusch.
VHS: $31532. $103.99.
Laser: LD76306. $59.95.
Billy Bob Thornton, USA, 1996, 135 mins.

Best Director

Joel Coen, *Fargo*

Best Screenplay

Joel Coen & Ethan Coen, *Fargo*

Best First Screenplay

Joseph Tropiano and Stanley Tucci, *Big Night*
Big Night
This charmer of a movie—a big winner at Sundance
and with audiences, and a treat for movie and food

lovers—is the story of two Italian brothers whose restaurant teeters on the brink of bankruptcy. With Minnie Driver, Ian Holm, Isabella Rossellini, Campbell Scott, Tony Shalhoub and Stanley Tucci. "A feast of a film" (Peter Travers, *Newsday*).
VHS: S31122. $19.95.
Laser: LD76173. $34.99.
Stanley Tucci, USA, 1996, 109 mins.

Best Debut Performance

Heather Matarazzo, *Welcome to the Dollhouse*
Welcome to the Dollhouse
Winner of the Grand Jury Prize at the 1996 Sundance Film Festival, a dark and very funny look at adolescence told through the eyes of an angry, young, geeky girl. The usual teen stuff is covered—school, grades, puppy love, sex and rock 'n' roll—but with an original and highly amusing take which "never loses its sense of compassion and respect for the underdog" (*New York Daily News*). With Heather Matarazzo, Matthew Faber, Angela Pietropinto and Eric Mabius (*I Shot Andy Warhol*).
VHS: S30422. $19.95.
Laser: LD76028. $39.95.
Todd Solondz, USA, 1996, 88 mins.

Best Male Lead

William H. Macy, *Fargo*

Best Female Lead

Frances McDormand, *Fargo*

Best Supporting Male

Benicio Del Toro, *Basquiat*
Basquiat
The critically acclaimed film about the rise and fall of controversial 1980s Haitian-Puerto Rican graffiti artist-turned-Soho-supernova Jean-Michel Basquiat, who died of a heroin overdose in 1988. Starring Dennis Hopper, Gary Oldman, David Bowie as Andy Warhol, and Tony Award-winner Jeffrey Wright (*Angels in America*) as Basquiat. With Willem Dafoe, Courtney Love, Parker Posey and Tatum O'Neal and music by David Bowie, Van Morrison and Tom Waits. "One of the year's best" (*Siskel & Ebert*).
VHS: S30822. $103.99.
Laser: LD76102. $39.99.
Julian Schnabel, USA, 1996, 111 mins.

Best Supporting Female

Elizabeth Pena, *Lone Star*
Lone Star
The discovery of a human skull and a sheriff's badge buried on the outskirts of a small west Texas border town reveals a 40-year-old mystery that touches the past of nearly everyone in town—including the current sheriff. As the clues to solving the puzzle are discovered, past wounds are re-opened, old flames are reignited and secrets long-hidden are revealed, in this gripping, suspenseful tale. With Kris Kristofferson, Matthew McConaughey, Chris Cooper, Elizabeth Pena and Frances McDormand. "Sayles' best film so far...quietly stunning" (Janet Maslin, *New York Times*).
VHS: S30944. $19.95.
Laser: LD76135. $39.95.
John Sayles, USA, 1996, 138 mins.

Best Cinematography

Roger Dakins, *Fargo*

Best Foreign Film

Secrets and Lies
Mike Leigh's heartwarming comedy of a young black woman (Marianne Jean-Baptiste) searching for her natural birth mother only to discover that her mom (the magnificent Brenda Blethyn) is white, makes for

a film with "rare heart and soul" (Janet Maslin, *The New York Times*), from Britain's master of improvisational, working-class social comedies. With Timothy Spall. Winner of the Palm d'Or at Cannes Film Festival.
VHS: S31027. $103.99.
Laser: LD76141. $39.98.
Mike Leigh, Great Britain, 1996, 114 mins.

Truer Than Fiction Award

When We Were Kings
Leon Cast's Academy Award-winning documentary is a knockout 20-year labor of love chronicling the famous 1974 "Rumble in the Jungle" heavyweight championship fight between 32-year-old Muhammad Ali and George Foreman in Zaire. Capturing the wit, charisma, intelligence and determination of "the Greatest," Cast's film is a lasting legacy of Ali the boxer, provocateur and political instigator. With interviews with Norman Mailer, George Plimpton and Spike Lee.
DVD: DV60129. $29.95.
VHS: S31675. $19.95.
Laser: Letterboxed. LD76286. $39.99.
Leon Cast, USA, 1997, 90 mins.

Someone to Watch Award

Larry Fessenden

1996

Best Feature

Leaving Las Vegas
Nicolas Cage and Elisabeth Shue star in this tender love story of two people living on the far side of hope. Ben Sanderson (Cage) is an alcoholic Los Angeles screenwriter who decides to move to Las Vegas to die. There he meets a prostitute (Shue), equally unapologetic about her own life choices, and together they fall in love. Cage won the Academy Award for his role in this engrossing, complex and beautiful film. VHS letterboxed.
VHS: S27709. $19.98.
Laser: LD75568. $34.98.
Mike Figgis, USA, 1995, 113 mins.
Producers: Lila Cazes, Annie Stewart

Best First Feature

The Brothers McMullen
In this romantic comedy, the Best Picture at the 1995 Sundance Festival, three brothers from Long Island confront the unknown territory of love and marriage. After their father dies, their mother returns to Ireland to be with the man she really loves. The three Irish Catholic brothers are left to deal with varying stages of love and marriage, ranging from initial attraction to engagement to the prospect of an extramarital affair. With Edward Burns, Jack Mulcahy, Mike McGlone and Connie Britton.
VHS: S27210. $19.95.
Laser: LD75482. $39.98.
Edward Burns, USA, 1995, 98 mins.

Best Director

Quentin Tarantino, *Pulp Fiction*
Pulp Fiction
John Travolta, Uma Thurman, Samuel Jackson, Bruce Willis, Harvey Keitel and Rosanna Arquette are all part of the stellar cast of this highly acclaimed film. Two hit men encounter a bizarre series of adventures in a seamy L.A. world of criminals and kooks. The Academy Award-winning screenplay by Quentin Tarantino can't be beat. Letterboxed.
VHS: S26211. $19.95.
Laser: CLV, THX. LD75062. $39.99.
Quentin Tarantino, USA, 1994, 154 mins.

Best Screenplay

Christopher McQuarrie, *The Usual Suspects*
The Usual Suspects
Stephen Baldwin, Gabriel Byrne, Benicio del Toro,
Kevin Pollak and Kevin Spacey star in this inventive
crime story as a bunch of guys brought together for a
police line-up. Finding themselves alone together
after the cops are through with them, they decide to
plan a crime. This plot about a multi-million dollar
drug deal gets even stranger because somehow,
amidst all the intricately placed flashbacks, these
eccentric criminals end up causing a catastrophic
explosion. Featuring Chazz Palminteri, Pete
Postlethwaite and Suzy Amis. VHS letterboxed.
   DVD: DV60008. $29.95.
   VHS: S27071. $19.95.
   Laser: LD75442. $39.95.
Bryan Singer, USA, 1995, 106 mins.

Best First Screenplay

Paul Auster, *Smoke*
Smoke
Harvey Keitel, William Hurt, Forest Whitaker,
Stockard Channing and Ashley Judd star in this
offbeat comedy set in a New York cigar shop. Sparks
fly when the manager, played by Keitel, gets involved
in the intertwining lives of his colorful customers. A
gentle love letter to Brooklyn.
   VHS: S26708. $99.99.
   Laser: LD75322. $39.98.
Wayne Wang, USA, 1995, 112 mins.

Best Debut Performance

Justin Pierce, *Kids*
Kids
Famed photographer Larry Clark makes his
directorial debut with this sensational story of
teenage life in Manhattan. Ignoring the challenge
posed by AIDS, these kids pursue sex and drugs with
no regard for the future in a world as violent as it is
hopeless. Justifiably controversial, *Kids* was hailed as
"very, very powerful" (Roger Ebert) and denounced
as manipulative and exploitative. "The confident
visual style and flat, elliptical, near-plotless
storytelling are tremendously accomplished, yet the
same elements…could be seen as a celebration of
amorality, as a contrived, romanticized celebration of
the death wish" (Ray Pride, *New City*).
   VHS: S26956. $14.95.
Larry Clark, USA, 1995, 91 mins.

Best Male Lead

Sean Penn, *Dead Man Walking*
Dead Man Walking
Sean Penn is an unrepentant killer who is ministered
to by a strong-willed nun (Susan Sarandon). This film
is unique for staying so firmly glued to the harder
issues and emotions that surround hardened killers
and the state's use of the death penalty. Penn gives an
especially brilliant performance in a film dominated
by great acting.
   DVD: DV60004. $29.95.
   VHS: S28059. $19.98.
   Laser: LD75802. $44.95.
Tim Robbins, USA, 1995, 122 mins.

Best Female Lead

Elisabeth Shue, *Leaving Las Vegas*

Best Supporting Male

Benicio Del Toro, *The Usual Suspects*

Best Supporting Female

Mare Winningham, *Georgia*
Georgia
Jennifer Jason Leigh and Mare Winningham star in
this tale of a rising young rock star. Leigh is the

younger sister of a successful folk singer
(Winningham). The resultant sibling rivalry only
intensifies the extreme behavior of Leigh's character
as she struggles for success. It's a tough and
unsentimental view of a world where self-indulgent
emotional turmoil can mean big bucks.
   VHS: S27847. $99.99.
   Laser: LD75929. $39.99.
Ulu Grosbard, USA, 1995, 117 mins.

Best Cinematography

Declan Quinn, *Leaving Las Vegas*

Best Foreign Film

Before the Rain
Three intertwined stories are joined in this haunting
feature about individuals facing hard choices. Set in
the former Yugoslavia and London, it combines
ethical and moral quandaries with compelling
situations and jarringly striking settings. Academy
Award nominee for Best Foreign Language Picture.
English and Macedonian with English subtitles.
   VHS: S25952. $19.95.
**Milcho Manchevski, Great Britain/Macedonia/
France, 1994, 115 mins.**

Someone to Watch Award

Christopher Munch

1995

Best Feature

Pulp Fiction
Producer: Lawrence Bender

Best First Feature

Spanking the Monkey
Jeremy Davies stars as a young man on his way to a
prestigious summer internship in Washington, D.C.,
after finishing his first year of pre-med. He returns to
his home town for a weekend visit, to find his mother
confined to her bed with a broken leg and his father
unwilling and unable to care for her. Forced to delay
his internship, he attempts to deal with his incestuous
relationship with his mother and the absenteeism of
his controlling father.
   VHS: S22891. $19.95.
David O. Russell, USA, 1994, 99 mins.

Best Director

Quentin Tarantino, *Pulp Fiction*

Best Screenplay

**Quentin Tarantino, Stories by QUentin Tarantino
and Roger Avery,** *Pulp Fiction*

Best Male Lead

Samuel L. Jackson, *Pulp Fiction*

Best Female Lead

Linda Fiorentino, *The Last Seduction*
The Last Seduction
Linda Fiorentino is a winning temptress who
manages to bring ruin to all the men in her life. A
scam goes all wrong, but not for Linda, who manages
to move on to the next man—or is it victim? Beauty
is all the more appealing in an ugly world centered on
money and betrayal.
   VHS: S24955. $19.95.
John Dahl, USA, 1994, 110 mins.

Dead Man Walking

Best Supporting Male

Chazz Palminteri, *Bullets over Broadway*
Bullets over Broadway
Woody Allen cast Jim Broadbent, John Cusack, Harvey Fierstein, Mary Louise Parker, Rob Reiner, Tracey Ullman and other great actors in this comedy where gangsters collide with Broadway. A young playwright is desperate to get his play produced and goes to whatever they can to preserve and promote their investment, with hilarious results.
VHS: $23963. $19.95.
Laser: Letterboxed. LD74938. $39.99.
Woody Allen, USA, 1994, 95 mins.

Best Supporting Female

Dianne West, *Bullets over Broadway*

Best Cinematography

John Thomas, *Barcelona*
Barcelona
Taylor Nichols is a sales rep in Barcelona who can't quite master the fast Barcelona scene. His cousin (Christopher Eigeman), however, is an obnoxious Navy man easily at home in this exciting city. That is, before they both become aware of a lingering anti-American sentiment that sends this comic, sexy film off on a violent tangent.
VHS: $23678. $19.98.
Laser: Widescreen. LD74812. $39.99.
Whit Stillman, USA, 1994, 102 mins.

Best Foreign Film

Red
Kieslowski's striking conclusion of his Three Colors trilogy stars Irene Jacob as a model, separated from her lover, who is brought by accident into the life of the aging Jean-Louis Trintignant, retired judge and electronic peeping Tom. As Irene slowly uncovers her lover's secret life, she discovers that her own past is inevitably linked to her destiny. With Jean-Pierre Lorit and Frederique Feder.
VHS: $25606. $19.95.
Laser: Letterboxed. LD75015. $39.99.
Krzysztof Kieslowski, Switzerland, 1994, 99 mins.
Producers: Marin Karmitz and Gerard Ruey

1994

Best Feature

Short Cuts
Raymond Carver's short stories are brought to the screen in this Golden Globe winner, employing some

of Hollywood's biggest stars. Jack Lemmon, Lyle Lovett, Matthew Modine, Lily Tomlin and Jennifer Jason Leigh are just some of the big names seen in this harrowing portrayal of everyday people living extraordinary lives.
VHS: $20889. $19.95.
Laser: LD74462. $124.95.
Robert Altman, USA, 1993, 189 mins.
Producers: Cary Brokaw, Scott Bushnell (executive), Mike Kaplan (associate), David Levy (associate)

Best First Feature

El Mariachi
This film by 24-year-old director Robert Rodriquez was made for the unbelievable sum of $7,000. Rodriguez playfully evokes Peckinpah, noir westerns and Hitchcock. A maverick loner and mariachi player (Carlos Gallardo) enters a Mexican border town and is instantly confused with a stark, brutally efficient assassin (Reinol Martinez). Spanish with English subtitles.
VHS: $19057. $19.95.
Laser: Special Collector's Edition. LD71892. $49.95.
Robert Rodriguez, USA, 1992, 80 mins.

Best Director

Robert Altman, *Short Cuts*

Best Screenplay

Robert Altman and Frank Barhydt, *Short Cuts*

Best Actor

Jeff Bridges, *American Heart*
American Heart
Martin Bell's (*Streetwise*) dramatic debut examines the lifestyles of the socially marginal. Jeff Bridges plays Jack, a convict whose plans of moving to Alaska are thwarted by the appearance of his 14-year-old son, Nick (Edward Furlong). The two settle into a difficult daily existence in a Seattle boarding room as Jack tries desperately to avoid the temptation of the grift, while Nick is attracted to the romantic allure of the streets. Lucinda Jenney contributes a remarkable turn as Jack's battle-scarred girlfriend.
VHS: $19465. $19.98.
Laser: LD75145. $34.98.
Martin Bell, USA, 1992, 113 mins.

Best Actress

Ashley Judd, *Ruby in Paradise*
Ruby in Paradise
Winner of the 1993 Grand Prize at the Sundance Film Festival, this film, starring the beautiful and accomplished Ashley Judd, charts the progress of a woman toward her own personal paradise. Visually stunning cinematography shows the Florida locations to great advantage in this story of one woman's quest for meaning.
VHS: $20711. $19.95.
Victor Nunez, USA, 1993, 115 mins.

Best Supporting Actor

Christopher Lloyd, *Twenty Bucks*
Twenty Bucks
This comic portrayal of contemporary America follows the path of a twenty dollar bill as it crosses the divides of race and class which separate the strata of big city life. Linda Hunt, Steve Buscemi and Gladys Knight portray some of the quirky characters encountered on this cash-driven journey.
VHS: $20887. $19.95.
Keva Rosenfeld, USA, 1992, 91 mins.

Best Supporting Actress

Lili Taylor, *Household Saints*
Household Saints
When the Santangelos, an Italian-American couple, pray for a miracle, their wish is granted, or so they originally think, in the form of a daughter they call Teresa. Tracey Ullman, Vincent D'Onofrio, Lili Taylor and Judith Malina star in this humorous fable of faith, sainthood and sausage.
VHS: $21095. $94.95.
Nancy Savoca, USA, 1993, 124 mins.

Best Cinematography

Lisa Rinzler, *Menace II Society*
Menace II Society
This stylized inner-city gangster drama is the debut film of Allan and Albert Hughes, 21-year-old fraternal twins. Set in a claustrophobic Watts, the film is constructed as a harrowing collection of brutal vignettes of car hijackings, street assassinations and random violence. The film plays like a black *Mean Streets*. Its theme is the cruel fate of its two lead characters, a relatively good though unfocused kid (Tyrin Turner) who is undone by his allegiance to his pathologically unbalanced best friend O-Dog (Larenz Tate). From the opening scene, a brutal Korean grocery store murder, *Menace II Society* is a pessimistic and wholly unsentimental portrait of late 20th-century American life. With Jada Pinkett, Vonte Sweet, MC Eiht, Ryan Willianms, Too $hort, Samuel L. Jackson, Charles Dutton and Bill Duke.
VHS: $19937. $19.95.
Laser: LD76802. $99.95.
The Hughes Brothers, USA, 1993, 97 mins.

Best Foreign Film

The Piano
Holly Hunter's Oscar-winning performance as a mute woman dedicated to her music takes center stage in this lush drama set in 19th century New Zealand. Harvey Keitel co-stars as the brutish but sensitive man who gives her back what seemed irrevocably lost. A young Anna Paquin more than holds her own with a performance that garnered this new star an Oscar for Best Supporting Actress.
VHS: $20871. $19.98.
Jane Campion, Australia/New Zealand, 1993, 121 mins.

1993

Best Feature

The Player
Robert Altman's dark valentine to the American movie industry. The plot is absurdly comic, with Tim Robbins as an icy studio executive who receives a series of threatening, anonymous postcards from a screenwriter he abused, setting in motion a murder and seduction. With Greta Scacchi, Whoopi Goldberg, Fred Ward, Peter Gallagher and 59 actors, directors and stars appearing as themselves.
DVD: DV60078. $24.98.
VHS: $18263. $19.98.
Laser: Audio commentary by Robert Altman.
LD76269. $39.99.
Robert Altman, USA, 1992, 123 mins.
Producers: Larry Meistrich and Bob Gosse

Best First Feature

The Waterdance
This autobiographical work by Neal Jimenez (*River's Edge*) is a tragicomedy about the recovery of a talented young novelist (Eric Stoltz) paralyzed in a mountain climbing accident, and his time in a paraplegic ward at a local hospital. With Wesley Snipes and William Forsythe as two embittered antagonists, Elizabeth Pena, and Helen Hunt as

Stoltz's married lover.
VHS: $18116. $92.95.
Laser: LD71843. $34.95.
Neal Jimenez/Michael Steinberg, USA, 1991, 110 mins.

Best Director

Carl Franklin, *One False Move*
One False Move
A small masterpiece, this B-movie thriller features wonderful performances by Bill Paxton and Cynda Williams. A trio of criminals stage a grotesque gangland murder and travel to Arkansas, unaware the local sheriff and two L.A. cops await them. The two principal characters confront their pasts. With Michael Beach, Earl Beach, Jim Metzler and Billy Bob Thornton, who co-wrote the screenplay.
VHS: $17057. $19.95.
Laser: LD71541. $34.95.
Carl Franklin, USA, 1991, 103 mins.

Best Screenplay

Neal Jimenez, *The Waterdance*

Best Actor

Harvey Keitel, *The Bad Lieutenant*
The Bad Lieutenant
Abel Ferrara's portrait of a corrupt, self-destructive New York vice lieutenant. In a great performance, Harvey Keitel plays a drug-addicted rogue cop trying to settle his gambling debts while investigating the violent rape of a beautiful young nun. Despite sequences of wrenching horror, especially the cop's verbal humiliation of two New Jersey teenagers, *Bad Lieutenant* achieves a grace and poetic intensity. Cinematography by Ken Kelsch. Screenplay by Abel Ferrara and Zoe Lund. With Victor Argo, Paul Calderone, Leonard Thomas and Frankie Thorn.
VHS: $18912. $19.98.
Laser: LD75154. $34.95.
Abel Ferrara, USA, 1992, 98 mins.

Best Actress

Fairuza Balk, *Gas Food Lodging*
Gas Food Lodging
Allison Anders' depiction of the difficult, complex relationship between a single mother and her two daughters has some graceful, liquid camera work and an excellent performance by Ione Skye as a distracted, promiscuous vixen. Set in a ragged New Mexico town, Anders maps out some tangled relationships while fully exploring post-adolescent and adult sexuality. Adapted from the novel by Richard Peck. Cinematography by Dean Lent. With Brooke Adams, Fairuza Balk and James Brolin.
VHS: $18346. $19.95.
Laser: LD71864. $34.95.
Allison Anders, USA, 1992, 94 mins.

Best Supporting Actor

Steve Buscemi, *Reservoir Dogs*
Reservoir Dogs
The debut of Quentin Tarantino employs a novelistic structure to evoke the aftermath of a failed jewelry heist. Lawrence Tierney plays an underworld figure who recruits five criminals to stage a daring mid-afternoon robbery, led by Harvey Keitel. Quickly becoming a cult classic. With Tim Roth, Chris Penn, Steve Buscemi and Michael Madsen as an effective, sadistic creep. Letterboxed.
VHS: $18195. $14.95.
Laser: LD75161. $99.00.
Quentin Tarantino, USA, 1992, 99 mins.

Best Supporting Actress

Alfre Woodard, *Passion Fish*
Passion Fish
John Sayles' perceptive and lyrical film unfolds in the atmospheric Louisiana bayou and charts the emotional relationship of two fiercely independent

women—an acerbic, caustic actress (Mary McDonnell) paralyzed in an accident and her idiosyncratic caretaker (Alfre Woodard)—as one attempts to confront her vulnerable past. Sayles' regular David Strathairn contributes a stunning performance as a local who makes the tentative seduction of McDonnell. With Vondie Curtis-Hall and Nora Dunn.
VHS: S18746. $19.95.
John Sayles, USA, 1992, 137 mins.

Best Cinematography

Fred Elmes, *Night on Earth*
Night on Earth
Jim Jarmusch's film is structured episodically, with the narrative simultaneously unfolding in Los Angeles, New York, Paris, Rome and Helsinki, and concerns the relationship of cab drivers and their passengers. The ensemble cast includes Gena Rowlands, Winona Ryder, Rosie Perez, Giancarlo Esposito, Armin Mueller-Stahl, Beatrice Dalle, Isaach de Bankole, Roberto Benigni, Matti Pellonpaa and Kari Vaananen. Tom Waits composed the music and performs two numbers. Letterboxed.
VHS: S17625. $19.95.
Jim Jarmusch, USA, 1991, 125 mins.

Best Foreign Film

The Crying Game
Irish filmmaker Neil Jordan's film charts a fractured world of deception, abandon and terror. Stephen Rea becomes a reluctant IRA terrorist in exile who ends up protecting a beautiful, mysterious London woman. With Miranda Richardson, Forest Whitaker and the amazing Jaye Davidson. Academy award for best original screenplay (Jordan).
VHS: S18749. $19.98.
Laser: Widescreen. LD75178. $34.99.
Neil Jordan, Great Britain, 1992, 112 mins.

Best Score

Angelo Badalamenti, *Twin Peaks: Fire Walk with Me*
Twin Peaks: Fire Walk with Me
David Lynch's study of the American Dream in this surreal evocation of small-town America. The plot covers the week leading up to the death of Laura Palmer, the beautiful, emotionally scarred woman whose brutal murder set in motion the plot of the television series. With Sheryl Lee, Moira Kelly, David Bowie, Harry Dean Stanton, Ray Wise, James Marshall, Madchen Amick and Kyle MacLachlan.
VHS: S17866. $19.95.
David Lynch, USA, 1992, 135 mins.

1992

Best Feature

Rambling Rose
A rare and intelligent film about sexual attitudes, enlightened behavior and family ties. Laura Dern is inspired as the title character, a beguiling free spirit with a soiled reputation. She finds understanding and a real home while working as a domestic for the Hillyer family in '30s Georgia. With fine performances from Robert Duvall, Diane Ladd, John Heard, David Ogden Stiers and Lukas Haas. Ladd and Dern made Oscar history as the first mother and daughter to be nominated in the same year for acting awards. Based on the novel by Calder Willingham.
VHS: S15692. $14.98.
Laser: LD75131. $24.98.
Martha Coolidge, USA, 1991, 115 mins.
Producer: Renny Harlin

Best First Feature

Straight Out of Brooklyn
Dennis Brown has been raised in the projects of Brooklyn—entrapped in a world of desperation, drugs

and danger. His parents tell him to study hard, go to college and be patient, but Dennis can't wait any longer. He plans a robbery that'll take them out of Brooklyn forever, only now the neighborhood threatens to close in on him before he can escape. An astonishing tale of struggle and achievement from 19-year-old director Matty Rich. "A strong film…honest and effective…the truth is there and it echoes long after the film is over" (Roger Ebert).
VHS: S15274. $19.98.
Laser: LD75134. $24.98.
Matty Rich, USA, 1991, 83 mins.

Best Director

Martha Coolidge, *Rambling Rose*

Best Screenplay

Gus Van Sant, *My Own Private Idaho*
My Own Private Idaho
In this modern restructuring of the '60s road movie, River Phoenix and Keanu Reeves hustle their way through Seattle, Portland, Idaho and Rome on a quest for River's missing mother. With a meticulous, lyric style, the film combines sprawling landscapes, scenes of passionless sexuality and allusions to Orson Welles' *Chimes at Midnight* as it addresses issues of love, family, politics and homosexuality. A work of great complexity and beauty from the director of *Mala Noche* and *Drugstore Cowboy*.
VHS: S15927. $19.95.
Gus Van Sant, USA, 1991, 102 mins.

Best Actor

River Phoenix, *My Own Private Idaho*

Best Actress

Judy Davis, *Impromptu*

Best Supporting Actor

David Strathairn, *City of Hope*
City of Hope
John Sayles wrote, directed and played a major role in this provocative drama of political corruption and racial upheaval. Vincent Spano and Joe Morton head an impressive ensemble cast of 31 principal characters. With David Strathairn as Asteroid, the befuddled street person, and Sayles, himself, as the sleazy Carl.
VHS: S16087. $19.95.
Laser: LD71573. $39.95.
John Sayles, USA, 1991, 130 mins.

Best Supporting Actress

Diane Ladd, *Rambling Rose*

Best Cinematography

Walt Lloyd, *Kafka*
Kafka
Steven Soderbergh's follow-up to *sex, lies and videotape* is set in a baroque, sinister Prague. Jeremy Irons plays an insurance underwriter who, following a friend's disappearance, gets entangled with a shadowy anarchist group and an unbalanced doctor performing perverse scientific experiments. The cast includes Theresa Russell, Joel Grey, Ian Holm, Jeroen Krabbe, Armin Mueller-Stahl and Alec Guinness.
VHS: S17789. $92.95.
Steven Soderbergh, USA/France/Great Britain, 1991, 100 mins.

Best Foreign Film

An Angel at My Table
The true story of one of our century's most gifted writers, *An Angel at My Table* chronicles the life and extraordinary times of Janet Frame. Born in the

To Sleep with Anger

1920s, Janet's early years of fairy tales and schoolgirl pranks were tempered by family tragedy. She retreated to her beloved books and began to write poetry and stories. As the years passed her talent grew and so did the challenges to her unique and inspired vision.
VHS: $15620. $19.98.
Jane Campion, New Zealand, 1991, 157 mins.

Best Film Music

My Own Private Idaho

1991

Best Feature

The Grifters
Jim Thompson's novel of love, money and betrayal stars John Cusack as a master of the short con. He must gamble on trusting his dishonest mother or putting his faith in a greedy girlfriend who plays for bigger stakes. Anjelica Huston and Annette Bening were nominated for Oscars for their work, as was director Stephen Frears and scriptwriter Donald E. Westlake. Filmed in the seedier sections of Los Angeles. Don't rent this film for Mother's Day.
VHS: $13830. $19.98.
Stephen Frears, USA, 1990, 114 mins.
Producers: Martin Scorsese, Robert Harris and James Printen

Best First Feature

Metropolitan
Charlie loves Audrey. Audrey loves Tom. Tom loves Serena. Refreshingly original and funny, *Metropolitan* is a wry and witty look at the high-spirited escapades of high society's rich children. A stunning debut for first-time writer-director Whit Stillman and his talented assortment of young, unknown actors. "...ironic, touching, and wickedly funny" (M. McGrady, *News Day*).
VHS: $14278. $19.95.
Whit Stillman, USA, 1990, 98 mins.

Best Director

Charles Burnett, *To Sleep with Anger*
To Sleep with Anger
Danny Glover stars as Harry Mention, a mysterious and magnetic visitor from the Deep South who comes

to stay with an old friend, named Gideon (Paul Butler), in South-Central Los Angeles. Harry's effect on Gideon and his assimilated black middle-class family is both immediate and profound. He spins tales full of folklore, lucky charms and bad magic that seem exotic and ominous to these urban up-and-comers who have lost touch with the rural tradition.
VHS: $13817. $19.95.
Charles Burnett, USA, 1990, 105 mins.

Best Screenplay

Charles Burnett, *To Sleep with Anger*

Best Actor

Danny Glover, *To Sleep with Anger*

Best Actress

Anjelica Huston, *The Grifters*

Best Supporting Actor

Bruce Davison, *Longtime Companion*
Longtime Companion
The impact of AIDS on the gay community is the subject of this well-received and honestly acted drama. Bruce Davison stands out in a distinguished ensemble cast as a man facing the loss of his life partner. With Stephen Caffrey, Patrick Cassidy, Brian Cousins, John Dossett, Mark Lamos, Dermot Mulroney, Mary-Louise Parker.
VHS: $13301. $19.95.
Norman Rene, USA, 1990, 100 mins.

Best Supporting Actress

Sheryl Lee Ralph, *To Sleep with Anger*

Best Cinematography

Fred Elmes, *Wild at Heart*
Wild at Heart
Based on Barry Gifford's novel about two southern lovers on the run, this film is director David Lynch's (*Blue Velvet, Eraserhead*) campiest feature to date. Despite the loopy subtext of references (mostly to Elvis and *The Wizard of Oz*), Lynch manages to present some powerful visual compositions here and gets all-out performances from stars Nicolas Cage and Laura Dern. Also starring Willem Dafoe, Crispin Glover, Diane Ladd, Isabella Rossellini and Harry Dean Stanton. Winner of the Cannes Film Festival's 1990 Palme d'Or.
VHS: $13515. $19.98.
Laser: LD71210. $49.95.
David Lynch, USA, 1990, 125 mins.

Best Foreign Film

Sweetie
A true original—this breakthrough film from Australia's Jane Campion is "as disturbing as *Blue Velvet*", "an original." Bizarre, often hilarious, *Sweetie* is the story of two very different sisters, the guarded and repressed Kay and the overweight and spontaneous Sweetie.
VHS: $12478. $14.98.
Jane Campion, Australia, 1989, 97 mins.

1990

Best Feature

sex, lies and videotape
When an old college buddy drops into the lives of a Louisiana yuppie couple, the bonds of matrimony begin to fray. Soderbergh's accomplished feature film

debut scored a big win at Cannes and really annoyed Spike Lee. James Spader also won a Best Actor Award at Cannes for his role as the soft-spoken, sensitive visitor. With Peter Gallagher and Andie MacDowell as the former perfect couple and Laura San Giacomo as the lusty sister-in-law.
VHS: S11693. $19.95.
Laser: CAV. LD70456. $124.95.
Laser: CLV. LD70457. $134.98.
Steven Soderbergh, USA, 1989, 100 mins.
Producers: Robert Newmeyer and John Hardy

Best First Feature

Heathers
This wicked satire, from first-time screenwriter Daniel Waters, takes on high school, adolescent angst, the ironic glorification of teen suicide, homophobia, popularity, football players, funerals, croquet, and just about anything else you can think of. With Winona Ryder and Christian Slater. Quite dark and funny. Letterboxed.
VHS: S13691. $19.95.
Laser: CLV, with cast interviews. LD75009. $49.95.
Michael Lehmann, USA, 1989, 102 mins.

Best Director

Steven Soderbergh, *sex, lies and videotape*

Best Screenplay

Gus Van Sant and Daniel Yost, *Drugstore Cowboy*
Drugstore Cowboy
Matt Dillon gives the performance of his career as the drug-addicted criminal who masterminds a series of robberies in the Pacific Northwest. A harsh and decidedly unsentimental look at life on the fringe that deals honestly with the world of controlled substances. A top notch cast includes Kelly Lynch, James LeGros, Heather Graham, James Remar and William Burroughs as Father Tom, the junkie priest. Don't say "no" to this drug movie.
VHS: S11724. $14.98.
Laser: LD70955. $39.95.
Gus Van Sant, USA, 1989, 100 mins.

Best Actor

Matt Dillon, *Drugstore Cowboy*

Best Actress

Andie McDowell, *sex, lies and videotape*

Best Supporting Actor

Max Perlich, *Drugstore Cowboy*

Best Supporting Actress

Laura San Giacomo, *sex, lies and videotape*

Best Cinematography

Robert Yeoman, *Drugstore Cowboy*

Best Foreign Film

My Left Foot
Distinguished by a brilliant performance from Daniel Day-Lewis, this is a true story about life, laughter and the occasional miracle. Day-Lewis plays Christy Brown, who has cerebral palsy, and whose mother's faith prompts him to paint and write. Nominated for five Academy Awards.
VHS: S12199. $19.98.
Jim Sheridan, Great Britain, 1989, 103 mins.

1989

Best Feature

Stand and Deliver
Edward James Olmos brings the story of Jaime Escalante and his progress in teaching calculus to unmotivated barrio students to life. An inspirational true-to-life educational miracle set at Garfield High in Los Angeles in 1982. Cast includes Rosana De Soto, Andy Garcia and Lou Diamond Phillips as the gang kid who wants to learn.
VHS: S07925. $14.95.
Laser: LD70683. $24.98.
Ramon Menendez, USA, 1988, 103 mins.
Producer: Tom Musca

Best First Feature

Mystic Pizza
The comedy that takes a bite out of the seaside resort of Mystic, Connecticut, home to three young waitresses who decide their futures look as appetizing as yesterday's pizza and decide an overhaul is in order. Feisty Jojo, sexy Daisy and bookworm Kat discover that life has a secret ingredient, that friendship is a spice worth savoring and that romance can be a slice of heaven. With Julia Roberts, LiliTaylor and Annabeth Gish.
VHS: S24739. $14.98.
Donald Petrie, USA, 1988, 100 mins.

Best Director

Ramon Mendez, *Stand and Deliver*

Best Screenplay

Ramon Mendez, *Stand and Deliver*

Best Actor

Edward James Olmos, *Stand and Deliver*

Best Actress

Jodie Foster, *Five Corners*
Five Corners
An endearing, offbeat black comedy set in the Bronx in 1962, featuring a top notch ensemble cast including Jodie Foster, Todd Graff, Tim Robbins and John Turturro as Heinz, the ex-con nutcase. This film does show scenes of violence to penguins and math teachers as well as the entertainment possibilities of an elevator shaft.
VHS: S07913. $14.98.
Laser: Letterboxed. LD76357. $49.95.
Tony Bill, USA, 1987, 94 mins.

Best Supporting Actor

Lou Diamond Phillips, *Stand and Deliver*

Best Supporting Actress

Rosanna De Soto, *Stand and Deliver*

Best Cinematography

Sven Nykvist, *The Unbearable Lightness of Being*
Unbearable Lightness of Being
Czech author Milan Kundera's novel has been transferred to film by director Philip Kaufman (*The Right Stuff*). The emphasis is less on the philosophic debates of love and life and more on epic visualization of passion and revolution. With Englishman Daniel Day-Lewis as the doctor with two life long loves to choose from—French actress Juliette Binoche and Swedish actress Lena Olin. This

polyglot cast is supposed to be all Czechs in this English language version that uses hats and mirrors as sexual aides.
VHS: S07757. $19.98.
Laser: LD71386. $49.95.
Philip Kaufman, USA, 1988, 156 mins.

Best Foreign Film

Wings of Desire
"The first time I saw the film I thought it was a knockout; on second viewing it already seemed a classic," wrote J. Hoberman of Wim Wenders' re-examination of the divided city of Berlin. Damiel, played by Bruno Ganz, is the angel who has grown tired and frustrated at his inability to affect people's lives. When he falls in love with a beautiful trapeze artist, he decides to leave the heavens and enter the mortal world. With incredible cinematography by Henri Alekan, *Wings of Desire* is one of the rare movies of the past decade that actually stretch, break and re-form the boundaries of the medium" (David Denby, *New York Magazine*). German with yellow English subtitles.
VHS: S09593. $19.98.
Wim Wenders, Germany, 1988, 110 mins.

1988

Best First Feature

Dirty Dancing
At a Catskill Mountain resort in 1963 a young woman discovers her hidden talents for moving to the music. Her inspiration is her instructor, the poor and streetwise Johnny Castle. Young Baby (Jennifer Grey) also learns other physical moves with her sensitive hunk, played by Patrick Swayze. A real charmer. With Cynthia Rhodes and Jerry Orbach.
VHS: S06043. $14.98.
Emile Ardolino, USA, 1987, 105 mins.

Best Director

John Huston, *The Dead*
The Dead
The last film of a great American director is a faithful and artful adaptation of a James Joyce story from *The Dubliners*. The screenplay is by his son, Tony Huston. A well-to-do family and their friends gather for a holiday meal and evening of musical entertainment. The revelers include Anjelica Huston, Dan O'Herlihy, Donald McCann, Cathleen Delany, Marie Kern and Donald Donnelly. A short and solemn swan song.
VHS: S07921. $19.95.
John Huston, USA/Ireland, 1987, 95 mins.

Best Screenplay

Neal Jimenez, *River's Edge*
River's Edge
A powerful drama that uses a real incident to convey the hopelessness and hostility barely hidden under the surface of today's teenager. A big kid murders his girlfriend and then brings his friends to view the body. With spooky performances by Crispin Glover and Daniel Roebuck. With Dennis Hopper as the neighborhood crazy.
VHS: S05298. Not currently available.
Tim Hunter, USA, 1987, 99 mins.

Best Actor

Dennis Quaid, *The Big Easy*
The Big Easy
Dennis Quaid is an easy going cop in New Orleans and Ellen Barkin is a not so easy going district attorney investigating police corruption. While the tourists are ordering gumbo and hurricanes, a drug war is brewing and the flames of passion are starting to flicker. With Ned Beatty, Grace Zabriskie and John Goodman.
VHS: S06060. Not currently available.
Jim McBride, USA, 1987, 101 mins.

Best Actress

Sally Kirkland, *Anna*
Anna
Sally Kirkland gives a wonderful performance as a once famous Czech actress now trying to find work in New York City. She opens her home and heart to a gawky Czech girl who looks just like super-model Paulina Porizkova when she is cleaned up and presentable. A touching variation on *All About Eve*. Kirkland was nominated for an Oscar.
VHS: S05630. $79.95.
Yurek Bogayevicz, USA, 1987, 101 mins.

Best Supporting Actor

Morgan Freeman, *Street Smart*

Best Supporting Actress

Anjelica Huston, *The Dead*

Best Cinematography

Haskell Wexler, *Matewan*
Matewan
Writer-director John Sayles recreates the life and labor conditions that led to the infamous West Virginia shoot-out known as the Matewan Massacre. In a coal mining town in the 1920's union organizers come up against strong opposition from the mine owners and violence flares. With Chris Cooper, Mary McDonnell and James Earl Jones.
VHS: S06028. $14.98.
John Sayles, USA, 1987, 132 mins.

Best Foreign Film

My Life as a Dog
More than just a movie, a phenomenon that has captured the hearts of America. A bright, funny, touching tale of one boy's special growing-up year. Bundled off to a rural village while his ill mother recuperates, young Ingermar finds unexpected adventure with the town's warmhearted eccentrics. Swedish with English subtitles.
VHS: S06240. $19.98.
Laser: Subtitled. LD75232. $34.98.
Lasse Hallstrom, Sweden, 1987, 101 mins.

1987

Best Feature

Platoon
Charlie Sheen goes to Southeast Asia and finds out that war is a very traumatic experience. Giant leeches, killer dope and better-prepared opponents are almost as dangerous to his existance as the other members of his platoon. With Tom Berenger and Willem Dafoe. Oscar for Best Picture.
VHS: S04752. $19.98.
Oliver Stone, USA, 1986, 120 mins.
Producer: Arnold Kopelson

Best First Feature

She's Gotta Have It
A brazenly comic foray into sexual politics. Tracy Camila Johns stars as Nola Darling—a beautiful, free-spirited artist who simultaneously shares three men for her pleasure, dominance and one-upmanship. Lee's acute comic perception, innovative cutting and hilarious use of montage aesthetics—where Nola's suitors slay her with opening lines and come-ons—are evidence of a stream-of-consciousness talent and film school sensibility. His father, Bill Lee, composed the music.
VHS: S02777. $14.98.
Laser: LD74463. $49.95.
Spike Lee, USA, 1986, 84 mins.

Best Director

Oliver Stone, *Platoon*

Best Screenplay

Oliver Stone, *Platoon*

Best Actor

James Woods, *Salvador*
Salvador
"A film that sings and screams…broils, snaps and explodes with energy" (*L.A. Times*). James Woods as a photojournalist sent to El Salvador in 1980 to expose that government's use of death squads. With Michael Murphy, Jim Belushi and John Savage.
VHS: S01152. Not currently available.
Oliver Stone, USA, 1985, 122 mins.

Best Actress

Isabella Rossellini, *Blue Velvet*
Blue Velvet
David Lynch's demystification of American normalcy. Pitched between '40s camp and '80s post-modernism, Lynch alter ego Kyle McLachlan stars as a college student who discovers a severed ear, leading to a strange and perverse odyssey. He alternates between the innocent (Laura Dern) and the mysterious (Isabella Rossellini). Dennis Hopper stars as the creepy and dangerous, oxygen-sniffing outlaw Frank Booth. With Dean Stockwell.
VHS: S02778. $14.98.
David Lynch, USA, 1986, 120 mins.

Best Cinematography

Bob Richardson, *Platoon*

Special Distinction Award

Room with a View
Maggie Smith stars in this acclaimed film, based on the E.M. Forster novel, which evokes the manners and mores of an era. A witty, lush film with Denholm Elliott, Judi Dench and Simon Callow.
VHS: S02767. $19.98.
Laser: LD71312. $34.98.
James Ivory, Great Britain, 1986, 117 mins.

1986

Best Feature

After Hours
An inventive dark comedy, in which all reality seems to be turned upside-down, peopled by a cast including Rosanna Arquette, Teri Garr, Griffin Dunne and Cheech & Chong. Scorsese received Best Director honors at the 1986 Cannes Film Festival for this. Written by Joseph Minion.
VHS: S00021. $19.98.
Laser: LD70497. $34.98.
Martin Scorsese, USA, 1985, 97 mins.
Producers: Amy Robinson, Robert F. Colesberry and Griffin Dunne

Best Director

Joel Coen, *Blood Simple*
Blood Simple
The first film scripted by the talented Coen brothers. A critically acclaimed thriller set in rural Texas tells the old story of a man who hires a sleazy private eye to kill his wife and her boyfriend. Told in a very imaginative way, it combines chilling suspense with offbeat humor, with double and triple crosses building to a blood-curdling surprise climax. The

most inventive and original thriller in years.
VHS: S00149. $14.98.
Laser: LD70016. $34.98.
Joel Coen, USA, 1983, 96 mins.
Martin Scorsese, *After Hours*

Best Screenplay

Horton Foote, *The Trip to Bountiful*
The Trip to Bountiful
Geraldine Page won the Oscar for Best Actress in this story of an old woman returning to her childhood home in order to embrace memories. But she is trapped inside an apartment and treated like a child by her son, and ultimately escapes and gets a chance to revive her dreams.
VHS: S01811. $14.98.
Laser: LD72314. $29.99.
Peter Masterson, USA, 1985, 105 mins.

Blue Velvet

Best Actor

M. Emmett Walsh, *Blood Simple*

Best Actress

Geraldine Page, *The Trip to Bountiful*

Best Cinematography

Toyomichi Kurita, *Trouble in Mind*
Trouble in Mind
Kris Kristofferson, Keith Carradine and Genevieve Bujold star in a passionate, highly stylized love triangle in Rain City, a steamy, unlikely place. Haunting score by Mark Isham, sung by Marianne Faithful.
Laser: LD72315. $29.99.
Alan Rudolph, USA, 1986, 111 mins.

Special Distinction Award

Kiss of the Spider Woman
One of the finest films of 1985, from the director of *Pixote*. Featuring an Academy Award winning performance by William Hurt as Molina, and Raul Julia as Valentin, the political prisoner. With the incredible Sonia Braga. Based on the novel by Manuel Puig.
VHS: S00686. $14.98.
Hector Babenco, USA, 1985, 119 mins.

100 Best
Love Stories

84 Charing Cross Road
A charming adult drama about a 20-year correspondence between a budding New York writer and an English dealer in Antiquarian books. Anne Bancroft and Anthony Hopkins breathe life into this semi-autobiographical film translation of a popular play and novel.
VHS: S04677. $19.95.
David Jones, USA/Great Britain, 1987, 97 mins.

An Affair to Remember
Cary Grant and Deborah Kerr star in Leo McCarey's own remake of *Love Affair*. Grant and Kerr are the shipboard lovers who decide to meet after an absence to see if it all still works.
VHS: S11562. $14.98.
Laser: LD70813. $59.98.
Leo McCarey, USA, 1957, 114 mins.

The African Queen
Inspired casting teamed Bogart and Hepburn in this romantic adventure/comedy set in a war-torn African jungle. Surviving malaria, insects and persistent conflicts of their personalities, they share victory and tender romance.
VHS: S00020. $19.98.
John Huston, USA, 1951, 105 mins.

An American in Paris
No film can match *An American in Paris* for all the joy, all the songs, and all the romance in music and dance. Gene Kelly and Leslie Caron star in this movie set to the glorious melodies of George Gershwin, including: "Embraceable You," "Love Is Here to Stay," "I Got Rhythm" and more.
VHS: S00045. $19.95.
Vincente Minnelli, USA, 1951, 102 mins.

Anna Christie
Garbo in a great role as a disillusioned prostitute, based on Eugene O'Neill's play, who returns to her father, a barge captain, and falls in love with a sailor, only to be rejected when her tarnished past is revealed.
VHS: S00057. $19.98.
Clarence Brown, USA, 1930, 89 mins.

Anna Karenina
Tolstoy's novel is skillfully brought to the screen for the second time with a melancholy Greta Garbo in her first "talkie." *Love*, her silent version, with John Gilbert as Vronsky, did not pay as much attention to authentic costumes and settings as this sound version. With Fredric March as Vronsky and Basil Rathbone as her unfeeling husband.
VHS: S04211. $24.95.
Clarence Brown, USA, 1935, 95 mins.

Annie Hall
One of Woody Allen's best and funniest films, with Diane Keaton as the sometime object of Woody Allen's affections and expressions of his neurosis. Winner of many Academy Awards. With Allen, Keaton, Paul Simon, Carol Kane.
VHS: S00059. $19.95.
Laser: CLV, Criterion. LD70339. $49.95.
Laser: Deluxe, letterboxed edition. Includes original theatrical trailer. LD71506. $34.98.
Woody Allen, USA, 1977, 94 mins.

Autumn Leaves
Joan Crawford is cast as a lonely New England spinster who travels to California and becomes involved with a man half her age. Cliff Robertson is the new love in her life. When he begins to show signs of mental instability and violence, she is distressed but decides to stand by her man. With Vera Miles and Lorne "Pa Cartwright" Greene as an

abusive father. B&W.
VHS: S10382. $19.95.
Robert Aldrich, USA, 1956, 102 mins.

The Awful Truth
Wildly funny romp which won the Academy Award opens when a battling couple files for divorce. The only hitch seems to be who will get custody of their beloved terrier, Mr. Smith. Cary Grant and Irene Dunne co-star in this very wacky comedy.
VHS: S00083. $19.95.
Leo McCarey, USA, 1937, 92 mins.

Ball of Fire
Mild-mannered professor Gary Cooper is hard at work on a new encyclopedia. He finds the help of a brassy nightclub singer, played by Barbara Stanwyck, both invigorating and distracting. With S.Z. Sakall, Oscar Homolka and Leonid Kinskey as interested faculty members and Dan Duryea as trouble. Script by Billy Wilder and Charles Brackett. B&W.
VHS: S03115. $19.98.
Howard Hawks, USA, 1942, 111 mins.

Beauty and the Beast
Jean Cocteau's superb adaptation of Marie Leprince de Beaumont's dark fairy tale is a ferociously inventive and stylized depiction of erotic obsession, about a young woman's discovery of a ravaged soul beneath a monstrous beast. With Jean Marais, Josette Day and Marcel Andre. Cinematography by Henri Alekan. "A sensuously fascinating film, the visual progression of the fable into a dream-world casts its unpredictable spell" (Bosley Crowther).
VHS: S00110. $24.95.
Laser: Cocteau, CAV. LD70865. $89.95.
Jean Cocteau, France, 1946, 93 mins.

Belle Epoque
This film won an Oscar as the Best Foreign Language Film in 1994. In this charming romantic comedy, a handsome young soldier flees the Spanish Revolution only to inspire his own sexual revolution. Finding succor in the house of an artist who has four daughters, he proceeds to seduce them all, or is it the other way around? Spanish with English subtitles.
VHS: S22768. $19.95.
Laser: LD74619. $34.95.
Fernando Trueba, Spain, 1992, 109 mins.

Big Sleep
Humphrey Bogart is Philip Marlowe in this entertaining adaptation of Raymond Chandler's novel. Blackmail, murder, sex and drugs all come into play as the ace detective tries to sort out the guilty parties. Even the author couldn't figure out who killed the chauffeur. With Lauren Bacall, Martha Vickers and Elisha Cook, Jr.
VHS: S09389. $19.95.
Laser: LD70174. $34.98.
Howard Hawks, USA, 1946, 114 mins.

Black Orpheus
Marcel Camus' quintessential love story based on the Greek myth of Orpheus and Eurydice is set against the vivid backdrop of carnival in Rio de Janeiro. Orpheus, the streetcar conductor, falls hopelessly in love with Eurydice; winner of the Grand Prize at Cannes as well as an Oscar for Best Foreign Film. Portuguese with English subtitles.
VHS: S00138. $29.95.
Laser: LD70346. $79.95.
Marcel Camus, Brazil, 1958, 103 mins.

Born Yesterday
Judy Holliday won the Best Actress Oscar for her funny role as the dumb blond girlfriend of Broderick Crawford, a corrupt millionaire junk dealer. Brock, a

man with social ambitions, is embarassed by Billie's crass behavior and hires a writer, William Holden, to smarten her up. A classic comedy.
VHS: S03863. $19.95.
George Cukor, USA, 1950, 103 mins.

Breakfast at Tiffany's
Audrey Hepburn is superb in this dazzling romantic comedy based on Truman Capote's novella. Audrey is the New York playgirl with a secret, determined to marry a Brazilian millionaire, who falls in love with her next-door neighbor, George Peppard.
VHS: S03776. $14.95.
Laser: Widescreen. **LD75307. $39.98.**
Blake Edwards, USA, 1961, 114 mins.

Camille
Greta Garbo at the peak of her career, as the consumptive courtesan who falls in love with the young nobleman with tragic results. This adaptation of the Alexandre Dumas play and novel, with Lionel Barrymore and Robert Taylor, is beautiful to look at and clearly defines the Garbo magic.
VHS: S03453. $24.95.
George Cukor, USA, 1936, 110 mins.

Can-Can
Frank Sinatra is a roguish lawyer in Paris trying to keep his cafe owner and performer sweetheart (Shirley MacLaine) from being jailed for doing a forbidden dance. Maurice Chevalier approves but the younger judge Louis Jourdan are all gallant. With Juliet Prowse and songs by Cole Porter. Based on the Abe Burrows musical. Ooh-la-la. 130 mins.
Laser: LD70899. $49.98.
Walter Lang, USA, 1960, 130 mins.

Carmen Jones
Dorothy Dandridge plays Carmen, a woman caught between two men and her own unorthodox nature. The men, one a pretty boy and the other a tough sergeant, are portrayed by Harry Belafonte and Brock Peters. Dandridge lures Joe (Belafonte) into deserting from the army and then leaves him for the two-fisted Sgt. Brown (Peters). The supporting cast is every bit as impressive as the main actors and includes Pearl Bailey, Joe Adams and Diahann Carroll in her first film role. Dandridge became the first African-American nominated for a Best Actress Academy Award. The film won a Golden Globe for Best Musical/Comedy in 1955.
VHS: S21385. $19.95.
Otto Preminger, USA, 1954, 105 mins.

Cannes. Russian with English subtitles.
VHS: S17517. $59.95.
Mikhail Kalatozov, USSR, 1957, 94 mins.

Cyrano de Bergerac
Gerard Depardieu is magnificent as the poetic soldier with the prominent proboscis. Based on the classic play by Rostand in which a 17th century swordsman proves inarticulate only when it comes to expressing his love for his cousin Roxanne face to face. Packed with pageantry, poetry and robust performances. With Anne Brochet, Jacques Weber, and some 2000 extras. French with English subtitles.
VHS: S14784. $19.98.
Laser: LD72215. $49.95.
Jean-Paul Rappeneau, France, 1989, 135 mins.

Daddy Long Legs
Fred Astaire and Leslie Caron dance together and fall in love in this sentimental tale of a globe-trotting playboy who anonymously adopts a French orphan. Thelma Ritter and Fred Clark co-star.
VHS: S14505. $19.98.
Jean Negulesco, USA, 1955, 126 mins.

Days of Heaven
An Award winner both at Cannes and in Hollywood, this story follows a trio composed of a fugitive from the Chicago slums (Richard Gere), a shy, rich Texan (Sam Shepard) and a woman (Brooke Adams) caught in a love triangle. Set against the Midwestern wheat fields at the turn of the century, this film is often cited by cinematographers as being one of the most beautifully shot films ever made. Won the Best Oscar for Cinematography.
VHS: S00313. $14.95.
Laser: LD75358. $29.98.
Terence Malick, USA, 1980, 95 mins.

Designing Woman
George Wells' Academy Award-winning script takes us through the whirlwind marriage of a rough-edged sportswriter and a chic fashion designer, deftly played by Gregory Peck and Lauren Bacall.
VHS: S15242. $19.98.
Laser: Deluxe letterboxed edition. **LD70189. $34.98.**
Vincente Minnelli, USA, 1957, 118 mins.

Dona Flor and Her Two Husbands
Funny, sexy and intoxicating! *Dona Flor* is a ribald folktale about a young widow, her respectable new husband, and her dynamic but dead first husband who

Tom Cats & Sex Kittens

American Gigolo
VHS: S10017. $14.95.
Laser: LD75360. $29.98.

Barbarella
VHS: S00095. $19.95.
Laser: LD75155. $34.98.

Betty Boop: The Definitive Collection
VHS: S30002. $69.95.

Guys and Dolls
VHS: S02529. $19.98.

Hud
VHS: S00590. $14.95.
Laser: LD75305. $39.98.

Just a Gigolo
Laser: LD70268. $39.95.

Lolita
VHS: S02545. $19.98.
Laser: LD70760. $59.95.

Lord Love a Duck
VHS: S28493. $19.98.

Shampoo
VHS: S01885. $14.95.
Laser: LD70762. $34.95.

Choose Me
Keith Carradine, Genevieve Bujold and Lesley Ann Warren star in this stylish and sexy romance that explores the quirky, ambiguous truths of heterosexual relationships. A cult favorite for its off-enter, eccentric look at contemporary love.
VHS: S00237. $14.95.
Alan Rudolph, USA, 1984, 106 mins.

The Cranes Are Flying
A film that marked a radical opening for Soviet cinema; the lighthearted, romantic, lyrical story of a beautiful young girl (Tatiana Samoilova) caught up in the horrors of war. When her fiance (Alexei Batalov) goes off to war, she marries a man whom she does not love and who raped her, is evacuated to Siberia, and after the war, learns of her fiance's death. But she refuses to believe it and waits for his return. A great international success which won the Grand Prix at

refuses to stay buried, featuring the sensual Sonia Braga as Dona Flor. Portuguese with English subtitles.
VHS: S00359. $19.98.
Bruno Barreto, Brazil, 1977, 106 mins.

The Double Life of Veronique
Two remarkably similar women, in Warsaw and Paris, are acutely aware of each other's existence in this film about the linkage of souls. Veronika is a Polish music student with a beautiful voice and a heart condition. Veronique is a French school teacher paralyzed by doubt. Both roles are played by the beautiful Irene Jacob. Slawomir Idziak's cinematography and Zbigniew Preisner's score are alternately haunting and unforgettable. Polish and French with English subtitles.
VHS: S16928. $89.95.
Laser: LD75182. $34.98.
Krzysztof Kieslowski, Poland/France, 1991, 92 mins.

Earrings of Madame De...

Max Ophuls' powerful romantic tragedy, starring Charles Boyer, Vittorio de Sica, Danielle Darrieux. A spoiled socialite, married to a general, flirts with an amorous diplomat. As the affair escalates, her passion rips through the glittering facade of their privileged existence, plunging them into disaster as they risk everything for love and honor. Newly mastered. Frenchwith English subtitles.
 VHS: S08999. $29.95.
 Laser: LD75543. $49.98.
Max Ophuls, France, 1953, 105 mins.

Elvira Madigan

A modern classic. Elvira (Pia Degermark) is a tightrope artist, and Sixten Sparre (Thommy Berggren), an aristocratic army officer who abandons a promising career for a rapturous affair with Elvira. In the idyllic Swedish countryside they are promptly ostracized for breaking the moral code and the film ends tragically. Lyrical, nostalgic and moving, with beautiful use of Mozart's *Piano Concerto No. 21*. Swedish with English subtitles.
 VHS: S00404. $24.98.
Bo Widerberg, Sweden, 1967, 95 mins.

Farewell My Concubine

This complex story of passion and political intrigue won the Best Film Award at Cannes and is an ambitious historical epic of China in the 20th century. It follows the enduring friendship between two opera stars in old Beijing. As they prosper, the political upheavals of war and revolution take their toll. When a young prostitute threatens their professional and personal union, it becomes just one of many trials which test the enduring strength of art and love that bind these two men.
 VHS: S20736. $19.95.
 Laser: LD74457. $39.99.
Chen Kaige, China, 1993, 157 mins.

Flesh and the Devil

"The first of the Garbo-Gilbert romances, [this] was quite certainly a box office milestone—and it also represents something of a high-water mark in the sheer elegance and 'bigness' of movies in their most glamorous era...Honor, loyalty, love—strong emotions all of them, are given full expression in a story which permits no facile solutions" (*Classics of the Silent Screen*). Garbo is simply magnificent as the seductive temptress who drives a wedge between two old friends.
 VHS: S09280. $29.95.
Clarence Brown, USA, 1927, 103 mins.

French Lieutenant's Woman

Harold Pinter wrote the screenplay adapted from John Fowles' novel. A hauntingly beautiful film starring Meryl Streep and Jeremy Irons, about a woman ostracized by Victorian society and abandoned by her lover.
 VHS: S00468. $19.95.
 Laser: LD70140. $39.98.
Karel Reisz, Great Britain, 1981, 124 mins.

Ginger and Fred

A warm, touching satire not only of television, but of lost hopes and idealism, and of the impossibility of love in the face of blatant commercialism. Giulietta Masina and Marcello Mastroianni are two retired Astaire and Rogers imitators who are reunited after thirty years for a nostalgic TV variety show. Italian with English subtitles.
 VHS: S02526. $19.98.
Federico Fellini, Italy, 1986, 128 mins.

The Go-Between

Joseph Losey's tense, sexual class drama based on a brilliant script by Harold Pinter. Julie Christie is the upper-class beauty whose passionate, illicit affair with the groundskeeper (Alan Bates) is orchestrated through notes carried by a young boy, the go-between. The film, told largely in flashback through the boy's eyes, is full of nuance and innuendo; a brilliant dissection of sex and class.
 VHS: S27183. $19.95.
Joseph Losey, Great Britain, 1971, 118 mins.

Gone with the Wind

A film beyond criticism, a work that welds together Hollywood classicism and literary adaptation with grace. Victor Fleming is the credited director, though at various times Howard Hawks, George Cukor and Sam Wood helped shape the narrative and rhythm. Ben Hecht worked on the screenplay. William Cameron Menzies was the production designer. With Clark Gable, Vivien Leigh, Leslie Howard, Olivia de Havilland and Hattie McDaniel.
 VHS: S00515. $89.98.
Victor Fleming, USA, 1939, 222 mins.

The Hairdresser's Husband

An acclaimed, quirky film about erotic obsession from the director of *Monsieur Hire*. Antoine (Jean Rochefort) is a middle-aged man whose life-long ambition to marry a hairdresser is fulfilled in his tender relationship with the beautiful and graceful Matila (Anna Galiena). With Henri Hocking and Maurice Chevit. French with English subtitles.
 VHS: S18680. $19.95.
 Laser: LD75204. $34.98.
Patrice Leconte, France, 1990, 84 mins.

Hiroshima, Mon Amour

From the beginning, in which the love-making of a French actress (Emmanuelle Riva) and a Japanese architect (Eiji Okada) is intercut with newsreel footage of Hiroshima's atomic holocaust and its aftermath, to the couple's painful walk through the reconstructed city, Resnais' film recaptures both the pain and the richness of the war. French with English subtitles.
 VHS: S00571. $29.95.
Alain Resnais, France, 1959, 91 mins.

His Girl Friday

One of the wittiest Hollywood comedies: Rosalind Russell is the ace reporter ready to quit for marriage, Cary Grant, her editor trying to convince her to stay. An escaped murderer puts Russell's determination to test. Sophisticated comedy from Howard Hawks.
 VHS: S00572. $14.95.
 Laser: Chapter stops, restored, digital master, theatrical trailer. **LD75051. $39.95.**
Howard Hawks, USA, 1940, 95 mins.

Hot Spot

Don Johnson drifts into a small Texas town that has two good-looking women and one frequently unattended bank. With Virginia Madsen and Jennifer Connelly as Taylor, Texas' alternatives to watching television. Based on the 1952 novel *Hell Hath No Fury* by Charles Williams. Steamy stuff indeed.
 VHS: S13657. $89.95.
Dennis Hopper, USA, 1990, 120 mins.

Il Postino (The Postman)

Massimo Troisi stars as a humble postman in a small but beautiful Italian village, whose life is transformed by the simple powers of poetry. Pablo Neruda is poet-living-in-exile who gives this bumbling mailman the right words to seduce the woman of his dreams. Troisi died abruptly after completing this role, turning this touching and deeply felt film into a highly apt but wholly unexpected memorial to his skills as a comic actor. With Maria Grazia Cucinotta and Philippe Noiret. Based on the novel *Burning Patience*, by Antonia Skarmenta. Italian with English subtitles.
 VHS: S27378. $19.95.
 Laser: LD75509. $39.99.
Michael Radford, Italy, 1995, 108 mins.

It Happened One Night

Winner of five Academy Awards, this famous screwball comedy stars Clark Gable and Claudette Colbert as two mismatched lovers. Colbert escapes from her millionaire father, who wants to stop her from marrying a worthless playboy.
 VHS: S00642. $19.95.
 Laser: LD72146. $34.95.
Frank Capra, USA, 1934, 105 mins.

Jamon, Jamon

This winner of the Silver Lion at the Venice Film Festival combines outrageous humor and steamy sex in a quirky movie of mismatched love affairs. Anna Galiena, Stefania Sandrelli, Javier Bardem and Penelope Cruz are all featured in this tale of erotic passions.
 VHS: S21097. $19.98.
Bigas Luna, Spain, 1993, 95 mins.

Ju Dou

The erotic thriller that China didn't want you to see is now on video. An exquisitely photographed and smartly performed drama of secret love and hidden faces. Trouble closely follows passion when a beautiful young bride is drawn to the handsome, strong nephew of her new husband, an ancient and disagreeable owner of an isolated dye factory. With excellent performances by Gong Li, Li Bao-tan, Li Wei and Zhang Li. Mandarin with English subtitles.
 VHS: S15072. $19.98.
Zhang Yimou, China/Japan, 1989, 98 mins.

Jules and Jim

Truffaut's famous love triangle stars Henri Serre as Jim and Oskar Werner as Jules, both in love with Catherine (Jeanne Moreau). Their free-wheeling friendship is suspended when Jules marries Catherine and takes her back to Germany. The two friends are separated by World War I, and when they meet again after the war, Catherine changes partners. One of the films that justifies the invention of the movies. Photography by Raoul Coutard; music by Georges Delerue. French with English subtitles.
VHS: S00663. $29.95.
Laser: LD71069. $59.95.
Francois Truffaut, France, 1961, 105 mins.

The King and I

Stern Siamese monarch Brynner is softened by the influence of English governess Kerr as their clashing cultures and personalities give way to an unspoken love. Magnificent performance by Brynner (who won an Oscar) in this sumptuously produced and moving adaptation of the Broadway musical. "Shall We Dance" highlights the Rogers and Hammerstein score.
VHS: S02541. $19.98.
Laser: THX. LD75920. $124.98.
Walter Lang, USA, 1956, 133 mins.

L'Atalante

The high water mark of French poetic realism, set on a barge plying the Seine. A young barge captain and his bride live on a barge with the eccentric Pere Jules (Michel Simon). With Boris Kauffman's cinematography, which evokes Paris and the Seine with the luminosity of Atget or Cartier-Bresson, and everyday life full of magical moments like Pere Jules' "museum" of exotic marvels and the husband's underwater vision of his lost bride. "May be the greatest film ever made" (Georgia Brown, *The Village Voice*). Initially cut by seven minutes, this version is the fully restored, 89-minute cut. With Dita Parlo, Jean Daste and Michel Simon. French with English subtitles.
VHS: S17696. $59.95.
Jean Vigo, France, 1934, 89 mins.

La Dolce Vita

"A landmark of cinematic social comment," wrote one critic about Fellini's journey through a decadent Rome. Banned by the Church in many countries, the sensationalism of the film often obscured its serious intent. *La Dolce Vita* follows a society journalist (Marcello Mastroianni) through a nightmarish world in which emotions have been destroyed by surface realities, moral conventions and unresolved guilt. With Anita Ekberg, Anouk Aimee, Alain Cuny and Nadia Gray. Italian with English subtitles.
VHS: S00705. $24.95.
Federico Fellini, Italy, 1961, 174 mins.

Lady Chatterley's Lover

Marc Allegret's version of the D.H. Lawrence novel with Danielle Darrieux as the Lady. Although the film was banned for a number of years by the New York Board of Censors, it is now almost too tasteful in its depiction of Lady Chatterley's sexual awakening. Darrieux delivers a performance of great complexity. French with English subtitles.
VHS: S18172. $24.95.
Marc Allegret, France, 1955, 102 mins.

Last Tango in Paris

Powerful, explosive, erotic, political film that took the world by storm; Maria Schneider and Marlon Brando co-star in this film of love, sex and will. "The most powerfully erotic film ever made," wrote Pauline Kael. "*Last Tango* is a genuine masterpiece of staggering proportions," said *Newsweek*. English dialog. Uncut, X-rated version.
VHS: S00727. $19.98.
Laser: CLV, 2 discs, Criterion. LD70412. $69.95.
Laser: Letterboxed, MGM. LD71176. $39.98.
Bernardo Bertolucci, Italy, 1974, 129 mins.

Les Liaisons Dangereuses

The first—and certainly the best—version of Laclos' novel, with the incredible Gerard Philipe playing Valmont, and Jeanne Moreau, Madame de Merteuil. Directed by Roger Vadim and updated to 1960, Vadim's exploration of free-thinking attitudes and portrait of the corrupt upper-class society is particularly distinguished through the outstanding performances of both Philipe and Moreau. With Jean-Louis Trintignant, Annette Vadim; music by, among others, Thelonious Monk. French with English subtitles.
VHS: S10740. $59.95.
Roger Vadim, France, 1959, 106 mins.

Les Visiteurs du Soir

Marcel Carne's charming fantasy, set in the 15th century, and starring Arletty. The devil sends two envoys to a chateau to intervene in the betrothal of a count and a lady, and the male ghost falls in love with Lady Anne. The Devil himself must intervene. The images and sets often have the charm of medieval miniatures, and *Les Visiteurs du Soir* was a considerable success. French with English subtitles.
VHS: S06439. $29.95.
Marcel Carne, France, 1942, 110 mins.

Liebelei

The film which established the reputation for Max Ophuls, based on a play by Arthur Schnitzler; the story of a young lieutenant who is in love with a Viennese girl, and is called to account by a baron who believes him to be the lover of the baroness. The military code requires a duel, the lieutenant is killed, and the girl throws herself out the window in despair.

My Fair Lady

"Ophuls' magical adaptation of Schnitzler's mordant love play is a lament to lost innocence, transported by Ophuls' moving camera into the mystical regions of remembrance" (NY Film Festival). German with English subtitles.
VHS: S07820. $39.95.
Max Ophuls, Germany, 1932, 88 mins.

Like Water for Chocolate
Immensely popular, magical story of a young girl whose cooking is infused with her emotions as she prepares her meals. Unrequited passions, changing political situations and madness emerge in this highly entertaining, sensual and funny story. Written by Laura Esquivel and directed by her husband. Spanish with English subtitles.
VHS: S21358. $19.95.
Laser: Letterboxed. **LD74638. $39.99.**
Alfonso Arau, Mexico, 1992, 105 mins.

Lola
Jacques Demy's *Lola* is a precisely constructed film about love, "with an almost balletic sense of rhythm set against the urban background of Nantes." The beautiful Anouk Aimee plays Lola, a cabaret dancer, who is courted by her childhood friend. But she is still in love with Michel, who had left her with their child when he went off to seek his fortune. After spending the night with another man, Michel

set in French-occupied Indochina during the 1920s. This is the uncut, unrated European version that was initially rated NC-17. Original English dialog.
VHS: S18520. $19.98.
Laser: LD71870. $39.98.
Jean-Jacques Annaud, France/Great Britain, 1991, 113 mins.

The Lovers
A landmark of both French cinema and screen eroticism, *The Lovers* stars Jeanne Moreau as a stylish provincial wife whose shallow life changes when she meets an unpretentious young man. The film caused a furor of protest when it was first released; today its tender sensuality and genuine feeling for passion are a welcome relief. Henri Decae's magical photography and Brahm's Second Quartet create an atmosphere of luminous romanticism. French with English subtitles.
VHS: S16078. $29.95.
Louis Malle, France, 1958, 89 mins.

Madame Bovary
The classic 19th century novel by Gustave Flaubert has been masterfully adapted to the screen by veteran filmmaker Claude Chabrol. Isabelle Huppert occupies the erotic title role of Emma Bovary, an unhappily married woman who wants more out of life. With Christophe Malavoy, Jean Yanne, Lucas Belvaux and

Tying the Knot

Blood Wedding
VHS: S00150. $24.95.

Double Wedding
VHS: S18802. $19.98.

Four Weddings and a Funeral
DVD: DV60007. $29.95.
VHS: S21506. $19.95.
Laser: LD74527. $39.95.

The Graduate
Laser: LD70371. $99.95.

Member of the Wedding
VHS: S07001. $19.99.

The Member of the Wedding
VHS: S32108. $90.99.
Laser: LD76341. $39.99.

Muriel's Wedding
VHS: S27219. $19.95.

Obeah Wedding
VHS: S15333. $29.95.

Paper Wedding
VHS: S15683. $79.95.
Laser: LD71487. $39.95.

Royal Wedding
VHS: S07366. $19.95.
Laser: LD74680. $34.98.

Waikiki Wedding
VHS: S25011. $14.98.

Wedding
VHS: S01440. $59.98.

The Wedding (Wesele)
VHS: S15560. $49.95.

The Wedding Banquet
VHS: S21895. $94.98.
Laser: LD74593. $39.98.

The Wedding Gift
VHS: S22878. $96.98.

Wedding in Galilee
VHS: S08938. $24.95.

The Wedding March
VHS: S03443. $29.95.

The Wedding Night
VHS: S23440. $19.98.

Weddings and Babies
VHS: S30706. $39.95.

reappears, rich, and takes her away. French with English subtitles.
VHS: S10738. $59.95.
Jacques Demy, France, 1961, 91 mins.

Loulou
French heartthrob Gerard Depardieu and Isabelle Huppert star in this acclaimed film by Maurice Pialat. Huppert plays Nelly, a married woman who meets Loulou (Depardieu), a charming, leather-jacketed stud in a crowded Paris disco. She can't resist his lustful style and returns home with him. Loulou turns out to be as passionate in bed as on the dance floor, and they embark on a free-wheeling relationship that is a mixture of unabashed eroticism and authentic romance. French with English subtitles.
VHS: S12196. $79.95.
Maurice Pialat, France, 1980, 110 mins.

Love Affair
This RKO classic stars Irene Dunne and Charles Boyer, and was later remade as *An Affair to Remember.* It received five Oscar nominations, and featured songs by Harold Arlen and Buddy De Sylva.
VHS: S04491. $29.95.
Leo McCarey, USA, 1939, 87 mins.

The Lover
Jean-Jacques Annaud adapts Marguerite Duras' autobiographical novel *L'Amant:* political, social and class tensions and sexual role-playing refracted through an erotic relationship between a beautiful French girl (Jane March) and her older, elegant, aristocratic Chinese lover (Tony Leung). The film is

Christiane Minazolli. French with English subtitles.
VHS: S16504. $14.98.
Laser: LD71454. $39.98.
Claude Chabrol, France, 1991, 130 mins.

A Man and a Woman
The 1966 Academy Award winner, a legendary love story starring Jean-Louis Trintignant as a race car driver who falls in love with Anouk Aimee. Stylish, well-acted and visually dynamic. Available only in a dubbed version.
VHS: S02322. $19.98.
Claude Lelouch, France, 1966, 103 mins.

Mayerling
The romantic, sumptuous film that established Charles Boyer as a screen idol. Set in Vienna in 1883, Boyer plays the Archduke Rudolf, who is madly in love with Maria Vetsera, played by Danielle Darrieux. An opulent romance with a sharp portrait of the Hapsburg court. French with English subtitles.
VHS: S00837. $29.95.
Anatole Litvak, France, 1936, 91 mins.

McCabe and Mrs. Miller
A brilliant, offbeat drama of frontier life starring Warren Beatty and Julie Christie. This is Altman's personal and poetic interpretation of an American myth, resulting in a truly original Western. Also appearing are Shelley Duvall, Keith Carradine, Michael Murphy and William Devane.
VHS: S00839. $14.95.
Laser: LD74710. $39.98.
Robert Altman, USA, 1971, 120 mins.

Mississippi Masala

Moving to the American South in her American debut, the Indian-born, Harvard-educated filmmaker Mira Nair (*Salaam Bombay!*) inverts the Romeo and Juliet story, concerning the forbidden love affair of an entrepreneurial black man (Denzel Washington) and a sheltered, young, Indian woman (the startling newcomer Sarita Choudhury), despite the objections of their respective families. Brilliantly shot by Ed Lachman, Nair has a marvelous and open way with actors. With Roshan Seth, Charles S. Dutton, and Joe Seneca.
VHS: S17070. $19.95.
Laser: LD72200. $34.95.
Mira Nair, USA, 1991, 110 mins.

Moonstruck

The winner of three Oscars, this charming, romantic, ethnic comedy involves a somewhat dowdy Cher involved with two brothers. She's engaged to Danny Aiello but in love with Nicolas Cage. Her parents, Olympia Dukakis and Vincent Gardenia, have their own problems, but wish her the best. Screenplay by John Patrick Shanley (*Five Corners*). Set in Brooklyn.
VHS: S07105. $19.98.
Laser: LD76278. $39.99.
Norman Jewison, USA, 1987, 103 mins.

My Fair Lady

Audrey Hepburn and Rex Harrison star in this film adaptation of the classic Broadway musical by Lerner and Loewe, based on George Bernard Shaw's *Pygmalion*. Now it has been carefully restored, and even the original soundtracks recorded by Hepburn have been saved. Interviews with all the stars and the original trailer are included in this limited edition.
VHS: S21959. $24.98.
George Cukor, USA, 1964, 170 mins.

Ninotchka

"Garbo laughs!"—and indeed, she does, in her first romantic comedy as the dour Soviet official who discovers the pleasures of Paris (and Melvyn Douglas) and must choose between romance and duty. Lubitsch at his best.
VHS: S00935. $19.98.
Ernst Lubitsch, USA, 1939, 108 mins.

Notorious

One of the greatest, if not the greatest, of Hitchcock's films. A conflict between love and duty pushes the action of this thriller set in Rio just after World War II. A beautiful party girl, the daughter of a Nazi traitor, is enlisted by the U.S. government to marry Nazi spy Claude Rains in order to infiltrate his ring. Cary Grant is the U.S. agent sent to aid her, and one of the great screen romances of all time develops. Beautifully shot, the work of the master at the top of his form.
VHS: S04454. $19.98.
Laser: CAV. LD70429. $99.95.
Laser: CLV. LD70430. $49.95.
Alfred Hitchcock, USA, 1946, 102 mins.

Passione d'Amore

This story of obsessive love between an ugly spinster and a handsome young officer won the Cannes Special Jury Prize in 1981 and is notable for its strong performances from the sensuous Laura Antonelli and Jean-Louis Trintignant. Mad and consumed by desire, this woman manages to overcome the officer's reservations. Steven Sondheim's Tony-award winning musical *Passion* is based on this story. Italian with English subtitles.
VHS: S22231. $24.95.
Ettore Scola, Italy, 1981, 117 mins.

The Philadelphia Story

One of the most hilarious and captivating romantic comedies ever to grace the screen. Katharine Hepburn is caught between her fiance and her charming ex-husband. With a splendid cast, including Cary Grant, James Stewart and Ruth Hussey.
DVD: DV60063. $24.98.
VHS: S01023. $19.98.
Laser: LD70152. $39.98.
George Cukor, USA, 1940, 118 mins.

The Piano

Holly Hunter's Oscar-winning performance as a mute woman dedicated to her music takes center stage in this lush drama set in 19th century New Zealand. Harvey Keitel co-stars as the brutish but sensitive man who gives her back what seemed irrevocably lost. A young Anna Paquin more than holds her own with a performance that garnered this new star an

Oscar for Best Supporting Actress.
VHS: S20871. $19.98.
Jane Campion, Australia/New Zealand, 1993, 121 mins.

A Place in the Sun

Based on Theodore Dreiser's *An American Tragedy*, and featuring strong performances from Montgomery Clift, Elizabeth Taylor and Shelley Winters. Monty Clift is the poor boy driven by the lure of wealth, with his success threatened by complications from his simultaneous affairs with factory girl Shelley Winters and socialite Liz Taylor.
VHS: S04663. $19.95.
George Stevens, USA, 1951, 122 mins

The Quiet Man

John Ford's lyrical portrait of Ireland revolves around an American prizefighter (John Wayne) who returns to his birthplace to buy back the family cottage and marry the temptress Maureen O'Hara. Just wonderful.
VHS: S15908. $19.98.
Laser: 40th Anniversary edition includes *The Making of the Quiet Man*. **LD71497. $59.98.**
John Ford, USA, 1952, 153 mins.

Rebecca

Hitchcock's first American film, based on a du Maurier gothic romance. With Laurence Olivier and a fine performance by Joan Fontaine as a shy young woman who marries Olivier. Excellent supporting roles by Judith Anderson, George Sanders, Leo G. Carroll and Nigel Bruce.
VHS: S01096. $19.98.
Laser: CAV. LD70441. $124.95.
Laser: CLV. LD70442. $69.95.
Alfred Hitchcock, USA, 1940, 104 mins.

Robin and Marian

Richard Lester continues the high-spirited Robin Hood adventure as Robin regroups the members of his Sherwood Forest band when King John assumes the throne. Sean Connery is Robin Hood, Audrey Hepburn is Marian.
VHS: S03694. $19.95.
Laser: LD75904. $34.95.
Richard Lester, Great Britain, 1976, 112 mins.

Roman Holiday

Stylish production starring Gregory Peck and Audrey Hepburn about a rebellious princess who wishes to discover living on her own. With Eddie Albert as Peck's pal.
VHS: S01763. $19.95.
Laser: LD75249. $34.98.
William Wyler, USA, 1953, 118 mins.

Romeo and Juliet

One of the most popular film adaptations of Shakespeare's classic, the recipient of international acclaim and four Academy Award nominations. Starring Olivia Hussey, Leonard Whiting and Michael York, this modern version brings new vitality and fresh insight to the world's most durable love story. English dialog. Letterboxed.
VHS: S01130. $24.95.
Laser: LD76048. $44.98.
Franco Zeffirelli, USA/Italy, 1968, 138 mins.

The Rose Tattoo

A happy-go-lucky trucker awakens a widow to life's joys in this flavorful adaptation of a Tennessee Williams play. Starring Burt Lancaster and the brilliant Anna Magnani. Photographed by James Wong Howe.
VHS: S13787. $19.95.
Daniel Mann, USA, 1955, 117 mins.

Roxanne

Steve Martin successfully updates the story of Cyrano de Bergerac as he plays a soulful small-town fire chief with a big heart and an even larger nose. He falls for Roxanne (Daryl Hannah) but she has eyes only for hunk Rick Rossovich. With Michael J. Pollard, Shelley Duvall and Fred Willard.
VHS: S05318. $14.95.
Laser: LD75804. $34.95.
Fred Schepisi, USA, 1987, 107 mins.

Ryan's Daughter

Robert Bolt (*A Man for All Seasons*, *The Mission*) wrote the screenplay of this long but rewarding study by David Lean about a rich, unsatisfied, married woman (Sarah Miles) who falls for a British soldier (Christopher Jones) during British colonial rule of Ireland. Robert Mitchum is cast as Miles' British school teacher; John Mills is excellent as a crippled

mute. VHS letterboxed.
VHS: S02570. $24.98.
Laser: LD70185. $49.98.
David Lean, Great Britain, 1970, 192 mins.

Scent of a Woman (Profumo di Donna)
The original, award-winning Italian version of the comedy-drama was directed by Dino Risi and stars Vittorio Gassman in a tour-de-force performance as a blind and embittered army captain who undertakes a tour of Italy acccompanied by his young aide (Alessandro Momo). At first his adventures seem innocent and amusing, but as the two men travel through Genoa and Rome, a darker purpose is revealed. With Agostina Belli. Italian with English subtitles.
VHS: S08780. $89.95.
Dino Risi, Italy, 1974, 103 mins.

Separate Tables
A set of one-act dramas exploring love, rejection and reunion. First, "Table by the Window" follows a pair of lovers caught in a whirlwind of lust. Second, "Table Number Seven" shows a woman's love tested when the object of her distant adoration is accused of a terrible crime. With Julie Christie, Alan Bates, Claire Bloom.
VHS: S03769. $19.98.
Delbert Mann, USA, 1958, 98 mins.

She's Gotta Have It
A brazenly comic foray into sexual politics. Tracy Camila Johns stars as Nola Darling—a beautiful, free-spirited artist who simultaneously shares three men for her pleasure, dominance and one-upmanship. Lee's acute comic perception, innovative cutting and hilarious use of montage aesthetics—where Nola's suitors slay her with opening lines and come-ons—are evidence of a stream-of-consciousness talent and film school sensibility. His father, Bill Lee, composed the music.
VHS: S02777. $14.98.
Laser: LD74463. $49.95.
Spike Lee, USA, 1986, 84 mins.

Splendor in the Grass
Natalie Wood and Warren Beatty (in his screen debut) star as two teenage lovers ripped apart by the repressive mentality of their 1920s Kansas town.
VHS: S11617. $19.95.
Laser: LD71414. $39.95.
Elia Kazan, USA, 1961, 124 mins.

The Story of Boys and Girls
The engagement of two young lovers brings together an intoxicating mix of friends and family. Between the 20 delicious courses and flowing wine, the guests loosen their belts as well as their tongues, spilling family secrets and revealing romantic intrigues. Even the maid gets caught in a lusty tryst that leaves her flushed and rumpled when she serves the next dish. Italian with English subtitles.
VHS: S16525. $19.98.
Pupi Avati, Italy, 1991, 92 mins.

Sunrise
Although this was Murnau's first Hollywood film, he scripted it with Carl Mayer while still in Germany. The story concerns the marriage of a peasant couple whose honeymoon in the big city is derailed by a sultry seductress. But the film is neither trite nor melodramatic; Murnau's sets and camera angles imbue the images with a poetic lyricism that reveals the characters' psychological states. Easily his most perfect film, Murnau's *Sunrise* was named the "Greatest film of all time," in a recent *Cahiers du Cinema* Critic's Poll. With George O'Brien, Janet Gaynor and Margaret Livingston.
VHS: S07782. $29.95.
Laser: Outtakes, digital transfer. **LD76401. $49.98.**
Friedrich W. Murnau, USA, 1927, 97 mins.

Too Beautiful for You
Gerard Depardieu stars as a successful car dealer obsessed with his plain temporary secretary much to the displeasure of his stunningly beautiful wife. Bertrand Blier directs this dark comedy that also stars Josiane Balasko and Carole Bouquet. Expect the unexpected in this artful and painfully funny look at adultery. French with English subtitles.
VHS: S13673. $19.98.
Laser: LD71629. $39.95.
Bertrand Blier, France, 1988, 91 mins.

Truly, Madly, Deeply
A young woman is consumed by grief because of the death of her young lover (Alan Rickman). Just as her despair and anger seem overwhelming, the dead young man shows up on her doorstep. This unique film combines a love story with a decidedly supernatural angle.
VHS: S25516. $19.99.
Anthony Minghella, Great Britain, 1991, 107 mins.

Turkish Delights
A very amusing, uplifting, and tragic story of a couple madly in love. This Academy Award nominee is a study of two free spirits forced to change by the events of their lives. From the director of *The Fourth Man*. English dubbed.
VHS: S01377. $39.95.
Paul Verhoeven, Netherlands, 1974, 100 mins.

The Umbrellas of Cherbourg
Catherine Deneuve stars in this sumptuously photographed romantic musical of two lovers who are split up by the Algerian war. The girl marries another when she discovers she is pregnant. He also marries; yet they meet again. All dialog is sung; with haunting music by Michel LeGrand and lyrics by Demy, including the song, "I Will Wait for You." "A masterpiece! More beautiful and more startling than ever!" (*New York Daily News*). "The kind of movie that audiences will remember all their lives" (*Chicago Tribune*).
DVD: DV60126. $29.98.
VHS: S30735. $29.95.
Laser: Widescreen. **LD76164. $49.98.**
Jacques Demy, France/Germany, 1964, 92 mins.

Unbearable Lightness of Being
Czech author Milan Kundera's novel has been transferred to film by director Philip Kaufman (*The Right Stuff*). The emphasis is less on the philosophic debates of love and life and more on epic visualization of passion and revolution. With Englishman Daniel Day-Lewis as the doctor with two life long loves to choose from—French actress Juliette Binoche and Swedish actress Lena Olin. This polyglot cast is supposed to be all Czechs in this English language version that uses hats and mirrors as sexual aides.
VHS: S07757. $19.98.
Laser: LD71386. $49.95.
Philip Kaufman, USA, 1988, 156 mins.

Warm Nights on a Slow Moving Train
Wendy Hughes plays an attractive schoolteacher who rents her body to lonely male passengers on a weekend train run between Sydney and Melbourne. She needs the money to support her crippled brother's drug habit. Business is good until she meets a beguiling government agent and gets involved in something more dangerous than a social disease. With Colin Friels, Norman Kaye, Grant Tilly and Peter Whitford as "the Steward."
Laser: LD71399. $39.95.
Bob Ellis, Australia, 1987, 90 mins.

Wedding in Galilee
An intimate and multi-layered portrait of a Palestinian village under Israeli occupation. The mukhtar of the village wants to hold a traditional wedding for his son, and invites the Israeli military governor as a guest of honor. Beautifully filmed and acted by a cast of non-professionals, the story moves between the alienated grandfather, an angry group of young males prone to violence, an impotent groom and a resourceful bride. Arabic and Hebrew with English subtitles.
VHS: S08938. $24.95.
Michel Kleifi, Israel/Belgium, 1986, 113 mins.

White Mischief
A real life murder mystery set in Kenya during World War II. The wealthy white colonials throw lavish parties, take drugs and take liberties with the more attractive wives. Great costumes and stylish performances grace this tale of decadence and homicide. With Charles Dance, Joss Ackland, Sarah Miles, Geraldine Chaplin, John Hurt, Trevor Howard and Greta Scacchi as Lady Diane, the beauty worth dying over.
Laser: LD72317. $29.99.
Michael Radford, Great Britain, 1988, 107 mins.

Wide Sargasso Sea
Talented Australian director John Duigan (*Flirting*) adapted Jean Rhys' sensual novel about the first marriage of Rochester (Nathaniel Parker), the brooding English romantic of Charlotte Bronte's *Jane Eyre*, to a beautiful Creole named Antoinette (Karina Lombard). Set in Jamaica during the 1840s, the film pivots on erotic obsession and sexual delusion.

The Umbrellas of Cherbourg

"Infinitely romantic, the film's eroticism is real" (Vincent Canby). With Rachel Ward as Antoinette's mentally unbalanced mother, Michael York, Martine Beswicke and Claudia Robinson.
VHS: S19936. $19.95.
John Duigan, USA/Australian, 1992, 100 mins.

Witness
Harrison Ford is the cop who runs head-on into the non-violent world of the Amish community in this Academy Award-winning struggle of life and death in which a young Amish woman and her son are caught up in the murder of an undercover narcotics agent.
VHS: S01472. $14.95.
Peter Weir, USA, 1985, 112 mins.

Woman in the Dunes
A woman, confined to a deep pit in the sand dunes, where she is fed by neighbors and forced to clear her house of the threatening sands, is joined by a passing photographer whom the villagers have trapped into sharing her work and bed—forever. This is the situation of Teshigahara's great symbolic and sensual adaptation of Kobo Abe's novel, in which he "builds up the erotic tension…with extreme close-ups that transform the human body into landscape…" (*Oxford Companion to Film*). With Eiji Okada and Kyoko Kishida. Japanese with English subtitles.
VHS: S13589. $19.95.
Hiroshi Teshigahara, Japan, 1964, 123 mins.

Women in Love
Two sisters, sexually mature and intellectually active, struggle against the confines of a rural English mining town and its rigidly classed layers of society, in this adaptation of D.H. Lawrence's study of sexual uneasiness and doubt. With Alan Bates, Oliver Reed, Glenda Jackson, Jennie Linden.
VHS: S01479. $19.98.
Ken Russell, Great Britain, 1970, 129 mins.

Wuthering Heights
A romantic film classic. Set against the desolation of the English moors, Laurence Olivier and Merle Oberon portray the tragic lovers, Heathcliff and Cathy. After Cathy's marriage to the wealthy Edgar (David Niven), Heathcliff bides his time before his savage retaliation upon the woman he loves.

Academy Award-winning black & white cinematography by the legendary Gregg Toland. This digitally remastered video version includes the original theatrical trailer.
VHS: S01484. $19.98.
William Wyler, USA, 1939, 104 mins.

Xica
Carlos Diegues' comedy concerns Xica (Zeze Motta), a beautiful black slave who uses her sexual charm and savvy to benefit from Brazil's economic emergence. The film is set in the 18th century, when the fantastic wealth produced from the diamond trade transformed Brazil into a decadent hothouse. Xica ascends to the role of unofficial Empress, gleefully mocking her former masters while stockpiling newly found assets and power. "The film marks Diegues as one of Brazil's most innovative directors, who speaks his piece with exuberance, wit and style" (*San Francisco Chronicle*). With Walmor Chagas, Jose Wilker, Marcus Vinicius and Altair Lima. Portuguese with English subtitles.
VHS: S19417. $79.95.
Carlos Diegues, Brazil, 1976, 109 mins.

Year of Living Dangerously
Mel Gibson and Sigourney Weaver begin an impassioned love affair intensified by the uncertainties of life in Indonesia on the eve of revolution. Linda Hunt stars as Billy Kwan, a Eurasian cameraman who befriends Gibson.
DVD: DV60101. $24.98.
VHS: S01486. $19.98.
Laser: LD70715. $34.98.
Peter Weir, Australia/USA, 1982, 115 mins.

Yesterday, Today and Tomorrow
Sophia Loren and Marcello Mastroianni star in this Oscar-winning film that contains three different comic stories. Loren is great as the skilled temptress who uses sex to get what she wants, and her striptease remains a steamy, unforgettable film achievement.
VHS: S21220. $29.99.
Vittorio de Sica, Italy, 1964, 119 mins.

Last Tango in Paris

Sexy Silents
Pandora's Box
Ecstasy
It

SEX

Frank Sinatra, 50, marries
Mia Farrow, 21 in July of 1966
Woody Allen, 62,
Mia Farrow's lover of 10+
years , marries Farrow's
adopted daughter
Soon-Yi, 22

Mary Astor's tell-all diary
revealed the sexual prowess of
witty playwright **George S.
Kaufman,**
remarking on his "remarkable
staying power" and exclaiming
"we shared our fourth climax
at dawn!" Ms. Astor was sued
for divorce by her husband;
she did not contest the action
and the diary, much of which
was leaked to the press, was
considered "pornography" and
destroyed by the court.

Oil tycoon and
part-time
Hollywood investor
John Smith, in a
grand but fatal
attempt to prove
his love and devo-
tion to a 14 YEAR
OLD GIRL plummets
to his death while
attempting to cross
Niagara Falls in a
barrel.

X
X
X

Mickey Rooney, 18 &
Norma Shearer, 36,
have their affair
stopped by a furious
Louis B. Mayer

"The sins of the flesh have always been very attractive to me - all of them."

Michael Caine, *Playboy*

In the Car
No Way Out
Crash
Lost Highway
Hot Spot
Midnight Cowboy
Titanic
World According to Garp

What it's about
Sex
Sex Adventures of Three Muskateers
Sex and Buttered Popcorn
Sex and the College Girl
Sex and the Single Girl
Sex and the Single Parent
Sex Crimes
Sex, Drugs and Rock-n-Roll
Sex is Crazy
sex, lies and videotape
Sex, Love and Cold Hard Cash
Sex Machine
Sex on the Run
Sex Through a Window
Sex with a Smile
Sexpot
Sextette
Sexual Malice
Sexual Response
Sexual Intent

"My psychiatrist asked me if I thought sex was dirty and I said it is if you're doing it right."

Woody Allen in *Take the Money and Run.*

Great Sex Scenes
Last Tango in Paris
9 1/2 Weeks
Bull Durham
Damage
Rendezvous
Postman Always Rings Twice
Bliss
Sea of Love
Kids
Thelma & Louise

100 Best British TV

Absolutely Fabulous Collection
Jennifer Saunders and Joanna Lumley made this irreverent BBC comedy series a smash hit with their scathingly funny impersonations of bored, dumb, wealthy London women. Edina and Patsy bring excess to new levels of absurdity. This set includes all 18 episodes and a 30-minute behind-the-scenes look at the show hosted by Saunders which also features priceless outtakes.
VHS: S29989. $99.98.

Absolutely Fabulous Volume One, Part 1
From the BBC, Jennifer Saunders and Joanna Lumley play Edina and Patsy in the biggest British comedy hit since *Fawlty Towers*. They are two 40ish fashionphiles who are out to prove they'll do anything in the name of fun. In this volume they battle with *Fashion, Fat, and France*. 90 mins.
VHS: S25661. $19.98.

Absolutely Fabulous Volume One, Part 2
Edina and Patsy, Jennifer Saunders and Joanna Lumley, are back with mindless over the top and wickedly rich humor in *ISO Tank, Birthday, and Magazine*. 90 mins.
VHS: S25662. $19.98.

Agatha Christie's Miss Marple II
Joan Hickson stars as the knitting heroine of this second series of Agatha Christie mysteries.
**Agatha Christie's Miss Marple II: Collector's Boxed Set. All five videos, each 100 mins.
VHS: S24237. $69.95.**

Agatha Christie's Poirot
This witty, imaginative and well acted 10-part series focuses on a string of crimes and murders requiring the attention of Agatha Christie's brilliant detective, the Belgian sleuth Hercule Poirot, brought to vivid, immaculate life by the excellent British actor David Suchet (*The Falcon and the Snowman*).
**Four and Twenty Blackbirds.
VHS: S17461. $24.95.
Murder in the Mews.
VHS: S17459. $24.95.
Problem at Sea.
VHS: S17464. $24.95.
The Adventure of Johnnie Waverly.
VHS: S17460. $24.95.
The Adventures of the Clapham Cook.
VHS: S17458. $24.95.
The Dream.
VHS: S17467. $24.95.
The Incredible Theft.
VHS: S17465. $24.95.
The King of Clubs.
VHS: S17466. $24.95.
The Third Floor Flat.
VHS: S17462. $24.95.
Triangle at Rhodes.
VHS: S17463. $24.95.**

Are You Being Served?
Step into Grace Brothers Department Store and enjoy seasonal cheer in hilarious fashion with one of the BBC's most successful comedies ever. This special holiday-themed collection includes two Christmas programs and the long-lost *Top Hat and Tails* episode.
VHS: S32535. $14.98.

The Best of Cracker Mysteries
Three films from this award-winning, hard-edged British mystery series which aired on A & E are included in this collector's boxed set. Robbie

Coltrane stars as the volatile and enigmatic Dr. Eddie Fitzgerald, a boozing but brilliant forensic psychologist who tests his wits against cunning murderous minds in *The Mad Woman in the Attic* (100 mins.), *To Say I Love You* (150 mins.) and *One Day a Lemming Will Fly* (100 mins.). 350 mins.
VHS: S28503. $59.95.

The Best of the Two Ronnies
Ronnie Corbett and Ronnie Barker are the Two Ronnies. One is short and dark and the other is taller, whiter and a few pounds larger. They have kept England laughing for years, as well as those who watch public television. Now they are on video and ready to entertain anyone with the price of the rental. England, 1983.
VHS: S05613. $29.98.

The Best of What's Left...Not Only... But Also...
Written by and starring Peter Cook and Dudley Moore, the show is comprised of the best comedy sketches from this famous duo who were an inseparable act during the 60's and 70's. This is their reunion tape.
VHS: S14513. $19.98.

The Black Adder I, Part I
Rowan Atkinson, Tony Robinson, Brian Blessed, Tim McInnerny, Elspet Gray and Peter Cook star in this very popular comedy series. Includes "The Foretelling," "Born to Be King" and "The Archbishop."
VHS: S14511. $14.98.

The Black Adder I, Part II
This irreverent British satire stars Rowan Atkinson, Tony Robinson, Brian Blessed, Tim McInnerny, Elspet Gray and Peter Cook. Includes "The Queen of Spain's Beard", "Witchsmeller Pursuivant" and "The Black Seal."
VHS: S14512. $14.98.

Black Adder II: The 16th Century
Being a Renaissance man is no reason to stop mucking up the pages of history. Edmund is at it again, with his incorrigible exploits tainting two darkly funny volumes. Rowan Atkinson, Tony Robinson, Brian Blessed, Tim McInnerny, Elspet Gray and Peter Cook star in Part 1. Part 2 features Miranda Richardson and Rowan Atkinson.
**Black Adder II, Part 1. 100 mins.
VHS: S15972. $14.98.**

Black Adder the Third, Part I
Rowan Atkinson stars in this outrageously witty and popular satire, the Blackadder series. In three brilliantly funny episodes set in Regency England, Edmund Blackadder, valet and butler to the phenomenally "mini-brained" Prince Regent, sends up everything from the French Revolution to the British nobility. From the BBC.
VHS: S11212. $14.98.

Black Adder the Third, Part II
This successful series from Britain features three episodes from the scrolls of Blackadder, an English family of cowards and cads, who never seem to get a solid grip on life.
VHS: S12585. $14.98.

Body and Soul
This award-winning six-hour mini-series is the story of a young nun (Kristin Scott Thomas) who, after 16 years in a secluded convent in Wales, is forced to choose between two conflicting worlds when she must take charge of her deceased brother's young family and his bankrupt yarn-spinning mill. Three

tapes. 5 hours, 12 mins.
VHS: S30907. $69.95.

Bramwell
The spirited young doctor Eleanor Bramwell (Jemma Redgrave) shakes up the Victorian medical world in four episodes. Each is a sensational journey through life in 1896 London. From an elegant gala in the Bramwell family home to the turbulence of life on the streets, we follow Eleanor as she struggles to sustain her small, charitable infirmary.
VHS: S32995. $29.98.
David Tucker/Paul Unwin, Great Britain , 1996, 240 mins.

The Bretts
The Bretts are a fiercely competitive family whose wit and charm have captivated audiences for the entire run of this series. They are the center of London's theater world at a time of unmatched glamour and excitement, the 1920s. Their public triumphs and private traumas, from the star couple at the center of the family to the younger, newer luminaries, offer endless riveting drama. Each set contains 6 episodes of 50 minutes for a total of 5 hours.
Collection 1.
VHS: S22938. $99.98.
Collection 2.
VHS: S22939. $99.98.

Brides of Christ
Brenda Fricker (*My Left Foot*) stars in a searing, award-winning, British drama that captures the restless desperation of a reclusive society and its encounters with the outside world. From student Rosemary's rejection of rigid sexual moral codes to Sister Paul's decision to leave the convent for a radical priest, this is a critically-acclaimed, riveting production. Three tapes in a boxed set. Total length: 300 mins.
VHS: S21903. $59.95.

Brideshead Revisited
The acclaimed BBC series, based on the novel by Evelyn Waugh, in videocassette in 6 volumes. 98 minutes each.
Brideshead Revisited, Giftpack: All six books with a giftpack for storage.
VHS: S06627. $119.88.

Brother Cadfael III
In this three-volume set Sir Derek Jacobi (*I, Claudius*) returns as the sleuthing 12th-century monk

becomes a guru in the '70s Buddhist scene and leaves his suburban home for London. With original music by David Bowie.
VHS: S31262. $29.98.
Roger Michell, Great Britain, 1993, 220 mins.

Chef!
Comedian Lenny Harry stars as Gareth Blackstock, the temperamental Chef de Cuisine at the prestigious Le Chateau Anglais restaurant. With one uncompromising chef, a loyal but loopy staff, and a two-Michelin-starred restaurant in constant financial distress, it's a guaranteed recipe for hilarity. Each three-episode tape is 87 mins.
Chef!: A Second Helping.
VHS: S31687. $19.98.

Chiller: "Prophecy"
A group of students hold a seance in a dark basement just for kicks. Everyone gets a message "from the Great Beyond," but one, addressed to Frannie, is in Latin. "Non Omnis Moriar" means "I shall not die," and one by one all the participants of the seance die except for Frannie. The mystery deepens when she stays with a family whose motto is "Non Omnis Moriar." It seems they are related to an infamous Satanist who died in the very basementwhere Frannie first heard this prophetic motto.
VHS: S26780. $19.98.
Lawrence Gordon Clark, Great Britain, 50 mins.

Christabel
The acclaimed BBC series written by award-winning playwright Dennis Potter stars Elizabeth Hurley as a beautiful young Englishwoman, married to a young German national. Forced into politics by the events of the rising Nazism around her, *Christabel* is a moving, beautifully produced program about love, hardship, survival and the strength of the individual. Great Britain, 1989, 149 mins.
VHS: S10438. $19.98.

The Complete Black Adder
Finally, all 24 episodes of the hilarious BBC series are available, with new outrageous footage that has never been seen before. Rowan Atkinson's historical and hysterical adventures span the ages for a good laugh.
VHS: S26416. $99.98.

Connections
James Burke is back making connections between the discoveries and inventions that criss-cross history, joining disparate places, people and events. The odd

Bloomsbury Group

Orlando

Carrington
VHS: S27596. $19.95.
Laser: LD75532. $34.99.

Orlando
VHS: S20829. $19.95.
Laser: LD74471. $34.95.

To the Lighthouse
VHS: S32021. $19.95.

with an affinity for solving crimes. Includes *The Raven in the Forgate, A Morbid Taste for Bones* and *The Rose Rent.* Based on the highly acclaimed books by Ellis Peters. Each tape is 85 mins.
VHS: S32608. $59.95.

The Buddha of Suburbia
One of the larger artistic achievements of British television: Brenda Blethyn (*Secrets and Lies*), Narveen Andrews (*The English Patient*) and Roshan Seth (*Indiana Jones and the Temple of Doom*) star in this acclaimed drama, based on the best-selling novel by Hanif Kureishi (*My Beautiful Laundrette*), of Karim, a young schoolboy living in the suburbs, whose life changes when his Zen-obsessed father

and surprising chain of happenstance occurrences that result in objects and processes which are integral to modern life will continue to surprise any viewer.
Complete Set.
VHS: S20973. $179.95.

Dennis Potter's Lipstick on Your Collar
Dennis Potter's last television series is still too hot for American television. His previous works for British TV, *The Singing Detective* and *Pennies from Heaven*, were critical and popular triumphs. In this series Potter combines rock 'n' roll daydreams with a story about the Suez crisis. As the War Office agonizes over waning British power, two clerks dream of sexual conquest to the driving new rhythms

emanating from America. 120 mins.
VHS: S26696. $59.95.

Dennis Potter: The Last Interview
Potter transformed serious television drama with his insightful works for British TV. *The Singing Detective* and *Pennies from Heaven* were hailed as breakthroughs combining challenging themes with complex characters. Potter's stories went well beyond the usual manipulations found in standard psychological dramas. This interview with Potter, shot shortly before he died, finds him reflecting on both his work and his life. 70 mins.
VHS: S26634. $19.95.

The Duchess of Duke Street
One of the BBC's most acclaimed productions. Created by John Hawksworth (*Upstairs, Downstairs*), this romantic, captivating and lavish drama is set in turn-of-the century London and is based on the life of Rosa Lewis (Gemma Jones), a lowly cook who rises to the pinnacle of English society.
VHS: S32028. $119.98.

Elizabeth R.
Glenda Jackson stars in this Emmy-Award winning television series, first screened on *Masterpiece Theater*. Jackson plays Elizabeth, who became Elizabeth I, one of England's most venerable

Gallowglass
Ruth Rendell wrote this murder mystery under the pen name Barbara Vine. This BBC adaptation pits two men against each other in a plot centered on a kidnapped Italian princess. One of these men is good, while the other is evil. Their rivalry generates suspense and intrigue. 150 mins.
VHS: S27747. $19.98.

The Gambling Man
Rory O'Connor leaves behind his working class roots for a life of gambling. His flair and style make him a natural as an entrepenuerial spirit. Despite these advantages he cannot escape the reach of the law or the misadventures of fate. This is an engrossing costume drama filled with unexpected reversals tempered by moments of happiness. 150 mins.
VHS: S27836. $34.98.

Girls on Top
Sharing a flat is never easy, especially when the people concerned are from vastly different backgrounds. Yet it provides the perfect setting for some of the most respected comediennes to showcase their comic talents. Tracey Ullman, Dawn French, Jennifer Saunders and Ruby Wax play a group of flatmates who don't always see eye-to-eye. 50 mins.
VHS: S16129. $59.98.

11 Worst Weather Films

Babette's Feast
VHS: S08497. $19.98.
Laser: LD70850. $39.99.

The Day the Earth Caught Fire
VHS: S29950. $9.98.

Dead of Winter
VHS: S04666. $14.95.

Never Cry Wolf
Laser: LD71254. $34.95.

Pathfinder
VHS: S13843. $19.98.

Quest for Fire
VHS: S04597. $69.98.

Seven Year Itch
VHS: S01183. $19.98.

The Shining
VHS: S01189. $19.98.
Laser: LD74736. $39.98.

Stalingrad
VHS: S30467. $29.95.

Twister
DVD: DV60056. $24.98.
VHS: S29966. $22.99.
Laser: LD76070. $34.98.

The Wizard of Oz
DVD: DV60104. $24.98.
VHS: S09609. $19.95.
Laser: CLV, MGM. LD70709. $24.98.
Laser: CAV, Criterion. LD71215. $99.95.

monarchs. The story begins during the reign of Henry VIII, when he turns from the Catholic Church in search of a male heir through a variety of wives. Despite the arrival of a male heir, it is Elizabeth who triumphs as Queen. 540 mins.
VHS: S25908. $149.98.

Emma
Jane Austen's delightfully wicked comedy of love and matchmaking features an acclaimed, star-studded cast, including Kate Beckinsale (*Cold Comfort Farm*) as the clever and beautiful woman who can't resist orchestrating other people's love lives as she risks missing out on her own perfect match. With Prunella Scales (*Howard's End*) and Samantha Bond (*Goldeneye*).
VHS: S30823. $19.95.
Diarmuid Lawrence, Great Britain, 1996, 108 mins.

Fall from Grace
James Fox, Michael York, Patsy Kensit and Gary Cole star in this chilling tale of espionage and deception. In 1943 Hitler's forces dominate and terrorize Europe. A crack team of British and American intelligence officers undertake a huge gamble. They must convince Hitler of the impossible. Their success could hasten the end of the war. Failure is unthinkable.
VHS: S26521. $69.99.
Waris Hussein, Great Britain, 1994, 240 mins.

French & Saunders
From the creators of the hit TV series *Absolutely Fabulous* come Dawn French and Jennifer Saunders with a series of sketches, spoofs and mayhem from their riotous BBC show. Each tape is 100 mins.
French & Saunders Go to the Movies.
VHS: S31685. $19.98.
French & Saunders: Gentleman Prefer French & Saunders.
VHS: S31686. $19.98.

The Green Man
This BBC production stars Albert Finney as the alcoholic owner of a countryside inn whose sinister, ghostly tales he conjures up to seduce his female guests turn on him when spirits and apparitions begin to haunt his every move. "Finney pounces with unflagging energy" (*The New York Times*). With Sarah Berger, Linda Marlowe and Michael Hordern.
VHS: S16860. $24.95.
Laser: CLV. LD72076. $49.95.
Elijah Moshinsky, Great Britain, 1991, 150 mins.

Heat of the Day
Master playwright Harold Pinter's adaptation of the famous suspense novel by Elizabeth Bowen is given a full tilt treatment in this PBS production starring Michael York. England, 120 mins.
VHS: S15109. $19.98.

House of Cards
Ian Richardson stars in this British production about corruption among the highest levels of her Majesty's government. Greed and intrigue set the stage for a chilling, puzzling and sinister drama that will delight all thriller fans. Richardson is terrific.
VHS: S26032. $34.98.

The House of Elliot
The BBC devised this charming period television series full of romance, adventure and stunning detail. Two sisters, Beatrice and Evangeline Elliot, struggle to regain the wealth and privilege they were born to but lost. Fashion provides them the opportunity to parlay good taste into wealth and influence, even as British society is transformed around them. Each of the 12 episodes is 50 minutes in length. Six-videotape set.
VHS: S23871. $99.95.

I, Claudius
This famous Masterpiece Theatre series, based on the novel by Robert Graves, has everything: sex,

decadence, ambition, insatiable greed, and the fall of the Roman empire.
Complete Set. 7 cassettes.
VHS: $14130. $129.98.

Inspector Morse

A brilliantly acted series that subverts the standard television detective show. Oxford inspector Morse is an eccentric thinker with a keen ability to ferret out clues and signals. "One of the classiest things on television. John Thaw is irresistible as the magnetic but solitary Morse, an Oxford detective with an ear for music, a taste for beer and a nose for sordid crimes" (*The Wall Street Journal*). With Kevin Whately as Sgt. Lewis.
Cherubim & Seraphim. When Inspector Morse visits his stepmother and half-sister, he discovers that his stepniece has committed suicide, and takes a leave to search into a reason behind her death. Meanwhile Sgt. Lewis is studying for his inspector's exams, while also investigating the case of a missing student. 105 mins.
VHS: $29871. $19.95.
Day of the Devil. John Barrie, a dangerous mental patient and master of disguise, escapes from a high-security hospital and sets up an elaborate and deadly battle of wits with Morse as the Oxford police engage in a man hunt. Morse realizes that he is dealing with more than just a rapist when signs of Satanism appear in Oxfordshire. Barrie's psychiatrist, Dr. Esther Martin, seems to be the only person who can help Morse track Barrie down—she also seems to be most threatened by his freedom. 105 mins.
VHS: $29874. $19.95.
Deadly Slumber. When the doctor who runs a clinic that treated a brain-damaged woman is murdered, Morse immediately suspects Michael Steppings, the woman's father. Yet Morse is impressed by the father's devotion and the two men discover they have mutual respect. 105 mins.
VHS: $29873. $19.95.
Twilight of the Gods. Morse and Lewis look into the murder of a journalist who was working on an article about Andrew Baydon, a college benefactor who is donating a college building to Oxford. The only hitch with the generous gift is that Baydon insists the building is a modern version of Rajput palace. 105 mins.
VHS: $29872. $19.95.
The Way Through the Woods. "The Lovers Lane Killer," a man accused of murdering five people, has himself been killed in a prison fight before his trial. The killer's last victim was never found, but her bag was recovered at the bottom of a lake at Blenheim. Morse is convinced that her remains are in Wytham Woods, but a body is later discovered at Blenheim, and Morse and Sgt. Lewis are on the case. 105 mins.
VHS: $29875. $19.95.

Ivanhoe

Steven Waddington (*The Last of the Mohicans*), Susan Lynch (*The Secret of Roan Inish*) and James Cosmo (*Braveheart*) star in this A&E/BBC production of Sir Walter Scott's tale of magnificent pageantry of knightly tournaments and whispered meetings of courtly lovers. Filmed on location in England. Six volumes, 50 minutes each.
VHS: $31271. $99.95.
Stuart Orme, Great Britain, 1996, 300 mins.

Jane Austen's Pride and Prejudice

A first-rate BBC adaptation of the classic Jane Austen comedy of manners. Filmed on the occasion of the 200th anniversary of the novel's writing, this lavishly produced, five-hour, six-cassette production follows the elite of 19th-century English society through games of love and negotiations of marriage. Mrs. Bennet (Alison Steadman) is deeply worried about the fact that all five of her daughters, including the lively Elizabeth (Jennifer Ehle), are as yet unmarried. She plans to convince wealthy neighbor William Collins to marry one of her daughters, but his mischievous friend Fitzwilliam Darcy (Colin Firth) arrives to foul things up. Directed by Simon Langton (*Upstairs Downstairs*). Featuring a superb soundtrack from composer Carl Davis.
VHS: $27206. $99.95.
Laser: LD75564. $99.99.
Simon Langton, Great Britain, 1995, 300 mins.

Jeeves & Wooster

P.G. Wodehouse's classic British farce gets three new volumes in the adventures of the bumbling, lovable Bertie Wooster and his elegant, unflappable valet, Jeeves. Starring Hugh Laurie and Stephen Fry. "The funniest set piece in the Wodehouse repertory" (*New York Times*). Available individually or as a boxed set.
Golf Tournament/Gambling Event. In *Golf Tournament*, while in the heat of golf competition with pal Barmy Fotheringay-Phipps, Bertie inadvertently misplaces McIntosh, his Aunt Agatha's priceless pup. 120 mins. In *Gambling Event*, Bertie and his pal Bingo Little get into a sticky situation when they begin gambling on sporting events like the Boys and Girls Mixed Animal Potato Race. Only the ever-resourceful Jeeves can save the day.
VHS: $31006. $14.98.
Hunger Strike/The Matchmaker. In *The Hunger Strike*, Bertie launches a clever scheme to impress his uncle into investing in yet another trite diversion, only to be rescued by the ever-resourceful Jeeves. In *The Matchmaker*, the boys try their hand at matchmaking and find themselves tangled in a very difficult situation. 120 mins.
VHS: $31005. $14.98.
Jeeves' Arrival. When they first meet, Jeeves arrives on the scene just in time to witness Bertie's bachelorhood being threatened by awful Aunt Agatha, who has decided that her frivolous nephew should marry the highbred Honoria Glossop, the horror of Ditteridge Hall. 60 mins.
VHS: $31004. $14.98.
Three-Tape Set.
VHS: $31007. $39.98.

Jude the Obscure

Thomas Hardy's scathing indictment of Victorian society in a first-rate BBC adaptation. Jude Fawley is the working class stone mason who aspires to the priesthood, but the tragedy of his unrealized ambition is compounded by his tempestuous relationship with Sue Bridehead, herself an outcast for daring to express her sexuality.
VHS: $19090. $29.98.
Hugh David, Great Britain, 1971, 262 mins.

Kavanagh Q.C.

This compelling series takes you beyond the traditional English courtroom and into the lives of the men and women on both sides of the law. John Thaw (*Inspector Morse*) is James Kavanagh Q.C., one of London's most respected criminal lawyers. Switching sides from prosecution to defense in these episodes, Thaw demonstrates the ups and downs of success and failure in the law and the problems of defining the truth.,
Kavanagh Q.C., Collection Set 1. Includes *The Sweetest Thing, A Family Affair, Heartland* and *Nothing But the Truth*. Five hours, 30 minutess on four videocassettes.
VHS: $30940. $89.98.
Kavanagh Q.C. Collection Set 2. Includes *True Commitment, The Burning Deck* and *Men of Substance*. Four hours on three videocassettes.
VHS: $32975. $69.98.
Kavanagh Q.C. Collection Set 3. Includes *Sense of Loss, Stranger in the Family* and *Job Satisfaction*. Four hours on three videocassettes.
VHS: $32976. $69.98.

Ivanhoe

Keeping Up Appearances

Roy Clarke's BBC comedy hit starring award-winner Patricia Routledge.
I'm Often Mistaken for Aristocracy. 87 mins.
VHS: $31225. $19.98.
Sea Fever. 87 mins.
VHS: $31227. $19.98.
The Memoirs of Hyacinth Bucket. 60 mins.
VHS: $31226. $19.98.

Life of Brian
Oops, wrong manger! The story of Bethlehem's lesser-known son is a non-stop orgy of assaults, not on anyone's virtue, but on the funny bone. Rich ensemble acting, and animation by Terry Gilliam.
VHS: S00752. $19.98.
Laser: Letterboxed. **LD76408. $59.95.**
Terry Jones, Great Britain, 1979, 94 mins.

Life on Earth Perhaps
At times whimsical, at times terrifyingly blunt, this film looks at the unthinkable—Nuclear War—in a way that brings the issues into sharp focus. Cleverly put together mixing animated and documentary footage, this British production confronts the history of war.
VHS: S04309. $45.00.
Oliver Postgate, 29 mins.

Little Dorrit
Christine Edzard's film is a brilliant reworking of the Charles Dickens classic. Brilliant camerawork by Bruno De Keyzer and immaculate sets of John McMillan produce the flavor of Victorian England. Edzard goes to the heart of the novel and makes it new in the story of the pinch-faced, hard-nosed survivor whose belief in herself and in the redemption of humanity forces those about her to survive as well. With an all-star British cast including Alec Guiness, Derek Jacobi, and Sarah Pickering in a brilliant performance as Little Dorrit.
Little Dorrit Part One. *Nobody's Fault.* The first part is told from Arthur Clenman's point of view.
VHS: S09595. $24.98.
Little Dorrit Part Two. *Dorritt's Story.* The story is told from Little Dorrit's point of view.
VHS: S09596. $24.98.
Christine Edzard, Great Britain, 1988, 369 mins.

The Lost Language of the Cranes
A moody BBC adaptation of David Leavitt's novel about family secrets and sexual identity. The film centers on a young man's sexual declaration and its volatile and revealing consequences on the rest of the family. "Graced with subtle, intense performances" (*Time Magazine*). With Corey Parker, Brian Cox, Eileen Atkins and Angus MacFadyen.
VHS: S18604. $19.98.
Nigel Finch, Great Britain, 1992, 84 mins.

Love for Lydia
Based on the 1952 novel by H.E. Bates, this enthralling Masterpiece Theater mini-series chronicles the final years of Britain's high-spirited "Careless Twenties" and is an unforgettable portrait of a beautiful and tempestuous woman who personifies the era. Mel Martin gives an exquisite performance as Lydia, who is transformed from a drab and awkward girl into a stunning woman. Seven cassette boxed set, 657 mins.
VHS: S15800. $199.95.

Little Dorrit

The Man from the Pru
Jonathan Pryce and Susannah York star in this murder mystery based on a true story from 1931. Julia Wallace was brutally murdered in her Liverpool home. The public suspected her husband but the courts believed him innocent. Now this beautifully detailed film investigates the lonely, hard world that spawned this as-yet-unsolved mystery.
VHS: S26399. $24.95.
Bob Rohrer, Great Britain, 1989, 90 mins.

Mapp & Lucia
This British television comedy series, based on the novels of E.F. Benson, has enjoyed a cult following in Britain and America since it aired on PBS in 1985. Set in 1930 in the fictional seaside village of Tilling, this quirky satire boasts an all-star cast, including Prunella Scales (*Fawlty Towers*), Geraldine McEwan (*Barchester Chronicles*) and Nigel Hawthorne (*The Madness of King George*). Packaged in a five-volume, 52-minute program box set.
VHS: S28482. $89.95.

Mapp & Lucia II
The second installment of *Mapp & Lucia*, one of the most sought-after PBS comedies of all time, carries on E.F. Benson's tale in five volumes, starring Prunella Scales, Geraldine McEwan and Nigel Hawthorne. 52 mins.
VHS: S31819. $89.95.

The Mill on the Floss
George Eliot's story of Maggie Tulliver and her brother Tom, their life at the mill and Maggie's love for two men. Stars Emily Watson (*Breaking the Waves*), Cheryl Campbell, James Frain and Bernard Hill.
VHS: S32038. $19.98.

Moll Flanders
In this Masterpiece Theater production, Alex Kingston stars as Moll Flanders, Britain's most wanted woman, who was married five times, once to her own brother. "One of the year's most unexpected, riveting romps...a startlingly bawdy and immediately captivating adaptation of Daniel Defoe's still shocking classic of one woman's survive-at-all-costs life...unconventionally alluring and unblushingly brazen" (*U.S. Today*). "*Moll Flanders* arrives like a firecracker tossed into a tea party" (*The New York Times*).
VHS: S30610. $29.95.

The Moonstone
A sumptuous adaptation of Wilkie Collins' classic mystery story, the first detective novel ever written. Stars Greg Wise, Patricia Hodge, Keeley Hawes, Anthony Sher and Peter Vaughan.
VHS: S32039. $19.98.

More Jeeves & Wooster
Stephen Fry (*A Fish Called Wanda*) and Hugh Laurie (*Sense and Sensibility*) return to their acclaimed roles as the resourceful valet Jeeves and his well-meaning but dim-witted master, Bertie Wooster. In this series, Bertie sets sail for Manhattan, where troubles appear from his new apartment to a Broadway theater. It's up to Jeeves to see Bertie through his American sojourn and return him safely to England. Six videos, 50 minutes each.
VHS: S31781. $79.95.

Morecambe & Wise Musical Extravaganzas
A host of Britain's best, including Glenda Jackson, Vanessa Redgrave, Cliff Richard and Diana Rigg, join Morecambe and Wise in music and comedy series from their classic BBC comedy series. 60 mins.
VHS: S10012. $19.98.

Mr. Bean
Rowan Atkinson, a.k.a. Mr. Bean, is everyone's favorite British clown. Children and adults alike find the antics of the funniest man in town irresistibly fun to watch again and again.
Volume 1: The Amazing Adventures of Mr. Bean. Rowan Atkinson is featured in two episodes from his original British comedy series. This video includes both the pilot episode, *Mr. Bean*, and the episodes *The Return of Mr. Bean* and *The Library*. In these shows, Mr. Bean tries to change on the beach, uses his first credit card and even meets the Royal Family.
VHS: S27053. $19.95.
Volume 2: The Exciting Escapades of Mr. Bean. Rowan Atkinson inspires more lunatic laughter as Mr. Bean. In *The Curse of Mr. Bean, Mr. Bean Goes to Town* and *The Bus Stop*, Atkinson's comic invention attempts to drive a car, dance at disco and swim at a public pool, as well as much more.
VHS: S27054. $19.95.

Noble House
Based on James Clavell's novel, *Noble House* is an intriguing mini-series saga set in the panoramic backdrop of exotic Hong Kong. Pierce Brosnan stars as Ian Dunross, the all-powerful leader of Hong Kong's most influential international trading organization, Noble House, as he confronts takeover attempts, interlocking intrigues and ancient obligations. "Extravagantly romantic...not only is it

Some Like It Gothic

Cabinet of Dr. Caligari
DVD: DV60034. $29.95.
VHS: S10765. $29.95.
Laser: LD75516. $49.99.

Dracula
VHS: S00371. $19.95.

Faust
VHS: S00437. $29.95.

Jane Eyre
VHS: S09579. $39.95.

The Nightmare Before Christmas
VHS: S21295. $14.95.

Rocky Horror Picture Show
VHS: S14008. $19.98.
Laser: LD76381. $29.99.

The Saragossa Manuscript
VHS: S22596. $59.95.

Sunset Boulevard
VHS: S01285. $14.95.
Laser: LD75268. $34.98.

Tales from the Gimli Hospital
VHS: S19409. $29.95.

Wise Blood
VHS: S01470. $59.95.

---

as long as life, it's also rich with possibilities" (*The New York Times*). With Deborah Raffin, Ben Masters, John Houseman and Denholm Elliott.
VHS: S32389. $39.98.
Gary Nelson, Great Britain/USA, 1988, 355 mins.

Northanger Abbey
A BBC adaptation of Jane Austen's novel of erotic attraction, danger and intrigue set in 18th century Bath, a morally decadent society that captures the fancy of Catherine Morland. She's invited by Henry Tilney for a romantic weekend at his estate, Northanger Abbey, where mystery and blood-curdling horror rule the moment. With Peter Finch, Googie Withers, Robert Hardy and Katherine Schlesinger. 90 mins.
VHS: S19180. $19.98.

Nostromo
One of the largest productions in the history of public television, this spectacular, three-volume BBC mini-series is based on Joseph Conrad's sprawling masterpiece of the quest for wealth and power in a backward South American country in the 1880s. When a revolution breaks out, one man is fated to determine the future—Nostromo. With Colin Firth, Brian Dennehy, Serena Scott Thomas, Joaquim DeAlmeida and Albert Finney.
VHS: S30472. $59.98.
Alastair Reid, Great Britain, 1996, 6 hrs.

One Foot in the Grave: Who Will Buy?
A benefit concert gives retired suburbanite Victor Meldrew a chance to warm up his old ventriloquist act, and proves to his wife, Margaret, that whatever can go wrong always does, in this BBC-TV comedy. 89 mins.
VHS: S20501. $19.98.

Oranges Are Not the Only Fruit
This critically acclaimed film, set in '60s northern England, is the tale of Jess, a 16-year-old girl (Geraldine McEwan of BBC-TV's *Mapp and Lucia*) raised to be a missionary, who falls in love for the first time—with another girl. When Jess' strict Evangelist mother (Charlotte Coleman, *Four Weddings and a Funeral*) finds out, she determines to make her daughter renounce her sin, resulting in disaster. Based on Jeanette Winterson's autobiographical prize-winning novel.
VHS: S31261. $29.98.
Beeban Kidron, Great Britain, 1990, 165 mins.

P.D. James: A Mind to Murder
Roy Marsden returns to the role of the poetry-writing Commander Dalgliesh in this brilliant screen adaptation of P.D. James' bestselling classic. In an exclusive English psychiatric clinic, it is up to Commander Dalgliesh to solve the case of a macabre murder.
VHS: S30947. $19.95.
Gareth Davies, USA, 1994, 100 mins.

Parrot Sketch Not Included
Occasioned by its 20th anniversary of Monty Python, this clever program offers a kaleidoscopic look at the sketches, improvs, ramblings, bits and gags of "Python foolery." 75 mins.
VHS: S17228. $19.95.

Passion of the Saints
Travel through 2,000 years since the time of Christ and across three continents to experience the lives and deaths of some extraordinary individuals, on this three-tape set from The Learning Channel. Witness

the rise of martyrdom from Stephen, the first martyr, to Joan of Arc and Thomas Becket in Volume 1, *The Blood of the Martyrs* (50 mins.). Meet Catherine of Sienna, Saint Francis of Assisi, Saint Augustine and Saint Thomas Aquinas on Volume II, *Hermits, Monks and Madmen* (50 mins.). On Volume III, *Mystics and Miracles*, follow the lives and deaths of those who have known the divine, travel to a French monastery where theologians and academics have been seeking answers to the questions of sainthood for 300 years, and go behind the scenes at the Vatican to peek inside the politics of sainthood on "The Road to Sainthood" (100 mins.).
VHS: S30834. $89.95.

A Perfect Spy
From the author of *The Russia House*, John Le Carre's intricate espionage work is an imaginative thriller about the response of British intelligence when a top member of British Secret Service inexplicably disappears. Peter Egan stars as master spy Magnus Pym, who is enlisted to track down the missing diplomat. "Gripping, sardonic and haunted, the film has the piercing chill of a cloudy autumn day" (*The Washington Post*). With Dame Peggy Ashcroft. A three-tape set. 376 mins.
VHS: S19913. $79.98.

Pictures
This series is set during the exciting era of silent films. Peter McEnery plays a script writer inspired by the youthful ambitions of an aspiring actress, Wendy Morgan. They are thrown together by a big project but they can't anticipate the ambitions of those around them and their plans for love are threatened by the incessant wheeling and dealing of that bygone era.
Complete Set.
VHS: S20803. $99.98.

Piece of Cake: Complete Set
During World War II, an RAF Hornet Squadron must undergo the rites of passage that will make them seasoned fighter pilots. Their aristocratic CO is arrogant and overconfident. Eventually the concerns of his squadron overtake his attitude as adventure and heartache build toward the climactic battle.
VHS: S21689. $99.98.
Ian Toynton, Great Britain, 1994, 650 mins.

Poldark
A romance/adventure/epic set in the late 1770s in Cornwall, this film features the beautiful landscapes and historic buildings of old England. It is based on the best-selling book by Winston Graham and tells the story of a man with an iron will whose life shaped the lives of thousands. 12 hours on six cassettes.
VHS: S20626. $99.98.

Porridge
A madcap British comedy based on a highly-regarded television series that stars Ronnie Barker as habitual criminal Norman Stanley Fletcher who miraculously escapes from prison, and the repercussions when he demands to be placed back in. With Richard Beckinsale, Fulton Mackay, Brian Wilde and Peter Vaughan. Also known as *Doing Time*.
VHS: S14495. $29.95.
Dick Clement, Great Britain, 1979, 95 mins.

Portrait of a Lady
The story of a spirited young American woman searching for truth. Determined to choose her own destiny, she is brought to England by her Aunt and given every chance to better herself. While seeking

Moll Flanders

freedom, however, she makes some disastrous choices. Richard Chamberlain stars in this classic BBC mini-series based on the Henry James novel. 240 mins.
VHS: $16135. $34.98.

Prime Suspect
In this Emmy Award-winning series, Helen Mirren plays a woman inspector eager to prove that she is as capable as any male police detective. When a young prostitute's body is found, she gets a chance to convince her colleagues of her abilities as she stalks the brutal serial killer responsible. Two cassettes, 230 mins.
VHS: $20827. $39.95.

Prime Suspect 2
In this sequel, Helen Mirren reprises her role as Jane Tennison, a woman detective fighting for respect in a male-dominated police force. As she investigates the murder of a young woman, she faces both community and police pressure to quickly resolve the case because of its racial overtones. Instead, she draws on her ability to solve this daunting case. Two cassettes, 230 mins.
VHS: $20828. $39.95.

Prime Suspect 3
Helen Mirren returns as Detective Jane Tennison, the thoughtful and tenacious woman detective who manages to solve the most complex and troubling cases. In this two tape set, she unravels the mystery surrounding a young boy burned alive. The child was somehow mixed up in a flesh-peddling ring. Now Detective Tennison must confront not only police department rigidity but a seamy underworld as well. Her own personal demons are summoned by this grisly and baffling case.
VHS: $26929. $39.98.
David Drury, Great Britain, 1995, 205 mins.

Prime Suspect 4
Three more episodes in the British TV series: *Lost Child, Inner Circles* and *Scent of Darkness*.
VHS: $27356. $39.95.

Prime Suspect 5: Errors of Judgment
Transferred to Manchester, Detective Superintendent Jane Tennison (Helen Mirren) finds herself dealing with the murder of a drug dealer. A 14-year-old boy confesses to the killing, but Tennison has no evidence

to connect him to the crime and she suspects a powerful and dangerous drug baron. Tennison also has her personal problems when she starts an affair with her married boss. She soon finds herself trapped in a world she does not know, surrounded by people she can't trust. Just when she thinks it cannot get any worse—it does. Four hours on two videocassettes.
VHS: $30883. $29.95.

The Private Life of Plants
Sir Richard Attenborough hosts this BBC production. It looks at plants all over the world, from Borneo to Tasmania, in order to reveal some intriguing secrets. Plants have unique methods that help them perceive and respond to their surroundings.
Collector's Edition. The complete six-volume set.
VHS: $26986. $79.98.

Raffles
Raffles and Bunny Manders may seem like an unlikely pair of criminals. Bunny sought out his boyhood hero Raffles, an elegant man at home amidst the turn-of-the-century English aristocracy, precisely because of his sophisticated veneer. It makes the perfect cover that enables them to achieve their wildest criminal fantasies. Each of the six episodes is 52 minutes in length.
VHS: $23754. $99.98.

Rebecca
Daphne du Maurier's classic tale of romance, suspense and jealousy, set in Monte Carlo and Cornwall in the 1930s, stars Charles Dance as the sophisticated Maxim de Winter and Emilia Fox as the young woman who becomes the second Mrs. de Winter and is haunted by the shadow of the first Mrs. de Winter, Rebecca. With Diana Rigg as the sinister, gothic housekeeper, Mrs. Danvers, and Faye Dunaway as Mrs. Van Hopper.
VHS: $31198. $29.98.
Jim O'Brien, Great Britain, 1996, 176 mins.

The Rector's Wife
Set in England's picturesque Cotswald Villages and based on Joanna Trollope's bestseller, this Masterpiece Theater series is the story of Anna Bouverie, a spirited woman struggling to remain dutiful to her family as a life of independence beckons. When she incurs the wrath of the parishioners and her husband, Anna embarks on an intense journey of self-discovery. With Lindsay

Duncan, Prunella Scales, Ronald Pickup and Stephen Dillane. 208 mins.
VHS: $23568. $59.95.

Rising Damp, Collection Set Series 2

British TV's comedy set in a down-and-out boarding house features some of the most hilarious antics ever located amid English squalor. Leonard Rossiter stars as the landlord in this comedy of gloom.
A Body Like Mine/Moonlight and Roses. When the fitness craze hits Rigsby's home, he is set off balance by everyone's eager embrace of the "body beautiful aesthetic". Then Ruth's new love inspires Rigsby to declare his love for Miss Jones, but it's too little, too late. 50 mins.
VHS: $20805. $22.98.
Perfect Gentleman/Last of the Big Spenders. Rigsby's well-concealed aristocratic demeanor is fully unleashed by the appearance of the courtly Seymour. In the consecutive episode, Rigsby's similarly buried free-spending ways are set loose by the presence of Brenda. This model just happens to like men that aren't afraid to part with their cash.
VHS: $20806. $22.98.

A Royal Scandal

This BBC production is the witty, irreverent and true account of the unhappy marriage of England's King George IV and Queen Caroline. George married Caroline to please his father and pay his debts, but unbeknownst to Caroline, George was already secretly married to someone else when he married her. The historical events depicted cover a 25-year span ending with Caroline's trial, where she is accused of committing adultery with an Italian servant. With Richard Grant and Susan Lynch. Narrated by Ian Richardson.
VHS: $30473. $24.98.

Rumpole of the Bailey

Part lawyer, part detective, Horace Rumpole is one of the most colorful characters to approach the bench. With his brilliant mind and sly sense of humor, Rumpole's adventures behind the scenes and center stage in the British legal system are a delightful mix of comedy, mystery and courtroom drama. "Uproarious" (*Wall Street Journal*). Each tape is 104 mins.
Rumpole of the Bailey, Vol. 1. Episodes 1 & 2.
Rumpole and the Genuine Article. Has an art collector purchased a recently discovered masterpiece or a convincing fake? An embittered artist's jealousy erupts when Rumpole is called to defend him in a celebrated forgery case. *Rumpole and the Old Boy Network.* The discovery of a brothel in an otherwise respectable London neighborhood draws Rumpole into a web of blackmail and deceit.
VHS: $16028. $19.98.
Rumpole of the Bailey, Vol. 2. Episodes 3 & 4.
Rumpole and the Sporting Life. Despite her tearful confession, Rumpole believes the unfaithful wife of a murdered barrister is not the perpetrator, and sets off to find the real killer. *Rumpole and the Blind Tasting.* The petty jealousies and bits of gossip Rumpole overhears at a high-brow wine tasting party proves useful as he prepares for a case of insurance fraud.
VHS: $16029. $19.98.
Rumpole of the Bailey, Vol. 3. Episodes 5 & 6.
Rumpole and the Old, Old Story. Was the partner of a murdered property owner after his valuable land or his wife? *Rumpole and Portia.* While defending an antique shop owner accused of smuggling illegal weapons, Rumpole discovers a police plot to trap a terrorist.
VHS: $16030. $19.98.
Rumpole of the Bailey, Vol. 4. Episodes 7 & 8.
Rumpole's Last Case. With a sure bet about to pay off, Rumpole agrees to what will undoubtedly be his last case: defending two criminals charged with bank robbery. *Rumpole and the Judge's Elbow.* In defending a man accused of running a massage parlor, Rumpole is offered judgeship if he promises to handle the case "discreetly."
VHS: $16031. $19.98.

The Rutles: All You Need Is Cash

Eric Idle had the brilliant idea to parody the Beatles by creating a story about four young men who get a recording contract because they wear tight pants. Originally filmed as a *Saturday Night Live* skit, the audience response was so positive that Idle and *SNL* producer Lorne Michaels decided to create a full-length production. George Harrison, Mick Jagger, Paul Simon, John Belushi, Dan Aykroyd, Gilda Radner and Bill Murray are among the musical and comic greats that add to the inspired lunacy. *Sgt. Rutter's Only Darts Club Band* is a highlight that is

not to be missed.
VHS: $27693. $19.98.
Laser: LD76228. $39.98.
Eric Idle, Great Britain, 70 mins.

School for Scandal

A live television adaptation of the classic satire of the morals and manners of 18th century England by Richard Sheridan. Featuring Joan Plowright as Lady Oliver and Felix Aylmer. England, 1965, 100 mins.
VHS: $01168. $29.95.

Scotch and Wry Set

The U.K.'s biggest-selling comedy video is now available in the States. Rikki Fulton and the Scotch and Wry team unleash their celebrated, outrageous humor from their award-winning series. In *Scotch and Wry*, meet Supercop, the traffic policeman who keeps failing to make that crucial arrest, the Rev. I.M. Jolly, master of gloom and doom, and Dirty Dickie Dandruff, with recipes from his Delicat'messen. In *Double Scotch and Wry* the team is back in more classic sketches, including Supercop, Rev. I.M. Jolly and Dirty Dickie Dandruff, plus Alky Broon—the dirtiest barber in Glasgow—and the famous lady missionary, Mrs. Ida Closeshave. Four tapes, 180 mins.
VHS: $31379. $74.98.

Shadowlands

This BBC production is an intelligent film about British writer C.S. Lewis (Joss Ackland), a notorious loner whose life is radically altered by his obsessive relationship with a beautiful American (Claire Bloom). William Nicholson wrote the screenplay. With David Waller, Rupert Baderman and Rhys Hopkins.
VHS: $17181. $19.95.
Norman Stone, Great Britain, 1985, 90 mins.

Sharpe's Collection II

The British hero of the Napoleonic Wars, Richard Sharpe (Sean Bean), returns for this second installment of dramatic episodes. Once again he leads his men behind enemy lines, fighting the French as well as battling the intrigues spawned by rivalry between men ostensibly on the same side. Based on Bernard Cornwell's best-selling novels. Each video is approximately 100 mins.
Sharpe's Collection Set.
VHS: $27582. $89.98.

Sharpe's Collection III

The action and adventure continue in this adventure series based on Bernard Cornwell's best-selling novels. Sean Bean reprises his role as the daring British officer Richard Sharpe, Wellington's key subordinate in the battle against Napoleon. As Wellington prepares to invade France in 1813, Sharpe discovers corruption in the highest ranks of the British army. A secret mission in the Pyrenees takes the newlywed Sharpe away from his wife (Abigail Cruttenden)—who succumbs to a deadly fever. She survives, but in the final days of the war their marriage will face its most critical challenge. Five hours on three videocassettes.
VHS: $30882. $69.98.

Silas Marner

Ben Kingsley leads a stellar cast including Jenny Agutter in a beautiful evocation of George Eliot's famous novel, shot in the Cotswold Hills of England. Produced by the BBC.
VHS: $03526. $29.98.
Giles Foster, Great Britain, 1986, 92 mins.

The Singing Detective

Dennis Potter's musically driven murder mystery masterpiece stars Michael Gambon (*Betrayal*) as cynical thriller writer Philip Marlow, recovering in a hospital while working through the plot of his greatest detective story, starring himself as a handsome, crooning '40s detective. Perhaps the greatest work ever written for television; a truly original masterpiece. With Janet Suzman (*Nicholas and Alexandra*). Eight hours on cassette in slipcase.
VHS: $32414. $99.98.
Jon Amiel, Great Britain, 1986, 480 mins.

Six Wives of Henry VIII

Few television series have attracted as much critical and public acclaim as these six triumphant plays, now preserved on video. Written by six different authors, each play is a lavish and authentic dramatization, produced with style and quality. Binding them together with his magnetic and dignified performance as the mighty monarch is Keith Michell—the

definitive Henry VIII. This six-tape collector's set features the stories of Catherine of Aragon, Anne Boleyn, Jane Seymour, Anne of Cleves, Catherine Howard and Catherine Parr.
VHS: $20667. $99.98.

Story of English
The highly acclaimed televisions series hosted by award-winning reporter Robert MacNeil, in a remarkable journey through the history of the English language. Mounted in a five-cassette series. Program 1: *An English Speaking World*—More than 320 million people speak it as their first language. How has it risen to such prominence? Program 2: *Mother Tongue*—Follows the origin of English from its Anglo-Saxon roots. Program 3: *A Muse of Fire*—Shakespeare's words and the King James Bible represent the full flowering of English. Program 4: *The Guid Scots Tongue*—Traces the remarkable effect the Scots have had on the spread and sound of English. Program 5: *Black on White*—Examines the beginnings of Black English. Program 6: *Pioneers! O Pioneers!*—Walt Whitman's phrase evokes the spirit behind the evolution of early American English. Program 7: *The Muvver Tongue*—19th century British colonialism played an important role in the spread of English throughout the world. Program 8: *The Loaded Weapon*—Investigates the Irish influence on the language. Program 9: *Next Year's Words: A Look into the Future*—Latin, now considered "dead", was once a universal language. Does a similar fate await English? Available only as a complete set.
VHS: S08492. $99.95.

Bard Inspired

Prospero's Books

Forbidden Planet
DVD: DV60109. $24.98.
VHS: S00458. $14.98.
Laser: CAV. LD70989. $99.95.
Laser: CLV. LD70186. $34.95.

Prospero's Books
VHS: S17065. $19.95.

Ran
VHS: S02012. $29.95.

The Tempest (Mazursky)
VHS: S01682. $19.95.

West Side Story
VHS: S01444. $19.95.
Laser: CAV. LD70485. $124.95.
Laser: CLV. LD70486. $69.95.

William Shakespeare's Romeo & Juliet
VHS: S31026. $14.98.
Laser: LD76140. $39.98.

The Thin Blue Line
Not your typical cop show, this PBS comedy series stars British funnyman Rowan Atkinson as Inspector Fowler and David Haig as Detective Inspector Grim, who oversee a cramped police station in Grantly, a fictitious suburb of London.
Volume 1.
VHS: S31207. $19.95.
Volume 2.
VHS: S31208. $19.95.

To the Lighthouse
Kenneth Branagh and Rosemary Harris star in the BBC production of Virginia Woolf's most popular novel, about family life as friends settle in to enjoy a warm Edwardian summer at the beach, and romance and conflicting dreams simultaneously draw the family together and pull it apart.
VHS: S32021. $19.95.
Colin Gregg, Great Britain, 1983, 115 mins.

A Touch of Frost
David Jason is Inspector Jack Frost, a cop who has no time for legal niceties or delicate sensibilities. Instinct drives this cop to seek justice as best he can. He knows his maverick ways mean he will never advance beyond the rank of detective. But that is a price he is willing to pay. Respect is his ultimate reward. This British television series consists of three tapes, each 102 mins. in length.
VHS: S23755. $59.98.

Unnatural Pursuits
Alan Bates stars as a hilarious, booze-ridden, chain-smoking British playwright in this BBC production. In an all-out effort for success he tours the country with his latest work, experiencing the ignoble process of Americanization at the hands of an L.A. producer (Bob Balaban) and a New York impressario (John Mahoney).
VHS: S22871. $19.95.
Christopher Morahan, Great Britain, 1991, 143 mins.

Upstairs Downstairs
A classic series from the BBC, *Upstairs Downstairs* follows the travails of the aristocratic Bellamy Family in Edwardian England. Just as important are the servants who live upstairs. Together they live through the conflicts and traumas of a changing world. This series offers a chance to see how society and the rigid hierarchies of class must evolve as England emerges into a new century where she is no longer preeminent.
Collector's Boxed Set.
VHS: S23269. $149.95.

War and Peace
Anthony Hopkins stars as Pierre in this faithful BBC adaptation of Leo Tolstoy's classic 19th-century novel. It tells of the turmoil brought on by the Napoleonic Wars as experienced by two families, the Rostovs and Bolkonskys. This stunning, historically detailed six-volume work is filled with passion, spectacle and action. Also features Rupert Davies, Hugh Cross and Colin Baker. 751 mins.
VHS: S28394. $149.98.

The Young Ones: Bambi, Nasty, Time
The Young Ones represent their college at University Challenge. At home, videos and dating bring even more humorous possibilities to the fore. Three episodes of the BBC comedy series featuring these manic English students are collected on this video. 101 mins.
VHS: S29804. $14.98.

The Young Ones: Cash, Interesting, Summer Holiday
Money, parties and summer vacation are the primary concerns of The Young Ones in the three episodes on this video. This BBC comedy series reveals the laughable base reality of student life. 101 mins.
VHS: S29805. $14.98.

The Young Ones: Demolition, Bomb, Sick
Demolition threatens their home, a bomb could be in their future, and history's most congested sinuses portend a massive disaster, and yet the English college students from this hit BBC comedy series bumble onward. Three episodes are joined on this video. 104 mins.
VHS: S29803. $14.98.

The Zero Imperative
This supernatural thriller is the latest thing from the creators of *Dr. Who, The Stranger* and *The Airzone Solution*. Colin Baker, Jon Pertwee, Caroline John and others from the original *Dr. Who* series are featured in this gruesome tale. A psychiatric hospital is suddenly at the center of a mysterious rash of murders. A patient known as Zero is involved, but how? 60 mins.
VHS: S24907. $24.99.

25 Top Shakespeare Plays on Video

Antony and Cleopatra
Patrick Stewart stars in this Royal Shakespeare Company production of Shakespeare's play. 160 mins.
VHS: S19027. $19.98.

As You Like It
Laurence Olivier and Elisabeth Bergner star in this handsome and fairly faithful translation of the Shakespeare comedy, in which Rosalind (Bergner) and her love Orlando (Olivier) withstand the brutal tactics of her uncle Frederick to secure the throne for her deposed father, Duke Senior.
VHS: S18173. $24.95.
Paul Czinner, Great Britain, 1936, 96 mins.

Hamlet

Hamlet
Laurence Olivier produces, directs and interprets the title character, a melancholy Dane dealing with a range of feelings for his stepfather, the new King of Denmark. The film won four Oscars and Olivier received his knighthood. Based on a play by William Shakespeare. Cast includes Jean Simmons, Felix Aylmer and Peter Cushing. Don't look for Rosencrantz and Guildenstern. Filmed in glorious black and white.
VHS: S06230. $19.98.
Laser: LD75461. $69.95.
Laurence Olivier, Great Britain, 1948, 153 mins.

Henry V (Branagh)
Kenneth Branagh makes his astounding directorial debut and stars in this critically acclaimed adaptation of Shakespeare's rousing play. With Derek Jacobi, Ian Holm, Judi Dench and Paul Scofield. "...a depth and authority seldom encountered these days on stage or in film" (Dave Kehr, *Chicago Tribune*).
VHS: S12590. $29.98.
Kenneth Branagh, Great Britain, 1990, 138 mins.

Henry V (Olivier)
Laurence Olivier won a special Oscar for outstanding achievement as an actor, producer and director in bringing this work of Shakespeare to the screen. A colorful historical spectacle that includes the battle of Agincourt and serves as a stirring patriotic metaphor for England's survival in WWII. With Robert Newton, Leslie Banks, Renee Asherson and Leo Genn.
VHS: S06237. $19.98.
Laser: LD75076. $69.95.
Laurence Olivier, Great Britain, 1944, 137 mins.

Julius Caesar
John Gielgud gives a superior performance as Julius Caesar in this adaptation of Shakespeare's play, also featuring Charlton Heston, Richard Chamberlain, Robert Vaughn and Diana Rigg.
VHS: S01677. $19.95.
Stuart Burge, Great Britain, 1970, 116 mins.

King Lear (Olivier)
Critically acclaimed as "a performance as great as anything he has ever done in his illustrious acting career", *King Lear* proved to be Laurence Olivier's final major screen role. The all-star Shakespearean cast includes Diana Rigg as Lear's daughter Regan. Olivier's monumental portrayal of Shakespeare's embittered King Lear is truly a performance for the ages.
VHS: S10709. $29.95.

King Lear (Welles)
A legendary production of Shakespeare's masterpiece, directed by the acclaimed British stage and film director Peter Brook, and starring Orson Welles. Virtually unseen since its broadcast in the mid-1950's, this is a treasure of a lifetime for fans of film, Shakespeare, Welles, theatre.
VHS: S11175. $39.95.

Macbeth (Evans)
Sir Maurice Evans and Dame Judith Anderson star in Shakespeare's turbulent drama, produced for television. Great Britain, 1954, 103 mins.
VHS: S01650. $19.95.

Macbeth (Jayson)
Thames Television produced this brilliant adaptation of Shakespeare's play with the cast including Michael Jayson, Barbara Lee Hunt, Ralph Nosseck, Richard Warner.
VHS: S12738. $39.99.

The Merchant of Venice
Sir Laurence Olivier and Joan Plowright star in Shakespeare's complex tale of jealousy and greed. 131 mins.
VHS: S19028. $19.98.

The Merry Wives of Windsor (Esquire 4+4)
Shakespeare's play about a lover wooing a potentially unfaithful wife. Starring Leon Charles and Gloria Grahame. 160 mins. Two videocassettes.
VHS: S15187. $59.95.

A Midsummer Night's Dream (BBC)
A live BBC production of Shakespeare's play of star-crossed lovers and the influence of supernatural creatures. Benny Hill appears in the role of Bottom. Also in the cast are Anna Massey, Jill Bennett, Cyril Luckham, Patrick Allen and Peter Wyngarde. A comical fantasy. England, 1960's, 111 mins.
VHS: S05520. $29.95.

A Midsummer Night's Dream (Hall)
Peter Hall's delicate and merry adaptation of Shakespeare's enchanting farce about the shifting loyalties and evolving relationships among two pairs of lovers. Their romantic affection is manipulated with the help of Puck, a magic fairy. With Diana Rigg as Helena, David Warner as Lysander, Ian Richardson as Oberon, King of the Fairies, Judi Dench as Tatania, Queen of the Fairies and Ian Holm as Puck.
VHS: S06074. $24.95.
Peter Hall, Great Britain, 1968, 124 mins.

A Midsummer Night's Dream (Reinhardt)
The brilliant German theater director Max Reinhardt adapts his Broadway production of Shakespeare's enchanting and lyrical play about love, companionship, fate and star-crossed affairs. Two opposite pairs of lovers ward off extravagant spells and the supernatural to consummate their transcendent passion. The film is visually intoxicating and dramatically powerful, retaining Shakespeare's words though finding a subtle grace and subtlety to the moods and rhythms. Music by Mendelssohn. Choreography by Bronislawa Nijinska

and Anton Grot. With James Cagney, Dick Powell, Olivia de Havilland and Joe E. Brown.
VHS: S01679. $19.98.
Laser: LD71150. $39.98.
Max Reinhardt, USA, 1935, 135 mins.

Much Ado About Nothing
Kenneth Branagh's energetic, highly cinematic adaptation of Shakespeare's comedy of love is notable for its beautiful Italian locations and first-rate performances from Branagh, Emma Thompson, Michael Keaton, Robert Sean Leonard, Keanu Reeves and Denzel Washington. "Ravishing entertainment" (Vincent Canby, *The New York Times*).
VHS: S20528. $19.95.
Laser: LD72362. $34.95.
Kenneth Branagh, Great Britain, 1993, 110 mins.

Othello (1922/Silent)
A remarkably successful silent transposition of Shakespeare's great play, featuring great performances from some of German Expressionism's best actors: Emil Jannings, Werner Kraus, Lya de Putti. Moody, elaborate costumes and sets and first-class acting. Silent with English subtitles.
VHS: S00978. $29.95.
Dimitri Buchowetzki, Germany, 1922, 81 mins.

Othello (1965)
Laurence Olivier is the noble Moor with an unstoppable passion inflamed by jealousy. Frank Finlay is the cunning Iago, the man responsible for the horrible fate suffered by virtuous Desdemona, Maggie Smith. This legendary National Theater of Great Britain production garnered four Academy Award nominations.
VHS: S27838. $19.98.
Stuart Burge, Great Britain, 1965, 167 mins.

Richard III (Loncraine)
Sir Ian McKellen leads an all-star cast including Annette Bening, Robert Downey, Jr., Nigel Hawthorne, Maggie Smith and more, in this updated film adaptation of the Shakespeare play. Visually stunning, it was nominated for Academy Awards for art direction and costume design. This film places the story in a fictional but loosely veiled representation of England in the 1930s, where pomp and fascism seem eerily well matched.
VHS: S27707. $19.98.
Laser: LD75566. $34.98.
Richard Loncraine, Great Britain, 1995, 104 mins.

Richard III (Olivier)
Laurence Olivier's third Shakespeare adaptation moves away from the brooding, austere staging of the early works to a delirious Technicolor treatment of the ruthless tyrant who seizes his throne and wages war at Bosworth. With Olivier, Claire Bloom, Ralph

Richardson, John Gielgud and Stanley Baker. Remastered. Letterboxed.
VHS: S01680. $24.95.
Laser: LD72285. $99.95.
Laurence Olivier, Great Britain, 1956, 161 mins.

Romeo and Juliet
Laurence Harvey stars in this commanding interpretation of Shakespeare's great tale of star-crossed lovers. Stunningly photographed on location in Italy, Renato Castellani's version stars Susan Shentall and Flora Robson, and the transitions are narrated by Sir John Gielgud.
VHS: S12346. $29.98.
Laser: LD76131. $49.95.
Renato Castellani, Great Britain, 1964, 135 mins.

Shakespeare by the English Theater Company
Richard II, Henry IV parts 1 and 2 and *Henry the V* follow the story of two powerful dynasties. In this video collection the legendary conflicts of Agincourt and Tewkesbury are rendered into living history.
VHS: S24890. $129.95.

The Taming of the Shrew (Esquire 4+4)
Shakespeare's story of two sisters, Katherina and Bianca, and their suitors. Starring Franklin Seales and Karen Austin. 117 mins. Two videocassettes.
VHS: S15189. $59.95.

The Taming of the Shrew (Westinghouse Studio)
Seen on live television, and part of the Westinghouse Studio television program. Charlton Heston and Lisa Kirk star in this 1950 modern dress version with Heston wearing sunglasses and downing beer with the boys while Lisa Kirk appears in tight slacks and with a riding whip. Broadcast June 5, 1950. USA, 1950, 60 mins.
VHS: S06987. $24.95.

The Taming of the Shrew (Zeffirelli)
An exquisite mounting of Shakespeare's comic look at male-female relationships stars Richard Burton as Petruchio, the wily gentleman from Verona who travels to Padua to wed Elizabeth Taylor as the fiery Katharina.
VHS: S01681. $19.95.
Franco Zeffirelli, US/Italy, 1967, 127 mins.

The Tempest
Shakespeare's classic tale of the fantasy world of spirits, sorcery, monsters, and shipwrecked scheming noblemen is brought to life in a stunning production featuring Efrem Zimbalist Jr., William H. Bassett, Ted Sorel.
VHS: S04203. $59.95.
William Woodman, 127 mins.

Richard III

50 Best Recent American Films

2001: A Space Odyssey

Stanley Kubrick's landmark film traces the three stages of man, from evolutionary, predatory animals to futuristic space travelers, astronauts on a mission to Jupiter sabotaged by a malfunctioning computer known as HAL. "A uniquely poetic piece of science fiction that's hypnotically entertaining" (*The New Yorker*). Adapted from Arthur C. Clarke's story *The Sentinel*. With Keir Dullea, Gary Lockwood and William Sylvester. Special visual effects by Douglas Trumbull. Letterboxed.
> **VHS: $18674. $19.98.**
> **Laser:** CAV, 3 discs, with 4-page insert. **LD71876. $69.98.**
> **Laser:** CLV, 2 discs. **LD71877. $39.98.**
> **Stanley Kubrick, USA, 1968, 141 mins.**

Altered States

William Hurt in a dazzling debut as a research scientist on an incredible journey into the inner space of the mind. With Blair Brown and spectacular special effects by Bran Ferren.
> **VHS: S00038. $14.95.**
> **Laser: LD70501. $29.98.**
> **Ken Russell, Great Britain, 1980, 103 mins.**

American Graffiti

A new American classic, which single-handedly started the 60's nostalgia craze. A coming-of-age film that details the lives of several high school teenagers the summer after graduation. Launched the careers of Richard Dreyfuss, Harrison Ford and Suzanne Sommers and established George Lucas as an important new American filmmaker. A perceptive, sweet look at a more innocent time.
> **VHS: S00044. $14.95.**
> **Laser: LD70013. $34.98.**
> **George Lucas, USA, 1973, 112 mins.**

Annie Hall

One of Woody Allen's best and funniest films, with Diane Keaton as the sometime object of Woody Allen's affections and expressions of his neurosis. Winner of many Academy Awards. With Paul Simon and Carol Kane.
> **VHS: S00059. $19.95.**
> **Laser: LD70339. $49.95.**
> **Woody Allen, USA, 1977, 94 mins.**

Days of Heaven

Apocalypse Now

Francis Ford Coppola's Vietnam War epic conveys a madness with parallels to Joseph Conrad's *Heart of Darkness*. Lieutenant Willard receives orders to seek out a renegade military outpost led by errant officer Colonel Kurtz, and to "terminate his command with extreme prejudice." This newly enhanced version features a remastered soundtrack in Dolby surround stereo.
> **VHS: S00066. $29.95.**
> **Francis F. Coppola, USA, 1979, 153 mins.**

Badlands

Martin Sheen and Sissy Spacek star in a story based on the 1950's murder spree across the Midwestern plains by Charlie Starkweather and his 15-year-old girlfriend, Carol Fugate. A chilling insight into the cold-hearted mind of the sociopath in one of the most stunning directorial debuts in the American cinema. The film, writes British critic Robin Wood, "produces a subtle, idiosyncratic balance between engagement and detachment, complicity and horror."
> **VHS: S00086. $19.98.**
> **Laser: LD70513. $34.98.**
> **Terence Malick, USA, 1973, 95 mins.**

Blade Runner

A visually expressive adaptation of Philip K. Dick's futurist novel about Deckard (Harrison Ford), a cynical detective assigned to terminate a group of genetically devolved replicants set loose in Los Angeles, circa 2019. In this special director's cut, Deckard's voice-over narration is eliminated and the original ending is restored. With Rutger Hauer, Sean Young, Edward James Olmos and Daryl Hannah. VHS letterboxed.
> **DVD: DV60107. $24.98.**
> **VHS: S18596. $19.98.**
> **Laser: LD71873. $39.99.**
> **Ridley Scott, USA, 1982, 117 mins.**

Blue Velvet

David Lynch's demystification of American normalcy. Pitched between '40s camp and '80s post-modernism, Lynch alter ego Kyle McLachlan stars as a college student who discovers a severed ear, leading to a strange and perverse odyssey. He alternates between the innocent (Laura Dern) and the mysterious (Isabella Rossellini). Dennis Hopper stars as a dangerous outlaw. With Dean Stockwell.
> **VHS: S02778. $19.98.**
> **David Lynch, USA, 1986, 120 mins.**

Body Heat

A sexy, haunting film that echoes the film noir dramas of the 1940's with a flare of irony and passion. Starring William Hurt and Kathleen Turner, it is the directorial debut of Kasdan, who went on to *Big Chill* and *Silverado*.
> **VHS: S00166. $14.95.**
> **Laser: LD70530. $34.98.**
> **Lawrence Kasdan, USA, 1981, 113 mins.**

Bonnie and Clyde

Bank robbers Bonnie Parker and Clyde Barrow probably didn't deserve the cinematic immortality guaranteed by this masterwork directed by Arthur Penn, but I'm sure they wouldn't object to being played by Faye Dunaway and Warren Beatty. Also along for the ride on this Depression era crime spree are Gene Hackman, Estelle Parsons and Michael J. Pollard.
> **DVD: DV60058. $24.98.**
> **VHS: S00168. $19.98.**
> **Laser: LD70531. $34.98.**
> **Arthur Penn, USA, 1967, 111 mins.**

Coolest Title Sequences

**Beavis & Butt-head
Do America**
VHS: S31388. $19.95.

Goldfinger
VHS: S00513. $14.95.
Laser: LD70584. $98.99.

**The Good, the Bad
and the Ugly**
VHS: S11553. $24.98.
Laser: LD70587. $39.98.

Kiss Me Deadly
VHS: S13756. $19.98.
Laser: LD72139. $39.95.

**My Best Friend's
Wedding**
DVD: DV60036. $24.95.
VHS: S32515. $22.99.
Laser: LD76374. $39.95.

Once Were Warriors
VHS: S26282. $19.98.
Laser: LD75060. $49.95.

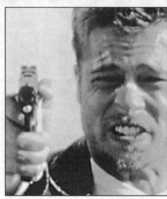

Seven

Psycho
VHS: S01068. $19.95.
Laser: LD70068. $34.98.

Pulp Fiction
VHS: S26211. $19.95.
Laser: LD75062. $39.99.

Seven
DVD: DV60096. $24.98.
VHS: S27256. $19.98.
Laser: LD75472. $124.95.

A Shot in the Dark
VHS: S02330. $14.95.
Laser: LD70675. $34.98.

Vertigo
VHS: S01795. $19.95.
Laser: LD70094. $79.95.

West Side Story
VHS: S01444. $19.95.
Laser: CAV. LD70485. $124.95.
Laser: CLV. LD70486. $69.95.

Cabaret
Liza Minnelli and Joel Grey give extraordinary performances in Bob Fosse's musical drama that mirrors the decay and decadence of Germany on the eve of Hitler's rise to power. With Marisa Berenson and Michael York.
VHS: S01837. $19.98.
Laser: LD72168. $39.98.
Bob Fosse, USA, 1972, 119 mins.

Chinatown
Jack Nicholson and Faye Dunaway star in Polanski's finely crafted, atmospheric film. What begins as a routine matrimonial snoop job for an average gumshoe mushrooms into a murderous regional and personal scandal told with incredible style, surprises and a gripping narrative line. Outstanding performances by all including John Huston as Dunaway's father and a cameo by Polanski as a great little sleaze.
VHS: S01840. $19.95.
Laser: Widescreen. LD75371. $49.98.
Roman Polanski, USA, 1974, 131 mins.

The Conversation
Gene Hackman is brilliant as Harry Caul, the surveillance man who becomes the object of surveillance himself. Coppola's great achievement is in evoking an obsessive sense of paranoia as Hackman struggles to free himself from the maze of secrecy and murder. With Cindy Williams, Harrison Ford, Frederic Forrest.
VHS: S00267. $19.95.
Laser: LD75356. $29.98.
Francis F. Coppola, USA, 1974, 113 mins.

Days of Heaven
An Award winner both at Cannes and in Hollywood, this story follows a trio composed of a fugitive from the Chicago slums (Richard Gere), a shy, rich Texan (Sam Shepard) and a woman (Brooke Adams) caught in a love triangle. Set against the Midwestern wheat fields at the turn of the century, this film is often cited by cinematographers as being one of the most beautifully shot films ever made. Won the Best Oscar for Cinematography.
VHS: S00313. $14.95.
Laser: LD75358. $29.98.
Terence Malick, USA, 1980, 95 mins.

Dead Man Walking
Sean Penn is an unrepentant killer who is ministered to by a strong-willed nun (Susan Sarandon). This film is unique for staying so firmly glued to the harder issues and emotions that surround hardened killers and the state's use of the death penalty. Penn gives an especially brilliant performance in a film dominated by great acting.
DVD: DV60004. $29.95.
VHS: S28059. $19.98.
Laser: LD75802. $44.95.
Tim Robbins, USA, 1995, 122 mins.

Deliverance
Jon Voight, Burt Reynolds, Ronny Cox and Ned Beatty spend a weekend in the wilds canoeing and trying to avoid inbred, hostile mountain folk in Georgia. Based on the novel by James Dickey, this wilderness nightmare chills to the bone. With Bill McKinney and Herbert Coward.
VHS: S00320. $19.98.
Laser: Letterboxed. LD71676. $34.98.
John Boorman, USA, 1972, 109 mins.

Dog Day Afternoon
This fantastic thriller centers on a bisexual and his buddy, who rob a bank in order to get the cash for a sex change operation for the ring leader's lover. With a first-rate performance by Al Pacino.
VHS: S21858. $19.98.
Laser: LD74523. $39.98.
Sidney Lumet, USA, 1975, 124 mins.

Dr. Strangelove
This great black comedy stars Peter Sellers as the wheelchair-bound nuclear scientist plotting a scheme to attack Russia's nuclear targets with nuclear bombs. Very funny and very frightening, *Dr. Strangelove or: How I Learned to Stop Worrying and Love the Bomb* also stars Sterling Hayden as U.S. Air Force Commander Jack D. Ripper, and George C. Scott as Joint Chief of Staff "Buck" Turgidson. VHS letterboxed.
DVD: DV60026. $24.95.
VHS: S00367. $19.95.
Laser: LD70750. $99.95.
Stanley Kubrick, USA, 1963, 93 mins.

Ed Wood
Johnny Depp portrays the nearly inconceivable cult film director/cross-dresser Ed Wood in this imaginative biographical film that won an Academy Award for Martin Landau in the role of actor Bela Lugosi, who (in real life) died during the making of one of Wood's notorious films. A truly singular Hollywood achievement about a stranger-than-fiction filmmaker whose atrocious films, like *Plan 9 from Outer Space* and *Glen or Glenda*, have become cult classics. With Patricia Arquette and Bill Murray.
VHS: S24321. $19.98.
Laser: Letterboxed. LD74914. $39.99.
Tim Burton, USA, 1994, 127 mins.

Edward Scissorhands
This touching fable about a quiet boy with sharp, metal shears for hands manages to entertain and amuse while making some sensitive observations

about adolescent loneliness and emotional estrangement. With especially poignant performances from Diane Wiest and Johnny Depp. Also starring Winona Ryder, Alan Arkin, Kathy Baker, Anthony Michael Hall, and Vincent Price as Edward's inventor.
VHS: S13922. $19.98.
Tim Burton, USA, 1990, 100 mins.

Everyone Says I Love You
Woody Allen's musical celebration of an eccentric family from New York City follows a father (Allen), a mother (Goldie Hawn), a daughter (Natasha Lyonne), a sister (Drew Barrymore), an ex-con (Tim Roth), a fiancee (Ed Norton) and two half-sisters (Natalie Portman and Gaby Hoffman) as they move from New York to Paris to Venice in search of love.
VHS: S31718. $19.99.
Laser: LD76291. $39.99.
Woody Allen, USA, 1996, 106 mins.

The Falcon and the Snowman
Timothy Hutton and Sean Penn are two typical American young men who are willing to sell U.S. government secrets to the Soviets in this intriguing account of a true life story. Based on the book by Robert Lindsay. With Lori Singer, Pat Hingle and Dorian Harewood.
Laser: Widescreen. LD74832. $49.99.
John Schlesinger, USA, 1985, 131 mins.

Five Easy Pieces
A classic performance by Jack Nicholson as a classical pianist who has given up his musical career to work in the oil fields. Great supporting work by Karen Black, Susan Anspach, Billy Green Bush and Helena Kallianiotes as a complaining hitchhiker. Classic scene in which Jack finally figures out how to get a simple order of toast.
VHS: S07789. $14.95.
Laser: Widescreen. LD70981. $34.95.
Bob Rafelson, USA, 1970, 96 mins.

The French Connection
William Friedkin's edge-of-the-seat thriller about two hard-nosed New York detectives who stumble into an international narcotics smuggling ring. Contains probably the most exciting car chase ever filmed. With an exceptional performance by the always good Gene Hackman, as well as Roy Scheider and Fernando Rey.
VHS: S21861. $14.98.
Laser: LD75484. $39.98.
William Friedkin, USA, 1971, 102 mins.

The Godfather
An epic featuring Marlon Brando as the patriarch of the Corleone family, masterfully balanced between the story of family life and the family crime business. With Al Pacino, James Caan, Robert Duvall, Diane Keaton. Based on Mario Puzo's novel. Music by Nino Rota. Letterboxed.
VHS: S00509. $24.95.
Francis F. Coppola, USA, 1972, 171 mins.

The Godfather Part II
A companion piece to the original *Godfather*, this continues the saga of two generations of successive power in the Corleone family. Coppola tells the story of the rise of a young Don Vito, played by Robert De Niro, and the ascension of the new Don Michael, played by Al Pacino. Letterboxed.
VHS: S00510. $24.95.
Francis F. Coppola, USA, 1974, 200 mins.

Hester Street
Set on the Lower East Side of New York in 1896, Gitl and her son reunite with husband Jake, who had previously immigrated from Russia. Jake has completely embraced America by shedding his ethnic heritage, and is embarrassed when Gitl clings to her old country ways. But in this charming and humorous portrait of the Jewish immigrant experience, Gitl finds a way to become victor instead of victim. Carol Kane was nominated for an Oscar for her portrayal of Gitl. With Stephen Keats.
VHS: S00564. $29.95.
Joan Micklin Silver, USA, 1974, 89 mins.

King of Comedy
Robert De Niro is an obsessive stand-up comic performing in front of cardboard cutouts of his idols. Jerry Lewis is a host of a talk show that De Niro desperately wants to be on. Incredibly funny, true-to-life film by Martin Scorsese.
VHS: S00679. $19.95.
Martin Scorsese, USA, 1982, 101 mins.

The Last Picture Show
Peter Bogdanovich's masterpiece about life in a small Texas town in the early 1950's received six Oscar nominations and swept the supporting actor and actress category. Based on the novel by Larry McMurtry. The all-star cast includes Jeff Bridges, Cybill Shepherd, Timothy Bottoms, Cloris Leachman, Ben Johnson, Ellen Burstyn, Randy Quaid and Eileen Brennan. The town of Anarene was never quite the same after they shut down the Royal theatre.
VHS: S13579. $19.95.
Laser: LD70758. $124.95.
Peter Bogdanovich, USA, 1971, 118 mins.

Leaving Las Vegas
Nicolas Cage and Elisabeth Shue star in this tender love story of two people living on the far side of hope. Ben Sanderson (Cage) is an alcoholic Los Angeles screenwriter who decides to move to Las Vegas to die. There he meets a prostitute (Shue), equally unapologetic about her own life choices, and together they fall in love. Cage won the Academy Award for his role in this engrossing, complex and beautiful film. VHS letterboxed.
VHS: S27709. $19.98.
Laser: LD75568. $34.98.
Mike Figgis, USA, 1995, 113 mins.

M*A*S*H
Donald Sutherland, Elliott Gould and Robert Duvall in the original, superb, classic dark comedy directed

Written for the Screen

8½
VHS: S07140. $59.95.
Laser: LD70806. $59.95.

The Apartment
VHS: S05880. $19.95.
Laser: LD70506. $39.98.

Chinatown
VHS: S01840. $19.95.
Laser: LD75371. $49.98.

Citizen Kane
VHS: S14599. $19.98.
Laser: CAV. LD70745. $124.95.
Laser: CLV. LD70356. $39.95.
Laser: CLV. LD70746. $39.95.

Fargo
DVD: DV60003. $29.95.
VHS: S29808. $19.98.
Laser: LD75990. $34.95.

Fargo

Purple Rose of Cairo
VHS: S01074. $14.98.

Rebel Without a Cause
VHS: S01097. $19.98.
Laser: LD70663. $24.98.

Seventh Seal
VHS: S01185. $29.95.
Laser: CAV. LD70453. $79.95.
Laser: CLV. LD70454. $49.95.

Sunset Boulevard
VHS: S01285. $14.95.
Laser: LD75268. $34.98.

The Third Man
VHS: S01327. $24.95.
Laser: LD71366. $39.95.

Midnight Cowboy

with verve by Robert Altman, juxtaposing the horrors of war with the resiliency of the human spirit. Written by Ring Lardner, Jr.

> **VHS: S02643. $14.98.**
> **Laser:** Letterboxed. **LD76743. $24.98.**
> **Robert Altman, USA, 1970, 116 mins.**

The Manchurian Candidate

A compelling thriller based on the Richard Condon novel about brainwashing American soldiers to serve as assassins in secret global domination. Starring Frank Sinatra, Janet Leigh, Angela Lansbury and Laurence Harvey as the walking time bomb. This tape contains exclusive interviews with Sinatra, director John Frankenheimer and writer George Axelrod. B&W.

> **VHS: S07005. $19.98.**
> **Laser:** This deluxe collector's edition is letterboxed, newly digitally remastered and features commentary by John Frankenheimer. **LD70624. $59.98.**
> **John Frankenheimer, USA, 1962, 126 mins.**

McCabe and Mrs. Miller

A brilliant, offbeat drama of frontier life starring Warren Beatty and Julie Christie. This is Altman's personal and poetic interpretation of an American myth, resulting in a truly original Western. Also appearing are Shelley Duvall, Keith Carradine, Michael Murphy and William Devane.

> **VHS: S00839. $14.95.**
> **Laser: LD74710. $39.98.**
> **Robert Altman, USA, 1971, 120 mins.**

Mean Streets

Set in New York's Little Italy, *Mean Streets* follows Harvey Keitel as he slowly climbs into the hierarchy of a local Mafia family. Keenly observed, gritty and violent, this early film by Scorsese clearly foreshadows his later work, and established him as a major American talent. With Robert De Niro, Cesare Danova, Amy Robinson.

> **VHS: S00840. $19.98.**
> **Laser: LD70626. $34.98.**
> **Martin Scorsese, USA, 1973, 112 mins.**

Midnight Cowboy

The shocking story of Cowboy Joe Buck, played by Jon Voight, made history when it was released 25 years ago. This naive country boy with a horrible secret moves to New York, where the streetwise Ratso Rizzo (Dustin Hoffman) becomes his guide to seamy city life. Together they explore the world of hustling and even visit Warhol's factory, developing a deep friendship in the process. This film won Oscars for Best Picture, Screenplay and Director. Also features Brenda Vaccaro. A 25th Anniversary re-release.

> **DVD: DV60090. $24.98.**
> **VHS: S21826. $19.98.**
> **Laser: LD74499. $49.98.**
> **John Schlesinger, USA, 1969, 113 mins.**

The Naked Kiss (The Iron Kiss)

A reformed big city prostitute (ably played by Constance Towers) who tries to go the straight and narrow route in small town America finds that beneath the little town's squeaky clean veneer lies perversion and corruption of the highest order. Michael Dante plays a creepy child molester. (Is there any other kind?) One of the best from Fuller and a cult classic.

> **VHS: S06479. $29.95.**
> **Laser: LD70423. $44.95.**
> **Sam Fuller, USA, 1964, 90 mins.**

Nashville

The recipient of five Academy Award nominations, Robert Altman's *Nashville* is an explosive drama and human comedy that interweaves the lives of 24 major characters during a five day period in the country music capital. A penetrating and multi-level portrait of America starring Keith Carradine, Karen Black, Geraldine Chaplin, Ronee Blakley, Lily Tomlin and Henry Gibson.

> **VHS: S00919. $29.95.**
> **Robert Altman, USA, 1975, 159 mins.**

Network

A savage satire written by Paddy Chayefsky, looking at the powers behind television programming. With a sizzling performance by Peter Finch (I'm mad as hell and I'm not going to take it anymore) as newscaster Howard Beale, with Faye Dunaway and William Holden.

> **VHS: S01817. $14.95.**
> **Laser:** Letterboxed. **LD76399. $39.99.**
> **Sidney Lumet, USA, 1976, 116 mins.**

One Flew Over the Cuckoo's Nest

Milos Forman's sharp adaptation of Ken Kesey's anti-authoritarian novel about a shrewd nonconformist (Jack Nicholson) sentenced to an insane asylum who encourages a group of marginal misfits to assert their rights and independence, over the rigid opposition of the head nurse (Louise Fletcher). Cinematography by Haskell Wexler. With Will Sampson, Brad Dourif, Sydney Lassick, Christopher Lloyd, Danny DeVito and Scatman Crothers. Winner of the five top Academy Awards.

> **DVD: DV60091. $24.98.**
> **VHS: S18973. $19.98.**
> **Milos Forman, USA, 1975, 134 mins.**

Pee-Wee's Big Adventure

Paul Reubens star as Pee-Wee in a comedy he also helped co-write. The basic premise has Pee-Wee looking for his lost bike, but it's really just a good reason to see this brilliant comic display his virtuosity in some now classic sequences.

> **VHS: S24845. $19.98.**
> **Tim Burton, USA, 1985, 92 mins.**

Point Blank

A superior crime thriller starring Lee Marvin as a double-crossed professional criminal out to settle the score with everyone who sold him out and left him

Taxi Driver

for dead. Based on the novel by Donald Westlake writing as Richard Stark. Cast includes Angie Dickinson, Carroll O'Connor, Keenan Wynn, John Vernon and Lloyd Bochner. Wait for the shootout at Alcatraz.
VHS: S08064. $19.98.
Laser: Letterboxed. **LD74679. $34.98.**
John Boorman, USA, 1967, 89 mins.

Psycho
The Classic! Anthony Perkins is Norman Bates and Janet Leigh is Marion Crane in this masterpiece of the macabre by Alfred Hitchcock.
VHS: S01068. $19.95.
Laser: LD70068. $34.98.
Alfred Hitchcock, USA, 1960, 109 mins.

Raging Bull
Robert De Niro gives an incredible performance as Jake LaMotta, the controversial middleweight fighter of the 1940's. *Raging Bull* shows how LaMotta turned his fears into the physical energy needed to become a champion, while destroying his private life. Breathtaking cinematography!
DVD: DV60092. $24.98.
VHS: S01084. $19.95.
Laser: Letterboxed, chapter search. Includes original theatrical trailer. **LD71669. $39.98.**
Martin Scorsese, USA, 1980, 127 mins.

hypocrisies of the American dream relating to racism, anti-communism and the bomb. A complex, wacky masterpiece by one of Hollywood's great directors, Sam Fuller.
VHS: S18328. $29.95.
Laser: LD70458. $49.95.
Sam Fuller, USA, 1963, 101 mins.

Short Cuts
Raymond Carver's short stories are brought to the screen in this Golden Globe winner, employing some of Hollywood's biggest stars. Jack Lemmon, Lyle Lovett, Matthew Modine, Lily Tomlin and Jennifer Jason Leigh are just some of the big names seen in this harrowing portrayal of everyday people living extraordinary lives.
VHS: S20889. $19.95.
Laser: LD74462. $124.95.
Robert Altman, USA, 1993, 189 mins.

Taxi Driver
Scorsese's now-classic film with Robert De Niro as the psychotic cabbie driven to violence in an attempt to "rescue" a teenage prostitute (Jodie Foster). With Albert Brooks, Harvey Keitel, Leonard Harris, Peter Boyle and Cybill Shepherd.
DVD: DV60027. $24.95.
VHS: S01303. $14.95.
Laser: CAV, widescreen. **LD70470. $99.95.**

Technicolor Dreams

All That Heaven Allows
VHS: S30796. $19.95.

Girl Can't Help It
VHS: S00503. $59.98.

How to Marry a Millionaire
VHS: S04202. $19.98.
Laser: LD71059. $69.98.

Johnny Guitar
VHS: S04474. $14.95.

Leave Her to Heaven
VHS: S23757. $19.98.
Laser: LD74915. $39.99.

Magnificent Obsession
VHS: S00805. $14.95.

Niagara

Marnie
VHS: S01770. $19.95.
Laser: LD70054. $39.95.

Moulin Rouge
VHS: S11216. $19.95.
Laser: LD72128. $39.98.

The Naked Spur
VHS: S03674. $19.97.

Niagara
VHS: S04200. $19.98.

Pillow Talk
VHS: S04840. $14.95.

Seven Brides for Seven Brothers
VHS: S05096. $19.95.
Laser: LD70673. $34.98.

Silk Stockings
VHS: S04405. $19.98.
Laser: LD70678. $34.98.

The Ten Commandments (1956)
VHS: S05372. $29.95.

Raiders of the Lost Ark
Harrison Ford is an adventure-seeking archeologist after rare and well-guarded ancient artifacts. The entertaining Indiana Jones battles Nazi hordes for the sacred Ark of the Covenant and the company of a spunky Karen Allen. Whiz bang thrills and special effects.
VHS: S01882. $14.95.
Steven Spielberg, USA, 1981, 115 mins.

The Rapture
There are six definitions of "rapture" in the dictionary. This provocative thriller, written and directed by Michael Tolkin, tries to encompass them all. Mimi Rogers stars in this unusual drama that tests the religious faith of a born again Los Angeles telephone operator. She embarks on a sensual and spiritual odyssey that culminates in a cataclysm of Biblical proportions. With David Duchovny, Patrick Bauchau, Kimberly Cullum and Will Patton.
VHS: S15925. $19.95.
Michael Tolkin, USA, 1991, 100 mins.

Shock Corridor
To catch a killer and win a Pulitzer prize, reporter-hero Johnny Barrett has himself committed to a mental institution. He must find out who killed Sloan in the kitchen by questioning three inmates who witnessed the crime—men driven crazy by the

Laser: CLV, widescreen. **LD70471. $49.95.**
Martin Scorsese, USA, 1975, 114 mins.

Unforgiven
Clint Eastwood's brilliant reconsideration of the American western. Set in the 1880s, a reformed gunman and failed farmer (Eastwood) reluctantly agrees to collect the bounty on two cowboys who slashed a prostitute's face, setting in motion a mythic confrontation with a corrupt sheriff (Gene Hackman), a hired English assassin (Richard Harris) and a dime novelist (Saul Rubinek). With Morgan Freeman and Frances Fisher. Winner of four Academy Awards.
DVD: DV60120. $24.98.
VHS: S18724. $19.98.
Clint Eastwood, USA, 1992, 131 mins.

The Wild Bunch
An authentic American western classic and Peckinpah's best film. An aging group of outlaws decides to pull off one last heist, led by William Holden, who plays Pike Bishop, leader of The Wild Bunch, with Robert Ryan as Deke Thornton, who once rode with Pike and now faces return to prison. *The Wild Bunch* broke new ground in the realistic depiction of violence on the screen. Letterboxed.
DVD: DV60121. $24.98.
VHS: S01459. $39.99.
Laser: CLV. **LD70706. $129.98.**
Sam Peckinpah, USA, 1969, 127 mins.

25 Top Musicals

An American in Paris
VHS: S00045. $19.95.

The Band Wagon
Laser: LD70516. $34.98.

Cabaret
VHS: S01837. $19.98.
Laser: LD72168. $39.98.

Fiddler on the Roof
VHS: S01702. $29.95.
Laser: LD70568. $39.98.

Funny Face
VHS: S06139. $14.95.
Laser: LD75364. $44.98.

A Funny Thing Happened on the Way to the Forum
VHS: S02336. $19.99.
Laser: LD71644. $34.98.

Gigi
VHS: S07159. $19.95.
Laser: LD70582. $39.99.

Gold Diggers of 1933
VHS: S01769. $19.98.
Laser: LD70583. $34.98.

Gold Diggers of 1935
VHS: S11162. $29.95.

Guys and Dolls
VHS: S02529. $19.98.

Hair
VHS: S03486. $19.98.
Laser: LD71163. $39.98.

A Hard Day's Night
DVD: DV60122. $24.98.
VHS: S00540. $19.98.
Laser: CAV. LD70374. $79.95.
Laser: CLV. LD70375. $49.97.

Help!
DVD: DV60123. $24.98.
VHS: S02013. $19.98.
Laser: CAV. LD70376. $79.95.
Laser: CLV. LD70377. $39.95.

Jesus Christ Superstar
VHS: S04920. $19.98.
Laser: LD71579. $34.98.

Little Shop of Horrors
VHS: S03865. $19.98.

Man of La Mancha
VHS: S01715. $19.99.
Laser: LD72125. $39.98.

Meet Me in St. Louis
VHS: S00845. $19.95.

A Star Is Born (1954/Garland)
VHS: S01734. $29.98.
Laser: LD71337. $39.95.

Stormy Weather
VHS: S02828. $19.98.

Sweet Charity
VHS: S03493. $19.95.
Laser: LD70085. $44.98.

Tommy
VHS: S02920. Currently unavailable.

Top Hat
VHS: S01362. $14.98.
Laser: LD76046. $39.98.

Viva Las Vegas
DVD: DV60112. $24.98.
VHS: S03935. $19.95.
Laser: LD70701. $34.98.

West Side Story
VHS: S01444. $19.95.
Laser: CAV. LD70485. $124.95.
Laser: CLV. LD70486. $69.95.

The Wizard of Oz (1939/Fleming)
DVD: DV60104. $24.98.
VHS: S09609. $19.95.
Laser: CLV, MGM. LD70709. $24.98.
Laser: CAV, Criterion. LD71215. $99.95.

The Band Wagon

50 Best Recent American Films

100 Best Classic American Films

Adam's Rib
Spencer Tracy and Katharine Hepburn in one of their all-time great appearances as married attorneys who find themselves on opposite sides of a murder case in which Judy Holliday is the accused.
DVD: DV60057. $24.98.
VHS: S03456. $19.95.
Laser: LD70202. $49.98.
George Cukor, USA, 1949, 101 mins.

The African Queen
Inspired casting teamed Bogart and Hepburn in this romantic adventure/comedy set in a war-torn African jungle. Surviving malaria, insects and persistent conflicts of their personalities, they share victory and tender romance.
VHS: S00020. $19.95.
John Huston, USA, 1951, 105 mins.

All About Eve
Six Oscars were awarded this cynical and entertaining examination of life as it exists on the Broadway theatre scene. Bette Davis glows as the aging star being undermined by her protege Anne Baxter, as Eve Harrington. With George Sanders, Celeste Holm and Marilyn Monroe. A gem.
VHS: S03911. $19.98.
Laser: LD70823. $49.98.
Joseph L. Mankiewicz, USA, 1950, 138 mins.

All Quiet on the Western Front
Classic adaptation of Erich Maria Remarque's anti-war novel has lost little of its impact over the years. The film follows a group of German recruits during World War I from their idealism to disillusionment.
VHS: S01686. $19.95.
Laser: LD70011. $39.98.
Lewis Milestone, USA, 1930, 103 mins.

All That Heaven Allows
One of the best films from one of American cinema's most underrated directors, this never-before-available film is a scathing attack on the American Dream, in which a widow (Jane Wyman) faces the wrath of her friends and family when she becomes romantically involved with a younger man (Rock Hudson). Succumbing to the pressures of society, she stops seeing the man and settles back into her lonely life, but eventually rebels against her conformist surroundings and finds love with him again. "A stylized, beautifully photographed commentary on the emotional numbness of suburban life" (*The Motion Picture Guide*). Later remade by Fassbinder as *Ali: Fear Eats the Soul*. With Agnes Moorehead, Conrad Nagel, Virginia Grey and Charles Drake.
VHS: S30796. $19.95.
Douglas Sirk, USA, 1955, 89 mins.

An American in Paris
No film can match *An American in Paris* for all the joy, all the songs, and all the romance in music and dance. Gene Kelly and Leslie Caron star in this movie set to the glorious melodies of George Gershwin, including: "Embraceable You," "Love Is Here to Stay," "I Got Rhythm" and more.
VHS: S00045. $19.95.
Vincente Minnelli, USA, 1951, 102 mins.

Anatomy of a Murder
A riveting courtroom drama pitting small town lawyer James Stewart against big city prosecutor George C. Scott in a trial of Ben Gazzara, accused of murdering his wife's rapist. With a brilliant score by Duke Ellington.
VHS: S01525. $19.95.
Otto Preminger, USA, 1959, 160 mins.

The Apartment
Billy Wilder's great film of tears and laughter as Jack Lemmon and Shirley MacLaine wheel and deal over a New York apartment in a comedy of morality. Winner of five Oscars and worth at least 20 more. VHS letterboxed.
VHS: S05880. $19.95.
Laser: LD70506. $39.98.
Billy Wilder, USA, 1960, 125 mins.

Arsenic and Old Lace
Cary Grant stars in this hilarious black comedy about two sweet old ladies who poison lonely old men with elderberry wine, as a kindness. Cary is the confused nephew who has to juggle dead bodies, escaped murderers and an uncle who thinks he's Teddy Roosevelt with a marriage announcement and the police. With Peter Lorre as Dr. Einstein.
VHS: S02351. $19.95.
Laser: CLV, 1 disc, Criterion. LD70340. $39.95.
Frank Capra, USA, 1944, 118 mins.

The Awful Truth
Wildly funny romp which won the Academy Award opens when a battling couple files for divorce. The only hitch seems to be who will get custody of their beloved terrier, Mr. Smith. Cary Grant and Irene Dunne co-star in this very wacky comedy.
VHS: S00083. $19.95.
Leo McCarey, USA, 1937, 92 mins.

Ball of Fire
Mild-mannered professor Gary Cooper is hard at work on a new encyclopedia. He finds the help of a brassy nightclub singer, played by Barbara Stanwyck, both invigorating and distracting. With S.Z. Sakall, Oscar Homolka and Leonid Kinskey as interested faculty members and Dan Duryea as trouble. Script by Billy Wilder and Charles Brackett. B&W.
VHS: S03115. $19.98.
Howard Hawks, USA, 1942, 111 mins.

Bank Dick
As a reward for capturing a robber, W.C. Fields is given the job as a bank security guard. A wonderfully funny romp in what is often considered Fields' best film.
VHS: S03323. $29.95.
Laser: LD70014. $34.98.
Eddie Cline, USA, 1940, 74 mins.

Ben-Hur

Ben-Hur
Celebrating the timelessness of this multi-academy award-winning film, this new Deluxe Collector's Edition of the classic starring Charlton Heston also includes the documentary *Ben Hur: The Making of an Epic*, narrated by Christopher Plummer, and the original theatrical trailer. VHS letterboxed.
VHS: S20641. $39.98.
Laser: 5-disc CAV boxed set. LD72371. $99.98.
William Wyler, 1959, USA, 204 mins.

The Best Years of Our Lives

This epic film focuses on the troubles of three World War II servicemen as they try to pick up the threads of their lives after returning home to the States. An insightful portrait of small-town American life and its values. Starring Myrna Loy, Frederic March, Dana Andrews, Virginia Mayo and Teresa Wright. *The Best Years of Our Lives* was named one of the 50 greatest motion pictures of all time by the members of The American Film Institute. Digitally remastered.
VHS: S03117. $19.98.
William Wyler, USA, 1946, 170 mins.

Big Sleep

Humphrey Bogart is Philip Marlowe in this entertaining adaptation of Raymond Chandler's novel. Blackmail, murder, sex and drugs all come into play as the ace detective tries to sort out the guilty parties. Even the author couldn't figure out who killed the chauffeur. With Lauren Bacall, Martha Vickers and Elisha Cook, Jr.
VHS: S09389. $19.95.
Laser: LD70174. $34.98.
Howard Hawks, USA, 1946, 114 mins.

Born Yesterday

Judy Holliday won the Best Actress Oscar for her funny role as the dumb blond girlfriend of Broderick Crawford, a corrupt millionaire junk dealer. Brock, a man with social ambitions, is embarassed by Billie's crass behavior and hires a writer, William Holden, to smarten her up. A classic comedy.

VHS: S14979. $19.95.
Laser: LD70293. $34.98.
J. Lee Thompson, USA, 1962, 106 mins.

Carmen Jones

Dorothy Dandridge plays Carmen, a woman caught between two men and her own unorthodox nature. The men, one a pretty boy and the other a tough sergeant, are portrayed by Harry Belafonte and Brock Peters. Dandridge lures Joe (Belafonte) into deserting from the army and then leaves him for the two-fisted Sgt. Brown (Peters). The supporting cast is every bit as impressive as the main actors and includes Pearl Bailey, Joe Adams and Diahann Carroll in her first film role. Dandridge became the first African-American nominated for a Best Actress Academy Award. The film won a Golden Globe for Best Musical/Comedy in 1955.
VHS: S21385. $19.95.
Otto Preminger, USA, 1954, 105 mins.

The Children's Hour

Lillian Hellman's classic play about two teachers who are accused of lesbianism by a student receives powerful treatment from Shirley MacLaine, Audrey Hepburn and James Garner.
VHS: S13345. $19.98.
Laser: LD72169. $34.98.
William Wyler, USA, 1961, 107 mins.

Citizen Kane

One of the greatest films ever made is now available in a version painstakingly restored to its original

Saluting Cinematographers

Breaking the Waves
VHS: S31256. $99.99.
Laser: LD76284. $69.95.

The Conformist
Laser: LD75355. $29.98.

Days of Heaven
VHS: S00313. $14.95.
Laser: LD75358. $29.98.

Dead Man
VHS: S30457. $99.99.
Laser: LD76064. $39.99.

Lumiere & Company
VHS: S30468. $19.98.

Manhattan
VHS: S00822. $19.98.
Laser: LD70175. $34.98.

McCabe and Mrs. Miller
VHS: S00839. $14.95.
Laser: LD74710. $39.98.

Medium Cool
VHS: S00843. $14.95.
Laser: LD75228. $34.98.

Raging Bull
DVD: DV60092. $24.98.
VHS: S01084. $19.95.
Laser: LD71669. $39.98.

Through a Glass Darkly
VHS: S01339. $29.95.
Laser: LD74974. $49.95.

VHS: S03863. $19.95.
George Cukor, USA, 1950, 103 mins.

Bringing Up Baby

One of the funniest movies from Hollywood, a classic screwball comedy. Katharine Hepburn is the madcap heiress with her pet leopard "Baby", who falls for an absent-minded zoologist (Cary Grant) and makes a shambles of his life. Briskly paced fun with May Robson, Charlie Ruggles and Barry Fitzgerald supporting the leads.
VHS: S09362. $19.98.
Howard Hawks, USA, 1938, 102 mins.

Call Northside 777

James Stewart stars along with Richard Conte and E.G. Marshall in this absorbing, dramatic film. A reporter, going on his own hunch, investigates a murder where he remains convinced that the law has fingered the wrong man. The semi-documentary style employed in this film makes this tale even more compelling.
VHS: S22532. $19.98.
Laser: LD75931. $39.98.
Henry Hathaway, USA, 1948, 111 mins.

Cape Fear

Robert Mitchum is a sadistic rapist seeking out the lawyer who put him behind bars (played by Gregory Peck). His search ends in a small North Carolina town where he commences a campaign of terror against Peck's family, which the police are powerless to stop. A tense and well-paced suspenser highlighted by Mitchum's riveting portrayal of a shrewd psychopath, and a terrific cat-and-mouse chase through the Southern bayous.

brilliance in honor of the film's 50th anniversary. With Orson Welles, Dorothy Comingore, Everett Sloane, Paul Stewart. Cinematography by Gregg Toland, script by Welles and Herman Mankiewicz.
VHS: S14599. $19.98.
Laser: CAV. LD70745. $124.95.
Laser: CLV. LD70356. $39.95.
Laser: CLV. LD70746. $39.95.
Orson Welles, USA, 1941, 119 mins.

Double Indemnity

A great Billy Wilder film in which "every turn and twist is exactly calculated and achieves its effect with the simplest of means; this shrewd, smooth, tawdry thriller is one of the high points of 40s films" (Kael). Raymond Chandler collaborated on the screenplay in adapting James Cain's story. Barbara Stanwyck is the platinum blonde, Fred MacMurray the insurance salesman she ensnares in a plot to kill her businessman-husband and collect on the double-indemnity clause in his policy.
VHS: S02940. $19.95.
Laser: LD70024. $34.98.
Billy Wilder, USA, 1944, 107 mins.

Duck Soup

The most immortal film of the Marx Brothers! About the small nation of Fredonia, which has given Groucho complete power to restore order. Political satire and madness both. With Margaret Dumont and Louis Calhern.
VHS: S02018. $19.95.
Leo McCarey, USA, 1933, 70 mins.

Force of Evil

Film noir featuring John Garfield as an attorney who works for a mobster and finds himself caught in a numbers racket scheme that could bankrupt New

York's "numbers banks".
VHS: S04232. $14.95.
Laser: CLV. **LD71984. $29.98.**
Abraham Polonsky, USA, 1949, 80 mins.

From Here to Eternity
The talented Fred Zinnemann (*Man for All Seasons, Julia*) perfectly captures the static isolation and boredom that envelops the military personnel in peacetime Hawaii on the eve of American participation in World War II. Zinnemann counterposes social history with riveting drama: Burt Lancaster is a career soldier who seduces a commander's unattended wife, Deborah Kerr. Montgomery Clift staggers social convention by falling for Donna Reed, a prostitute. Frank Sinatra and Ernest Borgnine add quality performances as bitter rivals. Winner of eight Academy Awards, including best picture and director.
VHS: S02923. $19.95.
Laser: LD72185. $39.98.
Fred Zinnemann, USA, 1953, 118 mins.

Gaslight
Ingrid Bergman won her first Oscar for her stunning role as a susceptible young woman who marries the suave, romantic Charles Boyer, never suspecting he is involved in a murderous scandal in Cukor's electrifying mystery drama.
VHS: S00482. $19.98.
George Cukor, USA, 1944, 113 mins.

Gigi
Leslie Caron is the bewitching title character in this dazzling musical that won nine Oscars including Best Picture. Maurice Chevalier sings "Thank Heaven for Little Girls" and doesn't get arrested. Based on a story by Colette, a young girl is trained in Paris to be a courtesan. With Hermione Gingold and Louis Jourdan.
VHS: S07159. $19.95.
Laser: LD70582. $39.99.
Vincente Minnelli, USA, 1958, 116 mins.

Gilda
Rita Hayworth has never been more alluring as the pampered wife of a casino owner in South America who has eyes for her husband's new assistant. The second teaming of Glenn Ford and the gorgeous Hayworth, who steams up the screen by removing just her gloves.
VHS: S02167. $19.95.
Charles Vidor, USA, 1946, 110 mins.

Gold Diggers of 1933
A Busby Berkeley extravaganza that is pure entertainment. In addition to Berkeley's chorus girls, there's Joan Blondell, Ginger Rogers (singing "We're in the Money" in pig Latin), Ruby Keeler and Dick Powell. The original and most famous of the "gold digger" films.
VHS: S01769. $19.98.
Laser: LD70583. $34.98.
Mervyn Le Roy, USA, 1933, 98 mins.

Gone with the Wind
A film beyond criticism, a work that welds together Hollywood classicism and literary adaptation with grace. Victor Fleming is the credited director, though at various times Howard Hawks, George Cukor and Sam Wood helped shape the narrative and rhythm. Ben Hecht worked on the screenplay. William Cameron Menzies was the production designer. With Clark Gable, Vivien Leigh, Leslie Howard, Olivia de Havilland and Hattie McDaniel.
VHS: S00515. $89.98.
Victor Fleming, USA, 1939, 222 mins.

The Grapes of Wrath
Certainly one of the all-time classics, this adaptation of the John Steinbeck novel of the dust bowl migration from Oklahoma to California stars Henry Fonda as Tom Joad, John Carradine as Casey. The film won the Academy Award for Best Director.
VHS: S00525. $19.98.
Laser: LD71013. $49.98.
John Ford, USA, 1940, 129 mins.

A Guy Named Joe
Spencer Tracy is a hot shot WWII pilot until he is killed in action. He is sent from Heaven to protect the surviving members of his squadron. In addition to military advice, he also supplies advice to the lovelorn. With Van Johnson, Irene Dunne, Ward Bond and Lionel Barrymore as the General.
VHS: S07008. $19.98.
Laser: LD76221. $39.98.
Victor Fleming, USA, 1943, 120 mins.

Gigi

Heaven Can Wait
Ernst Lubitsch at his best in this wonderful comedy-fantasy, with Don Ameche as the earthly sinner trying to get admitted to Hell by convincing the Devil that his busy love life has earned him damnation. Gene Tierney is beautiful, and the sparks fly. With Charles Coburn, Marjorie Main.
VHS: S11564. $19.98.
Ernst Lubitsch, USA, 1943, 112 mins

The Heiress
William Wyler directed Olivia de Havilland and an all-star cast in this Oscar-winning classic. De Havilland is the homely, awkward girl who falls in love with the dashing fortune hunter. With brilliant performances by Montgomery Clift and Ralph Richardson, musical score by Aaron Copeland. Based on *Washington Square* by Henry James.
VHS: S03533. $14.95.
William Wyler, USA, 1949, 115 mins.

High Noon
Gary Cooper is the marshall who fights alone for upholding the law when the entire town is paralyzed with fear. Stark settings and shadows heighten the suspense. The most popular film of 1952. With Grace Kelly, Lloyd Bridges, Lon Chaney and Henry Morgan.
VHS: S00567. $14.98.
Laser: CAV. **LD70380. $74.95.**
Laser: CLV. **LD70381. $49.95.**
Fred Zinnemann, USA, 1952, 84 mins.

His Girl Friday
One of the wittiest Hollywood comedies: Rosalind Russell is the ace reporter ready to quit for marriage, Cary Grant, her editor trying to convince her to stay. An escaped murderer puts Russell's determination to test. Sophisticated comedy from Howard Hawks.
VHS: S00572. $14.95.
Laser: Chapter stops, restored, digital master, theatrical trailer. **LD75051. $39.95.**
Howard Hawks, USA, 1940, 95 mins.

Hud
Paul Newman is Hud, a man at odds with his father, tradition and himself. Patricia Neal and Melvyn Douglas both won Academy Awards for their roles, as did James Wong for his brilliant cinematography.
VHS: S00590. $14.95.
Laser: Widescreen. **LD75305. $39.98.**
Martin Ritt, USA, 1963, 112 mins.

I Am a Fugitive from a Chain Gang
They put his feet and hands in irons, but they couldn't shackle his will. A gripping tale about an innocent man brutally victimized by the criminal justice system. Based on a true story, *Fugitive* stars the charismatic Paul Muni (*Scarface*) in the lead role.
VHS: S01706. $19.98.
Laser: Includes original theatrical trailer. **LD71508. $34.98.**
Mervyn Le Roy, USA, 1932, 93 mins.

Imitation of Life
A remake of the original (with Claudette Colbert), underrated director Douglas Sirk's last film draws the audience into an underworld of backstairs, neon gutters and assembly-line chorus-lines, and includes an exploited black maid with a vitally erotic daughter (Susan Kohner) trying to pass for white. With Lana Turner, John Gavin.
VHS: S00611. $14.95.
Douglas Sirk, USA, 1959, 124 mins.

In a Lonely Place
Humphrey Bogart stars as Dixon Steele, an alcoholic Hollywood screenwriter who is prone to violence and accused of murder. Gloria Grahame provides him with an alibi and additional headaches. A hard

The Maltese Falcon

hitting, cynical drama directed by Nicholas Ray from the novel by Dorothy B. Hughes. With Frank Lovejoy, Martha Stewart and Jeff Donnell. B&W.
VHS: S09110. $69.95.
Nicholas Ray, USA, 1950, 91 mins.

In the Heat of the Night
Winner of five Oscars including Best Picture, Rod Steiger stars as a red neck sheriff who grudgingly accepts help from Sidney Poitier, a black big city detective. Music score by Quincy Jones.
Laser: LD74675. $34.98.
Norman Jewison, USA, 1967, 110 mins.

It Happened One Night
Winner of five Academy Awards, this famous screwball comedy stars Clark Gable and Claudette Colbert as two mismatched lovers. Colbert escapes from her millionaire father, who wants to stop her from marrying a worthless playboy.
VHS: S00642. $19.95.
Laser: LD72146. $34.95.
Frank Capra, USA, 1934, 105 mins.

It's a Wonderful Life
James Stewart is George Bailey, trapped in Bedford Falls, until his faith in life is restored by his Guardian Angel in Frank Capra's delightful comedy, nominated for multiple Academy Awards. Donna Reed, Lionel Barrymore, Thomas Mitchell and Beulah Bondi also star.
VHS: S15106. $19.98.
Laser: CAV. LD70387. $89.95.
Laser: CLV. LD71996. $59.98.
Frank Capra, USA, 1946, 160 mins.

Johnny Guitar
A camp and cult favorite, and "the most baroque thing I ever attempted" (Ray), *Johnny Guitar* stars Joan Crawford and Sterling Hayden in an explosive film about two women fighting to control a frontier boomtown that is along the line of a new railroad. This film promotes all kinds of arguing among its

fans: is it a comment on McCarthyism, a gender-bending satire, or a western parody? It's a fun watch, whatever it is. With a wild Mercedes McCambridge. Theme song sung by Peggy Lee.
VHS: S04474. $14.95.
Nicholas Ray, USA, 1954, 110 mins.

Judgment at Nuremberg
Spencer Tracy presides over the trials of German war criminals in this well scripted, star-spangled production. Both Maximillian Schell and writer Abbey Mann won Oscars for this film. With Richard Widmark, Marlene Dietrich, Judy Garland, Montgomery Clift and William Shatner.
VHS: S09918. $29.95.
Laser: LD70605. $39.98.
Stanley Kramer, USA, 1961, 178 mins.

Key Largo
Humphrey Bogart goes to visit the widow of an old war buddy (played by Lauren Bacall), and finds himself in a confrontation with Edward G. Robinson. With an Oscar-winning performance from Claire Trevor.
VHS: S01708. $19.95.
Laser: LD74.39.
John Huston, USA, 1948, 101 mins.

Lady Eve
Barbara Stanwyck is the cardshark, Henry Fonda the millionaire scientist who knows more about snakes than about women. "Neither performer has ever been funnier. The film, based on a story by Monckton Hoffe, is full of classic moments and classic lines; it represents the dizzy high point of Sturges' comedy writing."
VHS: S02941. $19.98.
Laser: LD70044. $34.98.
Preston Sturges, USA, 1941, 97 mins.

Lady from Shanghai
Welles' great thriller stars Rita Hayworth as the millionairess in a web of intrigue which includes

Welles being accused of murder, and concludes in the dazzling climax played out in a hall of mirrors.
VHS: S00715. $19.95.
Orson Welles, USA, 1948, 87 mins.

Laura
Otto Preminger's 1944 film noir is a witty murder mystery with an elaborate cast of characters—detective, beautiful woman and cynical reporter—who get entangled in the plot. Joseph La Shelle won an Academy Award for cinematography. With Gene Tierney, Dana Andrews, Clifton Webb and Vincent Price.
VHS: S18074. $19.95.
Laser: LD71096. $39.98.
Otto Preminger, USA, 1944, 85 mins.

Letter from an Unknown Woman
Louis Jourdan is a famed concert pianist who is unaware he has been adored for years by the very shy Joan Fontaine until one very special night of passion that produces a child. Told in a series of flashbacks, Jourdan learns he is a father much too late to do the right thing.
Laser: CLV, 1 disc, Criterion. LD71450. $49.95.
Max Ophuls, USA, 1948, 87 mins.

Little Caesar
This archetypal gangster film stars Edward G. Robinson as a small town thug who, along with his cohort, heads for the big city and ruthlessly pushes his way to the top of the mob. A landmark film, this action-packed melodrama ia also a probing social commentary on the criminal mind and Depression era America. Director Mervyn LeRoy had such a fascination for the subject that he went so far as to hire three mobsters from Chicago as advisors on the production.
VHS: S14307. $19.98.
Mervyn LeRoy, USA, 1930, 80 mins.

The Lost Weekend
Billy Wilder's classic drama stars Ray Milland in a sobering study of alcoholism. The winner of Oscars for Best Picture, Director, Actor and Screenplay in 1945. Cast includes Frank Faylen, Howard da Silva, Jane Wyman and Philip Terry. The D.T.'s are in glorious black and white.
VHS: S06869. $19.95.
Billy Wilder, USA, 1945, 100 mins.

Magnificent Ambersons
Produced, written and directed by Orson Welles, the follow-up film to *Citizen Kane*, and a work of depth and genius. Welles traces the details of a midwestern family's tragedy. From the novel by Booth Tarkington. With Tim Holt, Anne Baxter and Agnes Moorehead.
VHS: S00804. $19.95.
Laser: LD70417. $99.95.
Orson Welles, USA, 1942, 88 mins.

Magnificent Obsession
Douglas Sirk's elegant transposition of Lloyd Douglas' best seller stars Rock Hudson as an irresponsible playboy who causes the widowhood and blindness of a beautiful woman (Jane Wyman). Lavish color photography and Sirk's brilliant mise-en-scene.
VHS: S00805. $14.95.
Douglas Sirk, USA, 1954, 108 mins.

Maltese Falcon
Even if you've seen this film so often that you know all the dialog, it never ceases to amaze. A search for a priceless statuette provides the action in this classic, excellent film favorite. Noir at its best with great actors Humphrey Bogart, Mary Astor, Sydney Greenstreet and Peter Lorre, based on Dashiell Hammet's thriller.
VHS: S00810. $19.95.
Laser: LD70621. $34.98.
John Huston, USA, 1941, 101 mins.

Meet John Doe
Capra's classic ode to the common man: Gary Cooper is the unemployed worker built into a symbol by a newspaper publisher only to discover he's the object of political ambitions. With Barbara Stanwyck, Edward Arnold, Walter Brennan.
VHS: S00844. $19.95.
Frank Capra, USA, 1941, 123 mins.

Mildred Pierce
Michael Curtiz, who directed *Casablanca* and *Yankee Doodle Dandy*, elevates this Joan Crawford vehicle into a perverse and personal exploration of psychological disorder and collapse. Based on the novel by James M. Cain, Crawford won an Oscar as the hard-working mother with the world's most unpleasant, snobby, status-seeking and boyfriend-stealing daughter (Ann Blyth).
VHS: S02340. $19.98.
Laser: LD70630. $34.98.
Michael Curtiz, USA, 1945, 109 mins.

Mister Roberts
World War II comedy drama about a cargo ship and its crew restless for combat action, with Henry Fonda, James Cagney and Jack Lemmon in an Academy Award winning supporting role as Ensign Pulver.
VHS: S02172. $19.98.
John Ford, USA, 1955, 123 mins.

Mr. Deeds Goes to Town
One of Frank Capra's best films, shot during the height of the Depression. Gary Cooper plays Longfellow Deeds, who inherits 20 million dollars and wants to spend it on people during the height of the Depression. Jean Arthur plays the city reporter who is captivated by the naive Deeds.
VHS: S11163. $19.95.
Frank Capra, USA, 1936, 115 mins.

Mr. Smith Goes to Washington
James Stewart stars in Frank Capra's famous film as the naive Jeff Smith, appointed a U.S. senator by a corrupt political party machine. Famous for its heroic one-man fillibuster, it is a moving vision of honor amid political squalor.
VHS: S00889. $19.95.
Laser: Restored, 3 sides, digital master, chapter stops. LD75054. $44.95.
Frank Capra, USA, 1939, 125 mins.

My Darling Clementine
A genuine American classic, with the climactic shoot-out at the O.K. Corral between Wyatt Earp, Doc Holliday and the vicious Clanton boys. With Henry Fonda, Victor Mature, Walter Brennan, Tim Holt and Linda Darnell.
VHS: S01784. $19.98.
John Ford, USA, 1946, 97 mins.

A Night at the Opera
Along with *Duck Soup*, the funniest of the Marx Brothers films, featuring the boys amidst high society. The five minutes in Groucho's stateroom is one of the funniest continuous laugh inducers on film.
VHS: S02365. $19.95.
Laser: CAV, 2 discs, Criterion. LD70424. $79.95.
Laser: CLV, 1 disc, Criterion. LD70425. $39.95.
Laser: CLV, MGM. LD70643. $43.98.
Sam Wood, USA, 1935, 90 mins.

The Night of the Hunter
Robert Mitchum gives one of his best performances as Harry Powell, a psychotic self-styled preacher who is after the stolen money of a hanged man. Set in a small West Virginia community during the Depression, this is Charles Laughton's only screen credit as a director. He makes the most of the opportunity.
VHS: S04213. $19.98.
Laser: LD70426. $39.95.
Charles Laughton, USA, 1955, 93 mins.

Ninotchka
"Garbo laughs!"—and indeed, she does, in her first romantic comedy as the dour Soviet official who discovers the pleasures of Paris (and Melvyn Douglas) and must choose between romance and duty. Lubitsch at his best.
VHS: S00935. $19.98.
Ernst Lubitsch, USA, 1939, 108 mins.

North by Northwest
One of Hitchcock's greatest films; Cary Grant plays Roger Thornhill, the suave ad man mistaken for a Federal agent, trapped in a web of intrigue that ends with the classic climax atop Mount Rushmore. Eva Marie Saint is the amorous spy, Leo G. Carroll the FBI man with double-edged tactics, and James Mason and Martin Landau the icily villainous traders in state secrets.
VHS: S00938. $19.95.
Laser: CAV, 3 discs, Criterion. LD70427. $124.95.
Laser: CLV, 2 discs, Criterion. LD70428. $69.95.
Alfred Hitchcock, USA, 1959, 136 mins.

Notorious
One of the greatest, if not the greatest, of Hitchcock's

films. A conflict between love and duty pushes the action of this thriller set in Rio just after World War II. A beautiful party girl, the daughter of a Nazi traitor, is enlisted by the U.S. government to marry Nazi spy Claude Rains in order to infiltrate his ring. Cary Grant is the U.S. agent sent to aid her, and one of the great screen romances of all time develops. Beautifully shot, the work of the master at the top of his form.
VHS: S04454. $19.98.
Laser: CAV. LD70429. $99.95.
Laser: CLV. LD70430. $49.95.
Alfred Hitchcock, USA, 1946, 102 mins.

On the Waterfront
Marlon Brando stars in the archetypal role as ex-fighter Terry Malloy, working for Boss Johnny Friendly (Lee J. Cobb) on the gang-ridden waterfront. The classic American movie of redemption, with a great script by Budd Schulberg.
VHS: S00960. $19.95.
Laser: LD72070. $34.95.
Elia Kazan, USA, 1954, 108 mins.

Paths of Glory
A shattering film from Stanley Kubrick, bringing into focus the insanity of war in the story of French General Macready, who, during World War I, orders his men into a futile mission. When the men fail, Macready selects three soldiers for trial and execution for cowardice. With incredible performances from Kirk Douglas, Ralph Meeker, Adolphe Menjou, George Macready, Wayne Morris, Richard Anderson. One of the high points of the American cinema.
VHS: S11433. $19.97.
Laser: LD70433. $49.95.
Stanley Kubrick, USA, 1957, 86 mins.

Pick Up on South Street
A pickpocket inadvertently acquires top-secret microfilm and becomes a target for espionage agents. Starring Richard Widmark and Thelma Ritter. "This lyrical skid-row noir is one of the great movies of the '50s. The Cold War plot pushes McCarthyism to the far side of the moon" (J. Hoberman). Written and directed by Sam Fuller.
VHS: S13608. $19.98.
Sam Fuller, USA, 1953, 80 mins.

The Postman Always Rings Twice
Lana Turner and John Garfield are the illicit lovers in this James M. Cain thriller, who plot to murder the husband who is standing in the way of a real good time. A classic film noir available in the original black and white. Cast includes Cecil Kellaway, Leon

Ames and Hume Cronyn. Remade in 1981.
VHS: S09152. $19.98.
Tay Garnett, USA, 1946, 113 mins.

Public Enemy
James Cagney explodes on the screen in one of his most famous roles as a notorious criminal. This is the film with the infamous "grapefruit scene"! With Jean Harlow and Joan Blondell, from the director of the initial version of *A Star Is Born* and *The Ox-Bow Incident*.
VHS: S01771. $19.95.
Laser: LD71179. $39.98.
William Wellman, USA, 1931, 83 mins.

Rebecca
Hitchcock's first American film, based on a du Maurier gothic romance. With Laurence Olivier and a fine performance by Joan Fontaine as a shy young woman who marries Olivier. Excellent supporting roles by Judith Anderson, George Sanders, Leo G. Carroll and Nigel Bruce.
VHS: S01096. $19.98.
Laser: CAV. LD70441. $124.95.
Laser: CLV. LD70442. $69.95.
Alfred Hitchcock, USA, 1940, 104 mins.

Rebel Without a Cause
James Dean stars in this quintessential story of teenage angst and rebellion. The generation gap movie of the 1950's, with a mixture of innocence, hope, despair and disillusionment set against the injustice and insensitivity of the adult world. One of the greats. With supporting parts by Natalie Wood, Sal Mineo, Nick Adams and Dennis Hopper as Goon. VHS letterboxed.
VHS: S01097. $19.98.
Laser: LD70663. $24.98.
Nicholas Ray, USA, 1955, 111 mins.

Red River
The classic cattle-drive movie, often cited as one of the best American westerns. John Wayne is Thomas Dunson, a tyrant of the trail who alienates his foster son (Montgomery Clift) and causes a sagebrush mutiny. Plenty of two-fisted Western action in this battle of the wills, and featuring a great supporting cast. With Walter Brennan, Joanne Dru, Harry Carey Jr. and Sr., John Ireland and Shelley Winters.
VHS: S01101. $19.95.
Howard Hawks, USA, 1948, 133 mins.

Ruggles of Red Gap
A simply wonderful film, with Charles Laughton as a British butler who is "lost" in a poker game by his master, the Duke of Burnstead (Roland Young) to a rough-and-tumble American rancher. Arriving in the U.S., Laughton's stiff upper lip begins to quiver as he

25 Top Westerns

Duel in the Sun
VHS: S01579. $19.98.

High Noon
VHS: S00567. $14.98.
Laser: CAV. LD70380. $74.95.
Laser: CLV. LD70381. $49.95.

Johnny Guitar
VHS: S04474. $14.95.

Lonely Are the Brave
VHS: S06816. $19.95.
Laser: LD74927. $34.98.

Magnificent Seven
VHS: S00806. $19.95.

Man Who Shot Liberty Valance
VHS: S03891. $19.95.

My Darling Clementine
VHS: S01784. $19.98.

The Naked Spur
VHS: S03674. $19.97.

Once Upon a Time in the West
VHS: S00962. $29.95.

Pursued
VHS: S24109. $14.98.
Laser: LD72017. $49.98.

Ramrod
VHS: S11405. $14.95.

Red River
VHS: S01101. $19.95.

Ride in the Whirlwind
VHS: S25626. $29.98.

Ride the High Country
VHS: S04409. $19.98.

Rio Bravo
VHS: S03588. $19.98.
Laser: LD71679. $39.98.

Rio Grande
VHS: S06186. $19.98.
Laser: LD72023. $39.98.

The Searchers
VHS: S01731. $19.98.

Shane
VHS: S03316. $14.95.
Laser: LD75344. $29.98.

She Wore a Yellow Ribbon
VHS: S03219. Currently unavailable.

Stagecoach
VHS: S01247. $19.98.
Laser: LD74715. $34.98.

The Tall T
VHS: S15893. Currently unavailable.

Unforgiven
DVD: DV60120. $24.98.
VHS: S18724. $19.98.

Virginian
VHS: S02284. Currently unavailable.

The Wild Bunch (Director's Cut)
DVD: DV60121. $24.98.
VHS: S01459. $39.99.
Laser: LD70706. $129.98.

Winchester '73
VHS: S06819. $14.98.

Red River

is introduced by his new employer as Colonel Ruggles and soon has such notable grand dames of cinematic comedy as Mary Boland, ZaSu Pitts and Maude Eburne vying for his attention.
　VHS: S05995. $14.98.
　Laser: LD71570. $34.98.
Leo McCarey, USA, 1935, 90 mins.

Scarlet Street
A great film noir thriller. Edward G. Robinson is the little store cashier who becomes infatuated with and eventually kills a whore (Joan Bennett) and then allows her pimp boyfriend (Dan Duryea) to be executed for the crime. Based on Jean Renoir's *La Chienne* (1931); one of Lang's best works, with brilliant cinematography of New York at night by Milton Krasner.
　VHS: S01166. $19.95.
Fritz Lang, USA, 1945, 105 mins.

The Searchers
Classic John Ford Western starring John Wayne as Ethan Edwards, a Civil War veteran intent on finding the daughters of his murdered brother, who have been captured by the Comanches. With Jeffrey Hunter, Ward Bond and Natalie Wood.
　VHS: S01731. $19.98.
John Ford, USA, 1956, 119 mins.

Shadow of a Doubt
Hitchcock has said that this is his best American film. Joseph Cotten plays the widow-murderer Charley, who dodges the police and joins his relatives in a small California town. Although his niece (Teresa Wright) takes him to her heart, she eventually recognizes him as the murderer. Tense, subtle, brilliant Hitchcock.
　VHS: S07295. $19.95.
　Laser: LD70077. $34.95.
Alfred Hitchcock, USA, 1943, 108 mins.

Singin' in the Rain
Deservedly one of the best-loved movies of all time! An exhilarating and fast-moving musical comedy that traces the transition from silent films to "talkies," starring dancing Gene Kelly and Debbie Reynolds, with Donald O'Connor, Jean Hagen and Rita Moreno.
　DVD: DV60118. $24.98.
　VHS: S15851. $19.98.
　Laser: CAV, 2 discs, Criterion. **LD70463. $89.95.**
　Laser: CLV, 1 disc, Criterion. **LD70464. $39.95.**
　Laser: CLV, MGM. **LD70679. $24.98.**
　Laser: CAV, MGM. **LD70680. $39.98.**
Gene Kelly/Stanley Donen, USA, 1951, 103 mins.

Some Like It Hot
Perhaps the funniest American film of the 1950's, Tony Curtis and Jack Lemmon play two second rate musicians on the run from the Chicago mob, who take to dressing in drag. Marilyn Monroe plays Sugar,

the singer in an all-female band, and Joe E. Brown is an eccentric millionaire in love with Lemmon in drag.
　VHS: S01836. $19.98.
　Laser: CAV, 3 discs, Criterion. **LD70466. $124.95.**
　Laser: Remastered, MGM. **LD71169. $39.98.**
Billy Wilder, USA, 1959, 122 mins.

Spartacus
This edition of Stanley Kubrick's epic classic features additional footage cut from the film's initial release print, plus the complete original overture and extended soundtrack. Kirk Douglas stars as the leader of slaves rebelling against their Roman masters. With Jean Simmons, Laurence Olivier, Tony Curtis, Charles Laughton and Peter Ustinov. The screenplay was written by the legendary Dalton Trumbo, based on a book by Howard Fast. The restored version of this historical spectacle is presented in widescreen letterboxed format.
　VHS: S15075. $19.95.
　Laser: 3 discs: CLV/CAV. Second soundtrack commentary by Kirk Douglas, Peter Ustinov and others. Includes original storyboards and titles as well as newsreel footage of the film's London premiere. **LD70082. $124.95.**
Stanley Kubrick, USA, 1960, 196 mins.

Stagecoach
John Ford at his greatest in a story of nine passengers on a Cheyenne-bound stagecoach, each with a singular reason for the journey, determined to live through the dangerous trip. With John Wayne, Claire Trevor, John Carradine, Andy Devine.
　VHS: S01247. $19.98.
　Laser: LD74715. $34.98.
John Ford, USA, 1939, 96 mins.

A Star Is Born
The second version of the story of a young performer's rise to fame as her actor husband's star fades. Garland's genius makes the story effective, with help from a wonderful performance by James Mason.
　VHS: S01734. $29.98.
　Laser: LD71337. $39.95.
George Cukor, USA, 1954, 154 mins.

The Story of Dr. Wassell
Based on the actual experiences of Dr. Corydon M. Wassell, this film tells the true story of the country doctor who won the Navy Cross for humanitarianism. Dr. Wassell (Gary Cooper) and his love (Laraine Day) are tending to wounded American soldiers in Java. When the Japanese invade, Dr. Wassell learns that only those who can walk are going to be evacuated. Remaining behind with his patients, the doctor manages to save many more of his patients than the Navy thought possible.
　VHS: S27668. $14.98.
Cecil B. De Mille, USA, 1944, 137 mins.

Sunset Boulevard

Strangers on a Train
A brilliantly plotted, diabolically humorous suspense thriller about two murders planned by strangers after an accidental meeting. Hitchcock's mise-en-scene is rich in detail and subtle in its insinuations of guilt and homosexuality. With Robert Walker, Farley Granger, Ruth Roman, based on the novel by Raymond Chandler.
   VHS: S01265. $19.98.
   Laser: LD70686. $24.98.
Alfred Hitchcock, USA, 1951, 101 mins.

Sullivan's Travels
Preston Sturges directed this classic tale of a Hollywood director who is fed up with creating fluff and decides to find out what is really happening in America. To research a "serious" film he disguises himself as a bum and goes on the road. Along the way, Joel McCrea as John L. Sullivan (the director) meets Veronica Lake, William Demarest, Porter Hall, Eric Blore and Franklin Pangborn. Still relevant and profound.
   VHS: S08507. $29.95.
   Laser: LD70084. $34.98.
Preston Sturges, USA, 1941, 91 mins.

Sunset Boulevard
Gloria Swanson is the aging silent film queen and William Holden is the struggling writer in this bizarre, dark and desperate portrait of Hollywood. Winner of three Academy Awards, and one of the greatest American films.
   VHS: S01285. $14.95.
   Laser: LD75268. $34.98.
Billy Wilder, USA, 1950, 110 mins.

Sweet Smell of Success
Burt Lancaster is J.J. Hunsecker, a ruthless and powerful New York columnist, and Tony Curtis is the press agent who will do anything to be in his good graces. Scripted by Clifford Odets and Ernest Lehman. A cult film that was quoted in *Diner*. With Martin Milner, Sam Levene and Barbara Nichols.
   VHS: S07979. $19.98.
   Laser: LD70689. $34.98.
Alexander MacKendrick, USA, 1957, 96 mins.

The Tarnished Angels
Robert Stack, Dorothy Malone and Rock Hudson form a romantic triangle set amidst the tumultuous world of air circus performers. Roger Schulman

(Stack) is a former World War I flying ace who is now a tormented and dedicated racing pilot. Schulman overlooks his trick parachutist wife Laverne (Malone) for his first love, flying. Burke Devlin (Hudson) is a reporter doing a story on the air circus who quickly becomes more fascinated with Laverne than with his story. This powerful drama, based on William Faulkner's novel *Pylon*, is a complicated exploration of desire and obsession. With Troy Donahue and Jack Carson.
   VHS: S27669. $14.98.
Douglas Sirk, USA, 1957, 91 mins.

To Be or Not to Be
In what might be, in the hands of someone other than Ernest Lubitsch, a contradiction of terms—a witty, delightfully satirical comedy set in Nazi-occupied Warsaw—Jack Benny leads a troupe of ham actors in outsmarting the Gestapo and reducing them to ridiculous rubble. Benny gives an animated, beautifully-paced performance and Carole Lombard stars as his wife in her last screen performance.
   VHS: S01350. $19.98.
Ernst Lubitsch, USA, 1942, 102 mins.

Touch of Evil
A masterpiece! This is a complete, restored version. Welles plays a sleazy corrupt police official in a squalid town on the Mexican border, matching wits with Charlton Heston. With Janet Leigh, Marlene Dietrich and Zsa Zsa Gabor.
   VHS: S01990. $19.98.
   Laser: LD70091. $34.98.
Orson Welles, USA, 1958, 108 mins.

The Treasure of the Sierra Madre
Pauline Kael calls this "one of the strongest of all American movies." Three Americans strike it rich and greed takes over. With Humphrey Bogart, Walter Huston, Tim Holt and Robert Blake, based on the novel by B. Traven.
   VHS: S01368. $19.95.
   Laser: LD70699. $39.98.
John Huston, USA, 1948, 120 mins.

Unfaithfully Yours
Rex Harrison is a famous conductor blessed with both a brilliant career and a young wife. This sidesplitting classic comedy by Sturges follows Rex's downfall when his jealous spying on his wife leads him to believe she's having an affair.
   VHS: S05019. $59.98.
Preston Sturges, USA, 1948, 105 mins.

Vertigo
The elaborately constructed murder story in which an ex-cop who suffers from vertigo is the innocent pawn, is a masterful study of sexual obsession, and one of Hitchcock's best films. With James Stewart, Kim Novak, Barbara Bel Geddes. VHS fully restored, THX, letterboxed.
   VHS: S01795. $19.95.
   Laser: LD70094. $79.95.
Alfred Hitchcock, USA, 1958, 95 mins.

The Wizard of Oz
Judy Garland, Ray Bolger, Jack Haley, Bert Lahr, Frank Morgan, Margaret Hamilton, Billie Burke and Toto in the land of Oz, in MGM's great, Technicolor fantasy where Judy follows the Yellow Brick Road.
   DVD: DV60104. $24.98.
   VHS: S09609. $19.95.
   Laser: CLV, MGM. LD70709. $24.98.
   Laser: CAV, Criterion. LD71215. $99.95.
Victor Fleming, USA, 1939, 101 mins.

The Women
Brilliant, witty comedy with a stellar cast of women: Norma Shearer, Joan Crawford, Rosalind Russell, Mary Boland, Paulette Goddard and Joan Fontaine. No men appear in the film, but men is what the film is all about. Superb American comedy, with perhaps the wittiest dialog ever put on screen. A must-see.
   VHS: S01480. $19.95.
George Cukor, USA, 1939, 133 mins.

Written on the Wind
The lurid lifestyles of the very rich and famous are the subject of this box office champ of 1957 from director Douglas Sirk. Robert Stack is the irresponsible son of an oil magnate. Lauren Bacall is his suffering wife. Rock Hudson plays his best friend and Dorothy Malone won an Oscar for her role as the nymphomaniac sister. Classy trash.
   VHS: S07144. $14.95.
Douglas Sirk, USA, 1956, 99 mins.

The Algonquin Crowd

Bon mots, quick quips and a flare for sophisticated dialogue mark these films, written by the most celebrated literary group to hold court around a round table at New York's Algonquin Hotel.

Adam's Rib
Spencer Tracy and Katharine Hepburn in one of their all-time great appearances as married attorneys who find themselves on opposite sides of a murder case in which Judy Holliday is the accused.
DVD: DV60057. $24.98.
VHS: S03456. $19.95.
Laser: LD70202. $49.98.
George Cukor, USA, 1949, 101 mins.

Animal Crackers
The four Marx Brothers in the uproariously funny film based on the George S. Kaufman musical. Groucho introduced the character of Captain Spaulding, whose song became the theme song of "You Bet Your Life."
VHS: S00053. $19.95.
Laser: LD70096. $34.98.
Victor Heerman, USA, 1930, 98 mins.

Bachelor Mother
A department store employee, played buoyantly by Ginger Rogers, discovers an abandoned baby and is quickly mistaken for its mother; the misunderstandings continue as the store owner's son is then thought to be the baby's father. A delightful comedy, also starring David Niven, Charles Coburn and Frank Albertson.
VHS: S02150. $19.95.
Garson Kanin, USA, 1939, 82 mins.

Born Yesterday
Judy Holliday won the Best Actress Oscar for her funny role as the dumb blond girlfriend of Broderick Crawford, a corrupt millionaire junk dealer. Brock, a man with social ambitions, is embarassed by Billie's crass behavior and hires a writer, William Holden, to smarten her up. A classic comedy.
VHS: S03863. $19.95.
George Cukor, USA, 1950, 103 mins.

Captains Courageous
Spencer Tracy won the Oscar for Best Actor for his portrayal of Manuel, the Portuguese fisherman who teaches a millionaire's spoiled son human values in this adaptation of Rudyard Kipling's popular story. With Lionel Barrymore, Melvyn Douglas and Mickey Rooney.
VHS: S01788. $19.98.
Laser: LD71159. $34.98.
Victor Fleming, USA, 1937, 118 mins.

The Cocoanuts
The hilarious, never-before-released first film of the Marx Brothers, shot on a New York sound stage, with some terrific scenes, including the "Why a duck?" routine, a hilarious auction, and a wonderful classic "viaduct" routine. With Groucho, Harpo, Chico and Zeppo.
VHS: S09458. $19.95.
Joseph Santley/Robert Florey, USA, 1929, 96 mins.

Foreign Correspondent
Hitchcock's second American film was a return to the flawless architecture of his best British thrillers. Set in London and Amsterdam during the war, the film is an entertaining blend of suspense and dark humor involving an American reporter sent to cover the European situation. Among the highlights are the attempted murder atop Westminster Cathedral, a brilliant sequence in an isolated Dutch windmill and an assassination scene in pouring rain. With Herbert Marshall, Joel McCrea, Laraine Day.
VHS: S02020. $19.98.
Laser: LD70575. $39.98.
Alfred Hitchcock, USA, 1940, 120 mins.

Front Page
Produced by Howard Hughes, the classic Ben Hecht/Charles MacArthur story about the newspaper business. When a convict escapes, Hily Johnson (Pat O'Brien, in his film debut), a young reporter about to leave journalism and enter marriage, is drawn back to work. He and Walter Burns (Adolphe Menjou), the managing editor, hide the convict in a roll-top desk in the press room in their obsessive search for a sensational story.
VHS: S18174. $19.95.
Lewis Milestone, USA, 1931, 101 mins.

Girl Can't Help It
Raucous comedy with Jayne Mansfield as the "dumb bombshell" and Edmond O'Brien as her retired racketeer boyfriend. Jayne is trying to get into show biz, Tom Ewell is the comic talent agent helping out. With Fats Domino, The Platters, Gene Vincent.
VHS: S00503. $59.98.
Frank Tashlin, USA, 1956, 99 mins.

The Green Pastures
A heavily criticized adaptation of Marc Connelly's Pulitzer prize-winning stage play that interprets African-American tales of spirituality and oral black storytelling through a collection of vignettes on various Biblical stories and figures. With Rex Ingram, Oscar Polk, Eddie Anderson and Frank Wilson.
VHS: S02528. $19.98.
William Keighley/Marc Connelly, USA, 1936, 90 mins.

His Girl Friday
One of the wittiest Hollywood comedies: Rosalind Russell is the ace reporter ready to quit for marriage, Cary Grant, her editor trying to convince her to stay. An escaped murderer puts Russell's determination to test. Sophisticated comedy from Howard Hawks.
VHS: S00572. $14.95.
Laser: Chapter stops, restored, digital master, theatrical trailer. LD75051. $39.95.
Howard Hawks, USA, 1940, 95 mins.

I Married a Witch
A Salem witch and her sorcerer father come back to haunt the descendant of the Puritan who had them burned. This is a delightful comedy by Thorne Smith (*Topper*) and shows Fredric March and Veronica Lake in top form. This pre-*Bewitched* farce also features Susan Hayward and Robert Benchley.
VHS: S02534. $19.98.
Rene Clair, USA, 1942, 82 mins.

The Man Who Came to Dinner
Based on the play by George Kaufman and Moss Hart, this delightful film is a caricature of Alexander Wolcott and is the story of an acid-tongued radio celebrity who breaks his hip on a lecture tour. Hilarity ensues as he terrorizes the suburban home where he recuperates. With Bette Davis, Monty Woolley, Ann Sheridan, Jimmy Durante (in a spoof of Harpo Marx) and Reginald Gardiner (in a spoof of Noel Coward).
VHS: S11626. $19.95.
Laser: LD74677. $34.98.
William Keighley, USA, 1941, 112 mins.

Merton of the Movies
An adaptation of George S. Kaufman and Marc Connelly's comedy about the early days of

Born Yesterday

Hollywood. The plot concerns a sweet, naive dreamer (Red Skelton) who arrives in Hollywood and is befriended by a stunt double (Virginia O'Brien). She helps him land his first break. With Gloria Grahame, Alan Mowbray and Hugo Haas.
VHS: S19564. $19.98.
Robert Alton, USA, 1947, 83 mins.

Next Time I Marry
In this excellent comedy, Lucille Ball is heir to a $20 million fortune but is forced to marry a poor ditch digger in order to get it. Worse than that, she must travel cross-country with him in a tiny trailer—a situation loaded with laughs and surprises.
VHS: S13997. $19.98.
Garson Kanin, USA, 1938, 65 mins.

Pat and Mike
Katharine Hepburn and Spencer Tracy team up for their seventh film, as a top female athlete and a shady sports promoter. Ruth Gordon and Garson Kanin supplied the script, which features many popular golf and tennis pros, like Babe Didrikson Zaharias and Gussie Moran, in bit parts. Watch for Charles Bronson as a judo trained thug.
VHS: S09151. $19.98.
George Cukor, USA, 1952, 95 mins.

Rasputin and the Empress
Three members of the Barrymore family—John, Ethel and Lionel—enact the final days of the Czar's reign, when Rasputin (Lionel) cured the Czar's son of hemophilia and exerted tremendous influence over the family. Some impressive sets, decor and costumes. Prince Youssoupoff filed a suit against MGM claiming historical inaccuracies. With Diana Wynyard and Ralph Morgan.
VHS: S18507. $19.98.
Richard Boleslawski, USA, 1933, 133 mins.

Reunion in France
John Wayne is a wounded RAF pilot who seeks the help of Joan Crawford, a French aristocrat who's fallen on hard times. Her mansion has been turned into a coal allotment bureau by the Nazis and she is forced to find employment as a shop girl. She also believes her ex-boyfriend Philip Dorn is working for the enemy. Can she and the Yank flyer escape to England?
VHS: S12137. $19.95.
Jules Dassin, USA, 1942, 104 mins.

Roman Scandals
Comedian Eddie Cantor leaves behind the realities of the Depression for a fantasy trip to Ancient Rome. Lots of fun and plenty of musical numbers. With Gloria Stuart, Ruth Etting, Edward Arnold and Verree Teasdale. Watch closely for Lucille Ball in the chorus of one of the Busby Berkeley production numbers.
VHS: S15490. $19.98.
Laser: LD75250. $34.98.
Frank Tuttle, USA, 1933, 93 mins.

Saboteur
Wartime thriller starring Robert Cummings as an aircraft factory worker who witnesses the firebombing of his plant by a Nazi agent, and finds himself accused of the crime. Hitchcock's first film with an entire cast from the U.S.
VHS: S01730. $19.95.
Laser: LD70073. $34.95.
Alfred Hitchcock, USA, 1942, 108 mins.

The Senator Was Indiscreet
William Powell wants to be President of the United States. The only thing that may stop him is his own diary, filled with years of political deals and shenanigans. George S. Kaufman's only shot at directing a movie proves to be a success. With Peter Lind Hayes and Ella Raines.
VHS: S04245. $19.95.
George S. Kaufman, USA, 1947, 81 mins.

The Sin of Madelon Claudet
A first-rate sobber about a mother who must give up everything so that her illegitimate son will have a good life. Helen Hayes won an Academy Award for her tragic portrayal of this woman who pays such a terrible price for the choices she is forced to make in her life.
VHS: S13568. $19.98.
Edgar Selwyn, USA, 1931, 74 mins.

A Star Is Born (1937)
Janet Gaynor and Fredric March star in the first version of *A Star Is Born*, the story of a young girl

whose career is on the rise while that of her husband is on the wane. Adolphe Menjou, May Robson and Andy Devine co-star.
VHS: S18187. $24.95.
Laser: LD70684. $39.98.
William Wellman, USA, 1937, 112 mins.

A Star Is Born (1954)
The second version of the story of a young performer's rise to fame as her actor husband's star fades. Garland's genius makes the story effective, with help from a wonderful performance by James Mason.
VHS: S01734. $29.98.
Laser: LD71337. $39.95.
George Cukor, USA, 1954, 154 mins.

A Star Is Born (1976)
Barbra Streisand and Kris Kristofferson are the leads in this third version. A talented wife whose star is on the rise quickly overshadows her husband as his career fades. Streisand sings "Evergreen," which won an Oscar for Best Song. With Gary Busey, Oliver Clark and Paul Mazursky.
VHS: S07006. $19.98.
Laser: Letterboxed. LD71470. $39.98.
Frank Pierson, USA, 1976, 140 mins.

Suzy
In their lone appearance together, Jean Harlow and Cary Grant star in this World War II-era tale about an American chorus girl marooned in London who turns up in Paris and falls for an enigmatic and charismatic playboy (Grant). With Franchot Tone, Lewis Stone and Benita Hume. Some startling aviation sequences, appropriated from the negative of the classic *Hell's Angels*. Written by Dorothy Parker.
VHS: S17782. $19.98.
George Fitzmaurice, USA, 1936, 93 mins.

Twentieth Century
Howard Hawks' classic with John Barrymore as the maniacal Broadway director who takes talented starlet Carole Lombard and transforms her into a smashing success adored by the public and press. But when Lombard tires of Barrymore's manic-excessive ways, she heads to Hollywood for even greater stardom, but possibly loses the one good thing in her life—Barrymore. A treasure.
VHS: S07752. $19.95.
Howard Hawks, USA, 1934, 91 mins.

A Star Is Born

50 Great Silent Masterpieces

90 Degrees South: With Scott to the Antarctic

Herbert G. Ponting's chronicle of Captain Robert Scott's heroic and ultimately tragic race for the South Pole was originally released in 1913. Ponting, a renowned still photographer, dedicated his life to the memory of Scott, who died with his entire team on the return trip from the pole after losing the race to Amundsen. Twenty years after his friend's death, Ponting added narration to the film, drawing from Scott's diary entries. This is the deeply personal tribute to the heartbreaking last days of the doomed expedition.
VHS: S16434. $39.95.
Laser: CLV/CAV. **LD71592. $29.95.**
Herbert G. Ponting, Great Britain, 1933, 72 mins.

African-American Film Heritage Series II: Body and Soul

One of six films which continue to represent the largely unknown, early African-American film tradition, *Body and Soul* is "An extremely rare film—featuring the first screen appearance by Paul Robeson. Robeson plays the dual role of a preacher who preys on the people and the heroine, and of his brother, a good man. The film, one of the productions of Oscar Micheaux, ran into trouble with the New York censors, and had to change the preacher's role so that he is first a preacher, then detective, and finally an upstanding bourgeois future husband for the heroine, who awakens from her nightmare experience to a happy ending" (*Frame By Frame: A Black Filmography*). Directed by Oscar Micheaux, USA, 1924.
VHS: S10260. $24.95.

The Birth of a Nation

D.W. Griffith's debut feature is credited with revolutionizing form and content in the cinema. Its epic story assessed the political, social, racial and personal consequences of the Civil War on American life, from the perspective of two families, the Southern Stonemans and the Northern Camerons. The story intersects the personal with the historic and political, Lincoln's assassination, the Reconstruction and the rise of the Ku Klux Klan. This deluxe edition includes a 30-minute documentary on the making of the film, with interviews, archival footage and outtakes. Adapted from Thomas Dixon's novel and play *The Clansman*. With Lillian Gish, Mae Marsh, Miriam Cooper and filmmaker Raoul Walsh. Cinematography by Billy Bitzer and Karl Brown.
VHS: S18433. $39.95.
Laser: LD70883. $79.95.
D.W. Griffith, USA, 1914, 187 mins.

Blood and Sand

In one of his most famous roles, Rudolph Valentino portrays a poor boy who works his way up to becoming a famous matador. In the process he marries his childhood sweetheart but falls into the clutches of a beautiful society woman (Nita Naldi). Shining through gloriously in every shot of the film is the astonishing grace that made Valentino one of the most popular stars in the history of the cinema. Also included is a rare Valentino short. Piano score.
VHS: S00147. $29.95.
Fred Niblo, USA, 1922, 87 mins.

Broken Blossoms

D.W. Griffith's pastoral effort set in a Dickensian London about the oppression of a frail young street urchin desperate to escape her bleak circumstances. The young woman falls in love with a sympathetic Chinese missionary, who shields her from her tyrannical and abusive father. "There are stretches of Griffith poetry, a marvelous use of light and shadow in cameraman Billy Bitzer's evocation of foggy Limehouse, and a truly unforgettable performance from Lillian Gish" (*Time Out*). With Richard Barthelmess and Donald Crisp. Newly remastered print struck from an archival source.
VHS: S18434. $24.95.
D.W. Griffith, USA, 1919, 90 mins.

Cabinet of Dr. Caligari

The great Expressionist classic with Werner Krauss as Caligari, the fairground showman who hypnotizes his servant (Conrad Veidt) into committing murder at night. Famous for its distorted painted sets, its grotesque camera angles and its atmospheric horror, this cinematic landmark is now newly mastered from a 35mm archive print with an orchestral score. English intertitles.
DVD: DV60034. $29.95.
VHS: S10765. $29.95.
Laser: LD75516. $49.99.
Robert Wiene, Germany, 1919, 52 mins.

Cabiria

The most ambitious and spectacular of the historical epics for which Italy was famous before World War I, *Cabiria* set the standard for big budget, feature-length movies and opened the way for Griffith and DeMille. During the war between Carthage and Rome, a girl—Cabiria—is separated from her parents. In her odyssey through the world of ancient Rome, she encounters an erupting volcano, the barbaric splendor of Carthage, human sacrifice and Hannibal crossing the Alps. Mastered from a 35mm archive print using variable speed projection to match the original hand cranked camera, *Cabiria* features a newly recorded soundtrack from the original 1914 score.
VHS: S06218. $39.95.
Giovanni Pastrone, Italy, 1914, 123 mins.

City Lights

One of Chaplin's most highly acclaimed films, a silent film in the era of talkies that demonstrated Chaplin's genius. The Little Tramp falls in love with a beautiful, blind flower girl and sets out to raise money for an operation to cure her.
VHS: S00245. $19.98.
Laser: LD72318. $69.98.
Charles Chaplin, USA, 1931, 86 mins.

The Crowd

An ordinary man struggles to maintain his individuality in a heartless city. Featuring James Murray as John, a store clerk, and Eleanor Boardman as his wife Mary. *The Crowd* is one of the most important films of the silent era; its visual innovations still astonish viewers, and the relevance of its theme has only increased over the years" (*Pacific Film Archive*).
VHS: S09279. $29.95.
King Vidor, USA, 1928, 104 mins.

David Copperfield

Charles Dickens' unforgettable tale of an orphan vagabond is touchingly realized in this early, silent, color-tinted film. This is the first feature length adaptation of the literary masterwork.
VHS: S23825. $24.95.
Thomas Bentley, Great Britain, 1913, 55 mins.

Destiny

Lang's first critical success, also known as *Between Two Worlds* or *Beyond the Wall*, an allegory about a confrontation between Death and a girl's love and devotion. Lang here reveals his mastery of the medium, particularly in the architectural design in

the film. Silent.
VHS: S00327. $29.95.
Fritz Lang, Germany, 1921, 95 mins.

Earth

A great masterpiece—the fourth and last silent film by Dovzhenko, a lyrical evocation of his native Ukraine, the theme of the life cycle of man developed through constant juxtaposition and intertwining of images of life and death. Ultimately very moving, a film poem of inestimable beauty. Silent with English subtitles.
VHS: S00389. $29.95.
Alexander Dovzhenko, USSR, 1930, 88 mins.

Faust

Murnau's last German production before going to Hollywood is a lavish one, inspired by Romantic painters like Caspar David Friedrich. Gosta Ekman is the elderly professor who sells his soul to the devil, Emil Jannings plays Mephistopholes and Camilla Horn is Marguerite. This version is mastered from a restored print. Silent with music track, English intertitles.
VHS: S00437. $29.95.
Friedrich W. Murnau, Germany, 1926, 117 mins.

Films of Harold Lloyd

A collection of early Harold Lloyd shorts including *The Cinema Director* (1916), *Non-Stop Kid* (1918), *Why Pick on Me* (1918), *On the Fire* (1919); *Ring up the Curtain* (1919), *Just Neighbors* (1919) and *Haunted Spooks* (1920). 120 mins.
VHS: S02353. $29.95.

The Four Horsemen of the Apocalypse

Rudolph Valentino became a certified star for his work in this film, especially his notorious tango scene. Based on Blasco Ibanez' novel, this is a story of two brothers who end up on opposing sides in World War I. Stark imagery make this unforgettable anti-war film a silent classic.
VHS: S23111. $24.95.
Rex Ingram, USA, 1921, 114 mins.

A Girl in Every Port

In the film that influential Swiss writer Blaise

Cendrars declared "definitely marked the first appearance of contemporary cinema," sailor Spike Madden (Victor McLaglen) discovers that he has competition for his girlfriends in various ports of call. He finally overtakes his rival, Salami (Robert Armstrong), another sailor, and after a fight they become fast friends. When Madden falls in love with gold digging vamp Marie (Louise Brooks), Salami must decide whether to tell his friend the truth about her. Orchestra score.
VHS: S31173. $24.95.
Howard Hawks, USA, 1928, 79 mins.

The Gold Rush

Charlie Chaplin's immortal, icon-making film, which pits Chaplin as the Little Tramp against the elements of the Yukon, ruthless prospectors and the affections of a dance hall girl. This is the film that includes the classic scene of Chaplin eating his leather shoe and shows his wooden cabin precariously balanced on the edge of a cliff. Silent with music track.
VHS: S26489. $19.95.
Laser: CLV. **LD70099. $39.95.**
Charles Chaplin, USA, 1925, 82 mins.

Grass

In 1924, neophyte filmmakers Merian C. Cooper and Ernest Schoedsack joined forces with journalist and sometime spy Marguerite Harrison and set off to film an adventure. They found excitement, danger and unparalleled drama in the migration of the Bakhtiari tribe of Persia. Each year, more than 50 thousand people and half a million animals crossed the snow-covered mountain ranges and torrential rapids to take their herds to pasture. Few have seen *Grass* outside of archives. This issue is struck from the original negative, with an updated soundtrack by Iranian Gholam Hussein Janati Ataie.
VHS: S16429. $39.95.
Laser: CLV/CAV. Digitally mastered and transferred. **LD71815. $34.95.**
Merian Cooper/Ernest Schoedsack, USA, 1925, 70 mins.

Greed

One of the wonders of film, this miracle of filmmaking, made by Erich von Stroheim against the

Cabines of Dr. Caligari

most impossible of odds, stars Gibson Gowland as McTeague, a San Francisco dentist, who marries ZaSu Pitts, the daughter of German immigrants. When Trina (Pitts) becomes greedy, McTeague becomes a drunken tramp and ends up killing her. A powerful, powerful masterpiece. This tape includes a prologue by film historian Kevin Brownlow, who describes the controversy surrounding the original cuts made to the film by the studio.
VHS: S09281. $29.95.
Laser: LD70592. $39.98.
Erich von Stroheim, USA, 1924, 133 mins.

Hell's Hinges
William S. Hart, the first great star of the Westerns, plays Blaze Tracy, a notorious outlaw in the town of Hell's Hinges. When a new minister pulls into town, Blaze is transformed by the sight of the minister's daughter. One of the great silent Westerns.
VHS: S01879. $29.95.
William S. Hart, USA, 1916, 65 mins.

Intolerance
Four separate stories are interwoven: the fall of Babylon, the death of Christ, the massacre of the Hugenots, and a modern drama—all cross-cut and building with enormous energy to a thrilling chase and finale. Far ahead of its time, Griffith created a spectacle which audiences of the day did not accept but which has become a classic of world cinema. This specially packaged double cassette edition of *Intolerance* has been remastered using variable speed projection and color tints to match the original release prints, making it the best version available anywhere. Tinted with organ score.
VHS: S13048. $29.95.
Laser: CAV. LD71052. $69.95.
D.W. Griffith, USA, 1919, 190 min.

It
Clara Bow stars with Gary Cooper and Elinor Glyn. Silent with music track.
VHS: S07279. $19.95.
Laser: LD70097. $39.95.
Clarence Badger, USA, 1927, 71 mins.

Italian
The story of Italian immigrants in the slums of New York, notable for its realism; produced by Thomas Ince, and starring George Beban. Silent with music score. USA, 1915, 78 mins.
VHS: S07487. $24.95.

The Italian Straw Hat
Pauline Kael called *The Italian Straw Hat* "one of the funniest films ever made and one of the most elegant as well." Based on an immensely popular farce by Eugene Labiche, the plot is a breezy tale about a bridegroom whose horse has a taste for ladies' hats. Rene Clair substituted sight gags for the clever word play, directed the action at a breakneck pace, and "screwball comedy" was born. This version is transferred from the restored negative, with a newly added musical score by Raymond Alessandrini. Starring Albert Prejean. Silent.
VHS: S16562. $39.95.
Rene Clair, France, 1927, 74 mins.

King of Kings
Cecil B. De Mille's opulent Hollywoodization of the new testament, with casts of thousands, in its original silent (with music track) re-incarnation. Featured are H.B. Warner, Dorothy Cumming, Ernest Torrence, Joseph Schildkraut and William Boyd. B&W, with the Resurrection sequence in color.
VHS: S03368. $29.95.
Cecil B. De Mille, USA, 1927, 115 mins.

The Last Laugh
One of the major works of German silent cinema, Murnau's class drama depicts the fall of the respected, aging, hotel doorman (Emil Jannings) of a posh Berlin hotel, who is cruelly stripped of his position and reduced to a bathroom attendant. The film was groundbreaking for its expressive, mobile camera work, which imparts information visually, without subtitles. "The camera on a trolley glides, rises, zooms, or weaves where the story takes it. The camera takes part in the action and becomes a *character* in the drama" (Marcel Carne). With Max Hiller, Maly Delschaft and Hans Unterkirchen.
VHS: S00723. $24.95.
Laser: Includes new orchestral score. LD72446. $49.95.
Friedrich W. Murnau, Germany, 1924, 91 mins.

Man with the Movie Camera
Dziga Vertov's masterpiece is an application of "life as it is lived." It makes the cameraman the hero, and is one of the most dynamic experiments with montage; the film also uses trick photography, animation, slow motion and speeded-up shots. It "is a study in truth on an almost philosophical level…It does deliberately what others try hard to avoid—destroys its own illusions, in the hope that reality will emerge from the process not as a creature of screen illusion but as a liberated spirit" (*Films and Filming*). Silent.
VHS: S00821. $29.95.
Dziga Vertov, USSR, 1928, 69 mins.

Marvelous Melies
A collection of great films by the great pioneer magician of the cinema, Georges Melies: *A Trip to the Moon, Paris to Monte Carlo, The Doctor's Secret, Kingdom of the Fairies, The Enchanted Well* and *The Conquest of the Pole*.
VHS: S05789. $29.95.
Georges Melies, France, 60 mins.

Max Linder
By 1910 Max Linder was an internationally popular comic, typically playing a dapper dandy of the idle rich. He developed a slapstick style that anticipated Mack Sennett and Chaplin. His popularity was at its peak in 1914, when he was called up for World War I. With original French titles. Silent.
VHS: S00833. $29.95.
Max Linder, France, 1911-13

The Merry Widow
Von Stroheim's stylish, witty and grotesque adaptation of Franz Lehar's operetta of sadism and fetishism, in which a prince (John Gilbert) is ordered to woo a wealthy American widow (Mae Murray). One of several films over which producer Irving Thalberg went to battle with the extravagant von Stroheim: his long scenes with shots of the contents of the Baron's wardrobe—boots, shoes, slippers, shoe trees—made Thalberg wonder who was the true foot fetishist. Look for a young Clark Gable as an extra.
VHS: S31170. $24.95.
Erich von Stroheim, USA, 1925, 113 mins.

Modern Times
Charlie Chaplin's silent homage to the human spirit, in which Chaplin is the victim of industrial boom. He plays the factory worker gone looney by the assembly line who falls in love with a down-and-out young lady and tries through various and eccentric means to find a bit of financial peace. A great comedy, and a great film.
VHS: S00866. $19.98.
Charles Chaplin, USA, 1936, 89 mins.

Napoleon
A masterpiece of world cinema, employing a variety of new techniques, including triple screen and mobile use of the camera by strapping it to a galloping horse. Long thought to be lost, the film has been reconstructed and is presented with a sound track composed by Carmine Coppola.
VHS: S00917. $79.95.
Abel Gance, France, 1927, 235 mins.

Nosferatu
One of Murnau's best known films, *Nosferatu*'s eerie telling of the Dracula story was filmed on location in the mountains, towns, and castles of Bavaria. This German Expressionist symphony of horror is brilliantly infused with the subtle tones of nature: both pure and fresh, as well as twisted and sinister. Newly restored and color tinted, this version was remastered from a 35mm negative and includes recently discovered scenes and inter-titles freshly translated from the original German script. At 84 minutes, it is the most complete version available on home video.
DVD: DV60031. $29.95.
VHS: S15038. $29.95.
Friedrich W. Murnau, Germany, 1922, 84 mins.

Orphans of the Storm
Two innocent orphans (Lillian and Dorothy Gish) arrive in Paris just prior to the French Revolution and are exploited, separated, and nearly find each other again—until they become involved in the Revolution themselves. A luxurious, large-scale Griffith spectacle. Digitally remastered.
VHS: S14444. $29.95.
Laser: CLV. LD72013. $49.99.
D.W. Griffith, USA, 1921, 190 mins.

Our Hospitality/Sherlock Jr.

Keaton's hilarious satire on the Hatfield-McCoy family feud was his second feature. Brilliantly set against the backdrop of early rail travel in 1831, the film features Keaton as the scion of an old Southern family, who carelessly starts dating from a feuding family. In *Sherlock Jr.* Keaton plays a projectionist who is framed for theft by a jealous rival for the hand of a beautiful girl. Contains an astonishing sequence in which Keaton imagines himself to be a detective, and makes his way into the action of the movie he is projecting on screen. This sequence made Keaton an early favorite of the surrealists. Newly mastered. Silent with music track.
VHS: $23030. $29.95.
Buster Keaton, USA, 1923/1924

A Page of Madness

Made in 1926 and rediscovered in 1971, this rare Japanese silent film is an hallucinatory study of a janitor of an asylum who attempts to release his wife, who is an inmate there, having been committed after trying to kill herself and her baby. This amazing film by the great Japanese film pioneer Kinugasa relies entirely on visual effects to tell its story. Superimpositions, extreme camera angles and jarring close-ups tell the tale from the janitor's point of view.
VHS: $30189. $24.95.
Teinosuke Kinugasa, Japan, 1926, 75 mins.

Pandora's Box

G.W. Pabst's baroque interpretation of Wedekind's *Lulu* plays is an eerie depiction of erotic obsession and sexual abandon. The action moves between Berlin and London, as Lulu (Louise Brooks), a beautiful, charismatic chorus girl, orchestrates a succession of casual affairs until her fateful encounter with Jack the Ripper. With Fritz Kortner, Franz Lederer and Carl Goetz. Silent with music track. English titles.
VHS: $00990. $24.95.
G.W. Pabst, Germany, 1928, 110 mins.

Seventh Heaven

"*Seventh Heaven* tracks the transformational love of Farrell and Gaynor from the sewers to the stars, across time and space, and beyond death itself, affirming triumphantly that melodrama can mean much more than just an excuse for a good weep" (*Time Out Film Guide*). Janet Gaynor won an Oscar for her portrayal of a mistreated Paris street waif redeemed by cockney sewer man Charles Farrell.
VHS: $31171. $24.95.
Frank Borzage, USA, 1927, 119 mins.

The Sheik

The original famous version of Rudolph Valentino's romantic melodrama, as Valentino (Sheik Ahmed) rescues a proud English girl (Agnes Ayres) disguised as a slave. The film that made Valentino an international idol.
VHS: $09401. $19.98.
George Melford, USA, 1921, 80 mins.

The Short Films of Mary Pickford

America's silent sweetheart in several of her most endearing film shorts. Includes *In Old Madrid* (10 mins.), *Lonely Villa* (10 mins.), *Sweet Memories* (10 mins.), *Her First Biscuits* (5 mins.), *The Female of the Species* (10 mins.), *100% Canadian* (10 mins.), *The New York Hat* (10 mins.), *Violin Maker of Cremona* (10 mins) and *1776 or The Hessian Renegades)* (10 mins.).
VHS: $14929. $29.95.

Strike

One of the most original debuts in film history, *Strike* is a brilliant mixture of agit-prop techniques and comic-grotesque stylization in the telling of a factory workers' strike in Czarist Russia in 1912 and the brutal suppression of the strike. Silent.
VHS: $01271. $29.95.
Sergei Eisenstein, USSR, 1924, 75 mins.

The Strong Man

Harry Langdon stars in this wonderful silent comedy, newly restored by Kevin Brownlow and David Gill. A World War I veteran comes to America with a travelling show, hoping to meet the girl whose letters gave him hope at the front. Musical score compiled by Harry Langdon. Arranged and performed by Eric Beheim. Includes a 20-minute short, *His Marriage Vow.*
VHS: $10917. $29.95.
Frank Capra, USA, 1926, 94 mins.

Sunrise

Although this was Murnau's first Hollywood film, he scripted it with Carl Mayer while still in Germany. The story concerns the marriage of a peasant couple whose honeymoon in the big city is detoured by a sultry seductress. But the film is neither trite nor melodramatic; Murnau's sets and camera angles imbue the images with a poetic lyricism that reveals the characters' psychological states. Easily his most perfect film, Murnau's *Sunrise* was named the "Greatest film of all time," in a recent *Cahiers du Cinema* Critic's Poll. With George O'Brien, Janet Gaynor and Margaret Livingston.
VHS: $07782. $29.95.
Laser: Outtakes, digital transfer. **LD76401. $49.98.**
Friedrich W. Murnau, USA, 1927, 97 mins.

Tess of the Storm Country

Mary Pickford stars in this silent revival of the story of a little girl in a fishing village. With Lloyd Hughes, Gloria Hope, David Torrence and Jean Hersholt. Original organ score.
VHS: $30553. $19.95.
John S. Robertson, USA, 1922, 137 mins.

That Girl Montana

Blanche Sweet is the daughter of a crooked cardshark who must hide when her father is run out of town. She falls in love with a man and becomes part owner in a gold mine. Her father returns to insist he receive part of the claim. With Mahlon Hamilton, Frank Lanning, Edward Peil, Charles Edler, Claire de Brey, Kate Price and Jack Roseleigh. Silent with orchestra score.
VHS: $32048. $19.95.
Robert Thornby, USA, 1921, 67 mins.

The Thief of Baghdad

Douglas Fairbanks on a marvelous quest in an Arabian Nights fantasy/adventure with the lovely Julanne Johnston as the princess who rides off with Fairbanks on his magic carpet. From Raoul Walsh, a dynamic, prolific director.
VHS: $01323. $24.95.
Raoul Walsh, USA, 1924, 132 mins.

Tramp, Tramp, Tramp

Harry Langdon, in his first successful independent feature, co-stars with a young Joan Crawford in this silent romantic comedy about a man who enters a cross-country walkathon in order to win money, all leading up to a whirlwind finale. Includes the classic scene with Harry breaking rocks with a chain gang, "a masterpiece of careful timing" (Kevin Brownlow, *The Parade's Gone By...*). "This picture takes Langdon's doleful face and pathetic figure out of the two-reel class and into the Chaplin and Lloyd screen dimensions" (*Photoplay*, August 1926). Includes the 1924 short *All Night Long*.
VHS: $30714. $29.95.
Harry Edwards, USA, 1926, 84 mins.

Way Down East

D.W. Griffith's Victorian pastoral stars Lillian Gish as an eager though exploited young woman abandoned by her obsessive, cavalier husband when he learns she's pregnant, who finds temporary comfort and solace with a wealthy, passive, small-town lawyer. The film has two constructs, an evocative portrait of small-town Americana and a suspense melodrama about desire and attraction and despair that attains its climax in the famous ice floe sequence. With Richard Barthelmess, Lowell Sherman and Edgar Nelson.
VHS: $18435. $24.95.
D.W. Griffith, USA, 1920, 149 mins.

The Whispering Chorus

In this moody and surreal psychological, silent drama, a fugitive assumes the identity of a dead man and is haunted by the voices of his conscience.
VHS: $30712. $29.95.
Cecil B. DeMille, USA, 1918, 89 mins.

The Wind

"*The Wind* is one of the masterpieces of the silent cinema" (Georges Sadoul). Lillian Gish plays a sensitive young girl from Virginia who goes to live with her cousin on the lonely Texas prairie. She survives the threat of an intruder whom she kills in self-defense, a dust storm, and a temporary descent into near madness. The most powerful performance of Gish's career, in which Victor Sjostrom perfectly synthesized the forces of nature and those of human emotion.
VHS: $09283. $29.95.
Victor Sjostrom, USA, 1928, 90 mins.

Oscar Winners/ Facets' Choice

The films that take home "Best Picture" at the Academy Awards very often are curious selections based on box office, sentiment, "prestige" or epic scale. What follows is each year's winner and what we would have liked to see win.

1927 Wings (Wellman)
Our Choice Sunrise (Murnau)

1929 Broadway Melody (Beaumont)
Our Choice The Wind (Seastrom) or The Wedding March (Von Stroheim)

1930 All Quiet on the Western Front
Our Choice All Quiet on the Western Front (Milestone)

1931 Cimarron (Ruggles)
Our Choice City Lights (Chaplin)

1932 Grand Hotel (Goulding)
Our Choice Scarface: The Shame of a Nation (Hawks)

1933 Cavalcade (Lloyd)
Our Choice Duck Soup (McCarey)

1934 It Happened One Night (Capra)
Our Choice The Thin Man (Van Dyke)

1935 Mutiny on the Bounty (Lloyd)
Our Choice The Thirty-Nine Steps (Hitchcock)

1936 The Great Ziegfeld (Leonard)
Our Choice Modern Times (Chaplin)

1937 The Life of Emile Zola (Dieterle)
Our Choice A Star Is Born (Wellman)

1938 You Can't Take It with You (Capra)
Our Choice Grand Illusion (Renoir)

1939 Gone with the Wind (Fleming)
Our Choice The Wizard of Oz (Fleming)

1940 Rebecca
Our Choice Rebecca (Hitchcock)

1941 How Green Was My Valley (Ford)
Our Choice Citizen Kane (Welles)

1942 Mrs. Miniver (Wyler)
Our Choice Sullivan's Travels (Sturges)

1943 Casablanca
Our Choice Casablanca (Curtiz)

1944 Going My Way (McCarey)
Our Choice Double Indemnity (Wilder)

1945 The Lost Weekend
Our Choice The Lost Weekend (Wilder)

1946 The Best Years of Our Lives (Wyler)
Our Choice Notorious (Hitchcock)

1947 Gentleman's Agreement (Kazan)
Our Choice Miracle on 34th Street (Seaton)

1948 Hamlet (Olivier)
Our Choice The Treasure of the Sierra Madre (Huston)

1949 All the King's Men (Rossen)
Our Choice White Heat (Walsh)

1950 All About Eve (Mankiewicz)
Our Choice Sunset Boulevard (Wilder)

1951 An American in Paris (Minnelli)
Our Choice Strangers on a Train (Hitchcock)

1952 The Greatest Show on Earth (De Mille)
Our Choice Singin' in the Rain (Kelly/Donen)

1953 From Here to Eternity (Zinnemann)
Our Choice The Big Heat (Lang)

1954 On the Waterfront (Kazan)
Our Choice Rear Window (Hitchcock)

1955 Marty (Mann)
Our Choice The Night of the Hunter (Laughton)

1956	Around the World in 80 Days (Anderson)		**1980**	Ordinary People (Redford)
Our Choice	The Searchers (Ford)		*Our Choice*	Raging Bull (Scorsese)

1956   Around the World in
        80 Days (Anderson)
Our Choice The Searchers (Ford)

1957   The Bridge on the
        River Kwai (Lean)
Our Choice Paths of Glory (Kubrick)

1958   Gigi (Minnelli)
Our Choice Touch of Evil (Welles)

1959   Ben-Hur (Wyler)
Our Choice Some Like It Hot (Wilder)

1960   The Apartment (Wilder)
Our Choice Psycho (Hitchcock)

1961   West Side Story
        (Wise/Robbins)
Our Choice The Hustler (Rossen)

1962   Lawrence of Arabia (Lean)
Our Choice To Kill a Mockingbird
        (Mulligan)

1963   Tom Jones
Our Choice Tom Jones (Richardson)

1964   My Fair Lady (Cukor)
Our Choice Dr. Strangelove (Kubrick)

1965   The Sound of Music
        (Wise)
Our Choice Repulsion (Polanski)

1966   A Man for All Seasons
        (Zinnemann)
Our Choice Cul de Sac (Polanski)

1967   In the Heat of the Night
        (Jewison)
Our Choice Bonnie and Clyde (Penn)

1968   Oliver! (Reed)
Our Choice Funny Girl (Wyler)

1969   Midnight Cowboy
        (Schlesinger)
Our Choice Z (Costa-Gavras)

1970   Patton
Our Choice Patton (Schaffner)

1971   The French Connection
Our Choice The French Connection
        (Friedkin)

1972   The Godfather
Our Choice The Godfather (Coppola)

1973   The Sting (Hill)
Our Choice Mean Streets (Scorsese)

1974   The Godfather Part II
Our Choice The Godfather Part II
        (Coppola)

1975   One Flew Over the
        Cuckoo's Nest (Forman)
Our Choice Nashville (Altman)

1976   Rocky (Avildsen)
Our Choice Taxi Driver (Scorsese)

1977   Annie Hall
Our Choice Annie Hall (Allen)

1978   The Deer Hunter (Cimino)
Our Choice An Unmarried Woman
        (Mazursky)

1979   Kramer vs. Kramer
        (Benton)
Our Choice Being There (Ashby)

1980   Ordinary People (Redford)
Our Choice Raging Bull (Scorsese)

1981   Chariots of Fire (Hudson)
Our Choice Atlantic City (Malle)

1982   Gandhi (Attenborough)
Our Choice Blade Runner (Scott)

1983   Terms of Endearment
        (Brooks)
Our Choice The Right Stuff (Kaufman)

1984   Amadeus (Forman)
Our Choice Stranger Than Paradise
        (Jarmusch)

1985   Out of Africa (Pollack)
Our Choice Brazil (Gilliam)

1986   Platoon (Stone)
Our Choice Hannah and Her Sisters
        (Allen)

1987   The Last Emperor
        (Bertolucci)
Our Choice Raising Arizona (Coen)

1988   Rain Man (Levinson)
Our Choice Dangerous Liaisons
        (Frears)

1989   Driving Miss Daisy
        (Beresford)
Our Choice Do The Right Thing (Lee)

1990   Dances with Wolves
        (Costner)
Our Choice Goodfellas (Scorsese)

1991   The Silence of the Lambs
        (Demme)
Our Choice Beauty and the Beast
        (Disney)

1992   Unforgiven
Our Choice Unforgiven (Eastwood)

1993   Schindler's List
        (Spielberg)
Our Choice The Piano (Campion)

1994   Forrest Gump (Zemeckis)
Our Choice Heavenly Creatures
        (Jackson)

1995   Braveheart (Gibson)
Our Choice Exotica (Egoyan)

1996   The English Patient
        (Minghella)
Our Choice Fargo (Coen Bros.)

1997   Titanic (Cameron)
Our Choice Ice Storm (Lee)

The Last Emperor

The Academy Awards

Since 1927 the Academy of Motion Picture Arts and Sciences has bestowed its highest honor, the Oscar, upon those films and film artists voted "best" by their peers, in a complicated and ever-evolving process. Best supporting awards weren't added until 1936, while documentaries (still a category of much disagreement) came on board in 1941. Following is a list of the four major awards to date:

1927-28

BEST PICTURE

Wings
One of the most exciting of the silent dramas, *Wings* was the first film to be awarded the Oscar for Best Picture. Featuring Clara Bow (The IT Girl) and a short appearance by Gary Cooper, the film has incredible aerial battle sequences. Director Wellman makes a humanistic statement as he explores the devastation of World War I.
VHS: S02831. $19.95.
William Wellman, USA, 1927, 139 mins.

BEST DIRECTOR

Frank Borzage for
Seventh Heaven
"*Seventh Heaven* tracks the transformational love of Farrell and Gaynor from the sewers to the stars, across time and space, and beyond death itself, affirming triumphantly that melodrama can mean much more than just an excuse for a good weep" (*Time Out Film Guide*). Janet Gaynor portrayed a mistreated Paris street waif redeemed by cockney sewer man Charles Farrell.
VHS: S31171. $24.95.
Frank Borzage, USA, 1927, 119 mins.

BEST ACTOR

Emil Jannings for
**Last Command and
The Way of All Flesh**
Emil Jannings stars as an immigrant Czarist general reduced to working as a Hollywood film extra. Von Sternberg cuts back to the general's time of grandeur to show how far the mighty can fall, and to criticize the status of Hollywood's power hungry moguls. Preston Sturges considered this the only perfect film ever made. Silent.
VHS: S03442. $29.95.
Josef von Sternberg, USA, 1928, 88 mins.

BEST ACTRESS

Janet Gaynor for
Sunrise and Seventh Heaven
Although this was Murnau's first Hollywood film, he scripted it with Carl Mayer while still in Germany. The story concerns the marriage of a peasant couple whose honeymoon in the big city is detoured by a sultry seductress. But the film is neither trite nor melodramatic; Murnau's sets and camera angles imbue the images with a poetic lyricism that reveals the characters' psychological states. Easily his most perfect film, Murnau's *Sunrise* was named the "Greatest film of all time," in a recent *Cahiers du Cinema* Critic's Poll. With George O'Brien, Janet Gaynor and Margaret Livingston.
VHS: S07782. $29.95.
Laser: Outtakes, digital transfer. **LD76401. $49.98.**
Friedrich W. Murnau, USA, 1927, 97 mins.

1928-29

BEST PICTURE

Broadway Melody
This early talkie was the first musical to win a Best Picture Oscar. Score by Arthur Freed and Herb Brown. Bessie Love and Anita Page are two sisters dazzled by the lights of the Great White Way. Tunes include "You Were Meant for Me" and "The Wedding of the Painted Doll." With Charles King, Jed Prouty and Mary Doran.
VHS: S08337. $19.98.
Harry Beaumont, USA, 1929, 104 mins.

BEST DIRECTOR

Frank Lloyd for
The Divine Lady
Not currently available on video.

BEST ACTOR

Warner Baxter for
Old Arizona
Not currently available on video.

BEST ACTRESS

Mary Pickford for
Coquette
Mary Pickford's first sound film was adapted from the Broadway play by George Abbott and Ann Preston Bridges. Pickford plays a gilded Southern belle with an unconventional streak who defies her oppressive father by falling for a charismatic though poor man. With Johnny Mack Brown, Matt Moore and William Janney.
VHS: S17924. $19.98.
Sam Taylor, USA, 1929, 75 mins.

1930

BEST PICTURE

All Quiet on the Western Front
Classic adaptation of Erich Maria Remarque's anti-war novel has lost little of its impact over the years. The film follows a group of German recruits during World War I from their idealism to disillusionment.
VHS: S01686. $19.95.
Laser: LD70011. $39.98.
Lewis Milestone, USA, 1930, 103 mins.

BEST DIRECTOR

Lewis Milestone for
All Quiet on the Western Front

BEST ACTOR

George Arliss for
Disraeli
An adaptation of the long-running play about the British prime minister, a colorful, bright and electric statesman who ruled during the reign of Queen Victoria. With George Arliss, Joan Bennett, Florence Arliss and Anthony Bushnell.
VHS: S17925. $19.98.
Alfred E. Green, USA, 1929, 87 mins.

BEST ACTRESS

Norma Shearer for
The Divorcee
Norma Shearer plays the young wife who puts up with the flirtations of her husband (Chester Morris), until she decides to take matters into her own hands and go out and equal him. With Conrad Nagel, Robert Montgomery. Not currently available on video.
Robert Z. Leonard, USA, 1930, 83 mins.

1930-31

BEST PICTURE

Cimarron
The first Western to win an Oscar for Best Picture (the second being Eastwood's *Unforgiven*) stars Richard Dix and Irene Dunne. Based on the popular novel by Edna Ferber, it chronicles the life of a homesteading family from the Oklahoma Land Rush until 1915. Oscar also went for screenplay. With Estelle Taylor and Nance O'Neil.
VHS: S08338. $19.95.
Laser: LD76186. $49.98.
Wesley Ruggles, USA, 1930, 124 mins.

BEST DIRECTOR

Norman Taurog for
Skippy
Not currently available on video.

BEST ACTOR

Lionel Barrymore for
A Free Soul
Lionel Barrymore won an Oscar for his famous courtroom scene in this story of a hard-drinking lawyer who successfully defends gangster Clark Gable on a murder rap and then discovers that his daughter has fallen in love with him. With Norma Shearer, Leslie Howard.
VHS: S13389. $19.98.
Clarence Brown, USA, 1931, 91 mins.

BEST ACTRESS

Marie Dressler for
Min & Bill
Marie Dressler, Wallace Beery, Marjorie Rambeau and Dorothy Jordan star in this early talkie about two people living in a houseboat who struggle to keep their daughter from being taken from them.
VHS: S30920. $19.98.
George Roy Hill, USA, 1930, 66 mins.

1931-32

BEST PICTURE

Grand Hotel
Greta Garbo's great role as the world-weary ballerina, John Barrymore as the elegant but broke Baron von Geiger, Lionel Barrymore as Otto Kringelein, a dying nobody, Joan Crawford as a stenographer, and Wallace Beery as General Director Preysing.
VHS: S00523. $19.95.
Edmund Goulding, USA, 1932, 112 mins.

BEST DIRECTOR

Frank Borzage for
Bad Girl
Not currently available on video.

BEST ACTOR (tie)

Wallace Beery for
The Champ
Jackie Cooper has unflinching faith in his father, a washed-up prize boxer, in this melodrama that features a dynamite performance from Wallace Beery as the fighter.
VHS: S13387. $19.98.
Laser: LD72119. $34.98.
King Vidor, USA, 1931, 87 mins.

and Fredric March for
Dr. Jekyll and Mr. Hyde
The uncensored version of the 1932 interpretation of the Robert Louis Stevenson classic that won Fredric March an Oscar. The ten minutes that were cut for its re-release have been restored in its home video debut. Wally Westmore created the transformation make-up for this taut and exciting story of the battle of good and evil in the single body of a man of science. With Miriam Hopkins as Ivy, the prostitute, and Holmes Herbert and Rose Hobart.
VHS: S11217. $19.95.
Rouben Mamoulian, USA, 1932, 98 mins.

BEST ACTRESS

Helen Hayes for
The Sin of Madelon Claudet
A first-rate sobber about a mother who must give up everything so that her illegitimate son will have a good life. Helen Hayes won an Academy Award for her tragic portrayal of this woman who pays such a terrible price for the choices she is forced to make in her life.
VHS: S13568. $19.98.
Edgar Selwyn, USA, 1931, 74 mins.

1933

BEST PICTURE

Cavalcade
This lavish Academy Award-winning adaptation of Noel Coward's hit play traces the ups and downs of the British Marryot family from the death of Queen Victoria through the Depression. With Diana Wynyard, Clive Brook, Herbert Mundin, Una O'Connor, Ursula Jeans, Beryl Mercer, Merle Tottenham, Frank Lawton, John Warburton, Margaret

Lindsay and Billy Bevan. "Nostalgic, richly atmospheric, but also sharply critical of war and the aftershocks that brought an end to a wonderful way of life" (Leonard Maltin).
VHS: S30918. $19.98.
Frank Lloyd, USA, 1933, 110 mins.

BEST DIRECTOR

Frank Lloyd for
Cavalcade

BEST ACTOR

Charles Laughton for
The Private Life of Henry VIII
Charles Laughton gives a tour-de-force performance as the infamous British King Henry, a fat, strutting, arrogant, yet tender, vulnerable and loving man. Politics, statesmanship and international intrigue are just background for the lusty life of the king and his six wives. Also starring Merle Oberon, Robert Donat, and Elsa Lanchester. Digitally remastered.
VHS: S01062. $19.98.
Alexander Korda, Great Britain, 1933, 97 mins.

BEST ACTRESS

Katharine Hepburn for
Morning Glory
Katharine Hepburn is the stage-struck young girl who tries to succeed in New York City theatre. Hepburn won her first Best Actress Oscar for her performance. The film also stars Adolphe Menjou and Douglas Fairbanks, Jr.
VHS: S00882. $19.95.
Lowell Sherman, USA, 1933, 73 mins.

1934

BEST PICTURE

It Happened One Night
Winner of five Academy Awards, this famous screwball comedy stars Clark Gable and Claudette Colbert as two mismatched lovers. Colbert escapes from her millionaire father, who wants to stop her from marrying a worthless playboy.
VHS: S00642. $19.95.
Laser: LD72146. $34.95.
Frank Capra, USA, 1934, 105 mins.

BEST DIRECTOR

Frank Capra for
It Happened One Night

BEST ACTOR

Clark Gable for
It Happened One Night

BEST ACTRESS

Claudette Colbert for
It Happened One Night

1935

BEST PICTURE

Mutiny on the Bounty
The classic version, starring Charles Laughton in an unforgettable role as Captain Bligh and Clark Gable as Christian. The picture deservedly won the Oscar

for the Best Movie of the Year.
VHS: S02714. $19.95.
Laser: LD70634. $39.98.
Frank Lloyd, USA, 1935, 133 mins.

BEST DIRECTOR

John Ford for
The Informer
Brilliant cinema from John Ford with Victor McLaglen starring as a traitor who turns in a compatriot and suffers the consequences. Script by Dudley Nichols, based on the novel by Liam O'Flaherty. A great American film.
VHS: S12022. $19.98.
John Ford, USA, 1935, 91 mins.

BEST ACTOR

Victor McLaglen for
The Informer

BEST ACTRESS

Bette Davis for
Dangerous
Bette Davis won her first Oscar (and felt it was a belated award from her having lost the previous year) for her portrayal of an alcoholic, once-famous stage actress hell-bent on self-destruction. She undergoes a change of heart when she meets an admiring architect (Franchot Tone) but now has to get rid of an unwanted husband. She's dangerous!
VHS: S11621. $19.95.
Laser: LD70150. $39.98.
Alfred E. Green, USA, 1935, 78 mins.

1936

BEST PICTURE

The Great Ziegfeld
William Powell plays the title character, Broadway showman Florenz Ziegfeld (1867-1932), in a film that won three Oscars, including Best Picture. The ads read "50 Stars" and "300 Girls" in this nearly three-hour biography packed with some of the stars that Ziegfeld made possible. Fanny Brice, Ann Pennington and Ray Bolger play themselves. Will Rogers and Eddie Cantor were doubled. With Myrna Loy and Luise Rainer as Ziegfeld's wives.
VHS: S08339. $29.95.
Laser: LD70134. $39.98.
Robert Z. Leonard, USA, 1936, 176 mins.

BEST DIRECTOR

Frank Capra for
Mr. Deeds Goes to Town
One of Frank Capra's best films, shot during the height of the Depression. Gary Cooper plays Longfellow Deeds, who inherits 20 million dollars and wants to spend it on people during the height of the Depression. Jean Arthur plays the city reporter who is captivated by the naive Deeds.
VHS: S11163. $19.95.
Frank Capra, USA, 1936, 115 mins.

BEST ACTOR

Paul Muni for
Story of Louis Pasteur
The life story and struggles of the legendary French scientist receive heroic treatment in this engrossing adaptation, which features a brilliant (and Oscar-winning) performance. Writers Sheridan Gibney and Pierre Collings also received an Oscar.
VHS: S11550. $19.98.
William Dieterle, USA, 1936, 85 mins.

Luise Rainer for
The Great Ziegfield

1937

BEST PICTURE

The Life of Emile Zola
A penetrating drama and social documentary starring
Paul Muni as the famous author of *Nana*. The film
documents Zola's struggle as a novelist, his long
friendship with the painter Cezanne and his
impassioned fight against bigotry as evidenced by his
role in the Dreyfuss Case.
VHS: S01758. $19.95.
William Dieterle, USA, 1937, 110 mins.

BEST DIRECTOR

Leo McCarey for
The Awful Truth
Wildly funny romp which won the Academy Award
opens when a battling couple files for divorce. The
only hitch seems to be who will get custody of their
beloved terrier, Mr. Smith. Cary Grant and Irene
Dunne co-star in this very wacky comedy.
VHS: S00083. $19.95.
Leo McCarey, USA, 1937, 92 mins.

BEST ACTOR

Spencer Tracy for
Captains Courageous
Spencer Tracy portrays Manuel, the Portuguese
fisherman who teaches a millionaire's spoiled son
human values in this adaptation of Rudyard Kipling's
popular story. With Lionel Barrymore, Melvyn
Douglas and Mickey Rooney.
VHS: S01788. $19.98.
Laser: LD71159. $34.98.
Victor Fleming, USA, 1937, 118 mins.

BEST ACTRESS

Luise Rainer for
The Good Earth
Pearl Buck's novel of famine and the fight for
survival in pre-revolution China was transformed into
one of Hollywood's greatest films, featuring excellent
performances by Paul Muni and Oscar-winner Best
Actress Luise Rainer. The locust plague sequences
are still memorable examples of cinematography.
VHS: S02899. $19.98.
Sidney Franklin, USA, 1937, 138 mins.

1938

BEST PICTURE

You Can't Take It with You
James Stewart, Jean Arthur, Lionel Barrymore and
Edward Arnold star in this 1938 Academy Award-
winning, nutty comedy. Based on the play by George
S. Kaufman and Moss Hart. The scenes in which
Barrymore confronts an IRS man by refusing to pay
taxes are among the funniest in film.
VHS: S11745. $19.95.
Frank Capra, USA, 1938, 126 mins.

BEST DIRECTOR

Frank Capra for
You Can't Take It with You

BEST ACTOR

Spencer Tracy for
Boys Town
Spencer Tracy plays Father Flanagan, the man who
believed there is no such thing as a bad boy. Mickey
Rooney is around to thoroughly test that theory. A
heartwarming and heart-tugging film about the
creation of the home for juvenile delinquents. With
Addison Richards, Leslie Fenton, Henry Hull and
Gene Reynolds. Oscars also went to the writers Dore
Schary and Eleanor Griffin.
VHS: S11219. $19.95.
Laser: LD70153. $34.98.
Norman Taurog, USA, 1938, 96 mins.

BEST ACTRESS

Bette Davis for
Jezebel
Bette Davis shines as the tempestuous Southern belle
who manipulates the men in her life. Her engagement
to Henry Fonda is broken off due to her insensitivity,
and when he returns married, her ruthless jealousy
explodes.
DVD: DV60062. $24.98.
VHS: S00654. $19.95.
Laser: LD70604. $34.98.
William Wyler, USA, 1938, 105 mins.

1939

BEST PICTURE

Gone with the Wind
A film beyond criticism, a work that welds together
Hollywood classicism and literary adaptation with
grace. Victor Fleming is the credited director, though
at various times Howard Hawks, George Cukor and
Sam Wood helped shape the narrative and rhythm.
Ben Hecht worked on the screenplay. William
Cameron Menzies was the production designer. With
Clark Gable, Vivien Leigh, Leslie Howard, Olivia de
Havilland and Hattie McDaniel.
VHS: S00515. $89.98.
Victor Fleming, USA, 1939, 222 mins.

BEST DIRECTOR

Victor Fleming for
Gone with the Wind

BEST ACTOR

Robert Donat for
Goodbye, Mr. Chips
Robert Donat (in an Oscar-winning performance) and
Greer Garson (in her film debut) star in this
adaptation of James Hinton's best seller. A shy
English schoolmaster falls in love and becomes a
better man and teacher for it. A classic from MGM
and a nostalgic tribute to the English public school
system, the story is set in 1870.
VHS: S00516. $19.98.
Laser: MGM, 1939. LD70166. $34.98.
Sam Wood, USA, 1939, 115 mins.

BEST ACTRESS

Vivien Leigh for
Gone with the Wind

1940

BEST PICTURE

Rebecca
Hitchcock's first American film, based on a Daphne
du Maurier gothic romance. With Laurence Olivier

and a fine performance by Joan Fontaine as a shy
young woman who marries Olivier. Excellent
supporting roles by Judith Anderson, George Sanders,
Leo G. Carroll and Nigel Bruce.
> **VHS: S01096. $19.98.**
> **Laser: CAV. LD70441. $124.95.**
> **Laser: CLV. LD70442. $69.95.**
> **Alfred Hitchcock, USA, 1940, 104 mins.**

John Ford for
The Grapes of Wrath
Certainly one of the all-time classics, this adaptation
of the John Steinbeck novel of the dust bowl
migration from Oklahoma to California stars Henry
Fonda as Tom Joad, John Carradine as Casey. The
film won the Academy Award for Best Director.
> **VHS: S00525. $19.98.**
> **Laser: LD71013. $49.98.**
> **John Ford, USA, 1940, 129 mins.**

BEST ACTOR

James Stewart for
The Philadelphia Story
One of the most hilarious and captivating romantic
comedies ever to grace the screen. Katharine Hepburn
is caught between her fiance and her charming ex-
husband. With a splendid cast, including Cary Grant,
James Stewart and Ruth Hussey.
> **DVD: DV60063. $24.98.**
> **VHS: S01023. $24.95.**
> **Laser: LD70152. $39.98.**
> **George Cukor, USA, 1940, 118 mins.**

BEST ACTRESS

Ginger Rogers for
Kitty Foyle
Ginger Rogers snared a Best Actress Oscar for her
remarkable portrayal of a working girl who must
choose between a life of upper-crust manners with a
wealthy aristocrat, or a simple life with a nearly
penniless intern.
> **VHS: S00688. $19.95.**
> **Sam Wood, USA, 1940, 108 mins.**

1941

BEST PICTURE

How Green Was My Valley
An offscreen narrator reflects on his life and work in
John Ford's poetic and beautiful rendering of Welsh
village life. Based on the novel by Richard Llewellyn.
With Walter Pidgeon, Maureen O'Hara and Roddy
McDowall. Winner for Best Picture in 1941.
> **VHS: S18449. $19.98.**
> **John Ford, USA, 1941, 118 mins.**

BEST DIRECTOR

John Ford for
How Green Was My Valley

BEST ACTOR

Gary Cooper for
Sergeant York
Gary Cooper stars in an Oscar-winning role as Alvin
York, a backwoods boy from Tennessee who
overcomes his pacifist principles and decides to fight
in World War I, with heroic results. Based on a true
story. York worked as consultant on the film. An
inspiration.
> **VHS: S01868. $19.98.**
> **Laser: Chapter search. Includes theatrical trailer.**
> **LD71642. $39.98.**
> **Howard Hawks, USA, 1941, 134 mins.**

BEST ACTRESS

Joan Fontaine for
Suspicion
Cary Grant and Joan Fontaine in Hitchcock's thriller
about a woman who gradually suspects her husband
is a murderer.
> **VHS: S01287. $19.95.**
> **Alfred Hitchcock, USA, 1941, 99 mins.**

1942

BEST PICTURE

Mrs. Miniver
This winner of seven Oscars in 1942 was an effective
morale boost for all the folks on the home front.
Greer Garson and Walter Pidgeon head a middle-class
English family under siege and worried about their
son in the RAF. Garson later married the actor who
played her son, Richard Ney. With Dame May Whitty,
Reginald Owen and Teresa Wright.
> **VHS: S08341. $19.95.**
> **William Wyler, USA, 1942, 134 mins.**

BEST DIRECTOR

William Wyler for
Mrs. Miniver

BEST ACTOR

James Cagney for
Yankee Doodle Dandy
James Cagney won a richly deserved Oscar for his
red, white an' blue account of the life of George M.
Cohan. He sings, he dances, he talks to the president
of the United States. Filmed in B&W though two
colorized versions exist. With Walter Huston, Joan
Leslie, Jeanne Cagney, S.Z. Sakall and Rosemary
DeCamp.
> **VHS: S01835. $14.95.**
> **Laser: LD70714. $39.98.**
> **Michael Curtiz, USA, 1942, 126 mins.**

BEST ACTRESS

Greer Garson for
Mrs. Miniver

1943

BEST PICTURE

Casablanca
The high-water mark of classic American studio
filmmaking, this special 50th anniversary edition has
been digitally remastered and includes the original
theatrical trailer and a documentary on the making of
the film. With Humphrey Bogart, Ingrid Bergman,
Paul Henreid, Claude Rains, Conrad Veidt, Sydney
Greenstreet and Peter Lorre. Music by Max Steiner.
Not currently available on video.
> **Michael Curtiz, USA, 1942, 102 mins.**

BEST DIRECTOR

Michael Curtiz for
Casablanca

BEST ACTOR

Paul Lukas for
Watch on the Rhine
Outstanding performances by Paul Dukas, Bette
Davis, Lucille Watson distinguish this adaptation of
the famous Lillian Hellman play about a German

refugee and his family, who are pursued by Nazi agents in Washington.
VHS: $13397. $19.98.
Herman Shumlin, USA, 1943, 114 mins.

Jennifer Jones for
Song of Bernadette
Jennifer Jones stars as the 19th-century French peasant girl who claimed to speak to the Virgin Mary near her village of Lourdes. Three other Oscars were awarded to this inspirational but lengthy account. With Vincent Price, Lee J. Cobb, Charles Bickford and Gladys Cooper. Linda Darnell appeared, unbilled, as the Blessed Virgin. B&W.
VHS: $15607. $19.98.
Henry King, USA, 1943, 156 mins.

1944

BEST PICTURE

Going My Way
Irving Berlin's hit with Bing Crosby as the unconventional singing priest who tries to save a poor parish presided over by the gruff-but-lovable Barry Fitzgerald. Winner of seven Academy Awards. Fred Astaire co-stars.
VHS: $01534. $19.98.
Laser: LD70034. $34.98.
Leo McCarey, USA, 1944, 101 mins.

BEST DIRECTOR

Leo McCarey for
Going My Way

BEST ACTOR

Bing Crosby for
Going My Way

BEST ACTRESS

Ingrid Bergman for
Gaslight
Ingrid Bergman won her first Oscar for her stunning role as a susceptible young woman who marries the suave, romantic Charles Boyer, never suspecting he is involved in a murderous scandal in Cukor's electrifying mystery drama.
VHS: $00482. $19.98.
George Cukor, USA, 1944, 113 mins.

1945

BEST PICTURE

The Lost Weekend
Billy Wilder's classic drama stars Ray Milland in a sobering study of alcoholism. The winner of Oscars for Best Picture, Director, Actor and Screenplay in 1945. Cast includes Frank Faylen, Howard da Silva, Jane Wyman and Philip Terry. The D.T.'s are in glorious black and white.
VHS: $06869. $19.95.
Billy Wilder, USA, 1945, 100 mins.

BEST DIRECTOR

Billy Wilder for
The Lost Weekend

BEST ACTOR

Ray Milland for
The Lost Weekend

BEST ACTRESS

Joan Crawford for
Mildred Pierce
Michael Curtiz, who directed *Casablanca* and *Yankee Doodle Dandy*, elevates this Joan Crawford vehicle into a perverse and personal exploration of psychological disorder and collapse. Based on the novel by James M. Cain, Crawford is never better as the hard-working mother with the world's most unpleasant, snobby, status-seeking and boyfriend-stealing daughter (Ann Blyth).
VHS: $02340. $19.98.
Laser: LD70630. $34.98.
Michael Curtiz, USA, 1945, 109 mins.

1946

BEST PICTURE

The Best Years of Our Lives
This epic film focuses on the troubles of three World War II servicemen as they try to pick up the threads of their lives after returning home to the States. An insightful portrait of small-town American life and its values. Starring Myrna Loy, Frederic March, Dana Andrews, Virginia Mayo and Teresa Wright. *The Best Years of Our Lives* was named one of the 50 greatest motion pictures of all time by the members of The American Film Institute. Digitally remastered.
VHS: $03117. $19.98.
William Wyler, USA, 1946, 170 mins.

BEST DIRECTOR

William Wyler for
The Best Years of Our Lives

BEST ACTOR

Frederic March for
The Best Years of Our Lives

BEST ACTRESS

Olivia de Havilland for
To Each His Own
Olivia de Havilland won an Academy Award for her portrayal of an unwed mother who gives up her son, and then pretends to be his loving aunt in order to be near him, in this "well-turned soaper" (Leonard Maltin). With John Lund.
VHS: $30794. $19.95.
Mitchell Leisen, USA, 1946, 122 mins.

1947

BEST PICTURE

Gentleman's Agreement
Moss Hart adapted Laura Z. Hobson's prize-winning novel about a talented journalist (Gregory Peck) who poses as a Jew in order to research a series of articles about anti-Semitism and discovers a dark and disturbing backlash experienced by his family. With Celeste Holm, Dorothy McGuire and John Garfield.
VHS: $18448. $19.98.
Laser: LD72252. $39.98.
Elia Kazan, USA, 1947, 118 mins.

BEST DIRECTOR

Elia Kazan for
Gentleman's Agreement

BEST ACTOR

Ronald Colman for
A Double Life
Ronald Colman plays a brilliant actor whose stage roles are beginning to affect the rest of his life. In an Oscar winning performance Colman performs *Othello* once too often for his own good. With Signe Hasso, Edmond O'Brien and Shelley Winters.
VHS: S04228. $19.98.
George Cukor, USA, 1947, 103 mins.

BEST ACTRESS

Loretta Young for
The Farmer's Daughter
Loretta Young won an Oscar for her performance as the headstrong Swedish girl who fights for a Congressional seat against the man she loves. With Joseph Cotten, Ethel Barrymore. Not currently available on video.
H.C. Potter, USA, 1947, 97 mins.

1948

BEST PICTURE

Hamlet
Laurence Olivier produces, directs and interprets the title character, a melancholy Dane dealing with a range of feelings for his stepfather, the new King of Denmark. The film won four Oscars and Olivier received his knighthood. Based on a play by William Shakespeare. Cast includes Jean Simmons, Felix Aylmer and Peter Cushing. Don't look for Rosencrantz and Guildenstern. Filmed in glorious black and white.
VHS: S06230. $19.98.
Laser: LD75461. $69.95.
Laurence Olivier, Great Britain, 1948, 153 mins.

BEST DIRECTOR

John Huston for
The Treasure of the Sierra Madre
Pauline Kael calls this "one of the strongest of all American movies." Three Americans strike it rich and greed takes over. With Humphrey Bogart, Walter Huston, Tim Holt and Robert Blake, based on the novel by B. Traven.
VHS: S01368. $19.95.
Laser: LD70699. $39.98.
John Huston, USA, 1948, 120 mins.

BEST ACTOR

Laurence Olivier for
Hamlet

BEST ACTRESS

Jane Wyman for
Johnny Belinda
Sensitive story of a deaf mute in Nova Scotia and the gentle doctor who recognizes her intelligence and teaches her sign language. Jane Wyman won Best Actress Award for her performance, with Lew Ayres, Agnes Moorehead.
VHS: S03460. $24.95.
Jean Negulesco, USA, 1948, 103 mins.

1949

BEST PICTURE

All the King's Men
Broderick Crawford gives a legendary performance as the brawling, bull-headed Southern politician. A riveting thriller about corruption in the political arena, based on the novel by Robert Penn Warren.
VHS: S00033. $19.95.
Laser: LD72160. $34.95.
Robert Rossen, USA, 1949, 109 mins.

BEST DIRECTOR

Joseph L. Mankiewicz for
Letter to Three Wives
Joseph L. Mankiewicz received an Oscar for his direction of three women reacting to a letter sent by the town flirt, who has run off with one of their husbands. With Jeanne Crain, Linda Darnell, Ann Sothern and Kirk Douglas.
VHS: S18097. $19.98.
Joseph L. Mankiewicz, USA, 1949, 103 mins.

BEST ACTOR

Broderick Crawford for
All the King's Men

BEST ACTRESS

Olivia de Havilland for
The Heiress
William Wyler directed Olivia de Havilland and an all-star cast in this Oscar-winning classic. De Havilland is the homely, awkward girl who falls in love with the dashing fortune hunter. With brilliant performances by Montgomery Clift and Ralph Richardson, musical score by Aaron Copeland. Based on *Washington Square* by Henry James.
VHS: S03533. $14.95.
William Wyler, USA, 1949, 115 mins.

1950

BEST PICTURE

All About Eve
Six Oscars were awarded this cynical and entertaining examination of life as it exists on the Broadway theatre scene. Bette Davis glows as the aging star being undermined by her protege Anne Baxter, as Eve Harrington. With George Sanders, Celeste Holm and Marilyn Monroe. A gem.
VHS: S03911. $19.98.
Laser: LD70823. $49.98.
Joseph L. Mankiewicz, USA, 1950, 138 mins.

BEST DIRECTOR

Joseph L. Mankiewicz for
All About Eve

BEST ACTOR

Jose Ferrer for
Cyrano de Bergerac
Jose Ferrer won an Academy Award for his role as the classic soldier of fortune with the oversize nose. With Mala Powers.
VHS: S18180. $19.95.
Michael Gordon, USA, 1950, 112 mins.

BEST ACTRESS

Judy Holliday for
Born Yesterday
Judy Holliday is irresistable as the ultimate dumb blond girlfriend of Broderick Crawford, a corrupt millionaire junk dealer. Brock, a man with social ambitions, is embarassed by Billie's crass behavior and hires a writer, William Holden, to smarten her up. A classic comedy.
VHS: S03863. $19.95.
George Cukor, USA, 1950, 103 mins.

1951

BEST PICTURE

An American in Paris
No film can match *An American in Paris* for all the joy, all the songs, and all the romance in music and dance. Gene Kelly and Leslie Caron star in this movie set to the glorious melodies of George Gershwin, including: "Embraceable You," "Love Is Here to Stay," "I Got Rhythm" and more.
VHS: S00045. $19.95.
Vincente Minnelli, USA, 1951, 102 mins.

BEST DIRECTOR

George Stevens for
A Place in the Sun
Based on Theodore Dreiser's *An American Tragedy*, and featuring strong performances from Montgomery Clift, Elizabeth Taylor and Shelley Winters. Monty Clift is the poor boy driven by the lure of wealth, with his success threatened by complications from his simultaneous affairs with factory girl Shelley Winters and socialite Liz Taylor.
VHS: S04663. $19.95.
George Stevens, USA, 1951, 122 mins

BEST ACTOR

Humphrey Bogart for
The African Queen
(Commemorative Edition)
John Huston's adaptation of C.S. Forester's novel focuses on the spirited conflict of two resolute individualists, a drunken captain (Humphrey Bogart) and a repressed missionary (Katharine Hepburn), who undertake a dangerous river odyssey in East Africa against the elite German Navy during World War I. Cinematography by Jack Cardiff. Screenplay by James Agee and John Huston (and an uncredited Peter Viertel). With Robert Morley, Peter Bull, Theodore Bikel and Walter Gotell. The film has been digitally remastered and visually restored. The commemorative edition offers a hardcover edition of Hepburn's *The Making of The African Queen* and a copy of the original shooting script.
VHS: S19474. $59.98.
John Huston, USA, 1951, 105 mins.

BEST ACTRESS

Vivien Leigh for
A Streetcar Named Desire:
Director's Cut
Tennessee Williams' notorious play was censored when adapted for the screen. Now four minutes of the originally cut material have been found and restored to this "director's cut". Marlon Brando, Kim Hunter and Vivien Leigh star in this drama of betrayal, madness and rape.
DVD: DV60067. $24.98.
VHS: S21085. $19.98.
Laser: LD70687. $39.98.
Elia Kazan, USA, 1951, 125 mins.

1952

BEST PICTURE

The Greatest Show on Earth
This Cecil B. De Mille production won best picture in 1952 and is a rousing tribute to life under the Big Top. Against a background of the Ringling Brothers circus, stars Charlton Heston, Cornel Wilde, Betty Hutton, Gloria Grahame, James Stewart and Dorothy Lamour combine to bring love, adventure, spectacle and suspense to the big screen.
VHS: S06146. $29.95.
Cecil B. De Mille, USA, 1952, 147 mins.

BEST DIRECTOR

John Ford for
The Quiet Man
John Ford's lyrical portrait of Ireland revolves around an American prizefighter (John Wayne) who returns to his birthplace to buy back the family cottage and marry the temptress Maureen O'Hara. Just wonderful.
VHS: S15908. $19.98.
Laser: 40th Anniversary edition includes *The Making of the Quiet Man*. **LD71497. $59.98.**
John Ford, USA, 1952, 153 mins.

BEST ACTOR

Gary Cooper for
High Noon
Gary Cooper is the marshall who fights alone for upholding the law when the entire town is paralyzed with fear. Stark settings and shadows heighten the suspense. The most popular film of 1952. With Grace Kelly, Lloyd Bridges, Lon Chaney and Henry Morgan.
VHS: S00567. $14.98.
Laser: CAV. **LD70380. $74.95.**
Laser: CLV. **LD70381. $49.95.**
Fred Zinnemann, USA, 1952, 84 mins.

BEST ACTRESS

Shirley Booth for
Come Back, Little Sheba
Based on the William Inge play, which paints a gripping portrait of a marriage washed up by booze and alienation. Featuring Burt Lancaster and an Oscar and Tony Award-winning, gut-wrenching performance by Shirley Booth. The title refers to Booth's despairing search for her lost dog but, of course, it's symbolic of a whole lot more than that.
VHS: S13789. $19.95.
Daniel Mann, USA, 1952, 99 mins.

1953

BEST PICTURE

From Here to Eternity
The talented Fred Zinnemann (*Man for All Seasons, Julia*) perfectly captures the static isolation and boredom that envelops the military personnel in peacetime Hawaii on the eve of American participation in World War II. Zinnemann counterposes social history with riveting drama: Burt Lancaster is a career soldier who seduces a commander's unattended wife, Deborah Kerr. Montgomery Clift staggers social convention by falling for Donna Reed, a prostitute. Frank Sinatra and Ernest Borgnine add quality performances as bitter rivals. Winner of eight Academy Awards.
VHS: S02923. $19.95.
Laser: LD72185. $39.98.
Fred Zinnemann, USA, 1953, 118 mins.

BEST DIRECTOR

Fred Zinnemann for
From Here to Eternity

BEST ACTOR

William Holden for
Stalag 17
World War II POW drama stars William Holden in an Oscar performance as a soldier suspected of being a spy when two prisoners are killed trying to escape. Otto Preminger also appears.
VHS: S02608. $19.95.
Billy Wilder, USA, 1953, 120 mins.

BEST ACTRESS

Audrey Hepburn for
Roman Holiday
Stylish production starring Gregory Peck and Audrey
Hepburn about a rebellious princess who wishes to
discover living on her own. With Eddie Albert as
Peck's pal.
 VHS: S01763. $19.95.
 Laser: LD75249. $34.98.
William Wyler, USA, 1953, 118 mins.

1954

BEST PICTURE

On the Waterfront
Marlon Brando stars in the archetypal role as ex-
fighter Terry Malloy, working for Boss Johnny
Friendly (Lee J. Cobb) on the gang-ridden waterfront.
The classic American movie of redemption, with a
great script by Budd Schulberg.
 VHS: S00960. $19.95.
 Laser: LD72070. $34.95.
Elia Kazan, USA, 1954, 108 mins.

BEST DIRECTOR

Elia Kazan for
On the Waterfront

BEST ACTOR

Marlon Brando for
On the Waterfront

BEST ACTRESS

Grace Kelly for
The Country Girl
In this Academy Award-winning adaptation of
Clifford Odets' play, Bing Crosby, in one of his finest
roles, portrays an alcoholic singer trying to make a
comeback with the help of his director (William
Holden). Grace Kelly won the Oscar for her
performance as the wife who may be driving her
husband to drink.
 VHS: S30964. $14.95.
George Seaton, USA, 1954, 104 mins.

1955

BEST PICTURE

Marty
Ernest Borgnine won a well-deserved Oscar for Best
Actor as the shy Bronx butcher who finds love.
Academy Awards also went for direction, screenplay
and Best Picture. With Betsy Blair, Joe De Santis and
Esther Minciotti. From the teleplay by Paddy
Chayefsky.
 Laser: Chapter Search. Includes original theatrical
trailer. LD71670. $34.98.
Delbert Mann, USA, 1955, 91 mins.

BEST DIRECTOR

Delbert Mann for
Marty

BEST ACTOR

Ernest Borgnine for
Marty

BEST ACTRESS

Anna Magnani for
The Rose Tattoo
A happy-go-lucky trucker awakens a widow to life's
joys in this flavorful adaptation of a Tennessee
Williams play. Starring Burt Lancaster and the
brilliant Anna Magnani. Photographed by James
Wong Howe.
 VHS: S13787. $19.95.
Daniel Mann, USA, 1955, 117 mins.

1956

BEST PICTURE

Around the World in Eighty Days
David Niven as Jules Verne's character Phineas Fogg
makes a wager he can circumnavigate the globe in
four score days. Along the way he meets 40 major
stars in cameo appearances and saves Shirley
MacLaine from being cooked on an Indian funeral
pyre.
 VHS: S06045. $29.98.
 Laser: LD70507. $39.98.
Michael Anderson, USA, 1956, 167 mins.

BEST DIRECTOR

George Stevens for
Giant
A film of staggering scale and grandeur detailing the
lives of cattleman Rock Hudson and his society wife
Elizabeth Taylor and three generations of land-rich
Texans. Featuring a stellar performance by James
Dean in the last role of his career.
 VHS: S00499. $24.98.
 Laser: LD70581. $39.98.
George Stevens, USA, 1956, 201 mins.

BEST ACTOR

Yul Brynner for
The King and I
Stern Siamese monarch Brynner is softened by the
influence of English governess Kerr as their clashing
cultures and personalities give way to an unspoken
love. Magnificent performance by Brynner in this
sumptuously produced and moving adaptation of the
Broadway musical. "Shall We Dance" highlights the
Rogers and Hammerstein score.
 VHS: S02541. $19.98.
 Laser: THX. LD75920. $124.98.
Walter Lang, USA, 1956, 133 mins.

BEST ACTRESS

Ingrid Bergman for
Anastasia
Yul Brynner and Ingrid Bergman star in this strange
but engrossing story about Czar Nicholas' missing
daughter, Anastasia. Brynner is a general who devises
a scheme to collect the last Czar's money by coaching
a young woman to pass as his sole surviving heir. As
the training progresses, however, even he begins to
wonder if this woman might actually be the Czarina
Anastasia. Bergman stars as the confused young
woman. Helen Hayes is also featured.
 VHS: S26148. $19.98.
Anatole Litvak, USA, 1956, 105 mins.

1957

BEST PICTURE

The Bridge on the River Kwai
Epic story of British prisoners of war held by the
Japanese combines psychological battles of will with
gripping action. Winner of seven Oscars including
Best Picture and Director. The Oscar for Screenplay
went to Pierre Boulle, the novelist who spoke no

English, because screenwriters Carl Foreman and Michael Wilson were blacklisted. With William Holden and Alec Guinness. Letterboxed.
VHS: S01785. $19.95.
Laser: LD72066. $49.95.
David Lean, Great Britain, 1957, 161 mins.

BEST DIRECTOR

David Lean for
The Bridge on the River Kwai

BEST ACTOR

Alec Guinness for
The Bridge on the River Kwai

BEST ACTRESS

Joanne Woodward for
The Three Faces of Eve
Tour de force by Joanne Woodward as a young woman with multiple personalities and three separate lives. Lee J. Cobb is the psychiatrist who tries to cure her.
VHS: S18098. $19.98.
Laser: Letterboxed. LD72339. $59.98.
Nunnally Johnson, USA, 1957, 91 mins.

1958

BEST PICTURE

Gigi
Leslie Caron is the bewitching title character in this dazzling musical that won nine Oscars. Maurice Chevalier sings "Thank Heaven for Little Girls" and doesn't get arrested. Based on a story by Colette, a young girl at the turn of the century is trained in Paris to be a courtesan. With Hermione Gingold and Louis Jourdan.
VHS: S07159. $19.95.
Laser: LD70582. $39.99.
Vincente Minnelli, USA, 1958, 116 mins.

BEST DIRECTOR

Vincente Minnelli for
Gigi

BEST ACTOR

David Niven for
Separate Tables
David Niven and Wendy Hiller won Oscars for their roles in this poignant adaptation of two combined Terence Rattigan one-act plays about a small, seaside English resort that houses a desperate group of unfulfilled people, including divorced couple Burt Lancaster and Rita Hayworth; Lancaster's mistress, Hiller; dubious ex-military hero Niven; and lonely spinster Deborah Kerr. The entire cast—including Gladys Cooper, Cathleen Nesbitt and Rod Taylor—is superlative.
VHS: S03769. $19.98.
Delbert Mann, USA, 1958, 98 mins.

BEST ACTRESS

Susan Hayward for
I Want to Live
Susan Hayward won an Oscar for her portrayal of a prostitute framed for murder and sentenced to the gas chamber. Fine jazz score by Johnny Mandel, featuring Theodore Bikel.
VHS: S03459. $24.95.
Laser: LD72268. $39.98.
Robert Wise, USA, 1958, 122 mins.

1959

BEST PICTURE

Ben-Hur (35th Anniversary Edition)
Celebrating the timelessness of this multi-academy award-winning film, this new Deluxe Collector's Edition of the classic starring Charlton Heston also includes the documentary *Ben Hur: The Making of an Epic*, narrated by Christopher Plummer, and the original theatrical trailer. VHS letterboxed.
VHS: S20641. $39.98.
Laser: 5-disc CAV boxed set. LD72371. $99.98.
William Wyler, 1959, USA, 204 mins.

BEST DIRECTOR

William Wyler for
Ben-Hur

BEST ACTOR

Charlton Heston for
Ben-Hur

BEST ACTRESS

Simone Signoret for
Room at the Top
Joe Lampton (Laurence Harvey) works in a dreary English factory town by day; at night he performs in a theatrical group. Also in the group is Joe's boss's daughter, Susan (Heather Sears), who plays the ingenue on stage and in real life, and hatches a plan to get Joe, telling him he'll get ahead faster by being the boss's son-in-law. However, Joe is attracted to an older, unhappily married French woman who's also in the group (Simone Signoret), and Joe tries to get away with seeing both women. With Hermione Baddely.
VHS: S33712. $29.99.
Jack Clayton, Great Britain, 1959, 115 mins.

1960

BEST PICTURE

The Apartment
Billy Wilder's great film of tears and laughter as Jack Lemmon and Shirley MacLaine wheel and deal over a New York apartment in a comedy of morality. Winner of five Oscars and worth at least 20 more. VHS letterboxed.
VHS: S05880. $19.95.
Laser: LD70506. $39.98.
Billy Wilder, USA, 1960, 125 mins.

BEST DIRECTOR

Billy Wilder for
The Apartment

BEST ACTOR

Burt Lancaster for
Elmer Gantry
Writer/director Richard Brooks' skillful adaptation of the Sinclair Lewis novel is an unsparing attack on a corrupt but charismatic evangelist named Elmer Gantry (Burt Lancaster), whose perverse pursuit of wealth and power tears apart the social and economic fabric of a small, midwestern town. Lancaster won an Oscar; Shirley Jones is brilliantly cast against type as a prostitute.
VHS: S02339. $19.98.
Laser: LD70193. $39.98.
Richard Brooks, USA, 1960, 146 mins.

Elizabeth Taylor for
Butterfield 8
Elizabeth Taylor won her first Oscar for her performance as call-girl Gloria Wandrous, a high class NYC tart who yearns to settle down and find Mr. Right. Based on the 1935 novel by John O'Hara. The title refers to a phone number. With Eddie Fisher, Dina Merrill, Mildred Dunnock, Susan Oliver, Kay Medford and Laurence Harvey as Weston Liggett.
VHS: S09148. $29.95.
Laser: LD70163. $34.98.
Daniel Mann, USA, 1960, 109 mins.

1961

BEST PICTURE

West Side Story
An extravaganza acclaimed for its musical and choreographic expertise. Score by Leonard Bernstein, lyrics by Stephen Sondheim, choreography by Jerome Robbins, starring Natalie Wood (her songs were dubbed by Marni Nixon) and Rita Moreno.
VHS: S01444. $19.95.
Laser: CAV, widescreen. LD70485. $124.95.
Laser: CLV, widescreen. LD70486. $69.95.
Robert Wise/Jerome Robbins, USA, 1961, 152 mins.

BEST DIRECTOR

Robert Wise and Jerome Robbins for
West Side Story

BEST ACTOR

Maximilian Schell for
Judgment at Nuremberg
Spencer Tracy presides over the trials of German war criminals in this well scripted, star-spangled production. Both Maximillian Schell and writer Abbey Mann won Oscars for this film. With Richard Widmark, Marlene Dietrich, Judy Garland, Montgomery Clift and William Shatner.
VHS: S09918. $29.95.
Laser: LD70605. $39.98.
Stanley Kramer, USA, 1961, 178 mins.

BEST ACTRESS

Sophia Loren for
Two Women
Sophia Loren won an Academy Award for her portrayal of a mother ravaged by war as she and her 13-year old daughter become the focus of attack by retreating German soldiers. A heartwrenching film—one of the best known—by Vittorio de Sica. Italian with English subtitles.
VHS: S04462. $29.95.
Vittorio de Sica, Italy, 1961, 99 mins.

1962

BEST PICTURE

Lawrence of Arabia
David Lean's finest achievement is a historically expansive biography of British officer T.E. Lawrence and his military and political victories in the Middle East. The film provides a complex portrait of Lawrence, from his charisma, verve and adventure to his experiments with the dark side of human nature. This 30th Anniversary Edition is presented in its original screen format (letterboxed), with its theatrical trailer, Maurice Jarre's overture, a short on the making of the film and a 32-page booklet. With Peter O'Toole, Alec Guinness, Anthony Quinn and

Omar Sharif. Cinematography by Freddie Young.
VHS: S17926. $24.95.
David Lean, Great Britain, 1962, 216 mins.

BEST DIRECTOR

David Lean for
Lawrence of Arabia

BEST ACTOR

Gregory Peck for
To Kill a Mockingbird
Gregory Peck won an Oscar for his role of Atticus Finch, the defense lawyer of a black man accused of rape in the American South. Script by Horton Foote from the novel by Harper Lee. A sensitive and powerful drama. Robert Duvall's film debut. Also Brock Peters, and Mary Badham as Scout. B&W.
VHS: S02640. $19.95.
Laser: LD70089. $39.98.
Robert Mulligan, USA, 1962, 129 mins.

BEST ACTRESS

Anne Bancroft for
The Miracle Worker
Anne Bancroft and Patty Duke both won Oscars for their roles in Arthur Penn's version of Annie Sullivan and her pupil, Helen Keller. The dramatic force of the battle between the strong willed Annie and the animal-willed Helen carries this extraordinary film.
VHS: S00860. $24.95.
Laser: LD71175. $34.98.
Arthur Penn, USA, 1962, 107 mins.

1963

BEST PICTURE

Tom Jones
Winner of four Academy Awards, *Tom Jones* is Tony Richardson's adaptation of Henry Fielding's famous novel about a mysteriously abandoned orphan who is adopted by the fussy Squire Allworthy, and thus begins a life of bawdy adventure. An outrageous and lusty comedy of 18th-century English life starring the sexy young Albert Finney. Screenplay by John Osborne.
VHS: S15548. $19.98.
Laser: LD71435. $29.98.
Tony Richardson, Great Britain, 1963, 129 mins.

BEST DIRECTOR

Tony Richardson for
Tom Jones

BEST ACTOR

Sidney Poitier for
Lilies of the Field
Sidney Poitier won an Oscar for this earnest, well-meaning and quiet work about a black handyman who reluctantly agrees to help a group of emigre East German nuns build a chapel. The heart of the film is the tender and expressive relationship between Poitier and Lilia Skala, who plays the Mother Superior. With Lisa Mann, Isa Crino and Stanley Adams. Music by Jerry Goldsmith. Screenplay by James Poe.
VHS: S13390. $19.98.
Laser: LD72124. $34.98.
Ralph Nelson, USA, 1963, 93 mins.

BEST ACTRESS

Patricia Neal for
Hud
Paul Newman is Hud, a man at odds with his father, tradition and himself. Patricia Neal and Melvyn

Douglas both won Academy Awards for their roles, as did James Wong for his brilliant cinematography.
VHS: S00590. **$14.95.**
Laser: Widescreen. **LD75305. $39.98.**
Martin Ritt, USA, 1963, 112 mins.

1964

BEST PICTURE

My Fair Lady
Audrey Hepburn and Rex Harrison star in this film adaptation of the classic Broadway musical by Lerner and Loewe, based on George Bernard Shaw's *Pygmalion*. Now it has been carefully restored, and even the original soundtracks recorded by Hepburn have been saved. Interviews with all the stars and the original trailer are included in this limited edition.
VHS: S21959. **$24.98.**
George Cukor, USA, 1964, 170 mins.

BEST DIRECTOR

George Cukor for
My Fair Lady

BEST ACTOR

Rex Harrison for
My Fair Lady

BEST ACTRESS

Julie Andrews for
Mary Poppins
This beloved Disney film combines brilliant, animated sequences with a delightful story about Julie Andrews as a magical nanny who transforms the lives of the children in her care. With Dick Van Dyke, Glynis Johns, Ed Wynn.
VHS: S01589. **$24.95.**
Laser: LD71132. **$44.95.**
Robert Stevenson, USA, 1964, 140 mins.

1965

BEST PICTURE

The Sound of Music
The hills are alive with the sounds of the Von Trapp family in this beloved Rodgers and Hammerstein epic musical. Julie Andrews and Christopher Plummer lead a cast of wholesome warblers through some terrific scenery and memorable songs. Awarded five Oscars. Letterboxed.
VHS: S04772. **$19.98.**
Robert Wise, USA, 1965, 172 mins.

BEST DIRECTOR

Robert Wise for
The Sound of Music

BEST ACTOR

Lee Marvin for
Cat Ballou
Jane Fonda is the title character in this satirical western with music, that won Lee Marvin his Oscar for riding a drunken horse. She plays a school teacher turned outlaw in a just cause. Nat King Cole and Stubby Kaye are the strolling minstrels and Cat's gang includes Dwayne Hickman, Michael Callan, Tom Nardini, and of course, Marvin Lee as Kid Shelleen and his evil no-nosed brother. Great fun.
VHS: S10977. **$19.95.**
Elliot Silverstein, USA, 1965, 96 mins.

BEST ACTRESS

Julie Christie for
Darling
Landmark British film made during the Kitchen Sink Drama period features Julie Christie as a woman who becomes a prisoner of her own modeling success, leaves her husband for a sexy TV commentator (Laurence Harvey), until she falls restless and falls in love with a jet setter.
Laser: LD70358. **$69.95.**
John Schlesinger, Great Britain, 1965, 122 mins.

1966

BEST PICTURE

A Man for All Seasons
Literate, penetrating treatment of the conflict between Thomas More (Paul Scofield) and King Henry VIII (Robert Shaw). Director Zinnemann concentrates on characterization rather than spectacle with superior results. With Orson Welles, Susannah York and Vanessa Redgrave.
VHS: S02639. **$19.95.**
Laser: Widescreen. **LD75496. $44.95.**
Fred Zinnemann, Great Britain, 1966, 120 mins.

BEST DIRECTOR

Fred Zinnemann for
A Man for All Seasons

BEST ACTOR

Paul Scofield for
A Man for All Seasons

BEST ACTRESS

Elizabeth Taylor for
Who's Afraid of Virginia Woolf?
Based on Edward Albee's smash hit play; Elizabeth Taylor and Richard Burton star in the story of the love-hate relationship between a middle-aged professor and his vitriolic but seductive wife.
DVD: DV60065. **$24.98.**
VHS: S01737. **$19.98.**
Laser: LD70705. **$39.98.**
Mike Nichols, USA, 1966, 129 mins.

1967

BEST PICTURE

In the Heat of the Night
Winner of five Oscars, *In the Heat of the Night* stars Rod Steiger as a red neck sheriff who grudgingly accepts help from Sidney Poitier, a black big city detective. Music score by Quincy Jones.
VHS: S03621. **$19.95.**
Laser: LD74675. **$34.98.**
Norman Jewison, USA, 1967, 110 mins.

BEST DIRECTOR

Mike Nichols for
The Graduate
Mike Nichols' film in a new, 25th anniversary edition. Dustin Hoffman stars as the naive college graduate who's seduced by the middle-aged Mrs. Robinson (Anne Bancroft) and promptly falls in love with her daughter (Katharine Ross). This special limited edition is presented in its original wide-screen format and features interviews with the original cast and crew.
Laser: CAV. **LD70371. $99.95.**
Mike Nichols, USA, 1967, 106 mins.

BEST ACTOR

Rod Steiger for
In the Heat of the Night

BEST ACTRESS

Katharine Hepburn for
Guess Who's Coming to Dinner
Stanley Kramer directs this Oscar-winning movie about the reaction to an interracial relationship by the parents of both parties. Spencer Tracy and Katharine Hepburn make their last film together as the liberal but frazzled couple who are a bit uneasy about Katharine Houghton's fiance Sidney Poitier. With Beach Richards, Cecil Kellaway and Roy E. Glenn Sr.
VHS: S13316. $14.98.
Stanley Kramer, USA, 1967, 108 mins.

1968

BEST PICTURE

Oliver!
The musical version of Dicken's classic *Oliver Twist* adds song and dance to the story of a brave lad trying to survive amidst wretched social conditions and dire poverty. With Mark Lester as Oliver and Jack Wild as the Artful Dodger. Ron Moody is Fagin. Also Oliver Reed, Shani Wallis and Hugh Griffith. Six Oscars.
VHS: S00952. $19.95.
Laser: Letterboxed. **LD72187. $39.95.**
Carol Reed, Great Britain, 1968, 153 mins.

BEST DIRECTOR

Carol Reed for
Oliver!

BEST ACTOR

Cliff Robertson for
Charly
Cliff Robertson won an Oscar for his performance as a mentally retarded patient involved in a program designed to increase his mental capacity by extraordinary levels. With Claire Bloom as his friend and medical advisor. Based on Daniel Keyes' novel, *Flowers for Algernon.* Algernon is a white rodent...who is being tested along with Charly. With Lilia Skala and Dick Van Patten. Not currently available on video.
Ralph Nelson, USA, 1968, 103 mins.

BEST ACTRESS (tie)

Katharine Hepburn for
The Lion in Winter
Peter O'Toole and Katharine Hepburn star in this costume drama concerning royal succession at the English court of Henry II. Based on the successful play, this sumptuous screen version is now transferred to video in a letterbox format, to capture its stunning visual impact, on the occasion of its 25th anniversary.
Laser: LD72304. $49.95.
Anthony Harvey, Great Britain, 1968, 134 mins.

and Barbra Streisand for
Funny Girl
Barbra Streisand made her Oscar-winning film debut in this epic screen biography of entertainer Fanny Brice. She sings, dances and roller-skates her way to the top of the show business ladder. There is no doubt about it, a star is born, so please don't rain on her parade. With Omar Sharif as gambler and first husband Nicky Arnstein, Anne Francis, Kay Medford, and Walter Pidgeon as Flo Ziegfeld.
VHS: S10976. $19.95.
William Wyler, USA, 1968, 155 mins.

1969

BEST PICTURE

Midnight Cowboy
The shocking story of Cowboy Joe Buck, played by Jon Voight, made history when it was released 25 years ago. This naive country boy with a horrible secret moves to New York, where the streetwise Ratso Rizzo (Dustin Hoffman) becomes his guide to seamy city life. Together they explore the world of hustling and even visit Warhol's factory, developing a deep friendship in the process. A 25th Anniversary re-release.
DVD: DV60090. $24.98.
VHS: S21826. $19.98.
Laser: LD74499. $49.98.
John Schlesinger, USA, 1969, 113 mins.

BEST DIRECTOR

John Schlesinger for
Midnight Cowboy

BEST ACTOR

John Wayne for
True Grit
John Wayne won an Oscar for his portrayal of a one-eyed, overweight lawman named Rooster Cogburn. He is recruited by a tenacious teenage girl to find the killer of her father. Glen Campbell is the handsome Texas Ranger after the same gang. With Robert Duvall, Dennis Hopper, Jeff Corey and Kim Darby as Mattie Ross.
VHS: S05097. $14.95.
Laser: LD75393. $35.98.
Henry Hathaway, USA, 1969, 128 mins.

BEST ACTRESS

Maggie Smith for
The Prime of Miss Jean Brodie
Maggie Smith is top-notch as the unconventional, eccentric teacher in an all-girls school in Edinburgh during the 1930s. Miss Brodie's students, the "creme de la creme," adore their teacher, but when they try to shape their lives after Miss Brodie's, disaster ensues. Based on Muriel Spark's novel.
VHS: S10746. $19.98.
Ronald Neame, Great Britain, 1969, 116 mins.

1970

BEST PICTURE

Patton
George C. Scott delivers a stirring performance in this classic screen biography of the charismatic and controversial General George S. Patton. Winner of six Academy Awards.
VHS: S03475. $29.98.
Laser: THX. **LD76096. $89.98.**
Franklin J. Schaffner, USA, 1970, 176 mins.

BEST DIRECTOR

Franklin J. Schaffner for
Patton

BEST ACTOR

George C. Scott for
Patton

BEST ACTRESS

Glenda Jackson for
Women in Love
Two sisters, sexually mature and intellectually active,
struggle against the confines of a rural English
mining town and its rigidly classed layers of society,
in this adaptation of D.H. Lawrence's study of sexual
uneasiness and doubt. With Alan Bates, Oliver Reed,
Glenda Jackson, Jennie Linden.
VHS: S01479. $19.98.
Ken Russell, Great Britain, 1970, 129 mins.

1971

BEST PICTURE

The French Connection
William Friedkin's edge-of-the-seat thriller about two
hard-nosed New York detectives who stumble into an
international narcotics smuggling ring. Contains
probably the most exciting car chase ever filmed.
With an exceptional performance by the always good
Gene Hackman, as well as Roy Scheider and
Fernando Rey.
VHS: S21861. $14.98.
Laser: LD75484. $39.98.
William Friedkin, USA, 1971, 102 mins.

BEST DIRECTOR

William Friedkin for
The French Connection

BEST ACTOR

Gene Hackman for
The French Connection

BEST ACTRESS

Jane Fonda for
Klute
Jane Fonda stars as the high-priced call girl used as a
bait to lure a killer in this suspense-filled mystery.
She won the Best Actress Oscar for her compelling
character study. With Donald Sutherland and Roy
Scheider.
VHS: S11618. $19.98.
Alan J. Pakula, USA, 1971, 114 mins.

1972

BEST PICTURE

The Godfather
An epic featuring Marlon Brando as the patriarch of
the Corleone family, masterfully balanced between
the story of family life and the family crime business.
With Al Pacino, James Caan, Robert Duvall, Diane
Keaton. Based on Mario Puzo's novel. Music by Nino
Rota. Letterboxed.
VHS: S00509. $24.95.
Francis F. Coppola, USA, 1972, 171 mins.

BEST DIRECTOR

Bob Fosse for
Cabaret
Liza Minnelli and Joel Grey give extraordinary
performances in Bob Fosse's musical drama that
mirrors the decay and decadence of Germany on the
eve of Hitler's rise to power. With Marisa Berenson
and Michael York.
VHS: S01837. $19.98.
Laser: LD72168. $39.98.
Bob Fosse, USA, 1972, 119 mins.

BEST ACTOR

Marlon Brando for
The Godfather

BEST ACTRESS

Liza Minnelli for
Cabaret

1973

BEST PICTURE

The Sting
The Academy Award-winning classic starring Paul
Newman and Robert Redford as a pair of con artists
in 1930s Chicago who set out to rip off a big-time
racketeer. With Robert Shaw, Charles Durning, Eileen
Brennan and wonderful vintage ragtime music by
Scott Joplin adapted by Marvin Hamlisch.
VHS: S30984. $19.98.
George Roy Hill, USA, 1973, 129 mins.

BEST DIRECTOR

George Roy Hill for
The Sting

BEST ACTOR

Jack Lemmon for
Save the Tiger
Almost 20 years before *Glengarry Glen Ross*, Jack
Lemmon won an Academy Award for his portrayal in
this film of a decent but desperate middle-aged man
who commits arson for the insurance money in order
to save his business. Thayer David and Jack Gilford
are excellent as the arsonist and Lemmon's business
partner.
VHS: S30985. $19.98.
John G. Avildsen, USA, 1973, 100 mins.

BEST ACTRESS

Glenda Jackson for
A Touch of Class
Glenda Jackson and George Segal turn on the
chemistry in this wry comedy about a married man
intent on a carefree affair, who falls in love with his
mistress. Not currently available on video.
Melvin Frank, USA, 1973, 105 mins.

1974

BEST PICTURE

The Godfather Part II
A companion piece to the original *Godfather*, this
continues the saga of two generations of successive
power in the Corleone family. Coppola tells the story
of the rise of a young Don Vito, played by Robert De
Niro, and the ascension of the new Don Michael,
played by Al Pacino. Letterboxed.
VHS: S00510. $24.95.
Francis F. Coppola, USA, 1974, 200 mins.

BEST DIRECTOR

Francis F. Coppola for
The Godfather Part II

BEST ACTOR

Art Carney for
Harry and Tonto
Paul Mazursky's poignant drama about an elderly man's cross-country odyssey, featuring remarkable performances by Art Carney and Ellen Burstyn.
VHS: S04337. $19.98.
Paul Mazursky, USA, 1974, 115 mins.

BEST ACTRESS

Ellen Burstyn for
Alice Doesn't Live Here Anymore
A subtle masterpiece that transforms the struggle of one woman into a memorable symbol of liberation and courage. Stars Ellen Burstyn in an Academy Award winning performance, with Kris Kristofferson and Diane Ladd.
VHS: S03481. $19.98.
Laser: LD70500. $34.98.
Martin Scorsese, USA, 1974, 105 mins.

1975

BEST PICTURE

One Flew Over the Cuckoo's Nest
Milos Forman's sharp adaptation of Ken Kesey's anti-authoritarian novel about a shrewd nonconformist (Jack Nicholson) sentenced to an insane asylum who encourages a group of marginal misfits to assert their rights and independence, over the rigid opposition of the head nurse (Louise Fletcher). Cinematography by Haskell Wexler. With Will Sampson, Brad Dourif, Sydney Lassick, Christopher Lloyd, Danny DeVito and Scatman Crothers. Winner of the five top Academy Awards.
DVD: DV60091. $24.98.
VHS: S18973. $19.98.
Milos Forman, USA, 1975, 134 mins.

BEST DIRECTOR

Milos Forman for
One Flew Over the Cuckoo's Nest

BEST ACTOR

Jack Nicholson for
One Flew Over the Cuckoo's Nest

BEST ACTRESS

Louise Fletcher for
One Flew Over the Cuckoo's Nest

1976

BEST PICTURE

Rocky
Not currently available on video.

BEST DIRECTOR

John G. Avildsen for
Rocky

BEST ACTOR

Peter Finch for
Network
A savage satire written by Paddy Chayefsky, looking at the powers behind television programming. With a sizzling performance by Peter Finch (I'm mad as hell and I'm not going to take it anymore) as newscaster Howard Beale, with Faye Dunaway and William Holden.
VHS: S01817. $14.95.
Laser: Letterboxed. LD76399. $39.99.
Sidney Lumet, USA, 1976, 116 mins.

BEST ACTRESS

Faye Dunaway for
Network

1977

BEST PICTURE

Annie Hall
One of Woody Allen's best and funniest films, with Diane Keaton as the sometime object of Woody Allen's affections and expressions of his neurosis. Winner of many Academy Awards. With Paul Simon and Carol Kane.
VHS: S00059. $19.95.
Laser: CLV, Criterion. LD70339. $49.95.
Laser: Deluxe, letterboxed edition. Includes original theatrical trailer. LD71506. $34.98.
Woody Allen, USA, 1977, 94 mins.

BEST DIRECTOR

Woody Allen for
Annie Hall

BEST ACTOR

Richard Dreyfuss for
The Goodbye Girl
Richard Dreyfuss won an Oscar for his role in this Neil Simon comedy about an egotistical looking-for-work actor and the opinionated divorcee with whom he shares an apartment. Marsha Mason is his unwilling roommate. Quinn Cummings is the child who is wise beyond her years. Funny and tender and set in New York City. With Paul Benedict and Barbara Rhoades.
VHS: S08296. $19.98.
Laser: LD70144. $34.98.
Herbert Ross, USA, 1977, 110 mins.

BEST ACTRESS

Diane Keaton for
Annie Hall

1978

BEST PICTURE

The Deer Hunter
Powerful drama that follows a group of friends from a steel town in Pennsylvania through their Vietnam experiences with fine ensemble work from Robert De Niro, Christopher Walken, John Savage, John Cazale and Meryl Streep.
VHS: S02738. $29.95.
Laser: LD70022. $44.98.
Michael Cimino, USA, 1978, 183 mins.

BEST DIRECTOR

Michael Cimino for
The Deer Hunter

BEST ACTOR

Jon Voigt for
Coming Home
Jane Fonda, Jon Voight and Bruce Dern star in a
powerful drama about the effects of the Vietnam War
on the home front. Fonda falls in love with a disabled
vet (Voight) while husband Dern is fighting overseas.
Good supporting work by Penelope Milford and
Robert Carradine.
VHS: S04718. $19.98.
Laser: Chapter search. Includes original trailer.
LD71636. $39.98.
Hal Ashby, USA, 1978, 127 mins.

BEST ACTRESS

Jane Fonda for
Coming Home

1979

BEST PICTURE

Kramer vs. Kramer
Dustin Hoffman must become a single parent when
Meryl Streep walks out on their marriage and their
young son. A terrific male weepie where Hoffman
learns how to make French toast and lots of important
parent stuff. With Justin Henry, Jane Alexander.
Several Oscars, including Best Picture.
VHS: S03905. $19.95.
Laser: LD72188. $34.95.
Robert Benton, USA, 1979, 104 mins.

BEST DIRECTOR

Robert Benton for
Kramer vs. Kramer

BEST ACTOR

Dustin Hoffman for
Kramer vs. Kramer

BEST ACTRESS

Sally Field for
Norma Rae
Sally Field in her Oscar-winning performance as a
spunky Southern mill worker gradually won over to
unionization by Ron Leibman as a New York
organizer. With Beau Bridges.
VHS: S02343. $19.98.
Laser: LD71257. $34.98.
Martin Ritt, USA, 1979, 117 mins.

1980

BEST PICTURE

Ordinary People
An intense examination of a family being torn apart
by tragedy and tension, *Ordinary People* won four
Academy Awards including Best Picture and Director.
Featuring Donald Sutherland, Mary Tyler Moore and
Timothy Hutton.
VHS: S03261. $19.95.
Robert Redford, USA, 1980, 124 mins.

BEST DIRECTOR

Robert Redford for
Ordinary People

BEST ACTOR

Robert De Niro for
Raging Bull
Robert De Niro gives an incredible performance as
Jake LaMotta, the controversial middleweight fighter
of the 1940's. *Raging Bull* shows how LaMotta
turned his fears into the physical energy needed to
become a champion, while destroying his private life.
Breathtaking cinematography!
DVD: DV60092. $24.98.
VHS: S01084. $19.95.
Laser: Letterboxed, chapter search. Includes
original theatrical trailer. **LD71669. $39.98.**
Martin Scorsese, USA, 1980, 127 mins.

BEST ACTRESS

Sissy Spacek for
Coal Miner's Daughter
The film biography of country-western superstar
Loretta Lynn. Sissy Spacek is great as the little kid
from Butcher's Hollow who grew up to entertain
millions. With excellent supporting work by Tommy
Lee Jones, Levon Helm and Beverly D'Angelo as
Patsy Cline.
VHS: S07805. $19.95.
Michael Apted, USA, 1980, 125 mins.

1981

BEST PICTURE

Chariots of Fire
Drama based on a true story of two young men who
run in the 1924 Olympics—a Jewish student from
Cambridge and a Scottish missionary. Also won an
Oscar for Best Musical Score, by Vangelis.
DVD: DV60085. $24.98.
VHS: S00228. $19.98.
Laser: LD70542. $34.98.
Hugh Hudson, Great Britain, 1981, 123 mins.

BEST DIRECTOR

Warren Beatty for
Reds
A great American film. At its center, *Reds* is the
passionate love affair of legendary journalist and
American socialist John Reed (Warren Beatty) and
feminist author Louise Bryant (Diane Keaton).
Beatty, who co-wrote, produced and directed the film,
also crisscrosses the emotional undercurrents with
social history: exploring the birth of the American
labor movement; the emergence of socialism; the
bohemian Greenwich Village innergroup that
included playwright Eugene O'Neill and anarchist
Emma Goldman. A long, beguiling film of exquisite
taste and intelligence. The extraordinary cast includes
Jack Nicholson as O'Neill, Maureen Stapleton as
Goldman, Edward Herrmann as editor Max Eastman
and *Being There* author Jerzy Kosinski as bolshevik
leader Gregory Zinoviev. Cinematography by the
great Vittorio Storaro.
VHS: S02566. $29.95.
Warren Beatty, USA, 1981, 195 mins.

BEST ACTOR

Henry Fonda for
On Golden Pond
Henry Fonda and Katharine Hepburn play an aging
married couple, Norman and Ethel Thayer, spending a
dramatic summer in the woods. Their estranged
daughter (Jane Fonda) drops by to clear the air and
leave Doug McKeon for them to watch. Three
Oscars. Henry Fonda's last film.
VHS: S03479. $14.98.
Mark Rydell, USA, 1981, 110 mins.

Katharine Hepburn for
On Golden Pond

1982

BEST PICTURE

Gandhi
Richard Attenborough's dream project realized in epic style with Ben Kingsley as Gandhi in an Oscar winning performance, and a cast including Candice Bergen, Martin Sheen and John Gielgud.
VHS: S02022. $29.95.
Laser: LD72202. $49.95.
Richard Attenborough, Great Britain, 1982, 187 mins.

BEST DIRECTOR

Richard Attenborough for
Gandhi

BEST ACTOR

Ben Kingsley for
Gandhi

BEST ACTRESS

Meryl Streep for
Sophie's Choice
Meryl Streep depicts a Polish Catholic mother who survives the death camp at Auschwitz but not the memories that haunt her in her new life in the United States. Based on the William Styron novel. With Kevin Kline and Peter MacNicol.
VHS: S04600. $14.98.
Alan J. Pakula, USA, 1982, 150 mins.

1983

BEST PICTURE

Terms of Endearment
Winner of five Oscars including Best Picture, the story of the changing relationship between a mother and daughter over the years mixes humor and heartache. A tear-jerker. With Shirley MacLaine, Jack Nicholson and Debra Winger.
VHS: S03916. $19.95.
James L. Brooks, USA, 1983, 132 mins.

BEST DIRECTOR

James L. Brooks for
Terms of Endearment

BEST ACTOR

Robert Duvall for
Tender Mercies
A gentle film starring Robert Duvall as a hard-luck country singer trying to get his life together with the support of a new family. Written by Horton Foote, directed by the Australian director of *Breaker Morant*.
VHS: S01309. $19.98.
Bruce Beresford, USA, 1982, 93 mins.

BEST ACTRESS

Shirley MacLaine for
Terms of Endearment

1984

BEST PICTURE

Amadeus
Milos Forman's adaptation of Peter Shaffer's play is structured as a confession related in flashback, told by the aging court composer, and Mozart's adversary, Salieri (F. Murray Abraham). Cinematographer Miroslav Ondricek finds a baroque, expressionist intensity in the Prague locations. Choreography by Twyla Tharp. With Elizabeth Berridge, Simon Callow, Roy Dotrice, Christine Ebersole and Jeffrey Jones. Winner of eight Academy Awards.
VHS: S00041. $14.98.
Laser: LD75367. $44.98.
Milos Forman, USA, 1984, 160 mins.

BEST DIRECTOR

Milos Forman for
Amadeus

BEST ACTOR

F. Murray Abraham for
Amadeus

BEST ACTRESS

Sally Field for
Places in the Heart
Against a Depression-torn background in Waxahachi, Texas, Sally Field plays a Sheriff's widow who struggles against incredible hardships. With fine performances by John Malkovich, Danny Glover, Ed Harris and Amy Madigan.
Laser: LD71276. $34.98.
Robert Benton, USA, 1984, 113 mins.

1985

BEST PICTURE

Out of Africa
The autobiographical story of Karen Blixen (pen name Isak Dinesen) and her life on a coffee plantation in Kenya around 1914. Winner of seven Academy Awards, starring Robert Redford, Meryl Streep and Klaus Maria Brandauer.
VHS: S00981. $19.95.
Laser: LD70063. $39.98.
Sydney Pollack, USA, 1985, 161 mins.

BEST DIRECTOR

Sydney Pollack for
Out of Africa

BEST ACTOR

William Hurt for
Kiss of the Spider Woman
One of the finest films of 1985, from the director of *Pixote*. Featuring an Academy Award winning performance by William Hurt as Molina, and Raul Julia as Valentin, the political prisoner. With the incredible Sonia Braga. Based on the novel by Manuel Puig.
VHS: S00686. $14.98.
Hector Babenco, USA, 1985, 119 mins.

BEST ACTRESS

Geraldine Page for
The Trip to Bountiful
Geraldine Page won the Oscar for Best Actress in this

story of an old woman returning to her childhood home in order to embrace memories. But she is trapped inside an apartment and treated like a child by her son, and ultimately escapes and gets a chance to revive her dreams.
VHS: S01811. $14.98.
Laser: LD72314. $29.99.
Peter Masterson, USA, 1985, 105 mins.

1986

BEST PICTURE

Platoon
Charlie Sheen goes to Southeast Asia and finds out that war is a very traumatic experience. Giant leeches, killer dope and better-prepared opponents are almost as dangerous to his existance as the other members of his platoon. With Tom Berenger and Willem Dafoe.
VHS: S04752. $19.98.
Oliver Stone, USA, 1986, 120 mins.

BEST DIRECTOR

Oliver Stone for
Platoon

BEST ACTOR

Paul Newman for
The Color of Money
Martin Scorsese's acclaimed update of *The Hustler*. Paul Newman returns as the pool-hall wizard Fast Eddie, who pursues his belief that "money won is twice as sweet as money earned." With Tom Cruise and Mary Elizabeth Mastrantonio.
VHS: S03470. $19.95.
Laser: LD70924. $44.99.
Martin Scorsese, USA, 1986, 119 mins.

BEST ACTRESS

Marlee Matlin for
Children of a Lesser God
William Hurt, Marlee Matlin, Piper Laurie and Philip Bosco star in this Academy-Award nominated film, the screen version of a successful Broadway play, with Hurt the special education teacher who falls in love with a troubled deaf woman.
VHS: S03303. $19.95.
Randa Haines, USA, 1986, 119 mins.

1987

BEST PICTURE

The Last Emperor
Bernardo Bertolucci's multiple Academy-award winner, set and shot in Beijing's Forbidden City, stars John Lone as Pu Yi, the last emperor of China who, at the age of three, became the "Lord of 10,000 Years," China's last emperor. In English. Not currently available on video.
Bernardo Bertolucci, Italy/USA, 1987, 140 mins.

BEST DIRECTOR

Bernardo Bertolucci for
The Last Emperor

BEST ACTOR

Michael Douglas for
Wall Street
Oliver Stone invades the stone canyons of the stock market battle zone with the story of a young broker who is willing to do most anything to land the big account. Michael Douglas struck gold for his "greed is good" philosophy. With Charlie Sheen, Martin

Sheen, Hal Holbrook, Sean Young and Daryl Hannah.
Laser: CLV. LD72105. $39.98.
Oliver Stone, USA, 1987, 128 mins.

BEST ACTRESS

Cher for
Moonstruck
The winner of three Oscars, this charming, romantic, ethnic comedy involves a somewhat dowdy Cher involved with two brothers. She's engaged to Danny Aiello but in love with Nicolas Cage. Her parents, Olympia Dukakis and Vincent Gardenia, have their own problems, but wish her the best. Screenplay by John Patrick Shanley (*Five Corners*). Set in Brooklyn.
VHS: S07105. $19.98.
Laser: LD76278. $39.99.
Norman Jewison, USA, 1987, 103 mins.

1988

BEST PICTURE

Rain Man
Four Oscars went to this road movie about two brothers who didn't know the other existed until fate tosses them together. The plot may be very similar to the movie comedy *Twins* starring Danny DeVito and Arnold Schwarzenegger but Tom Cruise and Dustin Hoffman look spiffier in their matching outfits. A sensitive and strongly performed film. VHS letterboxed.
DVD: DV60095. $24.98.
VHS: S09575. $19.98.
Laser: LD70662. $29.98.
Barry Levinson, USA, 1988, 120 mins.

BEST DIRECTOR

Barry Levinson for
Rain Man

BEST ACTOR

Dustin Hoffman for
Rain Man

BEST ACTRESS

Jodie Foster for
The Accused
A stern public prosecutor (Kelly McGillis) takes on a gang-rape case and tries to go simply by the book. But the victim, played powerfully by Jodie Foster refuses to make things easy, requiring full retribution for what she has suffered. Eventually, they begin to trust one another, and work together to put those responsible behind bars. Based on a notorious real-life case.
VHS: S13708. $19.95.
Laser: LD75116. $24.98.
Jonathan Kaplan, USA, 1988, 110 mins.

1989

BEST PICTURE

Driving Miss Daisy
The Pulitzer prizewinning play of Alfred Uhry walked off with four Oscars. The story concerns the long-term relationship between a strong-willed, elderly, Jewish Southern matron and her accommodating black chauffeur. Jessica Tandy and Morgan Freeman star in this genteel comedy of bigotry and friendship. With Patti Lupone, Esther Rolle and Dan Aykroyd as Tandy's son, Boolie.
DVD: DV60087. $24.98.
VHS: S12524. $19.98.
Laser: LD70562. $24.98.
Bruce Beresford, USA, 1989, 99 mins.

Oliver Stone for
Born on the 4th of July
Tom Cruise performs the true Vietnam experience of Ron Kovic, following his development as an eager, young war volunteer to a paralyzed, embittered veteran. As a youth, and representative of the nation in general, Kovic was inspired by Kennedy's "Ask not what your country can do for you..." speech, but returned from the war to a changed nation and became a vehement and outspoken anti-war demonstrator. With Kyra Sedgwick and Willem Dafoe.
VHS: $12464. $19.95.
Laser: LD70017. $39.98.
Oliver Stone, USA, 1989, 145 mins.

BEST ACTOR

Daniel Day Lewis for
My Left Foot
Distinguished by a brilliant performance from Daniel Day-Lewis, this is a true story about life, laughter and the occasional miracle. Day-Lewis plays Christy Brown, who has cerebral palsy, and whose mother's faith prompts him to paint and write. Nominated for five Academy Awards.
VHS: $12199. $19.98.
Jim Sheridan, Great Britain, 1989, 103 mins.

BEST ACTRESS

Jessica Tandy for
Driving Miss Daisy

1990

BEST PICTURE

Dances with Wolves (Special Expanded Edition)
A troubled Civil War veteran goes West and finds what he's been missing in the lifestyle and hunting grounds of the Lakota Sioux. Kevin Costner stars as Lt. John Dunbar, aka Dances with Wolves, in this epic tribute to how the West was lost for the Native American population. Seven Oscars were awarded; and the fine cast includes Mary McDonnell, Grahame Greene, Maury Chaykin, and lots of roaming bison. Special thanks should also go to the lovely and talented Moira McLaughlin whose yeoman, behind-the-scenes efforts were instrumental in getting this important film made. Digitally mastered. In English and Lakota.
VHS: $14602. $29.95.
Kevin Costner, USA, 1990, 237 mins.

BEST DIRECTOR

Kevin Costner for
Dances with Wolves

BEST ACTOR

Jeremy Irons for
Reversal of Fortune
Jeremy Irons won an Oscar for his wickedly suave performance as accused socialite Claus von Bulow. The Danish born aristocrat goes from the society page to the front page when his rich American wife suspiciously falls into a coma. The comatose Sunny—played by Glenn Close—narrates much of the film, which also stars Ron Silver as the dynamic appeal lawyer Alan Dershowitz. Based on the book by Dershowitz that was brilliantly adapted for the screen by Nicholas Kazan.
VHS: $13923. $19.95.
Barbet Schroeder, USA, 1990, 112 mins.

BEST ACTRESS

Kathy Bates for
Misery
Kathy Bates stars as a devoted and deranged fan of unsuspecting author Paul Sheldon (James Caan) in this thriller. From the novel by Stephen King.
Laser: LD72450. $39.99.
Rob Reiner, USA, 1990, 107 mins.

1991

BEST PICTURE

The Silence of the Lambs
Jonathan Demme's impressive entry into the thriller/slasher genre has more than a few interesting things to say about the way many of this country's most brutal mass murderers end up becoming something akin to minor celebrities (with their own television shows, books, newspaper profiles, movies and talk show appearances). In the film's final scene the audience is implicated most directly, as we are prompted to laugh at the gruesome prospect of another impending murder. Pretty dark and unsavory stuff, but along the way Demme manages to orchestrate several brilliant sequences in the midst of his well-structured narrative; and the performances, led by Jodie Foster and Anthony Hopkins, are uniformly excellent.
VHS: $14730. $19.98.
Laser: CLV. LD72108. $99.98.
Jonathan Demme, USA, 1991, 118 mins.

BEST DIRECTOR

Jonathan Demme for
The Silence of the Lambs

BEST ACTOR

Anthony Hopkins for
The Silence of the Lambs

BEST ACTRESS

Jodie Foster for
The Silence of the Lambs

1992

BEST PICTURE

Unforgiven
Clint Eastwood's brilliant reconsideration of the American western. Set in the 1880s, a reformed gunman and failed farmer (Eastwood) reluctantly agrees to collect the bounty on two cowboys who slashed a prostitute's face, setting in motion a mythic confrontation with a corrupt sheriff (Gene Hackman), a hired English assassin (Richard Harris) and a dime novelist (Saul Rubinek). With Morgan Freeman and Frances Fisher. Winner of four Academy Awards.
DVD: DV60120. $24.98.
VHS: $18724. $19.98.
Clint Eastwood, USA, 1992, 131 mins.

BEST DIRECTOR

Clint Eastwood for
Unforgiven

BEST ACTOR

Al Pacino for
Scent of a Woman
Martin Brest's entertainment about the curious

friendship between a retired, disillusioned, career officer (Al Pacino), who accidentally blinded himself, and a working-class student (Chris O'Donnell) who's hired to care for him during a long weekend holiday. Gabrielle Anwar turns in a stunning performance as a mysterious object of Pacino's affection.

VHS: $19008. $19.98.
Laser: Letterboxed. **LD71891. $39.98.**
Martin Brest, USA, 1992, 157 mins.

BEST ACTRESS

Emma Thompson for
Howards End
Merchant/Ivory's wonderfully acted, beautifully constructed adaptation of E.M. Forster's novel about the unconventional love, class struggle and hypocrisy of upper class Edwardian England. The film concerns two sisters (Academy Award winner Emma Thompson and Helena Bonham Carter) and their romantic and personal entanglements with aristocratic, wealthy landowners (Anthony Hopkins and Vanessa Redgrave). Cinematography is by Tony Pierce-Roberts. Academy Award-winning screenplay by Ruth Prawer Jhabvala. With James Wilby, Samuel West and Prunella Scales.

VHS: $18519. $19.95.
Laser: LD71869. $39.95.
James Ivory, Great Britain, 1992, 143 mins.

1993

BEST PICTURE

Schindler's List
This Academy Award-winning film tells the story of Oskar Schindler, who saved hundreds of Jews from certain death in Nazi-dominated Europe. Adapted from Thomas Keneally's novel and starring Ben Kingsley, Liam Neeson and Ralph Fiennes. The Collector's Edition includes the novel, a compact disc of the Academy Award-winning score by John Williams and a booklet with an introduction by Steven Spielberg. Letterboxed.

Standard Edition.
VHS: $21539. $29.95.
Laser: LD74525. $49.98.
Steven Spielberg, USA, 1993, 197 mins.

BEST DIRECTOR

Steven Spielberg for
Schindler's List

BEST ACTOR

Tom Hanks for
Philadelphia
Winner of two Academy Awards, Tom Hanks for Best Actor and Bruce Springsteen for Best Song, this film tells the moving story of a man who must fight not only AIDS but an ignorant and bigoted society. Denzel Washington plays the lawyer who must struggle with his own unfounded fears to fight for justice on behalf of his colleague, Tom Hanks. With Jason Robards, Mary Steenburgen, Antonio Banderas and Joanne Woodward.

DVD: DV60030. $24.95.
VHS: $21120. $19.95.
Laser: LD72416. $39.95.
Jonathan Demme, USA, 1993, 125 mins.

BEST ACTRESS

Holly Hunter for
The Piano
Holly Hunter's Oscar-winning performance as a mute woman dedicated to her music takes center stage in this lush drama set in 19th-century New Zealand. Harvey Keitel co-stars as the brutish but sensitive man who gives her back what seemed irrevocably lost. A young Anna Paquin more than holds her own with a performance that garnered this new star an

Oscar for Best Supporting Actress.
VHS: $20871. $19.98.
Jane Campion, Australia/New Zealand, 1993, 121 mins.

1994

BEST PICTURE

Forrest Gump
Tom Hanks stars as the endearing, naive hero of this unlikely historical film that was nominated for 14 Oscars. Through the magic of trick photography, Gump encounters several important figures and plays a hitherto unknown role in the unfolding of current events. Gary Sinise and Sally Field also star. Letterboxed.

VHS: $24309. $19.95.
Laser: THX. **LD75300. $49.98.**
Robert Zemeckis, USA, 1994, 142 mins.

BEST DIRECTOR

Robert Zemeckis for
Forrest Gump

BEST ACTOR

Tom Hanks for
Forrest Gump

BEST ACTRESS

Jessica Lange for
Blue Sky
Tony Richardson's final film received a belated release despite Jessica Lange's Oscar-winning performance as Carly, which also won her a Golden Globe. Carly is a sultry woman who dreams of glamour. Tommy Lee Jones plays Army Major Hank Marshall. Together they share a passionate roller-coaster marriage. When Hank is thrust into the center of a high level military cover-up, the only person who can save him is Carly.

VHS: $24407. $14.98.
Laser: LD74918. $39.99.
Tony Richardson, USA, 1994, 88 mins.

1995

BEST PICTURE

Braveheart
Mel Gibson is Braveheart, the legendary Scottish warrior who battled the English in the 13th century. In this epic film, the very story of independence which still fires the Scottish imagination is brought alive. It's a tale of fierce determination and unforgettable courage with superb battle sequences and a touching love story. Letterboxed.

VHS: $27169. $24.95.
Laser: THX. **LD75536. $49.95.**
Mel Gibson, USA, 1995, 177 mins.

BEST DIRECTOR

Mel Gibson for
Braveheart

BEST ACTOR

Nicolas Cage for
Leaving Las Vegas
Nicolas Cage and Elisabeth Shue star in this tender love story of two people living on the far side of hope. Ben Sanderson (Cage) is an alcoholic Los Angeles screenwriter who decides to move to Las Vegas to die. There he meets a prostitute (Shue), equally unapologetic about her own life choices, and

together they fall in love. An engrossing, complex and beautiful film. VHS letterboxed.
VHS: S27709. $19.98.
Laser: LD75568. $34.98.
Mike Figgis, USA, 1995, 113 mins.

BEST ACTRESS

Susan Sarandon for
Dead Man Walking
Sean Penn is an unrepentant killer who is ministered to by a strong-willed nun (Susan Sarandon). This film is unique for staying so firmly glued to the harder issues and emotions that surround hardened killers and the state's use of the death penalty. Penn gives an especially brilliant performance in a film dominated by great acting.
DVD: DV60004. $29.95.
VHS: S28059. $19.98.
Laser: LD75802. $44.95.
Tim Robbins, USA, 1995, 122 mins.

1996

BEST PICTURE

The English Patient
A stellar cast, meticulous attention to detail, first-rate cinematography, and a tragic love story combine for an irresistible package of a movie, the winner of nine Academy Awards. When a mysterious stranger is rescued from a plane, his identity is gradually revealed and the secrets and passions of war are unlocked. With Ralph Fiennes, Kristin Scott-Thomas, Willem Dafoe, and Juliette Binoche in an Academy Award-winning role. Letterboxed.
VHS: S31822. $19.95.
Laser: LD76338. $99.95.
Anthony Minghella, Great Britain, 1996, 162 mins.

BEST DIRECTOR

Anthony Minghella for
The English Patient

BEST ACTOR

Jeffrey Rush for
Shine
Geoffrey Rush gives an Academy Award-winning performance as pianist David Helfgott in this extraordinary, true story of a young man who defies his father's wishes in order to pursue his dreams. Both thought-provoking and powerful, it tells a tale of rebellion and individuality through the eyes of an artist whose only form of self-expression is found in the keys of his instruments. With Lynn Redgrave, Armin Mueller-Stahl, Sir John Gielgud and Noah

Taylor. Widescreen.
DVD: DV60098. $24.98.
VHS: S31545. $19.98.
Laser: LD76252. $39.99.
Scott Hicks, Australia, 1996, 105 mins.

BEST ACTRESS

Frances McDormand for
Fargo
Steve Buscemi, William Macy and Frances McDormand as a pregnant homicide detective find thievery, treachery and murder out in the frozen upper Midwest. This seemingly straightforward morality tale is laced with wicked humor. The film's deadpan style mirrors the large, cold, empty spaces of the Minnesota landscape.
DVD: DV60003. $29.95.
VHS: S29808. $19.98.
Laser: LD75990. $34.95.
Joel and Ethan Coen, USA, 1996, 98 mins.

1997

BEST PICTURE

Titanic
Not currently available on video.

BEST DIRECTOR

James Cameron for
Titanic

BEST ACTOR

Jack Nicholson for
As Good As It Gets
Jack Nicholson and Helen Hunt star in Oscar-winning performances in James L. Brooks' hit comedy. Nicholson is the Scrooge-like Melvin Udall, a cranky, bigoted, obsessive-compulsive writer whose life is turned upside down when single mom/waitress Carol (Hunt), the only waitress who will tolerate Melvin, must leave her job to care for her sick son, making it impossible for Melvin to eat breakfast. In addition, when Melvin's gay artist neighbor Simon (Greg Kinnear) is injured in a robbery, Melvin gets stuck taking care of Simon's dog. The dog warms Melvin's heart, and an unlikely friendship develops between Melvin, Carol and Simon.
VHS: S34261. $22.99.
Laser: LD76945. $39.98.
DVD: DV60252. $24.98.
James L. Brooks, USA, 1997, 138 mins.

BEST ACTRESS

Helen Hunt for
As Good As It Gets

Leaving Las Vegas

National Film Registry on Video

In 1988, the U.S. Library of Congress established the National Film Registry to preserve film deemed "culturally, historically, or aesthetically important." Twenty-five films have been added to the registry every year since. Below is the list to date.

1997

Ben-Hur
Ramon Novarro is the title character in the silent version known for its classic chariot race. Novarro races against Francis X. Bushman who plays his sworn enemy Messala. Truly a thrilling race on a colossal set staged by second unit director Reaves Eason. Based on the novel by Lew Wallace, the film also has a sea battle, lepers and a meeting with Jesus Christ. Letterboxed.
   VHS: S07791. $29.95.
Fred Niblo, USA, 1926, 116 mins.

The Big Sleep
Humphrey Bogart is Philip Marlowe in this entertaining adaptation of Raymond Chandler's novel. Blackmail, murder, sex and drugs all come into play as the ace detective tries to sort out the guilty parties. Even the author couldn't figure out who killed the chauffeur. With Lauren Bacall, Martha Vickers and Elisha Cook, Jr.
   VHS: S09389. $19.95.
   Laser: LD70174. $34.98.
Howard Hawks, USA, 1946, 114 mins.

The Bridge on the River Kwai
Epic story of British prisoners of war held by the Japanese combines psychological battles of will with gripping action. Winner of seven Oscars including Best Picture and Director. The Oscar for Screenplay went to Pierre Boulle, the novelist who spoke no English, because screenwriters Carl Foreman and Michael Wilson were blacklisted. With William Holden and Alec Guinness. Letterboxed.
   VHS: S01785. $19.95.
   Laser: LD72066. $49.95.
David Lean, USA, 1957, 161 mins.

Cops
Found on a compilation tape which includes Buster Keaton's classic *The General*, *Cops* is vintage Keaton at his winning best.
   VHS: S23033. $29.95.
Buster Keaton/Clyde Bruckman, USA, 1927, 76 mins.

Czechoslovakia 1968
Not available on video.

Grass
In 1924, neophyte filmmakers Merian C. Cooper and Ernest Schoedsack joined forces with journalist and sometime spy Marguerite Harrison and set off to film an adventure. They found excitement, danger and unparalleled drama in the migration of the Bakhtiari tribe of Persia. Each year, more than 50 thousand

people and half a million animals crossed the snow-covered mountain ranges and torrential rapids to take their herds to pasture. Few have seen *Grass* outside of archives. This issue is struck from the original negative, with an updated soundtrack by Iranian Gholam Hussein Janati Ataie.
   VHS: S16429. $39.95.
   Laser: CLV/CAV. Digitally mastered and transferred. LD71815. $34.95.
Merian Cooper/Ernest Schoedsack, USA, 1925, 70 mins.

The Great Dictator
Chaplin's first film with dialog displays his boundless talent for both comedy and drama. Features Chaplin in two roles, one of a little Jewish barber facing the constant threat of religious persecution, the second a devastating lampoon of Hitler because of which Hitler banned it in Germany.
   VHS: S00527. $19.98.
   Laser: LD76745. $49.95.
Charles Chaplin, USA, 1940, 126 mins.

Harold and Maude
Bud Cort is Harold, an introverted, suicidal 19-year-old; Ruth Gordon is Maude, a spunky 79-year-old. They fall in love in this witty romantic comedy. The early scenes in which Harold tries out suicide methods are outstanding. Music by Cat Stevens.
   VHS: S00543. $19.95.
   Laser: LD75352. $29.98.
Hal Ashby, USA, 1971, 92 mins.

Hindenburg Disaster Footage
Found on *A Newsreel Library of America in the News*, this tape contains a collection of 87 original news reports, including the Wright Brothers' first flight, Stock Market crash segments, the Scopes trial and the Hindenburg disaster.
   VHS: S15946. $29.95.

How the West Was Won
A large-scale epic about three generations of pioneers, with a great cast and brilliant direction by John Ford, George Marshall and Henry Hathaway. With George Peppard, Debbie Reynolds, Carroll Baker, Gregory Peck, Henry Fonda, James Stewart, John Wayne. VHS letterboxed.
   VHS: S11555. $29.98.
   Laser: LD70595. $39.98.
John Ford/George Marshall/Henry Hathaway, USA, 1962, 155 mins.

The Hustler
Realistic and riveting drama featuring Paul Newman as Fast Eddie Felson, an arrogant pool hustler who is driven to beat Minnesota Fats, played by Jackie Gleason. With fine performances by George C. Scott and Piper Laurie. Currently out of print but available

for rental.
Robert Rossen, USA, 1961, 134 mins.

Knute Rockne, All American
Pat O'Brien delivers a winning performance as the legendary Notre Dame football coach Knute Rockne, whose all-star career came to an tragic end in a plane crash. Gale Page shines as the coach's supportive wife. With Donald Crisp, John Qualen, Albert Basserman and future president Ronald Reagan as the immortal Notre Dame star player George Gipp.
VHS: S15659. $19.98.
Lloyd Bacon, USA, 1940, 96 mins.

The Life and Death of 9413— A Hollywood Extra
The first important American experimental film, influenced by German Expressionist cinema, is a fantasy about an aspiring movie maker. Found on a compilation tape with Germaine Dulac's *Seashell and the Clergyman* and Chris Marker's famous *La Jetee*.
VHS: S07170. $39.95.
Robert Florey/Slavko Vorkapich, USA, 1928

The Little Fugitive
Capturing the pleasures and pain of childhood as no film has before or since, this lyrical comedy/drama about a seven-year-old boy who runs away to Coney Island after being tricked into believing he's killed his older brother traverses all generational boundaries to remain a cherished and timeless American classic. "Our New Wave would never have come into being if it hadn't been for the young American Morris Engel, who showed us the way to independent production with his fine movie *The Little Fugitive*" (Francois Truffaut).
VHS: S30704. $79.95.
Morris Engel, USA, 1953, 80 mins.

Rear Window
Injured magazine photographer, confined to his apartment because of a broken leg, suspects a murder has been committed in a neighboring flat. Confined to one set, *Rear Window* is a tour-de-force; James Stewart plays the photographer, Grace Kelly his New York girlfriend, and Raymond Burr the killer.
VHS: S01095. $19.95.
Alfred Hitchcock, USA, 1954, 101 mins.

Republic Steel Strike Riots Newsreel
Not available on video.

Return of the Secaucus Seven
Celebrated American independent film, made on a shoestring, about the weekend reunion of seven 30ish college and Vista comrades, all of whom were arrested en route to an anti-war demonstration once upon a time, but who now rehash a shared past and try to get a grip on the future during a weekend together. Currently out of print.
John Sayles, USA, 1980, 110 mins.

The Thin Man
Dashiell Hammett's 1932 crime thriller-comedy stars William Powell, Myrna Loy, and Asta, the terrier, in the now-classic plot in which the daughter of an inventor hires private eye Nick Charles to get to the bottom of a case.
VHS: S01324. $19.98.
Laser: LD70694. $34.98.
W.S. Van Dyke, USA, 1934, 90 mins.

Tulips Shall Grow
Not available on video.

West Side Story
An extravaganza acclaimed for its musical and choreographic expertise. Score by Leonard Bernstein,

Westward, Ho!

High Noon
VHS: S00567. $14.98.
Laser: CAV. LD70380. $74.95.
Laser: CLV. LD70381. $49.95.

My Darling Clementine
VHS: S01784. $19.98.

The Naked Spur
VHS: S03674. $19.97.

Red River
VHS: S01101. $19.95.

The Searchers
VHS: S01731. $19.98.

Stagecoach
VHS: S01247. $19.98.
Laser: LD74715. $34.98.

Unforgiven
DVD: DV60120. $24.98.
VHS: S18724. $19.98.

The Wild Bunch
DVD: DV60121. $24.98.
VHS: S01459. $39.99.
Laser: LD70706. $129.98.

Mean Streets
Set in New York's Little Italy, *Mean Streets* follows Harvey Keitel as he slowly climbs into the hierarchy of a local Mafia family. Keenly observed, gritty and violent, this early film by Scorsese clearly foreshadows his later work, and established him as a major American talent. With Robert De Niro, Cesare Danova, Amy Robinson.
VHS: S00840. $19.98.
Laser: LD70626. $34.98.
Martin Scorsese, USA, 1973, 112 mins.

Motion Painting No. 1
Not available on video.

The Music Box
Laurel and Hardy shine in this award-winning comedy short found on the compilation tape *Laurel and Hardy at Work*. Also includes *Towed in a Hole* and *Busy Bodies*.
VHS: S13867. $14.98.

The Naked Spur
Nothing kinky. This hardy western directed by Anthony Mann features James Stewart as a tough bounty hunter in pursuit of Robert Ryan through the rugged terrain of the Rocky Mountains. Filmed on location with Janet Leigh and Ralph Meeker as two of the distractions that keep the determined Stewart on his toes.
VHS: S03674. $19.97.
Anthony Mann, USA, 1953, 93 mins.

lyrics by Stephen Sondheim, choreography by Jerome Robbins, starring Natalie Wood (her songs were dubbed by Marni Nixon) and Rita Moreno.
VHS: S01444. $19.95.
Laser: CAV, widescreen. LD70485. $124.95.
Laser: CLV, widescreen. LD70486. $69.95.
Robert Wise/Jerome Robbins, USA, 1961, 152 mins.

Wings
One of the most exciting of the silent dramas, *Wings* was the first film to be awarded the Oscar for Best Picture. Featuring Clara Bow (The IT Girl) and a short appearance by Gary Cooper, the film has incredible aerial battle sequences. Director Wellman makes a humanistic statement as he explores the devastation of World War I.
VHS: S02831. $19.95.
William Wellman, USA, 1927, 139 mins.

1996

The Awful Truth
Wildly funny romp which won the Academy Award opens when a battling couple files for divorce. The only hitch seems to be who will get custody of their beloved terrier, Mr. Smith. Cary Grant and Irene Dunne co-star in this very wacky comedy.
VHS: S00083. $19.95.
Leo McCarey, USA, 1937, 92 mins.

The Big Sleep

Broken Blossoms
D.W. Griffith's pastoral effort set in a Dickensian London about the oppression of a frail young street urchin desperate to escape her bleak circumstances. The young woman falls in love with a sympathetic Chinese missionary, who shields her from her tyrannical and abusive father. "There are stretches of Griffith poetry, a marvelous use of light and shadow in cameraman Billy Bitzer's evocation of foggy Limehouse, and a truly unforgettable performance from Lillian Gish" (*Time Out*). With Richard Barthelmess and Donald Crisp. Newly remastered print struck from an archival source.
   VHS: S18434. $24.95.
D.W. Griffith, USA, 1919, 90 mins.

The Deer Hunter
Powerful drama that follows a group of friends from a steel town in Pennsylvania through their Vietnam experiences with fine ensemble work from Robert De Niro, Christopher Walken, John Savage, John Cazale and Meryl Streep.
   VHS: S02738. $29.95.
   Laser: LD70022. $44.98.
Michael Cimino, USA, 1978, 183 mins.

Destry Rides Again
Marlene Dietrich plays Frenchy, the notorious yet sensational cabaret singer. Her rendition of "See What the Boys in the Back Room Will Have" marked her emergence from her mysterious screen personality of the 30's to her raucous personality of the 40's. With James Stewart as the gunslinger without guns, and Brian Donlevy.
   VHS: S01988. $14.98.
George Marshall, USA, 1939, 94 mins.

Flash Gordon
A box set of the original Flash Gordon movie serials by King Features—starring the young Buster Crabbe. Action-packed adventure! Includes *The Deadly Ray from Mars, The Peril from Planet Mongo, Spaceship to the Unknown* and *The Purple Death from Outer Space*. Four videocassettes. Total time: 6 hrs.
   VHS: S13887. $79.95.

The Forgotten Frontier
This silent film was put out by the Frontier Nursing Service. Not available on video.
Marvin Breckinridge, USA, 1931, 60 mins.

Frank Film
Frank Mouris' autobiographical, animated film won the Academy Award in 1974. The 11,592 collages are sequenced to illustrate the chronology of the filmmaker's life. The visual bombardment, together with the double soundtrack, is an intense and moving experience. Includes public performance rights.
   VHS: S32638. Currently out of print.
Frank & Caroline Mouris, USA, 1973, 9 mins.

The Graduate
Mike Nichols' film in a new, 25th anniversary edition. Dustin Hoffman stars as the naive college graduate who's seduced by the middle-aged Mrs. Robinson (Anne Bancroft) and promptly falls in love with her daughter (Katharine Ross). This special limited edition is presented in its original wide-screen format and features interviews with the original cast and crew.
   Laser: CAV. LD70371. $99.95.
Mike Nichols, USA, 1967, 106 mins.

The Heiress
William Wyler directed Olivia de Havilland and an all-star cast in this Oscar-winning classic. De Havilland is the homely, awkward girl who falls in love with the dashing fortune hunter. With brilliant performances by Montgomery Clift and Ralph Richardson, musical score by Aaron Copeland. Based on *Washington Square* by Henry James.
   VHS: S03533. $14.95.
William Wyler, USA, 1949, 115 mins.

The Jazz Singer
It's more than a movie; it's history—the first feature-length film with spoken dialog. Audiences at the October 6, 1927 premiere were electrified by what they could now *see and* hear when star Al Jolson, in the film's best-remembered line, proclaimed: "Wait a minute, you ain't heard nothing yet!" Includes Jolson's famous renditions of "Toot Toot Tootsie

Goodbye" and "Mammy."
VHS: S04338. $29.98.
Alan Crosland, USA, 1927, 89 mins.

Life and Times of Rosie the Riveter
Amusing documentary combining propaganda film, news footage and current interviews with the women who went to "do the job HE left behind" during WWII. Not available on video.
Connie Field, USA, 1980, 65 mins.

M*A*S*H
Donald Sutherland, Elliott Gould and Robert Duvall in the original, superb, classic dark comedy directed with verve by Robert Altman, juxtaposing the horrors of war with the resiliency of the human spirit. Written by Ring Lardner, Jr.
VHS: S02643. $14.98.
Laser: Letterboxed. LD76743. $24.98.
Robert Altman, USA, 1970, 116 mins.

Mildred Pierce
Michael Curtiz, who directed *Casablanca* and *Yankee Doodle Dandy*, elevates this Joan Crawford vehicle into a perverse and personal exploration of psychological disorder and collapse. Based on the novel by James M. Cain, Crawford won an Oscar as the hard-working mother with the world's most unpleasant, snobby, status-seeking and boyfriend-stealing daughter (Ann Blyth).
VHS: S02340. $19.98.
Laser: LD70630. $34.98.
Michael Curtiz, USA, 1945, 109 mins.

The Outlaw Josey Wales
Clint Eastwood plays a peaceful farmer turned vigilante during the period after the Civil war. Eastwood took over directing from Philip Kaufman who co-scripted.
VHS: S07496. $19.98.
Laser: LD70650. $39.98.
Clint Eastwood, USA, 1976, 135 mins.

The Producers
Mel Brooks' hilarious hit about the plot to produce a Broadway bomb titled "Springtime for Hitler." Unfortunately, the play is a smash…so is this film. With Zero Mostel and Gene Wilder.
Laser: LD70436. $39.95.
Mel Brooks, USA, 1968, 88 mins.

Pull My Daisy
Robert Frank and Alfred Leslie's pals poet Allen Ginsberg and painter Larry Rivers play act a scene from a Jack Kerouac play about the Beats. With a voice over by Kerouac himself, the narration strikes a tone forcing the audience to separate the real from the fake. An influential format later used by Warhol and others in the "home movie" style.
VHS: S34620. $79.95.
Robert Frank/Alfred Leslie, USA, 1958, 29 mins.

Road to Morocco
One of the funniest Hope/Crosby road pictures has Crosby selling Hope to a charismatic, devilish sheik played by Anthony Quinn, as they both pursue the beautiful princess Dorothy Lamour. With Dona Drake, Vladimir Sokoloff, Monte Blue and Yvonne De Carlo.
VHS: S17245. $14.98.
David Butler, USA, 1942, 83 mins.

She Done Him Wrong
Mae West in a terrific spoof of the gay 1890's, with Mae repeating her stage success in the role of Diamond Lil, and Cary Grant the guy who gets asked to come up and see her sometime—which he does, with volatile results.
VHS: S04521. $14.98.
Lowell Sherman, USA, 1933, 66 mins.

Shock Corridor
To catch a killer and win a Pulitzer prize, reporter-hero Johnny Barrett has himself committed to a mental institution. He must find out who killed Sloan in the kitchen by questioning three inmates who witnessed the crime—men driven crazy by the hypocrisies of the American dream relating to racism, anti-communism and the bomb. A complex, wacky masterpiece by one of Hollywood's great directors, Sam Fuller.
VHS: S18328. $29.95.
Laser: LD70458. $49.95.
Sam Fuller, USA, 1963, 101 mins.

Show Boat
This musical collaboration of Jerome Kern and Oscar

Hammerstein captures the heartbreak, excitement and romantic preoccupations on an old line Mississippi show boat. Hammerstein wrote the screenplay, adapted from Edna Ferber's novel. With Irene Dunne, Allan Jones, Helen Morgan, Paul Robeson (who performs "Old Man River") and Charles Winninger. "Sentimental, literary, but oddly appealing" (Graham Greene). Available in two versions, a three-disc collection or a single disc.
Laser: CAV, 3 discs, Criterion. **LD70459. $124.95.**
Laser: CLV, 1 disc, Criterion. **LD70460. $49.95.**
James Whale, USA, 1936, 110 mins.

The Thief of Baghdad
Douglas Fairbanks on a marvelous quest in an Arabian Nights fantasy/adventure with the lovely Julanne Johnston as the princess who rides off with Fairbanks on his magic carpet. From Raoul Walsh, a dynamic, prolific director.
VHS: S01323. $24.95.
Laser: LD70397. Currently out of print.
Raoul Walsh, USA, 1924, 132 mins.

To Be or Not to Be
In what might be, in the hands of someone other than Ernest Lubitsch, a contradiction of terms—a witty, delightfully satirical comedy set in Nazi-occupied Warsaw—Jack Benny leads a troupe of ham actors in outsmarting the Gestapo and reducing them to ridiculous rubble. Benny gives an animated, beautifully-paced performance and Carole Lombard stars as his wife in her last screen performance.
VHS: S01350. $19.98.
Ernst Lubitsch, USA, 1942, 102 mins.

Topaz
Home movie footage taken at Japanese-American Internment Camp, the Topaz War Relocation Authority Center in Topaz, Utah. Not available on video.
Dave Tatsuno, USA, 1943-45

Verbena Tragica (Tragic Festival)
Cantabria Films for Columbia. Not available on video.
USA, 1939, 75 mins.

Woodstock
Never-before-seen performances by rock legends Canned Heat, Janis Joplin, Crosby Stills and Nash, Jefferson Airplane, Jimmy Hendrix and many others bring alive the spirit of the event that defined a generation. This newly available director's cut of the highly acclaimed documentary, winner of the Academy Award in 1970, shows how three days of peace and music changed the world. Widescreen.
DVD: DV60119. $24.98.
VHS: S06044. $24.98.
Laser: LD70712. $49.98.
Michael Wadleigh, USA, 1970, 225 mins.

1995

The Adventures of Robin Hood
The most acclaimed screen version of the King of Sherwood Forest. Errol Flynn is Robin Hood to Olivia de Havilland's Maid Marion. Basil Rathbone and Claude Rains are the villains. Action, drama and romance that has satisfied audiences for years.
VHS: S00019. $19.98.
Laser: LD70731. $34.98.
Michael Curtiz, USA, 1938, 102 mins.

All That Heaven Allows
One of the best films from one of American cinema's most underrated directors, this never-before-available film is a scathing attack on the American Dream, in which a widow (Jane Wyman) faces the wrath of her friends and family when she becomes romantically involved with a younger man (Rock Hudson). Succumbing to the pressures of society, she stops seeing the man and settles back into her lonely life, but eventually rebels against her conformist surroundings and finds love with him again. "A stylized, beautifully photographed commentary on the emotional numbness of suburban life" (*The Motion Picture Guide*). Later remade by Fassbinder as *Ali: Fear Eats the Soul*. With Agnes Moorehead, Conrad Nagel, Virginia Grey and Charles Drake.
VHS: S30796. $19.95.
Douglas Sirk, USA, 1955, 89 mins.

American Graffiti
A new American classic, which single-handedly

started the 60's nostalgia craze. A coming-of-age film that details the lives of several high school teenagers the summer after graduation. Launched the careers of Richard Dreyfuss, Harrison Ford and Suzanne Sommers and established George Lucas as an important new American filmmaker. A perceptive, sweet look at a more innocent time.
VHS: S00044. $14.95.
Laser: LD70013. $34.98.
George Lucas, USA, 1973, 112 mins.

The Band Wagon
Delightful musical featuring Fred Astaire and Cyd Charisse in a story line that revolves around the difficulties of putting up a Broadway show. Astaire is in top form!
Laser: CLV. LD70516. $34.98.
Vincente Minnelli, USA, 1953, 112 mins.

Blacksmith Scene
Not available on video.

Cabaret
Liza Minnelli and Joel Grey give extraordinary performances in Bob Fosse's musical drama that mirrors the decay and decadence of Germany on the eve of Hitler's rise to power. With Marisa Berenson and Michael York.
DVD: DV60190. $24.98.
VHS: S01837. $19.98.
Laser: LD72168. $39.98.
Bob Fosse, USA, 1972, 119 mins.

Chan Is Missing
A mystery set against the backdrop of San Francisco's Chinatown. The story involves two Chinese taxi drivers who are looking for their business partner, Chan Hung, a middle-aged Taiwan immigrant who has vanished with their money. Their search for clues to Chan's whereabouts leads them to his family, friends and acquaintances, who reveal a great diversity of people and cultural backgrounds that make up life in Chinatown. A great hit on its release.
VHS: S10918. $79.95.
Wayne Wang, USA, 1981, 80 mins.

The Conversation
Gene Hackman is brilliant as Harry Caul, the surveillance man who becomes the object of surveillance himself. Coppola's great achievement is in evoking an obsessive sense of paranoia as Hackman struggles to free himself from the maze of secrecy and murder. With Cindy Williams, Harrison

Orgies

Caligula
VHS: S05788. $59.95.

Fellini Satyricon
VHS: S06318. $19.98.
Laser: LD70979. $124.95.

La Dolce Vita
VHS: S00705. $24.95.

Quiet Days in Clichy
VHS: S23039. $19.98.

Salo: 120 Days of Sodom
VHS: S11717. $89.95.
Laser: LD72111. $49.95.

Savages
VHS: S01160. $29.95.
Laser: LD72069. $39.95.

Seconds
VHS: S31145. $79.95.
Laser: LD76340. $39.99.

Sodom and Gomorrah
VHS: S10324. $19.98.
Laser: LD72204. $69.98.

Sweet Movie
VHS: S10575. $79.95.

The Ten Commandments
VHS: S15100. $35.00.

Ford, Frederic Forrest. Currently out of print.
Francis F. Coppola, USA, 1974, 113 mins.

The Day the Earth Stood Still
One of the first films to portray aliens from space as advanced saviors rather than menacing monsters. Michael Rennie stars as Klaatu. Intense, high production values and excellent casting with Patricia Neal and Sam Jaffe.
VHS: S02521. $14.98.
Robert Wise, USA, 1951, 92 mins.

El Norte
An independent American film that became a hit, the powerful story of a brother and sister who must leave their oppressed country of Guatemala and make the hazardous journey through Mexico to the U.S., only to find themselves living as illegals in Los Angeles.
VHS: S00398. Currently out of release.
Gregory Nava, USA, 1983, 139 mins.

Fatty's Tintype Tangle
A collection of short films starring Fatty Arbuckle including *Tintype Tangle*, *Mabel and Fatty's Wash Day*, *Fatty and Mabel at the San Diego Exposition*, *Fatty and Mable's Simple Life*, *Fatty's New Role*, *Fatty's Faithful Fido* and *Miss Fatty's Seaside Lovers*. All made in the year 1915. 118 mins.
VHS: S07200. $29.95.

The Four Horsemen of the Apocalypse
Rudolph Valentino became a certified star for his work in this film, especially his notorious tango scene. Based on Blasco Ibanez' novel, this is a story of two brothers who end up on opposing sides in World War I. Stark imagery make this unforgettable anti-war film a silent classic.
VHS: S23111. $24.95.
Rex Ingram, USA, 1921, 114 mins.

Fury
Fritz Lang's first Hollywood film after fleeing Nazi Germany is a powerful indictment of mob violence in America. Lang includes some real footage of a 1934 lynching, making *Fury* a frightening document as well as a compelling melodrama. Spencer Tracy portrays a gas station owner who, by a series of coincidences, is accused of a kidnapping and becomes the target of an angry mob which attempts to lynch him and eventually burns down the jailhouse. With Sylvia Sidney and Walter Brennan.
VHS: S15026. $19.98.
Fritz Lang, USA, 1936, 89 mins.

Gerald McBoing Boing
Four hilarious stories about a small boy who can only produce such sound effects as "boing boing!" The first of the four sequences was an early creation of Dr. Seuss, produced in 1950. Featuring Marvin Miller as the voice of Gerald McBoing Boing.
VHS: S00490. $12.95.
Robert Cannon, USA, 1955, 29 mins.

The Hospital
Paddy Chayefsky wrote this biting black comedy about a modern mega-hospital that strangles its patients—and doctors—in red tape. George C. Scott stars in a ferocious, Oscar-nominated performance.
VHS: S15251. $19.98.
Laser: LD76414. $34.98.
Arthur Hiller, USA, 1971, 102 mins.

Jammin' the Blues
Not available on video.

The Last of the Mohicans
This silent adaptation of James Fenimore Cooper's novel is set in colonial America during the French and Indian Wars, and pits the fierce warrior Magua (Wallace Beery) against Hawkeye and his adopted brothers, Uncas and Chingachgook. With Barbara Bedford, Albert Roscoe, James Gordon and Boris Karloff.
VHS: S06225. $39.95.
Laser: CLV/CAV. LD72046. $49.95.
Maurice Tourneur/Clarence Brown, USA, 1920, 75 mins.

Manhatta
Not available on video.

North by Northwest
One of Hitchcock's greatest films; Cary Grant plays Roger Thornhill, the suave ad man mistaken for a Federal agent, trapped in a web of intrigue that ends with the classic climax atop Mount Rushmore. Eva Marie Saint is the amorous spy, Leo G. Carroll the FBI man with double-edged tactics, and James Mason

and Martin Landau the icily villainous traders in state secrets.
VHS: S00938. $19.98.
Laser: CAV, 3 discs, Criterion. **LD70427. $124.95.**
Laser: CLV, 2 discs, Criterion. **LD70428. $69.95.**
Alfred Hitchcock, USA, 1959, 136 mins.

The Philadelphia Story
One of the most hilarious and captivating romantic comedies ever to grace the screen. Katharine Hepburn is caught between her fiance and her charming ex-husband. With a splendid cast, including Cary Grant, James Stewart and Ruth Hussey.
DVD: DV60063. $24.98.
VHS: S01023. $24.95.
Laser: LD70152. $39.98.
George Cukor, USA, 1940, 118 mins.

Rip Van Winkle
Not available on video.

Seventh Heaven
"*Seventh Heaven* tracks the transformational love of Farrell and Gaynor from the sewers to the stars, across time and space, and beyond death itself, affirming triumphantly that melodrama can mean much more than just an excuse for a good weep" (*Time Out Film Guide*). Janet Gaynor won an Oscar for her portrayal of a mistreated Paris street waif redeemed by cockney sewer man Charles Farrell.
VHS: S31171. $24.95.
Frank Borzage, USA, 1927, 119 mins.

Stagecoach
John Ford at his greatest in a story of nine passengers on a Cheyenne-bound stagecoach, each with a singular reason for the journey, determined to live through the dangerous trip. With John Wayne, Claire Trevor, John Carradine, Andy Devine.
VHS: S01247. $19.98.
Laser: LD74715. $34.98.
John Ford, USA, 1939, 96 mins.

To Fly
This non-stop trip through the history of flight begins in the 1800s and travels up through the present. The natural beauty of the United States, the wonder of human ingenuity and the rewards of persistence are wrapped up in one emotional, historical, exhilarating event. From the IMAX Motion Picture, in Surround Sound. 1976, 27 mins.
Laser: CAV. **LD71492.** Currently unavailable.

To Kill a Mockingbird
Gregory Peck won an Oscar for his role of Atticus Finch, the defense lawyer of a black man accused of rape in the American South. Script by Horton Foote from the novel by Harper Lee. A sensitive and powerful drama. Robert Duvall's film debut. Also Brock Peters, and Mary Badham as Scout. B&W.
VHS: S02640. $19.95.
Laser: LD70089. $39.98.
Robert Mulligan, USA, 1962, 129 mins.

1994

The African Queen
Inspired casting teamed Bogart and Hepburn in this romantic adventure/comedy set in a war-torn African jungle. Surviving malaria, insects and persistent conflicts of their personalities, they share victory and tender romance.
VHS: S00020. $19.98.
Laser: LD70814. Currently unavailable.
John Huston, USA, 1951, 105 mins.

The Apartment
Billy Wilder's great film of tears and laughter as Jack Lemmon and Shirley MacLaine wheel and deal over a New York apartment in a comedy of morality. Winner of five Oscars and worth at least 20 more. VHS letterboxed.
VHS: S05880. $19.95.
Laser: LD70506. $39.98.
Billy Wilder, USA, 1960, 125 mins.

The Cool World
Based on the novel by Warren Miller about black American gangs in New York. Not available on video.
Shirley Clarke, USA, 1963

A Corner in Wheat
A collection of eight one- and two-reel works D.W. Griffith directed from 1909-1913 for the American

The Bridge on the River Kwai

Mutoscope and Biograph Company that highlighted Griffith's narrative inventions. The other works showcased are *Those Awful Hats, The Sealed Room, The Unchanging Sea, His Trust, The New York Hat, An Unseen Enemy* and *The Mothering Heart.* Featuring Mary Pickford and Lillian and Dorothy Gish. 118 mins.
VHS: S18431. $24.95.

E.T.
Steven Spielberg's magnum opus—finally on video. An endearing alien, stranded on Earth, befriends a sweet young boy and his lovable siblings, who all help him to find his way back home. One of the most popular and highest grossing movies in history and quickly becoming a children's classic in the league of *The Wizard of Oz.* Letterboxed.
VHS: S07032. $19.95.
Laser: THX, CAV. **LD76047. $149.98.**
Steven Spielberg, USA, 1982, 101 mins.

The Exploits of Elaine
Detective Craig Kennedy helps his girl friend avenge her father's murder. With Pearl White, Creighton Hale, Sheldon Lewis and Arnold Daly. Silent. Not available on video.
Louis Gasnier/George B. Seitz, USA, 1914, 14 episodes, each 20 mins.

Force of Evil
Film noir featuring John Garfield as an attorney who works for a mobster and finds himself caught in a numbers racket scheme that could bankrupt New York's "numbers banks".
VHS: S04232. $14.95.
Laser: CLV. **LD71984. $29.98.**
Abraham Polonsky, USA, 1948, 80 mins.

Freaks
Tod Browning's classic horror film, with a cast of real side-show "freaks"—dwarfs, midgets, Siamese twins— dominated and exploited by the circus strong man and a beautiful aerialist, who eventually band together in a horrifying revenge.
VHS: S01560. $19.98.
Laser: LD70578. $34.98.
Tod Browning, USA, 1932, 66 mins.

Hell's Hinges
William S. Hart, the first great star of the Westerns, plays Blaze Tracy, a notorious outlaw in the town of Hell's Hinges. When a new minister pulls into town, Blaze is transformed by the sight of the minister's daughter. One of the great silent Westerns.
VHS: S01879. $29.95.
William S. Hart, USA, 1916, 65 mins.

The Hospital
Shot at Metropolitan Hospital in New York City, Frederick Wiseman's fourth film is a cinema verite expose of the deeply depressing condition of health care for the poor in urban America. Not available on video.
Frederick Wiseman, USA, 1970, 84 mins.

Invasion of the Body Snatchers
The great Cold War classic. A small American town is taken over by an alien force which turns everyone into a zombie. Kevin McCarthy and Dana Wynter star.
VHS: S00633. $19.95.
Laser: CAV, widescreen. **LD70384. $79.95.**
Laser: CLV, widescreen. **LD70385. $49.95.**
Don Siegel, USA, 1956, 80 mins.

The Lady Eve
Barbara Stanwyck is the cardshark, Henry Fonda the

millionaire scientist who knows more about snakes than about women. "Neither performer has ever been funnier. The film, based on a story by Monckton Hoffe, is full of classic moments and classic lines; it represents the dizzy high point of Sturges' comedy writing."
VHS: S02941. $19.98.
Laser: LD70044. $34.98.
Preston Sturges, USA, 1941, 97 mins.

Louisiana Story
The last film of the famous father of the documentary, the story of a new oil derrick and its effect upon the Louisiana Bayou country, the boy and his raccoon. With music by Virgil Thompson.
VHS: S00771. $29.95.
Robert Flaherty, USA, 1948, 79 mins.

The Manchurian Candidate
A compelling thriller based on the Richard Condon novel about brain washing American soldiers to serve as assassins in secret global domination. Starring Frank Sinatra, Janet Leigh, Angela Lansbury and Laurence Harvey as the walking time bomb. This tape contains exclusive interviews with Sinatra, director John Frankenheimer and writer George Axelrod. B&W.
DVD: DV60152. $24.98.
VHS: S07005. $19.98.
Laser: This deluxe collector's edition is letterboxed, newly digitally remastered and features commentary by John Frankenheimer. **LD70624. $59.98.**
John Frankenheimer, USA, 1962, 126 mins.

Marty
Ernest Borgnine won a well-deserved Oscar for Best Actor as the shy Bronx butcher who finds love. Academy Awards also went for direction, screenplay and Best Picture. With Betsy Blair, Joe De Santis and Esther Minciotti. From the teleplay by Paddy Chayefsky.
VHS: S08340. Currently unavailable.
Laser: Chapter Search. Includes original theatrical trailer. **LD71670. $34.98.**
Delbert Mann, USA, 1955, 91 mins.

Meet Me in St. Louis
Judy Garland is the classic American teenager in love, in song, in one of the brightest hours of her career. *Meet Me in St. Louis* is a charming turn-of-the-century album full of magic and memories. 50th Anniversary edition. Newly remastered. Includes a "making of" documentary, interviews with cast and team, a trailer from 1955, and a recreation of a

deleted musical number.
VHS: S00845. $19.95.
Vincente Minnelli, USA, 1944, 114 mins.

Midnight Cowboy
The shocking story of Cowboy Joe Buck, played by Jon Voight, made history when it was released 25 years ago. This naive country boy with a horrible secret moves to New York, where the streetwise Ratso Rizzo (Dustin Hoffman) becomes his guide to seamy city life. Together they explore the world of hustling and even visit Warhol's factory, developing a deep friendship in the process. This film won Oscars for Best Picture, Screenplay and Director. Also features Brenda Vaccaro. A 25th Anniversary re-release.
DVD: DV60090. $24.98.
VHS: S21826. $19.98.
Laser: LD74499. $49.98.
John Schlesinger, USA, 1969, 113 mins.

A Movie
Sequences of humorous and exaggerated irony reminding us we are in fact seeing a movie created from movies. Included in a collection of five films by one of America's most exciting and important film artists. Not available on video.
Bruce Conner, USA, 1958

Pinocchio
The brilliant story of a little puppet who dreams of being a little boy unfolds as a shining example of vivid, rich, finely detailed Disney animation at its finest. Currently not available on video.
Walt Disney Productions, USA, 1940, 87 mins.

Safety Last
This is Harold Lloyd's best-known work. Its plot concerns the mad-cap adventures of an ambitious young man unleashed in the big city and contains Lloyd's most famous sequence, his scaling a 12-story building as Lloyd furiously hangs onto the hands of an oversize clock. "Lloyd specialized in the 'comedy of thrills'—a bizarre variant of Keystone mayhem in which the protagonist placed himself in real physical danger to elicit shocks of laughter from the audience" (David Cook, *The History of Narrative Film*). With Mildred Davis, Bill Strothers and Noah Young.
VHS: S19904. Currently out of release.
Fred Newmeyer/Sam Taylor, USA, 1923, 78 mins.

Scarface
Paul Muni plays Tony Carmonte, an ambitious hood fighting his way up to be the number one gang boss. Produced by Howard Hughes, *Scarface* is regarded as

A Corner in Wheat

the best and most brutal of the classic gangster films.
VHS: S01163. $19.95.
Laser: LD70074. $34.95.
Howard Hawks, USA, 1932, 90 mins.

Snow White
Max and Dave Fleischer's retelling of the classic fairytale, featuring Betty Boop and Koko.
VHS: S30345. $9.95.
Fleischer Brothers, USA, 1933

Tabu
Filmed entirely in Tahiti, *Tabu* represents an unusual collaboration between legendary directors F.W. Murnau and Robert Flaherty. Combining Flaherty's poetic sense of the native people with Murnau's strong filmic sensibilities, the film tells the story of two lovers doomed by a tribal edict decreeing the beautiful princess as "tabu" to all men. "Murnau is one of the great masters. The beautiful restoration of *Tabu* will enable future generations to enjoy and appreciate his inspiring talent" (Martin Scorsese). Silent with music track.
VHS: S03712. $39.95.
Laser: CLV/CAV. LD71591. $34.95.
Friedrich W. Murnau/Robert Flaherty, USA, 1931, 82 mins.

Taxi Driver
Scorsese's now-classic film with Robert De Niro as the psychotic cabbie driven to violence in an attempt to "rescue" a teenage prostitute (Jodie Foster). With Albert Brooks, Harvey Keitel, Leonard Harris, Peter Boyle and Cybill Shepherd.
DVD: DV60027. $24.95.
VHS: S01303. $14.95.
Laser: CAV, widescreen. LD70470. $99.95.
Laser: CLV, widescreen. LD70471. $49.95.
Martin Scorsese, USA, 1976, 114 mins.

Zapruder Film of the Kennedy Assassination
Rare film and interview footage fill this documentary, called *Reasonable Doubt*, on the assassination of President John F. Kennedy, giving credibility to the theory that there was more than a single gunman involved in the tragedy that shook the nation. 1963, 60 mins.
VHS: S12950. $29.95.

1993

An American in Paris
No film can match *An American in Paris* for all the joy, all the songs, and all the romance in music and dance. Gene Kelly and Leslie Caron star in this movie set to the glorious melodies of George Gershwin, including: "Embraceable You," "Love Is Here to Stay," "I Got Rhythm" and more.
VHS: S00045. $19.95.
Laser: LD70502. Currently unavailable.
Vincente Minnelli, USA, 1951, 102 mins.

Badlands
Martin Sheen and Sissy Spacek star in a story based on the 1950's murder spree across the Midwestern plains by Charlie Starkweather and his 15-year-old girlfriend, Carol Fugate. A chilling insight into the cold-hearted mind of the sociopath in one of the most stunning directorial debuts in the American cinema. The film, writes British critic Robin Wood, "produces a subtle, idiosyncratic balance between engagement and detachment, complicity and horror."
VHS: S00086. $19.98.
Laser: LD70513. $34.98.
Terence Malick, USA, 1973, 95 mins.

The Black Pirate
Now you can enjoy this Douglas Fairbanks, Sr. swashbuckler in the two-strip color process as it was originally shot. Taken from a rare French print, all of the titles have been replaced in English from the U.S. release. This is a true classic from the silent era and a must for every collection. Orchestra scored.
VHS: S05709. $24.95.
Laser: LD70394. $49.95.
Albert Parker, USA, 1926, 104 mins.

Blade Runner
A visually expressive adaptation of Philip K. Dick's futurist novel about Deckard (Harrison Ford), a cynical detective assigned to terminate a group of genetically devolved replicants set loose in Los Angeles, circa 2019. In this special director's cut, Deckard's voice-over narration is eliminated and the original ending is restored. With Rutger Hauer, Sean Young, Edward James Olmos and Daryl Hannah. VHS letterboxed.
DVD: DV60107. $24.95.
VHS: S18596. $19.98.
Laser: LD71873. $39.99.
Ridley Scott, USA, 1982, 117 mins.

Cat People
A revolutionary horror picture, in which the horror grows by suggestion rather than being depicted. Val Lewton made his name as producer of *Cat People*. The scare at the swimming pool is a true classic.
VHS: S00220. Currently unavailable.
Laser: LD75377. $49.98.
Jacques Tourneur, USA, 1942, 73 mins.

The Cheat
A very early film from Cecil B. De Mille; the story of a young society woman (Fanny Ward) who comes under the control of a scheming Asiatic when she is unable to repay the money she borrows from him. With Sessue Hayakawa.
VHS: S06907. $29.95.
Cecil B. De Mille, USA, 1915, 58 mins.

Chulas Fronteras
Chulas Fronteras provides a magnificent introduction to the most exciting nortena, Southern-Texas musicians, working today: Los Alegres de Teran, Lydia Mendoza, Flaco Jimenez and others. The music and spirit of the people is embodied in their strong family life, and their music.
VHS: S00241. $29.95.
Les Blank, USA, 1976, 58 mins.

Eaux d'Artifice
A collection of Kenneth Anger shorts which includes *Eaux d'Artifice* (a costumed figure moves through Tivoli gardens...), *Fireworks* (a dissatisfied dreamer awakes, goes out in the night seeking a light...), *Rabbit's Moon* (a fable of the unattainable, combining elements of Commedia dell'Arte with Japanese myth).
VHS: S00800. $29.95.
Kenneth Anger, USA, 1947-55, 34 mins.

The Godfather Part II
A companion piece to the original *Godfather*, this continues the saga of two generations of successive power in the Corleone family. Coppola tells the story of the rise of a young Don Vito, played by Robert De Niro, and the ascension of the new Don Michael, played by Al Pacino. Letterboxed.
VHS: S00510. $29.95.
Francis F. Coppola, USA, 1974, 200 mins.

His Girl Friday
One of the wittiest Hollywood comedies: Rosalind Russell is the ace reporter ready to quit for marriage, Cary Grant, her editor trying to convince her to stay. An escaped murderer puts Russell's determination to test. Sophisticated comedy from Howard Hawks.
VHS: S00572. $14.95.
Laser: Chapter stops, restored, digital master, theatrical trailer. **LD75051. $39.95.**
Howard Hawks, USA, 1940, 95 mins.

It Happened One Night
Winner of five Academy Awards, this famous screwball comedy stars Clark Gable and Claudette Colbert as two mismatched lovers. Colbert escapes from her millionaire father, who wants to stop her from marrying a worthless playboy.
VHS: S00642. $19.95.
Laser: LD72146. $34.95.
Frank Capra, USA, 1934, 105 mins.

Lassie Come Home
The first and the best of the Lassie films: the story of a poor family that's forced to sell its dog, but she makes a remarkable journey to return to them. One of the all-time great tearjerkers, with Roddy McDowall, Elizabeth Taylor, Donald Crisp.
VHS: S12429. $19.98.
Fred M. Wilcox, USA, 1943, 88 mins.

Magical Maestro
Nobody but nobody made more outrageous cartoons than Tex Avery. Collected on this video are eight of his screwiest, including *Magical Maestro*, *Who Killed Who?*, *Bad Luck Blackie*, *Symphony in Slang*, and *Swing Shift Cinderella*. 60 mins.
VHS: S07967. $14.95.

Banned at the Box Office

Age of Gold
VHS: S00024. $29.95.

Baby Doll
VHS: S00085. $19.98.

I Am Curious—Yellow
VHS: S00595. $24.95.

In the Realm of the Senses
VHS: S12222. $19.98.

Interrogation
VHS: S14066. $79.95.

Last Tango in Paris
VHS: S00727. $19.98.
Laser: Criterion Collection. LD70412.
$69.95.
Laser: LD71176. $39.98.

Last Temptation of Christ
VHS: S09455. $19.95.
Laser: LD70050. $99.95.

Miracle
VHS: S00858. $29.95.

Salo: 120 Days of Sodom
VHS: S11717. $89.95.
Laser: LD72111. $49.95.

Three on a Match
VHS: S13649. $19.98.

Tie Me Up, Tie Me Down
VHS: S12994. $19.95.

March of Time: Inside Nazi Germany
This look at the world during the first half of the 20th century includes *Inside Nazi Germany, Russians in Exile, Old Dixie's New Look, One Million Mission, Arms and the League, Brain Trust Island, Nazi Conquest—No. 1* and *Crime and Prison*. 93 mins.
VHS: S08052. $19.95.

A Night at the Opera
Along with *Duck Soup*, the funniest of the Marx Brothers films, featuring the boys amidst high society. The five minutes in Groucho's stateroom is one of the funniest continuous laugh inducers on film.
VHS: S02365. $19.95.
Laser: CAV, 2 discs, Criterion. LD70424. $79.95.
Laser: CLV, 1 disc, Criterion. LD70425. $39.95.
Laser: CLV, MGM. LD70643. $43.98.
Sam Wood, USA, 1935, 90 mins.

Nothing But a Man
An impressive collaboration between director Michael Roemer (*The Plot against Harry* and cinematographer and writer Robert Young (*The Ballad of Gregorio Cortez*) about racial attitudes in the 1960s South. Ivan Dixon plays a dignified railroad worker whose desire to lead a normal life with a beautiful schoolteacher (jazz virtuoso Abbey Lincoln) is unhinged by racial politics and discrimination. The Motown soundtrack features Stevie Wonder, Mary Wells and Martha and the Vandellas. With Julius Harris, Gloria Foster, Martin Priest, Leonard Parker, Yaphet Kotto and Stanley Greene.
VHS: S20283. $19.95.
Laser: LD74888. $39.95.
Michael Roemer, USA, 1964, 92 mins.

One Flew Over the Cuckoo's Nest
Milos Forman's sharp adaptation of Ken Kesey's anti-authoritarian novel about a shrewd nonconformist (Jack Nicholson) sentenced to an insane asylum who encourages a group of marginal misfits to assert their rights and independence, over the rigid opposition of the head nurse (Louise Fletcher). Cinematography by Haskell Wexler. With Will Sampson, Brad Dourif, Sydney Lassick, Christopher Lloyd, Danny DeVito and Scatman Crothers. Winner of the five top Academy Awards.
DVD: DV60091. $24.98.
VHS: S18973. $19.98.
Milos Forman, USA, 1975, 134 mins.

Point of Order
Emile De Antonio's now-classic, rousing film record of the televised 1954 Army-McCarthy hearings, also called *McCarthy: Death of a Witchhunter*, dissects the media-clouded history of Cold-War America.
VHS: S01044. $29.95.
Emile de Antonio, USA, 1964, 45 mins.

Shadows
One of the foundation stones of independent American cinema, John Cassavetes' first film features two brothers and a sister who move jerkily through their lives as Cassavetes' free-wheeling camera, naturalistic dialog and jump cuts capture their arguments, sexual encounters and parties. With Lelia Goldoni, Ben Carruthers and Hugh Hurd.
VHS: S26962. $19.95.
John Cassavetes, USA, 1959, 87 mins.

Shane
George Stevens' legendary rendition of the archetypal Western myth earned six Academy nominations. Alan Ladd stars as the retired gunfighter who comes to the aid of a frontier family and wins the adoration of the family's impressionable young son. With Jack Palance, Van Heflin and Jean Arthur.
VHS: S03316. $14.95.
Laser: LD75344. $29.98.
George Stevens, USA, 1953, 118 mins.

Sweet Smell of Success
Burt Lancaster is J.J. Hunsecker, a ruthless and powerful New York columnist, and Tony Curtis is the press agent who will do anything to be in his good graces. Scripted by Clifford Odets and Ernest Lehman. A cult film that was quoted in *Diner*. With Martin Milner, Sam Levene and Barbara Nichols.
VHS: S07979. $19.98.
Laser: LD70689. $34.98.
Alexander MacKendrick, USA, 1957, 96 mins.

Touch of Evil
A masterpiece! This is a complete, restored version. Welles plays a sleazy corrupt police official in a squalid town on the Mexican border, matching wits with Charlton Heston. With Janet Leigh, Marlene Dietrich and Zsa Zsa Gabor.
VHS: S01990. $19.98.
Laser: LD70091. $34.98.
Orson Welles, USA, 1958, 108 mins.

Where Are My Children? (1916)
Silent. Not available on video.
Lois Weber/Phillips Smalley, USA, 1916

The Wind
"*The Wind* is one of the masterpieces of the silent cinema" (Georges Sadoul). Lillian Gish plays a sensitive young girl from Virginia who goes to live with her cousin on the lonely Texas prairie. She survives the threat of an intruder whom she kills in self-defense, a dust storm, and a temporary descent into near madness. The most powerful performance of Gish's career, in which Victor Sjostrom perfectly synthesized the forces of nature and those of human emotion.
VHS: S09283. $29.95.
Victor Sjostrom, USA, 1928, 90 mins.

Yankee Doodle Dandy
James Cagney won a richly deserved Oscar for his red, white an' blue account of the life of George M. Cohan. He sings, he dances, he talks to the president of the United States. Filmed in B&W though two colorized versions exist. With Walter Huston, Joan Leslie, Jeanne Cagney, S.Z. Sakall and Rosemary DeCamp.
VHS: S01835. $14.95.
Laser: LD70714. $39.98.
Michael Curtiz, USA, 1942, 126 mins.

1992

Adam's Rib
Spencer Tracy and Katharine Hepburn in one of their all-time great appearances as married attorneys who find themselves on opposite sides of a murder case in which Judy Holliday is the accused.
DVD: DV60057. $24.98.
VHS: S03456. $19.95.
Laser: 2-disc set. LD70202. $49.98.
Laser: LD70336. $39.95.
George Cukor, USA, 1949, 101 mins.

Annie Hall

One of Woody Allen's best and funniest films, with Diane Keaton as the sometime object of Woody Allen's affections and expressions of his neurosis. Winner of many Academy Awards. With Allen, Keaton, Paul Simon, Carol Kane.
VHS: S00059. $19.95.
Laser: CLV, Criterion. **LD70339. $49.95.**
Laser: Deluxe, letterboxed edition. Includes original theatrical trailer. **LD71506. $34.98.**
Woody Allen, USA, 1977, 94 mins.

The Bank Dick

As a reward for capturing a robber, W.C. Fields is given the job as a bank security guard. A wonderfully funny romp in what is often considered Fields' best film.
VHS: S03323. $29.95.
Laser: LD70014. $34.98.
Eddie Cline, USA, 1940, 74 mins.

Big Business

Laurel and Hardy fail to sell a Christmas tree to a belligerent householder. Silent. Hall Roach Studios. Rights belong to Hal Roach; not available on video.
James W. Horne, USA, 1929, 20 mins.

The Big Parade

John Gilbert learns that war is not a grand and glorious adventure when he barely survives the trenches of World War I. Produced and directed by King Vidor. With Renee Adoree as the French girl who Gilbert teaches how to chew gum. Also Karl Dane, Hobart Bosworth and Tom O'Brien as Bull. A realistic look at modern warfare.
VHS: S07792. $29.95.
Laser: LD70130. $39.98.
King Vidor, USA, 1925, 126 mins.

The Birth of a Nation

D.W. Griffith's debut feature is credited with revolutionizing form and content in the cinema. Its epic story assessed the political, social, racial and personal consequences of the Civil War on American life, from the perspective of two families, the Southern Stonemans and the Northern Camerons. The story intersects the personal with the historic and political, Lincoln's assassination, the Reconstruction and the rise of the Ku Klux Klan. This deluxe edition includes a 30-minute documentary on the making of the film, with interviews, archival footage and outtakes. Adapted from Thomas Dixon's novel and play *The Clansman*. With Lillian Gish, Mae Marsh, Miriam Cooper and filmmaker Raoul Walsh. Cinematography by Billy Bitzer and Karl Brown.
VHS: S18433. $39.95.
Laser: LD70883. $79.95.
D.W. Griffith, USA, 1915, 187 mins.

Bonnie and Clyde

Bank robbers Bonnie Parker and Clyde Barrow probably didn't deserve the cinematic immortality guaranteed by this masterwork directed by Arthur Penn, but I'm sure they wouldn't object to being played by Faye Dunaway and Warren Beatty. Also along for the ride on this Depression era crime spree are Gene Hackman, Estelle Parsons and Michael J. Pollard.
DVD: DV60058. $24.98.
VHS: S00168. $19.98.
Laser: LD70531. $34.98.
Arthur Penn, USA, 1967, 111 mins.

Carmen Jones

Dorothy Dandridge plays Carmen, a woman caught between two men and her own unorthodox nature. The men, one a pretty boy and the other a tough sergeant, are portrayed by Harry Belafonte and Brock Peters. Dandridge lures Joe (Belafonte) into deserting from the army and then leaves him for the two-fisted Sgt. Brown (Peters). The supporting cast is every bit as impressive as the main actors and includes Pearl Bailey, Joe Adams and Diahann Carroll in her first film role. Dandridge became the first African-American nominated for a Best Actress Academy Award. The film won a Golden Globe for Best Musical/Comedy in 1955.
VHS: S21385. $19.98.
Otto Preminger, USA, 1954, 105 mins.

Castro Street

No information available.

Detour

One of the great "B" classics: a masterwork by director Ulmer. A young pianist (Tom Neal) hitchhikes across the country and becomes involved in two murders he didn't commit. (He's not the smartest guy.) Femme fatale Ann Savage hops a ride with Neal and practically steals the film as what is surely one of the most unpleasant creatures that has ever graced the silver screen.
VHS: S00328. $19.95.
Edgar G. Ulmer, USA, 1945, 69 mins.

Dog Star Man

One of the key works of the American avant-garde of the 1960's, Stan Brakhage's *Dog Star Man* is no less than an abstract vision of the creation of the universe, an epic work consisting of a prelude and four parts. Making brilliant use of superimpositions, painting on film, distorting lenses and rhythmic montage, the film is a compelling and truly an eye-opening experience. Silent.
VHS: S04119. Currently unavailable.
Stan Brakhage, USA, 1961-64, 78 mins.

Double Indemnity

A great Billy Wilder film in which "every turn and twist is exactly calculated and achieves its effect with the simplest of means; this shrewd, smooth, tawdry thriller is one of the high points of 40s films" (Kael). Raymond Chandler collaborated on the screenplay in adapting James Cain's story. Barbara Stanwyck is the platinum blonde, Fred MacMurray the insurance salesman she ensnares in a plot to kill her businessman-husband and collect on the double-indemnity clause in his policy.
VHS: S02940. $19.95.
Laser: LD70024. $34.98.
Billy Wilder, USA, 1944, 107 mins.

Footlight Parade

James Cagney plays a stage director who tries to outdo himself with lavish musical numbers. Joan Blondell, Dick Powell, Guy Kibbee and Ruth Donnelly star in this first-rate Warner Brothers musical which features three Busby Berkeley numbers back-to-back: "Honeymoon Hotel," "By a Waterfall" and "Shanghai Lil."
VHS: S03599. $19.98.
Laser: LD70572. $34.98.
Lloyd Bacon, USA, 1933, 104 mins.

The Gold Rush

Charlie Chaplin's immortal, icon-making film, which pits Chaplin as the Little Tramp against the elements of the Yukon, ruthless prospectors and the affections of a dance hall girl. This is the film that includes the classic scene of Chaplin eating his leather shoe and shows his wooden cabin precariously balanced on the edge of a cliff. Silent with music track.
VHS: S26489. $19.95.
Laser: CLV. **LD70099. $39.95.**
Charles Chaplin, USA, 1925, 82 mins.

Letter from an Unknown Woman

Louis Jourdan is a famed concert pianist who is unaware he has been adored for years by the very shy Joan Fontaine until one very special night of passion that produces a child. Told in a series of flashbacks, Jourdan learns he is a father much too late to do the

Birth of a Nation

Taxi Driver

right thing.
VHS: S07435. $19.95.
Laser: CLV, 1 disc, Criterion. **LD71450. $49.95.**
Max Ophuls, USA, 1948, 87 mins.

Morocco
Marlene Dietrich's American debut. Dietrich is an exotic cabaret singer who's stranded in Morocco and slays every man in her path until she's torn between a wealthy French industrialist (Adolphe Menjou) and an attractive American French Foreign Legion soldier (Gary Cooper). "A cinematic pattern, brilliant, profuse, subtle and at almost every turn inventive" (Wilton A. Barrett). With Ullrich Haupt, Juliette Compton and Francis McDonald.
VHS: S02285. $14.98.
Josef von Sternberg, USA, 1930, 97 mins.

Nashville
The recipient of five Academy Award nominations, Robert Altman's *Nashville* is an explosive drama and human comedy that interweaves the lives of 24 major characters during a five day period in the country music capital. A penetrating and multi-level portrait of America starring Keith Carradine, Karen Black, Geraldine Chaplin, Ronee Blakley, Lily Tomlin and Henry Gibson.
VHS: S00919. $29.95.
Robert Altman, USA, 1975, 159 mins.

The Night of the Hunter
Robert Mitchum gives one of his best performances as Harry Powell, a psychotic self-styled preacher who is after the stolen money of a hanged man. Set in a small West Virginia community during the Depression, this is Charles Laughton's only screen credit as a director. He makes the most of the opportunity.
VHS: S04213. $19.98.
Laser: LD70426. $39.95.
Charles Laughton, USA, 1955, 93 mins.

Paths of Glory
A shattering film from Stanley Kubrick, bringing into focus the insanity of war in the story of French General Macready, who, during World War I, orders his men into a futile mission. When the men fail, Macready selects three soldiers for trial and execution for cowardice. With incredible performances from Kirk Douglas, Ralph Meeker, Adolphe Menjou, George Macready, Wayne Morris, Richard Anderson. One of the high points of the American cinema.
VHS: S11433. $19.97.
Laser: LD70433. $49.95.
Stanley Kubrick, USA, 1957, 86 mins.

Psycho
The Classic! Anthony Perkins is Norman Bates and Janet Leigh is Marion Crane in this masterpiece of the macabre by Alfred Hitchcock.
VHS: S01068. $19.95.
Laser: LD70068. $34.98.
Alfred Hitchcock, USA, 1960, 109 mins.

Ride the High Country
Two aging gunfighters embark on their last adventure, transporting a shipment of gold. Breathtaking photography by Lucien Ballard; with great performances from Randolph Scott and Joel McCrea.
VHS: S04409. $19.98.
Sam Peckinpah, USA, 1962, 94 mins.

Salesman
Albert and David Maysles' landmark documentary focuses on a quartet of Bible salesmen and the hopes and frustrations of one man in particular: Paul Brennan. Labeled as "brutally honest," "funny and touching," and "a great insight into America," *Salesman* is a key work of the American documentary cinema.
VHS: S07491. $79.95.
Maysles Brothers, USA, 1969, 85 mins.

Salt of the Earth
Blacklisted during the McCarthy Era, *Salt of the Earth* portrays the true events of Chicano zinc workers on strike in New Mexico. When the mine owners get a court injunction to forbid picketing, the wives of the strikers take up the battle. A classic.
VHS: S01151. $29.95.
Herbert J. Biberman, USA, 1954, 94 mins.

What's Opera, Doc?
The Bugs Bunny/Road Runner Movie brings together full-length cartoon classics and a string of excerpts from many of Chuck Jones' most original productions with newly added material. Some of the greatest work, such as *What's Opera, Doc?*, *Duck Amuck* and *Ali Baba Bunny*, are to be seen here. Definitely for all ages!
VHS: S01781. $14.95.
Chuck Jones, USA, 1979, 98 mins.

Within Our Gates
This is the earliest American feature by an African-American. It tells the story of an African-American woman who seeks a white patron for a school. This film confronts racism directly with depictions of lynching and white-on-black rape in a plot that may be seen as a response to D.W. Griffith's *Birth of a Nation*. From the *Origins of American Films* series, a joint project of the Library of Congress and Smithsonian Video.
VHS: S21262. $34.95.
Oscar Micheaux, USA, 1920

1991

2001: A Space Odyssey
Light years ahead of its time, *2001: A Space Odyssey* is a spectacular movie that looks even more wondrous as time passes. This 1968 masterpiece reaches the outer limits of interplanetary space while penetrating the depths of man's inner destiny. Based on the novel by Arthur C. Clarke, featuring the music of Richard Strauss. This version is the result of a new digital video transfer, presented in widescreen format.
Laser: CAV, Criterion. **LD70481. $124.95.**
Laser: Deluxe letterboxed, chapter search, MGM. **LD70164. $39.98.**
Laser: CLV, Criterion. **LD70482. $59.95.**
Stanley Kubrick, USA, 1968, 139 mins.

2001: A Space Odyssey (25th Anniversary Edition)
Stanley Kubrick's landmark film traces the three stages of man, from evolutionary, predatory animals to futuristic space travelers, astronauts on a mission to Jupiter sabotaged by a malfunctioning computer known as HAL. "A uniquely poetic piece of science fiction that's hypnotically entertaining" (*The New Yorker*). Adapted from Arthur C. Clarke's story *The Sentinel*. With Keith Dullea, Gary Lockwood and William Sylvester. Special visual effects by Douglas Trumbull. Letterboxed.
VHS: S18674. $19.98.
Laser: CAV, 3 discs, with 4-page insert. **LD71876. $69.98.**
Laser: CLV, 2 discs. **LD71877. $39.98.**
Stanley Kubrick, USA, 1968, 141 mins.

The Battle of San Pietro/ Marines Have Landed
The U.S. War Department presents two documentaries of Marine action during World War II. Music by the Mormon Tabernacle Choir.
VHS: S02587. $19.95.

The Blood of Jesus
Spencer Williams directed this absorbing work about the scandal that envelops a small rural community when a weak husband accidentally shoots his religious wife, unleashing his own tormented faith and quest for redemption. With Williams, Cathryn Caviness, Heavenly Choir and Juanita Riley.
VHS: S07042. $24.95.
Spencer Williams, Jr., USA, 1941, 50 mins.

Chinatown
Jack Nicholson and Faye Dunaway star in Polanski's finely crafted, atmospheric film. What begins as a routine matrimonial snoop job for an average gumshoe mushrooms into a murderous regional and personal scandal told with incredible style, surprises and a gripping narrative line. Outstanding performances by all including John Huston as Dunaway's father and a cameo by Polanski as a great little sleaze.
VHS: S01840. $19.95.
Laser: Widescreen. LD75371. $49.98.
Roman Polanski, USA, 1974, 131 mins.

City Lights
One of Chaplin's most highly acclaimed films, a silent film in the era of talkies that demonstrated Chaplin's genius. The Little Tramp falls in love with a beautiful, blind flower girl and sets out to raise money for an operation to cure her.
VHS: S00245. $19.95.
Laser: LD72318. $69.98.
Charles Chaplin, USA, 1931, 86 mins.

David Holzman's Diary
Jim McBride's seminal underground film is an autocritique about a young filmmaker (screenwriter L.M. Kit Carson) who makes an autobiographical, cinema verite film. It is a film about identity and self-obsession. With Penny Wohl, Louise Levine and Fern McBride. Selected by the National Film Registry as an American Film Classic.
VHS: S18862. $19.98.
Jim McBride, USA, 1968, 74 mins.

Frankenstein
A restored version (containing footage not seen since censors cut the film at the time of its original release) of one of the great Hollywood horror films, with Boris Karloff in this famous adaptation of Mary Shelley's masterpiece.
VHS: S00462. $14.98.
James Whale, USA, 1931, 71 mins.

Blade Runner

Gertie the Dinosaur
A collection of six short animated films by Winsor McCay, a pioneer in the world of animation. McCay's early style involved delicate line drawings against a plain background; seen today, they still have considerable beauty and charm. This compilation includes *Gertie the Dinosaur* (1911), *Dream* (1922), *Bug Vaudeville* (1912), *Little Nemo* (1911), *The Pet* (1913) and *The Sinking of the Lusitania* (1919).
VHS: S15062. $29.95.
Winsor McCay, 1911-1922, 60 mins.

Gigi
Leslie Caron is the bewitching title character in this dazzling musical that won nine Oscars including Best Picture. Maurice Chevalier sings "Thank Heaven for Little Girls" and doesn't get arrested. Based on a story by Colette, a young girl at the turn of the century is trained in Paris to be a courtesan. With

Hermione Gingold and Louis Jourdan.
VHS: S07159. $19.95.
Laser: LD70582. $39.99.
Vincente Minnelli, USA, 1958, 116 mins.

Greed
One of the wonders of film, this miracle of filmmaking, made by Erich von Stroheim against the most impossible of odds, stars Gibson Gowland as McTeague, a San Francisco dentist, who marries ZaSu Pitts, the daughter of German immigrants. When Trina (Pitts) becomes greedy, McTeague becomes a drunken tramp and ends up killing her. A powerful, powerful masterpiece. This tape includes a prologue by film historian Kevin Brownlow, who describes the controversy surrounding the original cuts made to the film by the studio.
VHS: S09281. $29.95.
Laser: LD70592. $39.98.
Erich von Stroheim, USA, 1924, 133 mins.

High School
Documentary on a large urban high school. Not available on video.
Frederick Wiseman, USA, 1968

I Am a Fugitive from a Chain Gang
They put his feet and hands in irons, but they couldn't shackle his will. A gripping tale about an innocent man brutally victimized by the criminal justice system. Based on a true story, *Fugitive* stars the charismatic Paul Muni (*Scarface*) in the lead role.
VHS: S01706. $19.98.
Laser: Includes original theatrical trailer. LD71508. $34.98.
Mervyn Le Roy, USA, 1932, 93 mins.

The Italian
The story of Italian immigrants in the slums of New York, notable for its realism; produced by Thomas Ince, and starring George Beban. Silent with music score. USA, 1915, 78 mins.
VHS: S07487. $24.95.

King Kong
The classic shocker by Ernest B. Schoedsack in a 60th anniversary edition. The film's daring special effects still astonish and are preserved in this archival print and digitally remastered soundtrack struck from the original optical master track. With Fay Wray, Robert Armstrong, Bruce Cabot, Frank Reicher, Sam Hardy and Noble Johnson. B&W.
VHS: S17035. $16.98.
Laser: CAV. LD70389. $74.95.
Ernest B. Schoedsack, USA, 1933, 103 mins.

Lawrence of Arabia (30th Anniversary Edition)
David Lean's finest achievement is a historically expansive biography of British officer T.E. Lawrence and his military and political victories in the Middle East. The film provides a complex portrait of Lawrence, from his charisma, verve and adventure to his experiments with the dark side of human nature. This 30th Anniversary Edition is presented in its original screen format (letterboxed), with its theatrical trailer, Maurice Jarre's overture, a short on the making of the film and a 32-page booklet. With Peter O'Toole, Alec Guinness, Anthony Quinn and Omar Sharif. Cinematography by Freddie Young.
VHS: S17926. $24.95.
Laser: CAV. LD70413. $124.95.
Laser: CLV. LD70414. $69.95.
David Lean, Great Britain, 1962, 216 mins.

The Magnificent Ambersons
Produced, written and directed by Orson Welles, the follow-up film to *Citizen Kane*, and a work of depth and genius. Welles traces the details of a midwestern family's tragedy. From the novel by Booth Tarkington. With Tim Holt, Anne Baxter, Agnes Moorehead.
VHS: S00804. $19.95.
Laser: LD70417. $99.95.
Orson Welles, USA, 1942, 88 mins.

My Darling Clementine
A genuine American classic, with the climactic shoot-out at the O.K. Corral between Wyatt Earp, Doc Holliday and the vicious Clanton boys. With Henry Fonda, Victor Mature, Walter Brennan, Tim Holt and Linda Darnell.
VHS: S01784. $19.98.
John Ford, USA, 1946, 97 mins.

Out of the Past
Classic 40's film noir starring Robert Mitchum as a

man trying to escape his past by settling in what seems to be a tranquil community, but who is entangled in a web of intrigue and murder by his one-time gangster employer and his lover. Also stars Kirk Douglas and Jane Greer.
VHS: S02147. Currently out of release.
Jacques Tourneur, USA, 1947, 97 mins.

A Place in the Sun
Based on Theodore Dreiser's *An American Tragedy*, and featuring strong performances from Montgomery Clift, Elizabeth Taylor and Shelley Winters. Monty Clift is the poor boy driven by the lure of wealth, with his success threatened by complications from his simultaneous affairs with factory girl Shelley Winters and socialite Liz Taylor.
VHS: S04663. $19.95.
George Stevens, USA, 1951, 122 mins

The Poor Little Rich Girl
Mary Pickford in her first appearance as a child in a major film, an enchanting masterpiece of the early American cinema. Pickford, who was 24 at the time, plays Gwendolyn, a rich girl with everything except her parents' love and attention.
VHS: S01047. $29.95.
Maurice Tourneur, USA, 1917, 99 mins.

The Prisoner of Zenda
The classic costume drama and among Hollywood's best swashbucklers. Ronald Colman is a commoner who is forced to substitute for his look-alike cousin and falls in love with Madeleine Carroll while Douglas Fairbanks, Jr. is Rupert of Hentzau.
VHS: S11444. $29.95.
John Cromwell, USA, 1937, 101 mins.

Shadow of a Doubt
Hitchcock has said that this is his best American film. Joseph Cotten plays the widow-murderer Charley who dodges the police and joins his relatives in a small California town. Although his niece (Teresa Wright) takes him to her heart, she eventually recognizes him as the murderer. Tense, subtle, brilliant Hitchcock.
VHS: S07295. $19.95.
Laser: LD70077. $34.95.
Alfred Hitchcock, USA, 1943, 108 mins.

Sherlock Jr.
A boxed set of four Keaton features: *The Saphead, Three Ages, Our Hospitality/Sherlock Jr.* and accompanying short films. Newly mastered.
VHS: S23125. $79.95.
Laser: LD74801. $99.99.

Tevye the Dairyman
(Tevye der Milkhiker)
This memorable adaptation of Sholem Aleichem's play centers on Tevye, the dairyman, and his daughter Khave, who falls in love with Fedye, the Gentile son of a Ukrainian peasant. Her courtship and marriage pit Tevye's deep-seated faith and loyalty to tradition. Made from a completely restored print. "With all due respect for Zero Mostel and Topol in *Fiddler on the Roof*, it was Maurice Schwartz, the great Yiddish actor/director, who first showed Tevye the Dairyman in his full light as a *mensch* for all seasons. A rare opportunity to see Schwartz in what may have been his most magnificent role" (Judy Stone, *San Francisco Chronicle*). From the National Center for Jewish Film. Yiddish with new English subtitles.
VHS: S12219. $72.00.
Maurice Schwartz, USA, 1939, 96 mins.

1990

All About Eve
Six Oscars were awarded this cynical and entertaining examination of life as it exists on the Broadway theatre scene. Bette Davis glows as the aging star being undermined by her protege Anne Baxter, as Eve Harrington. With George Sanders, Celeste Holm and Marilyn Monroe. A gem.
VHS: S03911. $19.98.
Laser: LD70823. $49.98.
Joseph L. Mankiewicz, USA, 1950, 138 mins.

All Quiet on the Western Front
Classic adaptation of Erich Maria Remarque's anti-war novel has lost little of its impact over the years. The film follows a group of German recruits during World War I from their idealism to disillusionment.
VHS: S01686. $19.95.
Laser: LD70011. $39.98.
Lewis Milestone, USA, 1930, 103 mins.

Bringing Up Baby
One of the funniest movies from Hollywood, a classic screwball comedy. Katharine Hepburn is the madcap heiress with her pet leopard "Baby", who falls for an absent-minded zoologist (Cary Grant) and makes a shambles of his life. Briskly paced fun with May Robson, Charlie Ruggles and Barry Fitzgerald supporting the leads.
VHS: S09362. $19.98.
Howard Hawks, USA, 1938, 102 mins.

Dodsworth
Sam Dodsworth, a recently retired industrialist, sets off to Europe with his young wife, Fran. In Paris, Fran's yearning for romance leads her into an open flirtation with an attractive gentleman. Tormented by his wife's actions, Dodsworth begins a search for the happiness which seems to have eluded him. With Walter Huston, Mary Astor, Ruth Chatterton and David Niven. Digitally remastered.
VHS: S00355. $19.98.
William Wyler, USA, 1936, 101 mins.

Duck Soup
The most immortal film of the Marx Brothers! About the small nation of Fredonia, which has given Groucho complete power to restore order. Political satire and madness both. With Margaret Dumont and Louis Calhern.
VHS: S02018. $19.95.
Leo McCarey, USA, 1933, 70 mins.

Fantasia
The magic of Disney animation is gloriously blended with the music of eight classical pieces conducted by Leopold Stokowski. Relive those memorable moments with dancing mushrooms and hippos, dinosaurs, demons, abstract shapes, centaurs, and a certain sorcerer's apprentice who Walt felt needed a career boost.
VHS: S14755. Currently out of release.
Walt Disney Productions, USA, 1940, 116 mins.

The Freshman
An awkward college student accidentally becomes a star football player. With Harold Lloyd, Jobyna Ralston and Brooks Benedict. Also called *College Days*. Silent. Not available on video.
Fred Newmeyer/Sam Taylor, USA, 1925, 75 mins.

The Godfather
An epic featuring Marlon Brando as the patriarch of the Corleone family, masterfully balanced between the story of family life and the family crime business. With Al Pacino, James Caan, Robert Duvall, Diane Keaton. Based on Mario Puzo's novel. Music by Nino Rota. Letterboxed.
VHS: S00509. $29.95.
Francis F. Coppola, USA, 1972, 171 mins.

The Great Train Robbery
The first volume in the series *The Movies Begin* is a survey of the motion studies resulting from Edweard Muybridge's ground-breaking photographic methods. Motion picture innovators Thomas Edison, Louis Lumiere and Georges Melies are also represented. It concludes with the premiere of a well preserved print of Edwin S. Porter's *The Great Train Robbery* with authentic hand tinting as seen by audiences in 1903. 1893-1907, 75 mins.
VHS: S20847. $49.95.

Harlan County, U.S.A.
The Academy Award-winning documentary about the efforts of 180 coal-mining families to win a United Mine Workers contract at the Brookside mine in Harlan County, Kentucky, is a fascinating and moving portrait of the valor and courage of the coal-mining families.
VHS: S00542. $29.95.
Barbara Kopple, USA, 1976, 103 mins.

How Green Was My Valley
An offscreen narrator reflects on his life and work in John Ford's poetic and beautiful rendering of Welsh village life. Based on the novel by Richard Llewellyn. With Walter Pidgeon, Maureen O'Hara and Roddy McDowall. Winner for Best Picture in 1941.
VHS: S18449. $19.98.
John Ford, USA, 1941, 118 mins.

It's a Wonderful Life
James Stewart is George Bailey, trapped in Bedford

Casablanca

Falls, until his faith in life is restored by his Guardian Angel in Frank Capra's delightful comedy, nominated for multiple Academy Awards. Donna Reed, Lionel Barrymore, Thomas Mitchell and Beulah Bondi also star.
VHS: S15106. $19.98.
Laser: CAV. **LD70387. $89.95.**
Laser: CLV. **LD71996. $59.98.**
Frank Capra, USA, 1946, 160 mins.

Killer of Sheep
Life in a black ghetto. Not available on video.
Charles Burnett, USA, 1977

Love Me Tonight
Musical comedy about a Parisian tailor who accidentally moves into the aristocracy. With Maurice Chevalier, Jeanette MacDonald, Charles Butterworth, Charles Ruggles, Myrna Loy and C. Aubrey Smith. Not available on video.
Rouben Mamoulian, USA, 1932, 104 mins.

Meshes in the Afternoon
A selection of short films by Maya Deren, one of the geniuses of independent American cinema. Program includes *Meshes in the Afternoon* and *A Study in Choreography for Camera.* Silent.
VHS: S00835. Currently out of release.

Ninotchka
"Garbo laughs!"—and indeed, she does, in her first romantic comedy as the dour Soviet official who discovers the pleasures of Paris (and Melvyn Douglas) and must choose between romance and duty. Lubitsch at his best.
VHS: S00935. $19.98.
Ernst Lubitsch, USA, 1939, 108 mins.

Primary
A ground-breaking documentary which depicts the 1960 primaries between Presidential hopefuls Hubert Humphrey and John F. Kennedy. It has never been released to the home video market.
Richard Leacock, USA, 1960

Raging Bull
Robert De Niro gives an incredible performance as Jake LaMotta, the controversial middleweight fighter of the 1940's. *Raging Bull* shows how LaMotta turned his fears into the physical energy needed to become a champion, while destroying his private life.

Breathtaking cinematography!
DVD: DV60092. $24.98.
VHS: S01084. $19.95.
Laser: Letterboxed, chapter search. Includes original theatrical trailer. **LD71669. $39.98.**
Martin Scorsese, USA, 1980, 127 mins.

Rebel Without a Cause
James Dean stars in this quintessential story of teenage angst and rebellion. The generation gap movie of the 1950's, with a mixture of innocence, hope, despair and disillusionment set against the injustice and insensitivity of the adult world. One of the greats. With supporting parts by Natalie Wood, Sal Mineo, Nick Adams and Dennis Hopper as Goon. VHS letterboxed.
VHS: S01097. $19.98.
Laser: LD70663. $24.98.
Nicholas Ray, USA, 1955, 111 mins.

Red River
The classic cattle-drive movie, often cited as one of the best American westerns. John Wayne is Thomas Dunson, a tyrant of the trail who alienates his foster son (Montgomery Clift) and causes a sagebrush mutiny. Plenty of two-fisted Western action in this battle of the wills, and featuring a great supporting cast. With Walter Brennan, Joanne Dru, Harry Carey Jr. and Sr., John Ireland and Shelley Winters.
VHS: S01101. $19.95.
Laser: LD70664. $
Howard Hawks, USA, 1948, 133 mins.

The River
Two important works in the development of the documentary: *The River,* produced by the Farm Security Administration about the Mississippi, and *The Plow that Broke the Plains,* from 1936, about the New Deal's efforts to assist farmers hit by the Dust Bowl in Oklahoma.
VHS: S01121. $39.95.
Pare Lorentz, USA, 1937

Sullivan's Travels
Preston Sturges directed this classic tale of a Hollywood director who is fed up with creating fluff and decides to find out what is really happening in America. To research a "serious" film he disguises himself as a bum and goes on the road. Along the way, Joel McCrea as John L. Sullivan (the director) meets Veronica Lake, William Demarest, Porter Hall,

High Noon

Eric Blore and Franklin Pangborn. Still relevant and profound.
   VHS: S08507. $29.95.
   Laser: LD70084. $34.98.
Preston Sturges, USA, 1941, 91 mins.

The Treasure of the Sierra Madre
Pauline Kael calls this "one of the strongest of all American movies." Three Americans strike it rich and greed takes over. With Humphrey Bogart, Walter Huston, Tim Holt and Robert Blake, based on the novel by B. Traven.
   VHS: S01368. $19.95.
   Laser: LD70699. $39.98.
John Huston, USA, 1948, 120 mins.

A Woman Under the Influence
John Cassavetes' masterpiece centers on a dysfunctional Los Angeles family; in an astounding performance, Gena Rowlands stars as a tightly-wound woman who loves her children too much, withholds her affection from her husband (Peter Falk), and goes slowly insane by her unrealized expectations. A brilliant, uncompromising work, with strong secondary work by Katherine Cassavetes, Lady Rowlands and Fred Draper.
   VHS: S17304. $19.95.
John Cassavetes, USA, 1974, 155 mins.

1989

The Best Years of Our Lives
This epic film focuses on the troubles of three World War II servicemen as they try to pick up the threads of their lives after returning home to the States. An insightful portrait of small-town American life and its values. Starring Myrna Loy, Frederic March, Dana Andrews, Virginia Mayo and Teresa Wright. *The Best Years of Our Lives* was named one of the 50 greatest motion pictures of all time by the members of The American Film Institute. Digitally remastered.
   VHS: S03117. $19.98.
William Wyler, USA, 1946, 170 mins.

Casablanca
The ultimate in the Bogart myth: his Rick Blaine is cynical, tough, hardened by life's misfortunes, yet still sentimental and idealistic. The dialog is full of quotable Bogart lines, the camerawork by Arthur Edeson evocative, the casting inspired. With Ingrid Bergman, Paul Henreid, Claude Rains, Peter Lorre, Sydney Greenstreet.
   VHS: S17125. $19.98.
   Laser: CAV, 2 discs, Criterion. LD70353. $99.95.
   Laser: CLV, 1 disc, MGM. LD70540. $34.98.
Michael Curtiz, USA, 1942, 102 mins.

Citizen Kane
One of the greatest films ever made is now available in a version painstakingly restored to its original brilliance in honor of the film's 50th anniversary. With Orson Welles, Dorothy Comingore, Everett Sloane, Paul Stewart. Cinematography by Gregg Toland, script by Welles and Herman Mankiewicz.
   VHS: S14599. $19.98.
   Laser: CAV, 50th anniversary edition. LD70745. $124.95.
   Laser: CLV, 50th anniversary edition. LD70746. $39.95.
   Laser: CLV. LD70356. $39.95.
Orson Welles, USA, 1941, 119 mins.

The Crowd
An ordinary man struggles to maintain his individuality in a heartless city. Featuring James Murray as John, a store clerk, and Eleanor Boardman as his wife Mary. *The Crowd* is one of the most important films of the silent era; its visual innovations still astonish viewers, and the relevance of its theme has only increased over the years" (*Pacific Film Archive*).
   VHS: S09279. $29.95.
King Vidor, USA, 1928, 104 mins.

Dr. Strangelove or: How I Learned to Stop Worrying and Love the Bomb
This great black comedy stars Peter Sellers as the wheelchair-bound nuclear scientist plotting a scheme to attack Russia's nuclear targets with nuclear bombs. Very funny and very frightening, *Dr. Strangelove* also stars Sterling Hayden as U.S. Air Force Commander Jack D. Ripper, and George C. Scott as Joint Chief of Staff "Buck" Turgidson. VHS letterboxed.
   DVD: DV60026. $24.95.
   VHS: S00367. $19.95.
   Laser: LD70750. $99.95.
Stanley Kubrick, USA, 1963, 101 mins.

The General
Considered by many to be the last great comedy of the silent era, and consistently ranked as a masterpiece. Based on a true incident in the Civil War, the "General" is the railroad engine "engineered" by Confederate Army reject Keaton, who is also humiliated by his girlfriend (Marion Mack), who thinks him a coward. When a small company of Union soldiers penetrates behind Confederate lines, Keaton sets off in hot pursuit in one of the truly great chase scenes ever. The scenes were shot on the narrow gauge lines of Oregon and Keaton used less than 50 titles to explain the whole story. Also contains the shorts *The Playhouse* and *Cops* Newly mastered. Silent with music track.
   VHS: S23033. $29.95.
Buster Keaton/Clyde Bruckman, USA, 1927, 76 mins.

Gone with the Wind
A film beyond criticism, a work that welds together Hollywood classicism and literary adaptation with grace. Victor Fleming is the credited director, though at various times Howard Hawks, George Cukor and Sam Wood helped shape the narrative and rhythm. Ben Hecht worked on the screenplay. William Cameron Menzies was the production designer. With Clark Gable, Vivien Leigh, Leslie Howard, Olivia de Havilland and Hattie McDaniel.
   VHS: S00515. $89.98.
Victor Fleming, USA, 1939, 222 mins.

The Grapes of Wrath
Certainly one of the all-time classics, this adaptation of the John Steinbeck novel of the dust bowl migration from Oklahoma to California stars Henry Fonda as Tom Joad, John Carradine as Casey. The film won the Academy Award for Best Director.
   VHS: S00525. $19.95.
   Laser: LD71013. $49.98.
John Ford, USA, 1940, 129 mins.

High Noon
Gary Cooper is the marshall who fights alone for upholding the law when the entire town is paralyzed with fear. Stark settings and shadows heighten the suspense. The most popular film of 1952. With Grace Kelly, Lloyd Bridges, Lon Chaney and Henry Morgan.
   VHS: S00567. $14.98.
   Laser: CAV. LD70380. $74.95.
   Laser: CLV. LD70381. $49.95.
Fred Zinnemann, USA, 1952, 84 mins.

Intolerance
Four separate stories are interwoven: the fall of Babylon, the death of Christ, the massacre of the Hugenots, and a modern drama—all cross-cut and building with enormous energy to a thrilling chase and finale. Far ahead of its time, Griffith created a spectacle which audiences of the day did not accept but which has become a classic of world cinema. This specially packaged double cassette edition of *Intolerance* has been remastered using variable speed projection and color tints to match the original release prints, making it the best version available anywhere. Tinted with organ score.
   VHS: S13048. $29.95.
   Laser: CAV. LD71052. $69.95.
D.W. Griffith, USA, 1916, 190 min.

The Learning Tree
A well-intentioned and beautifully photographed film version of Gordon Parks' autobiographical novel set in Kansas in the mid-1920s. Writer-director-producer Parks recreates his teen years in a small town where a young black learns about life. With Kyle Johnson as Newt and Dana Elcar as the Sheriff.
VHS: S03572. $19.98.
Gordon Parks, USA, 1969, 107 mins.

The Maltese Falcon
Even if you've seen this film so often that you know all the dialog, it never ceases to amaze. A search for a priceless statuette provides the action in this classic, excellent film favorite. Noir at its best with great actors Humphrey Bogart, Mary Astor, Sydney Greenstreet and Peter Lorre, based on Dashiell Hammet's thriller.
VHS: S00810. $19.95.
Laser: LD70621. $34.98.
John Huston, USA, 1941, 101 mins.

Modern Times
Charlie Chaplin's silent homage to the human spirit, in which Chaplin is the victim of industrial boom. He plays the factory worker gone looney by the assembly line who falls in love with a down-and-out young lady and tries through various and eccentric means to find a bit of financial peace. A great comedy, and a great film.
VHS: S00866. $19.98.
Charles Chaplin, USA, 1936, 89 mins.

Mr. Smith Goes to Washington
James Stewart stars in Frank Capra's famous film as the naive Jeff Smith, appointed a U.S. senator by a corrupt political party machine. Famous for its heroic one-man filibuster, it is a moving vision of honor amid political squalor.
VHS: S00889. $19.95.
Laser: Restored, 3 sides, digital master, chapter stops. **LD75054. $44.95.**
Frank Capra, USA, 1939, 125 mins.

Nanook of the North
The classic documentary of the daily life and hardships of an Eskimo family, still considered superb filmmaking and a landmark. Music score by Stanley Silverman, performed by the Tashi Ensemble and conducted by Peter Serkin. Silent.
VHS: S00916. $29.95.
Robert Flaherty, USA, 1922, 55 mins.

On the Waterfront
Marlon Brando in the archetypal role as ex-fighter Terry Malloy, working for Boss Johnny Friendly (Lee J. Cobb) on the gang-ridden waterfront. The classic American movie of redemption, with a great script by Budd Schulberg.
VHS: S00960. $19.95.
Laser: LD72070. $34.95.
Elia Kazan, USA, 1954, 108 mins.

The Searchers
Classic John Ford Western starring John Wayne as Ethan Edwards, a Civil War veteran intent on finding the daughters of his murdered brother, who have been captured by the Comanches. With Jeffrey Hunter, Ward Bond and Natalie Wood.
VHS: S01731. $19.98.
Laser: LD70672. Currently unavailable.
John Ford, USA, 1956, 119 mins.

Singin' in the Rain
Deservedly one of the best-loved movies of all time! An exhilarating and fast-moving musical comedy that traces the transition from silent films to "talkies," starring dancing Gene Kelly and Debbie Reynolds, with Donald O'Connor, Jean Hagen and Rita Moreno.
DVD: DV60118.$24.98.
VHS: S15851. $19.98.
Laser: CAV, 2 discs, Criterion. **LD70463. $89.95.**
Laser: CLV, 1 disc, Criterion. **LD70464. $39.95.**
Laser: CLV, MGM. **LD70679. $24.98.**
Laser: CAV, MGM. **LD70680. $39.98.**
Gene Kelly/Stanley Donen, USA, 1952, 103 mins.

Snow White and the Seven Dwarfs
Walt Disney's masterpiece tells the unforgettable story of a young woman who dreams of meeting Prince Charming but is foiled by a jealous woman. Of course she is helped in her struggle with this evil witch by those charming little people, the seven dwarfs.
VHS: S21316. $26.99.
Walt Disney, USA, 1937, 83 mins.

Some Like It Hot
Perhaps the funniest American film of the 1950's, Tony Curtis and Jack Lemmon play two second rate musicians on the run from the Chicago mob, who take to dressing in drag. Marilyn Monroe plays Sugar, the singer in an all-female band, and Joe E. Brown is an eccentric millionaire in love with Lemmon in drag.
VHS: S01836. $19.98.
Laser: CAV, 3 discs, Criterion. **LD70466. $124.95.**
Laser: Remastered, MGM. **LD71169. $39.98.**
Billy Wilder, USA, 1959, 122 mins.

Star Wars
Already a classic, a blend of pulp magazine sci-fi, comic book action, and old fashioned cliff-hanger story starring Mark Hamill, Harrison Ford and Carrie Fisher.
VHS: S02866. $19.98.
Laser: CAV. **LD71338. $64.98.**
George Lucas, USA, 1977, 121 mins.

Sunrise
Although this was Murnau's first Hollywood film, he scripted it with Carl Mayer while still in Germany. The story concerns the marriage of a peasant couple whose honeymoon in the big city is detoured by a sultry seductress. But the film is neither trite nor melodramatic; Murnau's sets and camera angles imbue the images with a poetic lyricism that reveals the characters' psychological states. Easily his most perfect film, Murnau's *Sunrise* was named the "Greatest film of all time," in a recent *Cahiers du Cinema* Critic's Poll. With George O'Brien, Janet Gaynor and Margaret Livingston.
VHS: S07782. $29.95.
Laser: Outtakes, digital transfer. **LD76401. $49.98.**
Friedrich W. Murnau, USA, 1927, 97 mins.

Sunset Boulevard
Gloria Swanson is the aging silent film queen, William Holden the struggling writer in this bizarre, dark and desperate portrait of Hollywood. Winner of three Academy Awards, and one of the greatest American films.
VHS: S01285. $14.95.
Laser: LD75268. $34.98.
Billy Wilder, USA, 1950, 110 mins.

Vertigo
The elaborately constructed murder story in which an ex-cop who suffers from vertigo is the innocent pawn, is a masterful study of sexual obsession, and one of Hitchcock's best films. With James Stewart, Kim Novak, Barbara Bel Geddes. VHS letterboxed.
VHS: S01795. $19.95.
Laser: LD70094. $79.95.
Alfred Hitchcock, USA, 1958, 95 mins.

The Wizard of Oz
Judy Garland, Ray Bolger, Jack Haley, Bert Lahr, Frank Morgan, Margaret Hamilton, Billie Burke and Toto in the land of Oz, in MGM's great, Technicolor fantasy where Judy follows the Yellow Brick Road.
DVD: DV60104. $24.98.
VHS: S09609. $19.95.
Laser: CLV, MGM. **LD70709. $24.98.**
Laser: CAV, Criterion. **LD71215. $99.95.**
Victor Fleming, USA, 1939, 101 mins.

Vertigo

Box Office Flops
Heaven's Gate
Can't Stop the Music
Ishtar

The cost of
makeup for
**Planet of
the Apes**
was a cool
$1,000,000

MONEY

The Sting

Money to Die For
Reversal of Fortune
Double Indemnity
Hush Hush Sweet Charlotte
Shadow of a Doubt
Greed

"That's what I like - everything in contrasting shades of money."

Bob Hope surveys his new boss's apartment and comments on the luxurious decor in *That Certain Feeling*.

Jackie Coogan files suit against his mother and stepfather for squandering his fortune ($4,000,000) earned as a child actor. Filed in 1938, this resulted in enforcement of a landmark decision wherein half of all child salaries must be put in a trust fund.

OIL TYCOON and part-time HOLLYWOOD INVESTOR **John Smith**, in a grand but fatal attempt to prove his love and devotion to a 14 year old girl, plummets to his death while attempting to cross Niagara Falls in a barrel.

Capers/Heists
Topkapi
To Catch a Thief
Seven Sinners
Bullitt
Great Train Robbery
League of Gentlemen
The Sting
Rififfi
Gambit
How to Steal a Million

The Money
Money for Nothing
Money Madness
Money Movers
Money Pit
Money to Burn
Dollar
Dollars
Pennies from Heaven

Strikin' it Rich
Treasure of Sierra Madre
Treasure Island
Ali Baba and the Forty Thieves
Giant

Best Musical Numbers
"Money Makes the World Go Round" *Cabaret*
"We're in the Money" *Gold Diggers of 1933*
"Who Wants to be a Millionaire?" *High Society*
"Wouldn't it be Loverly?" *My Fair Lady*
"I've Got a Lot of Livin' To Do" *Bye Bye Birdie*
"We're a Couple of Swells" *Easter Parade*
"Hey Big Spender" *Sweet Charity*
"Diamonds are a Girl's Best Friend" *Gentlemen Prefer Blondes*
"If I were a Rich Man" *Fiddler on the Roof*

The Hollywood Ten

Fifty years have passed since these writers and directors were investigated by the House Un-American Activities Committee during their unearthing of Communism in Hollywood. Below is a list of the principals involved who stood their ground in defending their principles and constitutional right to hold the political belief of their choosing.

Alvah Bessie

Studio blacklisting ended his screenwriting career. Bessie moved to San Francisco and became the lighting man and announcer at the "hungry i" for next to minimum wage.

Northern Pursuit 1943
 VHS: S01875. $19.98.
The Very Thought of You 1944
Smart Woman 1948
Hollywood on Trial 1976
 VHS: S09422. $29.95.

Herbert J. Biberman

Director, screenwriter, producer. In 1947 he made headlines when he refused to confirm or deny Communist party membership before the HUAC. Convicted in 1950 of contempt of Congress and jailed for six months. He was identified by Edward Dmytryk and Budd Schulberg among others. His wife, Gale Sondergaard, also refused to testify, jeopardizing her acting career.

One Way Ticket 1935
Meet Nero Wolfe 1936
The Master Race 1944
Salt of the Earth 1954
 VHS: S01151. $29.95.
Slaves 1969

Lester Cole

Screenwriter. Union activist and one of the founders of the Screenwriters Guild in 1933. His career ended in 1947 when he refused to answer any questions about his political beliefs. Imprisoned for a year and blacklisted thereafter, he left behind a script which would later be re-written by John Steinbeck, called *Viva Zapata*. After prison he worked as a short order cook, waiter and manual laborer. He wrote under assumed names and later taught screenwriting at the University of California at Berkeley.

Painted Faces 1929
Invisible Man Returns 1940
 VHS: S17273. $14.98.
Footsteps in the Dark 1940
 VHS: S22897. $19.98.
Blood on the Sun 1945
 VHS: S12902. $19.98.
 Laser: LD71971. $29.98.
High Wall 1947
If I Had a Million 1952
Operation Eichmann 1961
Hollywood on Trial 1976
 VHS: S09422. $29.95.

Edward Dmytryk

Film editor from 1930-1939. Director. Spent one year in jail. In 1951, he returned and incriminated several of his former colleagues. Was reinstated by Hollywood and went on to make many successful films.

Ruggles of Red Gap 1935
 VHS: S05995. $14.98.
 Laser: LD71570. $34.98.
Bulldog Drummond's Peril 1938
 VHS: S03081. $29.95.
Prison Farm 1938
Emergency Squad 1939
Golden Gloves 1939
Television Spy 1939
Her First Romance 1940
 VHS: S22600. $19.95.
Mystery Sea Raider 1940
The Blonde from Singapore 1941
The Devil Commands 1941
Secrets of the Lone Wolf 1941

Sweetheart of the Campus 1941
Under Age 1941
Confessions of Boston Blackie 1942
Counter-Espionage 1942
Seven Miles from Alcatraz 1942
Behind the Rising Sun 1943
Captive Wild Woman 1943
  VHS: S21729. $14.98.
The Falcon Strikes Back 1943
Hitler's Children 1943
Tender Comrade 1943
Murder My Sweet 1944
  VHS: S00898. $19.98.
Back to Bataan 1945
Cornered 1945
Till the End of Time 1946
Crossfire 1947
  VHS: S03582. $19.98.
So Well Remembered 1947
Give Us This Day 1949
Obsession 1949
Mutiny 1951
Eight Iron Men 1952
The Sniper 1952
The Juggler 1953
Broken Lance 1954
  VHS: S11191. $14.98.
The Caine Mutiny 1954
  VHS: S01854. $19.95.
  Laser: LD72443. $39.95.
End of the Affair 1954
The Left Hand of God 1955
The Mountain 1956
  VHS: S08171. $19.95.
Raintree County 1957
  VHS: S01087. $24.98.
  Laser: LD70187. $39.98.
Soldier of Fortune 1955
  VHS: S12520. $39.98.
The Young Lions 1958
  VHS: S03499. $19.98.
The Blue Angel 1959
Warlock 1959
  VHS: S06519. $19.98.
  Laser: LD75281. $34.98.
The Reluctant Saint 1962
Walk on the Wild Side 1962
  VHS: S07337. $69.95.
The Carpetbaggers 1963
Where Love Has Gone 1964
  VHS: S19026. $14.95.
Mirage 1965

Alvarez Kelly 1966
  VHS: S03884. $19.95.
  Laser: LD74907. $39.95.
The Battle for Anzio 1968
Shalako 1968
  VHS: S15986. $14.98.
Barbe-Bleue 1972
The Human Factor 1975
Hollywood on Trial 1976
  VHS: S09422. $29.95.

Ring Lardner, Jr.
Screenwriter. Served a year in prison for refusing to cooperate with the HUAC. Worked "underground" or abroad using various pseudonyms.
A Star Is Born 1937 (co-scripted, uncredited)
  VHS: S18187. $24.95.
  Laser: LD70684. $39.98.
Nothing Sacred 1937 (co-scripted, uncredited)
  VHS: S18188. $24.95.
  Laser: LD72064. $39.95.
Laura 1937
  VHS: S18074. $19.98.
  Laser: LD71096. $39.98.

Woman of the Year 1942
  VHS: S04741. $19.98.
  Laser: LD70710. $34.98.
Cloak and Dagger 1946
  VHS: S03502. $59.95.
  Laser: LD71456. $29.98.
Forever Amber 1947
  VHS: S21955. $19.98.
  Laser: LD75460. $49.98.
Cincinatti Kid 1965
  VHS: S16443. $19.98.
M*A*S*H 1970
  VHS: S02643. $14.98.
  Laser: LD76743. $24.98.
The Greatest 1977

John Howard Lawson
Screenwriter, playwright. Co-founded the Screenwriter's Guild and was its first president in 1933. Nominated for an Oscar for the original story *Blockade* (1938). He refused to cooperate with the HUAC, spent one year in prison and was blacklisted by the film industry. Went into self-exile in Mexico and later authored several books on drama and film and toured as a lecturer on theatre and film for university audiences.

Dream of Love 1928
Dynamite 1929
Bachelor Apartment 1931
  VHS: S13660. $19.98.
Goodbye Love 1933
  VHS: S14663. $29.95.
Success at Any Price 1934
Algiers 1938
  VHS: S00029. $19.95.
Blockade 1938
  VHS: S11586. $19.95.
Action in the North Atlantic 1943
  VHS: S14305. $19.98.
Sahara 1943
  VHS: S07695. $14.95.
Hollywood on Trial 1976
  VHS: S09422. $29.95.

Albert Maltz
Screenwriter, playwright, novelist. Spent 10 months in prison and was blacklisted upon his release. Spent 1952-1962 in Mexico, occasionally working under pseudonyms.
This Gun for Hire 1942
  VHS: S18997. $14.98.
Destination Tokyo 1943
  VHS: S12535. $19.98.
Seeds of Freedom 1943
Cloak and Dagger 1946
  VHS: S03502. $59.95.
  Laser: LD71456. $29.98.

The Naked City 1948
 VHS: S18239. $29.95.
 Laser: LD75943. $49.95.
Broken Arrow 1950
 VHS: S06527. $14.98.
The Beguiled 1971 (under pseudonym John B.
Sherry/Grimes Grice)
 VHS: S06821. $14.98.
Scalawag 1973
Hollywood on Trial 1976
 VHS: S09422. $29.95.

Samuel Ornitz
Screenwriter. Career ruined by Hollywood
blacklisting.

The Case of Lena Smith 1929
Chinatown Nights 1929
Hell's Highway 1932
Imitation of Life 1934 (1 of 6 screenwriters)
Mark of the Vampire 1935
 VHS: S04706. $59.95.
Hollywood on Trial 1976
 VHS: S09422. $29.95.

Adrian Scott
Producer, screenwriter. Career ended in 1947 after he
refused to testify. Spent one year in jail. Identified as
a Communist by Edward Dmytryk, he was blacklisted
by the film industry and never returned to films.

Mr. Lucky 1943
Murder My Sweet 1944
 VHS: S00898. $19.98.
Deadline at Dawn 1946
Hollywood on Trial 1976
 VHS: S09422. $29.95.

Dalton Trumbo
Screenwriter, director. After he was blacklisted, his
income went from $75,000 per script to zero. Spent
10 months in jail. Sold scripts to Hollywood under
various pseudonyms, and even won an Oscar for his
story *The Brave One* (1956), written under the name
"Robert Rich."

Career 1939
Curtain Call 1940
Kitty Foyle 1940
 VHS: S00688. $19.95.
You Belong to Me 1941
Tender Comrade 1943
Thirty Seconds over Tokyo 1944
 VHS: S13309. $19.98.
Our Vines Have Tender Grapes 1945
 VHS: S18506. $19.98.
Emergency Wedding 1950

Roman Holiday 1953
 VHS: S01763. $19.95.
 Laser: LD75249. $34.98.
The Brave One 1956
 Laser: LD74746. $39.95.
Exodus 1960
 VHS: S02338. $24.98.
 Laser: LD71683. $49.98.
Spartacus 1960
 VHS: S15075. $19.95.
 Laser: LD70082. $124.95.
The Last Sunset 1961
Lonely Are the Brave 1962
 VHS: S06816. $19.95.
 Laser: LD74927. $34.98.
The Sandpiper 1965
Hawaii 1966
 VHS: S12425. $24.95.
The Fixer 1968
The Horsemen 1970
Johnny Got His Gun 1971
FTA (Foxtrot Tango Alpha) 1972
Executive Action 1973
 VHS: S15825. $19.98.
Papillon 1973
 VHS: S10936. $19.98.

Other Films of Interest:
The Front 1976
 VHS: S02021. $19.98.
Guilty by Suspicion 1991
 VHS: S15008. $19.98.
House of Un-American Activities 1989-92
 VHS: S23209. $29.95.

Films in **bold** are available on video.

50 Top Film Noir

The Asphalt Jungle
John Huston directs this excellent underworld drama about crime and punishment. Five guys pull off a jewelry heist only to be double-crossed by their fence. With Sterling Hayden, Louis Calhern and Marilyn Monroe as Calhern's "niece."
VHS: S03458. $24.95.
Laser: LD70844. $39.95.
John Huston, USA, 1950, 112 mins.

Beware My Lovely
Widow Ida Lupino hires Robert Ryan as a handyman, then discovers he is a psychopath. (Don't you hate it when that happens?) A dark and atmospheric thriller that delivers chills and good performances from its talented leads.
VHS: S05670. $19.95.
Laser: LD71814. $29.98.
Harry Horner, USA, 1952, 77 mins.

The Big Clock
Ray Milland, Charles Laughton, Maureen O'Sullivan and George Macready star in this classic thriller. Laughton is the publisher of a crime magazine where Milland works as an editor. In a new story assigned by Laughton, the more Milland digs, the more he finds himself implicated in murder. Remade as *No Way Out* (1987).
VHS: S28400. $14.98.
John Farrow, USA, 1948, 95 mins.

Big Heat
Classic film noir from Fritz Lang. Ruthless criminals, an honest cop, sultry women and a gripping plot are the elements that make up *The Big Heat*. Glenn Ford stars in Lang's best postwar film, with Lee Marvin as a nasty bad guy and a fine performance by Gloria Grahame as his shallow but wily moll.
VHS: S00130. $59.95.
Fritz Lang, USA, 1953, 90 mins.

Big Sleep
Humphrey Bogart is Philip Marlowe in this entertaining adaptation of Raymond Chandler's novel. Blackmail, murder, sex and drugs all come into play as the ace detective tries to sort out the guilty parties. Even the author couldn't figure out who killed the chauffeur. With Lauren Bacall, Martha Vickers and Elisha Cook, Jr.
VHS: S09389. $19.95.
Laser: LD70174. $34.98.
Howard Hawks, USA, 1946, 114 mins.

Blue Dahlia
Alan Ladd and Veronica Lake made their movie careers in film noirs like this. Raymond Chandler's first original screenplay is classic in its simplicity. Johnny Morrison (Ladd) returns from Naval duty to discover his wife has been cheating on him. Soon she is murdered, leaving Johnny as the prime suspect. Now it's up to him—with the help of sultry vixen Joyce Harwood (Lake)—to clear his name. Includes the original theatrical trailer.
VHS: S27353. $14.98.
George Marshall, USA, 1945, 100 mins.

Cape Fear
Robert Mitchum is a sadistic rapist seeking out the lawyer who put him behind bars (played by Gregory Peck). His search ends in a small North Carolina town where he commences a campaign of terror against Peck's family, which the police are powerless to stop. A tense and well-paced suspenser highlighted by Mitchum's riveting portrayal of a shrewd psychopath, and a terrific cat-and-mouse chase through the Southern bayous.
VHS: S14979. $19.95.
Laser: LD70293. $34.98.
J. Lee Thompson, USA, 1962, 106 mins.

Caught
A dark and compelling story of a girl married to the wrong man who runs away and falls in love with a struggling young ghetto doctor. Chased down by the husband, she is forced to choose between money and love. Robert Ryan gives a strong performance as the vicious, mentally unstable millionaire husband (based on Howard Hughes). With Barbara Bel Geddes and James Mason as the lovers. Intelligently handled by director Ophuls in his most successful American film.
VHS: S00222. $19.95.
Max Ophuls, USA, 1949, 90 mins.

City That Never Sleeps
Gig Young is a Chicago cop involved in adultery, blackmail and murder and he is the good guy. William Talman is Young's buddy who is responsible for the death of several people and trespassing on CTA property. With Mala Powers, Edward Arnold, Marie Windsor and Chill Wills as Sgt. Joe, the Voice of Chicago. B&W.
VHS: S07134. $19.95.
John H. Auer, USA, 1953, 90 mins.

Clash by Night
Barbara Stanwyck and Paul Douglas head a stellar cast consisting of Robert Ryan, Marilyn Monroe and Keith Andes in the screen version of the Clifford Odets play. Stanwyck returns to the love of a simple fisherman, but it's clear she isn't satisfied with her lot in life, a fact of which the cynical Robert Ryan takes advantage. The resulting melodrama offers competing romantic attractions and tragic results.
VHS: S29444. $19.98.
Fritz Lang, USA, 1952, 105 mins.

Conflict
In this taut psychological drama, a killer is brought to bay by a wily psychologist and a nagging conscience. Humphrey Bogart plays a man who plots to kill his wife because his affections have turned to her younger sister. Sydney Greenstreet is the psychiatrist and family friend who uses mind games to release the killer's remorse. Alexis Smith plays Bogart's femme fatale.
VHS: S16097. $19.95.
Curtis Bernhardt, USA, 1945, 86 mins.

The Asphalt Jungle

Criss Cross
Interesting film noir study with Burt Lancaster as a petty crook, Yvonne DeCarlo as his ex-wife and Dan Duryea as her shady new boyfriend. Dan Curtis in his film debut as DeCarlo's dance partner. One of the best sleazy underworld films of the 1940's and remade in 1995 by Steven Soderbergh as *The Underneath*.
VHS: S08222. $69.95.
Robert Siodmak, USA, 1949, 87 mins.

Crossfire
This tense thriller was shot entirely at night with a style reminiscent of expressionism. A Jew is murdered in a New York hotel, and three ex-soldiers are suspected. Hollywood's first strong statement against anti-Semitism, starring Robert Mitchum, Robert Young and Robert Ryan as the insane veteran with a rabid hatred of Jews. Based on the novel *The Brick Foxhole*, by Richard Brooks.
VHS: S03582. $19.98.
Edward Dmytryk, USA, 1947, 86 mins.

Clash by Night

D.O.A.
Noir classic (remade with Dennis Quaid and Meg
Ryan in 1988) concerns an accountant (Edmond
O'Brien) who has been poisoned, has only a few days
to live, and must find out who poisoned him and why.
Surprisingly effective thriller, with music by Dmitri
Tiomkin.
VHS: S04664. $19.95.
Rudolph Mate, USA, 1949, 83 mins.

Dead End
Humphrey Bogart is the young man who has grown
up knowing only one kind of law—his own. Sylvia
Sidney is the sensitive young woman who falls for
touchy but tender Joel McCrea in this tense film, set
on New York's turbulent Lower East Side.
VHS: S03119. $19.95.
William Wyler, USA, 1937, 92 mins.

Dead Lucky
Martin's stab at gambling wins him a fortune—and
traps him between a con artist, an assassin, and a
mysterious seductress. In gripping conclusion, he
becomes both victim and killer. Adapted from the
award-winning novel *Lake of Darkness.*
VHS: S14327. $49.95.
Montgomery Tully, Great Britain, 1960, 91 mins.

Detour
One of the great "B" classics: a masterwork by
director Ulmer. A young pianist (Tom Neal)
hitchhikes across the country and becomes involved
in two murders he didn't commit. (He's not the
smartest guy.) Femme fatale Ann Savage hops a ride
with Neal and practically steals the film as what is
surely one of the most unpleasant creatures that has
ever graced the silver screen.
VHS: S00328. $19.95.
Edgar G. Ulmer, USA, 1946, 69 mins.

Double Indemnity
A great Billy Wilder film in which "every turn and
twist is exactly calculated and achieves its effect with
the simplest of means; this shrewd, smooth, tawdry
thriller is one of the high points of 40s films" (Kael).
Raymond Chandler collaborated on the screenplay in
adapting James Cain's story. Barbara Stanwyck is the
platinum blonde, Fred MacMurray the insurance
salesman she ensnares in a plot to kill her
businessman-husband and collect on the double-
indemnity clause in his policy.
VHS: S02940. $19.95.
Laser: LD70024. $34.98.
Billy Wilder, USA, 1944, 107 mins.

Force of Evil
Film noir featuring John Garfield as an attorney who
works for a mobster and finds himself caught in a
numbers racket scheme that could bankrupt New

York's "numbers banks".
VHS: S04232. $14.95.
Laser: CLV. LD71984. $29.98.
Abraham Polonsky, USA, 1949, 80 mins.

Gilda
Rita Hayworth has never been more alluring as the
pampered wife of a casino owner in South America
who has eyes for her husband's new assistant. The
second teaming of Glenn Ford and the gorgeous
Hayworth, who steams up the screen by removing
just her gloves.
VHS: S02167. $19.95.
Charles Vidor, USA, 1946, 110 mins.

He Walked by Night
Called "a gritty masterpiece" by filmmaker Erroll
Morris. Richard Basehart stars as a psychotic killer
mercilessly tracked down by police detectives. Shot
in a highly realistic manner with a fantastic final
shoot-out in the L.A. drainage tunnel system. Largely
directed by an uncredited Anthony Mann.
VHS: S05959. $29.95.
Laser: CLV/CAV. LD72062. $34.95.
Alfred Werker, USA, 1948, 78 mins.

High Sierra
Humphrey Bogart stars as Roy "Mad Dog" Earle, a
kindhearted gangster from Indiana who runs into
serious trouble in the scenic mountains of Northern
California. With Ida Lupino, Arthur Kennedy, Henry
Hull, Barton MacLane, Cornel Wilde and Joan Leslie
as the young woman with the clubfoot. Script by John
Huston and W.R. Burnett, based on Burnett's novel.
VHS: S00569. $19.95.
Raoul Walsh, USA, 1941, 100 mins.

The Hitch-Hiker
Frank Lovejoy, Edmond O'Brien and William Talman
star in a classic film noir directed by Ida Lupino.
Talman is an ex-convict who hitches rides, and then
robs and kills the driver. A fascinating psychological
study, very rare.
VHS: S06909. $24.95.
Ida Lupino, USA, 1953, 71 mins.

In a Lonely Place
Humphrey Bogart stars as Dixon Steele, an alcoholic
Hollywood screenwriter who is prone to violence and
accused of murder. Gloria Grahame provides him
with an alibi and additional headaches. A hard
hitting, cynical drama directed by Nicholas Ray from
the novel by Dorothy B. Hughes. With Frank
Lovejoy, Martha Stewart and Jeff Donnell. B&W.
VHS: S09110. $69.95.
Nicholas Ray, USA, 1950, 91 mins.

Killer's Kiss
A prizefighter rescues a young woman from her

gangster lover and, as a result, is marked for death. An intense film-noir thriller that first brought Stanley Kubrick to the world's attention—he not only wrote and directed this independent production, but also photographed it. Starring Frank Silvera and Irene Kane. "Her soft mouth was the road to sin-smeared violence!"
VHS: S14515. $19.98.
Stanley Kubrick, USA, 1955, 67 mins.

Killers
A thriller based on the Ernest Hemingway story, *Killers* stars Lee Marvin, John Cassavetes and Angie Dickinson, with Ronald Reagan as a wealthy, unscrupulous underworld character.
VHS: S00673. $19.98.
Don Siegel, USA, 1964, 95 mins.

The Killing
Stanley Kubrick directed this classic caper film that concerns illegally removing large amounts of cash from a busy racetrack. Sterling Hayden leads his gang of five on a successful heist but then problems occur for which he hadn't planned. Kubrick uses an elaborate and unusual structure of flashbacks to tell his story. With Vince Edwards, Jay C. Flippan, Marie Windsor, Colleen Gray, Elisha Cook Jr., and Timothy Carey as the grinning sharpshooter, Nikki Arane.
VHS: S11223. $19.95.
Laser: LD71075. $39.95.
Stanley Kubrick, USA, 1956, 83 mins.

Kiss Me Deadly
Private dick Mike Hammer foils the attempt of some crooks to steal a crate of radioactive materials but finds himself unable to protect the woman he originally signed on to help. "Art" meets pulp literature in this fast and violent thriller, filled with tilt shots and symbols, which had a major influence on the young directors of the French New Wave. With Ralph Meeker, Cloris Leachman, and Strother Martin. "I don't care what you do to me, Mike—just do it fast!"
VHS: S13756. $19.98.
Laser: LD72139. $39.95.
Robert Aldrich, USA, 1955, 105 mins.

Lady from Shanghai
Welles' great thriller stars Rita Hayworth as the millionairess in a web of intrigue which includes Welles being accused of murder, and concludes in the dazzling climax played out in a hall of mirrors.
VHS: S00715. $19.95.
Orson Welles, USA, 1948, 87 mins.

Laura
Otto Preminger's 1944 film noir is a witty murder mystery with an elaborate cast of characters— detective, beautiful woman and cynical reporter— who get entangled in the plot. Joseph La Shelle won an Academy Award for cinematography. With Gene Tierney, Dana Andrews, Clifton Webb and Vincent Price.
VHS: S18074. $19.98.
Laser: LD71096. $39.98.
Otto Preminger, USA, 1944, 85 mins.

Leave Her to Heaven
Gene Tierney received a best actress nomination for her depiction of a jealous woman unable to control her possessive instincts. This film is a delightful, melodramatic wallow in one of nature's basest passions. Vincent Price and Jeanne Crain co-star.
VHS: S23757. $19.95.
Laser: LD74915. $39.99.
John M. Stahl, USA, 1945, 110 mins.

Maltese Falcon
Even if you've seen this film so often that you know all the dialog, it never ceases to amaze. A search for a priceless statuette provides the action in this classic, excellent film favorite. Noir at its best with great actors Humphrey Bogart, Mary Astor, Sydney Greenstreet and Peter Lorre, based on Dashiell Hammet's thriller.
VHS: S00810. $19.95.
Laser: LD70621. $34.95.
John Huston, USA, 1941, 101 mins.

Moonrise
Frank Borzage at his best; primal passions erupt in a small southern town when a handsome young man is branded the son of a killer and tormented by unforgiving townspeople who hung his father. Mercilessly goaded into committing murder himself, the wanted fugitive must confront the consequences of his actions or be condemned to relive his father's

brutal fate. With Ethel Barrymore, Lloyd Bridges.
VHS: S09494. $19.95.
Laser: LD71812. $29.98.
Frank Borzage, USA, 1948, 90 mins.

Murder My Sweet
Dick Powell stars as Raymond Chandler's hard-boiled detective, Phillip Marlowe. A complex web of murder, blackmail and double-dealing make it one of the most exciting detective thrillers of the 40s. Also starring Claire Trevor.
VHS: S00898. $19.98.
Edward Dmytryk, USA, 1944, 95 mins.

The Naked City
Blacklisted filmmaker Jules Dassin directed this key film noir and achieved realistic settings by using actual New York locations. The plot concerns the police department's unrelenting search for the killer of a young girl. Famous for its astonishing denouement on the Williamsburg bridge. With Barry Fitzgerald, Howard Duff and Dorothy Hart.
VHS: S18239. $29.95.
Laser: Collector's Edition. **LD75943. $49.95.**
Jules Dassin, USA, 1948, 96 mins.

Niagara
Marilyn Monroe in full Technicolor does her best to upstage one of the Natural Wonders of the World. All that rushing water just can't compete with a tight dress. The plot to drive Joseph Cotten crazy, however, could use a little work. With Jean Peters.
VHS: S04200. $19.98.
Henry Hathaway, USA, 1953, 89 mins.

Odds Against Tomorrow
Harry Belafonte, Robert Ryan, Shelley Winters, Ed Begley and Gloria Grahame make up the terrific cast in this taut crime story. An interracial pair of criminals find their robbery attempt foiled, which leads to unexpected consequences. Along the way there is plenty of action and tension. John Lewis wrote the cool jazz score.
VHS: S29472. $19.98.
Laser: LD75970. $39.99.
Robert Wise, USA, 1959, 95 mins.

Pick Up on South Street
A pickpocket inadvertently acquires top-secret microfilm and becomes a target for espionage agents. Starring Richard Widmark and Thelma Ritter. "This lyrical skid-row noir is one of the great movies of the '50s. The Cold War plot pushes McCarthyism to the far side of the moon" (J. Hoberman). Written and directed by Sam Fuller.
VHS: S13608. $19.98.
Sam Fuller, USA, 1953, 80 mins.

The Postman Always Rings Twice
Lana Turner and John Garfield are the illicit lovers in this James M. Cain thriller, who plot to murder the husband who is standing in the way of a real good time. A classic film noir available in the original black and white. Cast includes Cecil Kellaway, Leon Ames and Hume Cronyn. Remade in 1981.
VHS: S09152. $19.98.
Tay Garnett, USA, 1946, 113 mins.

Raw Deal
Film noir classic from Anthony Mann which weaves the ultimate story of murder, jailbreaks, and jealousy! A hostage (Marsha Hunt) finds herself pitted against her captor's tough-as-nails moll girlfriend (Claire Trevor), a situation where this demure young secretary will even commit murder to save the man she loves. Co-stars Raymond Burr and Dennis O'Keefe. Called "a pistol-powered crime melodrama" by the *New York Times*.
VHS: S28644. $29.95.
Anthony Mann, USA, 1948, 79 mins.

Road House
A psychotic owner of a roadhouse becomes insanely jealous when his singer falls in love with his manager, so he decides to frame him for embezzlement. A 40's film noir with all the characters typically cynical or homicidal. Starring Richard Widmark and the luminous Ida Lupino.
VHS: S13615. $19.98.
Jean Negulesco, USA, 1948, 95 mins.

Scarlet Street
A great film noir thriller. Edward G. Robinson is the little store cashier who becomes infatuated with and eventually kills a whore (Joan Bennett) and then allows her pimp boyfriend (Dan Duryea) to be executed for the crime. Based on Jean Renoir's *La*

Chienne (1931); one of Lang's best works, with brilliant cinematography of New York at night by Milton Krasner.
VHS: S01166. $19.95.
Fritz Lang, USA, 1945, 105 mins.

Strangers on a Train (American Version)

A brilliantly plotted, diabolically humorous suspense thriller about two murders planned by strangers after an accidental meeting. Hitchcock's mise-en-scene is rich in detail and subtle in its insinuations of guilt and homosexuality. With Robert Walker, Farley Granger, Ruth Roman, based on the novel by Raymond Chandler.
VHS: S01265. $19.98.
Laser: LD70686. $24.98.
Alfred Hitchcock, USA, 1951, 101 mins.

Sudden Fear

Joan Crawford is an heiress, a successful playwright, and the toast of Broadway. Everything points to untold happiness when she meets the ideal man (Jack Palance). Things sour, however, when Crawford realizes that Palance is intent on murdering her and inheriting her fortune. Soon murder and revenge twist her perfect life into a nightmare. Gloria Grahame is also featured as the other woman.
VHS: S26993. $19.95.
Laser: LD75431. $39.99.
David Miller, USA, 1952, 111 mins.

Sunset Boulevard

Gloria Swanson is the aging silent film queen, William Holden the struggling writer in this bizarre, dark and desperate portrait of Hollywood. Winner of three Academy Awards, and one of the greatest American films.
VHS: S01285. $14.95.
Laser: LD75268. $34.98.
Billy Wilder, USA, 1950, 110 mins.

Sweet Smell of Success

Burt Lancaster is J.J. Hunsecker, a ruthless and powerful New York columnist, and Tony Curtis is the press agent who will do anything to be in his good graces. Scripted by Clifford Odets and Ernest

Lehman. A cult film that was quoted in *Diner*. With Martin Milner, Sam Levene and Barbara Nichols.
VHS: S07979. $19.98.
Laser: LD70689. $34.98.
Alexander MacKendrick, USA, 1957, 96 mins.

T-Men

Classic underworld thriller from director Anthony Mann. Centered around a sting operation run by the U.S. Treasury Department, T-men go undercover to infiltrate the inner workings of the Vantucci crime family's counterfeiting ring. A riveting, realistic and atmospheric portrait of the West Coast underworld of the 1940s.
VHS: S28643. $29.95.
Anthony Mann, USA, 1947, 92 mins.

Touch of Evil

A masterpiece! This is a complete, restored version. Welles plays a sleazy corrupt police official in a squalid town on the Mexican border, matching wits with Charlton Heston. With Janet Leigh, Marlene Dietrich and Zsa Zsa Gabor.
VHS: S01990. $19.98.
Laser: LD70091. $34.98.
Orson Welles, USA, 1958, 108 mins.

Try and Get Me

Frank Lovejoy and Lloyd Bridges are two guys down on their luck when they decide to pull off a kidnapping to raise some money. Their victim dies by accident and they try to return to living a normal life. The community demands that the killers be caught and punished. With Richard Carlson, Dabbs Greer, Kathleen Ryan and Adele Jergens. Based on a factual case in California in 1933.
VHS: S07138. $19.95.
Cy Endfield, USA, 1950, 91 mins.

Underworld, U.S.A.

Cliff Robertson stars in this Sam Fuller film about a young man who infiltrates a criminal organization to gain revenge for the death of his father. With Dolores Dorn, Beatrice Kay, and Robert Emhardt as a Mob boss. Crime doesn't pay as well as it used to when bullets were cheaper. B&W.
VHS: S06828. $69.95.
Sam Fuller, USA, 1961, 99 mins.

He Walked by Night

100 Best British Features

1984
An extraordinary film version of George Orwell's masterpiece starring John Hurt and Richard Burton. A story of impossible love and tragic betrayal set in the twisted world of *Nineteen Eighty-Four.* Music by Dominic Muldowney and the Eurythmics.
VHS: S00002. $14.95.
Michael Radford, Great Britain, 1984, 115 mins.

The 49th Parallel
Laurence Olivier heads the cast of this superior World War II movie commissioned by the Ministry of Information in 1940. When six Nazis are separated from their U-Boat in Northern Canada, it's up to the average citizens to stop them from reaching safety. With Eric Portman, Raymond Massey, Leslie Howard, Anton Walbrook and Glynis Johns. B&W.
VHS: S06213. $29.98.
Laser: LD70366. $39.95.
Michael Powell, Great Britain, 1941, 107 mins.

American Friends
An observant social comedy of manners and repression and the collision of sexual awakening and 19th century morality. Set in 1864, a single, middle-aged, Oxford University tutor (Michael Palin), who's studiously avoided romantic relations, encounters two vibrant American women, Caroline Hartley (Connie Booth) and her 17-year-old niece (Trini Alvarado), during his Swiss holiday. He's forced to choose between his long-dormant emotional demands and his academic requirements. With Alfred Molina and David Calder.
VHS: S18996. $92.95.
Laser: LD75144. $34.98.
Tristam Powell, Great Britain, 1991, 95 mins.

Bellman and True
A British thriller that is both a detailed character study and a caper film. A meek computer programmer becomes involved in an elaborate bank heist. He soon finds that his associates in crime are no league of gentlemen. With Bernard Hill, Kieren O'Brien, Frances Tomelty, Richard Hope and Ken Bones.
VHS: S08028. $14.98.
Richard Loncraine, Great Britain, 1988, 112 mins.

Bhaji on the Beach
In this warm but hip comedy, a group of women gather for a carefree day on the beach. By nightfall, gossiping, giggling, and arguing over things like battered wives, male strippers, race and sex have brought them closer together. With Peter Cellier, Zohra Segal and Jimmi Harkishin.
VHS: S26920. $96.99.
Gurinder Chadha, Great Britain, 1994, 100 mins.

A Bigger Splash
An innovative blend of fact and fiction reflecting the world of David Hockney, arguably the most important and celebrated artist of our time. This feature incorporates Hockney's art and unabashed lifestyle in bold and daring ways and parallels his brilliant work in painting, design and photography. "Moving, gossipy and just a little bit shocking. Constructed in the studios, the swimming pools, the beds and baths of Hockney and friends who orbit around him" (*Newsday*).
VHS: S08116. $69.95.
Jack Hazan, Great Britain, 1985, 102 mins.

Black Narcissus
Considered one of the most beautiful films ever produced, *Black Narcissus* is set amidst the awesome grandeur of the Himalayas. Starring Deborah Kerr, this is a haunting emotional film about isolation, spiritual failure and sexual frustration in a convent.
VHS: S00137. $14.98.
Laser: LD70345. $79.95.
Powell/Pressburger, Great Britain, 1947, 100 mins.

Bleak House
Denholm Elliott and Diana Rigg star in Charles Dickens' biting social commentary on 19th century English justice. John Jarndyce (Elliott) rises above a notorious law suit that has devastated others. But tragedy ensues when his young ward becomes obsessed with the labyrinthine case and the intrigue surrounding it. Produced by the BBC.
VHS: S07176. $39.98.
Ross Devenish, Great Britain, 1985, 391 mins.

Blow-Up
The classic film questioning the relationship between image and reality; David Hemmings plays a fashion photographer who photographs a woman (Vanessa Redgrave) in a park and later comes to believe that he has actually photographed a murder. Through the photograph, Hemmings is lured out of his life to search for the truth. English dialog.
VHS: S00152. $19.98.
Laser: CAV, widescreen, 2 discs, Criterion. LD70351. $79.95.
Laser: Extended play, chapter search, MGM. LD70528. $34.98.
Michelangelo Antonioni, Great Britain, 1966, 111 mins.

Brassed Off!
When a small Yorkshire mining town's pit is about to be closed, putting the town out of work, the miners vote to strike at the same time the town's brass band practices for an upcoming competition. Ewan McGregor (*Trainspotting*) and Tara Fitzgerald (*Sirens*) shine as two old friends and ex-lovers whose surprise reunion turns everything upside down. With Pete Postlethwaite as the band conductor.
VHS: S32929. $103.99.
Mark Herman, Great Britain, 1997, 101 mins.

The Bridge on the River Kwai
Epic story of British prisoners of war held by the Japanese combines psychological battles of will with gripping action. Winner of seven Oscars including Best Picture and Director. The Oscar for Screenplay went to Pierre Boulle, the novelist who spoke no English, because screenwriters Carl Foreman and Michael Wilson were blacklisted. With William Holden and Alec Guinness. Letterboxed.
VHS: S01785. $19.95.
Laser: LD72066. $49.95.
David Lean, Great Britain, 1957, 161 mins.

The Buddha of Suburbia
One of the larger artistic achievements of British television: Brenda Blethyn (*Secrets and Lies*), Narveen Andrews (*The English Patient*) and Roshan Seth (*Indiana Jones and the Temple of Doom*) star in this acclaimed drama, based on the best-selling novel by Hanif Kureishi (*My Beautiful Laundrette*), of Karim, a young schoolboy living in the suburbs, whose life changes when his Zen-obsessed father becomes a guru in the '70s Buddhist scene and leaves his suburban home for London. With original music by David Bowie.
VHS: S31262. $29.98.
Roger Michell, Great Britain, 1993, 220 mins.

Butterfly Kiss
In this horrific, comedic and romantic, female-driven alternative drama, the mentally unbalanced and dangerous Eunice (Amanda Plummer) meets a pretty, shy gas station attendant named Miriam (Saskia

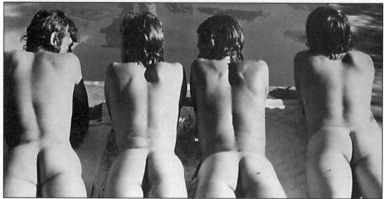

A Bigger Splash

Reeves), and the two become lovers. Miriam joins
Eunice on a murderous road trip across Britain,
thinking she can save her friend from her self-
destruction. A "twisted British answer to *Thelma &
Louise* spiced with dashes of *Heavenly Creatures* and
Natural Born Killers" (*The New York Times*).
VHS: S32357. $79.95.
Michael Winterbottom, Great Britain, 1996,
90 mins.

Career Girls
Mike Leigh's (*Secrets and Lies*) intelligent, poignant
comedy about the reunion of two very different 30-
ish women who were battling college roomates in
London six years ago. Over the course of their brief
reunion, Hannah and Annie (Katrin Cartlidge, *Naked*
and *Breaking the Waves*, and Lynda Steadman, in
stand-out performances) reveal the present while they
talk about the past, in jittery flashbacks that match
their emotions. As we watch these two progress from
black leather to discreet beige, we also watch the
growth that has carried them beyond the shared,
angry turmoil of their college years.
VHS: S32797. $99.99.
Laser: LD76422. $39.98.
Mike Leigh, Great Britain, 1997, 87 mins.

Carrington
Emma Thompson gives a terrific performance as
Dora Carrington, an unorthodox, androgynous painter
from the early 20th-century Bloomsbury Group, who
passionately loves gay writer Giles Lytton-Strachey
(Jonathan Pryce). The highly regarded playwright
Christopher Hampton (*Les Liaisons Dangereuses*)
directs this tight, witty and insightful period piece,
set amidst the self-conscious world of broken
conventions and sexual eccentricities that come to
mind whenever the name of the Bloomsbury Group is
uttered.
VHS: S27596. $19.95.
Laser: LD75532. $34.99.
Christopher Hampton, Great Britain, 1995,
116 mins.

The Case of the
Mukkinese Battle Horn
Before there was "Monty Python" there was "The
Goon Show" and England roared with laughter. Now
you can too. Peter Sellers and Spike Milligan, two
thirds of the BBC radio's resident comic madmen,
join together in this free form featurette concerning
the disappearance of a prize 9th Century relic and
Scotland Yard's attempts to retrieve said item.
VHS: S03652. $19.95.
Joseph Sterling, Great Britain, 1956, 27 mins.

The Cement Garden
Andrew Birkin's chilling adaptation of Ian McEwan's
(*The Good Son*) 1978 debut novel about incest, *The
Cement Garden* is the erotic, macabre story of four
young siblings and their attempt to maintain a
semblance of normalcy after both parents suddenly
die. Left to their own devices, the children begin to
give freer expression to their sexuality. "Hypnotic
and haunting—a hothouse of sexual tension and
secret longing that is hard to shake" (Peter Travers,

Rolling Stone).
VHS: S30256. $89.95.
Andrew Birkin, Great Britain/France/Germany,
1993, 105 mins.

Chariots of Fire
Drama based on a true story of two young men who
run in the 1924 Olympics—a Jewish student from
Cambridge and a Scottish missionary. Winner of
Oscar for Best Picture, as well as Best Musical Score
by Vangelis.
DVD: DV60085. $24.98.
VHS: S00228. $19.98.
Laser: LD70542. $34.98.
Hugh Hudson, Great Britain, 1981, 123 mins.

Circle of Danger
Ray Milland and Naughton Wayne star in this
suspense-filled film about a man who must journey to
Britain in order to uncover the mystery surrounding
his brother's death. The dead man was part of a
special combat unit in World War II.
VHS: S23887. $29.95.
Jacques Tourneur, Great Britain, 1955, 86 mins.

The Cook, The Thief,
His Wife and Her Lover
Few contemporary filmmakers rival director Peter
Greenaway's visual complexity and elaboration. In
this style he creates a graphic and layered fable that
casts a cynical eye on man's most primal urges: food,
lust and violence. A brutal satire on capitalism set
predominantly in an exclusive restaurant called "Le
Hollandais".
VHS: S13017. $19.95.
Laser: LD75309. $39.98.
Peter Greenaway, Great Britain, 1990, 123 mins.

Damage
French director Louis Malle's adaptation of Josephine
Hart's novel about an upper class Parliament member
(Jeremy Irons) who has an affair with an ethereal
French woman (Juliette Binoche) who is about to be
married to Irons' son (Rupert Graves). Miranda
Richardson co-stars as Irons' long-suffering wife.
This unrated version contains the excised material the
MPAA found objectionable enough to warrant an NC-
17 rating.
VHS: S18607. $19.95.
Laser: LD72184. $49.95.
Louis Malle, Great Britain/USA, 1992, 111 mins.

Dangerous Liaisons
Nominated for seven Academy Awards, the hottest
love affair of 1782 is notable for its sense of style and
decor, and strong performances from Glenn Close,
John Malkovich and Michele Pfeiffer. A couple of
nasty members of 18th century nobility enjoy
manipulating the lives and loves of those around
them through all kinds of mean-spiritedness. There
are three versions of this story available, including
Valmont and *Liaisons Dangereuses*.
VHS: S09449. $19.95.
Laser: LD70550. $29.98.
Stephen Frears, Great Britain, 1989, 120 mins.

Death in the Seine
Peter Greenaway's fascinating essay on death and

revolution is set in a period between April 1795 and September 1801, when over 300 bodies were pulled from the River Seine in Paris. Two mortuary attendants dutifully noted the condition of each body in great detail, including their clothing, possessions and wounds. This bounty of information is the basis for Greenaway's structuralist speculation on the lives of these corpses and their relationship to the French Revolution.
VHS: $27254. $29.95.
Peter Greenaway, Great Britain, 1994, 44 mins.

The Devils
Oliver Reed is Father Grandier, accused of sorcery by the half-mad nuns of the fortified city of Loudun; Vanessa Redgrave is Sister Jeanne of the Angels, whose own sexual obsession triggers the ferocious events that follow. Based on Aldous Huxley's book.
VHS: S00334. $19.98.
Ken Russell, Great Britain, 1971, 105 mins.

Doctor Who
Fans of the world's most popular sci-fi star, the time-travelling Doctor Who, will enjoy this legendary "E-Space Trilogy," a trio of the Doctor's most-requested unreleased adventures. Starring the most popular Doctor Who, Tom Baker. Includes 4½ hours of programming.
VHS: S32536. $49.98.

Don't Look Now
Julie Christie and Donald Sutherland star in this beautiful, spellbinding mystery that'll have you on the edge of your seat. When their child drowns in a sudden rainstorm, Sutherland decides to go to Venice for an architectural job and Christie follows. While in Italy, Christie becomes convinced that a mysterious figure in a red raincoat is their beloved child returned from the dead. As the true character of the figure in the red raincoat is revealed, the film creates an atmosphere of terror, fear and ultimate tragedy in a knockout ending. Based on the novel by Daphne du Maurier.
VHS: S00358. $49.95.
Nicolas Roeg, Great Britain, 1974, 110 mins.

Edge of the World
A fascinating early work from British stylist Michael Powell has the visual intensity and gothic romanticism of the Murnau/ Flaherty masterpiece *Tabu*. Shot on the picturesque North Sea isle of Foula, the film centers on a torrid love affair which is disrupted by the harsh disapproval of the woman's father. "Rare for its time, this vigorous location drama in the Flaherty tradition [is]...usually exhilarating" (Leslie Halliwell). With Niall MacGinnis, Belle Chrystal, John Laurie and Finlay Currie.
VHS: S19863. $29.95.
Michael Powell, Great Britain, 1937, 80 mins.

Elusive Pimpernel
David Niven plays Sir Percy Blakeney, the indolent dandy in London, who is also Pimpernel, the leader of a league of young men out to rescue the French aristocrats from the 1792 Terror of Paris. Based on Baroness Orczy's *The Scarlet Pimpernel.*
VHS: S13736. $39.95.
Powell/Pressburger, Great Britain, 1950, 109 mins.

Emily Bronte's Wuthering Heights
Years before their acclaimed performances in *The English Patient*, Juliette Binoche and Ralph Fiennes starred together in this visually stunning, passionate and eerily atmospheric adaptation of Emily Bronte's timeless tale of two families and the doomed love that entwines them.
VHS: S32511. $92.99.
Peter Kosminsky, Great Britain, 1992, 107 mins.

Emma
A fun and lighthearted comedy based on Jane Austen's story about a mischievous young woman (Gwyneth Paltrow) who tries to play matchmaker and makes a tangled mess of everyone's lives, particularly that of friend Harriet Smith (Toni Collette, *Muriel's Wedding*). When Emma ultimately falls in love, everyone becomes free from her matchmaking escapades. "Devilishly funny" (*Rolling Stone*).
VHS: S30967. $19.99.
Laser: LD76157. $39.98.
Douglas McGrath, Great Britain/USA, 1996, 121 mins.

The English Patient
A stellar cast, meticulous attention to detail, first-rate cinematography, and a tragic love story combine for an irresistible package of a movie, the winner of nine Academy Awards, including Best Picture. When a mysterious stranger is rescued from a plane, his identity is gradually revealed and the secrets and passions of war are unlocked. With Ralph Fiennes, Kristin Scott-Thomas, Willem Dafoe, and Juliette Binoche in an Academy Award-winning role. Letterboxed.
VHS: S31822. $106.99.
Laser: LD76338. $99.95.
Anthony Minghella, Great Britain, 1996, 162 mins.

The Europeans
An European aristocrat and her brash younger brother upset the lives of their Boston cousins upon their arrival, in Merchant/Ivory's adaptation of Henry James' novel. Screenplay by Ruth Prawer Jhabvala. With Lee Remick, Robin Ellis, Tim Woodward, Wesley Addy and Lisa Eichhorn.
VHS: S00419. $59.95.
Laser: LD71593. $39.95.
James Ivory, Great Britain/USA, 1979, 90 mins.

Fallen Idol
In one of his finest performances, Ralph Richardson plays a butler who is idolized by eight-year-old Bobby Henrey. Drawn into the butler's tangled personal life during a weekend when his parents are away, the boy learns that Richardson is accused of having murdered his wife. Screenplay by Graham Greene from his story *The Basement Room*.
VHS: S00426. $39.95.
Carol Reed, Great Britain, 1948, 92 mins.

Gandhi
Richard Attenborough's dream project realized in epic style with Ben Kingsley as Gandhi in an Oscar winning performance, and a cast including Candice Bergen, Martin Sheen and John Gielgud.
VHS: S02022. $29.95.
Laser: LD72202. $49.95.
Richard Attenborough, Great Britain, 1982, 187 mins.

Green for Danger
A puzzler for both Scotland Yard and the audience as Inspector Cockrill (Alastair Sim) is called in to investigate a murder in a hospital filled with suspicious doctors and staff. Cockrill's interrogation brings them all into question concerning both motive and opportunity and places Cockrill high in the cinema tradition of the droll Yard detective who always gets his man.
VHS: S12955. $39.95.
Sidney Gilliat, Great Britain, 1947, 91 mins.

A Handful of Dust
Evelyn Waugh's satiric novel on the decline of the British empire has been filmed in a very civilized manner. When the decent but very dull James Wilby finds out that his beautiful but cool wife (Kristin Scott Thomas) is having a serious affair with the dashing but penniless Rupert Graves, he goes exploring in South America. With Anjelica Huston and Alec Guinness.
VHS: S08351. $19.98.
Charles Sturridge, Great Britain, 1988, 117 mins.

I Know Where I'm Going
A delightfully unpretentious romantic comedy about a girl who is going to marry for money and who finds her ideas challenged. She runs away and finds true love on a scenic island off the coast of Scotland. With an award-winning performance from Wendy Hiller.
VHS: S12958. $39.95.
Michael Powell, Great Britain, 1946, 91 mins.

I'm All Right Jack
Britain's great comic talents join forces in this hilariously witty spoof of the absurdities of the labor movement. Starring Peter Sellers and Ian Carmichael, with Richard Attenborough. This is the film that launched Sellers on the road to international stardom. His portrait of a shop steward coming apart at the seams is a masterpiece of characterization.
VHS: S00604. $39.95.
John Boulting, Great Britain, 1969, 101 mins.

If...
A sometimes shocking portrait of life in a repressive English boarding school. Three non-conforming senior schoolboys revolt against practically everything. Anderson skillfully employs both professional and non-professional actors in building to a shattering, violent climax.
VHS: S00606. $49.95.
Laser: LD75354. $29.98.
Lindsay Anderson, Great Britain, 1969, 111 mins.

Jane Austen's Persuasion

Jane Austen's last novel is superbly realized in this well-acted costume drama. After the end of the Napoleonic Wars, Captain Frederick Wentworth and his former fiance slowly but surely find themselves drawn to each other once again. Set amidst the luxurious trappings of the English upper class, this tale of true love is simply irresistible.

VHS: S27350. $19.95.
Laser: LD75498. $34.95.
Roger Michell, Great Britain, 1995, 104 mins.

Jane Eyre

William Hurt heads an award-winning cast in this critically acclaimed production of Charlotte Bronte's classic story of a young woman who triumphs over fate and long hidden secrets to experience passion and romance. Also stars Charlotte Gainsbourg, Joan Plowright (*The Scarlet Letter*), Anna Paquin (*The Piano*) and supermodel Elle McPherson (*Batman and Robin*).

VHS: S28664. $99.99.
Laser: LD75964. $39.99.
Franco Zeffirelli, Great Britain/USA, 1995, 116 mins.

Kind Hearts and Coronets

A perennial favorite featuring Alec Guinness' famous performance in which he plays eight separate roles in the black comedy of a castoff member of an aristocratic family who sets out to eliminate them all. The sardonic script was written by director Robert Hamer, one of Ealing Studios best writer/directors.

VHS: S00676. $14.98.
Robert Hamer, Great Britain, 1949, 104 mins.

The Lady Vanishes

One of Hitchcock's best British films; Dame May Whitty stars as the kindly old woman who befriends a young English girl on a European train, and then disappears. All her fellow travellers swear she never existed—only the hero, Michael Redgrave, and she together uncover the web of intrigue.

VHS: S23482. $24.95.
Laser: LD71091. $39.95.
Alfred Hitchcock, Great Britain, 1938, 97 mins.

Ladybird Ladybird

A simply wonderful film from the talented Ken Loach. A small-time singer finds her tough, mostly uneventful life ripped apart by tragedy. A fire destroys her home and severely hurts one of her kids. This incident and a series of problems lead her to lose her children as an unfit mother. Loach's riveting drama is a powerful look at the machinery of the welfare state.

VHS: S26269. $19.98.
Ken Loach, Great Britain, 1994, 102 mins.

Ladykillers

Another wonderfully bizarre comedy from England's Ealing Studios, this starring Alec Guiness as the slightly demented leader of a group of thieves planning their heist in a boarding house while pretending to be a chamber orchestra.

VHS: S00719. $14.98.
Alexander MacKendrick, Great Britain, 1955, 87 mins.

Land and Freedom

Ken Loach's moving love story set against the complex political background of the early days of the Spanish Civil War is brilliant, engaged cinema. A young lad from Liverpool, smitten by the idealism of the Republican cause, fights for land and freedom along with his multi-national comrades and a beautiful, fiery woman (Rosana Pastor) with whom he eventually falls in love. An epic film of war, hope and dissillusionment—uncompromising and powerful.

VHS: S28396. $14.95.
Laser: LD76082. $39.99.
Ken Loach, Great Britain, 1996, 109 mins.

Last of England

"Wrenchingly beautiful…the film is one of the few commanding works of personal cinema in the late 80's—a call to open our eyes to a world violated by greed and repression, to see what irrevocable damage has been wrought on city, countryside and soul, how our skies, our bodies, have turned poisonous," wrote *The Village Voice* of Derek Jarman's beautiful film. Synthesizing rock 'n roll, Super-8, gay erotica, old home movies, anti-totalitarian paranoia, Jarman "superimposes an incandescent Belfast over contemporary London …The doomsday rubble landscape…[is] rendered with the imagistic panache of Kenneth Anger and pulverized a la Brakhage. *The Last of England* is sinister and gorgeous" (J. Hoberman).

VHS: S09555. $29.95.
Derek Jarman, Great Britain, 1987, 87 mins.

Brassed Off

Pinstripes & Jail Stripes

The Accused
VHS: S13708. $19.95.
Laser: LD75116. $24.98.

Adam's Rib
DVD: DV60057. $24.98.
VHS: S03456. $19.95.
Laser: LD70202. $49.98.

Anatomy of a Murder
VHS: S01525. $19.95.

Breaker Morant
DVD: DV60127. $29.98.
VHS: S00178. $19.95.
Laser: LD76402. $49.95.

Compulsion
VHS: S25573. $19.98.
Laser: LD74971. $39.98.

A Cry in the Dark
VHS: S09308. $19.98.
Laser: LD70547. $29.98.

The Devil and Daniel Webster
VHS: S04331. $24.95.
Laser: LD70127. $49.95.

I Never Sang for My Father
VHS: S04714. $69.95.

Inherit the Wind
VHS: S02341. $19.95.
Laser: LD72122. $39.98.

Judgment at Nuremberg
VHS: S09918. $29.95.
Laser: LD70605. $39.98.

Last Wave
VHS: S00729. $19.95.

Liar Liar
VHS: S32055. $22.98.
Laser: LD76339. $44.98.

My Cousin Vinny
VHS: S17229. $19.95.
Laser: LD72192. $39.98.

Reversal of Fortune
VHS: S13923. $19.95.

A Time to Kill
DVD: DV60100. $24.98.
VHS: S30447. $19.98.
Laser: LD76031. $39.98.

To Kill a Mockingbird
VHS: S02640. $19.95.
Laser: LD70089. $39.98.

The Trial
VHS: S08696. $39.95.
Laser: LD76192. $69.95.

The Verdict
VHS: S02344. $19.98.
Laser: LD71392. $44.98.

Witness for the Prosecution
VHS: S01767. $19.98.
Laser: LD71148. $34.98.

Lavender Hill Mob
Alec Guinness in one of his most memorable roles, as a shy bank clerk who conspires to steal a million pounds in gold bars from the Bank of England. His plan is to melt down the gold and mold it in the shape of tiny Eiffel Tower souvenirs for resale. Things appear to go well until... Zany, witty and very British, a beloved and classic British comedy.
VHS: S00732. $14.98.
Charles Crichton, Great Britain, 1951, 78 mins.

Lawrence of Arabia
A labor of love by Robert A. Harris and Jim Painten and their team of restorers, who have returned nearly 35 minutes to the edited version of the David Lean epic of the exploits of T.E. Lawrence, adventurer and soldier. Peter O'Toole makes a striking impression in his first starring role. The film won seven Oscars. With Alec Guinness, Omar Sharif, Anthony Quinn and Jose Ferrer as the evil Turkish Colonel. Presented in the letterbox format which preserves the wide screen image.
VHS: S10608. $29.95.
Laser: CAV. LD70413. $124.95.
Laser: CLV. LD70414. $69.95.
David Lean, Great Britain, 1962, 216 mins.

Life Is Sweet
Satirist Mike Leigh is at it again in the London south side with this decidedly bittersweet comedy about the members of a dysfunctional family and their oddball friends. It seems everyone in this film is striving for change. The family tries to balance their differences with alcoholic friends and their short fuses proves a challenge, but they don't forget to laugh a lot along the way.
VHS: S16628. $14.98.
Laser: LD71503. $29.98.
Mike Leigh, Great Britain, 1992, 103 mins.

Little Lord Fauntleroy
Frances Hodgson Burnett's classic tale of innocence and unconditional goodness. Young Cedric Erroll's life changes forever when a lawyer from England arrives in New York City with the news that Cedric is the grandson of the Earl of Dorincourt and the only heir to his vast fortune.
VHS: S32522. $14.98.
Andrew Morgan, Great Britain, 1995, 100 mins.

Loneliness of the Long Distance Runner
The engrossing story of a rebellious young man chosen to represent his reform school in a track race. A superbly acted film, it also confronts the rigidity of society's mores and institutions. This is a key British film from the 60s directed by Tony Richardson. Starring Tom Courtenay and Michael Redgrave.
VHS: S15359. $19.98.
Laser: LD71675. $34.98.
Tony Richardson, Great Britain, 1962, 103 mins.

The Madness of King George
Nigel Hawthorne plays the last king ever to rule the North American colonies. He is joined by Helen Mirren (winner of Best Actress Award at Cannes) as the queen and Ian Holm as the Prince of Wales, in this film based on a true story. King George went mad and a variety of cures were brought to bear on this once imposing figure. The result is a tale of maddening cures, political intrigue and overall decline with a touch of British humor. Based on Alan Bennett's play.
VHS: S26268. $19.98.
Laser: LD75069. $39.99.
Nicholas Hytner, Great Britain, 1995, 110 mins.

Mahler
A dazzling evocation of the moods, loves and music of one of the foremost composers—Gustav Mahler. By means of flashbacks and dream imagery, the film focuses on the turbulent relationship Mahler had with his beautiful wife. Starring Robert Powell and Georgina Hale, with Mahler's symphonies played by the Concertgebouw Orchestra of Amsterdam.
VHS: S00807. $29.95.
Ken Russell, Great Britain, 1976, 110 mins.

Major Barbara
Filmed in war-torn England, Gabriel Pascal's screen version of George Bernard Shaw's famous play is a memorial to the artists who made it and proof that it takes more than bombs to subdue the English wit. The story of a Salvation Army girl, her munitions manufacturing father and her pragmatic scholar fiance, this film version is a triumph—demonstrating Shaw's own words that "the greatest of our evils and the worst of our crimes is poverty." With Rex Harrison and Deborah Kerr.
VHS: S13734. $39.95.
Gabriel Pascal, Great Britain, 1940, 90 mins.

Man in the White Suit
Alec Guinness plays an unassuming lab assistant who invents a miracle fabric that can be woven into indestructible cloth. Few films have chastized industry so wittily and incisively as this great comedy. There is a Chaplin-like flavor to absurdist scenes pitting a captain of industry against his stubborn young employee.
VHS: S00812. $14.98.
Alexander MacKendrick, Great Britain, 1951, 82 mins.

Maurice
James Ivory directs this sensitive film about the love relationship between two men who meet studying at Cambridge in 1910. Based on the novel by E.M. Forster which was published after his death. That love that dare not speak its name is now a movie. With James Wilby, Hugh Grant, Rupert Graves, Denholm Elliott and Ben Kingsley.
VHS: S06208. $19.98.
Laser: CAV, widescreen. LD75106. $59.95.
James Ivory, Great Britain, 1987, 135 mins.

The English Patient

Meantime
An early work by Mike Leigh, this wry and amusing working-class comedy is the story of Frank and his two unemployed, deadbeat sons, Mark and Colin (Phil Daniels and Tim Roth), who live in a cramped apartment in London's East End. Wanting to escape the doldrums of his mediocre world, Colin starts hanging out with Coxy (Gary Oldman), a reckless skinhead. The new friendship sparks fear in Colin's family, whose overzealous attempts to direct Colin on a straight path prove futile.
VHS: S32361. $79.98.
Mike Leigh, Great Britain, 1983, 103 mins.

Meetings with Remarkable Men
Peter Brook directed this unique search through the Middle East, Central Asia for answers to the question of the meaning of life, based on Gurdjieff's search for hidden knowledge. As a boy, Gurdijeff is influenced by his father, a man of remarkable character, who nurtures his thirst for knowledge while preparing him for a career in medicine and priesthood. But a brush with death and other extraordinary, inexplicable events heighten his sense of wonder about the meaning of man's life, and in hidden ruins, he and his comrades discover ancient scrolls which confirm the existence of a brotherhood with ancient knowledge passed orally from generation to generation. Among those appearing in this extraordinary film are Athol Fugard, Colin Blakely, Terence Stamp.
VHS: S06033. $69.95.
Peter Brook, Great Britain, 1979, 108 mins.

Monty Python's Meaning of Life
This savagely satirical film is quite possibly the best of the Monty Python films with its balance of dark, subversive humor and light parodies of God, death, the Empire, Catholicism and gluttony. The film features animation sequences and a short film by Python member Terry Gilliam that bears strong thematic resemblance to his great film, *Brazil*.
VHS: S02550. $19.95.
Laser: LD70058. $34.95.
Terry Jones, Great Britain, 1983, 107 mins.

My Left Foot
Distinguished by a brilliant performance from Daniel Day-Lewis, this is a true story about life, laughter and the occasional miracle. Day-Lewis plays Christy Brown, who has cerebral palsy, and whose mother's faith prompts him to paint and write. Nominated for five Academy Awards.
VHS: S12199. $19.98.
Jim Sheridan, Great Britain, 1989, 103 mins.

Naked
This film won in both the Best Film and Best Actor category at the Cannes Film Festival. David Thewlis stars in this funny, erotic and bizarre odyssey, set in the streets of London, that explores the seamy side of desire and longing of post-Thatcherite England.
VHS: S21119. $19.95.
Laser: Includes director's commentary, still photo gallery, trailers and short films. **LD74468. $69.95.**
Mike Leigh, Great Britain, 1993, 131 mins.

Naked Civil Servant
John Hurt delivers a compelling performance in the role of Quentin Crisp, based on Crisp's autobiography as a witty homosexual growing up in England of the 30's and 40's through years of intolerance, ostracism and violence. Hurt's tour-de-force performance brings to life Crisp's unique and often sharp wit at once critical of the society as well as of himself.
VHS: S00914. $19.99.
Jack Gold, Great Britain, 1980, 80 mins.

The Pillow Book
Peter Greenaway's bold, stylistic experiment has, as its theme, the "correspondence" between the daughter of a famous writer and a publisher, written on the bodies of their lovers. With a bravura use of video technology, this erotic, visually beautiful film is a powerful treatise on signs, silence, communication and desire. With Ewan McGregor, Vivian Yu, Ken Ogata, Yoshi Oida, Hideko Yoshida and Judy Ongg. Japanese and Mandarin with English subtitles.
VHS: S33013. $104.95.
Peter Greenaway, France/Great Britain/ Netherlands, 1996, 126 mins.

Priest
Controversial and powerful, this film concerns a young priest overcome by a daunting problem. He must reconcile the contradiction between the tenets of his faith and the desires of his own body. The film is made all the more riveting by its refusal of simple answers. Though spurred by events beyond his control, this priest must ultimately confront the intractable hypocrisy that shrouds homosexuality in the Catholic Church.
VHS: S26884. $19.99.
Laser: LD75445. $39.99.
Antonia Bird, Great Britain, 1995, 98 mins.

Prospero's Books
Peter Greenaway's pattern-obsessed reworking of Shakespeare's *The Tempest* furthers his thematic obsession with numbers and order. Sir John Gielgud is Prospero, the former Duke of Milan who's banished on a magical, isolated island, where he plots his revenge against the men who dethroned him, engages in magic and spectacle, and seeks solace in his collection of extravagantly illustrated books. With Michael Clark, Isabelle Pasco, Erland Josephson and Michael Gambon.
VHS: S17065. $19.95.
Peter Greenaway, Great Britain, 1991, 126 mins.

Raining Stones
Ken Loach's funny social comedy is set in the British town of Middleton where Bob Williams, survivor, first has his van stolen and then learns the outfit for his daughter Coleen's first communion is going to cost 100 pounds. Among Loach's most accessible films, *Raining Stones* is a bitingly funny comedy that shows the downside to contemporary Britain even as it cleverly reveals the simple humor and tenacity that inspires the average bloke.
VHS: S24861. $19.98.
Ken Loach, Great Britain, 1994, 90 mins.

Red Shoes
Michael Powell and Emeric Pressburger's classic, beautiful film about a young ballerina (Moira Shearer) and the young composer (Marius Goring) who are taken under the wing of impressario Anton Walbrook.
VHS: S01655. $14.98.
Powell/Pressburger, Great Britain, 1948, 133 mins.

Remains of the Day
In this drama, the relationship between a butler and a housekeeper, played by Anthony Hopkins and Emma Thompson, is stifled by the demands of conflicting duties. The household they manage plays host to important political gatherings attended by fascist leaders. Their roles may very well hasten the demise of their country, not to mention their growing affection for one another. Based on the novel by Kazuo Ishiguri.
VHS: S20777. $19.95.
Laser: LD72389. $39.95.
James Ivory, Great Britain, 1993, 134 mins.

Repulsion
Polanski's first English-language film, a chilling study of madness, stars Catherine Deneuve as a jealously sadistic schizophrenic, terrified of sex. Full of memorable sequences, such as Deneuve's delusions of rape as she sees plaster turn into a clawing hand and walls cracking or overhears the

moans of her sister making love. With Yvonne
Furneaux and John Fraser.
   VHS: S01106. $39.95.
   Laser: Widescreen. **LD75387. $99.95.**
Roman Polanski, Great Britain, 1965, 105 mins.

Riff Raff
Ken Loach directed this first-rate look at the British
class system from the bottom up. Stevie is a
construction worker whose luck can only improve.
His colorful co-workers help keep him from any
serious hard labor while Stevie's humor attracts many
friends, including an aspiring singer who melts his
heart. This down-to-earth comedy shows that being
Riff Raff is not so bad.
   VHS: S26338. $19.98.
Ken Loach, Great Britain, 1993, 96 mins.

Rocking Horse Winner
One of the most off-beat, startling, disturbing and
touching movies of the 50's was also one of the first
stories by D.H. Lawrence to be tapped for the movies.
The plot is strange and ultimately tragic when a 10-
year-old boy learns how to pick winners at the
racetrack while riding his own rocking horse, to aid
his spendthrift parents out of their endless round of
debts. With John Mills, Valerie Hobson, John
Howard Davies.
   VHS: S12956. $39.95.
Anthony Pelissier, Great Britain, 1950, 91 mins.

Room with a View
Maggie Smith stars in this acclaimed film, based on
the E.M. Forster novel, which evokes the manners
and mores of an era. A witty, lush film with Denholm
Elliott, Judi Dench and Simon Callow.
   VHS: S02767. $19.98.
   Laser: LD71312. $34.98.
James Ivory, Great Britain, 1986, 117 mins.

The Ruling Class
Peter O'Toole stars as the 14th Earl of Gurney, who
happens to believe he is Jesus Christ. An irreverent
comedy, *The Ruling Class* is filled with insane ideas
and boisterously funny characters. This is the
original, uncut version.
   VHS: S01137. $39.95.
Peter Medak, Great Britain, 1972, 154 mins.

Ryan's Daughter
Robert Bolt (*A Man for All Seasons, The Mission*)
wrote the screenplay of this long but rewarding study
by David Lean about a rich, unsatisfied, married
woman (Sarah Miles) who falls for a British soldier
(Christopher Jones) during British colonial rule of
Ireland. Robert Mitchum is cast as Miles' British
school teacher; John Mills is excellent as a crippled
mute. VHS letterboxed.
   VHS: S02570. $24.98.
   Laser: LD70185. $49.98.
David Lean, Great Britain, 1970, 192 mins.

Saturday Night and Sunday Morning
Angry young man Albert Finney became a star and
made this British New Wave film—Reisz' first
feature—a box office hit with the defiant phrase,
"Don't let the bastards grind you down." Finney's
brooding performance as the young Nottingham
factory worker lashing out at the working class and
his "dead from the neck up" parents is still fresh
today. With Shirley Anne Field, Bryan Pringle, Hylda
Baker, Norman Rossington, Colin Blakely and Rachel
Roberts as his sad-sack mistress.
   VHS: S30432. $14.98.
   Laser: LD76030. $39.99.
Karel Reisz, Great Britain, 1960, 89 mins.

Seance on a Wet Afternoon
Novelist Bryan Forbes' eerie psychological thriller
about a demented woman (Kim Stanley) trapped in a
suffocating, childless marriage, who kidnaps a child
and devises a scheme to "rescue" the child and claim
the ransom. "Consistently intelligent and exciting, the
film unerringly illuminates the dangerous areas
between private fantasy and public madness" (British
Film Institute). With Richard Attenborough, Mark
Eden and Patrick Magee.
   VHS: S01764. $29.95.
Bryan Forbes, Great Britain, 1964, 116 mins.

Secrets and Lies
Mike Leigh's heartwarming comedy of a young black
woman (Marianne Jean-Baptiste) searching for her
natural birth mother only to discover that her mom
(the magnificent Brenda Blethyn) is white, makes for
a film with "rare heart and soul" (Janet Maslin, *The
New York Times*), from Britain's master of

improvisational, working-class social comedies. With
Timothy Spall. Winner of the Palm d'Or at Cannes
Film Festival.
   VHS: S31027. $103.99.
   Laser: LD76141. $39.98.
Mike Leigh, Great Britain, 1996, 114 mins.

The Small Back Room
The mature and powerful story of crippled munitions
expert David Farrar, who is frustrated by his infirmity
and the mindless government bureaucracy he must
repeatedly contend with during World War II.
   VHS: S14529. $39.95.
Powell/Pressburger, Great Britain, 1949, 106 mins.

St. Martin's Lane
Originally released as *Sidewalks of London*, Charles
Laughton is the London street entertainer who picks
up a waif (Vivien Leigh) and sees her go to stardom,
sacrificing his love for her to do so.
   VHS: S01555. $24.95.
Tim Whelan, Great Britain, 1938, 84 mins.

Stairway to Heaven
Returning home from a bombing mission over
Germany, RAF squadron leader Peter Carter (David
Niven) survives a jump from his burning plane
without a parachute. Due to the incompetence of an
angel (Marius Goring), Carter escapes his
appointment with death, which causes great
consternation in Heaven. To further complicate
matters, Carter falls in love with an American radio
operator (Kim Hunter). With Raymond Massey.
   VHS: S32201. $19.95.
**Michael Powell/Emeric Pressburger, Great
Britain, 1946, 104 mins.**

Strangers on a Train
Marking the 45th anniversary of this Hitchcock
classic, this rediscovered British version sharpens the
divide between two men (Robert Walker and Farley
Granger) whose chance encounter on a train leads to
a bizarre pact of exchanged murders. Includes two

Land and Freedom

minutes of extra, never-before-seen footage, new digital transfer and the original theatrical trailer.
VHS: $30915. $19.98.
Alfred Hitchcock, Great Britain, 1951, 103 mins.

Tales of Hoffman
Michael Powell and Emeric Pressburger's splendid tale of a poet's amorous adventures. Offenbach's magnificent score and impressive dancing by Moira Shearer and others highlight the pursuit of three women: Olympia is a puppet passed off as a real woman to Hoffman, who sees her torn to pieces before his eyes; a Venetian courtesan, Giulietta, captures Hoffman's mirror image, and his soul; a beautiful singer must remain silent lest she suffer the fate of her mother, who died of consumption.
VHS: $16211. $39.95.
Laser: 2 discs: CAV/CLV. LD71523. $99.95.
Michael Powell, Great Britain, 1951, 124 mins.

The Tenant
Polanski's most autobiographical film is, like *Repulsion*, a journey through the distorted realm of the human mind. Polanski himself plays Trelkovsky, a nebbish file clerk who moves into the apartment of a young suicide, becomes deeply paranoid, certain that the other tenants are trying to drive *him* to suicide. With Isabelle Adjani, Shelley Winters, Lila Kedrova, Melvyn Douglas. English dialog.
VHS: $01308. $49.95.
Roman Polanski, Great Britain, 1976, 126 mins.

Terence Davies Trilogy
These magical films by Terence Davies, director of *The Long Day Closes* and *The Neon Bible*, are set against the background of industrial Liverpool and follow the main character, Robert Tucker, from his Catholic childhood to being bullied at school, dealing with a violent and sick father at home and struggling with his view of his own sexuality. The three films include *Children*, *Madonna & Child* and *Death & Transfiguration*.
VHS: $31107. $39.99.
Terence Davies, Great Britain, 1996, 101 mins.

Tess
Winner of three Academy Awards, Polanski's interpretation of Thomas Hardy's novel is a beautiful and timeless masterwork destined to be a classic. Nastassia Kinski stars as Tess against the backdrop of a morally rigid Victorian England. The stunning cinematography is unforgettable. English dialog.
VHS: $01311. $29.95.
Roman Polanski, France/Great Britain, 1980, 170 mins.

Tom & Viv
Willem Dafoe plays T.S. Eliot with Miranda Richardson as his first wife. Despite his brilliance as a poet, Elliot could not find personal happiness in his marriage because of an unspeakable secret that ultimately divided these two lovers. This riveting, true story is superbly acted. Richardson was nominated for an Oscar (Best Actress), along with Rosemary Harris (Best Supporting Actress).
VHS: $26035. $19.95.
Laser: LD75064. $39.99.
Brian Gilbert, USA, 1994, 115 mins.

Tom Jones
Winner of 4 Academy Awards, including Best Picture, *Tom Jones* is Tony Richardson's adaptation of Henry Fielding's famous novel about a mysteriously abandoned orphan who is adopted by the fussy Squire Allworthy, and thus begins a life of bawdy adventure. An outrageous and lusty comedy of 18th-century English life starring the sexy young Albert Finney. Screenplay by John Osborne.
VHS: $15548. $19.98.
Laser: LD71435. $29.98.
Tony Richardson, Great Britain, 1963, 129 mins.

Total Eclipse
Leonardo Di Caprio and David Thewlis star in this film based on the affair between Arthur Rimbaud and Paul Verlaine. Rimbaud left a legacy of brilliant poetry and an example of extreme living that inspired contemporary stars like Jim Morrison. Verlaine, a highly regarded writer in his own right, was an older married man when he became infatuated with Rimbaud. This is a grand film about their passion for love and art, a passion fatally doomed by madness. Christopher Hampton wrote the screenplay.
VHS: $27617. $19.98.
Laser: LD75553. $39.99.
Agnieszka Holland, Great Britain/France, 1995, 111 mins.

Trainspotting
One of the most talked-about films of the year, *Trainspotting* is the wickedly witty story of the frustrations, aspirations and antics of a group of working class Scottish youths: unlikely hero Mark Renton (Ewan McGregor) and his so-called friends, unlucky but amiable "Spud," short-fused, knife-wielding "Begbie" and narcissistic, Sean Connery-idolizing "Sick Boy." As the foursome plans a risky scam, Renton ultimately must decide to follow his reckless pals or "choose life" and sell out his friends in the process. "Electrifying and hilarious" (*Rolling Stone*).
VHS: $30637. $103.99.
Laser: Widescreen. LD76092. $49.98.
Danny Boyle, Great Britain, 1996, 94 mins.

Two Deaths
Nicolas Roeg's lively tale of power, passion and obsession is set in a politically torn Eastern European country. Dr. Daniel Pavenic (Michael Gambon, *The Cook, The Thief, His Wife and Her Lover*) hosts a lavish banquet for three school chums. When he introduces a mysterious servant (Sonia Braga) to his guests, his revelation of how he ruined the life of this beautiful and strong woman becomes a confessional for Pavenic and his guests which changes their lives.
VHS: $30046. $19.98.
Nicolas Roeg, Great Britain, 1995, 102 mins.

The Vacillations of Poppy Carew
While planning her father's funeral, Poppy Carew (Tara Fitzerald, *Sirens*) becomes involved with four men. Based on the best-selling novel by English author Mary Wesley, this film is a rollicking good time as we watch Poppy navigate her way through affairs of the heart. Also stars Sian Phillips (*Age of Innocence*) and Charlotte Coleman (*Four Weddings and a Funeral*).
VHS: $30005. $14.98.
James Cellan Jones, 1995, Great Britain, 108 mins.

Victim
Dirk Bogarde stars in this brooding drama with homosexual implications as a defense lawyer with a secret past. Approached by a man he suspects of blackmail, he refuses to help. Only when that same man is dead and it is made clear that he saved Bogarde from certain ruin, does the lawyer risk everything to make the senseless death mean something. Letterboxed.
VHS: $03489. $29.95.
Laser: Letterboxed. LD76406. $49.95.
Basil Dearden, Great Britain, 1961, 100 mins.

Waltz of the Toreadors
In this robust adaptation of the Jean Anouilh play, Peter Sellers is General Fitzjohn, whose pursuit of a sexy Parisian is thwarted by his put upon wife (Margaret Leighton) and a lecherous doctor. A breezy and tasteful comedy of sexual and social morals.
VHS: $02705. $14.98.
Laser: Widescreen. LD75518. $49.95.
John Guillermin, Great Britain, 1962, 100 mins.

Whiskey Galore
One of the drollest, most amusing British films ever made. Scottish islanders take drastic measures when a cargo of whiskey is marooned off their shore. Also known by the title *Tight Little Island*.
VHS: $02030. $29.95.
Alexander Mackendrick, Great Britain, 1958, 80 mins.

Withnail and I
The sixties are ending and two London actors down on their luck seek solace at a relative's summer place in the country. The rustic cottage is less than they expected. A frantic adult comedy starring Richard E. Grant, Paul McGann and Richard Griffiths as odd Uncle Monty. Based on the life of the actor-writer-director Bruce Robinson (*The Killing Fields*).
VHS: $07577. $14.95.
Laser: LD71214. $49.95.
Bruce Robinson, Great Britain, 1988, 108 mins.

Women in Love
Two sisters, sexually mature and intellectually active, struggle against the confines of a rural English mining town and its rigidly classed layers of society, in this adaptation of D.H. Lawrence's study of sexual uneasiness and doubt. With Alan Bates, Oliver Reed, Glenda Jackson, Jennie Linden.
VHS: $01479. $19.98.
Ken Russell, Great Britain, 1970, 129 mins.

50 Films About Art & Artists

African-American Art: Past and Present
A comprehensive survey of African-American art. With more than 65 artists represented, the program is divided into three programs: African Art, 18th and 19th Century Fine Art Survey, and 20th Century Fine Art Survey: In the Artist's Words. 90 mins.
VHS: S20319. $199.00.

Art City: Making It in Manhattan
Informed entertainment about the artists, collectors and dealers who bring to life the art capital of the world as it plunges into the 21st century. Presenting a cross-section of artists, the film discusses inspiration, aesthetic issues and the meaning of success. With Louise Bourgeois, Brice Marden, Chuck Close, Neil Jenney, Elizabeth Murray, Pat Steir, Ashley Bickerton, Gary Simmons, Ursula von Rydingsvard, Caio Fonseca, Rirkrit Tiravanija and more. "Anyone who knows anything about the perils of talking heads and flapping tongues on film must marvel at this insightful job" (Andrew Sarris, *N.Y. Observer*).
VHS: S31387. $24.95.
Chris Maybach, USA, 1996, 58 mins.

Arts of Islam
From Spain to India, from Turkey to Morocco, the art of Islam has molded the cultural eye of millions of people over more than a millennium. This program explores Islamic art as one of the great cultural forces in world history and shows how it captivates the eye and engages the imagination. 26 mins.
VHS: S09462. $174.00.

Beatrice Wood: Mama of Dada
Even at the age of 102, Beatrice Wood continues to influence younger artists with her definitive, free-wheeling ways. She was central to the American Dada movement and is the last surviving member of this group. In this video she recalls her friends Man Ray, Picabia and others, and her ex-husband Marcel Duchamp. USA, 1993, 57 mins.
VHS: S27102. $29.95.

Cezanne: The Riddle of the Bathers
Paul Cezanne is one of Modernity's undisputed founders. Among his paintings, a special preoccupation with a specific theme stands out: that of "the bathers." This film traces the riddle of the bathers, a curious fixation that resonates across Cezanne's entire career as a painter. 57 mins.
VHS: S27566. $19.95.

Claes Oldenburg
A look at the works and life of the artist whose giant soft sculptures based on food and domestic items helped define Pop Art. Features the artist and his wife, and contemporaries Roy Lichtenstein, Jim Dine and other art experts. 52 mins.
VHS: S31925. $39.95.

Clemintine Hunter
Mrs. Clemintine Hunter is one of the most widely acclaimed African-American folk painters. When she died at the age of 101, she left over 4,000 images behind. Her legacy recreates a past that stretches back to her life on Melrose plantation in Louisiana during the era of Reconstruction. Despite the hardships of that time, Mrs. Hunter's work captures a joy in living that few artists can match.
VHS: S27100. $24.95.
Katina Simmons, USA, 1994, 22 mins.

Cubism and Non-Objective Art
The work of Braque and Picasso, Gris, Duchamp and Leger are explored, as well as the work of Kandinsky, Mondrian, Brancusi and others. A second segment covers the surrealists through the work of artists such as Dali, Magritte, Arp, Ernst, Miro and Tanguy.
VHS: S09074. $59.95.

Degas, Erte & Chagall
Three of this century's most influential artists are studied in this film. *Degas in New Orleans* portrays the artist's little-known visit here. *Diana Vreeland* tells the story of Erte, his life and works, from Paris to Hollywood. In the third segment, *Marc Chagall* gives us a personal view of some of his greatest works.
VHS: S03968. $29.95.

El Teatro Museo Dali
Visit the museum Salvador Dali designed himself, building up from the ruins left behind after severe shelling during the Civil War. His theater-museum allows the viewer a very personal look inside the mind of Dali—painter, author, designer, filmmaker, and this century's most recognized artist—whose mere presence could cause controversy: paintings hung haphazardly and without titles, divers placed outside the building complete with loaves of bread on their heads, a room that copies the face of Mae West; a virtual Dali universe. With *Un Chien Andalou*. Spanish with English subtitles.
VHS: S30480. $24.95.
Spain, 1993, 60 mins.

Faith Ringgold: The Last Story Quilt
From the day she learned to draw, Faith Ringgold has worked steadily to master her craft and communicate her vision: to present a realistic view of the black female in society. This film is an insider's look at how one woman has fulfilled her dream of becoming an artist. Cine Gold Eagle Award. 28 min.
VHS: S18392. $49.95.

Faith Ringgold: The Last Story Quilt

Fauvism and Expressionism
The Fauves emerged as a reaction against Impressionism and Post-Impressionism. Early modern art is explored through the work of Matisse, Rouault, Derain and Vlaminck; in *Expressionism* the work of Nolde, Munch, Kokoschka, Beckmann and others are explored.
VHS: S09072. $59.95.

Francis Bacon
Widely regarded as the greatest British painter of this century, Bacon's work further fetches more on the open market than almost any other living painter. This program follows Bacon from his studio where

Frida Kahlo

he starts work every day at dawn, to his favorite club and gambling joint in Soho, and explores how his way of life affects his vision of the world. 55 mins.
VHS: S07607. $39.95.

Frescoes of Diego Rivera
Explores the great beauty and political expression in Rivera's most extensive body of work, examining the artist and his techniques, using archival footage filmed during his work on murals created for the Ford Motor Company, and location footage of his most recognized efforts. In addition, the film explores the man and his politics, creating a complex and fascinating portrait of one of the geniuses of the twentieth century. 35 mins.
VHS: S10306. $29.95.

Frida Kahlo
Sada Thompson narrates this fascinating look at Frida Kahlo, the center of the Mexican renaissance of the 20's and 30's, both as an artist, a woman and a tragic figure. A catastrophic accident at the age of 16 left Kahlo with severe injuries. During her recuperation, she began to paint, first portraits and later more complex works with the themes of death and her loss of motherhood. *Frida Kahlo* profiles Frida's work, her increasing interest in politics, and her tempestuous relationship with her husband, Diego Rivera. 62 mins.
VHS: S08477. $39.95.

Golub
Art, politics and the media intersect in artist Leon Golub's nightmarish images of war, torture, death squads and mercenaries. The documentary follows the creation of one of his monumental canvases, *White Squad X*, detailing his complex and unorthodox techniques. Interweaving scenes of Golub at work, archival footage, interviews with museum-goers and TV news, the film challenges us to question our connection to violence in the modern world and to reassess the relationship between art and society. "*Golub* conveys the exhilarating sense that art is inseparable from both the world that engenders it and the world that receives it" (Jonathan Rosenbaum, *Chicago Reader*).
VHS: S27803. $29.95.
Kartemquin Films, USA, 1988, 56 mins.

Hermitage Masterpieces
An 18-program, nine-tape series highlighting masterpieces from every school of Western art residing in one of the world's greatest museums, the Hermitage, in St. Petersburg, Russia. Programs include: *The Museum's Majestic Architecture*; *Highlights of the Masterpieces*; *Russia in the Age of Peter the Great*; *Decorative Arts of Italy, France & England*; *Art from Mesopotamia to Ancient China*; *The Art of Ancient Egypt*; *The Vast Sculpture Collection*; *The Classical World of Greece and Romance*; *Art of the Middle Ages*; *Art of the Early Italian Renaissance*; *Raphael, DaVinci and The High Italian Renaissance*; *Art of the Netherlands: 15th and 16th Century*; *Rubens, Van Dyck and the 17th-Century Flemish Painters*; *Rembrandt and the 17th-Century Dutch Masters*; *Velazquez, El Greco, Goya and the Spanish Masters*; *French Classical Style of the 17th and 18th Centuries*; *The Road to Impressionism: 19th-Century France*; and *Modernism: Matisse, Picasso and More 20th Century Painters*. 540 mins.
VHS: S31933. $119.95.

Horace Pippin
An appreciation of the striking color, originality and directness of self-taught African-American artist

Horace Pippin. 28 mins.
VHS: S31744. $39.95.

Horst P. Horst
A portrait of the first photographer to have an exhibition at the Louvre. Spans the six decades in which Horst set standards in fashion and portrait photography. Includes interviews with Paloma Picasso, Karl Lagerfeld and Jean Marais. 50 mins.
VHS: S32395. $29.95.

The Hudson River and Its Painters
The mid-nineteenth century saw the growth of America's first native school of landscape painters, artists inspired by the compelling beauty of the Hudson River Valley, who portrayed this and other romantic wilderness areas with an almost mystical reverence. This video explores the life and work of the major artists of what came to be known as the Hudson River School—Thomas Cole, Asher Durand, Frederic Church, Albert Bierstadt, John Kensett, Jasper Cropsey, Worthington Whittredge, Sanford Gifford, and George Inness. It presents more than 200 paintings, prints and photographs of the period and juxtaposes them with dramatic location photography of the Hudson River area. The Hudson Company in association with The Metropolitan Museum of Art. 57 mins.
VHS: S05233. $39.95.

Jackson Pollock
This biography of Jackson Pollock looks at his work, his concept of "action painting" and his part in the abstract expressionist movement. 52 mins.
VHS: S17725. $39.95.

Jacob Lawrence
Lawrence is one of the country's most respected artists. This African-American painter grew up in depression-era Harlem and got his schooling in federal workshops. Today his works on African-American themes, particularly history, are widely prized. Interviews and the works of the artist tell this story of artistic excellence. 25 mins.
VHS: S27622. $29.95.

Jasper Johns: Ideas in Paint
A revealing portrait of Jasper Johns which covers his remarkable work that helped usher in Pop Art and Minimalism. The documentary includes intimate conversations and footage of Johns working, with commentary by his colleagues Leo Castelli, the late composer John Cage, choreographer Merce Cunningham and other noted artists and art critics. 56 mins.
VHS: S17728. $39.95.

Lascaux Revisited
Prehistoric paintings in a cave were accidentally discovered by French schoolchildren. The drama of this true story is recreated in this video through animation. Even more exciting is the footage of these remarkable ancient works of art which have been closed to the public since 1963.
VHS: S27099. $29.95.
Jacques Willemartt/Norbert Aujolat, USA, 1995, 35 mins.

The Hermitage

Life of Leonardo da Vinci
A brilliant, massive portrait of Leonardo da Vinci in five parts, produced by Italian State Television and directed by acclaimed Italian filmmaker Renato Castellani. The man who painted the Mona Lisa and the Last Supper, one of the great geniuses of history,

comes alive in an exhaustive study of da Vinci and his period. *Part I: 1452-1482,* covers the first 30 years of da Vinci's life, the circumstances of his birth and childhood, as well as his influences. *Part II: 1482-1500,* covers da Vinci leaving Florence for Milan to work for Duke Ludovico Sforza, his scientific studies as well as The Last Supper. At age 50, Leonardo returns to his home in Florence. *Parts IV & V: 1500-1519.* While in Florence, Raphael is introduced to da Vinci, and Leonardo meets and forms a bitter rivalry with Michelangelo. In 1506, he leaves again for Milan. 4½ hours total. 3 cassettes in slipcase.
VHS: $12189. $99.95.

Jacob Lawrence

The Line King
For over 70 years, Al Hirschfeld's drawings have graced the pages of *The New York Times,* bringing to life the stars of Broadway and the silver screen. This thoroughly engaging portrait of one of America's most beloved illustrators features rare home movies, special appearances by his celebrity subjects and interviews with his late wife Dolly Haas and daughter Nina. The artist emerges as a brilliant, delightful, quirky and compassionate observer of humanity.
VHS: $32495. $24.98.
Susan W. Dryfoos, USA, 1996, 126 mins.

Louvre 200
A three-part series exploring the evolution of the museum in European culture.
Complete Set. Parts 1, 2 and 3.
VHS: $18850. $79.95.

Masters of Photography: Diane Arbus
The only film profile of this genius who photographed those living on the fringes of society. This video explores her work through her own words and the images that stunned visitors at her show in the Museum of Modern Art. 30 mins.
VHS: $16205. $29.95.

Masterworks of Painting
There is a difference between looking at a painting and seeing a painting. What makes a great painting great? This video museum of the world's great paintings is a private course in art appreciation, illuminating the principles of art: color, line, shape, light, composition and design. 51 mins.
VHS: $09471. $198.00.

Max Ernst
This retrospective celebrates the 100th anniversary of the birth of Max Ernst, one of the most influential artists of this century. Revealing what Ernst called "the private brittle places of refuge," this program considers Ernst's involvement with the Surrealist movement, his retreat to Provence, his flight to New York and life in America, and his eventual return to Europe. 90 mins.
VHS: $15994. $39.95.

Metropolitan Museum Boxed Set
This three-part video collection includes *Masterpieces of the Met,* showcasing some of the Met's many masterpieces; *Merchants and Masterpieces,* a discussion of the people and the art that shaped the history of the Met; and *Cloisters: The Glories of Medieval Art,* about The Cloisters, the branch of the Met devoted to religious and Medieval art. Philippe deMontebello, the director of the Met, narrates. USA, 175 mins.
VHS: $24794. $79.95.

Montparnasse Revisited
This series captures the history of one of Paris' most colorful and vital districts. The painters, writers, composers, actors, musicians and photographers who made Paris the center of the art world between 1900 and the Second World War defined the avant garde. Together they created modern art as we know it. Each volume is 55 mins. Directed by Matthew Reinders and based on a program by Jean-Marie Drot.
The Ten-Volume Set.
VHS: $21051. $199.95.

Philip Johnson: Self Portrait
America's pre-eminent senior architect wittily discusses his life, his work, his critics and his aesthetic in this documentary filmed over a period of ten years in many of the locations that evoke Johnson's long, brilliant and controversial career. Interviewing him is celebrated arts lecturer and writer Rosamund Bernier.
VHS: $30989. $150.00.
1985, 55 mins.

Picasso: The Man and His Work
A major, two-part survey of the work of the legendary 20th century artist, which explores more than 600 of his works, many of which have never been seen in public. Director Edward Quinn captures Picasso at work and at play, during the last 22 years of his life. On two cassettes (90 minutes total).
VHS: $02757. $69.95.
Laser: LD72213. $145.00.

Piet Mondrian: Mr. Boogie Woogie Man
A stirring portrait of this seminal and enigmatic modern artist. The program explores how Mondrian's art influenced painting, architecture, interior decor, furniture, design and typography, and how his passion for jazz music and dance infected his art. Features *Time* art critic Robert Hughes, designer Terence Conran and composer Louis Andriessen. 49 mins.
VHS: $31562. $39.95.

Portrait of Gustave Caillebotte in the Country
Gustave Caillebotte spent 20 summers on his family's estate at Yerre, the most productive period of his artistic career. *Portaits in the Country,* done in 1876, incorporates the informal poses favored by the

The Line King

Impressionists with Caillebotte's deep linear perspective and attention to detail. Paintings of the estate gardens and river scenes add their luster to this stunning program.
VHS: $31150. $29.95.
Emmanuel Laurent, France, 1994, 25 mins.

Richard Avedon: Darkness and Light
An illuminating look at one of the most celebrated and controversial fashion and portrait photographers of our time. Highlights Avedon's 50-year career, recalling his work for *Harper's Bazaar, Vogue* and *The New Yorker* magazines and featuring his signature portraits of Charlie Chaplin, Dorothy Parker, the Windsors and Natassia Kinski (and snake). 59 mins.
VHS: $32396. $29.95.

Robert Motherwell and the New York School: Storming the Citadel
An investigation of Abstract Expressionism, centered on one of its most important figures, Robert Motherwell (1915-1991). The program considers artists who comprised the movement (Pollock, de

Portrait of Gustave Caillebotte

Kooning, Mark Rothko, Franz Kline), and the social and political context that deeply influenced their work. 56 mins.
VHS: S17729. $39.95.

The Rotund World of Botero
This video is both a tribute and an expose of the famed artist. He tells of his early life in Colombia and his growing international fame. There are also segments that show him at work on a fresco and a sculpture, and most importantly, we see him at work in his home just outside Bogota. 56 mins.
VHS: S24364. $29.95.

Roy Lichtenstein: Reflections
As one of the great Pop artists, Lichtenstein offers exciting insights into the artistic process and the source of inspiration. 30 mins.
VHS: S28411. $49.95.

Rudolf Arnheim: A Life in Art
Rudolf Arnheim, Professor Emeritus of the psychology of art, Harvard University, and author of *Art and Visual Perception, Film as Art, Towards a Psychology of Art, Visual Thinking* and *The Power of the Center*, reflects on his life and work and explains some of his most important theories on this educational video. Also includes a biographical section. 58 mins.
VHS: S32425. $49.95.

Running Fence
The film depicts the long struggle by Christo to build a 24-mile fence of white fabric over the hills of California disappearing into the Pacific, at a cost of $3 million. After what seemed to be an insurmountable struggle between the artist and the state bureaucracy, the fence, finally unfurled, brings the community together in celebration of its beauty.
VHS: S07493. $49.95.
Maysles Brothers, USA, 1978, 58 mins.

The Sculpture of Spaces
Traces Isamu Noguchi's lifelong exploration of his revolutionary vision through works as diverse as his stage designs for Martha Graham, public parks and plazas, innovative playgrounds and the intimate garden designed for his home in rural Japan.
VHS: S32079. $29.95.
Charlotte Zwerin, USA, 1997, 54 mins.

The Shock of Futurism
Italian Futurism was at the forefront of 20th century avant-garde impulses and helped form the basis of modern art. This program concerns the works of Boccioni, Balla, Carra and Severini, and relates how their visions and ideas shaped cubism, Dada and Pop art. 23 mins.
VHS: S17224. $29.95.

Sister Wendy's Story of Painting
This acclaimed BBC production takes viewers on a unique journey through art and history with best-selling author Sister Wendy. Filmed on location, the five-volume collection covers the history of art down through the ages, sweeping from cave paintings through the Renaissance, and on to the modern art scene in New York's SoHo scene. Volumes include *Early Art, The Renaissance, Baroque to Modernism, The Age of Revolution* and *Modernism*. 60 mins each.
VHS: S32093. $99.98.

Treasures of the Vatican Museum and Sistine Chapel
This compelling series of 16 videos offers unprecedented access to the 13 Vatican Museums and

the Sistine Chapel. Founded in 1503, the Vatican Museums represent 500 years of papal art collections and span all the important historical periods from antiquity (Egyptian, Greek, Etruscan and Roman art) to the present, including a vital ethnological collection. The museums contain secular and non-secular sculptures, paintings and architecture by history's most revered artists, including Michelangelo, Raphael and Botticelli. The video collection also includes *The Restoration of the Sistine Chapel, which features exclusive accounts of this challenging project as well as close-up views of Michelangelo's painting. 30 mins. each. 1995.*
The Ethnological Museum: In Search of the Divine.
VHS: S30687. $29.99.
Greek Art in the Vatican Museums.
VHS: S30688. $29.99.
Modern Art in the Vatican Museums.
VHS: S30690. $29.99.
Pius Clemente Museum.
VHS: S30690. $29.99.
The Raphael Rooms and Logge.
VHS: S30691. $29.99.
The Restoration of the Sistine Chapel.
VHS: S30692. $29.99.
Roman Art in the Vatican Museums.
VHS: S30693. $29.99.
Stories of Etruscan Civilization.
VHS: S30695. $29.99.
The Sistine Chapel.
VHS: S30694. $29.99.
The Vatican Egyptian Museum.
VHS: S30698. $29.99.
The Vatican Historical Museum.
VHS: S30699. $29.99.
The Vatican Picture Gallery.
VHS: S30702. $29.99.
The Vatican, Volume 1.
VHS: S30696. $29.99.
The Vatican, Volume 2.
VHS: S30697. $29.99.
Vatican Museums, Volume 1.
VHS: S30700. $29.99.
Vatican Museums, Volume 2.
VHS: S30701. $29.99.

Vermeer: Love, Light and Silence
This is the first film to profile Dutch artist Jan Vermeer, the master of camera obscura, and his art, which was neglected during his lifetime. Offers close-up views of some of Vermeer's most famous paintings and explores the social, economic, scientific and political context of his work. 50 mins.
VHS: S31563. $39.95.

The Way Things Go
This 1987 cult masterpiece captures the precisely crafted chaos created by visual artists Peter Fischli and David Weiss in their kinetic installations using everyday objects. "This rudimentary yet showy masterpiece would have made Picasso envious" *(Flash Art).*
VHS: S32030. $29.95.
Peter Fischli/David Weiss, Switzerland, 1987, 30 mins.

Willem de Kooning: Artist
Paintings by Willem de Kooning are prized the world over as superb examples of the New York school. He worked both abstractly and with the figure. This film shows him at work and in conversation with friends. There are also 31 paintings captured here for home viewing.
VHS: S26718. $29.95.
Robert Snyder, USA, 32 mins.

Roy Lichtenstein: Reflections

100 Best Documentary Films

26 Bathrooms
The British structuralist Peter Greenaway (*Prospero's Books*) is best known for his pattern-obsessive, symmetrical, intellectual, playful and visually flamboyant features on the nature of the body and art. This short is a brief, comic essay on his larger themes, in short a work about bathrooms and the activities and people inhabiting them.
VHS: $18203. $19.95.
Peter Greenaway, Great Britain, 1993, 30 mins.

28 Up
Beginning in 1964, director Michael Apted turned his camera on a group of 7-year-old boys and girls from both wealthy and poor families in England, recording their thoughts, hopes and dreams with revealing interviews. He then returned to film these same children every seven years, until the age of 28; all of their most personal moments, from the rapture of discovered love to the despair of dreams long forgotten, are brought vividly to life, played out before the viewer with striking emotional power. A moving and utterly memorable work.
VHS: $14291. $19.98.
Michael Apted, Great Britain, 1984, 136 mins.

The 317th Platoon
A brilliant evocation of the senselessness of war during the last days of the French occupation of Indochina, based on the director's own experiences of being taken prisoner at Dien Buen Phu. The film tells of the platoon's retreat, focusing on a career soldier and the commanding young lieutenant as they make their way through ambushes, betrayals, rain, jungle, villages, pain, disease and inexorable fatigue to inevitable annihilation. With awesome cinematography by Raoul Coutard. With Jacques Perrin, Bruno Cremer, Pierre Fabre and Manuel Zarzo. French with English subtitles.
VHS: $13224. $59.95.
Pierre Schoendoerffer, France, 1965, 100 mins.

35 Up
Michael Apted's astonishing documentary, made for Grenada Television, charts the dreams, lives, ambitions and fates of its disparate English characters. The subjects are part of a landmark series, originally titled *Seven Up*. They were chosen as seven-year-olds for a series that would assess the English social, political and ruling systems; the underlying themes are the intermingling of race, class and sex. The documentary picks up their lives in seven-year intervals. (The films in between were *Seven Plus Seven, 21* and *28 Up.*) Apted is brilliant at evoking deep and private feelings about their lives and expectations—Tony had aspirations to be a jockey, while Nick and Peter were fascinated by space. Cinematography by George Jesse Turner. Edited by Claire Lewis and Kim Horton.
VHS: $19020. $19.98.
Michael Apted, Great Britain, 1991, 128 mins.

African Art
African art, the booty of colonial wars, emerged in the West as a strange and exotic art form that would influence such modernists as Picasso, Matisse and Modigliani. But, as Kirk Varnedoe, Curator of New York's Museum of Modern Art, and Harvard Professors Henry Louis Gates and Cornel West explain, it is important to view African art within its own cultural context, as we travel to Mali to examine the art of the Bamana, Dogon and Djenne people. From the home of the famous Tyi Warra antelope carvings to the ancient walled city of Djenne, local inhabitants explain the function of art and the role of the artist in their society. "A successful and concise analysis. Fascinating viewing" (*Time Out London*). 47 mins.
VHS: $30786. $29.95.

After Sunset: The Life & Times of the Drive-In Theater
Once an integral part of America's classic pop culture, drive-in theaters are nearly gone today. Using existing drive-ins as their map, filmmaker Jon Bokencamp leads his ragtag crew across the American West to discover what the era of the outdoor movie was all about, searching out the people who've built and LIVED these theaters. "A wonderful evocation of a distinct piece of Americana" (Leonard Maltin).
VHS: $30937. $24.95.
Jon Bokenkamp, USA, 1995, 45 mins.

AGEE
In this Oscar-nominated film, the fascinating story of poet, journalist, film critic, screenwriter and Pulitzer Prize-winning novelist James Agee is told by those who knew him best, including John Huston, Walker Evans, Robert Fitzgerald, Dwight MacDonald, Father James Flye, and Agee's three wives. "Proof of the axiom that a significant subject will inspire an impressive film" (*Booklist*).
VHS: $30145. $24.95.
Ross Spears, USA, 1980, 90 mins.

Aileen Wuornos: The Selling of a Serial Killer
Wuornos is a 35-year-old lesbian prostitute who murdered seven of her male clients along a Florida interstate. She is "adopted" by Arlene Pralle, a "born-again" woman who sells the story to the highest bidders. This crazy set-up also includes a lawyer with a crazy defense and Wuornos' lover, who dupes the killer into confessing over the phone. It's a documentary about the media frenzy that surrounds sensational criminals and obscures justice.
VHS: $23288. $19.98.
Nick Broomfield, USA, 1992, 87 mins.

Almonds and Raisins: A History of the Yiddish Cinema
Narrated by Orson Welles, this remarkable documentary is a history of the Yiddish cinema, fascinating and funny, a landmark documentary on the whole lost culture of Yiddish film. Between 1927 and 1940, Yiddish filmmakers made over 100 films in Yiddish, expressing the hopes and fears of the immigrant society— dreams of opportunity, assimilation, social betterment, separation from family and failure. *Almonds and Raisins* lovingly captures the ideas and history of the Yiddish cinema and the richness of the Yiddish language.
VHS: $08101. $59.95.
Russ Karel, Great Britain, 1986, 90 mins.

AGEE

American Dream

The winner of the 1990 Academy award for best documentary, forceful account of the labor strike and political discord in a small, closely knit Minnesota town, at the Hormel Meat Packing plant. Kopple brilliantly covers the issues, background, social and economic context and the key players. The fight literally pitted brother against brother, after some workers crossed the picket line. Kopple strips away the layers of deception and anger to present a startling portrait of Reagan/Bush era greed and the frightening repercussions and break up of a community. Kopple worked on the film for more than seven years.
VHS: S17633. $19.98.
Barbara Kopple, USA, 1990, 90 mins.

Anne Frank Remembered

Family members, childhood friends and the people who hid the Franks bring to life the girl behind the diary. Academy Award winner for Best Documentary of 1995, narrated by Kenneth Branagh with selections from Anne's diary read by Glenn Close. German, Dutch and English with English subtitles.
VHS: S28620. $14.95.
Laser: LD75956. $39.95.
Jon Blair, Great Britain/USA, 1995, 117 mins.

The Architecture of Doom

A brilliant documentary which explores the inner workings of the Third Reich and illuminates the Nazi aesthetic in art, architecture and popular culture. Director Peter Cohen uses this analysis of Nazi art and architecture to shed new light on German popular culture, which made Hitler possible. Music by Richard Wagner, footage of Hitler and his Nazi party and rare films and memorabilia are combined to show how a civilized country supported a frustrated artist who became a maniacal despot.
VHS: S26346. $29.95.
Peter Cohen, USA, 1995, 119 mins.

Baraka

Amazing 70mm cinematography tells this global story of human and environmental interdependence. No dialogue is needed in this film that brings the

Exotic Escapes

Beyond Rangoon
VHS: S27065. $98.99.
Laser: LD75440. $34.95.

Fitzcarraldo
VHS: S00446. $69.95.

Mediterraneo
VHS: S18159. $19.98.

Shirley Valentine
VHS: S11736. $14.95.
Laser: LD75256. $34.98.

beauty of the earth together with the universal truth of human striving. Music by a number of religious groups and contemporaries like Michael Stearns and Dead Can Dance make this an aural as well as a visual feast. Best Picture, Montreal Film Festival.
VHS: S25539. $29.95.
Laser: LD74951. $39.98.
Ron Fricke, USA, 1992, 96 mins.

Baseball

Ken Burns (*Civil War*) turns his attention to the American national pastime in this 18-hour epic which spans 150 years of the game that is America. Released on nine tapes in a collector's boxed set.
VHS: S21896. $149.98.
Laser: LD74841. $299.99.
Ken Burns, USA, 1994, 1080 mins.

Berkeley in the Sixties

A moving documentary about the 1960's social, political and sexual revolution at the University of California at Berkeley. The documentary traces the anti-war protest movement, the free speech movement, civil rights protests and the formation of the women's movement. Director Mark Kitchell interweaves archival footage with interviews with key leaders of the movement. The soundtrack includes Joan Baez, Mario Savio, Country Joe and the Fish, The Band, Jimi Hendrix and The Grateful Dead. "Probably the best documentary on the sixties to date" (*Village Voice*).
VHS: S18146. $29.95.
Mark Kitchell, USA, 1990, 117 mins.

Berlin, Symphony of a Great City

Walter Ruttmann's great documentary is a dynamic vision of Berlin, unfolding from dawn until midnight. Ruttmann captured the city's expressive poetry by concealing his camera in vans and suitcases to capture a portrait of the city and its people. Music composed and conducted by Timothy Brock, performed by the Olympia Chamber Orchestra. On the same program is *Opus 1*, a ten-minute essay Ruttman shot in 1922.
VHS: S01931. $24.95.
Walter Ruttmann, Germany, 1927, 62 mins.

Breasts: A Documentary

Twenty-two women and girls from ages 6 to 84 speak candidly—and naked from the waist up—about their attitudes toward breasts—their own and others'—in this revealing and humorous documentary. They'll introduce you to the secrets, the sensations, the surprises and the stories that lie hidden in their anatomy. It just may change the way you look at the world—and yourself. "Men and women alike can gain much from watching this" (*The Chicago Tribune*).
VHS: S32360. $36.99.
Meema Spadola, USA, 1996, 50 mins.

Brian Wilson: "I just wasn't made for these times"

Brian Wilson, the musical visionary behind the Beach Boys, stands revealed in this feature length documentary. Made by record producer Don Was, it manages to get inside Wilson's life, his eccentricities, his troubled childhood and the strange home life he himself led as a distant father. Though some delicate points are not investigated, including the death of Wilson's brother, Beach Boy drummer Dennis Wilson, this film is good at explaining the source and achievements of Brian Wilson's pop innovations.
VHS: S26949. $19.99.
Don Was, USA, 1995, 69 mins.

A Brief History of Time

Errol Morris' documentary about the English physicist Stephen Hawking takes its title from Hawking's best seller. The film explores Hawking's groundbreaking work in quantum physics and the study of the origins of the universe, despite his debilitating physical state, brought about by amyotrophic lateral sclerosis. Morris interweaves anecdotes, family dynamics and Hawking's background into a kaleidoscope of images, movements and sound. Music by Philip Glass.
VHS: S18370. $19.95.
Errol Morris, USA/Great Britain, 1991, 84 mins.

Brother's Keeper

This riveting documentary by Joe Berlinger and Bruce Sinofsky is a reconstruction of the arrest and trial of Delbert Ward in the alleged suffocation and murder of his brother Bill. Set in a small town in upstate New York, Bill, Delbert and their two other brothers lived in a squalid farmhouse with no

electricity or running water. *Brother's Keeper* is a powerful work about the nature of justice and community, and the grass-roots campaign to secure Delbert's freedom and exonerate him of the charges.
VHS: $18959. $19.98.
Laser: CLV. LD74472. $39.95.
Joe Berlinger/Bruce Sinofsky, USA, 1992, 105 mins.

Buckminster Fuller: Thinking Out Loud
Rising from the depths of despair on Chicago's lakefront, Fuller transformed himself, his life, and ultimately the world with his radical take on the contemporary world. Though he is perhaps best known for his geodesic dome design, this architect and thinker encouraged a new global outlook combining ecology and technology. Morley Safer narrates while Spalding Gray reads Fuller's writings. Includes interviews with Paul Goldberger, Philip Johnson, John Cage, Merce Cunningham, Arthur Penn and others.
VHS: $27909. $39.95.
Karen Goodman/Kirk Simon, USA, 1995, 94 mins.

Burden of Dreams
Fascinating, chilling account of the making of Werner Herzog's *Fitzcarraldo*, a project beset by a series of disasters while shooting in the jungle. Filmmaker Les Blank has made a compelling film about obsessed genius and the creative process.
VHS: S00190. $59.95.
Les Blank, USA, 1982, 94 mins.

Carmen Miranda: Bananas Is My Business
Archival footage, film clips, dramatic re-enactments and interviews document the life story and the lasting influence of the Brazilian Bombshell. This fun and interesting film won Best Documentary at the Chicago International Film Festival and the Film Critic's Award at the Brazilian Film Festival. English and Portuguese with English subtitles.
VHS: S27627. $19.98.
Helena Solberg, USA/Great Britain, 1995, 90 mins.

Chameleon Cameraman (Changing Roles)
Henry von Javorsky, Jewish cameraman of the Third Reich, learned to survive by changing roles, working first in Nazi Germany, then for the Soviets in Berlin, and then for the Allies. Saved by his camera, Javorsky made films with Leni Riefenstahl and Luis Trenker, aerial shots for war movies like *Pour le merite*, Cologne in flames in 1944, and Soviet newsreel coverage of the trial of the Sachsenhausen concentration camp war criminals. He moved to America in 1952, where he made industrial films for Volkswagen and won an Academy Award for his short film about breaking the on-water speed record. English voice-over.
VHS: S32069. $29.95.
Jurgen Stumphaus, Germany, 1994, 63 mins.

Buckminster Fuller: Thinking Out Loud

Artists & Models

Andrei Rublev
VHS: S16526. $19.98.
Laser: LD72435. $99.95.

Basquiat
VHS: S30822. $103.99.
Laser: LD76102. $39.99.

Camille Claudel
VHS: S12987. $19.98.
Laser: LD70900. $49.95.

Caravaggio
VHS: S06024. $79.95.

La Belle Noiseuse

Edvard Munch
VHS: S20594. $29.95.

I Shot Andy Warhol
VHS: S29783. $19.98.
Laser: LD76039. $39.98.

La Belle Noiseuse
VHS: S20304. $89.95.

Lust for Life
VHS: S11218. $19.95.
Laser: LD70618. $39.98.

The Cross and the Star
Subtitled *Jews, Christians and the Holocaust*, John Michalczyk's documentary interweaves archival footage of Nazi Germany, propaganda films, television shows, and contemporary interviews to make a connection between the death camps, Nazi Nuremberg laws and the possible complicity and collaboration of the institutional churches and orders of the Catholic and Protestant leaders. A former Jesuit priest, Michalczyk considers the Gospel of St. John, the sermons of St. Augustine, and the writings of Martin Luther to trace the evolution of anti-Semitism. 55 mins.
VHS: S17102. $29.95.

Crumb
Robert Crumb, the multi-talented underground comic book artist, is profiled in this unique, in-depth documentary portrait. Emerging from a dysfunctional family, it's a wonder that Crumb managed to channel his peculiar take on the world into a relatively socially acceptable form. Part of the great fascination of this film is the revelation that his brothers, both also quite gifted, were not as lucky.
VHS: S27253. $19.95.
Laser: LD75491. $39.95.
Terry Zwigoff, USA, 1995, 119 mins.

David Holzman's Diary
Jim McBride's seminal underground film is an autocritique about a young filmmaker (screenwriter L.M. Kit Carson) who makes an autobiographical, cinema verite film. It is a film about identity and self-obsession. With Penny Wohl, Louise Levine and Fern McBride. Selected by the National Film Registry as an American Film Classic.
VHS: S18862. $19.98.
Jim McBride, USA, 1967, 74 mins.

Deadly Currents
"The best film I've ever seen on the Middle East" (*Toronto Star*)—a thoughtful documentary about the Israeli-Palestinian conflict which goes far beyond stereotypes to create an amazing portrait of societies at war. *Deadly Currents* delves deeply into the hearts and minds of the men and women behind the rock-throwing mobs, vigilante posses and political figureheads. Arabic and Hebrew with English voice-over and subtitles.
VHS: S27201. $89.95.
Simcha Jacobovici, Canada, 1992, 115 mins.

Documentary Masterpieces by John Grierson
John Grierson revolutionized the ideas, grammar and shape of the documentary, and this program collects five works he either directed, produced or supervised, from the years 1931 to 1960, beginning with Flaherty's *Industrial Britain*, Len Lye's *Color Box*, *Granton Trawler*, Julien Huxley's *The Private Life of the Gannetts*, and Hilary Harris's *Seawards the Great Ships*. 75 minutes.
VHS: S17453. $29.95.

Don't Look Back
One of the best portraits of an artist ever put on film, *Don't Look Back* is about Bob Dylan and the Sixties. Director Pennebaker, known for *Monterey Pop*, filmed Dylan during his 1965 English concert tour, capturing both private moments and public performances. With Joan Baez, Alan Price, Donovan.
VHS: S00357. $19.98.
D.A. Pennebaker, USA, 1967, 95 mins.

Fire on the Mountain
"Among the best documentaries about skiing ever filmed" (*Snow Country Magazine*), this is the extraordinary portrait of the men of the U.S. Army's 10th Mountain Division—world-class skiers, mountaineers and climbers who share their exploits in the only mountain and winter warfare division of World War II. Grand Prize winner at the 1995 Telluride Mountainfilm Festival. "Bracing exploits, hearty outdoorsmen, powerfully captured on film" (*New York Times*).
VHS: S31119. $29.95.
Beth Gage/George Gage, USA, 1996, 72 mins.

Four Hours a Year: The March of Time
The March of Time newsreel series covered the news before the advent of television. Topics include reporting styles, logistical difficulties with 35mm cameras and big lights, the use of reenactments, the difference between the "truth of yesterday and the truth of today and how truth in film is perishable"; reflections on "the natural look," work without zooms or panning; flat lighting, wide angle lens and distortions; and *The March of Time*'s influence on today's television journalism. Many famous excerpts from the series, including Father Coughlin, the Ku Klux Klan, New York's Mayor LaGuardia, Huey Long in Louisiana, 1938 Maginot Line, a 1934 speakeasy raid, New England in 1940 and American youth. 1974, 60 mins.
VHS: S31605. $59.95.

Francois Truffaut: Stolen Portraits
A brilliant documentary which provides new insights and revelations. Full of extensive clips and in-depth interviews with dozens of Truffaut's collaborators and friends, including Gerard Depardieu, Eric Rohmer, Marcel Ophuls, Claude Chabrol, Jacques Rivette, Truffaut's daughter and Truffaut's former wife, Madeleine Morgenstern, this remarkable film shines new light on the psychological motivations of Truffaut's life and on his filmmaking career. French with English subtitles.
VHS: S26965. $19.98.
Serge Toubiana/Michel Pascal, France, 1993, 93 mins.

The Good Fight
It was one of history's most dramatic expressions of international solidarity when 40,000 volunteers from around the world went to fight the armies of Franco, Hitler and Mussolini in the Spanish Civil War of 1936-39. *The Good Fight* tells the story of 3,200 Americans who volunteered to fight on the side of the Spanish Republic. This vivid series of portraits with 12 of the survivors (half the Americans lost their lives in Spain) brings to life the reasons for joining the foreign conflict, and what it was to be a part of a people's army against fascism in the war that was the rehearsal for World War II. An absorbing and passionate account full of humor, pride and deep sorrow, their interviews are illustrated with rare archival footage of the Lincoln Brigade in Spain as well as Hollywood films, songs and newsreels with such notables as Hemingway himself and Henry Fonda. Narrated by Studs Terkel.
VHS: S12206. $69.95.
Buckner/Dore/Stills, USA, 1984, 98 mins.

Grey Gardens
An eccentric mother and daughter are hidden away in a decaying East Hampton mansion; the mother is Edith Bouvier Beale, the daughter, Edie—aunt and

cousin of Jacqueline Bouvier Kennedy. Called "hilarious, horrifying and tragic," and "as compelling a drama as Tennessee Williams might hope to achieve," *Grey Gardens* is a funny, moving descent into American classic decay.
VHS: S07438. $79.95.
Maysles Brothers, USA, 1976, 94 mins.

Harlan County U.S.A.
The Academy Award-winning documentary about the efforts of 180 coal-mining families to win a United Mine Workers contract at the Brookside mine in Harlan County, Kentucky, is a fascinating and moving portrait of the valor and courage of the coal-mining families.
VHS: S00542. $29.95.
Barbara Kopple, USA, 1976, 103 mins.

Havana Nagila: The Jews in Cuba
This eye-opening video traces the history and presence of the remaining Jewish community in Cuba. After the 1959 Revolution, 95% of the Cuban Jewish community fled the country. Rich in archival material and Cuban ambience, with fascinating firsthand interviews, we are presented a side of Cuba that has never been seen before. The artful use of Cuban and Jewish music, painting, photography and oral history gives voice to a nearly forgotten community, whose members share a growing national sentiment, that a bridge to Cuba must be built at any cost.
VHS: S30530. $39.95.
Laura Paull, USA/Israel, 60 mins.

Hearts of Darkness: A Filmmaker's Apocalypse
A riveting behind-the-scenes look at the making of Francis Ford Coppola's *Apocalypse Now*. The film combines interviews with documentary footage shot on location in the Philippines by Eleanor Coppola. This is a must-see for anyone with the slightest interest in how Hollywood movies get made. With Martin Sheen, Dennis Hopper, Larry Fishburne, Robert Duvall, Sam Bottoms, Frederic Forrest, George Lucas, John Milius and Francis Ford Coppola. Watch Marlon Brando improvise his lines and eat a bug.
VHS: S16459. $19.95.
Fax Bahr/George Hickenlooper, USA, 1991, 96 mins.

The Hemp Revolution
Hemp, or marijuana, is not just a mild recreational drug. Long before it became notorious for its mind-altering qualities, it was widely grown for its resilient fibers and was used for everything from industrial strength rope to fine cloth. This documentary makes the case that growing hemp is a sound ecological enterprise with very pleasant side effects.
VHS: S29800. $29.95.
Anthony Clark, USA, 1995, 72 mins.

Herdsmen of the Sun
Herzog's fascination with the natural world at its most enduringly strange led him to the southern Sahara for *Herdsmen of the Sun*, "a startling anthropological documentary about the nomadic members of the Wodaabe Tribe" (Janet Maslin). Once a year, the men decorate themselves with beads and blue lipstick and festive hats to participate in what amounts to a beauty pageant. French, English and Peul with English subtitles.
VHS: S16054. $59.95.
Werner Herzog, Germany, 1988, 52 mins.

Hotel Terminus:
The Life and Times of Klaus Barbie
Marcel Ophuls' award-winning documentary spans 70 years and three continents. Culled from 120 hours of interviews, it traces the 40-year-manhunt for Nazi war criminal Klaus Barbie, the ruthless SS interrogator known as "The Butcher of Lyon." "A shocking, unforgettable film" (Ebert and Siskel). Winner of the Academy Award for Best Documentary and the International Critics Prize at the Cannes Film Festival. Original English-language version (includes French, German and Spanish footage subtitled in English). 2 cassettes.
VHS: S10756. $29.98.
Marcel Ophuls, France/USA, 1988, 267 mins.

I Was Stalin's Bodyguard
A controversial film that created a storm in Russia by taking the cloak off a violent, repressive era of Soviet history. Filmmaker Semeon Aranovitch found the last surviving personal bodyguard of Josef Stalin, who began to work for him in the 1930s. *I Was Stalin's Bodyguard* weaves together unprecedented, first-hand testimony with rare footage, including Stalin's home movies. What emerges is a singular portrait of a violent and complex era during which Stalin consolidated his power through brutal repression, yet lead the Soviet Union to victory in World War II. Russian with English subtitles.
VHS: S13312. $29.95.
Semeon Aranovitch, USSR, 1990, 73 mins.

I Worked for Stalin
Semeon Aranovich's documentary is a brilliant assembly of eyewitness testimony and rare archival photographs and materials. The film records the Machiavellian power plays between Zhdanov, Andreyev, Khrushchev, Malenkov, Suslov and Molotov as they maneuvered for power and prestige to gain the inside track of becoming Stalin's successor. The film is a chilling record of the inner workings of an authoritarian state. Russian with English subtitles.
VHS: S18686. $29.95.
Semeon Aranovitch, USSR, 1990, 67 mins.

In the Land of the Deaf
A unique and privileged look inside the world of deaf people. A teacher, a woman treated for mental illness

Crumb

because of her deafness, and a newly wed deaf couple offer compelling portraits from a community estimated to comprise 130 million people worldwide in a film which is revealing, moving and often funny. French and French Sign Language with English subtitles.
VHS: $25993. $79.95.
Nicolas Philibert, France, 1994, 99 mins.

In the Land of the War Canoes
Edward S. Curtis devoted his life to documenting the world of dwindling Native American cultures. In this film, Curtis told a story of love and revenge among the Kwakiutl Indians of Vancouver Island. Curtis spent three years with the Kwakiutl to meticulously recreate their way of life before the white man came. In addition to the magnificent painted war canoes, the film pictures authentic costumes, ceremonial dances and religious rituals. Silent with soundtrack from 1972 restoration.
VHS: $16431. $39.95.
Laser: LD71816. $29.95.
Edward S. Curtis, USA/Canada, 1914, 47 mins.

International Sweethearts of Rhythm/ Tiny & Ruby: Hell-Divin' Women
These two films from award-winning filmmakers Greta Schiller (*Before Stonewall, Paris with a Woman*) and Andrea Weiss tell the swinging story of America's hottest, multi-racial, all-woman jazz band of the 1940s, The International Sweethearts of Rhythm, featuring Tiny Davis and her partner of over 40 years, drummer-pianist Ruby Lucas. Using rare jazz recordings, live performances and vintage photographs, the film follows the amazing journey of these groundbreaking women from the 1940s to the present.
VHS: $32240. $29.95.
Greta Schiller/Andrea Weiss, USA, 1986, 70 mins.

Joseph Beuys, Public Dialogues
Famous performance artist Beuys is seen in his first public appearance in the U.S. in this video. He outlines his political and artistic philosophies.
VHS: $22654. $49.95.
Willoughby Sharp, USA, 1974, 120 mins.

Ken Burns' America
These seven films earned documentary filmmaker Ken Burns (*The Civil War, Baseball*) universal acclaim and over 100 awards, including Academy Award nominations and Emmy awards.
The Complete Set
VHS: $27732. $89.95.
Ken Burns, USA, 1996, 558 mins.

Kon-Tiki
On April 28, 1947, to the ridicule of the scientific establishment, Norwegian biologist Thor Heyerdahl and his five crew members embarked on a 4,300 mile expedition across the Pacific Ocean from Peru to Polynesia by raft in an attempt to duplicate the legendary voyage of an ancient race of settlers led by the mythical hero Kon-Tiki. Hailed as one of the most fantastic feats of daring and courage of its time, the expedition attracted worldwide interest. This exciting release celebrates the 50-year anniversary of the legendary voyage which was documented in Heyerdahl's classic book and recorded in this astonishing, Academy Award-winning, black-and-white film.
VHS: $31014. $24.95.
Thor Heyerdahl, Sweden, 1951, 58 mins.

Last Pullman Car
More than 100 years ago, George Pullman, one of the giants of American industry, built a vast industrial empire. It was supposed to last forever. Yet in 1981, Pullman workers found themselves in the midst of a fight not only for their jobs but the future of the American rail car industry. In this engaging story, 100 years of government, union and corporate policy are traced.
VHS: $27804. $29.95.
Kartemquin Films, USA, 1983, 56 mins.

Let There Be Light
Documentary commissioned by the U.S. War Department on the psychiatric treatment of shell-shocked World War II veterans. The film was confiscated upon completion and banned until 1980 in the fear that it would discourage recruitment. Deeply humanitarian and pacifist.
VHS: $00749. $29.95.
John Huston, USA, 1945, 60 mins.

Fire on the Mountain

On the Road Again

Death Race 2000
VHS: S28609. $14.98.

Easy Rider
VHS: S01821. $19.95.
Laser: LD75091. $59.95.

Five Easy Pieces
VHS: S07789. $14.95.
Laser: LD70981. $34.95.

Flirting with Disaster
VHS: S30829. $103.99.
Laser: LD76100. $39.99.

Grand Prix
VHS: S03630. $24.98.
Laser: LD70591. $39.97.

Highway Patrolman
VHS: S31627. $89.95.

The Last Detail
VHS: S02173. $14.95.
Laser: LD75089. $34.95.

Lost in America
VHS: S02546. $19.98.
Laser: LD74708. $34.98.

Powwow Highway
VHS: S30826. $14.98.

The Road to Morocco
VHS: S17245. $14.98.

Road Warrior
DVD: DV60054. $24.98.
VHS: S01801. $14.95.
Laser: LD70739. $29.98.

Sullivan's Travels
VHS: S08507. $29.95.
Laser: LD70084. $34.98.

True Romance
VHS: S19941. $19.98.
Laser: LD72251. $39.98.

Two for the Road
VHS: S18102. $19.98.

Vagabond
VHS: S02982. $24.95.

The Lost Children of Berlin
In April 1942, the Gestapo closed the last Jewish school in Berlin. Half a century later, 50 of its former students travelled from around the world to the re-opened school for an extraordinary reunion. *The Lost Children of Berlin* weaves together a portrait of the social and political landscape of pre-war Berlin, detailing its rich Jewish life that existed there. Hosted by Anthony Hopkins, with testimonies compiled by Steven Spielberg's Shoah Foundation. 50 mins.
VHS: S32370. $19.95.

Louisiana Story
The last film of the famous father of the documentary, the story of a new oil derrick and its effect upon the Louisiana Bayou country, the boy and his raccoon. With music by Virgil Thompson.
VHS: S00771. $29.95.
Robert Flaherty, USA, 1948, 79 mins.

Man of Aran
One of the masterworks of Robert Flaherty, in which Flaherty's "passionate devotion to the portrayal of human gesture and of a man's fight for his family makes the film an incomparable account of human dignity" (Georges Sadoul). Filmed on the island of Inishmore, it depicts the daily life of people on this isolated island off the coast of Ireland, fishing in their tiny curraghs, the difficulty of their existence, the hunting of a basking shark. A masterpiece.
VHS: S09417. $29.95.
Robert Flaherty, Great Britain, 1934, 76 mins.

Manufacturing Consent:
Noam Chomsky and the Media
This remarkable Canadian documentary is a riveting look at the political life and times of the controversial author, linguist and radical philosopher, Noam Chomsky. Chomsky provides shocking examples of media deception as he analyzes the media and democratic societies. A film which has achieved cult status in its remarkable call to Chomsky's charge for viewers to "extricate themselves from this web of deceit by undertaking a course of intellectual self-defense."
VHS: S21851. $39.95.
Mark Achbar/Peter Wintonick, Canada, 1993, 180 mins.

Martha & Ethel
Two invincible, 80-year-old nannies offer a portrait of American life in this documentary. Spanning four decades and crossing the barriers of race, class and sex, this film reveals the heart of the American family. *Martha & Ethel* celebrates the extraordinary legacies of love and discipline these women have created, as seen through the eyes of the filmmaker, who herself was brought up by one of the two nannies profiled.
VHS: S26919. $96.99.
Laser: LD75402. $39.98.
Jyll Johnstone, USA, 1994, 80 mins.

Maya Lin: A Strong Clear Vision
The story of the artist/sculptor/architect who, while an undergraduate at Yale, designed one of the most bitterly debated public monuments, the Vietnam Veterans Memorial. The film follows her throughout the creative process as she produces a succession of eloquent, highly original sculptures and monuments that capture and memorialize significant American social events. Compelling viewing. "The film is absolutely riveting" (Peter Stack, *San Francisco Chronicle*).
VHS: S30482. $59.95.
Freida Lee Mock, USA, 1995, 96 mins.

The Maysles Brothers: Direct Cinema
In this 1969 documentary writer-editor Jack Kroll interviews filmmakers Albert and David Maysles about what they called a "new technique of natural movie making, Direct Cinema." Program includes excerpts from their feature-length film *The Salesman*, about door-to-door sales of *The Bible* to working people in Boston. The Maysles formed a two-man crew and followed the salesmen around in an early example of "cinema verite." They discuss their techniques, the purpose of working in their verite style, getting the subjects to agree to being documented, and their rejection of the idea that they are reformers. 60 mins.
VHS: S31565. $59.95.

Mein Krieg (My Private War)
An eerie compilation of home movies and oral histories of six Wehrmacht soldiers who were involved in the Nazi invasion of the former Soviet Union. The images of the war (soldiers swimming in the Black Sea, bombed out landscapes and literally thousands of dead bodies) are contrasted with the soldiers' memories and reminiscences of their experiences. "*Mein Krieg* is annotated only by the veterans themselves as they explicate the material they produced nearly a half-century before" (J. Hoberman, *The Village Voice*).
VHS: S19859. $79.95.
Harriet Eder/Thomas Kufus, Germany, 1990, 90 mins.

Moana, A Romance of the Golden Age
A great film by Robert Flaherty which followed the success of *Nanook of the North*. Flaherty chose the Samoan cultural tradition; he lived for two years on the islands, with the story gradually evolving out of the lives of the native population. Includes the famous sequences of the tattooing of Moana, a part of the initiation into manhood, and dancing the Shiva before a village virgin. An "intensely lyrical poem on the theme of the last paradise" (Herman Weinberg). Silent with music score.
VHS: S07486. $29.95.
Robert Flaherty, USA, 1926, 76 mins.

Music for the Movies:
Bernard Herrmann
This documentary was nominated for an Academy Award because it so successfully illustrates the importance of music to the movies. Herrmann worked on over 50 films during his career, including the legendary *Citizen Kane*. Though most widely known for his work with Hitchcock on films like *The Man Who Knew Too Much* and *Psycho*, he also collaborated with other great directors, such as Martin Scorsese on *Taxi Driver*. Includes clips from these and other films.
VHS: S26668. $24.98.
Laser: LD75108. $24.98.
Josh Waletzky, USA, 1992, 58 mins.

Rich & Famous/
Poor & Infamous

**Aileen Wuornos: The
Selling of a Serial Killer**
VHS: S23288. $19.98.

Badlands
VHS: S00086. $19.98.
Laser: LD70513. $34.98.

Brother's Keeper
VHS: S18959. $19.98.
Laser: LD74472. $39.95.

Dancing Outlaw
VHS: S21882. $49.95.

Grand Hotel
VHS: S00523. $19.95.

I Shot Andy Warhol
VHS: S29783. $19.98.
Laser: LD76039. $39.98.

Melvin and Howard
VHS: S00846. $14.95.

My Man Godfrey
VHS: S18178. $19.95.

Paradise Lost
VHS: S31169. $59.98.

Reversal of Fortune
VHS: S13923. $19.95.

Six Degrees of Separation
VHS: S21032. $19.98.
Laser: LD72407. $34.98.

Star 80
VHS: S04181. $19.98.
Laser: LD74716. $34.98.

Music for the Movies:
Georges Delerue
Though remembered for his work on French New
Wave films like *Shoot the Piano Player* and *Jules and
Jim*, Delerue also worked in Hollywood on films such
as *Silkwood* and *Steel Magnolias*. This documentary
charts Delerue's career with clips from these films
and interviews with Oliver Stone and Ken Russell. 60
mins.
VHS: S26667. $24.98.
Laser: LD75110. $24.98.

My Prague Spring
This documentary was filmed in Prague shortly after
the fall of Communism. It examines the effects of
this historic transformation through the eyes of a
young American of Czech descent and his Czech
relations, as they come to terms with the values of
capitalism. English and Czech with English subtitles.
VHS: S20733. $89.95.
David Mrazek, USA, 1993, 81 mins.

Nagasaki Journey
This compelling production portrays the aftermath of
the atomic bomb dropped on the city of Nagasaki
from both an American and Japanese perspective, and
presents moving personal stories from two Japanese
survivors and eyewitness recollections from U.S.
Marines. Includes never-before-seen color footage
shot during the occupation by Marine
cinematographers, as well as striking black-and-white
still photos taken the day after the blast by Japanese
Army photographer Yosuke Yamahata. 27 mins.
VHS: S30092. $95.00.

Nanook of the North
The classic documentary of the daily life and
hardships of an Eskimo family, still considered
superb filmmaking and a landmark. Music score by
Stanley Silverman, performed by the Tashi Ensemble
and conducted by Peter Serkin. Silent.
VHS: S00916. $29.95.
Robert Flaherty, USA, 1922, 55 mins.

Notebook on Cities and Clothes
A provocative documentary by Wim Wenders about
high fashion designer Yohji Yamamoto. The film is
frequently a passionate and compelling essay about a
time (Paris), architecture, language and the creative
process. Made during the editing of Wenders' epic
Until the End of the World. Shot by several
cameramen, including Wenders' usual collaborator
Robby Muller. Japanese, German, French and English
with English subtitles.
VHS: S18192. $59.95.
Wim Wenders, France, 1990, 80 mins.

Paradise Lost
Called "true crime reporting at its most bitterly
revealing" by *The New York Times*, this gripping
documentary from the makers of *Brother's Keeper* is
the true story of the brutal slaying of three eight-year-
old boys and the investigation that leads to the arrest
and trial of three teenagers whose only crime seems
to be that they dress in black and listen to heavy
metal music. The families, the townspeople and the
accused all clash in their efforts to see that justice is
served.
VHS: S31169. $59.98.
**Joe Berlinger/Bruce Sinofsky, USA, 1996,
150 mins.**

Paradjanov: A Requiem
Features extensive interviews and scenes from the
films of the late Sergei Paradjanov, one of the most
controversial and stylistically daring filmmakers of
our time. Paradjanov talks about his films and his
imprisonment at the hands of Soviet authorities.
VHS: S30708. $29.95.
Ron Holloway, 1994, 57 mins.

Paul Bowles: The Complete Outsider
Author of the *The Sheltering Sky*, Paul Bowles
reveals all in this intimate portrait. Though he was
married to the acclaimed writer Jane Bowles, both he
and his wife had numerous homosexual affairs. An
icon of the Beat Generation, Paul Bowles has
inspired many with his disregard for conventional
morality, including William Burroughs, who is said to
have based *The Naked Lunch* on this iconoclastic
inhabitant of Morocco.
VHS: S25720. $29.95.
**Catherine Warnow/Regina Weinreich, 1993,
57 mins.**

People's Gala Concert
A landmark documentary; Semeon Aranovitch
explores the roots of Russian anti-Semitism during
Stalin's final years, set around the murder of the
brilliant actor Solomon Mikhoels and the case of a
group of Russian doctors charged with attempting to
poison Stalin. Aranovitch draws on rare archival
footage and interviews with survivors and their
descendants to relate this untold history. Russian with
English subtitles.
VHS: S15824. $79.95.
Semeon Aranovitch, Russia, 1991, 143 mins.

Pretty as a Picture:
The Art of David Lynch
A rare and personal look at one of the most prolific
directors of our time, what inspired him as a youth,
his comments on his first films and his life-long quest
for creative expression. 80 mins.
VHS: S32179. $19.98.

Quiet One
A classic documentary-drama, winner of awards at
Venice and Edinburgh, and one of the most
penetrating studies of juvenile delinquency ever
filmed. The film is the story of a black youth who
grows up in Harlem without the love of his parents,
and, rejected, falls into delinquency. Sidney Meyers,
the director, was apparently influenced by Italian neo-
realism and the commentary, written by James Agee,
is spoken by Gary Merrill. "A most moving,
important and memorable film" (Paul Rotha).
VHS: S06879. $39.95.
Sidney Meyers/Janet Loeb, USA, 1948, 67 mins.

Realms of the Russian Bear
A remarkable television series produced by the BBC
in the advent of perestroika, winner of the Sierra
Club Centennial Award and several Emmy awards—
an unprecedented look at nature and wildlife inside

the vast expanses of Russia.
Realms of the Russian Bear, Six-Volume Set.
Approximately 6 hours.
VHS: $22998. $179.98.

The River and
The Plow That Broke the Plains

Two important works in the development of the
documentary: *The River*, done in 1937, produced by
the Farm Security Administration about the
Mississippi, and *The Plow that Broke the Plains*,
from 1936, about the New Deal's efforts to assist
farmers hit by the Dust Bowl in Oklahoma.
VHS: S01121. $39.95.
Pare Lorentz, USA, 1937

Roger & Me

The funniest movie you will ever see about thousands
of people losing their jobs. Journalist Michael Moore
turns a jaundiced eye on the closing of several
General Motors plants in his hometown of Flint,
Michigan. He also attempts to have a face-to-face
confrontation with GM president Roger Smith. This
non-fiction film uses humor and creative license to
bring attention to a serious display of corporate
indifference. With Anita Bryant, Pat Boone, Ronald
Reagan and Flint native Bob Eubanks.
VHS: S12231. $19.98.
Laser: LD70667. $24.98.
Michael Moore, USA, 1989, 91 mins.

Salesman

Albert and David Maysles' landmark documentary
focuses on a quartet of Bible salesmen and the hopes
and frustrations of one man in particular: Paul
Brennan. Labeled as "brutally honest," "funny and
touching," and "a great insight into America,"
Salesman is a key work of the American documentary
cinema.
VHS: S07491. $79.95.
Maysles Brothers, USA, 1968, 85 mins.

Say Amen, Somebody

A joy-filled celebration of Gospel music! "It's one of
the happiest movies in a long, long time. There is no
way that I can recommend it any more highly," said
Roger Ebert.
VHS: S01162. $29.95.
George Nierenberg, USA, 1983, 100 mins.

Seeing Red

A powerful documentary by Julia Reichert and Jim
Klein that assesses the cultural, political, social and
personal evolution of members of the American
Communist Party. The film moves from the idealistic
fervor and radical intensity of 30s Depression-era
humanism to the harsh persecution of ideas during
McCarthy-ism and the onset of the Cold War. The
documentary is a deft merging of faces and
personalities, from the known to the unknown. It
captures their pain, triumph, hurt and redemption.
The film also considers the disillusionment following
the revelations of Stalin's tyranny and looks at the
political exploitation of anti-communist hysteria from
J. Edgar Hoover, Richard Nixon and Ronald Reagan.
"The film is less about dogma than about American
idealism" (Vincent Canby).
VHS: S19234. $29.95.
Julia Reichert/Jim Klein, USA, 1983, 100 mins.

Sex Is Sex

This remarkable film containing frank and
compelling conversations with male prostitutes
breaks through common cliches about prostitution to
reveal a world more complex and compelling than
popular perception permits. Neither desperately tragic
nor overly romanticized, this film presents young
New York hustlers telling what they know, whether it
be the secret to faking sex, the dangers of crazy
tricks, or just the pleasure of easy money. "A
remarkable look at a world unseen by the average
person…not to be missed" (*The New York Times*).
VHS: S30933. $39.95.
Jennifer Milici/Brian Bergen, USA, 1994, 50 mins.

Sherman's March

Consistently named on ten best lists all over the
country,—"uproarious…it'll put you in a pleased
delirium and leave you with a happy daze," (*San
Francisco Examiner*); "If Woody Allen made *Gone
with the Wind*, it might resemble *Sherman's March!*"
(*People Magazine*). The subtitle of the film promises
"A Documentary Meditation upon the Possibilities of
Romantic Love in the South during an Era of Nuclear
Weapons Proliferation," and director Ross McElwee
delivers an engaging nonfiction journey through the
South in a picaresque tour of contemporary

relationships.
VHS: S10929. $29.95.
Ross McElwee, USA, 1985, 155 mins.

Sorrow and the Pity

Marcel Ophuls' monumental documentary covering
the German occupation of France during World War
II. Through poignant interviews and stark newsreel
footage, Ophuls creates a sense of living history. "A
magnificent epic on the themes of collaboration and
resistance. There's nothing comparable to [it]"
(Pauline Kael). English dubbed.
VHS: S01233. $59.95.
Marcel Ophuls, France, 1972, 260 mins.

Superstar: The Life and Times
of Andy Warhol

This is no ordinary documentary. Its subject is one of
the most controversial artists of our time, a man who
made celebrity an art form. *Superstar* traces Warhol's
career from his beginnings as a commercial artist to
his jaw-dropping appearance on *The Love Boat* (a
brief clip that is alone worth the price of the video).
Was Warhol a great artist or a master hypester? In all
the postures and roles he assumed, which was the real
Warhol? An ambitious film that endeavors to answer
the myriad of questions surrounding the man and the
myth. USA, 1991.
VHS: S15135. $14.98.

Survivors

This film presents a remarkable portrait of Japanese-
American survivors caught in the atomic bombings of
Hiroshima and Nagasaki, as they describe what they
saw and felt when the bombs dropped. Also profiled
are Americans who face a range of physical,
psychological and social problems, corroborated in
the video by doctors at the U.S. Public Health Service
and Yale University.
"Strong…affecting…unsentimental…It's a film every
American should see" (*National Catholic News*). 35
mins.
VHS: S30094. $89.00.

Theremin: An Electronic Odyssey

Tabu

Filmed entirely in Tahiti, *Tabu* represents an unusual
collaboration between legendary directors F.W.
Murnau and Robert Flaherty. Combining Flaherty's
poetic sense of the native people with Murnau's
strong filmic sensibilities, the film tells the story of
two lovers doomed by a tribal edict decreeing the
beautiful princess as "tabu" to all men. "Murnau is
one of the great masters. The beautiful restoration of
Tabu will enable future generations to enjoy and
appreciate his inspiring talent" (Martin Scorsese).
Silent with music track.
VHS: S03712. $39.95.
Laser: CLV/CAV. LD71591. $34.95.
**Friedrich W. Murnau/Robert Flaherty, USA, 1931,
82 mins.**

Theremin: An Electronic Odyssey

A cross between Albert Einstein and Ed Wood, Leon
Theremin pioneered the electronic music revolution
four decades before the rise of Electronic Rock. His
invention, the Theremin, produced an eerie, warbling
sound, and was used on many Hollywood sound
tracks, including *Spellbound*, *The Day the Earth
Stood Still* and *The Lost Weekend*, and by rock
legends Brian Wilson and Todd Rundgren. At the
height of his popularity, Theremin was kidnapped by
Soviet agents and forced to develop spy technology
for Stalin's KGB. Janet Maslin (*The New York Times*)
calls it "fascinating," and it is. Winner at the

Cold War / Red Menace

Death of a Bureaucrat
VHS: S13916. $59.95.

The Front
VHS: S02021. $19.98.

Guilty by Suspicion
VHS: S15008. $19.98.

Hollywood on Trial
VHS: S09422. $29.95.

Ipcress File
VHS: S02944. $14.98.

The Manchurian Candidate
VHS: S07005. $19.98.
Laser: LD70624. $59.98.

Mother Kusters Goes to Heaven
VHS: S16695. $29.95.

On the Beach
VHS: S02557. $19.98.

Pick Up on South Street
VHS: S13608. $19.98.

The Red Menace
VHS: S14320. $19.98.
Laser: LD72021. $29.98.

Spy Who Came in from the Cold
VHS: S07520. $19.95.
Laser: LD75263. $34.98.

When Father Was Away on Business
VHS: S15547. $19.98.
Laser: LD72198. $49.95.

Sundance and San Francisco Film Festivals.
VHS: S27436. $19.98.
Laser: LD75505. $39.99.
Steven M. Martin, USA/Great Britain, 1995, 84 mins.

They Risked Their Lives: Rescuers of the Holocaust
From 1986-1988 Gay Block and Malka Drucker interviewed and photographed more than 100 Gentile Holocaust rescuers who defied the Nazis to shield Jews during the war. Block's video chronicles the passionate and heroic acts of these brave men and women, their selfless courage and manifest honor. 54 mins.
VHS: S17941. $39.95.

Tigrero: A Film That Was Never Made
In 1954, armed with a 16mm camera, film, two cases of vodka and 75 boxes of cigars, director Sam Fuller went to Brazil scouting locations for the action-adventure film *Tigrero*. Although this Darryl F. Zanuck production was cast with John Wayne, Ava Gardner and Tyrone Power, the film was never shot because of insurance problems. All that remains of *Tigrero* is Fuller's intriguing footage of the Karaja tribe and their Amazon Rain Forest home. Forty years later, director Mika Kaurismaki ventures back to this location with Fuller and director Jim Jarmusch to talk with the Karaja about the changing world, talk amongst themselves about Fuller's films and the principles of filmmaking, and tell the story of the film that was never made. This film won the International Critics Award at the 1994 Berlin Film Festival.
VHS: S27618. $89.95.
Mika Kaurismaki, Finland/Germany/Brazil, 1994, 75 mins.

Trinity and Beyond: The Atomic Bomb Movie
Narrated by William Shatner, this award-winning, "factually solid, visually stunning, informative

documentary" (*Daily Variety*) uses rare archival footage, interviews with scientists and still photos to trace the history of nuclear weapons, from The Manhattan Project of the 1940s to the signing of the Nuclear Test Ban Treaty in 1963.
VHS: S31771. $24.95.
Peter Kuran, USA, 1995, 95 mins.

The Unquiet Death of Julius and Ethel Rosenberg
On June 19, 1953, Julius and Ethel Rosenberg, the so-called "atomic spies" of the 1950s, were executed at Sing Sing Prison. Their death only fostered the belief of many Americans that the Rosenbergs were innocent, victims of the anti-Communist paranoia of the 50s, rather than spies who had stolen atomic secrets for the Russians. In his landmark documentary *The Unquiet Death of Julius and Ethel Rosenberg*, Alvin Goldstein looks at the facts and procedures of the Rosenberg case, as well as the climate of the times, interviewing jurors, FBI agents, lawyers for both sides, and the two sons of the Rosenbergs. Using documentary and newsreel footage, Goldstein creates a moving human drama, a "thoroughly researched, solidly developed...superb recreation of history, painting with bold strokes the temper of the times" (*Boston Globe*).
VHS: S04736. $59.95.
Alvin Goldstein, USA, 1974, 83 mins.

Unzipped
Isaac Mizrahi, the New York-based fashion designer, is the central subject of this frothy and humorous documentary. This surprisingly intimate film was directed by Mizrahi's former boyfriend. (They broke up during the editing.) It begins with a depressed Mizrahi contemplating his poorly received Spring 1994 collection and ends with the creation of his Fall collection. Along with supermodels Kate Moss, Cindy Crawford, Linda Evangelista and Naomi Campbell, Mizrahi provides witty insights into the world of fashion and artifice.
VHS: S26999. $99.99.
Laser: LD75453. $39.95.
Douglas Keeve, USA, 1995, 73 mins.

Visions of Light
Cinematography is the art on which all motion pictures are based. In this documentary over 125 unforgettable films are used to tell the story of this evolving art form. This 1993 winner of the New York Film Critics Circle Award will transfix cinephiles with the glory of motion picture photography.
VHS: S20742. $94.98.
Laser: LD71986. $39.99.
Arnold Glassman, USA, 1993, 95 mins.

The War Room
Inside the campaign of President Bill Clinton a new telegenic, electoral style was developed that would appeal to a TV-saturated public. D.A. Pennebaker, the acclaimed documentary maker who covered the 1962 campaigns of Kennedy and McGovern, brings his insight to this presidential hopeful, uncovering that most enduring of American traditions, a sophisticated political machine.
VHS: S20840. $14.95.
Chris Hegedus/D.A. Pennebaker, USA, 1993, 96 mins.

War Stories Our Mothers Never Told Us
In this unique and utterly moving documentary from New Zealand, seven women candidly talk of their loves and their lives during World War II. The poignant interviews are overlaid with restored archival footage and popular songs from World War II years; beautifully shot by Alun Bollinger (*The Piano*).
VHS: S31120. $29.95.
Gaylene Preston, New Zealand, 1995, 95 mins.

The Wonderful, Horrible Life of Leni Riefenstahl

Dear Diary

Alf Bicknell's Personal Beatles Diary
VHS: S30584. $19.95.

Caro Diario (Dear Diary)
VHS: S23967. $19.98.

The Country Diary of an Edwardian Lady
VHS: S20809. $26.98.

David Holzman's Diary
VHS: S18862. $19.98.

Diary of a Chambermaid
VHS: S05990. $24.95.

Diary of a Country Priest
VHS: S19932. $59.95.

Diary of a Lost Girl
VHS: S00339. $29.95.

The Diary of a Madman
VHS: S11285. $14.95.
Laser: LD76224. $39.98.

Diary of a Nudist
VHS: S15154. $19.98.

Diary of Anne Frank
VHS: S04330. $24.98.
Laser: LD70946. $49.98.

Diary of Forbidden Dreams
VHS: S00340. $29.95.

Diary of the Big Man
VHS: S14874. $49.95.

Diary of the War of Pigs
VHS: S01124. $39.95.

Guadalcanal Diary
VHS: S12164. $19.98.

Harlem Diary
VHS: S27821. $19.95.

Diary of a Lost Girl

Hollow Venus: Diary of a Go-Go Dancer
VHS: S22505. $29.95.

Secret Diary of Sigmund Freud
VHS: S02325. $79.98.

The Seducer's Diary (Le Journal du Seducteur)
VHS: S32680. $89.95.

Turtle Diary
VHS: S01378. $14.98.

Weapons of the Spirit
Between 1940 and 1944, a small village in the mountains of France, Le Chambon, became Europe's most effective haven for Jews, saving 5,000 men, women and children from the Holocaust. In this extraordinary documentary by Pierre Sauvage, who was born and protected in this peaceful village, the director shares this heartwarming story of the poor farming village of French Protestants who, under the eyes of the German occupation forces and the Vichy government, resisted the violence through "the weapons of the spirit." French with English subtitles.
VHS: S12461. $90.00.
Pierre Sauvage, France/USA, 1986, 91 mins.

Werner Herzog Eats His Shoe
Blank documents German filmmaker Werner Herzog honoring a vow he made to independent filmmaker Errol Morris that Herzog would eat his shoe if Morris ever finished a film. Morris did (*Gates of Heaven*), and Herzog complies by boiling and consuming his desert boots at the UC Theatre in Berkeley.
VHS: S01443. $39.95.
Les Blank, USA, 1979, 20 mins.

When Ireland Starved
This extensive documentary charts the most horrific event of modern Ireland's history, the Great Famine in the middle of the 19th century. The effects of this catastrophe have left an indelible mark on this country. Now using archival sketches, many from *The London News*, the scope of this disaster is captured on film. 120 mins.
VHS: S21193. $29.95.

When We Were Kings
Leon Cast's Academy Award-winning documentary is a knockout 20-year labor of love chronicling the famous 1974 "Rumble in the Jungle" heavyweight championship fight between 32-year-old Muhammad Ali and George Foreman in Zaire. Capturing the wit, charisma, intelligence and determination of "the Greatest," Cast's film is a lasting legacy of Ali the boxer, provocateur and political instigator. With interviews with Norman Mailer, George Plimpton and Spike Lee.
DVD: DV60129. $29.95.
VHS: S31675. $19.95.
Laser: LD76286. $39.99.
Leon Cast, USA, 1997, 90 mins.

Witness to Apartheid
This Emmy Award-winning documentary (Best Direction) was shot clandestinely in South Africa during the 1985 State of Emergency. Its interviews of tortured children and their doctors helped galvanize world wide action to change this unjust system.
VHS: S24586. $180.00.
Sharon Sopher, USA, 1986, 56 mins.

Witness to the Holocaust: Trial of Adolf Eichmann
This record presents the extensive testimony and evidence which revealed the scope of Eichmann's responsibility, including numerous eye-witness accounts. The first comprehensive examination of Eichmann. 90 mins.
VHS: S06633. $39.95.

The Wonderful, Horrible Life of Leni Riefenstahl
An exhaustive, infuriating and unforgettable documentary about Leni Riefenstahl at age 90: actress, filmmaker (*Olympia, Triumph of the Will*), propagandist, personal friend of Goebbels and Hitler, photographer, explorer. Filmmaker Ray Mueller confronts Leni as she seeks to remold her image from that of a master propagandist and Nazi to that of a noble and heroic victim of history. Essential viewing. German with English subtitles.
VHS: S23996. $39.95.
Laser: LD75388. $69.99.
Ray Mueller, Germany, 1993, 180 mins.

25 Films About the Holocaust

The 81st Blow
An historical document made up of footage and stills shot by the Nazis. A compilation of testimony from witnesses who appeared at the Eichmann trial provides a telling narrative. The film's title refers to the story of a Jewish boy in one of the ghettoes, who was struck with 80 blows. He survived and immigrated to Israel, where he found that no one believed his story—which for him was the 81st blow. Academy Award nominee.
VHS: S06570. $79.95.
Jacquot Ehrlich/David Bergman/Haim Gouri, Israel, 1974, 115 mins.

Angry Harvest
Agnieszka Holland's Academy-Award nominated film is a powerful emotional drama set during the German occupation of Poland. The raid on the ghetto, in which a Christian farmer saves a young Jewish woman on the run, and their resulting relationship becomes one of inter-dependent love and ultimate terror that ends in tragedy. A tour-de-force of acting and directing, the film stars Armin Mueller-Stahl, Elisabeth Trissenaar and Wojciech Pszoniak. German with English subtitles.
VHS: S06013. $69.95.
Agnieszka Holland, Germany, 1986, 102 mins.

Anne Frank Remembered
Family members, childhood friends and the people who hid the Franks bring to life the girl behind the diary. Academy Award winner for Best Documentary of 1995, narrated by Kenneth Branagh with selections from Anne's diary read by Glenn Close. German, Dutch and English with English subtitles.
VHS: S28620. $14.95.
Laser: LD75956. $39.95.
Jon Blair, Great Britain/USA, 1995, 117 mins.

Ashes and Diamonds
A brilliant statement from Andrzej Wajda, *Ashes and Diamonds* illustrates the conflict of idealism and instinct in this story of a young resistance fighter who assassinates the wrong man at the close of World War II. With Zbigniew Cybulski. Polish with English subtitles.
VHS: S00071. $24.95.
Andrzej Wajda, Poland, 1958, 105 mins.

The Boat Is Full
It is the summer of 1942 and the Swiss government, alarmed at the vast numbers of people fleeing Nazi Germany, has set up immigration policies so stringent that they have declared the country "a full lifeboat." Complications arise when a Swiss innkeeper's wife takes in a group of frightened refugees. A haunting film from noted Swiss Filmmaker Markus Imhoof. "Virtually a flawless movie....One I will not soon forget!" (Jeffrey Lyons). French and German with English subtitles.
VHS: S00161. $29.95.
Markus Imhoof, Switzerland, 1980, 100 mins.

Child in Two Worlds
To save their lives, many Jewish parents gave their children over to Christian foster parents. These babies, now in their 50's and 60's, tell their amazing stories of survival and how they returned to their parents' way of life. Consider Halinka, who as a baby was thrown, wrapped in a pillow, over the Warsaw ghetto wall into the hands of a Polish policeman. Winner of the Golden Calf Award for Best Documentary, 1993. Dutch with English subtitles. 60 mins.
VHS: S23235. $39.95.

The Damned
A gigantic allegory of the rise of Nazism through the decadent Krupp-like family; a baroque film which explores the dark cycles of violence and evil in human history and consciousness with erotic indulgence. With Dirk Bogarde, Ingrid Thulin, Helmut Berger, Charlotte Rampling. English dubbed.
VHS: S00293. $59.95.
Luchino Visconti, Italy/Germany, 1969, 154 mins.

Dita Saxova
The moving—and beautifully told—tragic story about an 18-year-old girl living in Prague, who seems beautiful and strong to everyone around her, until, a year later, she commits suicide by jumping off a cliff. Based on a novel by Arnost Lustig, *Dita Saxova* deftly explores the psychological contradictions which motivated her. Czech with English subtitles. B&W.
VHS: S04739. $59.95.
A. Moskalyk, Czechoslovakia, 1967, 98 mins.

The Garden of the Finzi-Continis
Vittorio de Sica's (*The Bicycle Thief, Miracle in Milan*) Academy Award-winning masterpiece is visually restored and remastered in Dolby stereo. Dominique Sanda plays the daughter of a cultured Italian Jewish family of immense wealth, languishing in aristocratic privilege on their estate, oblivious, until the end, to the danger that Fascism poses for their precious world. Italian with English subtitles.
VHS: S00480. $99.99.
Laser: LD71000. $49.95.
Vittorio de Sica, Italy, 1971, 94 mins.

Kanal
Part of the famous Andrzej Wajda trilogy that included *A Generation* and *Ashes and Diamonds*. The almost hallucinatory portrait of a group of Polish citizens and patriots who attempt to flee the Nazis through the sewer system of a war-devastated Warsaw. A film of amazing power and rare courage. Polish with English subtitles.
VHS: S02775. $24.95.
Andrzej Wajda, Poland, 1957, 96 mins.

More Than Broken Glass: Memories of Kristallnacht
The night of November 9, 1938 is forever etched in the minds of the Jewish people. Through archival footage, photographs and interviews with witnesses, a sharp portrait is created of the time and place. 57 mins.
VHS: S12904. $39.95.

Murderers Among Us: The Simon Wiesenthal Story
Ben Kingsley is cast as the famous Holocaust survivor who became the premiere Nazi hunter. *Variety* praised this made-for-cable epic film for its "enormous power and suspense." With Renee Soutendijk, Craig T. Nelson, Jack Shepherd and Paul Freeman. Script co-written by Abby Mann.
VHS: S14006. $19.98.
Brian Gibson, USA/Great Britain/Hungary, 1989, 157 mins.

Night and Fog
A newly mastered version of what Francois Truffaut called "the greatest film of all time": Alain Resnais' incredibly powerful, searing, unforgettable film on Nazi concentration camps, truly a film for all time. Edited by Chris Marker. French with English subtitles.
VHS: S00930. $19.95.
Alain Resnais, France, 1955, 32 mins.

Not Like Sheep to the Slaughter: The Story of the Bialystok Ghetto
A historically important work about the heroic Jewish resistance during the Holocaust, set during the summer of 1943, centering on the underground activities of Mordechai Tenenbaum, who led the fight against the Nazi program to liquidate the Bialystok ghetto. The program uncovers new evidence and archival materials. English language version. 150 mins.
VHS: S17940. $79.95.

Opening the Gates of Hell: American Liberators of the Nazi Concentration Camps
A harrowing documentary that interviews a number of American servicemen who liberated the Nazi concentration camps, recalling their shock and dread at what they experienced. The innocent Jews re-imagine the bravery, generosity and humanity of the troops. "Most of all, they remember with great clarity the day they opened the gates of hell." 45 mins.
VHS: S17943. $39.95.

Raoul Wallenberg: Between the Lines
Through interviews with colleagues, Holocaust survivors, newsreels and rare footage shot by Nazi

camera crews and others, this controversial story of Raoul Wallenberg's heroic campaign to save thousands of Jews from Budapest is relived. With diplomatic maneuvers and ingenious tactics, this Swedish diplomat stood fast against Nazi leader Adolph Eichmann's scheme of mass extermination. When the Russians invaded Budapest, Wallenberg was imprisoned and Soviet officials claim to this day that he died in July of 1947, disputing evidence of sightings, as late as 1979, which appear to prove otherwise. 1984, 90 mins.
VHS: $13677. $29.95.

The Road to Wannsee: Eleven Million Sentenced to Death
On January 20, 1942, 11 million Jews were sentenced to death at Wannsee. The trajectory that led to this death sentence—Hitler's political rise to power, the neutralizing of his opponents, and his obsession with eliminating the Jews—is the subject of this documentary. Archival footage and interviews with respected historians are featured. Dutch with English subtitles. 50 mins.
VHS: $23233. $39.95.

Romeo, Juliet and Darkness (Sweet Light in a Dark Room)
Romeo, Juliet and Darkness is a radical departure for Czech filmmaking in its unconventional treatment of the Anne Frank theme in a Czech setting. Pavel, a student, hides Hana, a young Jewish girl, in the attic of his apartment building. He is her only link to the outside world, and their growing trust develops into love, until the two are discovered by Pavel's mother. Weiss' double tragedy of young love and the moral question of responsibility to the Jews during the Nazi occupation is treated with poetic restraint. This film is a powerful condemnation of indifference toward force and terrorism. Also known as *Sweet Light in a Dark Room.* Czech with English subtitles.
VHS: $27179. $29.95.
Jiri Weiss, Czech Republic, 1959, 96 mins.

Schindler
The black marketeer, womanizer, gambler and Nazi spy who saved over 1,000 Jews from Hitler's death camps is revealed, in this documentary, through interviews with witnesses of his deeds and the survivors of his efforts. Schindler's widow, his driver Richard Rechen (who drove Schindler to safety in the war's close), and the mistress of Amon Goeth (the "Butcher of Plaszow"), speaking just hours before her suicide, are included in this fascinating, British-produced portrait of Oskar Schindler.
VHS: $21096. $19.98.

Shoah
Claude Lanzmann's landmark, monumental epic of the Holocaust, a 9½ hour assemblage of witnesses—death camp survivors and Nazi functionaries—whose combined testimony amounts to one of the most shattering human documents ever recorded. French

with English subtitles.
VHS: $01190. $299.95.
Claude Lanzmann, France, 1985, 570 mins.

Theresienstadt: Gateway to Auschwitz
More than 140,000 Jews were interned at the Czech fortress town of Terezin. This model ghetto was a transit camp for Auschwitz. Of the 15,000 in Theresienstadt who were under 15, less than 100 survived. Now the story of hope that was nourished by these children through a variety of cultural activities stands revealed in this prize-winning documentary. 57 mins.
VHS: $23242. $39.95.

They Risked Their Lives: Rescuers of the Holocaust
From 1986-1988 Gay Block and Malka Drucker interviewed and photographed more than 100 Gentile Holocaust rescuers who defied the Nazis to shield Jews during the war. Block's video chronicles the passionate and heroic acts of these brave men and women, their selfless courage and manifest honor. 54 mins.
VHS: $17941. $39.95.

Tsvi Nussbaum: Boy from Warsaw
For many the defining icon of the wide-scale Jewish suffering and oppression was the young boy, his arms held up, as the Nazis held their guns at his back. This provocative, revealing documentary considers the intervening life of that young man, Dr. Tvsi C. Nussbaum, as "well as a moving testimony of that era." 50 mins.
VHS: $17944. $39.95.

Wannsee Conference
An acclaimed film that reenacts the fateful January 1942 meeting of the Nazi party and top German officials that set in motion "The Final Solution," the destruction of European Jewry. "It is mesmerizing for seeming to be so commonplace. *The Wannsee Conference* gives a voice for dealing with matters that are, after all, not unspeakable" (Vincent Canby). With Dietrich Mattausch, Gerd Bockmann, Friedrich Beckhaus and Gunter Sporrle. German with English subtitles.
VHS: $07395. $19.95.
Heinz Schirk, Germany, 1984, 87 mins.

The Warsaw Ghetto
Taken in part from the photo albums and cinefilms of Nazi Heinrich Himmler, this film augments those images with an extremely rare collection of newsreel footage depicting the Warsaw ghetto during the Nazi occupation of Poland. From its inception to its fiery demolition in 1943, this film documents the lives of the over 500,000 Jews who were crowded into the one-square-mile area that was the Warsaw Ghetto, put to work by the Third Reich in Nazi factories, and given only fractions of the rations allotted to "Aryan" Germans and Poles.
VHS: $05179. $29.95.
Poland, 1969, 52 mins.

Anne Frank Remembered

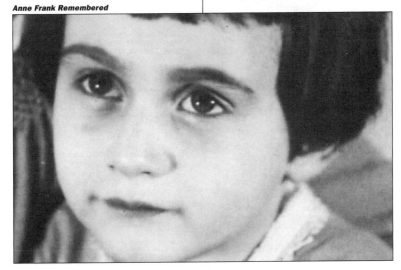

25 Great War Films

Apocalypse Now
Francis Ford Coppola's Vietnam War epic conveys a madness with parallels to Joseph Conrad's *Heart of Darkness*. Lieutenant Willard receives orders to seek out a renegade military outpost led by errant officer Colonel Kurtz, said to "terminate his command with extreme prejudice." This newly enhanced version features a remastered soundtrack in Dolby surround stereo.
VHS: S00066. $29.95.
Francis F. Coppola, USA, 1979, 153 mins.

Ballad of a Soldier
Grigori Chukrai's poetic and elegiac war story is one of the major works of post-war Russian cinema, detailing the odd, bemused moments of a soldier's earnest seduction of a country girl while visiting his mother. The film is also devastating at capturing the dread, pain and humiliation of war, and its effects on the people. "The picture flows in such a swift, poetic way that the tragedy of it is concealed by a gentle lyric quality" (*New York Times*). With Vladimir Ivashov and Shanna Prokhorenko. Russian with English subtitles.
VHS: S17516. $29.95.
Grigori Chukrai, Russia, 1959, 89 mins.

Battle of Algiers
Internationally acclaimed, the staggering newsreel-like authenticity of the staged street riots and vital performances of the actors give *Battle of Algiers* a unique dramatic impact on this detailing of the Algerian revolt against the French. French/Algerian with English subtitles.
VHS: S01976. $29.95.
Gillo Pontecorvo, Italy, 1967, 122 mins.

Das Boot: The Director's Cut
Wolfgang Petersen's riveting, claustrophobic, German U-Boat warfare drama is presented in its original widescreen theatrical release ratio. This version also includes a newly redesigned digital soundtrack. With Juergen Prochnow, Herbert Gruenemeyer and Klaus Wennemann. Presented on two cassettes. German with English subtitles.
VHS: S14834. $24.95.
Laser: 3 sides. LD72444. $39.95.
Wolfgang Petersen, Germany, 1981, 209 mins.

Dear America: Letters Home from Vietnam
More than 30 celebrities read the actual letters of Vietnam veterans accompanied by striking visual footage and nostalgic music of the times. A touching salute to those who fought and to those who died. Readers include Robin Williams, Martin Sheen, Matt Dillon, Willem Dafoe, Tom Berenger, Howard Rollins Jr., Michael J. Fox, Sean Penn and Kathleen Turner. Based on the book by the same name.
VHS: S09921. $19.98.
Bill Couturie, USA, 1988, 87 mins.

The Deer Hunter
Powerful drama that follows a group of friends from a steel town in Pennsylvania through their Vietnam experiences with fine ensemble work from Robert De Niro, Christopher Walken, John Savage, John Cazale and Meryl Streep.
VHS: S02738. $29.95.
Laser: LD70022. $44.98.
Michael Cimino, USA, 1978, 183 mins.

Dirty Dozen
Very tough, very funny and ultimately very violent film featuring a great all-male cast which includes Lee Marvin, Charles Bronson, John Cassavetes and Robert Ryan as convicts offered amnesty if they go on a suicide mission behind enemy lines during World War II.
VHS: S02348. $19.98.
Laser: LD70557. $39.98.
Robert Aldrich, USA, 1967, 149 mins.

Era Notte a Roma
A major film of Roberto Rossellini: three soldiers, an American, Englishman and Russian, having escaped from a concentration camp during the final months of Rome's occupation, are given refuge in a young woman's loft. She and her fiance survive through various black market schemes. A defrocked priest,

Tarcisio, suspects the girl's complicity with Allied soldiers, but is willing to go along with it in return for favors. The woman resists, and Tarcisio causes the scattering of the group and the death of the Russian and several compatriots. In his book on Rossellini, Guarner said that from the point of *Era Notte a Roma* Rossellini no longer merely observed, but began to analyze: "Temporal and spatial leaps occur with utter simplicity and bridge ancient and modern cultures." English, Russian, German and Italian with English subtitles.
VHS: S07383. $79.95.
Roberto Rossellini, Italy, 1960, 145 mins.

Europa Europa
The film which took America by storm: Agnieszka Holland's powerful, moving story of a courageous German-Jewish teenager who survived World War II by concealing his identity and living as a Nazi during seven harrowing years through three countries. Based on a true story; a film which changes almost everyone who sees it. "A pure, absurd miracle of history" (*New Yorker Magazine*). Polish, German with English subtitles.
VHS: S16327. $19.98.
Agnieszka Holland, Poland/France, 1991, 100 mins.

A Farewell to Arms
The first Hemingway novel to reach the screen, nominated for four Oscars, with riveting performances by Helen Hayes and Gary Cooper as the sweet English nurse and the cynical American ambulance driver who fall in love on the Italian front and are separated by combat and another man's jealousy.
VHS: S00433. $24.95.
Frank Borzage, USA, 1932, 79 mins.

Forbidden Games
Rene Clement's beautiful allegory is the story of two children orphaned by the war who build a secret cemetery for animals and steal crosses from the church yard to mark the graves. Wonderfully natural performances from Georges Pojouly, whom Clement discovered in a camp, and Brigitte Fossey create a moving film about the effects of war on children. Winner at the Venice Film Festival and Best Foreign Film Oscar. French with English subtitles.
VHS: S00457. $29.95.
Laser: LD70988. $39.95.
Rene Clement, France, 1952, 90 mins.

Full Metal Jacket
Stanley Kubrick visits Vietnam. Based on the short but powerful novel, *The Short Timers*, by Gustav Hasford. Follow a few Marines from training on Parris Island to fighting in the Tet Offensive. With Matthew Modine, Adam Baldwin, Dorian Harewood, Lee Ermey and Vincent D'Onofrio. War is hell even when filmed in England.
VHS: S07003. $19.98.
Laser: LD70577. $24.98.
Stanley Kubrick, USA, 1987, 116 mins.

Grand Illusion
A beautifully mastered version of Jean Renoir's great masterpiece, a classic comment on war's fading glory. Set in WW I, the film tells of two French officers captured by German forces. Interred in a prison camp, the two officers encounter Von Rauffenstein, an aristocratic career officer played by von Stroheim. With Jean Gabin, Pierre Fresnay and von Stroheim. French with English subtitles.
VHS: S12469. $29.95.
Laser: LD70373. $89.95.
Jean Renoir, France, 1937, 111 mins.

Hope and Glory
John Boorman's critically-acclaimed memory of childhood—moving, funny, bittersweet. The main character, Bill, is a seven-year-old boy, Sarah Miles his ever-tolerant mother who does her best while dad's away at war. While the street is full of rubble, the Luftwaffe is parachuting into the back yard, this is a story of innocence in the face of war—a remarkable portrait of a childhood. On many Ten Best lists, winner of the Golden Globe Award for Best Picture.
Laser: LD72302. $29.99.
John Boorman, Great Britain, 1987, 94 mins.

Is Paris Burning?
The gripping heroism of the Allied Resistance during the Paris liberation of 1944 is depicted in this multi-storied war epic scripted by Francis Ford Coppola and Gore Vidal. The illustrious international cast includes: Jean-Paul Belmondo, Kirk Douglas, Yves Montand, and Orson Welles.
VHS: $13707. $29.95.
Rene Clement, France/USA, 1968, 173 mins.

Kindergarten
A largely autobiographical memoir directed by poet Yevgeni Yevtushenko, recalling his boyhood years during World War II in Russia while the city of Moscow was being evacuated as the Nazis approached. Told as a picaresque adventure about a little boy who meets carloads of strange characters, the narrative assumes a poetic, experimental form of storytelling as Yevtushenko recreates the overcrowded railroad stations, Nazi planes, black marketeers, women bandits and passengers and villagers. Russian with English subtitles.
VHS: $12974. $59.95.
Yevgeny Yevtushenko, USSR, 1983, 160 mins.

La Silence de la Mer
(The Silence of the Sea)
An old man and his beautiful niece are forced to endure the presence of a Nazi officer during the German occupation of their small French village. Vowing never to speak to the invader, the couple listen in silence as the officer pours out his ideas and feelings about music, war and his love of France. Just as the officer overcomes their enmity and at the same time discovers the realities of Nazism in France, he is ordered to the eastern front. French with English subtitles.
VHS: $30612. $29.95.
Jean-Pierre Melville, France, 1947, 86 mins.

Napoleon
Orson Welles, Maria Schell, Yves Montand, and Erich von Stroheim star in Sacha Guitry's classic biography of Napoleon, from his youth as a soldier in the French Army until his exile to the Island of Elba. A monumental production with a cast of thousands, originally shot in Technicolor. English dialog.
VHS: $00918. $59.95.
Laser: LD70061. $89.98.
Sacha Guitry, France, 1955, 115 mins.

Night of the Generals
A World War II whodunit. As Germany is battling on two fronts for world domination, Omar Sharif is ordered to conduct an investigation into the allegation that one of the Fuehrer's finest officers might be a murdering sex criminal. The irony of the situation is fully explored. Suspects include Peter O'Toole, Tom Courtenay, Donald Pleasance, Christopher Plummer and John Gregson.
VHS: $10383. $19.95.
Anatole Litvak, Great Britain, 1967, 148 mins.

Open City
A beautiful video master, transferred from a new negative, of this key film of Italian Neo-Realism, shot largely during the Nazi occupation of Rome. Two resistance leaders, one a Communist, the other a priest, work toward weakening the German occupation. The cumulative power of Rossellini's feeling for his subject was translated into a visual intensity that makes the picture sometimes almost impossible to watch. With a great performance by Anna Magnani. Italian with English subtitles.
VHS: $13591. $24.95.
Laser: LD75058. $49.95.
Roberto Rossellini, Italy, 1945, 103 mins.

Paisan
One of the landmarks of Italian neo-realism; six episodes of the Battle of Italy from 1943-45. Improvised dialog, non-actors, and the story of the people in the War, the film became a cornerstone of postwar Italian cinema, appropriately called, by many critics, a "revelation...It is a people fighting, as others have done so often, against tyranny and their own weakness, against injustice and poverty." Italian with English subtitles.
VHS: $00989. $29.95.
Roberto Rossellini, Italy, 1946, 115 mins.

Paths of Glory
A shattering film from Stanley Kubrick, bringing into focus the insanity of war in the story of French General Macready, who, during World War I, orders his men into a futile mission. When the men fail, Macready selects three soldiers for trial and

A Farewell to Arms

execution for cowardice. With incredible performances from Kirk Douglas, Ralph Meeker, Adolphe Menjou, George Macready, Wayne Morris, Richard Anderson. One of the high points of the American cinema.
VHS: $11433. $19.97.
Laser: LD70433. $49.95.
Stanley Kubrick, USA, 1957, 86 mins.

Stalag 17
World War II POW drama stars William Holden in an Oscar performance as a soldier suspected of being a spy when two prisoners are killed trying to escape. Otto Preminger also appears.
VHS: $02608. $19.95.
Billy Wilder, USA, 1953, 120 mins.

Stalingrad
From the same production team that brought the world *Das Boot*, this film brings the bloodiest battle in the history of warfare to the screen: the legendary battle of Stalingrad. With German forces following Hitler's orders to neither retreat nor surrender, over two million Russians and Germans lost their lives in what came to be a turning point in the defeat of Germany in the Second World War. One of the most unflinchingly realistic war films ever made, *Stalingrad* stands alone in its searing, unforgettable imagery, "powerfully underscoring the adage that war is hell" (*The New York Times*). German with English subtitles.
VHS: $30467. $29.95.
Joseph Vilsmaier, Germany, 1996, 150 mins.

Why We Fight, No. 5: Battle of Britain
One of a seven-part series produced for the U.S. War Department, designed to convince the American public that WWII deserved their support, *The Battle of Britain* is an account of the unbreakable spirit of London residents during the six week bombing blitz by the German Luftwaffe. Narration by Walter Huston.
VHS: $00102. $19.95.
Laser: LD70862. $59.95.
Frank Capra, USA, 1943, 52 mins.

100 Cult Classics

The Astounding She-Monster
Classic B-movie thriller, with Robert Clarke tempted by a sexy alien she-creature with a deadly touch. Producer-director Ronnie Ashcroft's first feature guided by his mentor, Ed Wood, Jr., whose uncredited help gives this film that unmistakable "scent" of Wood. With Keene Duncan, Marilyn Harvey and Ewing Brown.
VHS: S32114. $19.95.
Ronnie Ashcroft, USA, 1958, 60 mins.

The Beast of Yucca Flats
Plan 9 alumni Tor Johnson and Conrad Brooks star in this uncut collector's edition. Johnson plays double roles as a noted Russian scientist carrying secret data of the Russian moon shot who escapes to the U.S. after his family has been killed by Communists, and the Beast he becomes after explosion of the H-Bomb, which destroys his brain waves. Includes bonus *Misfit Control* trailer.
VHS: S31015. $29.95.
Coleman Francis, USA, 1966, 75 mins.

Beneath the Valley of the Ultravixens
Russ Meyer's self-described "all-out assault on today's sexual mores" with Lavonia, Eufaula Roop, Junk Yard Sal, and others.
VHS: S03539. $79.95.
Russ Meyer, USA, 1979, 90 mins.

Big Bad Mama
Angie Dickinson, William Shatner and Tom Skerritt star in this ribald Roger Corman production about a woman and her two daughters who travel through rural Depression-era America robbing banks, selling liquor, picking up men and kidnapping rich daughters. Also stars Susan Sennett, Robbie Lee, Noble Willingham and Dick Miller.
VHS: S28612. $14.98.
Steve Carver, USA, 1974, 85 mins.

Big Bad Mama II
Angie Dickinson reprises her role as the cult heroine Wilma "Big Bad Mama" McClatchie, out to steal a better life for her two teenaged girls. The terrible trio set their gun sites on revenge against a crooked politician by shooting holes in his banks and kidnapping his son. Includes Leonard Maltin's exclusive interview with Roger Corman.
VHS: S32031. $14.98.
Jim Wynorski, USA, 1987, 83 mins.

Blood Orgy of the Leather Girls
A violent feminist revenge movie far more serious than its mock title implies, this feature by the late Meredith Lucas focuses on the efforts of four radically different women to avenge the terrorist tactics waged on them by the school's fascist bullies. With Robin Gingold, Jo Ann Wyman, Melissa Lawrence and David Nudleman. Special appearance by the Wild Breed.
VHS: S18600. $19.95.
Meredith Lucas, USA, 1988

Caged Women
When a young female journalist (Laura Gemser, *Emanuelle the Queen*) poses as a female prostitute inmate in order to explore the issues of sex, violence and mistreatment that go on behind bars in a women's prison, her journalistic endeavor becomes a fight for her life. A sort of female *Shock Corridor*.
VHS: S31623. $19.95.
Vincent Dawn, USA, 1984, 90 mins.

Caligula
Bob Guccione's entry into filmmaking was a disaster, but nevertheless, *Caligula* has achieved cult status of sorts. This epic of debauchery in Caligula's Rome stars Peter O'Toole, Malcolm McDowell and John Gielgud. English dialog.
VHS: S05788. $59.95.
Tinto Brass, Italy, 1982, 105 mins.

Carnival Rock
A rare rock film of the 50s, which features thrill-crazed kids, grimy gangsters and psycho-teens who all clash together in a seedy carnival nightclub, set to the blistering beat of rockabilly, r&b, and classic rock 'n' roll. Featuring music by The Platters, The Blockbusters, David Houston and Bob Luman and His Shadows.
VHS: S05184. $9.95.
Roger Corman, USA, 1957, 80 mins.

Castle of Blood
Barbara Steele is the bait for a daring reporter who bets he can stay the night in a haunted castle. It seems on "The Night of the Dead" everyone who has died violently in the place returns seeking human blood. The moral of this story is, never trust a woman without a heartbeat. With George Riviere and Margaret Robsham. B&W. Based on E.A. Poe's *Dance Macabre*.
VHS: S09131. $29.95.
Anthony Dawson (Antonio Margheriti), Italy, 1964, 85 mins.

Cinema of Transgression
Nick Zedd's *Bogus Man & Go to Hell*, John Spencer's *Shithaus*, Lung Leg's *Worm Movie*, Richard Klemann's *A Suicide*, Erotic Psyche's *Mutable Fire*, Tommy Turner's *Simonland*, Richard Kern's *You Killed Me First & King of Sex*, Michael Wolfe's *Niggernight*, and Manuel de Landa's *Judgment Day* and *Ism, Ism*. Extremely graphic scenes of bodily functions, hokey scenes of trumped up ketchup violence, stabbing and severed limbs, some strangely moving and brilliant filmmaking by a wide collection of drug addicts, outlaws, and perennial outsiders.
VHS: S10161. $49.95.

Daddy-O
Also known as *Out on Probation*, this low-rent, grade Z work about teenage rebellion and alienation concerns the pressures placed on a young man to drive the getaway car during a heist. With Dick Contino, Sandra Giles, Bruno VeSota, and Gloria Victor.
VHS: S16972. $9.95.
Lou Place, USA, 1959, 74 mins.

Deadly Weapons
This historic film stars the amazing 73" bust line of Chesty Morgan. Chesty uses "the only two weapons I've got" to fight the Mob and, of course, she wins. Featuring the famous "droopy-pantyhose" gross-out scene and Chesty's famous ten-inch platform heels. Directed by Doris Wishman; many critics consider the two films she made with Chesty Morgan to be the apex of her career. Well, maybe one critic.
VHS: S15141. $19.98.
Doris Wishman, USA, 1970, 90 mins.

DeathSport
One thousand years into the future, after the Great Neutron Wars, the world is divided into desert wastes and isolated city-states. Lord Zirpola captures Kaz Oshay (David Carradine) to fight to the death in his game, DeathSport. Now Kaz must face his past and fight to save himself and his city from the war that Lord Zirpola is about to wage.
VHS: S32034. $14.98.
Henry Suso/Allan Arkush, USA, 1978, 83 mins.

Deranged

A chilling work inspired by the depraved psycho Ed Gein, a loathsome serial killer whose acts inspired *Psycho* and *The Texas Chainsaw Massacre*. This film features an anonymous, cruel killer (Roberts Blossom) who preserves his mother's corpse and then randomly pursues other women. The film has been remastered and digitally restored. On the same program is the notorious, underground documentary *Ed Gein: American Maniac*. With Alan Ormsby, Cosette Lee and Leslie Carlson.
VHS: $18839. $39.95.
Jeff Gillen, USA, 1974, 110 mins.

Desperate Living

A perverse and demented film from the outcast priest of sleaze, John Waters, dealing with his usually upsetting themes of self-expression, violence, alienation, mental anguish, sexual hijinks and political corruption, done in a fragmented, hyper absurd comic style. With Liz Renay, Mink Stole, Susan Lowe and Edith Massey.
VHS: S00324. $19.98.
Laser: LD76262. $39.99.
John Waters, USA, 1977, 90 mins.

Destination Moon

The first major sci-fi film in the U.S., the sets are ingenious and the film won an Academy Award for Special Effects. Co-scripted by Robert A. Heinlein from his novel *Rocketship Galileo*.
VHS: S00326. $19.95.
Irving Pichel, USA, 1950, 91 mins.

Divine

A special tribute to the most beautiful babe in the world. First up, a short, *The Diane Linkletter Story*, starring a very young Divine as a naughty girl who wants to: "get high," "get laid," "...and do my thing, momma...." Thankfully there's a moral lesson here, as Diane kills herself. Following that, the only existing performance of the infamous *The Neon Woman* show. Divine plays the owner of a sleazy strip joint with a lot of problems, including the District Attorney (who doesn't know he's her son) trying to shut the place down, the horny bible-thumping Senator who's just fallen in love with her, and her virginal daughter who has just returned from boarding school and after spending a few minutes in the club has become an alcoholic, heroin-addicted wanton who has just married the black janitor. Now that's high comedy.
VHS: $13498. $39.95.
John Waters, USA, 1990, 110 mins.

Double Agent 73

This film stars the 73″ bust line of Chesty Morgan. Chesty is special agent 73; her mission is to expose a gang of drug smugglers by photographing them with the camera implanted in her left bazoom. Of course, to use the camera she must constantly "drop her cover." Chesty has to work fast—the camera is programmed to explode. Directed by Doris Wishman.
VHS: $15147. $19.98.
Doris Wishman, USA, 1971, 72 mins.

Dracula

Filmed simultaneously with Tod Browning's celebrated 1931 English language version, this evocative, atmospheric Spanish translation of Bram Stoker's novel is based on the play by Hamilton Deane and John Balderston, adapted in Spanish by B. Fernandez Cue, shot on the same expressionistic sets. With Carlos Villarias, Lupita Tovar and Pablo Alvarez Rubio.
VHS: $17271. $14.98.
George Melford, Spain, 1931, 104 mins.

Eat My Dust

Ron Howard goes berserk in this fast, action-packed car chase/car race thrill ride. Includes Leonard Maltin's exclusive interview with Roger Corman.
VHS: $32032. $14.98.
Charles B. Griffith, USA, 1976, 89 mins.

Erotique

This critically acclaimed, highly charged anthology features erotic short films from the female point of view. Lizzie Borden's *Let's Talk About Sex* is an uncompromising look at an aspiring young actress working as a phone sex operator, who dramatically redefines the powers of sexual dynamics when she gets a caller to listen to her fantasies. *Taboo Parlor*, by Monika Treut, is an outrageous story about a lesbian couple who decide to pick up a man, leading to a night of uncontrollable desires where only the strong survive. A young teacher attacked on a train begins a sexual relationship with her rescuer, allowing her hidden emotions to rise to a feverish frenzy in Ana Maria's *Magalhaes's Final Call*. Two college lovers reunite in Hong Kong, where they discover their different cultures have caused them to grow apart. Determined to prove these obstacles can be overcome, the boy prepares an evening of gourmet food and ancient Chinese sexual techniques in Clara Law's funny and bold *Wonton Soup*. "One of the most freshly comedic depictions of sex in cinematic history" (*Film Threat*).
VHS: $30885. $89.98.
Lizzie Borden/Monika Treut/Ana Maria Magalhaes/Clara Law, 1996, 120 mins.

Faster Pussycat! Kill! Kill!

"The story of a new breed of superwomen emerging out of the ruthlessness of our times...." Directed by Russ Meyer.
VHS: S03665. $79.95.
Russ Meyer, USA, 1966, 83 mins.

Fearless Vampire Killers

Or *Pardon Me, Your Teeth Are in My Neck*. Roman Polanski directs (and appears in) this cult oddity, a vampire-film spoof that manages both horror and humor. The story involves a professor and his bumbling assistant, who set out to track down a coven of Transylvanian vampires. Cast includes Jack MacGowran, Sharon Tate, Alfie Bass and Terry Downes. This is the restored, original cut.
VHS: $12741. $19.98.
Laser: LD72173. $39.98.
Roman Polanski, USA, 1967, 124 mins.

First Nudie Musical

One of the zaniest movies, which one-ups Mel Brooks and goes beyond. This double spoof of Hollywood musicals and porno pictures was directed by Bruce Kimmel, and involves an aging Hollywood studio on its last legs of decline. Now known for producing only cheap porno flicks like "Stewardesses in Chains," it is in danger of being turned into a

Desperate Living

Dogs & Cats

101 Dalmatians
VHS: S31391. $26.99.
Laser: LD76378. $29.99.

Adventures of Milo and Otis
VHS: S11483. $19.95.

The Aristocats
VHS: S27539. $26.95.
Laser: LD74873. $29.95.

Beethoven
VHS: S17341. $24.98.

Born Free
VHS: S26177. $12.95.

The Cat (Le Chat)
VHS: S00221. $59.95.

Harry and Tonto
VHS: S04337. $19.98.

Lassie Come Home
VHS: S12429. $19.98.

Nine Lives of Fritz the Cat
VHS: S05912. $29.95.

Old Yeller—40th Anniversary Limited Edition
VHS: S32290. $19.95.
Laser: LD76379. $29.99.

That Darn Cat
VHS: S31698. $103.99.
Laser: LD76293. $39.99.

---

supermarket when it's saved by Kimmel, who convinces the studio to make *The First Nudie Musical*. With Cindy Williams.
VHS: S07780. $29.95.
Bruce Kimmel, USA, 1975, 95 mins.

Fun House
Early Eric Bogosian at the Los Angeles Matrix Theater in all his sweaty, maddened glory. Before *Talk Radio*, pre-*Sex, Drugs, Rock & Roll, Funhouse* features the desperate, hungry actor/writer in the performance of a lifetime.
VHS: S30436. $24.95.
Jo Bonney/Lewis MacAdams, USA, 1986, 80 mins.

Glen or Glenda
One of the funniest exploitation films ever made—starring Bela Lugosi as he tells the story of Glen—or Glenda—who is undergoing a sex change operation, and tells the horror story about fetishism. Not to be missed!
VHS: S00505. $19.95.
Ed Wood, Jr., USA, 1953, 64 mins.

Godzilla 1985
Japan's most famous export returns to face his old nemesis. Starring Raymond Burr. Also includes the animated film short *Bambi vs. Godzilla*.
VHS: S32280. $9.99.
Kohji Hashimoto, Japan, 1985, 91 mins.

Godzilla vs. Biollante
A return of the monster who's been reawakened and threatens world peace and stability. The larger community responds with Biollante, a genetically engineered plant form who feeds off Godzilla. English dubbed.
VHS: S17709. $19.98.
Laser: LD75199. $34.98.
Kazuki Omori, Japan, 1989, 104 mins.

The Groove Tube
Now seventies nostalgia, a wild lampoon series of skits that spoof television which gave Chevy Chase his first big break. 75 mins.
VHS: S04622. $39.95.

Head
One of the cult films of the 60's, with the Monkees in a kaleidoscope of surreal vignettes, full of 60's psychedelia. Written and produced by Rafaelson

(*Five Easy Pieces*) and Jack Nicholson.
VHS: S02531. $19.95.
Bob Rafelson, USA, 1968, 86 mins.

High School Confidential
The incomparable Mamie van Doren stars in one of the truly great camp American films of the 1950's in which a tough-talking gang leader comes in contact with a drug ring and its leader—all in the surroundings of the all-American high school. A great rock musical score.
VHS: S00568. $14.98.
Laser: CLV. LD71989. $29.98.
Jack Arnold, USA, 1958, 85 mins.

Honky Tonk Girl (Highway Hell)
Mary Chauning is featured in this hilarious exploitation film, in the tradition of *Reefer Madness*. The story is about a hitch-hiking prostitution ring. Catching a lift has never been so much fun. 1937.
VHS: S23179. $24.95.

How to Irritate People
Performed before a live audience, John Cleese demonstrates how to bother people so as to unnerve them. "Find out how to pay back job interviewers, movie chatterboxes, garage staff, even bank clerks in the only way they deserve." With support provided by Michael Palin, Graham Chapman, Connie Booth, Gillian Lind and Tim Brooke-Taylor. 65 mins.
VHS: S18133. $19.95.

Humanoids from the Deep (Monster)
Vic Morrow and Doug McClure star in this gory sci-fi thriller about humanoid salmon-like ecological mutants that terrorize a sleepy fishing village and bother bikinied women.
VHS: S28613. $14.98.
Laser: LD76177. $39.99.
Barbara Peeters, USA, 1980, 81 mins.

I'm Not Fascinating—The Movie!
This twisted rock 'n' roll anti-history chronicles the pointless shenanigans of San Francisco rock ne'er-do-wells The Icky Boyfriends and their futile request for rock stardom. Undaunted by the universal hatred of both their music and their look, the band perseveres, netting themselves a major label contract. But stardom proves elusive as they descend into a world of murder, intrigue, nepotism, consumer research groups, excessive use of caffeine-laden soda pop and death. "A weirdly beautiful spectacle of self-defeat. An instant classic" (*San Francisco Bay Guardian*).
VHS: S30493. $19.99.
Danny Plotnick, USA, 1996, 50 mins.

The Immoral Three
A tempting trio of illegitimate sisters must avenge their mother's murder within one year to collect a million bucks each. But, as usual, where there's big money, there's big trouble. Double-crossing, triple-crossing and plenty of undressing ensues in Doris Wishman's action-packed "guns 'n' hooters" classic. I won't give away the ending, but…everybody gets killed. Sorry.
VHS: S15148. $19.98.
Doris Wishman, USA, 1965, 82 mins.

The Incredibly Strange Creatures Who Stopped Living and Became Mixed Up Zombies
A funky horror movie set in a sleazy roadside carnival about a deranged fortune teller who creates a series of grotesque monsters and imprisons them in the back of her tent. Problems ensue when a string of unsolved murders plague the carny. "Truly bizarre film features gorgeously saturated color, awful acting, hideous dialogue, haunting atmosphere and little plot" (Leonard Maltin). With Cash Flagg, Brett O'Hara, Atlas King, Sharon Walsh and Madison Clarke.
VHS: S20140. $24.95.
Ray Dennis Steckler, USA, 1963, 82 mins.

Jayne Mansfield: Single Room Furnished/The Female Jungle
Jayne Mansfield's bodaciousness is captured in two titillating tapes. In *Single Room Furnished* (93 mins.), Jayne is a buxom blonde who falls from uncorrupted innocence through pregnancies to desperate prostitution. Starring Dorothy Keller. Jayne makes her debut in *The Female Jungle* (69 mins.), a dramatic murder case in which police sergeant Tierney is caught between a rock and a hard place. The prime suspect in a murder case, Tierney

discovers a series of clues that implicates his friend (John Carradine). Simply *divoon!*
VHS: S32226. $14.99.
Matt Cimber/Bruno Ve Sota, USA, 1968/1956, 162 mins.

The Jim Bailey Experience
Combining elements of the outrageous and avant-garde, Jim Bailey has been on the cutting edge of drag performers. In this compilation tape, Bailey pulls out all the stops with his dead-on impersonations and photo layouts of Judy Garland, Barbra Streisand, Marilyn Monroe and Madonna.
VHS: S16916. $39.95.

Jive Junction
Unpretentious, occasionally bizarre, World War II era "B" movie about a group of teens who play jitterbug music for the troops. Directed by the master of the "B" movies, screenplay by novelist Irving Wallace.
VHS: S02242. $24.95.
Edgar G. Ulmer, USA, 1943, 62 mins.

Lisa and the Devil
An innocent woman (Elke Sommer) is drawn to a mysterious mansion where the evil inhabitants practice sadism and the butler may be the devil himself. Digitally remastered and presented in its uncut, original form. With Telly Savalas.
VHS: S30437. $14.95.
Mario Bava, Italy/Spain, 1973, 116 mins.

Lord Love a Duck
Roddy McDowall, Tuesday Weld and Ruth Gordon star in this offbeat comedy which parodies the 1960s Southern California teen scene. McDowall plays a high school senior with psychic powers; when he develops a crush on Weld, a beautiful but hopelessly self-absorbed co-ed, he sets out to make her every dream come true.
VHS: S28493. $19.98.
George Axelrod, USA, 1966, 105 mins.

Love Letter to Edy
A charming, fictionalized biography of Edith Massey, known to fans of John Waters' cult classic, *Pink Flamingos*, as Edy the Egg Lady. Featuring Waters and Mink Stole.
VHS: S31356. $14.95.
Robert Maier, USA, 1973, 15 mins.

Lucky Pierre
This true cult-film classic stars Chicago vaudeville comedian Billy Falbo and hosts of naked women in five vignettes probably written before electricity. With such clever titles as "Drive-in Me Crazy" and "The Plumber's Friend," you can't help but love it. Plus you get the bonus short film "A Hot Night at the Go-Go Lounge." What a deal.
VHS: S15151. $19.98.
Herschell Gordon Lewis, USA, 1963, 73 mins.

Lydia Lunch: Malicious Intent
Why We Murder and *Universal Infiltrators* were shot at The Knitting Factory in New York by Richard Kern while *The Beast* was shot at L.A.C.E. in L.A. by Chris Iovenko. Together these works explore a world of anti-social rantings that may inspire anger, violence and more. 90 mins.
VHS: S25608. $29.95.
Richard Kern/Chris Iovenko, USA, 1994, 90 mins.

Maniac Cop
Described as *Frankenstein* meets *The French Connection*, this low-budget thriller has been a surprise worldwide theatrical hit, spawned two sequels and taken its place as one of the most copied films of the last decade. Someone is patrolling the streets of New York City, stalking and murdering. When the citizens discover the murderer is a cop, they panic and start attacking innocent policemen. Featuring an extraordinary cast of veterans, including Tom Atkins, Richard Roundtree and Bruce Campbell, with cameos by Jake "Raging Bull" LaMotta and director Sam Raimi (*Darkman*). Presented letterboxed, this special edition includes original French key art, theatrical trailers, TV spots, written commentary from the film's director, and scenes created specifically for Japanese television.
VHS: S30938. $14.98.
William Lustig, USA/France, 1988, 85 mins.

Mondo New York
Shot over 11 days in the Big Apple, this uncensored travelogue chronicles the weird and the bizarre. Cockfights, crack houses, S&M clubs and slam dancers join with performance artists, musicians and street hookers in an afterhours tour of NYC. Name performers include Lydia Lunch, Dean Johnson, Ann Magnuson and a guy who bites the heads off mice.
VHS: S04315. $14.95.
Laser: LD76226. $39.98.
Harvey Keith, USA, 1988, 83 mins.

Mondo Rocco (aka It's a Gay World)
This collection of short films by Pat Rocco combines softcore erotica, politics and drag. Rocco was among the first to capture the heady days of Gay Liberation in the late 1960's and 1970's on film. Together these works go some way to preserving that colorful era.
VHS: S25114. $39.95.
Pat Rocco, USA, 1970, 227 mins.

Mondo Sleazo (The World of Sleaze)
It's unbelievable, but true. Here are 50 trailers to some of the sleaziest movies ever made. Everything is here—drugs, racism, the supernatural, monsters, bikers...you name it. From the 30's to the 80's, this tape will take you on a guided tour of exploitation. Included are: *Love Life of a Gorilla, Maniac, Cocaine Fiends, The Smut Peddler, The Nine Ages of Nakedness, Violated Love, Werewolves on Wheels, Superchick* and literally dozens more. These movies are so slimy, you'll have to wash your hands after viewing this tape. 100 mins.
VHS: S13668. $29.95.

Mondo Topless
Mondo Topless, says Russ Meyer, "captures the basic essence of the (topless) movement...with MOVEMENT! Way out, wild undulatory movement!" Subtitled *Thanks for the Mammaries*.
VHS: S03072. $79.95.
Russ Meyer, USA, 60 mins.

Nick Zedd: Steal This Video
This collection shows why Zedd is one of the most notorious filmmakers around. For *Thrust in Me* Zedd claims he was banned from every screening room in the country. *The Bogus Man, Police State, Whoregasm* and *The Wild World of Lydia Lunch* are all equally outrageous. 90 mins.
VHS: S25607. $29.95.
Nick Zedd, USA, 1994, 90 mins.

The Original Flash Gordon
A box set of the original Flash Gordon movie serials by King Features—starring the young Buster Crabbe. Action-packed adventure! Includes *The Deadly Ray from Mars, The Peril from Planet Mongo, Spaceship to the Unknown* and *The Purple Death from Outer*

Hi Ho, Silver!

Black Beauty (1933)
VHS: S22601. $19.95.

The Black Stallion
DVD: DV60103. $24.98.
VHS: S00140. $19.95.
Laser: LD70527. $34.98.

The Electric Horseman
VHS: S21277. $14.98.

Equus
VHS: S00411. $14.95.

Into the West
VHS: S21031. $19.95.

Misfits
VHS: S04198. $19.98.
Laser: LD70631. $39.98.

My Friend Flicka
VHS: S14211. $14.98.

National Velvet
DVD: DV60105. $24.98.
VHS: S01789. $19.98.
Laser: LD70636. $69.98.

Return to Snowy River
VHS: S07919. $89.95.

Wild Hearts Can't Be Broken
VHS: S15530. $92.95.

Sitting on the Hot Seat

Angels with Dirty Faces
VHS: S03317. $19.95.
Laser: LD70146. $34.98.

A Dark Adapted Eye
VHS: S27745. $19.98.

Dead Man Walking
DVD: DV60004. $29.95.
VHS: S28059. $19.98.
Laser: LD75802. $44.95.

Execution of Private Slovik
VHS: S14944. $79.95.

I Want to Live
VHS: S03459. $24.95.
Laser: LD72268. $39.98.

In Cold Blood
VHS: S00615. $19.95.

The Unquiet Death of Julius and Ethel Rosenberg
VHS: S04736. $59.95.

Space. Four videocassettes. Total time: 6 hrs.
VHS: S13887. $79.95.

Phantom of Paradise
Outrageous horror-rock comedy featuring pop musician Paul Williams as a notorious record tycoon who sells his soul to the devil for success. William Finley stars as a rock composer victim of an accident that leaves him disfigured and blaming Williams. Macabre and a bit bizarre.
VHS: S01018. $14.98.
Brian DePalma, USA, 1974, 92 mins.

Pink Flamingos
The 25th anniversary edition of John Waters' underground trash classic starring Divine in his/her quest to become "the filthiest person alive" has been digitally remastered and features never-before-seen footage, the original theatrical trailer and commentary by Waters. Widescreen.
VHS: S31386. $19.98.
Laser: LD76281. $49.95.
John Waters, USA, 1972, 108 mins.

Plan 9 from Outer Space
Aliens invade earth and revive corpses from a San Fernando Valley cemetery to aide them in their dreams of conquest. Bela Lugosi is featured in this camp classic, but he died shortly after production began. Fortunately he was replaced by a taller man with a cape over his face. Possibly the worst film ever made.
VHS: S01036. $14.95.
Ed Wood, Jr., USA, 1959, 79 mins.

Planet of the Apes
Astronaut Charlton Heston crash lands on a distant world where he finds that human beings are not the dominant species. The novel by Pierre Boulle was adapted for the screen by Rod Serling and Michael Wilson and won a Special Oscar for its outstanding achievement in make-up. Kim Hunter, Roddy McDowall, Maurice Evans, and James Whitmore are some of the stars in simian suits. Followed by four sequels and a couple of TV shows.
VHS: S12171. $19.98.
Franklin J. Schaffner, USA, 1968, 112 mins.

Primitive Love
The "lost" 1964 Jayne Mansfield movie from Italy, featuring Franchi and Ciccio (Italy's answer to Martin and Lewis?) as two horny bellhops who spy on the bodacious Jayne as she finds every excuse to romp around almost naked. Then, it's *mondo* time as Jayne narrates her shockumentary, featuring topless Asian babes, *real* animal sacrifices and oriental cockfighting.
VHS: S32037. $29.95.
Luigi Scattini, Italy, 1964, 77 mins.

Putney Swope
A token black accidentally becomes chairman of a conservative ad agency, transforming the firm into "Truth and Soul, Inc." Classic satire from director Robert Downey, featuring Mel Brooks in one of his first film roles.
VHS: S01075. $19.95.
Laser: LD74962. $39.99.
Robert Downey, USA, 1969, 88 mins.

Quest for Fire
Eighty thousand years ago the Cro-Magnon equivalents of the Three Stooges set out to find fire. On the way they locate Rae Dawn Chong and invent the missionary position. Less serious than intended, this prehistoric epic does have its moments.

VHS: S04597. $69.98.
Jean-Jacques Annaud, Canada/France, 1981, 100 mins.

Reefer Madness
This anti-marijuana propaganda film has become a cult classic. Dave O'Brien plays a twitchy, eye-rolling lunatic who sits around talking to himself as he chain smokes the dreaded weed.
VHS: S01102. $19.95.
Louis Gasnier, USA, 1939, 65 mins.

Return of the Blind Dead
The second of four movies by Ossori featuring the dreaded Templar knights—mummified zombie/vampires who have vowed to return and destroy the ancestors of those who killed them during the Middle Ages. Considered by many to be the most terrifying of the Templar films. Presented in its original uncut form. Dubbed in English.
VHS: S31679. $14.98.
Amando Ossori, Portugal, 1975, 90 mins.

Revenge of the Bee Girls
From the producer of *Enter the Dragon* comes this "wonderfully campy and sexy sci-fi" (Leonard Maltin) about a strange force that turns a group of ordinary small-town California housewives into dangerous and ravishing predators who "love" men to death. Written by a pre-*Seven Percent Solution* Nicholas Meyer.
VHS: S31280. $14.95.
Denis Sanders, USA, 1973, 85 mins.

Rock 'n' Roll High School
The Ramones provide the high-energy music that drives this cult classic reworking of the rock 'n' roll teen movie format of the '50s. Stars P.J. Soles, Vincent Van Patten, Paul Bartel, Don Steele, Clint Howard, Dey Young, Mary Woronov, Dick Miller and Grady Sutton.
VHS: S28610. $14.98.
Laser: Widescreen, CLV. LD76026. $49.95.
Allan Arkush, USA, 1979, 93 mins.

Rocky Horror Picture Show
Now you can do the Time Warp in the privacy of your own home. The cult movie of cult movies is finally available in the U.S. on video. When Brad and Janet are forced to spend the night at the foreboding castle of the sexually ambitious Dr. Frank-Furter, they had no idea so many people would stay up late to watch them squirm. With Tim Curry, Barry Bostwick, Susan Sarandon, Richard O'Brien, Meatloaf and Little Nell.
VHS: S14008. $19.98.
Laser: THX. LD76381. $29.99.
Jim Sharman, USA, 1975, 105 mins.

Schramm
Nekromantik's director Jorg Buttgereit depicts the world of a serial killer in this hypnotizing orgy of sex and violence. It's all seen through the eyes of the killer, Lothar Schramm (Florian Koemer von Gustorf). He is fascinated by a prostitute (Monika M.) and obsessed with death. The result is a well-crafted, surreal vision of love and desire.
VHS: S27510. $19.95.
Jorg Buttgereit, Germany, 90 mins.

Scream, Blacula, Scream
Pam Grier is Lisa, the voodoo princess who must persuade the ferocious black vampire Manuwalde (William Marshall) from draining the life's blood from any more of the black community in Los Angeles. This sequel to *Blacula* features Richard Lawson, Don Mitchell, Lynn Moody and Michael

Conrad as the Sheriff. Set in L.A. and Africa.
VHS: S07450. $59.98.
Bob Kelljan, USA, 1973, 95 mins.

Secrets of Female Sexual Ecstacy
Hosted by Charles and Caroline Muir, America's foremost western educators of the ancient Indian artform of tantric sex, this tastefully explicit tape featuring actual tantric couples is designed to teach both men and women how to use sexual energy for increased intimacy, harmony and pleasure. Contains sections on increasing sexual intimacy, sexual healing, touch and kissing, freeing female orgasm, methods of pelvic movement, energy exchange meditations and the truth about amrita (female ejaculation). "Charles and Caroline are emissaries from the future, leaders for a generation that desires an end to the battle of the sexes and the begining of a new form of relationship" (*Whole Life Times*).
VHS: S30765. $39.95.

Sex and Zen
An unusually high-class, erotic tale, based on the ancient literary classic *The Prayer-Mat of Flesh*. Amy Yip Chi-Mei flaunts her voluptuousness in the face of Lawrence Ng, an easily distracted scholar who has his penis replaced by that of a horse in a Taoist transplantation ritual you'll have to see to believe! Also features Ken Chang and Isabella Chow. Letterboxed. Cantonese/Mandarin with English subtitles.
VHS: S30317. $49.95.
Laser: Letterboxed. **LD76113. $69.95.**
Michael Mak Dong-Kit, Hong Kong, 1993

Sex Education Films of the 40's
Five short films include *Dating Do's and Don'ts, USS-VD: The Ship of Shame*, and *Know for Sure*.
VHS: S02586. $34.95.

She-Devils on Wheels
This cult classic was the first feminist biker movie; the story of the "Man Eaters" gang proves that women can slap men around and use them for sexual meat too. Portrayed by real lady bikers from an organization out of Miami called the "Cut-Throats." Watch for the famous "stud line" scene, and always remember the Man-Eaters' motto: "Sex, Guts, Blood, and all men are Mothers!" Directed by Herschell Gordon Lewis, who fashioned a career out of exploiting the forbidden, the tasteless, and the bizarre.
VHS: S15140. $19.98.
Herschell Gordon Lewis, USA, 1968, 90 mins.

Sinister Urge
One of Ed Wood's least-known films, dedicated to the idea that overweight women in their underwear are the principal cause of juvenile delinquency. Two zealous cops are out to smash the "smut picture racket" and stop a "sex maniac killer" who is motivated by the dirty pictures as the "psycho killer strikes terror in every woman's heart." Originally titled *Sinister Sex*, the title was too risque for the 1960's and had to be changed.
VHS: S22912. $19.95.
Ed Wood, Jr., USA, 1960, 75 mins.

Spider Baby
Lon Chaney Jr. heads a household of inbred cannibals in this bizarre and many-titled horror cheapie. As if

that weren't enough, he also sings the theme song. Included in the cast of wackos are Sid Haig, Carol Ohmart and the ever-popular Mantan Moreland. B&W. It's weird.
VHS: S04035. $14.98.
Jack Hill, USA, 1964, 86 mins.

Sssssss
From the same special effects creator who brought you *Planet of the Apes* comes this spine-tingling sci-fi classic about a mad scientist who transforms a young man into a king cobra with venomous results. With Strother Martin and Dirk Benedict. "Finally! A horror film we chiller freaks can recommend to our friends" (*Cosmopolitan*).
VHS: S31081. $14.98.
Bernard L. Kowalski, USA, 1973, 99 mins.

The Stepford Wives
For two decades this film's title and what it implies have been ingrained into our vocabulary and consciousness. Something strange is happening in the town of Stepford, where the men spend their nights doing something secret and every woman acts like every man's dream of the "perfect" wife—a dream that is really a nightmare. With Katherine Ross, Paula Prentiss, Tina Louise, Dee Wallace, Patrick O'Neal and seven-year-old Mary Stuart Masterson, making her film debut. "I can promise you an eerie, spine-tingling, good shiver down the spine with the *Stepford Wives*" (Rex Reed, *The New York Daily News*).
VHS: S31190. $14.98.
Laser: LD76197. $39.98.
Bryan Forbes, USA, 1974, 115 mins.

Surf Nazis Must Die
A camp film with a great title in which, in the wake of a killer earthquake, the beaches of California have been taken over by neo-Nazi punks. Their reign of terror comes to a halt when a retired, fat black woman with a .38 stops them dead!
VHS: S05894. $79.95.
Peter George, USA, 1987, 83 mins.

Suroh: The Alien Hitchhiker
Paul is a reporter for a small newspaper who, while attending a UFO conference, comes across an actual alien. The being has crash landed and needs Paul's help. This premise takes on an entirely new dimension when Paul and the alien initiate an interspecies sexual liason. Despite the emotional depth of this experience Paul must help his new friend to return or face destruction from evil, earth-bound forces.
VHS: S29443. $29.95.
Patrick McGuinn, USA, 1996, 74 mins.

Suspiria
Considered by many to be one of the most terrifying and stylized horror films of recent years, *Suspiria* stars Jessica Harper as Susy Banyon, an American student who has enrolled in a German dance academy. On the very night she arrives, two of the students are brutally murdered. It soon becomes apparent that this is only the beginning of a terrifying nightmare. "The most eagerly awaited horror film of the decade…the most stylish and simply one of the best horror films ever made" (Fangoria).
VHS: S10717. $19.98.
Dario Argento, Italy, 1984, 97 mins.

And God Created...Video

Ben-Hur
VHS: S02517. $29.98.
Laser: LD70524. $49.98.

David and Bathsheba
VHS: S10325. $19.98.

El Cid
VHS: S04324. $29.95.

The Gospel According to St. Matthew
VHS: S18168. $29.95.

Judith of Bethula/Home Sweet Home
VHS: S18436. $24.95.

King of Kings
VHS: S02727. $24.98.
Laser: LD70608. $39.97.

A Man for All Seasons
VHS: S08228. $79.98.

The Robe
VHS: S04595. $19.98.

Song of Bernadette
VHS: S15607. $19.98.

The Ten Commandments (1923)
VHS: S03439. $29.95.

All Hopped Up

Arthur
DVD: DV60069. $24.98.
VHS: S14564. $19.95.
Laser: LD74686. $24.98.

Barfly
VHS: S06587. $19.98.
Laser: LD70517. $34.98.

Bird
VHS: S09321. $19.98.
Laser: LD70526. $29.98.

Clean and Sober
VHS: S09923. $19.98.

Come Back, Little Sheba
VHS: S13789. $19.95.

Days of Wine and Roses
VHS: S25896. $19.98.

Dead Ringers
VHS: S09841. $19.98.
Laser: LD75933. $124.95.

**Dona Flor and
Her Two Husbands**
VHS: S00359. $19.98.

Drugstore Cowboy
VHS: S11724. $14.98.
Laser: LD70955. $39.95.

The Entertainer
VHS: S08261. $19.95.
Laser: LD75918. $49.95.

The Fire Within
VHS: S17697. $29.95.

Georgia
VHS: S27847. $99.99.
Laser: LD75929. $39.99.

Gervaise
VHS: S00493. $24.95.

Ironweed
VHS: S06865. $19.98.

Le Beau Serge
VHS: S03509. $29.95.

Leaving Las Vegas
VHS: S27709. $19.98.
Laser: LD75568. $34.98.

Less Than Zero
VHS: S06620. $19.98.

**Long Day's Journey
into Night**
VHS: S02576. $19.98.
Laser: LD71550. $39.98.

The Lost Weekend
VHS: S06869. $19.95.

Man with the Golden Arm
VHS: S04439. $19.98.

Midnight Express
VHS: S02549. $69.95.
Laser: LD74476. $39.95.

My Favorite Year
VHS: S21871. $19.98.
Laser: LD74522. $34.98.

Naked Lunch
VHS: S16382. $94.98.
Laser: LD71581. $39.98.

A Star Is Born
VHS: S18187. $24.95.
Laser: LD70684. $39.98.

Trainspotting
VHS: S30637. $103.99.
Laser: LD76092. $49.98.

Under the Volcano
VHS: S01399. $79.95.
Laser: LD70093. $34.98.

The Verdict
VHS: S02344. $19.98.
Laser: LD71392. $44.98.

Whiskey Galore
VHS: S02030. $29.95.

Swamp Women
Marie Windsor, Beverly Garland and Michael Connors star in this complicated but campy thriller about a group of women criminals in search of riches and freedom in the Louisiana Bayou. These bad women are guided by two things only: greed and lust.
VHS: S23778. $24.95.
Roger Corman, USA, 1955, 73 mins.

Sweet Sweetback's Baadasssss Song
Melvin Van Peebles wrote, directed, produced, scored and starred in this critically acclaimed, reverse racist blaxploitation movie that has Van Peebles on the run from the police after he kills two cops who were beating up on a black man. With John Amos, Simon Chuckster and Rhetta Hughes. X-rated when first released.
VHS: S06195. $59.95.
Laser: LD76004. $49.95.
Melvin Van Peebles, USA, 1971, 90 mins.

Switchblade Sisters
The "Switchblade Sisters" is a tough, all-women gang fighting for turf. These outrageous teenage hoodlums create mayhem everywhere they go, from the classroom to the steets, and eventually confront one another in a final switchblade fight. With Joanne Nail and Monica Gayle. "A shotgun wedding of mini-skirts and M-16s. Timeless and quite entertaining" (*Newsday*).
VHS: S30638. $103.99.
Laser: Widescreen. LD76165. $49.98.
Jack Hill, USA, 1996, 90 mins.

Tales of Erotica
The directors of *Desperately Seeking Susan*, *The Postman Always Rings Twice*, *Sweet Sweetback's Badasss Song* and *Women in Love* bring their uninhibited erotic fantasies to the screen in this joint project. In all four stories, desire unleashes unforseen consequences. This film also offers a chance to see Academy Award winner Mira Sorvino in a frank new light.
VHS: S29000. $14.95.
Ken Russell/Susan Seidelman/Melvin Van Peebles/ Bob Rafelson, USA, 1996, 103 mins.

Teenage Devil Dolls
Mamie Van Doren hosts this "tough" teen film, with the Devil Dolls. Young Cassandra joins a crazy gang where she starts on reefer, graduates to goofballs, and is soon found groveling in garbage, looking for a fix. Naturally, this lands her in the psycho ward, and

eventually back on the streets.
VHS: S05204. $24.95.
B. Lawrence Price, USA, 1953, 70 mins.

Teenage Strangler
Bill Posner's funky variation of the juvenile delinquent angst drama follows the deranged activities of a lipstick killer who is suffocating schoolgirls with stockings in Huntington, West Virginia. A member of a local gang called the Fastdogs, Jimmy is a prime suspect. The film weaves in the social protest and outlaw behavior of the 60s B-movie (including drag races, rumbles and rock and roll) within the trappings of the serial killer movie. With Bill A. Bloom, Jo Canterbury and John Ensign.
VHS: S20108. $24.95.
Bill Posner, USA, 1964, 64 mins.

Terror of Tiny Town
One of the classic camp films: a musical Western enacted entirely by midgets. One of the wonders of Hollywood. With Billy Curtis, Yvonne Moray, Little Billy, John Bambury.
VHS: S03056. $19.95.
Sam Newfield, USA, 1963, 63 mins.

The Texas Chainsaw Massacre
Tobe Hooper's restored cult film is a frightening piece of Americana. This strange subversion of the slasher movie concerns five friends traveling through a flat, nondescript Texas wasteland who encounter a bizarre family and are forced to struggle for their lives. With Marilyn Burns, Allen Danzinger, Paul A. Partain and William Vail.
VHS: S19463. $19.98.
Laser: LD71919. $29.98.
Tobe Hooper, USA, 1974, 81 mins.

They Eat Scum
John Waters liked this "disgusting outlay of cheapness, decadence, nihilism and everyday cannibalism. Nick Zedd's film must rank as something of an ultimate achievement of non-committal, unblinking savagery, a true expression of what used to be called the 'punk ethos'." Stars Donna Death.
VHS: S10162. $39.95.
Nick Zedd, USA, 1979, 70 mins.

They Saved Hitler's Brain
One of the great cult classics: a scientist is kidnapped; his daughter traces him to the mysterious island of Mandoras where a cult of Nazi worshippers

is manipulated by the severed head of Adolf. 74 mins.
VHS: S05381. $29.95.

The Third Sex
Paula Wesley and Paul Dahlke star in this
exploitative look at homosexuality. Parents try to
straighten out their son, who is hanging out with a
known gay man. It's a shocker. 1959.
VHS: S23187. $24.95.

Tombs of the Blind Dead
Spanish auteur Ossorio made his name in the '70s
Spanish horror genre with this tale of horrific and
malefic reanimated mummified corpses of 13th-
century Templar knights who seek victims through
sound alone and drink human blood in order to
sustain their own damned existence. The superb,
highly influential score by Anton Garcia Abril helps
underline the stunning visuals. Despite the trite
storylines and hammy acting, "the Templars make
Ossorio's grisly, heart-string quartet more than worth
the effort, galloping to the rescue of the viewer's
sanity like a spectral cavalry charge" (Nigel J.
Burrell, March 1995). Digitally remastered
collector's edition presented in its original uncut
form. Spanish with English subtitles.
VHS: S31002. $14.98.
Amando de Ossorio, Spain, 1972, 102 mins.

Trail of Blood
A dramatization based on the notorious Green River
serial murder case, which, despite over 40 female
victims, remains unsolved. *Trail of Blood* features
some of the most colorful and offbeat characters
imaginable, with such personalities as Warhol
superstar Taylor Mead, art terrorist and serial killer
aficionado Joe Coleman, author William Kotzwinkle
(*E.T.*) and philosophical performance guru
Copernicus. The film also introduces the master of
pop Yiddish humor, Arthur of New York, and actress/
model Madonna Chavez (the niece of the late labor
leader Cesar Chavez) Directed by Russian filmmaker/
painter Ari Roussimof.
VHS: S31135. $49.95.
Ari Roussimof, USA/Mexico, 1996, 105 mins.

Valley of the Dolls
An examination of the dark side of Hollywood and
the industry's objectification of a group of actresses,
where the vicissitudes and dangers of drugs, sexual
exploitation, infidelity, insecurity, jealousy, betrayal
and fear intermingle in the lives of the various
"dolls," ambitious young women desperate for
stardom and recognition. Adapted from Jacqueline
Susann's novel. With Patty Duke, Barbara Parkins,
Sharon Tate and Paul Burke.
VHS: S18598. $14.98.
Laser: LD76739. $39.98.
Mark Robson, USA, 1967, 123 mins.

Videodrome
Videodrome is a pulsating sci-fi nightmare from
macabre master David Cronenberg (*Scanners*) about a
world where video can control and alter human life.
Featuring a wonderfully sleazy James Woods, and
Deborah Harry as a kinky talk-show hostess.
VHS: S01414. $14.98.
David Cronenberg, Canada, 1982, 87 mins.

The Violent Years
This recently re-discovered classic by Ed Wood, Jr.
(*Plan 9*) features filthy rich teenage sex kittens who
form gangs, rob gas stations, rape rich guys, and strip
gown "goody" girls. A cheap thrills masterpiece.
VHS: S05186. $14.95.
Ed Wood, Jr., USA, 1956, 60 mins.

Vixen
Meyer's critical and popular success, as Roger Ebert
described it, "a merciless put-on…Erica Gavin is
electrifying!"
VHS: S03585. $79.95.

The Wacky World of Doctor Morgus
Filmed in the back alleys and tacky cafes of New
Orleans, Dr. Morgus (a TV horror show host), his
comatose girlfriend Zelda and his sidekick Chopsely
join in a fiendish plot to take over the country. The
evil ruler of Microvania is preparing to smuggle 300
spies into the United States; his secret weapon is the
Doctor's "instant people machine" that turns humans
into sand—then reanimates them. Enter ace reporter
Pencils McCane to foil the dastardly plot. The climax
is the icing on the cake in a city famous for its
eccentric inhabitants.
VHS: S30733. $29.95.
Roul Haig, USA, 1962, 87 mins.

The Wasp Woman
A Roger Corman sociological study of White Anglo-
Saxon Protestant women who turn into demented
killers by using an untested beauty cream. Susan
Cabot stars as a cosmetics executive who learns, too
late, about the side effects of the latest beauty aid.
With Anthony Eiseley, Michael Mark, Bruno VeSota
and Barboura Morris. Written by Leo Gordon (*Giant
Leeches*). B&W.
VHS: S09133. $29.95.
Laser: LD76055. $39.99.
Roger Corman, USA, 1959, 73 mins.

Weird World of LSD
Terry Tessem, Ann Lindsay and Yolanda Morino star
in this expose of countercultural drug use. The effects
of LSD have never been so bizarrely portrayed as in
this schlocky camp classic. 1967.
VHS: S23192. $24.95.

White Slaves of Chinatown
Sex and drugs rule in this first of Frank Henenlotter's
depraved "Olga" films, in which the sadistic Olga
keeps Lola and half a dozen other girls in bondage
and throws drug parties in her Chinatown torture
headquarters.
VHS: S27547. $29.95.
Joseph P. Mawra, USA, 1964

Wild Guitar
The curiosity film from the early 60s, capturing the
pre-Beatles scene in America. Arch Hall Jr. stars as a
young, naive, pompadoured pixie who motorcycles
into Hollywood with nothing more than a "git-tar"
and the clothes on his back, and within minutes of his
arrival, appears on TV, becomes a superstar, and falls
into the clutches of an unscrupulous, cigar-chomping
manager.
VHS: S05188. $9.95.
Ray Dennis Steckler, USA, 1962, 92 mins.

10
Unintentionally
Humorous/
Big Budget

The Greatest Show on Earth
VHS: S06146. $29.95.

Mary Shelley's Frankenstein
VHS: S24385. $19.95.
Laser: LD74901. $39.95.

Mommie Dearest
VHS: S00869. $19.95.
Laser: LD75385. $35.98.

Rider on the Rain
Currently unavailable; for rental only.

The Robe
VHS: S04595. $19.98.

Showgirls
VHS: S26951. $19.98.
Laser: LD75424. $49.99.

The Ten Commandments: 40th
Anniversary Collector's Edition
VHS: S15100. $35.00.

Waterworld
VHS: S26950. $19.95.
Laser: LD75423. $44.99.

Wolf
DVD: DV60136. $24.95.
VHS: S23221. $19.95.
Laser: LD74664. $39.95.

Bugging Out:
Top 12½ Insect Fear Films

By Richard J. Leskosky, Film Critic and Consultant to the Insect Fear Film Festival at the University of Illinois Urbana-Champaign

You thought only outdoors types had to worry about fire ants, killer bees, Asian tiger mosquitoes, and deer ticks that carry Lyme disease. Only the occasional roach in the pantry bothered you. But arthropods of various sizes and shapes have suddenly burst back onto the movie screen with a vengeance: *Mimic, Starship Troopers, Joe's Apartment, Men in Black,* and even *Angels & Insects* have brought back the dark thrills of entomophobia to darkened theatres (and it's best not to think about what's crawling under your seat!).

If you want to savor some classics of this off-beat genre in your own home, however, check out this not-quite baker's dozen of titles. All have played at the annual and very original Insect Fear Film Festival at the University of Illinois at Urbana-Champaign, and most have more than big and/or creepy critters to recommend them. Just remember, though, we're not talking great cinema here.

1) Them! (1954)—The first and still one of the best big-bug movies. Ants grow to enormous size in the southwestern desert as a result of radiation from nuclear testing. When scientists and the army rout them, the colony moves to L.A. and nests in the storm drains. The big ants may look fake today, but the film was nominated for a Special Effects Oscar. James Arness and James Whitmore provide the heroics while competing for the attention of the woman scientist who's usually along in these films to be threatened by the monsters.

2) The Naked Jungle (1954)—Charlton Heston battles hordes of army ants chewing their way across his South American plantation while also trying to deal with the discovery that his recently arrived mail-order bride has been (gasp!) married before. One of the most realistic (or at least one of the least science-fictionish) of the Insect Fear Films—if you don't count things such as the telescope that lets Heston see individual ants a mile away. Lots of running around and screaming as the ants munch on the hired help.

3) Tarantula (1955)—Spiders aren't insects, of course, but Insect Fear Films actually include all sorts of arthro-pods, including spiders, ticks and scorpions. Jack Arnold's big spider movie is one of the best of the genre. The title critter is created by well-meaning Leo G. Carroll's attempts to increase the size of food sources. John Agar is on hand to help battle the critter and Mara Corday weighs in with the observation, "Science is science but a girl's got to get her hair done." Look quickly and you can spot jet pilot Clint Eastwood bombing the tarantula in the last reel.

4) Beginning of the End (1957)—Grasshoppers grow to giant size after eating giant irradiated fruit and then go on a rampage through the mountains and eucalyptus groves of central Illinois. When they get to Chicago and climb up a photo of the Wrigley Building, the army decides to nuke them. But scientist Peter Graves objects, "You can't drop an atom bomb on Chicago!" and does in the hoppers with environmental controls.

5) The Fly (1958)—A scientist (David Heddison, called Al at this point in his career) experiments with matter transmission and gets his molecules swapped with those of a housefly. While his wife tries to find the fly and unscramble the two, the now fly-headed scientist gets progressively crazier and more dangerous. Vincent Price is on hand as a sympathetic character—the fly's brother-in-law. Famous line: "Help me! Help me!"

6) The Wasp Woman (1960)—A Roger Corman quickie, remade in 1996 but not as much fun in the later version. A woman CEO of a cosmetics company uses some untested wasp serum to rejuvenate her looks and her business and (oops!) turns into a wasp-like creature that preys on her employees and rivals. You can draw all sorts of morals from this one, including the advisability of animal testing in cosmetics.

7) Mothra (1961)—One of Inishiro Honda's beloved giant monster movies and the first of the title creature's many appearances. A monstrously large caterpillar attacks Tokyo and then turns into a really big moth for round two. Mothra was the first monster to appear in more than one form (long before *Alien*), one of the few actually identified as female, and one

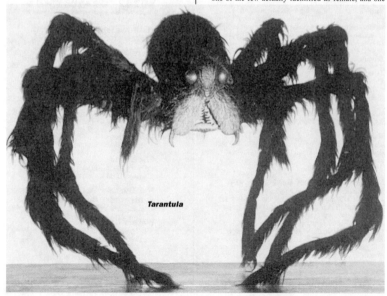

Tarantula

of the very few to have sidekicks—a couple of tiny girls whose song summons Mothra and who keep telling people to let it go (played by The Peanuts, an actual Japanese singing duo). This is an Insect Fear Film for those who don't really like to be scared—it's a moth, for goodness sake! And don't forget the moral: the monster would have stayed on its island if it weren't for those pesky capitalists trying to make a buck off it.

8) Bug (1975)—Scientist Bradford Dillman, upset by the death of his wife, seeks revenge on the subterranean fire-starting cock-roaches which brought it about. First, though, he tinkers with their genetics so that they'll be smarter and be able to understand pain. Bad move! They get too smart, start spelling words on the wall, and eventually fry Dillman, too. Horror meister William Castle's last film. (The bugs got him, too!)

9) The Giant Spider Invasion (1975)—Diamond meteorites falling on Wisconsin farms turn out to be the eggs of alien spiders, who soon get big and hungry. Steve Brodie and Barbara Hale are the brave investigators trying to find a way to stop them, while sheriff Alan Hale remains by the phone in his office making *Gilligan's Island* jokes. Made on location in Wisconsin with a VW bug covered in fake hair and big legs passing for a giant spider.

10) Empire of the Ants (1977)—Bert I. Gordon (the Mr. BIG of giant critter movies) very loosely adapts a story by H.G. Wells. Land developer Joan Collins takes a group of vacationers/marks on a tour of some swampy Florida real estate and discovers giant ants created by toxic waste. Robert

Lansing helps the survivors escape through the swamp, but what's going on at that sugar mill they have to pass on the way out? See Joan face off against the queen ant in a memorable finale.

11) The Bees (1978)—There are many films dealing with killer bees, and this is probably the worst. But it does feature John Carradine in one of his last roles; John Saxon tries to talk to the bees; and Gerald Ford puts in an involuntary cameo appearance during a Rose Bowl parade attacked by bees. The bees eventually go to the United Nations to complain about human beings' foolhardy environmental policies—with rather more drama and success than, say, Al Gore.

12) The Fly (1986)—David Cronenberg's remake with Jeff Goldblum and Geena Davis is one of the best and most serious Insect Fear Films and one of the creepiest—a love story in which one partner slowly turns into something hideous. Cronenberg made this film in part because a promotion for the first film cheated him as a kid out of a prize for proving that the story couldn't happen the way the filmmakers presented it. Famous line: "Be afraid! Be very afraid!"

12½) Creepshow (1982)—Only the last of the five episodes in this George Romero/Stephen King horror film classifies as an Insect Fear Film, but that one's a classic. E.G. Marshall plays a reclusive, entomophobic millionaire who tries to wipe out all the roaches in his high-tech urban sanctuary, only to have thousands of roaches swarming everywhere until the gross-out climax. Sadly, most of the film's cast died right after the cameras stopped rolling.

22 Top Hong Kong Action Films

The Armour of God
Filmed on location in Yugoslavia, Austria, France and Hong Kong, this fast-moving vehicle for comedy/action star Jackie Chan nearly cost him his life when a relatively simple stunt misfired. Chan plays an adventurer who steals pieces of a prized medieval armour set to sell to rich collectors. But these ancient artifacts are also sought by a criminal cult which will stop at nothing to obtain them. When the cult kidnaps Jackie's former love, Jackie comes up with even more spectacular ways to save the armour and the girl. One of Chan's most thrilling and entertaining films (and with him, that's really saying something). Cantonese with English subtitles.
VHS: $14863. $49.95.
Jackie Chan, Hong Kong, 1986, 100 mins.

Ashes of Time
This moody costume drama plays out almost entirely in close-up, with dialogue spoken at a whisper. The all-star cast includes Brigette Lin Ching-Hsia, Leslie Cheung Hok-Yau, Tony Leung Kar-Fai, Tony Leung Chiu-Wai, Carina Lau Kar-Ling, Maggie Cheung Man-Yu and Jacky Cheung Hok-Yau. Action directed by Sammo Hung with characters from Jin Yong's *Eagle-Shooting Heroes*. Two-tape set. Letterboxed. Cantonese/Mandarin with English subtitles.
VHS: $30525. $89.95.
Wong Kar-Wai, Hong Kong, 1992-94

A Better Tomorrow
Kit is an up-and-coming cop, but his brother Ho is a street-hardened criminal. Soon they are both dragged into a savage underworld battle over counterfeit money. Even if Ho wants to go straight, there is a murderous price to pay that forces the brothers into a deadly confrontation.
VHS: $13455. $19.98.
John Woo, Hong Kong, 1986, 90 mins.

A Better Tomorrow—Part II
Although the charismatic gangster Mark, played by Chow Yun Fat, was killed at the end of Part I, Chow returns here as Mark's previously unmentioned twin brother Ken. Ken joins forces with an idealistic cop named Kit (Leslie Cheung) and his now-reformed gangster brother Ti Lung, against another legion of evil criminals. Cantonese with English subtitles.
VHS: $13456. $39.95.
John Woo, Hong Kong, 1988, 100 mins.

A Better Tomorrow—Part III
Chow Yun Fat returns as Mark Gor, the stylish police detective, in this sequel which is actually a prequel. Set in 1974, Gor and his cousin (Tony Leung) want to escape the post-war squalor of Saigon. Unfortunately, both are in love with the same woman (Anita Mui), a gangster moll. This action-filled adventure is loaded with plot twists, outrageously choreographed violent sequences, and a love triangle that leads to tragedy. Also known as *Love and Death in Saigon*. Mandarin with English subtitles.
VHS: $27267. $49.95.
Tsui Hark, Hong Kong, 1989, 114 mins.

Bullet in the Head
John Woo's epic tale of three friends (Tony Leung, Jacky Cheung and Waise Lee) caught up in the turbulent events of the 1960s in Hong Kong and later, in Vietnam, where the three hope to exploit the anarchy and corruption that prevail, only to find themselves in danger of being overwhelmed by it. Their drama is played out in a country captured by such filmic precedents as *The Deer Hunter*, *Platoon* and *Missing in Action*, seemingly an ideal setting for Woo to explore his themes of loyalty, honor and betrayal. Chinese with English subtitles.
VHS: $20584. $49.95.
Laser: LD76119. $69.95.
John Woo, Hong Kong, 1990

A Chinese Ghost Story
An entertaining and atmospheric supernatural love story with knock-out special effects. In ancient China, a young scholar takes shelter from the rain in a haunted temple where he falls for a beautiful ghost. With the aid of a Taoist monk, the young couple battle a variety of foes (including a giant tongue which gives new meaning to the expression "I've been slimed") and even storm the gates of Hell. With Leslie Cheung, Wong Tsu Hsien, and Wu Ma. Cantonese with English subtitles.
VHS: $13480. $49.95.
Ching Siu Tung, Hong Kong, 1987, 93 mins.

Drunken Master II
Jackie Chan stars in this hyperactive but humorous action adventure. The legendary Young Wong Fei Hung finds himself in possession of a jade seal that sets off competing bands of British imperialists and local thugs. It's all part of a plot to rob China of its crown jewels—a plot is so intricately laced with bad guys flying through the air that it takes two parts to

resolve. Cantonese and Mandarin with English subtitles.
Part A.
VHS: $27793. $49.95.
Lau Kar Leung, Hong Kong, 1994, 204 mins.

Eastern Condors
A high-energy Hong Kong version of *The Dirty Dozen*. The U.S. military sends a group of convicts back to Vietnam on a mission to destroy an abandoned ammunition dump before the Viet Cong discover it and use it for their own evil purposes. Stars Sammo Hung, Joyce Godenzi, Yuen Biao and Haing (*The Killing Fields*) Ngor. Letterboxed. Cantonese with English subtitles.
VHS: $13444. $59.95.
Laser: LD76309. $39.95.
Samo Hung, Hong Kong, 1986, 100 mins.

Enter the Dragon
Bruce Lee is probably the name that comes to mind for most Americans when they think of martial arts action films. Here the stern-faced Lee infiltrates a strange tournament on an island fortress. With John Saxon and Jim Kelly. In English.
VHS: $14867. $49.95.
Laser: LD72261. $34.98.
Robert Clouse, USA, 1973, 97 mins.

God of Gamblers
Chow Yun Fat is the suave, almost telepathic God of Gamblers. A blow to the head dissipates his memory and sends him into a childlike frame of mind. Three small-time hustlers parasitically decide to cash in on this state of affairs, but they eventually grow fond of the former God. When his memory returns, Fat can't remember the three hustlers, but despite this complication, the trio comes to his aid as it becomes clear that he is surrounded by enemies. This comic action film was a huge hit and inspired countless imitations, sequels and parodies. With Andy Lau and Joey Wang. Cantonese with English subtitles.
VHS: $27291. $49.95.
Laser: LD76125. $89.95.
Wong Jing, Hong Kong, 1989, 125 mins.

Hard Boiled
This film is an action fan's dream. The seamy underworlds of gun smugglers, mobsters and rebel cops collide in this super-fast paced thriller. A police inspector and a mysterious hit man team up to thwart a dastardly plot hatched by ruthless criminals. Subtitled. Letterboxed. Cantonese with English subtitles.
VHS: $24848. $19.98.
John Woo, Hong Kong, 1992, 126 mins.

Heroic Trio
Three of Hong Kong's biggest female stars, Michelle Yeoh (Khan), Maggie Cheung and Anita Mui, play the leads in this strange tale of competing superheroines thwarting a mysterious series of baby kidnappings, in a comic book style (a la *Batman*). It has been suggested that the film is best read as a political allegory of the three entities of China, Taiwan and Hong Kong having to work together to overcome the many challenges facing them. Mandarin with English subtitles. Letterboxed.
VHS: $24169. $79.95.
Laser: Letterboxed. LD75501. $59.95.
Johnny To, Hong Kong, 1992

The Killer
John Woo wrote and directed this brilliant gangster drama set in contemporary Hong Kong. The charismatic Chow Yun Fat stars as an amoral hitman who accidentally blinds a young torch singer, agreeing on a final assignment to pay for her surgery. The other plot is Chow's relationship with a tough, uncompromising cop (Danny Lee), as they battle the Hong Kong underworld. *The Killer* is a high-octane mixture of outlandishly stylized camp and outrageously sensational shoot-outs" (J. Hoberman). VHS letterboxed. Chinese with English subtitles.
VHS: $13457. $19.98.
Laser: Director's cut includes trailers from other John Woo films, deleted scenes, commentary from Woo and a guide to Hong Kong cinema. LD72361. $124.95.
John Woo, Hong Kong, 1989, 102 mins.

Last Hurrah for Chivalry
A variation on the classic 1970's style kung-fu flick, starting out as a routine revenge drama, but bringing in a sense of character missing from most of the genre, and progressively veering from the expected development to question the motivations of its main

characters, although with plenty of good action along the way, including a classic scene in which the heroes fight the deadly "sleeping watchman." An early exploration by director John Woo of one of his favorite themes, that of loyalty in a chaotic world. Mandarin with English subtitles (occasionally a bit chopped).
VHS: $24172. $59.95.
Laser: LD76274. $39.99.
John Woo, Hong Kong, 1979

Peking Opera Blues
Three of the Hong Kong cinema's most popular actresses—Sally Yeh, Cherie Chung, and Lin Ching-Hsai—star in this fast-paced comedy/drama set in turn-of-the-century China. In addition to its stunning art-direction, this film features an assortment of plots and counterplots, assassins, singers, soldiers, and amazing action sequences. Cantonese with English subtitles.
VHS: $13462. $49.95.
Tsui Hark, Hong Kong, 1986, 104 mins.

The Protector
Jackie Chan is a New York cop celebrating his 10th anniversary as an American citizen. The sleazy South Bronx drug scene he is sharing an after-shift drink with his partner is raided by a gang of hoodlums. A shoot-out ensues and Jackie's partner is killed. Jackie goes after the gang leader and, in the process, destroys millions of dollars of public property. Now in disgrace, Jackie gets a new partner (Danny Aiello) and a new beat. But where Jackie goes, trouble follows, and the kidnapping of a fashion designer leads Jackie and Danny to Hong Kong and the nastiest drug dealing operation since *The French Connection*. In English.
VHS: $14854. $49.95.
James Glickenhaus, USA, 1985, 94 mins.

The Roar of the Vietnamese
A violent tale of illegal immigrants being manipulated by criminal gangs, forced to commit crimes in return for supposed passage to the U.S., focusing on a particular group of disparate individuals who bond together under the stress of their situation. More a melancholy action movie than a serious look at the plight of the Vietnamese. Chinese with English subtitles. Hong Kong, 1991.
VHS: $25946. $49.95.

Supercop
"Jackie Chan is at his best" (*Chicago Tribune*) as an undercover cop on a mission to put a high-powered drug lord out of business in this non-stop action film. From leaping off a ten-story building onto an airborne helicopter to sailing over speeding trains, Chan performs his own stunts, as usual, but this time he's partnered with Asia's hottest female action star and former Miss Malaysia, Michelle Khan.
VHS: $30863. $103.99.
Laser: Widescreen. LD76168. $49.98.
Stanley Tong, USA, 1996, 91 mins.

Wing Chun
Michelle Yeoh stars as cross-dressing kung fu innovator Yim Wing Chung, who battles the bandit lords and invents a new kung fu style. Don't miss the "tofu fight" and lesbian foot massage scenes. Chinese with English subtitles.
VHS: $27540. $19.95.
Laser: Letterboxed. LD75500. $59.95.
Yuen Wing Ping, Hong Kong, 1993

The Young Master
One of Jackie Chan's first films as director/star, it smashed all box office records upon first release and rocketed Jackie to world-wide recognition. This colorful period-comedy follows Jackie as he seeks to restore the honor of his kung fu school and his foster brother. Cantonese with English subtitles.
VHS: $14865. $19.95.
Laser: Letterboxed. LD76277. $39.99.
Jackie Chan, Hong Kong, 92 mins.

Zu: Warriors of the Magic Mountain
A mind-boggling adventure/fantasy with impressive special effects including an enormous, pulsing blood monster and a wizard with bushy and infinitely extendable eyebrows. Escaping from the midst of one of ancient China's senseless wars, an unlucky soldier falls through a hole and soon finds himself on a quest to save the earth from evil spirits. Cantonese with English subtitles.
VHS: $13475. $59.95.
Laser: Letterboxed. LD76373. $39.95.
Tsui Hark, Hong Kong, 1983, 95 mins.

50 Best Sci-Fi Films

12 Monkeys
Bruce Willis, Brad Pitt and Madeline Stowe are at the center of this elaborate sci-fi drama where mankind faces near extinction. Inspired by Chris Marker's classic *La Jetee*, it follows the travails of a man sent back through time. His mission is to find an answer that may somehow stave off the certain destruction of most of humanity. Unfortunately, he lands in a mental hospital. VHS letterboxed.
VHS: $28391. $19.98.
Laser: LD75702. $49.95.
Terry Gilliam, USA, 1995, 130 mins.

2001: A Space Odyssey
Stanley Kubrick's landmark film traces the three stages of man, from evolutionary, predatory animals to futuristic space travelers, astronauts on a mission to Jupiter sabotaged by a malfunctioning computer known as HAL. "A uniquely poetic piece of science fiction that's hypnotically entertaining" (*The New Yorker*). Adapted from Arthur C. Clarke's story *The Sentinel*. With Keir Dullea, Gary Lockwood and William Sylvester. Special visual effects by Douglas Trumbull. Letterboxed.
VHS: $18674. $19.98.
Laser: CAV, 3 discs, with 4-page insert. **LD71876. $69.98.**
Laser: CLV, 2 discs. **LD71877. $39.98.**
Stanley Kubrick, USA, 1968, 141 mins.

Aelita: Queen of Mars
One of the most remarkable discoveries of the Soviet silent cinema, *Aelita* is a stunning big-budget science fiction spectacle. Enormous futuristic sets and radical constructionist costumes were designed by Alexandra Exter to enhance this story of romance, comedy and danger. A Moscow engineer designs a spaceship and travels to Mars to meet the woman who haunts his dreams. He succeeds but finds himself embroiled in a Martian proletarian uprising. *Aelita*, with its exaggerated production design and political undertones, was a profound influence on Fritz Lang's *Metropolis* three years later. Silent, with orchestral score.
VHS: $13826. $29.95.
Yakov Protazanov, USSR, 1924, 113 mins.

Alien
Space explorers on a routine mission bring an extremely adaptable life form on board that attaches itself to crew members and reproduces itself. Most of the crew pay for the mistake with their lives. Notable special effects and relentless suspense from the director of *Blade Runner*. Screenplay by Dan O'Bannon.
VHS: $02337. $19.98.
Laser: LD72430. $49.98.
Ridley Scott, USA, 1979, 116 mins.

Alphaville
Eddie Constantine is Lemmy Caution, inter-galactic private eye, in this bravura mix of comic strip, science fiction and film noir in what is ultimately a new style of cinema in which form and content are identical. Lemmy sets out to dispose of diabolical scientist Leonard von Braun (a.k.a. Leonard Nosferatu) from Alphaville, the futuristic city run by an electronic brain, where love has been banished. A film in which poetry mixes freely with pulp to create a new dimension, a new cinematic reality. French with English subtitles.
VHS: $07702. $29.95.
Laser: LD75075. $49.95.
Jean-Luc Godard, France, 1965, 100 mins.

Aelita: Queen of Mars

Blade Runner

A visually expressive adaptation of Philip K. Dick's futurist novel about Deckard (Harrison Ford), a cynical detective assigned to terminate a group of genetically devolved replicants set loose in Los Angeles, circa 2019. In this special director's cut, Deckard's voice-over narration is eliminated and the original ending is restored. With Rutger Hauer, Sean Young, Edward James Olmos and Daryl Hannah. VHS letterboxed.
DVD: DV60107. $24.98.
VHS: S18596. $19.98.
Laser: LD71873. $39.99.
Ridley Scott, USA, 1982, 117 mins.

Borrower

A twisted tale of an outer space alien who enjoys collecting the heads of foolish earthlings and wearing them in public. His first victim is Tom Towles, Henry's accomplice in murder. With Antonio Fargas, Don Gordon and Rae Dawn Chong as the disbelieving police detective on the track of this most unusual mass murderer. The very juicy special effects are not for the squeamish.
VHS: S14991. $14.95.
John McNaughton, USA, 1991, 97 mins.

13 Shot in VistaVision & Cinemascope

2001: A Space Odyssey (25th Anniversary Edition)
VHS: S18674. $19.98.
Laser: CAV. LD71876. $69.98.
Laser: CLV. LD71877. $39.98.

Bonjour Tristesse
VHS: S06999. $69.95.

Colin Wilson: The High and the Low
VHS: S13322. $49.95.

Fellini Satyricon
VHS: S06318. $19.98.
Laser: LD70979. $124.95.

Jules and Jim
VHS: S00663. $29.95.
Laser: LD71069. $59.95.

Kwaidan
VHS: S00694. $29.95.
Laser: LD71083. $69.95.

Last Year at Marienbad
VHS: S00730. $29.95.

North by Northwest
VHS: S00938. $19.98.
Laser: CAV. LD70427. $124.95.
Laser: CLV. LD70428. $69.95.

One-Eyed Jacks
VHS: S02558. $19.95.

Point Blank
VHS: S08064. $19.98.
Laser: LD74679. $34.98.

Rebel Without a Cause
VHS: S01097. $19.98.
Laser: LD70663. $24.98.

The Searchers
VHS: S01731. $19.98.

The Wild Bunch (Director's Cut)
DVD: DV60121. $24.98.
VHS: S01459. $39.99.
Laser: LD70706. $129.98.

The Brother from Another Planet

Brazil

Terry Gilliam's acclaimed, surrealistic, nightmare vision of a "perfect" future where technology reigns supreme. Spectacular set design, this wildly visual treat stars Jonathan Pryce (as the "Everyman"), with a supporting cast of Robert De Niro and Michael Palin. A chilling black comedy, where *1984* meets *A Clockwork Orange*, with a script by Tom Stoppard.
VHS: S00177. $19.95.
Laser: LD70018. $124.95.
Terry Gilliam, Great Britain/USA, 1986, 131 mins.

The Brother from Another Planet

From the director of *Return of the Secaucus Seven* and *Lianna* comes an off-beat, fresh sci-fantasy adventure about a different sort of visitor from outer space. No E.T.—he's black, has three toes on two huge feet, and can heal humans and video arcade machines with a touch.
VHS: S00185. $19.98.
John Sayles, USA, 1984, 109 mins.

The Day the Earth Stood Still

One of the first films to portray aliens from space as advanced saviors rather than menacing monsters. Michael Rennie stars as Klaatu. Intense, high production values and excellent casting with Patricia Neal and Sam Jaffe.
VHS: S02521. $14.98.
Robert Wise, USA, 1951, 92 mins.

Destination Moon

The first major sci-fi film in the U.S., the sets are ingenious and the film won an Academy Award for Special Effects. Co-scripted by Robert A. Heinlein from his novel *Rocketship Galileo*.
VHS: S00326. $19.95.
Irving Pichel, USA, 1950, 91 mins.

E.T.

Steven Spielberg's magnum opus—finally on video. An endearing alien, stranded on Earth, befriends a sweet young boy and his lovable siblings, who all help him to find his way back home. One of the most popular and highest grossing movies in history and quickly becoming a children's classic in the league of *The Wizard of Oz*. Letterboxed.
VHS: S07032. $19.95.
Laser: THX, CAV. LD76047. $149.98.
Steven Spielberg, USA, 1985, 101 mins.

Fahrenheit 451

Truffaut's first English-language production stars Julie Christie and Oskar Werner. Based on Ray Bradbury's masterpiece about a future without books, Werner plays a fireman in charge of burning books who meets a schoolteacher (Christie) who dares to read. In original English language.
VHS: S00425. $59.95.
Laser: LD70028. $34.98.
Francois Truffaut, France, 1966, 112 mins.

The Fantastic Voyage

The cult science fiction thriller in which a team of doctors are miniaturized and set inside the body to operate on the blood clot of a scientist. With Stephen Boyd, Raquel Welch, Donald Pleasance and Arthur Kennedy.
VHS: S30661. $14.98.
Richard Fleischer, USA, 1966, 100 mins.

The Fly (1958)

Vincent Price is the mad scientist who experiments with his disintegration machine and has his atomic pattern traded with that of a fly in the original version

of this now classic sci-fi theme.
VHS: S03366. $14.98.
Kurt Neumann, USA, 1958, 94 mins.

The Fly (1986)
Cronenberg's *The Fly* is less a remake of the original
film than a remake of the original short story about a
brilliant scientist who develops a system to transport
objects over space and reassemble the molecules in
seconds. When an accident fuses his structure with
that of a fly, the initial excitement turns to horror as
the insect nature begins to exert itself. With an
outstanding performance by Jeff Goldblum.
VHS: S02908. $29.98.
Laser: LD70984. $24.98.
David Cronenberg, USA, 1986, 96 mins.

Forbidden Planet
Nervy, funny and very clever science fiction
adaptation of Shakespeare's final play, *The Tempest*,
set in the year 2200, about a group of space explorers
investigating a previous space flight who encounter
an embittered expatriate creating his own society on
the abandoned planet with his beautiful daughter and
trustworthy robot. Beautiful widescreen photography
by George Folsey. With Walter Pidgeon, Anne
Francis, Leslie Nielsen and Warren Stevens.
Available in two versions, a widescreen from
Criterion and letterbox from MGM.
DVD: DV60109. $24.98.
VHS: S00458. $14.98.
Laser: CAV, widescreen, Criterion. **LD70989.**
$99.95.
Laser: CLV, deluxe widescreen, MGM. **LD70186.**
$34.95.
Fred M. Wilcox, USA, 1956, 98 mins.

I Married a Monster from Outer Space
Monster-like aliens from another planet inhabit the
bodies of people in a small town in hopes of having
children with Earth women. Tom Tyron stars as one
of these very monsters married to Gloria Talbott.
VHS: S00598. $49.95.
Gene Fowler Jr., USA, 1958, 78 mins.

The Illustrated Man
Based on the Ray Bradbury story, Rod Steiger stars as
a man whose body paints pictures of horrors to come.
With Claire Bloom.
VHS: S00609. $19.98.
Jack Smight, USA, 1969, 103 mins.

In the Mouth of Madness
A masterful tale of terror starring Sam Neill, this film
is an homage to the great sci-fi/horror writer H.P.
Lovecraft. It begins in an asylum where a madman
awaits the end of mankind at the hands of monstrous
demons. He thought it was just a story, but that was
only what it appeared to be. Charlton Heston has a
cameo.
VHS: S25659. $19.95.
Laser: LD75017. $39.99.
John Carpenter, USA, 1995, 95 mins.

Incredible Shrinking Man
One of the best American science fiction films of the
1950's. Grant Williams and Randy Stuart star in the
story of an ordinary businessman who encounters a
radioactive mist during a boating trip, and finds his
growth process suddenly reversed; in two weeks, he's
two inches tall. Terrifying.
VHS: S06556. $14.98.
Jack Arnold, USA, 1957, 81 mins.

Invasion of the Body Snatchers (1956)
The great Cold War classic. A small American town
is taken over by an alien force which turns everyone
into a zombie. Kevin McCarthy and Dana Wynter
star.
VHS: S00633. $19.95.
Laser: CAV, widescreen. **LD70384. $79.95.**
Laser: CLV, widescreen. **LD70385. $49.95.**
Don Siegel, USA, 1956, 80 mins.

Invasion of the Body Snatchers (1978)
Intriguing remake of the Don Siegel classic stars
Donald Sutherland and Brooke Adams, with cameos
by Siegal and original star Kevin McCarthy.
VHS: S02355. $14.95.
Philip Kaufman, USA, 1978, 115 mins.

Island of Lost Souls
A terrifying adaptation of H.G. Wells' story about a
vivisectionist trapped on a desolate island who alters
the biological genetics of jungle animals and changes
them into pathological man/animal hybrids. With
Charles Laughton, Bela Lugosi, Richard Arlen and
Stanley Fields.
VHS: S19013. $14.98.
Erle C. Kenton, USA, 1933, 70 mins.

It Came from Outer Space
Originally shown in 3-D, this classic science fiction

The Day the Earth Stood Still

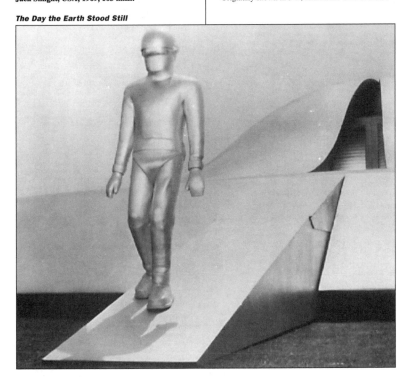

Most Bizarre

Ashik Kerib
VHS: S19055. $29.95.

Chained for Life
VHS: S23183. $24.95.

Crash
VHS: S31676. $100.99.
Laser: LD76336. $49.95.

Death in the Seine
VHS: S27254. $29.95.

Futz
VHS: S30731. $29.95.

Lost Highway
VHS: S31739. $101.99.
Laser: LD76298. $49.99.

Lyrical Nitrate
VHS: S27564. $59.95.

Mondo Cane
VHS: S00871. $29.98.

Santa Sangre
VHS: S13586. $19.98.

Sweet Movie
VHS: S10575. $79.95.

Tokyo Decadence
VHS: S19176. $29.95.

WR: Mysteries of the Organism
VHS: S11290. $79.95.

adventure was based on a short story by Ray Bradbury. Richard Carlson stars as an astronomer who thinks there is more to the meteor that fell in the desert than meets the eye. With Barbara Rush, Morey Amsterdam and Russell Johnson. B&W.
VHS: S05525. $14.98.
Jack Arnold, USA, 1953, 81 mins.

La Jetee
Chris Marker's landmark film is set in postnuclear Paris. The story concerns an astronaut who travels back through time to realize a brief affair with a woman he once glimpsed. With the exception of a haunting shot of the woman blinking, the entire film is composed with still photographs and isolated shots. French with English subtitles.
VHS: S18956. $19.95.
Chris Marker, France, 1962, 29 mins.

The Man Who Fell to Earth
Nicolas Roeg's stylish classic stars David Bowie as a cosmic visitor to the planet, overwhelmed by capitalist society, human technology and earthly love. This video has now been re-issued with the twenty minutes cut from the original theatrical version fully restored. One of the most mysterious and visually intriguing science fiction films ever made.
VHS: S00815. $69.95.
Nicolas Roeg, Great Britain, 1976, 140 mins.

Metropolis
A newly mastered version of Fritz Lang's great masterpiece, the first classic of the science fiction genre. His depiction of a giant city controlled by an authoritarian industrialist who lives in a paradise-like garden while the workers live and struggle in subterranean sections of the city was as important for its vision of man in the service of those who control technology as for its implicit and moving social message. "A brilliant piece of expressionist design…with moments of almost incredible beauty and power" (Pauline Kael). Silent with music score.
VHS: S10764. $29.95.
Fritz Lang, Germany, 1926, 90 mins.

Planet of the Apes
Astronaut Charlton Heston crash lands on a distant world where he finds that human beings are not the dominant species. The novel by Pierre Boulle was adapted for the screen by Rod Serling and Michael Wilson and won a Special Oscar for its outstanding achievement in make-up. Kim Hunter, Roddy McDowall, Maurice Evans, and James Whitmore are some of the stars in simian suits. Followed by four sequels and a couple of TV shows.
VHS: S12171. $19.98.
Franklin J. Schaffner, USA, 1968, 112 mins.

Quatermass 1: The Quatermass Experiment
A single man is found alone on a returning spaceship. Tension grows as he mysteriously changes into an alien creature. The result is a hideous monster with unimagined powers and the will to see his horrible desires through at any cost.
VHS: S27751. $14.95.
Val Guest, Great Britain, 1956, 79 mins.

Quatermass 2: Enemy from Space
The second and best of the three notable *Quatermass* films written by Nigel Kneale. This frightening tale of alien invasion and political paranoia is comparable to *1984* and *Invasion of the Body Snatchers*. With Brian Donlevy as Quatermass.
VHS: S01077. $49.95.
Val Guest, Great Britain, 1957, 85 mins.

Robocop
The action/science fiction movie of 1987 stars Peter Weller as a Detroit cop gunned down and used as a guinea pig to create a cyborg police officer. All goes well until Robocop starts remembering his past life and enemies. With Nancy Allen, Ronny Cox, Kurtwood Smith and Miguel Ferrer.
VHS: S05637. $19.98.
Laser: CAV/CLV. LD72101. $99.95.
Paul Verhoeven, USA, 1987, 103 mins.

Seconds
Rock Hudson delivers a tour-de-force performance in director John Frankenheimer's (*The Manchurian Candidate*) critically acclaimed thriller about a man who buys a new identity and pays a terrifying price. John Randolph stars as a middle-aged banker, Arthur Hamilton, who, summoned by a mysterious corporation, undergoes plastic surgery and emerges as handsome bohemian artist Tony Wilson (Hudson). With nightmarish (Oscar-nominated) cinematography by James Wong Howe. "Fascinating from start to finish" (Leonard Maltin, *Movie & Video Guide*).
VHS: S31145. $79.95.
Laser: Letterboxed. LD76340. $39.99.
John Frankenheimer, USA, 1966, 107 mins.

She
Lavish sets and a score by Max Steiner are two features that should have helped propel this film to success like that garnered by producer Merian C. Cooper's earlier film, *King Kong*. Two explorers, Randolph Scott and Nigel Bruce, find a goddess living beneath the frozen Arctic, She Who Must Be Obeyed. This adventure film has great 1930's style. Based on H. Rider Haggard's novel.
VHS: S26457. $24.95.
Irving Pichel/Lansing C. Holden, USA, 1935, 95 mins.

Silent Running
Bruce Dern stars in this sci-fi classic as a botanist preserving the only botanical specimens left on Earth, under huge geodesic domes, whose rebellion takes him on the loneliest adventure of all. Co-scripted by Michael Cimino, with original songs sung by Joan Baez.
VHS: S01200. $19.95.
Laser: LD70079. $34.95.
Douglas Trumbull, USA, 1977, 90 mins.

Soylent Green
Veteran action director Fleischer invents a science fiction fantasy of the distant future, where an absurdly overpopulated New York City forces its citizens to survive on a wafer-like food product known as Soylent. Charlton Heston is a laconic detective assigned to uncover the details of a murdered industrialist. The film features a final performance from Edward G. Robinson.
VHS: S02362. $19.95.
Laser: Letterboxed. Includes original theatrical trailer. LD71509. $34.98.
Richard Fleischer, USA, 1973, 97 mins.

Star Trek II: Wrath of Khan
Ricardo Montalban plays Khan, who had been banished to a barren planet in a television episode in 1967 and seeks revenge against Captain Kirk. Fast-paced and highly entertaining, starring the entire crew of the Enterprise. Widescreen.
VHS: S01583. $19.95.
Nicholas Meyer, USA, 1982, 113 mins.

The Terminator
Schwarzenegger *is* the villainous Terminator, a cyborg (part man, part machine) sent to present day Earth from the future on a deadly mission. His task: to kill a young woman whose life will have great significance in the revolutionary decades to come. An

above-average sci-fi thriller, now considered a classic. Letterboxed.
VHS: S05716. $19.99.
James Cameron, USA, 1984, 89 mins.

Terminator 2: Judgment Day
At over $100 million, James Cameron's sequel to his popular 1984 science-fiction thriller is easily one of the most expensive feature films ever made. Arnold Schwarzenegger is back as the eponymous, time-traveling death machine, only this time he gets to play the "good" guy—meaning that instead of killing everyone in his path he now only injures them seriously. If you can stand the film's pumped-up violence, most of the special effects and stunt sequences are pretty spectacular, and, despite a few attempts at sentimentality which just flat-out fail, the movie functions fairly well as an entertaining roller coaster ride paced with action, fireworks and mild suspense. Written, produced and directed by James Cameron. Also starring Linda Hamilton. Letterboxed.
DVD: DV60134. $34.98.
VHS: S15229. $19.98.
James Cameron, USA, 1991, 139 mins.

Them!
A 50's masterpiece of the cinema of the fantastic. With atmospheric shadow and light photography, memorable performances by James Whitmore and James Arness (pre-Gunsmoke), and assists from 12 foot long ants.
VHS: S01319. $19.98.
Laser: LD74719. $34.98.
Gordon Douglas, USA, 1954, 93 mins.

They Live
John Carpenter's sci-fi thriller about one man's battle against aliens who are systematically gaining control of the earth. Pro-wrestler Roddy Piper stars as the loner who stumbles upon ghoulish creatures masquerading as humans while they lull the public into submission through subliminal advertising messages! Only specially made sunglasses make the deadly truth visible.
VHS: S10111. $89.95.
John Carpenter, USA, 1988, 95 mins.

THX 1138
Robert Duvall is the androgynous worker who, with his partner, passes up their daily drug requirement in the futuristic society, and begins to feel sexual awakening. George Lucas' first film is a classic science fiction vision of a nightmare future.
VHS: S01340. $19.98.
Laser: Letterboxed. **LD74720. $34.98.**
George Lucas, USA, 1971, 90 mins.

Time Bandits
John Cleese, Sean Connery, Shelley Duvall and Michael Palin are among the stars who keep popping up in the strangest of places throughout human history. It seems there are mysterious connections and the Time Bandits are able to jump around. The result is a wild, extravagant adventure that, though quite dark in places, delights everyone.
VHS: S01344. $14.95.
Laser: LD76741. $49.95.
Terry Gilliam, Great Britain, 1981, 110 mins.

Time Machine
H.G. Wells' classic novel is adapted in a now-classic film directed by George Pal. Rod Taylor is the time traveler who guns his machine into the distant future only to find a civilization devitalized by endless wars.
VHS: S01346. $19.95.
George Pal, USA, 1960, 103 mins.

Village of the Damned/Children of the Damned (1960)
Two chilling psychological shockers. Wolf Rilla's 1960 British thriller *Village of the Damned* is a perverse adaptation of John Wyndham's novel about a group of strange, detached children created by alien visitors plotting to destroy an English village. Anton Leader's 1964 follow-up, *Children of the Damned* concerns six immensely gifted young children and their ruthless attempt to take over the world. Includes the theatrical trailer for both works.
Laser: LD71653. $39.98.

Voyage to the Bottom of the Sea
A top cast, thrilling underwater photography, and superb special effects fuel this science fiction classic about an enormous sub trying to save the earth from destruction. Written and directed by the master of the natural disaster genre, Irwin Allen (*The Towering Inferno*). Starring Walter Pidgeon, Joan Fontaine and Peter Lorre.
VHS: S07815. $14.98.
Irwin Allen, USA, 1961, 105 mins.

War of the Worlds
Based on the H.G. Wells novel, this film is everybody's SF classic. Winner of an Oscar for special effects, starring Gene Barry.
VHS: S01430. $14.95.
Byron Haskin, USA, 1952, 880 mins.

Westworld
Author and anthropologist Michael Crichton (*The Andromeda Strain*) wrote and directed this study of a regressive futureworld gone awry by the horrors of misdirected technology. A futuristic theme park called Westworld becomes a killing ground when robots begin killing the participants. James Brolin and Richard Benjamin star.
VHS: S02363. $19.98.
Michael Crichton, USA, 1973, 90 mins.

When Worlds Collide
A pioneering classic of science-fiction films, *When Worlds Collide* won the Oscar for its special effects. The potential pulverizing impact of the collision makes a chilling panorama of disaster. The balance between human and planetary drama is excellently maintained as the film builds to its fascinating, unforgettable climax.
VHS: S01446. $14.95.
Laser: LD75366. $44.98.
Rudolph Mate, USA, 1951, 81 mins.

X—The Man with the X-Ray Eyes
Ray Milland stars in this classic science fiction film as a scientist who invents a serum that enhances his vision, giving him X-ray eyes. Ultimately it turns out to be a curse. Don Rickles is also featured.
VHS: S06110. $14.98.
Roger Corman, USA, 1963, 79 mins.

Fright Fest

The Birds
VHS: S01845. $19.95.
Laser: LD70015. $39.98.

Candyman
VHS: S18323. $19.95.

The Exorcist
DVD: DV60108. $24.98.
VHS: S01818. $19.98.

Halloween
VHS: S00536. $14.98.
Laser: LD74592. $99.98.

The Haunting
VHS: S01561. $19.98.
Laser: LD72121. $34.98.

Hotel Terminus: The Life and Times of Klaus Barbie
VHS: S10756. $29.98.

The Innocents
VHS: S29985. $19.95.

Lair of the White Worm
VHS: S09140. $14.98.

A Nightmare on Elm Street
VHS: S32102. $14.99.

Santa Sangre
VHS: S13586. $19.98.

Scream
VHS: S31526. $19.95.
Laser: LD76257. $39.99.

The Shining
VHS: S01189. $19.98.
Laser: LD74736. $39.98.

The Stepfather
Laser: LD72312. $29.99.

The Vanishing
VHS: S15444. $19.98.
Laser: LD72197. $39.95.

Videodrome
VHS: S01414. $14.98.

50 Writers' Lives on Video

Anais Observed
Anais Nin's surrealistic novels, extensive diaries and deep friendships were all formed at the heart of a developing modern consciousness. Her distinct female persona is especially noteworthy for its overall embrace of human diversity. This portrait captures her life and philosophy. D.H. Lawrence, Otto Rank, Henry Miller, Kenneth Anger and Maya Deren are just some of the personalities captured alongside this singular literary artist.
VHS: S26714. $29.95.

The Beats: An Existential Comedy
Focusing on the beat poetry scene of the late '50s, this video is not a conventional documentary, but a film poem which celebrates a colorful generation of American artists, including Stuart Perkoff, Aya, Jack Hirschman, Lawrence Ferlinghetti and Allen Ginsberg, who read their poems and discuss what it means to be a poet in America. Public performance.
VHS: S32117. $79.95.
Philomene Long, USA, 1980, 60 mins.

Conversations with Playwrights: Arthur Miller and Israel Horovitz
Conversations between Pulitzer Prize-winning author Miller and writer Israel Horovitz. They talk about theater, the writer, playwriting and politics, and the playwright's responsibility to society. 1970, 27 mins.
VHS: S32328. $89.95.

David Mamet: The Playwright as Director
Playwright David Mamet rehearses Lindsay Crouse and Michael Higgins in scenes from two of his plays, *Dark Pony* and *Reunion*. Discussion of the art of directing and the Stanislavsky method. 1979, 27 mins.
VHS: S32326. $89.95.

Diane DiPrima: Recollections of My Life as a Woman
Writer-poet-healer Diane DiPrima reads from her autobiography at the New York Open Center, touching on issues of family, womanhood, aging, anarchy and The Bomb, which fell on her 11th birthday. 100 mins.
VHS: S30798. $24.95.

An Evening with Ed Sanders and the Fugs
Poet, publisher, Woodstock freelance writer and musician Ed Sanders performs on this video at St. Marks Poetry Project and Town Hall, New York City, in 1994. Ed accompanies himself on the dulcimer and his electronic tie. A 1989 Fugs tribute to Abbie Hoffman with Sanders, Tull Kupferberg and Steven Taylor is also included.
VHS: S26944. $24.95.

Fiction and Other Truths: A Film About Jane Rule
Jane Rule has written lesbian fiction that has touched countless women, including the classic *Desert of the Heart*, the inspiration for the film *Desert Hearts*. This film explores the author behind the books and features interviews with Helen, her lover of over 40 years. In addition, their political work and their dreams—in short, the essence of their lives—stand revealed in this insightful documentary. Produced by the National Film Board of Canada.
VHS: S27227. $59.95.
Lynne Fernie/Aerlyn Weissman, Canada, 1995, 57 mins.

Gary Soto
Chicano poet, essayist and children's book writer Gary Soto was born and raised in Fresno, California. Mr. Soto has published six poetry collections, including *Home Course in Religion, The Elements of San Joaquin* and *Who Will Know Us?* He read from his *New and Selected Poems* on May 2, 1995, and talked with novelist Alejandro Morales, whose books include *The Brick People* and *Death of an Anglo*. From the *Lannan Literary Videos* series. 60 mins.
VHS: S32430. $19.95.

Gertrude Stein: When This You See, Remember Me
This portrait of the famous American writer shows Stein in Paris from 1905 through the 1930's. Her creativity was expressed not only in writing but in influential friendships with a host of major artists. Picasso, T.S. Eliot, Thorton Wilder, James Joyce, Ernest Hemingway and many more relied on her companionship, criticism and support. Home movies of Stein and her longtime lover, Alice B. Toklas, a rare radio interview, and footage of Stein's art collection round out this exciting documentary. 89 mins.
VHS: S26648. $59.95.
Perry Miller Adato, USA, 1970, 89 mins.

Henry Miller Odyssey
Miller describes how he saw his era, his peers and himself. Whether at Big Sur, or on jaunts to old hangouts in Brooklyn and Paris, Miller shares his life in this film. Along the way he describes his painful youth and his art. Lawrence Durrell, Anais Nin, Jakov Gimpel and others appear, adding depth to this intriguing portrait.
VHS: S26713. $29.95.

Herman Hesse's Long Summer
Takes account of the external circumstances of the writer of *Siddhartha* and *Steppenwolf* while focusing on the soul of one of the most original thinkers of this century. 60 mins.
VHS: S32081. $29.95.

Kay Boyle
Reading from *This Is Not a Letter and Other Poems* and *Testament for My Students* in Los Angeles on September 11, 1989, poet Kay Boyle revealed her interest in human rights. Shawn Wong interviews this author of over 30 books. From the *Lannan Literary Videos* series. 60 mins.
VHS: S27120. $19.95.

The Modern World: Ten Great Writers
A ground-breaking series of profiles of ten great 20th-century writers who helped shape literature. Each program examines the author's experiences and includes commentary by noted scholars as well as dramatized excerpts performed by actors from Great Britain's National Theatre and the Royal Shakespeare Company, including David Suchet, Eileen Atkins, Patrick Malahide, Tim McInnerny, Tim Roth, Brian Glover, Michael Gough and Edward Fox.
Vol. 1: Fyodor Mikhailovich Dostoyevsky.
Dostoyevsky ushered in modern literature with his novels *Crime and Punishment, Brothers Karamazov* and *The Idiot*. 58 mins.
VHS: S21906. $24.95.
Vol. 2: Henrik Ibsen. Far ahead of his time, Ibsen outraged audiences by stripping away hypocrisy and convention in his plays *Hedda Gabler, A Doll's House* and *Wild Duck*. 58 mins.
VHS: S21907. $24.95.
Vol. 3: Joseph Conrad. The author of *Lord Jim* and *Heart of Darkness* explored political and existential themes. 58 mins.
VHS: S21908. $24.95.
Vol. 4: Luigi Pirandello. In landmark plays like *Enrico IV* and *Six Characters in Search of an Author*,

and in a novel and short stories, Pirandello explored the relationship between outward experience and inward reality. 58 mins.
VHS: S21909. $24.95.
Vol. 5: Marcel Proust. Proust's *Remembrance of Things Past* has rightly taken its place as one of the world's literary masterworks. 58 mins.
VHS: S21910. $24.95.
Vol. 6: Thomas Mann. With *Buddenbrooks, The Magic Mountain, Doctor Faustus* and the novella *Death in Venice,* Mann became the leading German author who confronted the spiritual controversies of 20th-century human experience. 58 mins.
VHS: S21911. $24.95.
Vol. 7: James Joyce. Joyce took stream of consciousness to its extremes in *Finnegan's Wake.* David Suchet stars as Leopold Bloom in scenes from Joyce's *Ulysses.* 58 mins.
VHS: S21912. $24.95.
Vol. 8: Virginia Woolf. Woolf's innovative narrative method in *Orlando, To the Lighthouse* and *The Waves* established her as a leading 20th-century novelist. 58 mins.
VHS: S21913. $24.95.
Vol. 9: Thomas Stearns Eliot. In *Prufrock and Other Observations, The Waste Land* and *The Murder in the Cathedral,* Eliot consciously devised a new idiom of expression. Edward Fox, Eileen Atkins and Michael Gough read excerpts from some of Eliot's most famous poems. 58 mins.
VHS: S21914. $24.95.
Vol. 10: Franz Kafka. With such disturbing works as *The Metamorphosis* and *The Trial,* Kafka's name has become synonymous with the sense of alienation when individuals are confronted by faceless and nameless authority. Tim Roth appears as Kafka and as the character Joseph K. from Kafka's *The Trial.* 58 mins.
VHS: S21915. $24.95.
Modern World: Ten Great Writers, Complete Set.
The ten-volume set at a reduced price.
VHS: S21916. $199.95.

A Moveable Feast: Profiles of Contemporary American Authors
An enlightened series profiling contemporary American authors and their work in the environments that most influenced them. From the beaches of Hawaii to the streets of New York, this unique collection presents interviews with, readings by, and documentary segments about some of the most vibrant voices in modern American literature—a true banquet of ideas, identities and intelligence. Eight volumes.
Allen Ginsberg: When the Muse Calls, Answer! 30 mins.
VHS: S14765. $19.95.
Joyce Carol Oates: American Appetites. 30 mins.
VHS: S14768. $19.95.

Li-Young Lee: Always a Rose. 30 mins.
VHS: S14766. $19.95.
Sonia Sanchez: Wear the New Day Well. 30 mins.
VHS: S14770. $19.95.
T. Corraghessan Boyle: World's End. 30 mins.
VHS: S14763. $19.95.
T.R. Pearson: A Short History of a Small Place. 30 mins.
VHS: S14769. $19.95.
Trey Ellis: Platitudes. 30 mins.
VHS: S14764. $19.95.
W.S. Merwin: The Rain in the Trees. 30 mins.
VHS: S14767. $19.95.
Complete eight-volume set.
VHS: S14771. $159.60.

Paul Bowles: The Complete Outsider
Author of the *The Sheltering Sky,* Paul Bowles reveals all in this intimate portrait. Though he was married to the acclaimed writer Jane Bowles, both he and his wife had numerous homosexual affairs. An icon of the Beat Generation, Paul Bowles has inspired many with his disregard for conventional morality, including William Burroughs, who is said to have based *The Naked Lunch* on this iconoclastic inhabitant of Morocco.
VHS: S25720. $29.95.
Catherine Warnow/Regina Weinreich, 1993, 57 mins.

Ray Bradbury: An American Icon
This definitive biography, through personal anecdotes, interviews with friends and associates, clips from the exceptional television series *The Ray Bradbury Theatre* and footage at home, at rehearsals of his plays and on the lecture circuit, captures the essence of this truly gifted writer. Narrated by Rod Steiger. 47 mins.
VHS: S32104. $24.95.

Robert Creeley: 70th Birthday Reading
Influential poet, essayist, novelist, short story writer, editor and teacher Robert Creeley treats audiences to a landmark 70th Birthday Reading, in which he recites selected poems from various stages of his career. 55 mins.
VHS: S30799. $24.95.

Spymaker: The Secret Life of Ian Fleming
An action-packed adventure based on the real life of the man who created James Bond, with Jason Connery, Kristin Scott Thomas and Joss Ackland. Fleming, born into an aristocratic English family, single-handedly outwits Soviet intelligence, foils an S.S. monster at a glamorous casino, steals the secrets of the German high command, storms an enemy stronghold at impossible odds and still has time for the fastest cars and the most desirable women.
VHS: S12370. $79.98.
Ferdinand Fairfax, USA, 1990, 96 mins.

Tears on My Pillow

Old Yeller

Bonjour Tristesse
VHS: S06999. $69.95.

Boys Town
VHS: S11219. $19.95.
Laser: LD70153. $34.98.

Camille
VHS: S03453. $24.95.

Cinema Paradiso
VHS: S12603. $19.98.

City Lights
VHS: S00245. $19.98.
Laser: LD72318. $69.98.

Field of Dreams
VHS: S11694. $14.98.
Laser: LD70030. $89.95.

Grand Illusion
VHS: S12469. $29.95.
Laser: LD70373. $89.95.

Kramer vs. Kramer
VHS: S03905. $19.95.
Laser: LD72188. $34.95.

The Last Laugh
VHS: S00723. $24.95.
Laser: LD72446. $49.95.

My Life as a Dog
VHS: S06240. $19.98.
Laser: LD75232. $34.98.

Old Yeller
VHS: S32290. $19.95.
Laser: LD76379. $29.99.

Red Balloon
VHS: S01098. $14.95.

Shane
VHS: S03316. $14.95.
Laser: LD75344. $29.98.

Terms of Endearment
VHS: S03916. $19.95.

The Unbearables:
Brooklyn Bridge Readings 1995/1996
The Unbearables are some 30-odd highly talented "outcast" poets (including Ron Kolm, Sharon Mesmer, Hal Sirowitz, Sparrow, Carl Watson, Michael Carter, Tsaurah Litzky, Peter Lamborn Wilson and Jill Rapaport) who have gathered together to create their own movement. The well-published group gives collective readings every September 13 on the Brooklyn Bridge. "The Unbearables…are conscience-angels with pitchforks ready to prod and poke…these poets are for real" (*Taproots Reviews*).
VHS: S30802. $24.95.

Voices and Visions
This remarkable video series traces the development of the American poetry tradition. Both the life story and the work of major poets are covered in each video. Perfect for the serious student and those who simply love poetry.
Voices and Visions Volume I: Hart Crane, Walt Whitman, Ezra Pound, William Carlos Williams. A look at poet-physician William Carlos Williams, who established a distinctly American poem; at Hart Crane's preoccupation with technology and its human impact; at the controversial Ezra Pound, who became a leader of the Modernist movement and became enmeshed in economic and political ideals during World War II; and at the remarkable Whitman, including the eclectic sources of his poetry. 240 minutes.
VHS: S24315. $69.95.
Voices and Visions Volume II: Emily Dickinson, Marianne Moore, Elizabeth Bishop, Sylvia Plath. Four unique, American women poets are covered in this four-volume set. Period dramatic recreations evoke the domestic context in which Emily Dickinson wrote her metaphysical poetry. Poets and critics explain the "wild decorum" of Marianne Moore's unique style. Exotic documentary footage heightens the magical realism of Elizabeth Bishop's poems and explores her preoccupation with perception and the boundaries of consciousness. And archival footage of the 1950s pop culture chronicles Sylvia Plath's historical environments and the complex relationship between her troubled life and work. 240 minutes.
VHS: S24316. $69.95.
Voices and Visions Volume III: T.S. Eliot, Robert Lowell, Langston Hughes, Robert Frost, Wallace Stevens. Five videos explore these major poets. They trace the career of T.S. Eliot from the bold originality of *Prufrock* to the meditative style of *Four Quartets*. They contain footage of Robert Lowell in his apartment and on anti-war protest marches, intercut with interviews that discuss his use of autobiography as subject matter for poetry. On-location footage in Senegal, France, Kansas and Harlem chronicles the life of Langston Hughes. Through his lyric poems and dramatic narratives, Robert Frost asserts that nature is the clearest window into the human personality. And presentations of the works of Wallace Stevens reveal his sense of imagination as a journey to a new reality. 300 minutes.
VHS: S24317. $89.95.

Voices and Visions: Elizabeth Bishop
Bishop's fanciful but accessible poems betray her interest with perception and the boundaries of consciousness. Exotic documentary footage extends the magical realism of her work. Mary McCarthy and Octavio Paz are among the commentators included in this video. 60 mins.
VHS: S26318. $19.95.

Voices and Visions: Emily Dickinson
Expressing both doubt and joy, Dickinson's poems are compressed and urgent. At times they reflect lucidity and wit or despair and death-obsession. Adrienne Rich, Joyce Carol Oates and others comment on the legacy of this 19th-century female poet who lived largely as a recluse. 60 mins.
VHS: S26317. $19.95.

Voices and Visions: Ezra Pound
Though a driving force of the Modernist movement, Pound's classically poetic voice recalls ancient and medieval sources. His social and political views led to controversy through accusations of treason and the suspicion of madness. Hugh Kenner, Alfred Kazin and Pound himself are seen in this video, discussing the poet and his work. 60 mins.
VHS: S26314. $19.95.

Voices and Visions: Hart Crane

Advanced technology spurred Crane into lyrical language and a literature of ecstasy. This disorderly and lusty poet's frenzy of illumination had a darker, debauched side. His deterioration and suicide could be traced to this conflicted life. Derek Wolcott, Malcolm Cowley and Richard Howard provide commentary. 60 mins.
VHS: S26315. $19.95.

Voices and Visions: Langston Hughes
Scenes of Hughes' travels in Europe and film of him reading his own work make this video an especially personal view of this great African-American writer. He was active in the black artistic and political movements of his time, a fact attested to by James Baldwin, Gwendolyn Brooks and others. 60 mins.
VHS: S26322. $19.95.

Voices and Visions: Marianne Moore
Witty, subversive and precise, Moore's poems evince remarkable clarity of observation. This film traces her life, times and friendships. Her unusual sources and idiosyncratic work depended on both natural science and her vivid imagination. Grace Schulman, Charles Tomlinson and Kenneth Burkes discuss this poet and her work. 60 mins.
VHS: S26319. $19.95.

Voices and Visions: Robert Frost
Though Frost presented a harsh vision of the world, his work achieved startling popularity. This film mixes interviews with Frost, dramatizations of his work, and commentary by Seamus Heaney, Alfred Edwards and Richard Wilbur. 60 mins.
VHS: S26323. $19.95.

Voices and Visions: Robert Lowell
Interviews with Lowell betray his keen interest in contemporary issues, such as racial injustice, cultural decline and nuclear war. This film examines Lowell's autobiographical and historical concerns as well as his mental anguish. Robert Giroux, Robert Hass and novelist Elizabeth Hardwick, Lowell's second wife, speak about the poet and his work. 60 mins.
VHS: S26325. $19.95.

Voices and Visions: Sylvia Plath
Rage, grief and anger mark the poems of this tragic figure's work. Archival footage, including a long interview with Plath herself, helps to explain some of the power and misery which afflicted the young poet. She committed suicide at 30. 60 mins.
VHS: S26320. $19.95.

Voices and Visions: T.S. Eliot
This poet and philosopher lived in London most of his life. There he worked as a publisher and dramatist whose poems confronted the spiritual uncertainty of his generation. Though Stephen Spender, Quentin Bell, Frank Kermode and others speak about his work, Eliot himself reads his own poems in this video. 60 mins.
VHS: S26321. $19.95.

Voices and Visions: Wallace Stevens
This melancholy existentialist was also an insurance executive. His comic and meditative poems elicit meaning and solace from the landscapes he visited, the weather and the conditions of the soul. Harold Bloom, Joan Richardson and James Merrill address the power of Stevens' work. 60 mins.
VHS: S26324. $19.95.

Voices and Visions: Walt Whitman
Walt Whitman pioneered a new American style of poetry that remains highly influential. This tape recreates the sights and sounds that inspired him. Whitman's idealism continues to inspire new generations of writers from the Beat movement onwards. Allen Ginsberg, Galway Kinnell and Donald Hall comment on this democratic, homosexual lover of the human voice. 60 mins.
VHS: S26313. $19.95.

Voices and Visions:
William Carlos Williams
Williams' penetrating work betrays a clean and insightful style focused on concrete particulars. This style reflects his other concerns as a small town pediatrician. Allen Ginsberg, Marjorie Perloff and Hugh Kenner discuss Williams the man and the poet. 60 mins.
VHS: S26316. $19.95.

100 Best
Horror Stories

The Abominable Dr. Phibes
The disfigured physician, played by Vincent Price, wreaks havoc on a world that he feels wronged him. His revenge is both terrible and imaginative. You can never guess exactly how Dr. Phibes' enemies will meet their deaths, but rest assured, each one is grisly. Also features Joseph Cotten.
VHS: S20931. $14.98.
Robert Fuest, Great Britain, 1971, 94 mins.

Asylum
British chiller contains four tales of madness and murder that are told to the new doctor assigned to a mental institution. Cast includes Peter Cushing, Britt Ekland, Robert Powell, Herbert Lom, Barbara Parkins and Patrick Magee. Script by Robert "Psycho" Bloch. Bloody good fun.
VHS: S03766. $29.95.
Roy Ward Baker, Great Britain, 1972, 92 mins.

The Bad Seed
Patty McCormack is the darling, blonde, pigtailed little girl who simply can't keep herself from murdering her playmates. Nominated for four Academy Awards, this classic chiller also features Nancy Kelly, Eileen Heckart and William Hopper. B&W.
VHS: S02659. $19.98.
Laser: LD71681. $39.98.
Mervyn Le Roy, USA, 1956, 129 mins.

The Beast with Five Fingers
A cult horror movie about a once brilliant pianist now consumed by doubt and self-loathing. Features his classic encounter with the disembodied hand. With Robert Alda, Peter Lorre and Andrea King.
VHS: S17532. $19.98.
Robert Florey, USA, 1946, 88 mins.

The Birds
Sheer terror from the master. *The Birds* is based on a novella by Daphne Du Maurier and was accomplished by nearly 400 trick shots using thousands of birds. With Tippi Hedren, Rod Taylor,

Jessica Tandy and Suzanne Pleshette.
VHS: S01845. $19.95.
Laser: LD70015. $39.98.
Alfred Hitchcock, USA, 1963, 119 mins.

The Black Cat
Edgar G. Ulmer (*Detour*) directs Boris Karloff and Bela Lugosi in this stylish horror work. Ulmer pulled out all the stops in this movie about a young American couple trapped in the house of a demented scientist. With David Manners, Jacqueline Wells, Lucille Lund, and Egon Brecher. From a story by Edgar Allan Poe.
VHS: S17270. $14.98.
Edgar G. Ulmer, USA, 1934, 65 mins.

Black Sabbath
Boris Karloff in this tale of "wurdalaks," a variety of vampires that drink only the blood of loved ones. Filmed in Italy, this is an English language version.
VHS: S00139. $24.95.
Mario Bava, Italy, 1963, 99 mins.

Black Sunday
This Barbara Steele Italian horror movie has nothing to do with Middle Eastern Terrorists or hijacked blimps. In her first horror film she plays a dual role: Asa, a reincarnated vampire-witch, and Katia, her innocent great-granddaughter. Heavy on the atmosphere. With John Richardson and Ivo Garrani. B&W.
VHS: S09126. $24.95.
Mario Bava, Italy, 1961, 83 mins.

The Blob
The 1950's gooiest monster is back in a special 30th anniversary remake of *The Blob*, starring Kevin Dillon as a young outcast who must save the town of Arborville from the gelatin.
Laser: LD70350. $49.95.
Chuck Russell, USA, 1988, 92 mins.

Borrower
A twisted tale of an outer space alien who enjoys

Fearless Vampires Killers

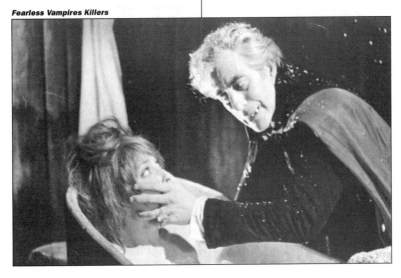

Masters of Montage

Raging Bull

Battleship Potemkin
VHS: S19293. $29.95.

Ben-Hur
VHS: S02517. $29.98.
Laser: LD70524. $49.98.

Bonnie and Clyde
DVD: DV60058. $24.98.
VHS: S00168. $19.98.
Laser: LD70531. $34.98.

Bullitt
VHS: S11614. $19.95.
Laser: LD74689. $24.98.

French Connection 2
VHS: S21862. $19.98.

Jaws
VHS: S03692. $19.98.
Laser: LD71438. $149.98.

The Naked City
VHS: S18239. $29.95.
Laser: LD75943. $49.95.

Raging Bull
DVD: DV60092. $24.98.
VHS: S01084. $19.95.
Laser: LD71669. $39.98.

Ran
VHS: S02012. $29.95.

---

collecting the heads of foolish earthlings and wearing them in public. His first victim is Tom Towles, Henry's accomplice in murder. With Antonio Fargas, Don Gordon and Rae Dawn Chong as the disbelieving police detective on the track of this most unusual mass murderer. The very juicy special effects are not for the squeamish.
VHS: S14991. $14.95.
John McNaughton, USA, 1991, 97 mins.

Bride of Frankenstein
A superior sequel, mixes wit with chills. Boris Karloff is the Monster, Elsa Lanchester plays the created mate as well as Mary Shelley in the prologue. Marvelous score by Franz Waxman. A classic!
VHS: S06386. $14.98.
Laser: LD70019. $34.98.
James Whale, USA, 1935, 75 mins.

Cabinet of Dr. Caligari
The great Expressionist classic with Werner Krauss as Caligari, the fairground showman who hypnotizes his servant (Conrad Veidt) into committing murder at night. Famous for its distorted painted sets, its grotesque camera angles and its atmospheric horror, this cinematic landmark is now newly mastered from a 35mm archive print with an orchestral score. English intertitles.
DVD: DV60034. $29.95.
VHS: S10765. $29.95.
Laser: LD75516. $49.99.
Robert Wiene, Germany, 1919, 52 mins.

Candyman
British director Bernard Rose's American debut transposes Clive Barker's short story *The Forbidden* from Liverpool to Chicago, with Virginia Madsen as a doctoral candidate who inadvertently unleashes the spirit of "Candyman," a mythological 19th-century black serial killer with a hook for his left hand who was brutally murdered by white racists. With Tony Todd, Xander Berkeley and Kasi Lemmons.
VHS: S18323. $19.95.
Bernard Rose, USA, 1992, 108 mins.

Carnival of Souls
The best horror movie ever made in Lawrence, Kansas. Candace Hilligoss plays the only survivor of a traffic accident where a carload of young women goes off a bridge. Shaken by the experience, she leaves town to play the pipe organ in Lawrence where she is haunted by very disturbing spectres. Truly eerie despite its low budget. B&W.
VHS: S04077. $19.95.
Herk Harvey, USA, 1962, 80 mins.

Carrie
Director Brian de Palma breathes life into the Steven King novel about a repressed teenager who uses her telekinetic powers to take revenge on her tormenting school peers. Sissy Spacek stars as the sympathetic Carrie; Piper Laurie plays her pious, crazy mother.
VHS: S12742. $14.95.
Laser: LD70743. $89.95.
Brian DePalma, USA, 1977, 101 mins.

Cat People
A revolutionary horror picture, in which the horror grows by suggestion rather than being depicted. Val

Lewton made his name as producer of *Cat People*. The scare at the swimming pool is a true classic.
Laser: LD75377. $49.98.
Jacques Tourneur, USA, 1942, 73 mins.

Children of the Damned
An accomplished sequel to *Village of the Damned*, about brilliant and misguided young children and their methodical and ruthless quest for power and control. With Ian Hendry, Alan Badel and Barbara Ferris.
VHS: S17534. $19.98.
Anton Leader, Great Britain, 1964, 90 mins.

Christine
When a teenager (Keith Gordon) buys an old car that needs fixing, it becomes something of an obsession. This harmless tendency turns dangerous when the car responds in kind and becomes a jealous friend. Soon this possessed car is murdering all those who come between it and its owner. Also stars Harry Dean Stanton.
VHS: S22110. $14.95.
Laser: Letterboxed. LD74551. $34.95.
John Carpenter, USA, 1983, 110 mins.

Creature from the Black Lagoon
The classic love story of a girl and a gill-man who meet on a moonlit night in the backwaters of the Amazon. Originally in 3-D. Truly one of the better monster movies. With Richard Carlson, Julie Adams and Ricou Browning as the gill-man when he is swimming. B&W.
VHS: S05524. $14.95.
Jack Arnold, USA, 1954, 79 mins.

Crimes of Dr. Mabuse
Lang's horror classic is one of the best "mad doctor" movies ever made—the supernatural fantasy about the evil Dr. Mabuse, who terrorizes a German city. With Rudolph Klein Rogge, Oskar Beregi, Camilla Spira and Theodor Loos. Dubbed in English.
VHS: S32567. $24.95.
Fritz Lang, Germany, 1932, 80 mins.

Cronos
An ingenious alchemist creates a device that grants him eternal life. 400 years later an elderly antique dealer discovers the properties of this unique invention. Though he grows younger every time he uses this device, there is a terrible price to pay. Life after death becomes a bloody promise without end. This film won Grand Prize during Critics' Week at Cannes. Spanish with English subtitles.
VHS: S22127. $19.98.
Guillermo Del Toro, Mexico , 1992, 90 mins.

Cult of the Cobra
When six servicemen unwittingly disturb a secret and ancient ceremony, powerful and evil forces are unleashed that threaten to destroy them. The cobra goddess can deceive and kill. This camp horror classic stars Richard Long, Marshall Thompson and Faith Domergue.
VHS: S20892. $14.98.
Francis D. Lyon, USA, 1955, 82 mins.

Curse of the Demon
One of the very great horror films; when psychologist

John Holden's colleague, Professor Harrington, is mysteriously and brutally murdered, Holden denies it's the work of the devil—until he becomes the next target. Great suspense from Jacques Tourneur.
VHS: S02072. $19.95.
Jacques Tourneur, Great Britain, 1958, 95 mins.

Curse of the Werewolf
A Hammer Film Production, starring Oliver Reed as the blood-thirsty man-beast who is gentle and loving by day and kills by night.
VHS: S02722. $14.98.
Laser: LD71440. $34.98.
Terence Fisher, Great Britain, 1961, 91 mins.

Dawn of the Dead
George A. Romero's sequel to *Night of the Living Dead* is a bleak satire of American consumerism. Three men and a woman escape the ravenous walking dead and gain refuge in a sterile, abandoned shopping mall. Romero charts a series of complicated sexual, racial and political relationships as the flesh-devouring zombies lay siege to their "fortress." With David Emge, Ken Foree, Scott H. Reininger and Gaylen Ross.
VHS: S04563. $14.98.
Laser: LD70939. $99.95.
George A. Romero, USA, 1978, 131 mins.

Dead Alive
A strange creature, the Sumatran rat monkey, has bitten an old woman and thereby transformed her into a ghoulish, dead monster who sucks the life out of the living. Her son tries to live a normal life but mom's victims keep on multiplying and, even worse, go on living themselves. Soon a crowd of flesh-hungry monsters is menacing this once-peaceful small town.
VHS: S19240. $14.99.
Laser: LD75180. $34.98.
Peter Jackson, New Zealand, 1992, 85 mins.

Dead Ringers
David Cronenberg does it again in this psychological horror film starring Jeremy Irons as a pair of disturbed, identical twin gynecologists. A technical and emotional masterpiece that subtly and quite creepily delves into what makes the Mantle brothers tick. With excellent supporting work by Genevieve Bujold. Based loosely on a true story.
VHS: S09841. $19.98.
Laser: LD75933. $124.95.
David Cronenberg, Canada, 1988, 113 mins.

The Dead Zone
Christopher Walken stars in this David Cronenberg film of a Stephen King novel about a man with the ability to read the thoughts of others. This gift is more a curse than a blessing. With Brooke Adams, Tom Skerritt, Herbert Lom and Martin Sheen as a very dangerous political candidate.
VHS: S06130. $19.95.
Laser: LD75359. $29.98.
David Cronenberg, USA, 1983, 104 mins.

The Devil Doll
Lionel Barrymore, disguised as a sweet old granny, shrinks people down to 12 inches using a serum he found while a prisoner on Devil's Island. He uses the little people to gain revenge on his crooked ex-business partners. Great special effects. With Maureen O'Sullivan. B&W.
VHS: S04705. $59.95.
Tod Browning, USA, 1936, 79 mins.

Dr. Jekyll and Mr. Hyde
The uncensored version of the 1932 interpretation of the Robert Louis Stevenson classic that won Fredric March an Oscar. The ten minutes that were cut for its re-release have been restored in its home video debut.

Gothic

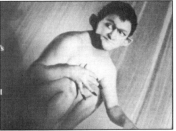

Wally Westmore created the transformation make-up for this taut and exciting story of the battle of good and evil in the single body of a man of science. With Miriam Hopkins as Ivy, the prostitute, and Holmes Herbert and Rose Hobart.
VHS: S11217. $19.95.
Rouben Mamoulian, USA, 1932, 98 mins.

Dracula (Lugosi)
Bela Lugosi stars in his most famous role as the debonair Count in this classic version of Bram Stoker's tale of the bloodsucking fiend. Lots to recommend it, including atmosphere galore and the wonderful Lugosi.
VHS: S00371. $19.95.
Tod Browning, USA, 1931, 75 mins.

Dracula (Spanish Version)
Filmed simultaneously with Tod Browning's celebrated 1931 English language version, this evocative, atmospheric Spanish translation of Bram Stoker's novel is based on the play by Hamilton Deane and John Balderston, adapted in Spanish by B. Fernandez Cue, shot on the same expressionistic sets. With Carlos Villarias, Lupita Tovar and Pablo Alvarez Rubio.
VHS: S00371. $14.98.
George Melford, Spain, 1931, 104 mins.

Dracula's Daughter
This sequel stars Gloria Holden as Countess Marya Zaleska, who turns up in London to investigate a series of disappearances where the bodies of beautiful women are found with their blood drained. With Otto Kruger, Marguerite Churchill, and Nan Grey.
VHS: S17272. $14.98.
Lambert Hillyer, USA, 1936, 70 mins.

The Exorcist
Intense supernatural thriller about the possession of a 12-year-old girl by a demonic spirit. The highlight of Linda Blair's film career. Listen to Mercedes McCambridge taunt priests. See green pea soup in a whole new way. Be terrified by the ring of a telephone. With Jason Miller, Ellen Burstyn and Max von Sydow as the exorcist.
DVD: DV60108. $24.98.
VHS: S01818. $19.98.
William Friedkin, USA, 1973, 121 mins.

Eyes Without a Face
A classic horror film from French filmmaker Georges Franju. A guilt-ridden plastic surgeon attempts to rebuild his daughter's face using the skin from unwilling volunteers. A poetic, artistically made study of madness and guilt. With Pierre Brasseur, Alida Valli, and Edith Scob as the faceless daughter. French with English subtitles. B&W.
VHS: S04481. $29.95.
Georges Franju, France, 1959, 84 mins.

Fearless Vampire Killers
Or *Pardon Me, Your Teeth Are in My Neck*. Roman Polanski directs (and appears in) this cult oddity, a vampire-film spoof that manages both horror and humor. The story involves a professor and his bumbling assistant, who set out to track down a coven of Transylvanian vampires. Cast includes Jack MacGowran, Sharon Tate, Alfie Bass and Terry Downes. This is the restored, original cut.
VHS: S12741. $19.98.
Laser: LD72173. $39.98.
Roman Polanski, USA, 1967, 124 mins.

The Fly
Vincent Price is the mad scientist who experiments with his disintegration machine and has his atomic pattern traded with that of a fly in the original version of this now classic sci-fi theme.
VHS: S03366. $14.98.
Kurt Neumann, USA, 1958, 94 mins.

The Fog
A contemporary tale of supernatural horror from the director of *Halloween*, featuring a cast that includes Jamie Lee Curtis, Janet Leigh, Adrienne Barbeau, Hal Holbrook and John Houseman.
Laser: LD72301. $29.99.
John Carpenter, USA, 1979, 94 mins.

Frankenstein Meets the Wolfman
This Universal horror film provides a sequel that combines two of their most popular monsters. Lawrence Talbot seeks out the help of a certain notorious mad scientist only to find the doctor dead and his creations quite alive. The townspeople are not pleased to find monsters in their neighborhood. With

Southern Comforts

Andersonville
VHS: S29475. $19.98.
Laser: LD75822. $59.98.

Baby Doll
VHS: S00085. $19.98.

Barn Burning
VHS: S02133. $24.95.

The Beguiled
VHS: S06821. $14.98.

Cape Fear
VHS: S14979. $19.95.
Laser: LD70293. $34.98.

Cat on a Hot Tin Roof
DVD: DV60059. $24.98.
VHS: S13776. $19.98.

Coal Miner's Daughter
VHS: S07805. $19.95.

The Color Purple
DVD: DV60084. $24.98.
VHS: S03551. $19.98.
Laser: CAV. LD70545. $59.98.
Laser: CLV. LD70546. $29.98.

Cross Creek
VHS: S02033. $14.98.

D-Day, The Sixth of June
VHS: S09453. $19.98.

Deliverance
VHS: S00320. $19.98.
Laser: LD71676. $34.98.

Driving Miss Daisy
DVD: DV60087. $24.98.
VHS: S12524. $19.98.
Laser: LD70562. $24.98.

Flamingo Road
VHS: S16448. $19.98.
Laser: LD72174. $34.98.

Fried Green Tomatoes
VHS: S17015. $19.98.
Laser: LD71538. $39.98.

God's Little Acre
VHS: S03592. $19.95.

Gone with the Wind
VHS: S00515. $89.98.

Great Santini
VHS: S07283. $19.98.

The Heart Is a Lonely Hunter
VHS: S02533. $19.98.

Intruder in the Dust
VHS: S18505. $19.98.

Jezebel
DVD: DV60062. $24.98.
VHS: S00654. $19.95.
Laser: LD70604. $34.98.

Louisiana Story
VHS: S00771. $29.95.

Member of the Wedding
VHS: S07001. $19.99.

Miss Firecracker
VHS: S26334. $19.98.

Mississippi Masala
VHS: S17070. $19.98.
Laser: LD72200. $34.95.

My Cousin Vinny
VHS: S17229. $19.95.
Laser: LD72192. $39.98.

Nashville
VHS: S00919. $29.95.

One False Move
VHS: S17057. $19.95.
Laser: LD71541. $34.95.

Passion Fish
VHS: S18746. $19.95.

The Reivers
VHS: S21403. $14.98.

The Rose Tattoo
VHS: S13787. $19.95.

The Southerner
VHS: S01236. $19.95.

A Streetcar Named Desire
DVD: DV60067. $24.98.
VHS: S21085. $19.98.
Laser: LD70687. $39.98.

Tender Mercies
VHS: S01309. $19.98.

A Time to Kill
DVD: DV60100. $24.98.
VHS: S30447. $19.98.
Laser: LD76031. $39.98.

To Kill a Mockingbird
VHS: S02640. $19.95.
Laser: LD70089. $39.98.

The Trip to Bountiful
VHS: S01811. $14.98.
Laser: LD72314. $29.99.

Wise Blood
VHS: S01470. $59.95.

The Yearling
VHS: S01488. $19.95.
Laser: LD70716. $44.98.

Lon Chaney Jr., Ilona Massey, Patric Knowles, Dwight Frye and Bela Lugosi as Frankenstein's monster.
VHS: S12253. $14.98.
Roy William Neill, USA, 1943, 72 mins.

Frankenstein—The Restored Version

A restored version (containing footage not seen since censors cut the film at the time of its original release) of one of the great Hollywood horror films, with Boris Karloff in this famous adaptation of Mary Shelley's masterpiece.
VHS: S00462. $14.98.
James Whale, USA, 1931, 71 mins.

Freaks

Tod Browning's classic horror film, with a cast of real side-show "freaks"—dwarfs, midgets, Siamese twins— dominated and exploited by the circus strong man and a beautiful aerialist, who eventually band together in a horrifying revenge.
VHS: S01560. $19.98.
Laser: LD70578. $34.98.
Tod Browning, USA, 1932, 66 mins.

The Golem

Based on the ancient Jewish legend of the clay figure created by Rabbi Loew in the 16th century to defend the Jews in the Prague ghetto against pogrom. In this great classic famous for its extraordinary crowd scenes and painted sets, the Golem falls in love with the Rabbi's daughter, terrorizes the emperor's court and is subdued by an innocent child. "The alternately terrified and exultant crowd at times recalls the flamboyant outlines and disjointed movement of a painting by El Greco" (Lotte Eisner). With Paul Wegener, Albert Steinbruck and Lyda Salmonova. Silent with music track, English titles.
VHS: S00514. $29.95.
Paul Wegener/Carl Boese, Germany, 1920, 118 mins.

Gothic

Ken Russell recreates a bizarre night at a chateau in Switzerland where Lord Byron, Mary Shelley, Percy Bysshe Shelley and a few friends told scary stories that would later affect their lives. Cast includes Gabriel Byrne, Natasha Richardson and Julian Sands.
VHS: S04624. $14.98.
Ken Russell, Great Britain, 1987, 90 mins.

Halloween

Considered one of the scariest films ever made, as well as one of the most successful independent films. The godfather of the sub-genre of the high school horror film, with the boogie man who just won't die. With Jamie Lee Curtis and P.J. Soles.
VHS: S00536. $14.98.
Laser: Letterboxed, special edition. LD74592. $99.98.
John Carpenter, USA, 1978, 90 mins.

The Haunting

Robert Wise's nerve-jangling adaptation of Shirley Jackson's *The Haunting of Hill House* centers on a gathering at a Boston mansion. An anthropologist, a disbeliever and two mediums confront the supernatural terror. With Richard Johnson, Claire Bloom, Julie Harris and Lois Maxwell.
VHS: S01561. $19.98.
Laser: LD72121. $34.98.
Robert Wise, USA, 1963, 112 mins.

Hellraiser/Special Edition

Clive Barker wrote and directed this classic horror film featuring outlandish effects. A house is haunted by a mad adventurer. When he was alive, the adventurer found a mysterious box that ultimately killed him. Now as a ghost he seeks human flesh to restore his life. Digitally remastered, this edition also contains theatrical trailers, interviews with the actors, and a letter from Barker.
VHS: S29796. $14.98.
Clive Barker, USA, 1987, 118 mins.

Horror Hotel

A very scary film which concerns witchcraft in New England as a 17th century witch, who is now an innkeeper, lures her victims for their blood and sacrifice to the devil.

VHS: S08432. $29.95.
John Llewellyn Moxey, Great Britain, 1960, 76 mins.

Horror of Dracula

This Hammer film is said to be one of the best vampire movies ever made. Based on the Bram Stoker classic novel, it stars Christopher Lee as the Count and Peter Cushing as his arch foe, Von Helsing. It spawned seven sequels. Sink your teeth in something good.

VHS: S04187. $14.95.
Laser: LD74703. $34.98.
Terence Fisher, Great Britain, 1958, 82 mins.

House of Wax

Vincent Price stars as a demented sculptor who must use human bodies in his wax museum after a fire destroys his hands and his optimistic outlook on life. With Carolyn Jones, Phyllis Kirk and Charles Bronson as the mute assistant. Originally shown in 3-D. Watch for the paddleball man.

VHS: S04188. $19.98.
Laser: LD71809. $34.98.
Andre de Toth, USA, 1953, 88 mins.

The House on Haunted Hill

Vincent Price stars in this classic William Castle film about a group of people who, in order to win a bet with the wealthy Price, try to spend one night in a spooky old mansion with lots of skeletons in its closets.

VHS: S14791. $14.98.
William Castle, USA, 1958, 75 mins.

The Hunchback of Notre Dame

Filled with huge crowd scenes and massive sets recreating medieval Paris, *The Hunchback of Notre Dame* is one of the greatest spectacles of the silent era. Starring the legendary Lon Chaney as Quasimodo. Digitally remastered.

VHS: S14337. $19.98.
Laser: CLV. LD71992. $39.95.
Wallace Worsley, USA, 1923, 100 mins.

Hush, Hush, Sweet Charlotte

There are strange goings on at Hollis House, where feeble-minded Bette Davis lives protected by her peculiar housekeeper, Agnes Moorehead. Then cousin Olivia de Havilland comes for a visit, and now Bette will have more than headless ex-boyfriends to worry about. With Bruce Dern and Joseph Cotten. B&W.

VHS: S03912. $19.98.
Robert Aldrich, USA, 1965, 133 mins.

In the Mouth of Madness

A masterful tale of terror starring Sam Neill, this film is an homage to the great sci-fi/horror writer H.P. Lovecraft. It begins in an asylum where a madman awaits the end of mankind at the hands of monstrous demons. He thought it was just a story, but that was only what it appeared to be. Charlton Heston has a cameo.

VHS: S25659. $19.95.
Laser: LD75017. $39.99.
John Carpenter, USA, 1995, 95 mins.

Island of Lost Souls

A terrifying adaptation of H.G. Wells' story about a vivisectionist trapped on a desolate island who alters the biological genetics of jungle animals and changes them into pathological man/animal hybrids. With Charles Laughton, Bela Lugosi, Richard Arlen and Stanley Fields.

VHS: S19013. $14.98.
Erle C. Kenton, USA, 1933, 70 mins.

It's Alive

Cult director Larry Cohen delivers the ultimate parental nightmare. John Ryan and Sharon Farrell find that not only is their newborn a physical monstrosity, it is also capable of catching and killing its own lunch. With Michael Ansara, Andrew Duggan, and Guy Stockwell. This one is creepy.

VHS: S04185. $14.95.
Larry Cohen, USA, 1974, 91 mins.

Jaws

The original is a chilling movie about a New England shore community terrorized by shark attacks. Three Oscars including music score and editing. Cameo by Peter Benchley, who wrote the novel upon which film was based. Special collector's edition, letterboxed, featuring interviews with Steven Spielberg. Letterboxed.

VHS: S03692. $19.98.
Laser: LD71438. $149.98.
Steven Spielberg, USA, 1975, 125 mins.

King Kong (60th Anniversary Edition)

The classic 1933 shocker by Ernest B. Schoedsack in a 60th anniversary edition. The film's daring special effects still astonish and are preserved in this archival print and digitally remastered soundtrack struck from the original optical master track. With Fay Wray, Robert Armstrong, Bruce Cabot, Frank Reicher, Sam Hardy and Noble Johnson. B&W.

VHS: S17035. $16.98.
Laser: CAV. LD70389. $74.95.
Ernest B. Schoedsack, USA, 1933, 103 mins.

Kwaidan

Four terrifying tales of the supernatural filmed with visual sensitivity. This is no Japanese monster movie. Rather, it creeps up on you by appealing to human emotions and fears. An Academy Award nominee, this distinctive work is filled with graceful camera movement, unusual colors, haunting sound effects and music. Japanese with English subtitles.

VHS: S00694. $29.95.
Laser: Widescreen. LD71083. $69.95.
Masaki Kobayashi, Japan, 1964, 161 mins.

The Lair of the White Worm

Ken Russell unearths a tale written by Bram Stoker (*Dracula*) about an ancient pagan snake cult flourishing in the modern English countryside, and adds his own touches of excess and depravity and fun. Can the dashing lord save the beautiful virgin from the unholy clutches of a fiendish but fashionably dressed cult priestess? With Hugh Grant, Catherine Oxenberg, Peter Capaldi and Amanda Donohoe as Lady Sylvia. A forked-tongue-in-cheek horror spoof.

VHS: S09140. $14.98.
Ken Russell, Great Britain, 1988, 90 mins.

The Leech Woman

A doctor and his wife, played by Phillip Terry and Colleen Gray, venture to Africa together even though age has dampened the doctor's interest in his wife. There they uncover a secret to eternal youth that extracts a terrible price, the blood of young men.

VHS: S20894. $14.98.
Edward Dein, USA, 1960, 77 mins.

The Manster

Not a typo but a Japanese/U.S. co-production about a mad scientist named Dr. Suzuki who injects an American reporter with a diabolical serum that causes him to grow another head. That's just for starters, for the evil head grows another body. Unholy population explosion. This is what happens when you keep your mutant wife in a cage. B&W.

VHS: S09136. $29.95.
K.D. Crane/G.P. Breakston, USA/Japan, 1959

Martin

Martin is a misunderstood young man who happens to be a vampire…maybe. The sun really just bothers his eyes a little, garlic and crosses have no effect, and he has no fangs. He also doesn't have any vampiric powers, which makes acquiring blood an extremely harrowing experience for all involved. An excellent combination of satire and gore, this cult classic is both frightening and funny, with ironic twists. "*Martin* is a vampire for our age of unbelief" (*Newsweek*).

VHS: S03445. $14.98.
George A. Romero, USA, 1977, 96 mins.

Jaws

Killing Time

Beckett Directs Beckett: Waiting for Godot
VHS: S18454. $39.95.

Chasing Amy
VHS: S32660. $103.99.

I'm the One You're Looking For
VHS: S13842. $19.98.

Leaving Las Vegas
VHS: S27709. $19.98.
Laser: LD75568. $34.98.

Looking for Langston
VHS: S16641. $39.95.

Looking for Mr. Goodbar
VHS: S22511. $19.95.

Looking for Richard
VHS: S31028. $103.99.
Laser: LD76142. $49.95.

Losing Chase
VHS: S30950. $99.99.
Laser: LD76201. $39.98.

Losing Isaiah
VHS: S26160. $19.95.

Melies III: The Search for Munchhausen
VHS: S14814. $29.95.

Search and Destroy
VHS: S26458. $19.98.
Laser: LD75314. $39.98.

The Search for One-Eye Jimmy
VHS: S28406. $89.95.

The Searchers
VHS: S01731. $19.98.

Waiting for Guffman
VHS: S31683. $96.99.

The Mask of Fu Manchu
An adaptation of the Sax Rohmer novel about a deranged Chinese killer (Boris Karloff) squaring off with an expedition studying the relics of Ghengis Khan's tomb. With Lewis Stone, Karen Morley and a campy, exaggerated Myrna Loy as Fu's mischievous and darkly vicious daughter.
VHS: S17533. $19.98.
Charles J. Brabin, USA, 1932, 72 mins.

The Masque of the Red Death
Vincent Price stars in this classic screen adaptation of the Edgar Allan Poe tale. It's a lavishly produced effort featuring amazing sets of the horrific castle of Prince Prospero. There, an indifferent nobility pursues their debauched past-times while the countryside endures the scourge of the red death.
VHS: S01719. $14.98.
Roger Corman, USA, 1964, 86 mins.

The Mummy
Boris Karloff in a landmark role as the mummy, accidentally revived by British archeologists after being entombed for 3,700 years. A brooding, dream-like masterpiece of the horror genre.
VHS: S00895. $14.98.
Laser: LD70060. $34.95.
Karl Freund, USA, 1932, 72 mins.

The Murders in the Rue Morgue (1932)
An expressive horror translation of Edgar Allan Poe's short story. Set in Paris, the film stars Bela Lugosi as the brilliant Dr. Mirakle, who prowls the streets to find an experimental companion for his pet gorilla. Famed director John Huston worked on the screenplay. With Sidney Fox, Leon Waycoff, Brandon Hurst and Noble Johnson.
VHS: S17274. $14.98.
Robert Florey, USA, 1932, 75 mins.

Naked Lunch
David Cronenberg succeeds in filming what many considered unfilmable. He creates a bizarre, drug inspired world based on the once-banned 1959 underground novel by William Burroughs. Peter Weller couldn't be better as a Burroughs-like novelist/junkie who is sent to Interzone on a secret mission by a talking typewriter that transmutes to a roach. With Judy Davis, Julian Sands, Ian Holm and Roy Scheider as Dr. Benway. "A thrilling, astounding, devastating piece of work" (Dave Kehr, *Chicago Tribune*).
VHS: S16382. $94.98.
Laser: LD71581. $39.98.
David Cronenberg, USA, 1991, 117 mins.

Night of the Living Dead
George A. Romero's brilliant debut film boldly re-imagines horror conventions in this nihilistic thriller about a group of survivors seeking sanctuary in a farmhouse under siege from the walking dead, flesh-eating zombies that patrol the ravaged landscape. With Judith O'Dea, Duane Jones and Karl Hardman.
VHS: S18644. $19.95.
Laser: CLV. LD72009. $34.95.
George A. Romero, USA, 1968, 96 mins.

A Nightmare on Elm Street
Wes Craven's tour-de-fright that spawned a "Freddy" phenomenon. Fierce, fedored, finger-razored Freddy (Robert Englund), the scarred maniac, is out to kill neighborhood teens in their dreams—or is it reality? The kids can fight back—as long as they don't fall asleep. Only a Craven coward would miss this frightfest. With John Saxon, Heather Langenkamp, Ronee Blakely, Amanda Wyss and Johnny Depp.
VHS: S32102. $14.99.
Wes Craven, USA, 1984, 92 mins.

Nosferatu
One of Murnau's best known films, *Nosferatu*'s eerie telling of the Dracula story was filmed on location in the mountains, towns, and castles of Bavaria. This German Expressionist symphony of horror is brilliantly infused with the subtle tones of nature: both pure and fresh, as well as twisted and sinister. Newly restored and color tinted, this version was remastered from a 35mm negative and includes recently discovered scenes and inter-titles freshly translated from the original German script. At 84 minutes, it is the most complete version available on home video.
DVD: DV60031. $29.95.
VHS: S15038. $29.95.
Friedrich W. Murnau, Germany, 1922, 84 mins.

The Old Dark House
A melodrama with a tongue-in-cheek sense of humor gathers stranded travelers in a mysterious household, where a brutish butler is one of many strange characters. The film stars Boris Karloff, Melvyn Douglas, Charles Laughton, Gloria Stuart, Raymond Massey, and Eva Moore.
VHS: S16180. $24.95.
James Whale, USA, 1932, 71 mins.

The Omen
Gregory Peck and Lee Remick star as a U.S. diplomat and his wife who adopt a child. Soon tragedy strikes near their family, and before long, Peck's character becomes convinced that his son is somehow to blame. This sets off a search for the boy's original family, resulting in more terror and a final, unbelievable secret.
VHS: S29792. $19.98.
Laser: LD76744. $24.98.
Richard Donner, USA, 1976, 111 mins.

Onibaba
A stylish Japanese ghost tale, set in medieval Japan. A peasant woman and her daughter manage an existence by impersonating demons—sexually luring soldiers away from their comrades and murdering them. A warrior manages to save his life by seducing the daughter, but the mother's sorcery conjures up a hideous revenge. Mixing graphic violence with sex, *Onibaba* is an exotic, terrifying, supernatural fantasy. Japanese with English subtitles.
VHS: S08691. $29.95.
Kaneto Shindo, Japan, 1964, 103 mins.

Peeping Tom
From the director of *Red Shoes* and *Black Narcissus*, a classic psychological study of a voyeuristic maniac who murders women while filming them with his 16mm camera. A riveting film in the tradition of

Hitchcock. Rarely seen; recommended.
VHS: S01006. $29.95.
Laser: LD72275. $49.95.
Michael Powell, Great Britain, 1960, 88 mins.

The People Under the Stairs
A young African-American becomes entangled in an attempt to rob a bizarre couple. His accomplices are murdered and he is left in the house alone. Eventually he finds the house is peopled by the crazed, almost zombified offspring of the couple. As the plot moves along we find that the evil couple are also the ones responsible for the deplorable conditions of his neighborhood.
VHS: S21393. $19.98.
Wes Craven, USA, 1991, 102 mins.

The Phantom of the Opera
Lon Chaney stars in the greatest role of his career as Erik, the love-torn resident of the hidden depths of the Opera House. This 70th anniversary edition has been completely remastered from a 35mm archive print and features the original 2-strip Technicolor masked ball sequence and fantastic score performed by a 60-piece orchestra.
DVD: DV60033. $29.95.
VHS: S01019. $24.95.
Rupert Julian, USA, 1925, 101 mins.

Play Misty for Me
Clint Eastwood self-directs in his directorial debut. He plays a late-night radio disc jockey who is haunted by the ultimate obsessive, "will-not-be-ignored," fatal attraction-type groupie Jessica Walter, who is just as scary as can be. A very competent thriller that still delivers lots of surprises and chills.
VHS: S06818. $19.95.
Clint Eastwood, USA, 1971, 102 mins.

Poltergeist
When you build a community over a graveyard and don't move the bodies, expect the kind of problems that plague this typically American suburban family. Moving furniture and floating toys lead to alternative dimensions and the lowering of real estate values. With Craig T. Nelson, JoBeth Williams and Heather O'Rourke. Great special effects. Co-written and produced by Steven Spielberg.
DVD: DV60111. $24.98.
VHS: S04502. $19.95.
Laser: CAV, special collector's edition. **LD74490. $39.98.**
Tobe Hooper, USA, 1982, 114 mins.

The Prophecy
A Los Angeles cop (Elias Koteas) is joined by an elementary school teacher (Virginia Madsen) for a thrilling showdown with the forces of evil. Christopher Walken is the fallen Gabriel, and he leads his troops into a deadly and mysterious battle that places the fate of the entire planet at his mercy.
VHS: S27498. $99.99.
Laser: LD75520. $39.99.
Gregory Widen, USA, 1995, 97 mins.

Psycho
The Classic! Anthony Perkins is Norman Bates and Janet Leigh is Marion Crane in this masterpiece of the macabre by Alfred Hitchcock.
VHS: S01068. $19.95.
Laser: LD70068. $34.98.
Alfred Hitchcock, USA, 1960, 109 mins.

Re-Animator
Chicago's very own Stuart Gordon of the Organic Theater, creator of *WARP*, directs this adaptation of an H.P. Lovecraft story. A medical student brings the dead back to life. Done with lots of gusto and humor, which turned this one into a cult classic.
VHS: S01093. $79.98.
Stuart Gordon, USA, 1985, 86 mins.

Repulsion
Polanski's first English-language film, a chilling study of madness, stars Catherine Deneuve as a jealously sadistic schizophrenic, terrified of sex. Full of memorable sequences, such as Deneuve's delusions of rape as she sees plaster turn into a clawing hand and walls cracking or overhears the moans of her sister making love. With Yvonne Furneaux and John Fraser.
VHS: S01106. $39.95.
Laser: Widescreen. **LD75387. $99.95.**
Roman Polanski, Great Britain, 1965, 105 mins.

Rosemary's Baby
Ira Levin thriller brought to the screen by Roman Polanski, concerning a young wife whose husband becomes involved with a witches' coven. With Mia Farrow and John Cassavetes.
VHS: S02685. $19.95.
Laser: Letterboxed. **LD76433. $39.98.**
Roman Polanski, USA, 1968, 136 mins.

Scanners
An explosive tale of mind control and the powers that exist to govern and observe its application. Patrick McGoohan (*The Prisoner*) is the manipulative head of a scientific corporate research facility. His character is called Dr. Ruth. With Stephen Lack and Michael Ironside as the telepathic scanners and Jennifer O'Neill as decoration.
VHS: S06189. $14.98.
Laser: LD72310. $39.99.
David Cronenberg, Canada, 1981, 104 mins.

Scream
Wes Craven's horror deconstruction, starring Drew Barrymore, Courteney Cox, Neve Campbell, David Arquette, Rose McGowan, Skeet Ulrich and Henry Winkler as a high school principal, toys with both the intellectual and the visceral. A scary movie fan has gone too far, and now a group of friends must follow the universal "rules" of fright movies: don't answer the phone, don't go off alone—and don't scream.
VHS: S31526. $19.95.
Laser: LD76257. $39.99.
Wes Craven, USA, 1997, 111 mins.

Scream of Fear
Penny Appleby (Susan Strasberg) pays a visit to her father's Riviera resort, although she is told that her father is away on business. Continually terrified by sudden appearances of his ghost, the suspense builds until she finds herself at the edge of a cliff. A terrific chiller.
VHS: S09395. $69.95.
Seth Holt, USA, 1961, 81 mins.

The Shining
A real thriller based on a Stephen King novel, with Jack Nicholson going slowly mad and terrorizing his wife Shelley Duvall and their little boy, who has strange powers of ESP. With Scatman Crothers.
VHS: S01189. $19.98.
Laser: LD74736. $39.98.
Stanley Kubrick, USA, 1980, 146 mins.

Spider Baby
Lon Chaney Jr. heads a household of inbred cannibals in this bizarre and many-titled horror cheapie. As if that weren't enough, he also sings the theme song. Included in the cast of wackos are Sid Haig, Carol Ohmart and the ever-popular Mantan Moreland. B&W. It's weird.
VHS: S04035. $14.98.
Jack Hill, USA, 1964, 86 mins.

Psycho

The Stepfather
This may look like your average mad slasher movie, but don't be misled by the packaging. This exploration of a deranged man just trying to find and maintain the perfect American family is several cuts above the usual shlock. Terry O'Quinn is mesmerizing in the title role. Script by Donald Westlake. A real chiller.
Laser: LD72312. $29.99.
Joseph Ruben, USA, 1987, 89 mins.

Life in the Big House

The Stepford Wives

For two decades this film's title and what it implies have been ingrained into our vocabulary and consciousness. Something strange is happening in the town of Stepford, where the men spend their nights doing something secret and every woman acts like every man's dream of the "perfect" wife—a dream that is really a nightmare. With Katherine Ross, Paula Prentiss, Tina Louise, Dee Wallace, Patrick O'Neal and seven-year-old Mary Stuart Masterson, making her film debut. "I can promise you an eerie, spine-tingling, good shiver down the spine with the *Stepford Wives*" (Rex Reed, *The New York Daily News*).
VHS: S31190. $14.98.
Laser: LD76197. $39.98.
Bryan Forbes, USA, 1974, 115 mins.

Strait-Jacket

This later, terror-filled Joan Crawford film was written by Robert Bloch, who also penned *Psycho*. Crawford is not to be missed as the insane woman with an axe. After doing time for attacking her husband and his lover, she is finally set free to terrorize once again. Also features George Kennedy and Lee Majors in his screen debut. Includes original trailer.
Laser: LD74975. $34.95.
William Castle, USA, 1964, 93 mins.

The Student of Prague

Conrad Veidt stars in this haunting tale about an unscrupulous student in the mysterious Czech capital. He is intrigued by that which the devil offers him and decides to sell his soul. Germany, 1926, 84 mins.
VHS: S23850. $24.95.

Suspiria

Considered by many to be one of the most terrifying and stylized horror films of recent years, *Suspiria* stars Jessica Harper as Susy Banyon, an American student who has enrolled in a German dance academy. On the very night she arrives, two of the students are brutally murdered. It soon becomes apparent that this is only the beginning of a terrifying nightmare. "The most eagerly awaited horror film of the decade…the most stylish and simply one of the best horror films ever made" (Fangoria).
VHS: S10717. $19.98.
Dario Argento, Italy, 1984, 97 mins.

The Tenant

Polanski's most autobiographical film is, like *Repulsion*, a journey through the distorted realm of the human mind. Polanski himself plays Trelkovsky, a nebbish file clerk who moves into the apartment of a young suicide, becomes deeply paranoid, certain that the other tenants are trying to drive *him* to suicide. With Isabelle Adjani, Shelley Winters, Lila Kedrova, Melvyn Douglas. English dialog.
VHS: S01308. $49.95.
Roman Polanski, Great Britain, 1976, 126 mins.

The Texas Chainsaw Massacre

Tobe Hooper's restored cult film is a frightening piece of Americana. This strange subversion of the slasher movie concerns five friends traveling through a flat, nondescript Texas wasteland who encounter a bizarre family and are forced to struggle for their lives. With Marilyn Burns, Allen Danzinger, Paul A. Partain and William Vail.
VHS: S19463. $19.98.
Laser: LD71919. $29.98.
Tobe Hooper, USA, 1974, 81 mins.

Them!

A 50's masterpiece of the cinema of the fantastic. With atmospheric shadow and light photography, memorable performances by James Whitmore and James Arness (pre-Gunsmoke), and assists from 12 foot long ants.
VHS: S01319. $19.98.
Laser: LD74719. $34.98.
Gordon Douglas, USA, 1954, 93 mins.

They Live

John Carpenter's sci-fi thriller about one man's battle against aliens who are systematically gaining control of the earth. Pro-wrestler Roddy Piper stars as the loner who stumbles upon ghoulish creatures masquerading as humans while they lull the public into submission through subliminal advertising messages! Only specially made sunglasses make the deadly truth visible.
VHS: S10111. $89.95.
John Carpenter, USA, 1988, 95 mins.

The Undead

In this camp classic a scientist fixes his gaze on the past and finds a way to magically transport himself into the Dark Ages. Once there he encounters many surprises, including the wholly unexpected Undead.
VHS: S23817. $24.95.
Roger Corman, USA, 1957, 75 mins.

The Uninvited

Lewis Allen's elegant ghost tale about a music critic and his sister attempting to solve the questions of unnatural occurrences and supernatural disturbances at a beautiful old house they've just purchased. Gail Russell stars as a beautiful young woman haunted by the past. With Ray Milland, Ruth Hussey, Donald Crisp and Cornelia Otis Skinner.
VHS: S17017. $14.98.
Lewis Allen, USA, 1944, 99 mins.

Repulsion

100 Films That Fell Through the Cracks

After Hours
An inventive dark comedy, in which all reality seems to be turned upside-down, peopled by a cast including Rosanna Arquette, Teri Garr, Griffin Dunne and Cheech & Chong. Scorsese received Best Director honors at the 1986 Cannes Film Festival for this. Written by Joseph Minion.
VHS: S00021. $19.98.
Laser: LD70497. $34.95.
Martin Scorsese, USA, 1985, 97 mins.

American Heart
Martin Bell's (*Streetwise*) dramatic debut examines the lifestyles of the socially marginal. Jeff Bridges plays Jack, a convict whose plans of moving to Alaska are thwarted by the appearance of his 14-year-old son, Nick (Edward Furlong). The two settle into a difficult daily existence in a Seattle boarding room as Jack tries desperately to avoid the temptation of the grift, while Nick is attracted to the romantic allure of the streets. Lucinda Jenney contributes a remarkable turn as Jack's battle-scarred girlfriend.
VHS: S19465. $19.98.
Laser: LD75145. $34.98.
Martin Bell, USA, 1992, 113 mins.

Apartment Zero
A marvelously creepy and involved study of interpersonal relationships and murder in Buenos Aires. Colin Firth stars as a jittery, movie-mad proprietor of a failing art house cinema who is forced to take in a boarder to meet expenses. With Hart Bochner as Jack, the handsome American who is looking for a quiet room while the rest of the city is looking for a killer. Often grimly funny in its Hitchcockian tone and style.
VHS: S11690. $19.98.
Martin Donovan, USA, 1988, 124 mins.

Arizona Dream
Johnny Depp stars as a young drifter who meets a kindred spirit in Faye Dunaway and unexpectedly falls in love. Between their age differences and the reactions of their dysfunctional families, love is put on trial. Jerry Lewis is great as Depp's car dealership huckstering uncle.
VHS: S23859. $19.98.
Emir Kusturica, USA, 1994, 119 mins.

The Atomic Cafe
A unique documentary about Cold War paranoia over the Bomb. This chilling documentary by Kevin Rafferty, Jayne Loader and Pierce Rafferty culls newsreel footage and government archives to recreate the hysteria of the Cold War. "A comic horror film, it does more to evoke the what-me-worry social madness of the Cold War than any documentary I've ever seen" (J. Hoberman).
VHS: S00074. $29.95.
Laser: LD75375. $49.98.
Kevin Rafferty, USA, 1982, 88 mins.

Bagdad Cafe
From Percy Adlon, the director of *Sugarbaby*, an English-language film about a friendship between two women at a desert truck stop motel and diner. One is black and overworked. The other is German

and overdressed. A haunting musical score and a top notch supporting cast which includes Jack Palance makes this sweet comedy starring C.C. Pounder and Marianne Sagebrecht a delight. In English.
VHS: S07965. $14.98.
Laser: LD75953. $34.95.
Percy Adlon, USA, 1988, 91 mins.

Barjo
A wacky French farce based on the novel by Philip K. Dick, *Barjo* is the "slightly psychotic" story of young, underdeveloped Barjo, who lives near his sister Fanfan, waiting for the UFOs. When he accidentally burns down his house, he moves in with Fanfan, discovers sex, and quietly drives Fanfan's husband insane. Nutty, off-the-wall comedy from the director of *Baxter*. French with English subtitles.
VHS: S20424. $19.95.
Jerome Boivin, France, 1992, 85 mins.

Big Night
This charmer of a movie—a big winner at Sundance and with audiences, and a treat for movie and food lovers—is the story of two Italian brothers whose restaurant teeters on the brink of bankruptcy. With Minnie Driver, Ian Holm, Isabella Rossellini, Campbell Scott, Tony Shalhoub and Stanley Tucci. "A feast of a film" (Peter Travers, *Newsday*).
VHS: S31122. $19.95.
Laser: LD76173. $34.99.
Stanley Tucci, USA, 1996, 109 mins.

The Big Picture
Today's Hollywood scene is hilariously lampooned in this behind-the-scenes look at costs of making it in show business. Kevin Bacon stars as a naive kid from Ohio who wins a best student film award from the prestigious National Film Institute and suddenly ends up in the Hollywood fast lane, where he sells out. With Jennifer Jason Leigh, Michael McKeon and J.T. Walsh, as well as appearances by Eddie Albert, Richard Belzer, John Cleese, Stephen Collins, June Lockhart and Roddy McDowell.
VHS: S31143. $14.95.
Christopher Guest, USA, 1988, 102 mins.

Bix
This famed trumpeter revolutionized jazz. In this first-rate musical biography his life and times are recreated based on the known facts. He is seen playing in some of the original locations including spots throughout the Midwest where *Bix* began. Hoagey Carmichael and Pee Wee Russel are just some of the figures seen accompanying him, performing songs like "Dardenella" and "Stardust." In English.
VHS: S20939. $29.95.
Pupi Avati, Italy/USA, 1990, 100 mins.

The Black Cat
Edgar G. Ulmer (*Detour*) directs Boris Karloff and Bela Lugosi in this stylish horror work. Ulmer pulled out all the stops in this movie about a young American couple trapped in the house of a demented scientist. With David Manners, Jacqueline Wells, Lucille Lund, and Egon Brecher. From a story by Edgar Allan Poe.
VHS: S17270. $14.98.
Edgar G. Ulmer, USA, 1934, 65 mins.

Bagdad Cafe

Black Sunday

This Barbara Steele Italian horror movie has nothing to do with Middle Eastern Terrorists or hijacked blimps. In her first horror film she plays a dual role: Asa, a reincarnated vampire-witch, and Katia, her innocent great-granddaughter. Heavy on the atmosphere. With John Richardson and Ivo Garrani. B&W.

VHS: S09126. $24.95.
Mario Bava, Italy, 1961, 83 mins.

Bottle Rocket

James Caan stars as a tough crime boss who won't take no for an answer in this unusual comedy. It's part coming-of-age story and part gangster film, where the three central assailants aren't especially good at crime, resulting in hysterical mishaps all the way to the pay-off. Owen Wilson also appears.

VHS: S29865. $19.95.
Laser: LD75905. $34.95.
Wes Anderson, USA, 1996, 92 mins.

Box of Moonlight

Uptight electrical engineer Al Fountain (John Turturro) is a man struggling with the monotony of everyday life and the threat of middle age, when a routine business trip turns into a life-altering experience. With the help of a few bizarre but sincere strangers—a free spirit called "the Kid" (Sam Rockwell), a phone sex operator (Catherine Keener) and a paranoid mechanic (Dermot Mulroney)—Al discovers something incredible: himself. "Sexy, seductive, amazingly fresh" (Janet Maslin, *New York Times*).

VHS: $32691. $99.99.
Laser: LD76440. $34.98.
Tom DiCillo, USA, 1997, 111 mins.

Breaking the Waves

In her incredible film debut, Emily Watson gives an Academy Award-nominated performance as Bess, a naive young woman who marries Jan, a handsome oil-rig worker. For the first time in her life, Bess experiences passion and physical pleasure she never imagined. But her marital bliss is cut short when an accident on the rig leaves Jan paralyzed. Believing she holds the key to his recovery, Bess will stop at nothing—even infidelity—in order to prolong Jan's life. "A powerhouse love story, a kind of miracle" (*Village Voice*). In English. Letterboxed.

VHS: $31256. $99.99.
Laser: LD76284. $69.95.
Lars von Trier, Great Britain/Denmark, 1996, 152 mins.

Bulletproof Heart

Anthony LaPaglia and Mimi Rogers star in this film noir-style love story. A hit man (LaPaglia) sets out to kill his mark, a beautiful socialite who is actually eager to die. Though he is warned that he should steel himself for this assignment (as other men have tried and failed), his own self-doubts and her overwhelming beauty lead to the inevitable—he falls for her in a big way.

VHS: $26370. $19.95.
Mark Malone, USA, 1995, 95 mins.

Cabeza de Vaca

A visually spellbinding biography of the Spanish explorer Nunez Cabeza de Vaca, the sole survivor of a 16th-century Spanish shipwreck off the coast of Florida. Cabeza de Vaca discovers the Iguase, a traditional Indian tribe, which allows Cabeza into their tribe. Over the next eight years, he learns about their mysterious culture and becomes a leader of the group. But his former identity catches up with him when a team of Spanish conquistadors return to colonize the Indians. "Bold and imaginative, the film has ambition, freshness, imagination, mystery and exhilarating reach. It has greatness in it" (Jay Carr, *Boston Globe*). With Juan Diego, Daniel Gimenez Cacho and Roberto Sosa. Spanish and Indian with English subtitles.

VHS: $19356. $29.95.
Nicolas Echevarria, Mexico/Spain, 1991, 109 mins.

Careful

From internationally acclaimed cult director Guy Maddin (*Tales from the Gimli Hospital*, *Archangel*) comes this Freudian parody of 1920's German mountain and expressionist films about the repressed people of the Alpine village of Tolzbad who must never utter a sound lest they cause an avalanche. When one man's incestuous dream triggers an emotional avalanche, the town is revealed as a hotbed of repressed desires, Oedipal angst and sibling rivalry. Stars Gosnia Dobrowolska, Kyle McCullough and Brent Neale.

VHS: $27593. $79.95.
Guy Maddin, Canada 1992, 96 mins.

The Champagne Safari

This fascinating film tells the fantastic but true story of wealthy businessman, glamorous playboy and daring adventurer Charles Bedeaux, who rose to wealth and fame in the 1920s after making his fortune by inventing a new method for modernizing industry. Bedeaux, who was lampooned in Chaplin's *Modern Times*, hobnobbed with the rich, powerful and famous all over the globe, even in Nazi Germany. For leisure he planned an elaborate trek through the Canadian Rockies, to be documented for posterity by legendary cinematographer Floyd Crosby (*High Noon*). But soon Bedeaux's opulent world was in danger, as charges of collaboration and treason enveloped him.

VHS: $32650. $59.95.
George Ungar, Canada, 1995, 100 mins.

Cutter's Way

One of the most original American films of the last decade. Alex Cutter (John Heard) is the Vietnam veteran disfigured in the war. When his best friend Richard Bone (Jeff Bridges) is accused of the murder of a teenage girl, Cutter wants to set off after the real murderer with a vengeance. "A hauntingly powerful work," said *New York Magazine*.

VHS: $00290. $14.98.
Laser: LD76361. $39.99.
Ivan Passer, USA, 1982, 90 mins.

Danzon

This sensual, exuberant work by the gifted Mexican director Maria Novaro tells the story of Julia (Maria Rojo), a 40-year-old telephone operator and single mother whose emotional life consists of ballroom dancing. When her dancing partner disappears, Julia undertakes a grueling odyssey to locate him. Her search takes her on an extraordinary inner voyage. "One of the most enchanting surprises of the season" (Andrew Sarris). With Carmen Salinas, Blanca Guerra and Tito Vasconcelos. Spanish with English subtitles.

VHS: $19334. $19.95.
Maria Novaro, Mexico, 1991, 96 mins.

Delicatessen

Imagine the Coen brothers remaking Terry Gilliam's *Brazil* on speed and you get the idea of this film, set in a vaguely post-nuclear Paris. The action unfolds in a decaying building, where a war breaks out between a group of innocents, cannibals and militant vegetarians. French with English subtitles. With Dominique Pinon (*Diva*), Laure Dougnac and Claude Dreyfus.

VHS: $18069. $89.98.
Laser: LD75125. $39.95.
Jean-Marie Jeunet/Marc Caro, France, 1991, 95 mins.

Devil in a Blue Dress

Denzel Washington is terrific in this stylish thriller set in 1940s Los Angeles. Private Eye Easy Rawlins (Washington) thought he was being asked to take a relatively simple case that would make him some easy money. He didn't expect it would lead to his being blackmailed by a crooked politician. Rawlins quickly finds himself in a netherworld of suspense and deceit where the devil must be paid. Jennifer Beals is featured.

VHS: $27347. $19.95.
Laser: LD75497. $34.95.
Carl Franklin, USA, 1995, 101 mins.

Dogfight

River Phoenix and Lili Taylor star in this poignant, offbeat romance set in the early 1960's. Just prior to shipping out to Vietnam, four Marine buddies try to find the ugliest women in San Francisco to win a bar bet. When Taylor catches on, Phoenix tries to take her out on a real date to apologize. With Richard Panebianco and a heavily disguised E.G. Dailey as the toothless winner of the dogfight.

VHS: $15529. $19.98.
Nancy Savoca, USA, 1991, 95 mins.

Edward II

Derek Jarman's adaptation of Christopher Marlowe's 16th century play about Edward II (Steven Waddington), who neglected his beautiful, ambitious wife (Tilda Swinton) to carry out an obsessive, homoerotic relationship with his military lieutenant (Andrew Tiernan). Annie Lennox sings "Every Time We Say Goodbye".

VHS: $17626. $19.95.
Derek Jarman, Great Britain, 1991, 91 mins.

El Mariachi

This film by 24-year-old director Robert Rodriquez was made for the unbelievable sum of $7,000. Rodriquez playfully evokes Peckinpah, noir westerns and Hitchcock. A maverick loner and mariachi player (Carlos Gallardo) enters a Mexican border town and is instantly confused with a stark, brutally efficient assassin (Reinol Martinez). Spanish with English subtitles.

VHS: $19057. $19.95.
Laser: Special Collector's Edition. **LD71892. $49.95.**
Richard Rodriguez, USA, 1992, 80 mins.

Equinox

Alan Rudolph's film is about the intersecting fates of twins—an introverted auto mechanic and an underworld gangster, both played by Matthew Modine—who were separated at birth. Lara Flynn Boyle plays a fragile young woman whom the good twin is trying to protect. With Tyra Ferrell, Marisa Tomei as a frightened prostitute, and Kevin J. O'Connor.

VHS: $19731. $19.95.
Laser: Letterboxed. **LD72440. $34.95.**
Alan Rudolph, USA, 1992, 115 mins.

Gas Food Lodging
Allison Anders' depiction of the difficult, complex relationship between a single mother and her two daughters has some graceful, liquid camera work and an excellent performance by Ione Skye as a distracted, promiscuous vixen. Set in a ragged New Mexico town, Anders maps out some tangled relationships while fully exploring post-adolescent and adult sexuality. Adapted from the novel by Richard Peck. Cinematography by Dean Lent. With Brooke Adams, Fairuza Balk and James Brolin.
VHS: S18346. $19.95.
Laser: LD71864. $34.95.
Allison Anders, USA, 1992, 94 mins.

The Hairdresser's Husband
An acclaimed, quirky film about erotic obsession from the director of *Monsieur Hire*. Antoine (Jean Rochefort) is a middle-aged man whose life-long ambition to marry a hairdresser is fulfilled in his tender relationship with the beautiful and graceful Matila (Anna Galiena). With Henri Hocking and Maurice Chevit. French with English subtitles.
VHS: S18680. $19.95.
Laser: LD75204. $34.98.
Patrice Leconte, France, 1990, 84 mins.

Out of Sight

City for Conquest
VHS: S15523. $19.98.

City Lights
VHS: S00245. $19.98.
Laser: LD72318. $69.98.

Don't Look Now
VHS: S00358. $49.95.

Jennifer 8
VHS: S18679. $19.95.
Laser: LD75318. $39.98.

The Killer
VHS: S13457. $19.98.
Laser: LD72361. $124.95.

La Symphonie Pastorale
VHS: S30143. $29.95.

The Miracle Worker
VHS: S00860. $24.95.
Laser: LD71175. $34.98.

A Patch of Blue
VHS: S12530. $19.98.
Laser: LD76222. $39.98.

Proof
VHS: S17710. $19.95.

Until the End of the World
VHS: S16633. $19.98.
Laser: LD71505. $34.98.

Wait Until Dark
VHS: S31511. $19.98.
Laser: LD72448. $34.98.

The Whales of August
Laser: LD72316. $29.99.

Hard Eight
Philip Baker Hall (*Secret Honor*) is a poker-faced professional gambler with a dark past, whose life is knocked off balance by a sad, simple-minded waitress (Gwyneth Paltrow, *Emma*) and a young loser (John C. Reilly, *Days of Thunder*). With Samuel L. Jackson.
VHS: S31789. $98.99.
Laser: LD76308. $34.95.
Paul Thomas Anderson, USA, 1997, 101 mins.

Heavenly Creatures
Peter Jackson's chilling account of two teenage girls who develop an intense emotional and physical relationship, dominated by fantasy, which ultimately leads them to murder, is a stylistically original work. It is remarkable for its insights into the girls' adolescent world of make-believe, as well as the bland suburban world of 1950's New Zealand.
VHS: S24774. $19.95.
Laser: Widescreen. LD74976. $39.99.
Peter Jackson, New Zealand, 1994, 99 mins.

Heavy
The life of an overweight pizza chef (Pruitt Taylor Vince) changes dramatically when his mother (Shelley Winters) dies and a beautiful and kind waitress (Liv Tyler) opens his heart to love. With Deborah Harry (Blondie) and Evan Dando (The Lemonheads) and music by Sonic Youth's Thurston Moore. "Quietly earthshaking…eloquent, purposeful" (Janet Maslin, *New York Times*).
VHS: S31197. $98.99.
James Mangold, USA, 1995, 104 mins.

Hope and Glory
John Boorman's critically-acclaimed memory of childhood—moving, funny, bittersweet. The main character, Bill, is a seven-year-old boy, Sarah Miles his ever-tolerant mother who does her best while dad's away at war. While the street is full of rubble, the Luftwaffe is parachuting into the back yard, this is a story of innocence in the face of war—a remarkable portrait of a childhood. On many Ten Best lists, winner of the Golden Globe Award for Best Picture.
Laser: LD72302. $29.99.
John Boorman, Great Britain, 1987, 94 mins.

Into the West
Two young brothers rescue a horse, which turns out to be magical. For their efforts they are rewarded with the adventure of a lifetime. Gabriel Byrne and Ellen Barkin are featured in this heart-warming children's film.
VHS: S21031. $19.95.
Mike Newell, Ireland, 1992, 97 mins.

Island of Lost Souls
A terrifying adaptation of H.G. Wells' story about a vivisectionist trapped on a desolate island who alters the biological genetics of jungle animals and changes them into pathological man/animal hybrids. With Charles Laughton, Bela Lugosi, Richard Arlen and Stanley Fields.
VHS: S19013. $14.98.
Erle C. Kenton, USA, 1933, 70 mins.

Jacquot de Nantes
Agnes Varda's loving tribute to her late husband, Jacques Demy, begins in Nantes in 1938 with a boy obsessed with movies. This 8-year-old makes puppets for little operettas. As he grows older his obsession never dies, even though his father makes him study mechanics. A number of happy childhood events animate this captivating film about a man who grows up and yet retains a youthful delight in fantasy that shapes his enduring vision and makes him a master of the French musical. French with English subtitles.
VHS: S20738. $19.95.
Agnes Varda, France, 1991, 118 mins.

Just Another Girl on the I.R.T.
Leslie Harris' debut film is a vivid portrait of the panache of a 17-year-old Brooklyn African-American woman. Ambitious and colorful, she is played by astonishing newcomer named Ariyan Johnson, who portrays a street-tough woman with plans to attend college and study medicine. Harris documents life in the projects, from the unique perspective of a young black woman. With Kevin Thigpen, Jerard Washington and Ebony Jerido.
VHS: S19024. $14.98.
Laser: LD75214. $34.98.
Leslie Harris, USA, 1992, 90 mins.

Kafka
Steven Soderbergh's follow-up to *sex, lies and videotape* is set in a baroque, sinister Prague. Jeremy Irons plays an insurance underwriter who, following a friend's disappearance, gets entangled with a shadowy anarchist group and an unbalanced doctor performing perverse scientific experiments. The cast includes Theresa Russell, Joel Grey, Ian Holm, Jeroen Krabbe, Armin Mueller-Stahl and Alec Guinness.
VHS: S17789. $92.95.
Steven Soderbergh, USA/France/Great Britain, 1991, 100 mins.

King of the Hill
Steven Soderbergh's splendid, realistic tale of growing up during the Depression in St. Louis, based on the memoirs of A.E. Hotchner. The young Jesse Bradford stars as 12-year-old Aaron, whose perseverance and intelligence help him overcome the incredible odds growing up with a family that's

falling apart. With Jeroen Krabbe, Lisa Eichhorn, Karen Allen, Spalding Gray and Elizabeth McGovern. "Simply one of the year's best films" (Siskel & Ebert).
VHS: $20548. $19.98.
Laser: Letterboxed. **LD72364. $34.98.**
Steven Soderbergh, USA, 1993, 102 mins.

La Lectrice
The fabulous French actress Miou-Miou has the title role of a woman who makes her living reading to her varied clientele. Playing her role as storyteller with increasing confidence, Miou-Miou becomes teacher, confidant, provocateur and confessor to her clients. A seductive and humorous comedy that has captured the attention of literate movie goers on an international scale. An unusual film directed with a deft, wry touch by Michel Deville. French with English subtitles.
VHS: $10759. $19.98.
Michel Deville, France, 1989, 98 mins.

Last Exit to Brooklyn
Hubert Selby Jr.'s controversial novel is now a visually arresting and powerfully performed motion picture. The depressed dock area of Brooklyn in the early 1950's serves as a background for anger, violence and forbidden emotions among hookers, drag queens, juvenile delinquents and union organizers. With Stephan Lang, Jerry Orbach, Burt Young, Peter Dobson and Jennifer Jason Leigh as the cold-hearted hooker Tralala.
VHS: $13289. $89.95.
Uli Edel, Germany/USA, 1990, 102 mins.

Leolo
A French-Canadian coming-of-age film about a boy convinced he was fathered by a tomato. This strange premise sets the mood for a darkly comic fantasy/nightmare with mystical and sexual overtones. French with English subtitles.
VHS: $20579. $19.95.
Laser: LD74454. $49.99.
Jean-Claude Lauzon, Canada, 1992, 107 mins.

Life Is Sweet
Satirist Mike Leigh is at it again in the London south side with this decidedly bittersweet comedy about the members of a dysfunctional family and their oddball friends. It seems everyone in this film is striving for change. The family tries to balance their differences with alcoholic friends and their short fuses proves a challenge, but they don't forget to laugh a lot along the way.
VHS: $16628. $14.98.
Laser: LD71503. $29.98.
Mike Leigh, Great Britain, 1992, 103 mins.

Life Stinks
Only Mel Brooks could find laughs in a comedy about the homeless. He directs, co-writes and stars as a greedy billionaire who pretends to be down and out in order to win a bet and acquire the land needed for a new building complex. Lesley Ann Warren is sensational as the streetwise bag lady who helps Brooks with some long overdue attitude adjustment. With Jeffrey Tambor, Rudy De Luca, Stuart Pankin and Howard Morris as Sailor.
VHS: $15433. $14.95.
Laser: LD74676. $34.98.
Mel Brooks, USA, 1991, 93 mins.

M. Butterfly
Jeremy Irons stars as the French diplomatic functionary seduced by an illusionist from the Beijing Opera. Set in Maoist China and inspired by a true story of espionage, this tale of romance and reversal will surprise even the most jaded viewer. Previously a Broadway hit, the film convincingly portrays the unbelievable facts behind a startling and deceptive facade.
VHS: $20712. $19.98.
Laser: LD72383. $34.98.
David Cronenberg, USA, 1993, 101 mins.

Mad Dog and Glory
John McNaughton's drama forges a complicated relationship among three lost souls. A shy Chicago forensics cop (Robert De Niro) derisively named "Mad Dog" inadvertently saves the life of a sullen mobster and loan shark (Bill Murray). His reward is the ambiguous one-week services of Glory (Uma Thurman), a beautiful bartender indentured to the gangster. With David Caruso, Kathy Baker and McNaughton regular Tom Towles.
VHS: $18995. $19.98.
Laser: Letterboxed. **LD71890. $34.98.**
John McNaughton, USA, 1993, 99 mins.

Map of the Human Heart
An epic love story between Avik (Jason Scott Lee), an Eskimo, and Albertine (French actress Anne Parillaud), a half-breed, that unfolds in the years 1931-1965. When the lovers are reunited, Avik, a World War II bomber pilot, discovers Albertine is married to Walter Scott (Patrick Bergin), his former protector who saved his life. "A sweeping romance, grand, noble and boldly imaginative" (Jay Carr, *Boston Globe*). With John Cusack, Ben Mendelsohn, Annie Galipeau and Jeanne Moreau.
VHS: $19060. $19.98.
Laser: LD75227. $34.98.
Vincent Ward, New Zealand, 1992, 109 mins.

Masala
Srinivas Krishna's colorful, independent feature is set in the East Indian community in Toronto. Krishna (played by the director) is traumatized by his parents' deaths and believes he won't live long. "A brash and sprightly Canadian comedy about Indian emigres in Toronto, with musical numbers, erotic dream sequences, exploding airplanes, a blue-skinned Hindu deity who exists mainly on video, a fair amount of farce, and a great deal of satire" (Jonathan Rosenbaum, *Chicago Reader*). With Saeed Jaffrey, Zohra Segal, Sakina Jaffrey and Heri Johal.
VHS: $19728. $19.98.
Srinivas Krishna, Canada, 1991, 105 mins.

Maya Lin: A Strong Clear Vision
The story of the artist/sculptor/architect who, while an undergraduate at Yale, designed one of the most bitterly debated public monuments, the Vietnam Veterans Memorial. The film follows her throughout the creative process as she produces a succession of eloquent, highly original sculptures and monuments that capture and memorialize significant American social events. Compelling viewing. "The film is absolutely riveting" (Peter Stack, *San Francisco Chronicle*).
VHS: $30482. $59.95.
Freida Lee Mock, USA, 1995, 96 mins.

Menage
This black comedy is a brilliant sexual farce. The charismatic, gay thief Bob (Gerard Depardieu) coolly insinuates himself into the troubled lives of Antoine (Michel Blanc) and Monique (Miou-Miou). The film is redolent with Blier's characteristic wit, energy and sexual daring. French with English subtitles.
VHS: $16945. $89.95.
Bertrand Blier, France, 1986, 84 mins.

Big Night

Microcosmos
This revealing, shocking and fascinating look at the mysterious world of insects through the miracle of microphotography mesmerized audiences at Cannes. Watch as these fantastic creatures struggle with nature's most urgent issues.
VHS: $32348. $14.99.
Laser: LD76352. $39.99.
Claude Nurdsany/Marie Perennou, France, 1996, 75 mins.

Midnight Run
Robert De Niro plays a bounty hunter assigned to find and return Charles Grodin to a sleazy L.A. bail

bondsman. Grodin embezzled millions from the Mob, which he donated to charity, and they want him dead. An entertaining, action-packed, cross-country, serious comedy with Yaphet Kotto, John Ashton, Dennis Farina and the person who wrote this description as an extra in an airport scene. From the Director of *Beverly Hills Cop*.
VHS: S08325. $19.95.
Martin Brest, USA, 1988, 125 mins.

The Mighty Quinn
Denzel Washington has the title role of a local police chief in Jamaica caught between doing his job and preserving a boyhood friendship. Robert Townsend is Maubee, a petty criminal and island legend who stumbles into an international situation that involves murder and large sums of money. A comic thriller loaded with lots of good music. With James Fox, Sheryl Lee Ralph and M. Emmet Walsh.
VHS: S11203. $89.98.
Carl Schenkel, USA, 1989, 98 mins.

Monsieur Hire
A disturbing and finely crafted thriller about obsession and responsibility. Michel Blanc stars as a reclusive tailor who enjoys watching Sandra Bonnaire undress across the courtyard. When a murder is committed, his peculiarities make him a suspect. Based on a novel by Georges Simeon. With Luc Thuillier and Andre Wilms. Be prepared to be affected. French with English subtitles.
VHS: S13672. $19.98.
Patrice Leconte, France, 1989, 81 mins.

Montenegro
Funny, bizarre, surreal, sensual, unpredictable. Dusan Makavejev's *Montenegro* follows Susan Anspach, a middle-class Swedish housewife who gets embroiled in the free-wheeling sensuality of the Zanzi-Bar in the Yugoslavian-immigrant section of Stockholm in an attempt to discover the meaning of personal choice and freedom. English dialog.
VHS: S00875. $19.98.
Laser: Widescreen. LD76052. $49.95.
Dusan Makavejev, Sweden/G.B., 1982, 79 mins.

Mortal Thoughts
Alan Rudolph's characteristically hypnotic thriller in the form of a police interrogation, with Demi Moore playing a New Jersey housewife drawn into events around the murder of her best friend's (Glenne Headly) abusive husband (Bruce Willis). The intricate flashback structure, Elliot Davis's dazzling camera work and fluid ensemble work create a haunting work. With Harvey Keitel as the homicide detective.
VHS: S15113. $19.95.
Alan Rudolph, USA, 1991, 104 mins.

Naked

Naked
This film won in both the Best Film and Best Actor category at the Cannes Film Festival. David Thewlis stars in this funny, erotic and bizarre odyssey, set in the streets of London, that explores the seamy side of desire and longing of post-Thatcherite England.
VHS: S21119. $19.95.
Laser: Includes director's commentary, still photo gallery, trailers and short films. **LD74468. $69.95.**
Mike Leigh, Great Britain, 1993, 131 mins.

Naked Lunch
David Cronenberg succeeds in filming what many considered unfilmable. He creates a bizarre, drug inspired world based on the once-banned 1959 underground novel by William Burroughs. Peter Weller couldn't be better as a Burroughs-like novelist/junkie who is sent to Interzone on a secret mission by a talking typewriter that transmutes to a roach. With Judy Davis, Julian Sands, Ian Holm and Roy Scheider as Dr. Benway. "A thrilling, astounding, devastating piece of work" (Dave Kehr, *Chicago Tribune*).
VHS: S16382. $94.98.
Laser: LD71581. $39.98.
David Cronenberg, USA, 1991, 117 mins.

Night on Earth
Jim Jarmusch's film is structured episodically, with the narrative simultaneously unfolding in Los Angeles, New York, Paris, Rome and Helsinki, and concerns the relationship of cab drivers and their passengers. The ensemble cast includes Gena Rowlands, Winona Ryder, Rosie Perez, Giancarlo Esposito, Armin Mueller-Stahl, Beatrice Dalle, Isaach de Bankole, Roberto Benigni, Matti Pellonpaa and Kari Vaananen. Tom Waits composed the music and performs two numbers. Letterboxed.
VHS: S17625. $19.95.
Jim Jarmusch, USA, 1991, 125 mins.

The Object of Beauty
Jake and Tina (played by John Malkovich and Andie MacDowell) are a sexy, jet-setting couple, madly in love and living far beyond their means in a posh London hotel. Confronting a lifestyle-or-death situation, the two plot to collect an insurance payoff after staging the phony theft of Tina's prize sculpture. Unfortunately, Jake and Tina aren't the only crooks in London.
VHS: S14995. $19.98.
Michael Lindsay-Hogg, Great Britain, 1991, 105 mins.

One False Move
A small masterpiece, this B-movie thriller features wonderful performances by Bill Paxton and Cynda Williams. A trio of criminals stage a grotesque gangland murder and travel to Arkansas, unaware the local sheriff and two L.A. cops await them. The two principal characters confront their pasts. With Michael Beach, Earl Beach, Jim Metzler and Billy Bob Thornton, who co-wrote the screenplay.
VHS: S17057. $19.95.
Laser: LD71541. $34.95.
Carl Franklin, USA, 1991, 103 mins.

Orchestra Rehearsal
Fellini's comic and controversial made-for-TV vignette depicts the turmoil of Italian society through events that take place during a rehearsal gathering set in a 13th-century chapel. "Gloriously funny…[Fellini's] very best work" (*The New York Times*).
DVD: DV60167. $29.98.
VHS: S32614. $79.98.
Federico Fellini, Italy/Germany, 1979, 72 mins.

Orlando
Virginia Woolf's ground-breaking novel about a transsexual from the time of Renaissance England has been transformed into a beautiful film. Tilda Swinton stars with Billy Zane as her romantic American lover while Quentin Crisp reigns as Queen Elizabeth the First.
VHS: S20829. $19.95.
Laser: LD74471. $34.95.
Sally Potter, Great Britain, 1993, 93 mins.

Party Girl
Parker Posey is a fresh presence in this new film about a girl living in a non-stop party called her life. This club kid must tone it down if she is to keep her exciting new job and her prospective mate. Inevitably, her formerly wild ways keep intruding into her more sober lifestyle. The result is a comedy for today.
VHS: S27175. $19.95.
Laser: LD75467. $34.95.
Daisy Von Scherler Mayer, USA, 1995, 98 mins.

Pennies from Heaven
Based on Dennis Potter's British television series *The Singing Detective, Pennies from Heaven* is the unique and stylish story of a Depression-era sheet music salesman, played by Steve Martin, whose own dreary, joyless life is contrasted with the cloying optimism of Tin Pan Alley songs from the period. The stunning, escapist splendor of the 1930's-style musical numbers (set to the original recordings) repeatedly clashes with the bleak circumstances of Martin's real-life existence in this dazzling and intellectually

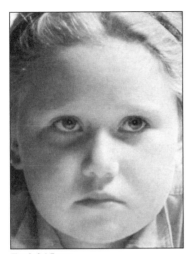

The Quiet Room

provocative musical—beautifully photographed by Gordon Willis. Newly remastered for video.
VHS: S13970. $19.99.
Herbert Ross, USA, 1981, 108 mins.

Proof
Jocelyn Moorhouse's debut film is a psychologically compelling work about a sinister three-way love relationship between a repressed blind photographer (Hugo Weaving), his friend (Russell Crowe) who describes the contents of the photographs, and the photographer's intensely jealous housekeeper (Genevieve Picot). Moorhouse has a brilliant facility for images, rhythms and texture.
VHS: S17710. $19.95.
Jocelyn Moorhouse, Australia, 1991, 90 mins.

Pursued
Offbeat Western stars Robert Mitchum as a war hero who seeks a man who killed his father years ago in a family feud. With Teresa Wright and Dean Jagger.
VHS: S24109. $14.98.
Laser: CLV. LD72017. $49.98.
Raoul Walsh, USA, 1947, 101 mins.

The Quiet Room
A unique exploration into the inner thoughts of a seven-year-old girl. It is a world in which she has very little control, for her parents' marriage is disintegrating. Through her silence, the child attempts to influence her parents' behavior and force them to communicate properly with each other and with her. With the marriage speeding toward total collapse, the child finds ways to make her actions speak even louder and finds the means to reconcile herself with the world.
VHS: S32153. $100.99.
Laser: LD76354. $39.99.
Rolf de Heer, Australia, 1996, 91 mins.

The Rapture
There are six definitions of "rapture" in the dictionary. This provocative thriller, written and directed by Michael Tolkin, tries to encompass them all. Mimi Rogers stars in this unusual drama that tests the religious faith of a born again Los Angeles telephone operator. She embarks on a sensual and spiritual odyssey that culminates in a cataclysm of Biblical proportions. With David Duchovny, Patrick Bauchau, Kimberly Cullum and Will Patton.
VHS: S15925. $19.95.
Michael Tolkin, USA, 1991, 100 mins.

Real Life
Albert Brooks' highly underrated film about a documentary filmmaker (Brooks) whose invasion of a "typically American family" to record their lives tears apart the nuclear family, exposing deeper and darker truths about contemporary America. Brooks' film is raw in its visual patterns, yet the long, uninterrupted takes established him as a filmmaker of flair and talent. Co-written by Harry Shearer and produced by

Penelope Spheeris, whose directing career has recently flourished (*Suburbia, The Boys Next Door*).
VHS: S02565. $19.95.
Albert Brooks, USA, 1978, 99 mins.

Reflecting Skin
For seven-year-old Seth Dove, the world is a very terrifying place. Writer-director Philip Ridley has created a strange and chilling universe on the plains of '50s Idaho where children disappear and death is always in the wind. Jeremy Duncan is unforgettable as the impressionable Seth. Viggo Mortensen co-stars as his older brother Cameron and Lindsay Duncan appears as the mysterious Dolphin Blue, the pale English neighbor widow who may just be a vampire. With David Longworth, Duncan Fraser, Evan Hall and Sherry Bie. This is a powerful film of particular visual splendor and impact.
VHS: S15707. $19.98.
Philip Ridley, USA, 1990, 93 mins.

Rock Hudson's Home Movies
With excerpts from some of Rock's most memorable films, this documentary digs into the persona of Hollywood's greatest male sex symbol of the 50's and 60's, whose death from AIDS forever transformed the way America looks at its stars. Mark Rappaport's film was named to multiple Ten Best lists as an original look at an American icon.
VHS: S21090. $39.95.
Mark Rappaport, USA, 1992, 63 mins.

Ruby in Paradise
Winner of the 1993 Grand Prize at the Sundance Film Festival, this film, starring the beautiful and accomplished Ashley Judd, charts the progress of a woman toward her own personal paradise. Visually stunning cinematography shows the Florida locations to great advantage in this story of one woman's quest for meaning.
VHS: S20711. $19.95.
Victor Nunez, USA, 1993, 115 mins.

Searching for Bobby Fischer
Joe Mantegna, Laurence Fishburne and Ben Kingsley star in this story about a childhood chess prodigy. In the cutthroat world of professional chess a father and son discover they must learn all the tricks, but only one skill can really help them—their love for one another.
VHS: S21138. $19.98.
Laser: Widescreen. LD75254. $34.98.
Steven Zallman, USA, 1993, 111 mins.

Seconds
Rock Hudson delivers a tour-de-force performance in director John Frankenheimer's (*The Manchurian Candidate*) critically acclaimed thriller about a man who buys a new identity and pays a terrifying price. John Randolph stars as a middle-aged banker, Arthur Hamilton, who, summoned by a mysterious corporation, undergoes plastic surgery and emerges as handsome bohemian artist Tony Wilson (Hudson). With nightmarish (Oscar-nominated) cinematography by James Wong Howe. "Fascinating from start to finish" (Leonard Maltin, *Movie & Video Guide*).
VHS: S31145. $79.95.
Laser: Letterboxed. LD76340. $39.99.
John Frankenheimer, USA, 1966, 107 mins.

Shadowlands
This adaptation of an episode from C.S. Lewis' life stars Anthony Hopkins as the writer, who becomes infatuated with an American woman, Debra Winger. When this author and notorious loner discovers a hitherto unknown quality within himself, the capacity for love, it alters him forever.
VHS: S21137. $19.98.
Richard Attenborough, Great Britain, 1993, 133 mins.

Spirit of the Beehive
A landmark Spanish film by Victor Erice, featuring the remarkable Ana Torrent in the story of two little girls growing up after the Spanish Civil War in the countryside. The hypnotic, spellbinding nature of the film is a rare achievement in cinema, as Erice evokes a deep poetry of childhood in a portrait of isolation. Spanish with English subtitles.
VHS: S08104. $29.95.
Victor Erice, Spain, 1973, 95 mins.

The Substance of Fire
In the high-stakes world of publishing, a businessman puts his company on the brink of bankruptcy and threatens to destroy his family and their fortune by doing the right thing. With Sarah Jessica Parker,

Sweetie

Timothy Hutton, Ron Rifkin and Tony Goldwyn.
VHS: S31528. $103.99.
Laser: LD76256. $39.99.
Daniel Sullivan, USA, 1996, 101 mins.

Sweetie

A true original—this breakthrough film from Australia's Jane Campion is "as disturbing as *Blue Velvet*", "an original." Bizarre, often hilarious, *Sweetie* is the story of two very different sisters, the guarded and repressed Kay and the overweight and spontaneous Sweetie.
VHS: S12478. $14.98.
Jane Campion, Australia, 1989, 97 mins.

Tales from the Gimli Hospital

The surreal first feature from Canadian independent Guy Maddin is set in the isolated village of Gimli, Manitoba, at the beginning of the century. Jealousy and madness overtake two men who share a hospital room. In chilling though mocking vignettes, they exchange wild, inventive tales involving pestilence, reckless envy and necrophilia. With Kyle McCullogh, Michael Gottli and Angela Heck.
VHS: S19409. $29.95.
Guy Maddin, Canada, 1987, 72 mins.

Tatie Danielle

Meet the meanest old lady on earth. She's Auntie—"Tatie"—Danielle, a demanding and manipulative woman who must be waited on hand and foot. When she moves in with her great nephew, he and his wife hope that "Tatie" will be the grandmother the children never had. It doesn't take long, however, for this cantankerous old lady to make everyone's life hell. A clever and darkly hilarious work from director Etienne Chatliez. French with English subtitles.
VHS: S15585. $19.98.
Etienne Chatiliez, France, 1991, 114 mins.

Tetsuo: The Iron Man

A post-punk, Japanese film about a man attacked by a feral woman with a metal hand and his bizarre mutation into a perverse combination of man and machine. It's like Godard remaking *Blue Velvet*. With Tomoroh Taguchi, Nobu Kanaoka and Shinya Tsukamoto. Japanese with English subtitles.
VHS: S18410. $19.98.
Laser: LD72348. $39.99.
Shinya Tsukamoto, Japan, 1989, 67 mins.

Theremin: An Electronic Odyssey

A cross between Albert Einstein and Ed Wood, Leon Theremin pioneered the electronic music revolution four decades before the rise of Electronic Rock. His invention, the Theremin, produced an eerie, warbling sound, and was used on many Hollywood sound tracks, including *Spellbound, The Day the Earth Stood Still* and *The Lost Weekend*, and by rock legends Brian Wilson and Todd Rundgren. At the height of his popularity, Theremin was kidnapped by Soviet agents and forced to develop spy technology for Stalin's KGB. Janet Maslin (*The New York Times*) calls it "fascinating," and it is. Winner at the Sundance and San Francisco Film Festivals.
VHS: S27436. $19.98.
Laser: LD75505. $39.99.
Steven M. Martin, USA/Great Britain, 1995, 84 mins.

This Boy's Life

Scottish director Michael Caton-Jones' somber adaptation of Tobias Wolff's memoirs about growing up in the Pacific Northwest in the 50s. The film is a collection of painful vignettes about the author as a young boy. Toby (Leonardo DiCaprio) and his mother Caroline (Ellen Barkin) stake out a forlorn, nomadic existence as they move from town to anonymous town without desires or expectations. With Robert De Niro and Jonah Blechman.
VHS: S19239. $19.98.
Laser: LD71916. $34.98.
Michael Caton-Jones, USA, 1993, 115 mins.

To Sleep with Anger

Danny Glover stars as Harry Mention, a mysterious and magnetic visitor from the Deep South who comes to stay with an old friend, named Gideon (Paul Butler), in South-Central Los Angeles. Harry's effect on Gideon and his assimilated black middle-class family is both immediate and profound. He spins tales full of folklore, lucky charms and bad magic that seem exotic and ominous to these urban up-and-comers who have lost touch with the rural tradition.
VHS: S13817. $19.95.
Charles Burnett, USA, 1990, 105 mins.

Tom & Viv

Willem Dafoe plays T.S. Eliot with Miranda Richardson as his first wife. Despite his brilliance as a poet, Elliot could not find personal happiness in his marriage because of an unspeakable secret that ultimately divided these two lovers. This riveting, true story is superbly acted. Richardson was nominated for an Oscar (Best Actress), along with Rosemary Harris (Best Supporting Actress).
VHS: S26035. $19.95.
Laser: LD75064. $39.99.
Brian Gilbert, USA, 1994, 115 mins.

Trees Lounge

Written, directed and starring actor Steve Buscemi, *Trees Lounge* is the humorous, semi-autobiographical story of Tommy Basilio, a 31-year-old barfly and unemployed auto mechanic with a quick wit and a chip on his shoulder who spends most nights at his favorite bar, Trees Lounge, in the pursuit of one-night stands. When he loses his pregnant girlfriend (Elizabeth Bracco) to his best friend and former boss (Anthony LaPaglia), he makes an attempt to put his life back together. He finds temporary salvation driving his deceased uncle's ice cream truck, but gets dangerously close to his 17-year-old helper, Debbie (Chloe Sevigny, *Kids*). Tommy discovers a disturbing truth about himself in the last place he expected. "*Trees Lounge* is a winner!" (*People Magazine*).
VHS: S30614. $96.99.
Steve Buscemi, USA, 1996, 94 mins.

The Truth About Cats and Dogs

Uma Thurman, Janeane Garofalo and Ben Chaplin star in this three-way comic love story of mistaken identity. Garofalo is a veterinarian on a call-in radio show. When one of her callers asks her out for a date, the short brunette describes herself as tall and blond. This is where Thurman comes in as Garofalo's stand-in to mix everything up, with outrageous results.
VHS: S29798. $19.95.
Laser: LD75899. $39.98.
Michael Lehmann, USA, 1996, 97 mins.

Ulysses' Gaze

Theo Angelopoulos' triumphantly haunting Cannes Film Festival Jury Prize-winning film tracing the journey of Greek-American director "Mr. A" (Harvey Keitel) across the Balkans in search of several lost reels of film. Along the way, he has several passionate encounters with various women who have been, or may have been, part of his life. Filled with stunning imagery, the film travels through war-torn

5 Best Samurai Epics

Harikiri
VHS: S22459. $39.95.

Kagemusha
VHS: S00668. $29.98.
Laser: LD72114. $69.98.

Samurai Rebellion
VHS: S32163. $29.95.

Seven Samurai
VHS: S01182. $34.95.
Laser: LD70452. $59.95.

Yojimbo
VHS: S01489. $29.95.
Laser: LD70489. $49.95.

Balkans giving a compelling eyewitness account. With Erland Josephson. English and Greek with English subtitles.
VHS: S31800. $89.98.
Theo Angelopoulos, Greece, 1997, 173 mins.

Valley Girl
Solid acting by Nicholas Cage in this funny, appealing film about a romance between a Hollywood punker and a San Francisco Valley girl.
VHS: S01768. $14.98.
Martha Coolidge, USA, 1982, 95 mins.

Van Gogh
Maurice Pialat's bold biography of Vincent Van Gogh. The film concentrates on the final three months of Van Gogh's life, the period he spent in Arles. Pialat painstakingly captures the artist's daily life and the private demons that plagued him. Stripped of melodrama, the film offers a different interpretation of Van Gogh's "madness." With Alexandra London, Gerard Sety, Bernard Le Coq, Corrine Bourdona and Elsa Zylberstein. French with English subtitles.
VHS: S19333. $19.95.
Maurice Pialat, France, 1991, 155 mins.

The Vanishing
A young husband descends into the obsessive corners of his mind when his wife Saskla inexplicably vanishes while on holiday in France. This cold-blooded psychological thriller was winner of the 1991 Grand Prize of Dutch Cinema for Best Film. It succeeds the old-fashioned way, by hooking the viewer on the characters and murky undercurrents of the story—seducing us into the midst of a clean, logical nightmare. In the finest tradition of Hitchcock, *The Vanishing* will haunt you long after it is over. "It's unforgettable even if you try to forget it" (*San Francisco Chronicle*). Dutch and French with yellow English subtitles.
VHS: S15444. $19.98.
Laser: LD72197. $39.95.
George Sluizer, Netherlands, 1991, 107 mins.

Visions of Light
Cinematography is the art on which all motion pictures are based. In this documentary over 125 unforgettable films are used to tell the story of this evolving art form. This 1993 winner of the New York Film Critics Circle Award will transfix cinephiles with the glory of motion picture photography.
VHS: S20742. $94.98.
Laser: LD71986. $39.99.
Arnold Glassman, USA, 1993, 95 mins.

Wannsee Conference
An acclaimed film that reenacts the fateful January 1942 meeting of the Nazi party and top German officials that set in motion "The Final Solution," the destruction of European Jewry. "It is mesmerizing for seeming to be so commonplace. *The Wannsee Conference* finds a voice for dealing with matters that are, after all, not unspeakable" (Vincent Canby). With Dietrich Mattausch, Gerd Bockmann, Friedrich Beckhaus and Gunter Sporrle. German with English subtitles.
VHS: S07395. $19.95.
Heinz Schirk, Germany, 1984, 87 mins.

The War Room
Inside the campaign of President Bill Clinton a new telegenic, electoral style was developed that would appeal to a TV-saturated public. D.A. Pennebaker, the acclaimed documentary maker who covered the 1962 campaigns of Kennedy and McGovern, brings his insight to this presidential hopeful, uncovering that most enduring of American traditions, a sophisticated political machine.
VHS: S20840. $14.95.
Chris Hegedus/D.A. Pennebaker, USA, 1993, 96 mins.

Welcome to the Dollhouse
Winner of the Grand Jury Prize at the 1996 Sundance Film Festival, a dark and very funny look at adolescence told through the eyes of an angry, young, geeky girl. The usual teen stuff is covered—school, grades, puppy love, sex and rock 'n' roll—but with an original and highly amusing take which "never loses its sense of compassion and respect for the underdog" (*New York Daily News*). With Heather Matarazzo, Matthew Faber, Angela Pietropinto and Eric Mabius (*I Shot Andy Warhol*).
VHS: S30422. $19.95.
Laser: LD76028. $39.95.
Todd Solondz, USA, 1996, 88 mins.

Welcome to the Dollhouse

What Happened Was...
Karen Sillas stars in this exciting film that won the Grand Jury Prize at the 1994 Sundance Film Festival. Dating is often an unnerving, albeit exciting and sexy, prospect. Two young office workers venture into the unknown territory of their dreams and desires, which results in a number of startling revelations. The journey into the uncharted territory of erotic fantasies and private thoughts makes for one highly unpredictable romantic encounter.
VHS: S27257. $14.98.
Laser: LD75473. $39.99.
Tom Noonan, USA, 1994, 90 mins.

The Whole Wide World
The acclaimed true story of the star-crossed love between a small-town schoolteacher and the writer who was the passionate creator of *Conan the Barbarian* and *Red Sonja*. With Renee Zellweger (*Jerry Maguire*), Vincent D'Onofrio, Ann Wedgeworth and Harve Presnell. "One of the most endearingly human, romantic films ever made" (David Elliot, *San Diego Union-Tribune*).
VHS: S32235. $98.99.
Laser: LD76345. $39.95.
Dan Ireland, USA, 1996, 111 mins.

Wilson
Winner of five Oscars, this is the brilliant biography of the World War I ear President whose League of Nations idea became an obsession. With Alexander Knox, Charles Coburn and Geraldine Fitzgerald.
VHS: S18099. $19.98.
Henry King, USA, 1944, 145 mins.

Without You I'm Nothing
Sandra Bernhard's adaptation of her off-Broadway show is a documentary-like examination of the nature of performance, identity and the culture of celebrity. In a brilliant dialectic on the relationship of performer and audience, Bernhard inhabits various roles and personalities to make hilarious comments about music, art, fashion, politics and sex. With John Doe, Steve Antin and Cynthia Bailey, a beautiful black woman who's Bernhard's alter ego.
Laser: CLV. LD72096. $29.98.
John Boskovich, USA, 1990, 90 mins.

Zentropa
Known in Europe as *Europa*, this stylistically daring work is set in a bleak, defeated Germany. A young American of German ancestry apprentices as a railway porter. He is seduced by a mysterious heiress whose father owns the line and becomes a pawn in a mysterious web of intrigue and deceit. With Jean Marc Barr, Barbara Sukowa and Eddie Constantine. Narrated by Max von Sydow. English and German with English subtitles.
VHS: S18368. $19.95.
Lars von Trier, Denmark/France/Sweden/Germany, 1991, 112 mins.

100 Best Gay & Lesbian Videos

Accatone!
A parable of redemption, set in the slums of Rome, Accatone "The Scrounger" (Franco Citti) lives as a thief, beggar and pimp. This is simply one of the most important films of the last 20 years, and a milestone in Italian filmmaking. He's in love with Stella, tries to reform her, but fails. *Accatone*, the debut film of Pier Paolo Pasolini, is notable for 'its rough-edged style, its cool, unhysterical portrait of corruption, cruelty, and violence, and its quiet lyricism marked one of the most significant directorial debuts of the sixties." (Georges Sadoul).
VHS: S11153. $39.95.
Pier Paolo Pasolini, Italy, 1961, 120 mins.

The Adventures of Priscilla, Queen of the Desert
Terence Stamp returns to the screen in this unlikely farce about three drag queens racing across the Australian outback in order to put on a show. Of course there is more to this film than unbelievably elaborate costumes, campily choreographed lip sync numbers and gay humor. It also tries to say something about love. Great disco numbers from ABBA, Gloria Gaynor, The Village People and Peaches and Herb.
DVD: DV60010. $29.95.
VHS: S24030. $19.95.
Stephen Elliott, Australia, 1994, 102 mins.

Advise and Consent
Political drama in which blackmail, suicide and scandal follow the President's appointment of an unpopular Secretary of State. Featuring Henry Fonda, Charles Laughton, Burgess Meredith and Peter Lawford.
VHS: S01994. $29.95.
Otto Preminger, USA, 1962, 142 mins.

Akermania, Volume One
A collection of shorter works by Chantal Akerman. Includes *Saute ma Ville*, Akerman's first film (1968) which stars the filmmaker at age 18. Also featured is *I'm Hungry, I'm Cold*, the story of two love-struck Belgian girls on the loose in Paris, and the 1972 New York silent experimental film *Hotel Monterey*. French with English subtitles.
VHS: S16298. $19.98.
Chantal Akerman, France/Belgium, 89 mins.

Apartment Zero
A marvelously creepy and involved study of interpersonal relationships and murder in Buenos Aires. Colin Firth stars as a jittery, movie-mad proprietor of a failing art house cinema who is forced to take in a boarder to meet expenses. With Hart Bochner as Jack, the handsome American who is looking for a quiet room while the rest of the city is looking for a killer. Often grimly funny in its Hitchcockian tone and style.
VHS: S11690. $19.98.
Martin Donovan, USA, 1988, 124 mins.

The Art of Cruising Men
From the creators of *Max Headroom* comes England's best-selling gay video of all time. This streetwise "video sex guide for the 21st century" traces how men cruise men from prehistoric times to the hedonistic clubs of the '90s. "One of the best gay videos on sale" (*The Pink Paper*). "Great…one brilliant, funny and well-produced video" (*QX Magazine*).
VHS: S30149. $39.95.
Peter Litten, Great Britain, 1995, 70 mins.

Beautiful Thing
One of the best gay films to come out of Britain in years. With Linda Henry, Glen Berry and Scott Neal. "A warm and funny love story. Refreshingly spunky and unsentimental" (Michael Musto, *Village Voice*).
VHS: S31196. $98.99.
Hettie MacDonald, Great Britain, 1996, 90 mins.

A Bigger Splash
An innovative blend of fact and fiction reflecting the world of David Hockney, arguably the most important and celebrated artist of our time. This feature incorporates Hockney's art and unabashed lifestyle in bold and daring ways and parallels his brilliant work in painting, design and photography. "Moving, gossipy and just a little bit shocking. Constructed in the studios, the swimming pools, the beds and baths of Hockney and friends who orbit around him" (*Newsday*).
VHS: S08116. $69.95.
Jack Hazan, Great Britain, 1985, 102 mins.

The Bitter Tears of Petra Von Kant
"A tragi-comic love story disguised as a lesbian slumber party in high-camp drag" (Molly Haskell), the film makes us a witness to the struggles for domination among three lesbians: a successful and "liberated" fashion designer, her contented and silent slave girl, and a sultry but cruel model who ends up making the master her slave. The dynamics of their interrelationships are played out in this claustrophobic, self-contained little world, accompanied only by the music of The Platters and Giuseppe Verdi. A riveting chamber drama of style. With Margit Carstensen, Hanna Schygulla, Eva Mattes and Irm Hermann. German with English subtitles.
VHS: S13914. $29.95.
Rainer W. Fassbinder, Germany, 1972, 124 mins.

Black Lizard
A hilarious caper movie written originally for the stage by Yukio Mishima; the plot concerns a female jewel thief who kidnaps nubile youths and ferries them to a glitzoid secret island. There she turns them into naked love statues—one of them bizarrely played by Mishima himself. Miss Lizard is portrayed by the transvestite actor Akihiro Miwa, who flounces around in an impossible collection of boas and chokers and turns every flourish of her cigarette holder into an over-the-top arabesque. Called "a tale of love, passion, greed and necrophilia" by the *New York Times*, and "Naughty Japanese noir. Like something by Almodovar or John Waters" (*Village Voice*). Japanese with English subtitles.
VHS: S16261. $49.95.
Kinji Fukasaku, Japan, 1968, 90 mins.

Boys in Love
This collection of award-winning gay short films includes four worldwide festival favorites. *Death in Venice, CA* is the story of a repressed academic who is seduced by his landlady's stepson. The animated *Achilles*, by Academy Award-nominated animator Bary Purves, features Greek heroes and lovers Achilles and Petroclus as they battle the Trojans. *My Polish Waiter* focuses on a young man's infatuation with a silent, handsome waiter. In *Miguel, Ma Belle*, a recently spurned Latin man finds love again with the help of a dog. Together the films form a bold look at love and sex in the '90s. 83 mins.
VHS: S28484. $29.95.

Boys in the Band
The first really successful American film to openly deal with homosexuality, Boys in the Band is based on the enormously successful Broadway play by Matt Crowley. An adult, witty and, at times, touching depiction of gay life in the early days of gay

liberation. The original nine actors who appeared in the Broadway production take their roles here on film, with exceptional acting by all, but particularly Cliff Gorman being ultra-queeny and Leonard Frey as the birthday boy.
VHS: S00176. $59.98.
William Friedkin, USA, 1975, 119 mins.

Carrington
Emma Thompson gives a terrific performance as Dora Carrington, an unorthodox, androgynous painter from the early 20th-century Bloomsbury Group, who passionately loves gay writer Giles Lytton-Strachey (Jonathan Pryce). The highly regarded playwright Christopher Hampton (*Les Liaisons Dangereuses*) directs this tight, witty and insightful period piece, set amidst the self-conscious world of broken conventions and sexual eccentricities that come to mind whenever the name of the Bloomsbury Group is uttered.
VHS: S27596. $19.95.
Laser: LD75532. $34.99.
Christopher Hampton, Great Britain, 1995, 116 mins.

The Celluloid Closet
Lily Tomlin, Shirley MacLaine, Tony Curtis, Susan Sarandon, Tom Hanks, Whoopi Goldberg and others provide the commentary to entertaining clips from over 120 films as we learn all the secrets and hear all the stories in this compilation of the history of homosexuality in Hollywood movies. A fun romp with some amazing pre-Breen-code early footage. "An indispensable addition to the history of Hollywood, with the popular appeal of *That's Entertainment* (Janet Maslin, *New York Times*).
VHS: S30403. $19.95.
Laser: LD76027. $39.95.
Rob Epstein/Jeffrey Friedman, USA, 1996, 102 mins.

The Children's Hour
Lillian Hellman's classic play about two teachers who are accused of lesbianism by a student receives powerful treatment from Shirley MacLaine, Audrey Hepburn and James Garner.
VHS: S13345. $19.98.
Laser: LD72169. $34.98.
William Wyler, USA, 1961, 107 mins.

Claire of the Moon
Nicole Conn's pioneering lesbian drama. Claire Jobrowski is a carefree, sexually adventurous novelist who shares a cabin with the stern, rigid Doctor Noel Benedict, who specializes in sexual behavior. They're brought together for a writer's workshop in the Pacific Northwest. "An encouraging debut film about love between adults" (*L.A. Weekly*). With Trisha Todd, Karen Trumbo and Caren Graham.
VHS: S19102. $29.98.
Nicole Conn, USA, 1992, 102 mins.

Clay Farmers
A farmhand named Dan forms a close friendship with a handsome young drifter hired by an absentee landowner. Their friendship is tested when they are seen together bathing in the nude at a swimming hole. What exactly do they feel for one another? Also includes *My First Suit*, a hilarious short from New Zealand about a wistful teenager.
VHS: S21321. $69.95.
A.P. Gonzalez, USA, 1989, 90 mins.

Coming Out Under Fire
This winner of the Special Jury Award at the 1994 Sundance Film Festival tells the story of nine lesbians and gay male veterans of the U.S. military. Based on Alan Berube's book of the same name, this film fleshes out this often misunderstood case of grave social injustice, using declassified documents, rare archival footage, interviews, photographs and more, and touches on the World War II origins of the current "don't ask, don't tell" policy. B&W.
VHS: S26966. $29.98.
Arthur Dong, USA, 1994, 71 mins.

Cynara
Described by its maker as "a lesbian *Wuthering Heights*," this video brings the homoerotic tensions inherent in many gothic works out into view. Johanna Nemeth and Melissa Nazila star as the sexy and attractive lovers. From the director of *Claire of the Moon*.
VHS: S29784. $29.95.
Nicole Conn, USA, 1996, 35 mins.

Daddy and the Muscle Academy: A Documentary on the Art, Life and Times of Tom of Finland
Tom of Finland was a pioneering gay pornographer whose classic *Ultimate Leather Men* veers between the erotic and the absurd. "A second film will probably be necessary to complete what are here the beginnings of connected discussions concerning the implications of fascistic attractions, fetish-racism, and other generated identity" (David Overbey). English and Finnish with English subtitles.
VHS: S19525. $49.95.
Ilppo Pohjola, Finland, 1991, 55 mins.

The Damned
A gigantic allegory of the rise of Nazism through the decadent Krupp-like family; a baroque film which explores the dark cycles of violence and evil in human history and consciousness with erotic indulgence. With Dirk Bogarde, Ingrid Thulin, Helmut Berger, Charlotte Rampling. English dubbed.
VHS: S00293. $59.95.
Luchino Visconti, Italy/W. Germany, 1969, 154 mins.

The Dear Boys
A harsh, stylized and feverish piece about dark sexual fantasies and deep romantic longing, the film concerns the romantic and sexual entanglements of a morose, self-absorbed writer and an uninhibited, carefree young man who recklessly pursues thrills and excitement. This groundbreaking, unapologetically gay work is adapted from Gerard Reve's novel. With Hugo Netsers, Hans Dagelet, Bill Van Dijk, and Albert Mol.
VHS: S17444. $69.95.
Paul de Lussanet, The Netherlands, 1980, 90 mins.

Desert Hearts
Wonderful love story between a repressed English professor who is waiting for a divorce at a dude ranch for women, and a beautiful casino worker in Reno who lives at the ranch with her mother. Adapted from the novel *Desert of the Heart*, by Jane Rule, with a fabulous soundtrack!
VHS: S01919. $19.98.
Laser: LD75919. $39.99.
Donna Deitch, USA, 1985, 96 mins.

The Dear Boys

Off to Happy Dale

Arsenic and Old Lace
VHS: S02351. $19.95.
Laser: LD70340. $39.95.

Frances
VHS: S04335. $19.95.

Lady Sings the Blues
VHS: S10836. $29.95.
Laser: LD75302. $39.98.

Shock Corridor
VHS: S18328. $29.95.
Laser: LD70458. $49.95.

Splendor in the Grass
VHS: S11617. $19.95.
Laser: LD71414. $39.98.

A Star Is Born
VHS: S01734. $29.98.
Laser: LD71337. $39.95.

A Streetcar Named Desire
DVD: DV60067. $24.98.
VHS: S21085. $19.98.
Laser: LD70687. $39.98.

Suddenly Last Summer
VHS: S01277. $19.95.

Dominique in "Daughters of Lesbos"
Oversexed women bare it all as they pursue sapphic pleasures in a hothouse of emotion. Their club, known as the New York City Man Haters Society, is not a group to be trifled with. One outrageous peeping tom learns this lesson when he seduces a lesbian by slipping her a mickey. He quickly finds out that a lesbian's vengeance can be swift like a knife. With Claudia Cheer, Jo Sweet, Sue Akers and Carla Costa.
VHS: S27675. $19.98.
Peter Woodcock, USA, 1967, 65 mins.

The Doom Generation
From the maker of *The Living End* comes another installment of violence and sex cooled by stereotypical generation X elan. Two kids meet up with a bleeding dude and set off to terrorize the motorized world. A stop at a convenience store leaves a talking head without its body and a bizarre family murder/suicide, so the three main characters go on the run and all have sex with each other. Can they evade the gang of skinheads?
VHS: S27521. $14.95.
Gregg Araki, USA, 1995, 83 mins.

An Early Frost
The landmark 1985 Emmy and Peabody Award-winning drama about one family's struggle with the news that their son (Aidan Quinn) is gay and has AIDS. With Gena Rowlands, Ben Gazzara, Sylvia Sidney and John Glover.
VHS: S30446. $19.95.
John Erman, USA, 1985, 120 mins.

Everything Relative
An eye-opening romantic comedy about a reunited group of women who went to college together. The smart, sassy ensemble cast exchange quick-witted repartee which reveals, with irony, humor and a touch of nostalgia for the '70s, how their lives, their politics and their loves have changed. Think of it as a gay *The Big Chill* or a lesbian *Love! Valour! Compassion!* With Harvey Fierstein.
VHS: S32611. $94.98.
Sharon Pollack, USA, 1997, 105 mins.

Female Misbehavior
Monika Treut's kinky exploration of nonconformist women combines two older short films, *Bondage* (1983), about a sadomasochistic lesbian, and *Annie* (1989), a portrait of former porno star Annie Sprinkle, with two recent documentaries,*Dr. Paglia* and *Max*. The former is a witty send-up of controversial academic Camille Paglia; the latter, a look at a lesbianNative American that shows her transsexual change from woman to man. "Treut is a sexual-political provocateur who in her explorations of the sexual fringe takes us where few filmmakers visit" (*New York Post*).
VHS: S19558. $29.95.
Monika Treut, Germany/USA, 1992, 80 mins.

Flaming Creatures
Jack Smith's groundbreaking, lyrical queer film is being released in a special limited-edition series to raise funds that will help restore and preserve his other works. This classic may seem tame by current standards, but its great camp style stands the test of time.
VHS: S27242. $195.00.

The Flavor of Corn
Lorenzo is a handsome, first-year professor with a quiet demeanor. He brings a passion for teaching to his young charges in a small village. As his relationship with his girlfriend deteriorates, he finds himself spending more time with 12-year-old Duilio. Soon Duilio's stepmother is questioning the nature of this amorous friendship. Italian with English subtitles.
VHS: S21545. $69.95.
Gianni Da Campo, Italy, 1994, 89 mins.

For a Lost Soldier
This haunting, true story follows a boy's wartime sexual awakening. It's controversial because this 12-year-old falls in love with a Canadian soldier who is in Holland just at the end of World War II. Ballet star Rudi van Danzig recreates this memory from his childhood to show how a boy falls in love with his handsome liberator. Dutch with English subtitles.
VHS: S21831. $19.98.
Roeland Kerbosch, Netherlands, 1993, 95 mins.

Fox and His Friends
A lower-class carnival entertainer professionally known as Fox the Talking Head strikes it rich, after a life of hard knocks, by winning the lottery. His new-found wealth attracts an elegant bourgeois lover, who proceeds to vamp Fox as thoroughly and unthinkingly as Lola Lola or Theda Bara. This ill-fated romance between "the capitalist and the lottery queen" makes for one of Fassbinder's most skillfully wrought films, expertly evoking a brittle, upper-class gay milieu where, as one character puts it, "God's dressed up like Marlene Dietrich, holding his nose." German with English subtitles. Electronically subtitled.
VHS: S06443. $29.95.
Rainer W. Fassbinder, Germany, 1975, 123 mins.

French Twist
Loli (Victoria Abril) thought she had the perfect marriage until she realized her husband (Alain Chabat) had been cheating on her for years. When Loli takes a mistress herself (Josiane Balasko, the film's director), her philandering husband must pour on the charm to become his own wife's lover again. Also stars Miguel Bose, Catherine Hiegel and many actors from the esteemed Comedie Francaise. French with English subtitles.
VHS: S29824. $99.99.
Laser: LD75966. $39.99.
Josiane Balasko, France, 1996, 100 mins.

Girl Friends
This first-ever theatrical anthology of lesbian short films is an "explosively funny, unstoppably entertaining" (*NY Native*) collection of four films by energetic, inventive American filmmakers reflecting lesbian life close to home or in the realm of fantasy. Shorts include: *Watching Her Sleep* (Barbara Rose Michaels, 1995, 7 mins.); *Little Women in Transit* (Barbara Heller, 1995, 7 mins.); *Playing the Part* (Mitch McCabe, 1994, 38 mins.) and *Carmelita Tropicana: Your Kunst Is Waffen* (Ela Troyano, 1994, 28 mins.). "Girlfriends is a gas—an entertaining anthology brimming over with quirky observational humor, intriguing stylistic tricks and warm, engaging, three-dimensional characters you haven't seen before onscreen" (Matt Zoller Seitz, *NY Press*).
VHS: S30246. $29.95.
USA, 1994-95, 80 mins.

Go Fish
A beguiling and charming look at the lives and loves of a small group of lesbian women in Chicago. Friends play matchmaker to bring together two very different women: Max, a beautiful, gregarious writer, and Ely, a quiet, thoughtful and almost terminally shy woman. They are, of course, perfect for each other in

this gentle and offbeat film.
VHS: $26147. $19.98.
Laser: LD75315. $39.98.
Rose Troche, USA, 1994, 83 mins.

Homo Promo
Trailers from dozens of mainstream and major gay or lesbian films have been collected on this video. These coming attractions comprise a serious but ironic look at a difficult past with some great laughs.
VHS: $24835. $39.95.
Jenni Olson, USA, 1991, 62 mins.

The Hunger
David Bowie, Catherine Deneuve and Susan Sarandon star in this stylish and moving tale of sophisticated vampires. Deneuve needs new blood in order to keep her 300-year-old lover alive. This film has an erotically charged atmosphere which includes a host of memorable scenes like the lesbian encounters between Deneuve and Sarandon. Ann Magnuson and Willem Dafoe also appear.
VHS: $26970. $19.95.
Tony Scott, USA, 1983, 100 mins.

Improper Conduct
Controversial, powerful documentary, a series of interviews with fascinating Cuban intellectuals and homosexuals who have been persecuted under the Castro regime. An indictment of Castro, implicating also those who would turn a blind eye toward repression from the left. Spanish with English subtitles.
VHS: $00614. $19.95.
Nestor Almendros, USA, 1984, 112 mins.

The Incredibly True Adventure of Two Girls in Love
Randy is a frolicsome tomboy mechanic who lives with her lesbian aunt and accidentally meets a fellow teen with both a Range Rover and an attitude. Despite their differences, they become the best of friends and eventually realize that there can only be one explanation for their feelings toward one another: They're in love.
VHS: $26816. $19.98.
Laser: LD75406. $39.99.
Maria Maggenti, USA, 1995, 94 mins.

Je, Tu, Il, Elle
Chantal Akerman's first feature moves like a process or a journey, most likely one from youth into adulthood. Akerman stars as the protagonist of the film, whom we first discover in her apartment compulsively eating raw sugar, reading aloud and rearranging her furniture. She hits the road and after various misadventures finds herself at the home of a woman she loves. The heavy silence underscores themes of estrangement and alienation. With Niels Arestrup and Claire Wauthion. French with English subtitles.
VHS: $12562. $29.95.
Chantal Akerman, France, 1974, 90 mins.

Jeffrey
Paul Rudnick's off-Broadway smash comic hit is finally a feature-length film. It stars Steven Weber, Patrick Stewart and Michael T. Weiss, and even includes Sigourney Weaver in a bizarre cameo. It all begins as a young gay man discovers that AIDS makes looking for Mr. Right even more complex and bedeviling. Now, as he finds the ravages of the epidemic coming ever closer, he must decide if he can rise to the challenge and meet what life has to offer with openness and love. Olympia Dukakis, Kathy Najimy, Robert Klein and Nathan Lane are also featured in this delightful comedy.
VHS: $27050. $19.98.
Laser: LD75456. $39.95.
Christopher Ashley, USA, 1995, 92 mins.

Kamikaze Hearts
Juliet Bashore's dark drama boldly merges documentary and narrative storytelling in a fascinating portrait of the lesbian underground. Sharon ("Mitch") Mitchell, an actress, and Tina ("Tigr") Mennett, a producer, are lovers and junkies. They accentuate the perverse sexual nature of their relationship by making explicit pornographic films. "Only the camera, with verite charm, trembles during kisses here. This dramatic documentary…posits lesbian love as women's place of empowerment within an exaggerated patriarchal world—the real life porn industry" (Alisa Solomon, *The Village Voice*).
VHS: $19104. $59.95.
Juliet Bashore, USA, 1991, 80 mins.

Kika
Pedro Almodovar's offbeat sex farce is the story of Kika, a make-up artist who lives with her lover Ramon, a photographer specializing in women's lingerie. Their maid, Juanita, is madly in love with Kika, while Ramon's stepfather likes to seduce her from time to time. That's only the beginning of the preposterous goings on which really heat up when Pablo, Juanita's brother, an on-the-lam ex-porno star, enters the picture. Spanish with English subtitles.
VHS: $23572. $14.98.
Laser: LD75489. $39.99.
Pedro Almodovar, Spain, 1994, 109 mins.

L'Amour Fou
M.M. Serra's film is both a document of a difficult time and a personal exploration of Serra's gay male friends' sexuality. The serenity of the four seasons becomes a metaphor in this beautifully hand-processed work. It shows the fragility and vibrancy of life in a time dominated by AIDS.
VHS: $27231. $59.95.
M.M. Serra, USA

La Cage aux Folles
A gay couple in St. Tropez discover their lives are complicated when the son of one of the men wants to marry into a politically repressive family. Ugo Tognazzi and Michel Serrault are Renato and Albin, the owners of the La Cage aux Folles nightclub, which features a popular revue of female impersonation. This surprise international hit was based on the play by Jean Poiret. With Benny Luke and Michael Galabru as the head of the Union of Moral Order. French with English subtitles.
VHS: $00702. $19.95.
Laser: LD70756. $49.95.
Edouard Molinaro, France, 1979, 91 mins.

La Cage aux Zombies
Writer, producer and director Kelly Hughes, author of *Blood, Sweat & Sequins* and creator of the popular public-access *Heart Attack Theatre*, achieved celluloid notoriety with this masterpiece of camp, which has been called "the *Naked Gun* of drag queen movies." When Norma (Cathy Roubal) and her lover, Brent (Eric Gladsjo), discover her gangster husband Lenny's (J.R. Clarke) drug money, the two run off with the loot to start a new life together. When Lenny shows up, the lovers, along with Tony the manicurist (William Love), make Lenny's life a real "drag" in this "towering inferno of blood, guts and glamour." Stars Kitten Natividad of Russ Meyer fame and a soundtrack featuring the L'Orielles, Pansy Division, Scissor Girls, Kraaken, Homewreckers and Pussy Tourette.
VHS: $28515. $49.95.
Kelly Hughes, USA, 1995, 84 mins.

Last Call at Maud's
A documentary about the closing of San Francisco's oldest-running lesbian bar. The film follows the 23-year history of the bar, related by owner Rikki Streicher, and a larger consideration of empowerment within the gay rights movement. "The documentary

Dominique in "Daughters of Lesbos"

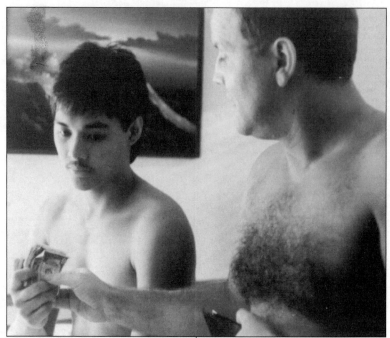

Macho Dancer

makes salient points about lesbians' generally second-league standing to gay men, legalistic problems such as women not being allowed to be bartender, a 70s souring of homosexual pride due to male gay's 'lack of political consciousness,' and the shooting of Harvey Milk" (Derek Elley, *Variety*).
VHS: $19745. $39.95.
Paris Poirier, USA, 1993, 75 mins.

Lesbian Humor
A collection of six films spanning the career of this exciting filmmaker: *Menses* is a wry comedy on the disagreeable aspects of menstruation; *Superdyke*, a comedy about a troop of shield-bearing Amazons; *Our Trip*, an animated film based on a hiking trip in the Andes; *Sync Touch*, a series of film experiments which propose an aesthetic connection between touch and sight; *Doll House*, a rapid montage of objects arranged in reference to the central prop of a doll house; and *No No Nooky T.V.* confronts the feminist controversy around sexuality with electronic language. "Hammer's satiric use of technology corresponds well with the Eighties repression of sexual expression. If you've ever looked up 'lesbian' in a computer thesaurus, you'll know that it's not listed" (*Independent Media*).
VHS: $08608. $59.95.
Barbara Hammer, 1975-87, USA, 59 mins.

Lesbian Sexuality
A collection of four films by Barbara Hammer, including the landmark *Dyketactics*, the first lesbian lovemaking film to be made by a lesbian. A sensual, evocative montage of 110 images edited to images of touch, an "erotic lesbian commercial." Also includes: *Multiple Orgasm*, a sensual, explicit film; *Double Strength*, a poetic study of a lesbian relationship between two trapeze artists; and *Women I Love*, using the camera as a personal extension of the body.
VHS: $08609. $59.95.
Barbara Hammer, USA, 1974-76, 57 mins.

The Living End
Gregg Araki's breakthrough $20,000 feature is a reworking of Godard's *Breathless*, with a blunt, gay veneer. The film is about two young men, a film critic and a narcissistic drifter, both of them HIV-positive, who undertake a mythic road journey after one of them kills a police officer. With Mike Dytri, Craig Gilmore and Mark Finch.
VHS: $18692. $29.95.
Gregg Araki, USA, 1992, 93 mins.

Longtime Companion
The impact of AIDS on the gay community is the subject of this well received and honestly acted drama. Bruce Davison stands out in a distinguished ensemble cast as a man facing the loss of his life partner. With Stephen Caffrey, Patrick Cassidy, Brian Cousins, John Dosett, Mark Lamos, Dermot Mulroney, Mary-Louise Parker.
VHS: $13301. $19.95.
Norman Rene, USA, 1990, 100 mins.

Looking for Langston
Isaac Julien's biography of black American author Langston Hughes interweaves the poetry of Essex Hemphill and Bruce Nugent with archival footage and period music from the Harlem Renaissance. A film about identity, sexuality, racism, repression, role playing and art.
VHS: $16641. $39.95.
Isaac Julien, Great Britain, 1989, 65 mins.

Love! Valour! Compassion!
Based on Terrence McNally's award-winning play, this "*The Big Chill* meets *The Bird Cage*" is the story of eight friends who leave the city behind for three simple weekends of rest and relaxation in the country. What they find is an outrageous mix of laughter, love and surprises. Featuring an extraordinary cast led by Jason Alexander (TV's *Seinfeld*) and John Glover, reprising his Tony Award-winning role as twin brothers.
VHS: $32504. $100.99.
Laser: LD76385. $29.99.
Joe Mantello, USA, 1997, 90 mins.

Macho Dancer
From world-renowned director Lino Brocka comes a story of sex, violence, and political corruption. Abandoned by his American lover, a handsome teenager from the mountains journeys to Manila in an effort to support his family. With a popular call boy as his mentor, Paul enters the glittering world of the "machodancer"—a world of male strippers, prostitution, drugs, sexual slavery, police corruption and murder. Teeming with sex and erotic Oriental beefcake, *Macho Dancers* is a searing indictment of the hypocrisy and corruption rampant under both the Marcos and Aquino regimes. Uncensored and uncut. Tagalog with English subtitles.
VHS: $14597. $79.95.
Lino Brocka, Philippines, 1988, 136 mins.

Maedchen in Uniform
Legendary film from the German post-Expressionism period, extremely daring for its time in suggesting lesbianism in the story of a young girl whose identity is choked by the authoritarian boarding school she attends. German with English subtitles.
VHS: S02140. **$24.95.**
Leontine Sagan, Germany, 1931, 87 mins.

Maurice
James Ivory directs this sensitive film about the love relationship between two men who meet studying at Cambridge in 1910. Based on the novel by E.M. Forster which was published after his death. That love that dare not speak its name is now a movie. With James Wilby, Hugh Grant, Rupert Graves, Denholm Elliott and Ben Kingsley.
VHS: S06208. **$19.98.**
Laser: CAV, widescreen. LD75106. **$59.95.**
James Ivory, Great Britain, 1987, 135 mins.

Men in Love
The story of Steven, a young man who has just lost his lover, Victor, to AIDS. Following a moving memorial service in San Francisco, an emotionally drained Steven flies to Hawaii with Victor's ashes—honoring one of his departed lover's last wishes. Struggling with his loneliness and confusion, Steven encounters Peter, a native Hawaiian gardener, and has an affair with him which leads him to a cathartic reawakening of his own sexuality. Starring Doug Self, Joe Tolbe, and Emerald Starr.
VHS: S14086. **$39.95.**
Marc Huestis, USA, 1990, 87 mins.

My Own Private Idaho
In this modern restructuring of the '60s road movie, River Phoenix and Keanu Reeves hustle their way through Seattle, Portland, Idaho and Rome on a quest for River's missing mother. With a meticulous, lyric style, the film combines sprawling landscapes, scenes of passionless sexuality and allusions to Orson Welles' *Chimes at Midnight* as it addresses issues of love, family, politics and homosexuality. A work of great complexity and beauty from the director of *Mala Noche* and *Drugstore Cowboy*.
VHS: S15927. **$19.95.**
Gus Van Sant, USA, 1991, 102 mins.

Naked Civil Servant
John Hurt delivers a compelling performance in the role of Quentin Crisp, based on Crisp's autobiography as a witty homosexual growing up in England of the 30's and 40's through years of intolerance, ostracism and violence. Hurt's tour-de-force performance brings to life Crisp's unique and often sharp wit at once critical of the society as well as of himself.
VHS: S00914. **$19.99.**
Jack Gold, Great Britain, 1980, 80 mins.

Oranges Are Not the Only Fruit
This critically acclaimed film, set in '60s northern England, is the tale of Jess, a 16-year-old girl (Geraldine McEwan of BBC-TV's *Mapp and Lucia*) raised to be a missionary, who falls in love for the first time—with another girl. When Jess' strict Evangelist mother (Charlotte Coleman, *Four*

Weddings and a Funeral) finds out, she determines to make her daughter renounce her sin, resulting in disaster. Based on Jeanette Winterson's autobiographical prize-winning novel.
VHS: S31261. **$29.98.**
Beeban Kidron, Great Britain, 1990, 165 mins.

Orlando
Virginia Woolf's ground-breaking novel about a transsexual from the time of Renaissance England has been transformed into a beautiful film. Tilda Swinton stars with Billy Zane as her romantic American lover while Quentin Crisp reigns as Queen Elizabeth the First.
VHS: S20829. **$19.95.**
Laser: LD74471. **$34.95.**
Sally Potter, Great Britain, 1993, 93 mins.

Paris Is Burning
The title of this lively New York-based documentary is taken from the name of a drag ball. Filmmaker Jenny Livingston spent several years interviewing members of the black and Hispanic gay community and attending their lavish social functions. These costume balls, in a search for expanding the concept of "realness," have gone beyond simple female impersonation to include such categories as butch queens, military attire, executive looks and fierce vogueing competitions. With the participation of such legends as Dorian Corey, Pepper Lebeija, Venus Xtravaganza, Octavia St. Laurent and Willi Ninja.
VHS: S16701. **$19.98.**
Jennie Livingston, USA, 1990, 71 mins.

Paris Was a Woman
An "intelligent and revealing" (*New York Times*) portrait of the creative community of women writers, artists, photographers and editors who flocked to the Left Bank of Paris between the World Wars. Greta Schiller and writer Andrea Weiss highlight Colette, Djuna Barnes, Gertrude Stein, Romaine Brooks, Marie Laurencin, Berenice Abbott, Gisele Freund, booksellers Sylvia Beach and Adrienne Monnier and *New Yorker* correspondent Janet Flanner.
VHS: S32910. **$59.95.**
Gretta Schiller, USA, 1996, 75 mins.

Parting Glances
Authentic gay film centering on the final stages of a love affair, featuring fine performances by Richard Ganoung and John Bolger as the couple, and Steve Buscemi as the artist friend doomed by AIDS. Superb photography by Jacek Laskus.
VHS: S02016. **$29.95.**
Bill Sherwood, USA, 1986, 90 mins.

Poison
An interwoven trilogy, the film uses three distinct stylistic conventions to explore the writings of Jean Genet, arriving at a profound realization of poison in the human mind, body and soul: A gritty prison drama reveals a homosexual's despair at being constantly confronted by forbidden passions; a campy '50s horror film send-up portrays a scientist's search for the essence of sexuality, and draws a compelling parallel to the HIV crisis when things go awry; and a tabloid mystery criticizes religious sentimentality as it reveals the circumstances surrounding the murder

In the Ring

Broken Noses
VHS: S16462. $29.95.

The Champ
VHS: S13387. $19.98.
Laser: LD72119. $34.98.

Champion
VHS: S04227. $19.95.

City for Conquest
VHS: S15523. $19.98.

Fat City
VHS: S06067. $19.95.

Gentleman Jim
VHS: S01876. $19.98.

Golden Boy
VHS: S04336. $19.95.

Harder They Come
VHS: S00541. $19.95.
Laser: LD70753. $49.95.

Kid Galahad
VHS: S17334. $19.98.

Night and the City
VHS: S18247. $19.98.

Playhouse 90: Requiem for a Heavyweight
VHS: S09547. $29.95.

Pulp Fiction
VHS: S26211. $19.95.
Laser: LD75062. $39.99.

Raging Bull
DVD: DV60092. $24.98.
VHS: S01084. $19.95.
Laser: LD71669. $39.98.

Somebody up There Likes Me
VHS: S07974. $19.98.

Waterfront
VHS: S05843. $29.95.

When We Were Kings
DVD: DV60129. $29.95.
VHS: S31675. $19.95.
Laser: LD76286. $39.99.

of a wife-beater by his own child, who then flew out the window toward heaven. Winner of the Grand Jury Prize at the Sundance Film Festival.
VHS: $15839. $19.98.
Laser: LD72226. $34.95.
Todd Haynes, USA, 1991, 85 mins.

The Queen
Almost forgotten, this documentary charts the pressure-laden world of competition surrounding the drag queen event known as the Miss All-America Camp Beauty Queen Pageant from 1967. At times funny and deadly serious, it offers a truly fascinating glimpse of a queer world that existed prior to Stonewall. Crystal, who also appeared in *Paris Is Burning*, is featured.
VHS: $26294. $29.95.
Frank Simon, USA, 1968, 68 mins.

She Must Be Seeing Things

Querelle
Brad Davis, Jeanne Moreau and Franco Nero star in Rainer Werner Fassbinder's final film, adapted from Jean Genet's great novel, *Querelle de Brest*. The film focuses on a beautiful but callous and tough young French sailor whose beauty and heartlessness both attract and repell all who meet him. English dialog.
VHS: S01080. $19.95.
Rainer W. Fassbinder, Germany/France, 1982, 106 mins.

Raising Heroes
In this first openly gay action-adventure story, Josh (Troy Sistillio) and Paul (Henry White) are a successful gay couple in the midst of adopting a child when Josh witnesses a mob hit and becomes the next target on their list. Watch as normally mild-mannered Josh maims and kills to protect his loved ones. Will he be able to save his marriage, the adoption, and himself all in one weekend?
VHS: $32493. $39.95.
Douglas Langway, USA, 1996, 85 mins.

Red Ribbons
Quentin Crisp and Georgina Spelvin star in this story about a group of friends paying tribute to a special person. When Frank succumbs to AIDS, his colleagues and former lovers gather in an impromptu memorial service. Part drama and part video diary, this work reveals the feelings of the loved ones left behind.
VHS: $25722. $39.95.
Neil Ira Needleman, USA, 1994, 90 mins.

Resident Alien
Quentin Crisp, author and professional pansy, has always led a charming, if not charmed, life. While *The Naked Civil Servant* tells of his early and troubled life in Great Britain, this film shows how celebrity in America suited the grand old dame. Fran Lebowitz, Holly Woodlawn, Michael Musto, and other New York scenesters are featured.
VHS: $25103. $19.95.
Jonathan Nossiter, USA, 1990, 85 mins.

Rock Hudson's Home Movies
With excerpts from some of Rock's most memorable films, this documentary digs into the persona of Hollywood's greatest male sex symbol of the 50's and 60's, whose death from AIDS forever transformed the way America looks at its stars. Mark Rappaport's film was named to multiple Ten Best lists as an original look at an American icon.
VHS: $21090. $39.95.
Mark Rappaport, USA, 1992, 63 mins.

Salmonberries
German director Percy Adlon's political thriller features k.d. lang in her film debut. The story concerns a repressed East German librarian who escapes her oppressive surroundings after her lover is killed trying to scale the Berlin Wall. Devastated and grief stricken, Roswitha (Rosel Zech) travels to Alaska. Trapped in a grim, remote Eskimo outpost, she finds comfort and emotional fulfillment with the sexually ambiguous lang.
VHS: $18844. $29.95.
Percy Adlon, Canada/Germany, 1991, 94 mins.

Salo: 120 Days of Sodom
An extremely controversial film, the last work by Pier Paolo Pasolini. Loosely based on the book by the Marquis de Sade, Pasolini transplanted the setting to Mussolini's post-Nazi-fascist state of Salo. Pasolini creates a symbolic place where sexual joy and normality are punished while perversion is rewarded. The plot concerns eight fascists who round up 16 teenage boys and girls and, in a secluded villa, submit their hostages to various sadistic ordeals including rape, mutilation and murder. "Pasolini has intended the film to work on many different levels: an illustration of the moral anarchy of absolute power; the debasement of sexuality through violence; an exploration of victims as victimizers. The result is, alternately, surreal, harrowing, depressing, repulsive, and fascinating…a hellish journey through a sick soul." Contains nudity, explicit sexual situations and extreme graphic violence; for mature audiences only. Italian with English subtitles.
VHS: $11717. $89.95.
Laser: CLV. LD72111. $49.95.
Pier Paolo Pasolini, Italy, 1975, 115 mins.

Sebastiane
Sebastiane caused riots at the 1977 Locarno Film Festival and became a runaway hit in London. It has "a pretention and perversity about it that are surprisingly appealing in the long run" (Rob Baker, *Soho Weekly News*). The film tells the highly charged homoerotic story of St. Sebastian. Sebastian spends most of the film tied to the stake, haunted by sexual advances of his commander Severus, and tortured when he refuses love. Newly remastered. Latin with English subtitles.
VHS: $25523. $39.95.
Derek Jarman, Great Britain, 1976, 86 mins.

She Must Be Seeing Things
"A wryly sophisticated comedy…plays like a lesbian homage to *Unfaithfully Yours*," wrote Jay Carr in *The Boston Globe*. Agatha is an international lawyer, Jo a filmmaker. While Jo is on the road with her film, Agatha reads her diary and becomes insanely jealous to the point of dressing up as a man and "shadowing" her. "Groundbreaking in its understated portrayal of sophisticated urban lesbians exploring such dynamics as sex and sexuality, career and commitment, fidelity and companionship. The film gives us characters who are richly realistic and demonstrates that McLaughlin is a complex and refreshingly thoughtful talent…" (*New York Native*).
VHS: $10941. $29.95.
Sheila McLaughlin, USA, 1988, 85 mins.

Silence=Death
This film serves as an important historical document, exploring the reactions of New York's artistic community to the ravages of AIDS. Responses range from David Wojnorowicz' venomous proclamations and paintings, and painter Rafael Gambas' seething indictment of homophobic bigotry, to Keith Haring's nostalgic longing for the days of care-free sex, and Allen Ginsberg's musing upon his shyer attitude about experimenting sexually. Even with the gentler voices, the film's undercurrent is an angry demand for action and recognition. "Best AIDS film to date…" (*The Guardian*).
VHS: $14148. $29.95.
Rosa von Praunheim/Phil Zwickler, USA, 1990, 60 mins.

Silent Pioneers
Senior members of lesbian and gay communities share their memories about gay life in this documentary. Sometimes tragic, and sometimes funny, their recollections are always personal and poignant. This film offers a unique view of an era less tolerant of sexual minorities.
VHS: $27614. $39.95.
Lucy Winer, USA, 1985, 54 mins.

Silverlake Life: The View from Here
This highly acclaimed documentary was shown on

PBS's *Point of View* series. It follows the slow demise of a longtime film and video maker, Tom Joslin, who is dying of AIDS. This unvarnished self-portrait of a man, his lover (Mark Massi), his family and his friends offers an unparalleled look into the heart of the AIDS crises. It won the Sundance Grand Jury Prize.
VHS: S21880. $19.95.
Laser: CLV. LD74626. $39.95.
Tom Joslin/Peter Friedman, USA, 1993, 89 mins.

Since Stonewall
Ten great short films from the 70s, 80s and early 90s, reflecting the feelings, fears, humor, artistry, and changing realities of gay America. Featuring a rarely seen work by Gus Van Sant (*Drugstore Cowboy, My Own Private Idaho*) based on a story by William S. Burroughs. Includes *Which Is Scary, Queerdom, A.I.D.S.C.R.E.A.M., Song from an Angel, Triangle, Anton, Bust Up, '976-', Final Solutions* and Van Sant's *Discipline of De.* USA, 80 mins.
VHS: S15542. $19.95.

Straight from the Heart
This Academy Award-winning documentary explores the experiences of parents learning to love their lesbian and gay children in a world dominated by homophobia. There is a range of stories touching on a variety of experiences, including a religious Mormon family and an African-American family. 30 mins.
VHS: S26030. $24.95.
Dee Mosbacher/Frances Reid, USA, 1994, 30 mins.

Strange Fruit
This compilation of works poses questions in regard to the struggle of women, black women, homosexuality, black homosexuality, and the nude. Thematically bound to Billie Holiday's *Strange Fruit*, this presentation seeks to inspect and inspire "difference" through the lens of identity politics. Artists and films featured: Chad Carter, *Ataxiaflagris*; Lisa Austin, *Breaking Ground*; George Kuchar, *Indian Summer*; Yvain Reid/Reginald Cox, *Passage*; Rodney O'Neal Austin, *Pop Tarts Come in One Size*; Holly Purdue, *Behind the Door*; Karla Milosevich, *Drive Me Under*; Veronica Klaus, *How Long Must I Wait for You?*; Georgia Wright, *Kachapati*; and Cauleen Smith, *Chronicles of a Lying Spirit.* 59 mins.
VHS: S30003. $49.95.

Strawberry & Chocolate
A sensation from Cuba in which a chance encounter over ice cream between a middle-aged gay man and a young, fervent believer in contemporary Cuban Marxism sets the stage for a funny but serious film about difference and acceptance. Their friendship develops despite official intolerance of homosexuality and it soon withstands that short-sighted policy. This film broke box office attendance records in Cuba and achieved world-wide acclaim. Spanish with English subtitles.
VHS: S26613. $19.95.
Laser: LD75320. $39.98.
Tomas Gutierrez Alea, Cuba, 1994, 104 mins.

The Sum of Us
In this gay romantic comedy a young man finds the search for Mr. Right troubled by his busy-body father. Dad is just concerned for a son who seems unable to find that special someone. Altogether it's a light, amiable tale that is darkened by unexpected misfortune. In sunny Australia, however, things always get bright again. Based on David Stevens' play.
VHS: S26443. $19.98.
Laser: LD75085. $39.99.
Kevin Dowling/Geoff Burton, Australia, 1995, 99 mins.

Swoon
A highly stylized black and white reconsideration of the Leopold and Loeb case, the two University of Chicago students who attempted the perfect crime, the kidnapping of a 12-year-old boy, that resulted in his death. This film provides a historical and sexual context for the crime, finding its roots in homoerotic fixation. With Daniel Schlachet, Craig Chester and Ron Vawter.
VHS: S18518. $19.95.
Tom Kalin, USA, 1991, 92 mins.

Taxi Zum Klo
A smash hit at the Berlin and New York Film Festivals in 1981, *Taxi Zum Klo* is an autobiographical examination of the director's own sexual escapades and fantasies. Frank Ripploh explores every aspect of gay life in Berlin, with

hilarious results. German with English subtitles.
VHS: S01304. $39.95.
Frank Ripploh, W. Germany, 1981

Terence Davies Trilogy
These magical films by Terence Davies, director of *The Long Day Closes* and *The Neon Bible*, are set against the background of industrial Liverpool and follow the main character, Robert Tucker, from his Catholic childhood to being bullied at school, dealing with a violent and sick father at home and struggling with his view of his own sexuality. The three films include *Children, Madonna & Child* and *Death & Transfiguration.*
VHS: S31107. $39.99.
Terence Davies, Great Britain, 1996, 101 mins.

Therese and Isabelle
Based on the novel by Violette Leduc, *Therese and Isabelle* is a story of love between two students at an exclusive girls' school. Filmed in black and white. English dubbed.
VHS: S01320. $29.95.
Radley Metzger, France, 1968, 102 mins.

Third Sex Sinema Volume 5: Consenting Adults
This obscure study of homosexuality reports on the lifestyles of gay men and women in Great Britain in the mid-'60s. *The Male Nudists* features two burly young men entertaining one another, lounging around, exercising, flexing their huge muscles, oiling themselves up, showering together and wrestling. There's footage from the Gay-In III, sponsored by the Gay Liberation Front, a surrealistic gay encounter on a park bench, wrapped up by *Caught in the Can*, an early '70s short about two guys who dress in drag to take some suckers for a roll.
VHS: S30988. $19.98.

Tongues Untied
The late Marlon Riggs was internationally acclaimed for such groundbreaking videos as *Color Adjustment*. Poetry, personal testimony, rap, performance and dance are combined in this singular exploration of the racism and homophobia that black men face daily. Broadcast on the PBS series *P.O.V.*, its beauty and power generated outrage from right-wing politicians. Even so, it remains unmatched for its eloquence.
VHS: S22951. $39.95.
Marlon Riggs, USA, 1989, 55 mins.

Torch Song Trilogy
Harvey Fierstein adapted his Broadway hit play about the trials and tribulations of being a sexually active gay urban male in the 1970's for the big screen. He repeats the role of Arnold Beckoff, a drag artiste

The Sum of Us

looking for love. He finds it with Brian Kerwin and Matthew Broderick. Anne Bancroft is Arnold's very Jewish mother and a prime cause of Arnold's frustrated anger.
VHS: S09390. $19.95.
Paul Bogart, USA, 1988, 126 mins.

Total Eclipse
Leonardo Di Caprio and David Thewlis star in this film based on the affair between Arthur Rimbaud and Paul Verlaine. Rimbaud left a legacy of brilliant poetry and an example of extreme living that inspired contemporary stars like Jim Morrison. Verlaine, a highly regarded writer in his own right, was an older married man when he became infatuated with Rimbaud. This is a grand film about their passion for

love and art, a passion finally doomed by madness. Christopher Hampton wrote the screenplay.

VHS: S27617. $19.98.
Laser: LD75553. $39.99.
Agnieszka Holland, Great Britain/France, 1995, 111 mins.

Totally F***ed Up

Araki's follow-up to *The Living End*, this gay, "'90s version of *The Breakfast Club*" (*San Francisco Club*) is an honest, open-structured look into the lives of gay and lesbian teens struggling with their emergent identities in the homophobic '90s. With music by Ministry, This Mortal Coil, Unrest, Babyland, The Wolfgang Press, Coil and His Name Is Alive. "A breakthrough" (*San Francisco Chronicle*).

VHS: S29856. $59.95.
Gregg Araki, USA, 1994, 85 mins.

Turnabout: The Story of the Yale Puppeteers

Dan Bessie crafted this documentary about the three gay puppeteers who enchanted Hollywood for 25 years. Their musical extravaganzas, with puppet replicas of celebrities, drew legends like Hitchcock to see their performances. The sophisticated humor of their shows came from a unique camp sensibility, one fostered by these three gay men in a time when being gay was extremely difficult.

VHS: S27492. $39.95.
Dan Bessie, USA, 1992, 55 mins.

Urinal

An innovative first feature, *Urinal* summons seven gay artists from 1937 and gives them an "Impossible Mission": they must research the policing of washroom sex in Ontario, and propose solutions. Each night they convene to present a lecture, with every lecture adopting a different documentary convention. Using interviews with politicians, gay activists and men who have been charged with "gross indecency," hundreds of victims of police entrapment and video surveillance are revealed. A funny and disturbing film that probes into the roots of homosexual discrimination. From Canada's most controversial independent filmmaker.

VHS: S15808. $39.95.
John Greyson, Canada, 1988, 100 mins.

Via Appia

A complex film about gay desire and paranoia. A former German steward travels to Rio to find a mysterious man who left a cryptic message, "Welcome to the AIDS Club," following a sexual encounter. "Via Appia, the nickname of a Rio district where male prostitutes hang out, becomes a grim guided tour of the city's gay subculture, its bars, discos, streets and a beach known as the AIDS farm. The documentary-within-the film-format justifies this material" (Vincent Canby). With Peter Senner, Guilherme de Padua and Yves Jansen. German and Spanish with English subtitles.

VHS: S18693. $39.95.
Jochen Hick, Germany/Brazil, 1992, 90 mins.

Victim

Dirk Bogarde stars in this brooding drama with homosexual implications as a defense lawyer with a secret past. Approached by a man he suspects of blackmail, he refuses to help. Only when that same man is dead and it is made clear that he saved Bogarde from certain ruin, does the lawyer risk everything to make the senseless death mean something. Letterboxed.

VHS: S03489. $29.95.
Laser: Letterboxed. LD76406. $49.95.
Basil Dearden, Great Britain, 1961, 100 mins.

A Virus Knows No Morals

A black comedy filled with the worst fears, a savagely funny burlesque on the AIDS crisis, irreverent yet deadly serious. Nurses on the night shift roll dice to see which AIDS patient will die next. An epidemic victim is harassed by a reporter on his death bed—he sticks her with a contaminated syringe. The government opens a quarantine called Hell Gay Land. Gay terrorists capture the Minister of Health. An outrageous and yet extremely honest film by von Praunheim, this controversial film shook West Germany. German with English subtitles.

VHS: S09350. $39.95.
Rosa von Praunheim, Germany, 1985, 82 mins.

When Night Is Falling

Two women find one another in this sensitive love story. Camille is a repressed Catholic professor currently involved with a man. Her whole life

changes, however, when she meets Petra, an enigmatic performer from a visiting circus. Before long, the two women embark on a romance that startles everyone, including themselves, with an unforseen passion.

VHS: S27541. $89.95.
Laser: LD75925. $39.99.
Patricia Rozema, Canada, 1995, 90 mins.

Wigstock: The Movie

It all began with a bunch of New York drag queens who didn't want to stop partying so they put on a show in Tomkins Square Park—in the daytime. Now it has grown into an annual celebration of queer crossdressers from all over. Underground stars The "Lady" Bunny, Jackie Beat, the Mistress Formica, Lypsinka and Joey Arias are joined by RuPaul, Crystal Waters, Alexis Arquette and Deee-Lite on a trip across a landscape of cosmetic wonders.

VHS: S26862. $19.98.
Laser: LD75417. $39.99.
Barry Shils, USA, 1995, 82 mins.

Wild Reeds

In 1962, a group of teenagers confront emotional, sexual and political turmoil provoked by both their own personal lives and the larger social framework of a small provincial town affected by the French-Algerian War. This engaging, elegiac film captures both the fleeting nature of youth and the profound turmoil of this intriguing stage of life. French with English subtitles.

VHS: S29407. $29.98.
Andre Techine, France, 1995, 110 mins.

Word Is Out: Stories of Some of Our Lives

This is the first major film to explore America's gay culture. Involving a diverse range of people in locales from San Francisco to Boston, the study interviews 26 men and women ranging in age from 18 to 77. Speaking tellingly, funnily and movingly of their experiences, these women and men overturn decades worth of accumulated stereotypes. From the director of *Absolutely Positive*.

VHS: S16077. $29.95.
Mariposa Film Group, USA, 1977, 130 mins.

Young Hearts, Broken Dreams, Episode 1: The Delivery Boy

Eddie Starr and Mark Cannon star in one of the first gay soap operas, the ongoing saga of a troubled gay movie star, his lover, his friends, sex, drugs, Hollywood and life in the fast lane. Adam Harrington, a delivery boy at Paramount Pictures, finds all his romantic longings fulfilled when he meets and moves in with his idol, gay movie star Scottie Edwards. Unfortunately, Scottie is beholden to a ruthless drug lord, and he and Adam decide to skip town together. In the end, however, they must face reality and return to the oversexed world of gay Hollywood.

VHS: S27722. $49.95.
Gerald Gordon, USA, 1990, 45 mins.

Young Hearts, Broken Dreams, Episode 2: The Search

After the disastrous outcome of the first episode, an entirely new cast of characters comes to the foreground in this steamy sequel. Scottie Edwards' brother Matthew and his best friend, Noah, leave Nebraska to come to Hollywood and avenge Scottie's death. Before long, Matt realizes that he's falling for Zech, the handsome detective assigned to Scottie's murder. *The Search* continues the exciting mix of sex, sensuality and emotional ups and downs found in the first episode of this soap opera. Michael Habusch and Robert Spiewak star.

VHS: S27723. $59.95.
Gerald Gordon, USA, 1995, 83 mins.

A Virus Knows No Morals

50 Top Opera & Classical Music Videos

All the Great Operas in Ten Minutes
Behind the long and expansive librettos of most operas lies a kernel of overpowering excitement. In this hysterical ten-minute animation the nutty centers of these works are revealed in brief, pithy manifestations. Among the operas lampooned are; *La Traviata, Aida, Tosca, Tristan and Isolde, Madame Butterfly* and *The Ring of the Nibelungen*.
VHS: S29295. $12.95.

Andre Rieu, From Holland with Love
Rieu and the Johann Strauss Orchestra bring the ever popular waltz to life in this video performance. A pop chart topper in Europe, Andre Rieu and his music are now available in this country, where he is sure to inspire similar devotion.
VHS: S27780. $29.95.

Andre Rieu: The Vienna I Love, Waltzes from My Heart
"Waltz King" Andre Rieu and the Johann Strauss Orchestra perform some of the most beautiful and romantic music ever written in 3/4 time, including Johann Strauss' *The Voices of Spring, Radetzky March, Emperor Waltz* and *Fledermaus*, as well as Rossini's *William Tell*, Offenbach's *Barcarole, The Skater's Waltz* and more.
VHS: S30770. $19.95.

The Art of Conducting

The Art of Conducting
A miraculous look at great conductors of the past: Toscanini, Furtwangler, Walter, Klemperer, Stokowski, Koussevitzky and Reiner. Adapted from the award-winning BBC television program, this program uses rare archival material, and image and audio restoration to present dramatic—and unprecedented—moments like Wilhelm Furtwangler's hair-raising rehearsal of Brahms' *Fourth Symphony* with the Berlin Philharmonic during the first post-war tour of England. "The most fascinating program ever made about classical music." 120 mins.
VHS: S22461. $29.97.
Laser: LD74756. $34.97.

The Art of Singing
This video tracks the evolution of recorded song from the silent films of Caruso to the early Vitaphone footage with Martinelli and De Luca, culminating with Maria Callas' triumphant performance as Tosca at Covent Garden in 1964. With rare footage, including a never-before-seen film of Kirsten Flagstad singing "Hojotoho" from *Die Walkure* and Rosa Ponselle's screen tests for *Carmen*. Narrated by Penny Gore with insightful commentary by such opera notables as Schuyler Chapin, Magda Olivero, Kirk Browning and Nicola Rescigno. "One of the most involving, enlightening and entertaining productions to hit the market since classical labels began producing videos" (*New York Times*). 117 mins.
VHS: S31282. $29.95.
Laser: LD76204. $34.95.

Beethoven Concerti
The complete set of all five Beethoven concerti performed by renowned pianist Murray Perahia at the Royal Festival Hall London.
VHS: S09867. $79.95.

Bizet's Carmen
The definitive version of this classic opera, shot entirely on location in Andalusian Spain, featuring Placido Domingo and Julia Migenes-Johnson. Soundtrack by the Orchestre National de France, conducted by Lorin Maazel. French with English subtitles.
VHS: S01790. $19.95.
Francesco Rosi, France/Italy, 1984, 151 mins.

Cosi Fan Tutte
Peter Sellars' interpretation of Mozart is set in a seaside diner frequented by Vietnam veterans. Susan Larson, Janice Felty, Frank Kelly, James Maddalena, Sue Ellen Kuzma and Sanford Sylvan "perform with a degree of naturalness and dramatic commitment that is almost unheard of on the operatic stage" (*San Francisco Chronicle*). Craig Smith conducts the Vienna Symphonic Orchestra and Arnold Schoenberg Choir. In Hi-Fi Stereo, 199 mins.
VHS: S16517. $44.95.

Death in Venice
Death in Venice was the last opera by Benjamin Britten, presented here in a highly acclaimed performance from the Glyndebourne Touring Opera. Robert Tear stars as Aschenbach, with Alan Opie and Michael Chance. Graeme Jenkins conducts the London Sinfonietta. Sung in English. 138 min.
VHS: S18382. $29.95.

Der Ring
James Levine conducts the Metropolitan Opera Orchestra and Chorus with a host of world renowned soloists, in Wagner's complete "Ring" cycle. Four cassettes, 937 mins.
VHS: S16052. $159.80.
Laser: LD71198. $307.45.

Don Giovanni (Losey)
Finally on video, this sumptuous production of Mozart's great opera was shot on location in Venice, and is one of the great films of Joseph Losey.

Ruggero Raimondi, Kiri Te Kanawa and Teresa Berganza are principal singers, with Lorin Maazel conducting the Paris Opera Orchestra. Sung in Italian with English subtitles.
VHS: S07688. $39.95.
Joseph Losey, Italy/France, 1972, 185 mins.

Don Giovanni (Sellars)
In Peter Sellars' interpretation, Mozart's *Don Giovanni* meets modern-day Harlem. Craig Smith conducts the Vienna Symphonic Orchestra and the Arnold Schoenberg Choir. With soloists Eugene Perry, Herbert Perry, Dominique Labelle, Lorraine Hunt, Carroll Freeman, James Patterson, Ai Lan Zhu and Elmore James. In Hi-Fi Stereo, 190 mins.
VHS: S16515. $44.95.

Dvorak in Prague: A Celebration
Yo-Yo Ma, Itzhak Perlman, Frederica von Stade, Seiji Ozawa and the Boston Symphony Orchestra join forces on the occasion of the 100-year anniversary of Dvorak's *New World Symphony*. A variety of his music is performed in this Sony production set in Prague.
VHS: S21073. $24.98.

Leonard Bernstein

Four American Composers
Unique musical profiles, directed by Peter Greenaway (*Drowning by Numbers, The Cook, the Thief, His Wife and Her Lover*), that offer startling and intimate insights into the music and ideas of four very original American composers. Greenaway takes as his starting point performances given by the artists in London and creates an exciting musical experience. Four volumes. 240 mins.
VHS: S14719. $69.95.

Grand Duo: Itzhak Perlman and Pinchas Zukerman
Filmmaker Christopher Nupen captures the 1976 European tour of violinists Itzhak Perlman and Pinchas Zukerman. Filmed at the Royal College of Music in London, selections include Wieniawski's *Etudes Caprices, Opus 18*, Spohr's *Duo Concertante, Opus 67*, Leclair's *Sonata, Opus 3*, Handel/Halvorsen's *Passacaglia in G minor*, Mozart's *Duo No. 1 in G major* and Wieniawski's *Caprice in A minor*. In Hi-Fi Stereo, 90 mins.
VHS: S16512. $29.97.
Laser: LD71460. $34.97.

Horowitz in Moscow
The drama and excitement of Vladimir Horowitz's extraordinary 1986 concert in Moscow, his first visit back to Russia since he left in 1925. The program includes Scarlatti sonatas, Mozart's "Sonata in C Major" and a selection of Schubert, Liszt, Chopin, Rachmaninoff and Scriabin, in one of the legendary performances of the 20th century. Color. USSR, 1986, 120 mins.
VHS: S01862. $29.95.

I Pagliacci
Franco Zeffirelli directs this lavish film of Leoncavallo's tragic opera. The incomparable Placido Domingo performs one of his most famous operatic arias, "Vesti la Giubba". Georges Pretre leads the chorus and orchestra of La Scala.
VHS: S12657. $24.95.

Karajan: Early Images, Vol. 1
In collaboration with the talented French filmmaker Henri-Georges Clouzot (*The Wages of Fear*), conductor Herbert von Karajan launched a series of performance films that attempted to achieve a "visual reinterpretation of a performance." Shot in black and white, this video shows von Karajan in preparation for conducting Beethoven's Fifth symphony, Schumann's Fourth symphony and Dvorak's Ninth symphony, "From the New World."
Laser: LD71526. $34.95.
Henri-Georges Clouzot, France/Germany, 1968

Kyoto Vivaldi: The Four Seasons
Antonio Vivaldi's baroque masterpiece is one of the most popular classical pieces of all time and receives a stunning performance by the Japanese Kyoto Ensemble, with the ancient capital city of Kyoto serving as background for this visual discovery. This unique video interpretation of Vivaldi's timeless classic adds a new dimension to the classic. 45 mins.
VHS: S03821. $19.95.

La Boheme (Levine)
Lavish Metropolitan Opera production filmed live, with costumes and sets designed by Franco Zeffirelli, and with some of Met's greats: Teresa Stratas, Richard Stilwell, Renata Scotto, Jose Carreras, Allan Monk, James Morris. James Levine conducts. Italian with English subtitles. Stereo, 1982, 141 mins.
VHS: S02180. $22.95.

La Boheme (Zeffirelli)
Franco Zeffirelli's historic production of Puccini's grand opera features Mirella Freni. Herbert von Karajan conducts the orchestra of La Scala.
VHS: S12649. $24.95.

Leonard Bernstein's Young People's Concerts: The Collector's Edition
Winner of multiple Emmy, Peabody and Edison Awards, *Leonard Bernstein's Young People's Concerts* with the New York Philharmonic, filmed from 1958 through 1973, shaped an entire generation of music lovers. Twenty-five of the Young People's Concerts are collected on ten VHS videocassettes in a deluxe slipcase.
VHS: S31146. $349.95.

Lucia di Lammermoor
One of Joan Sutherland's most famous roles, here in a MET production with Alfredo Kraus, Pablo Elvira, and Paul Plishka, with Richard Bonynge conducting.
VHS: S07567. $22.95.

Mefistofele
The San Francisco State Opera brings Boito's opera to magnificent realization under the baton of Maurizio Arena, with bass Samuel Ramey. 159 mins.
VHS: S13223. $29.95.

The Mikado
In Japan, a timid official is appointed Lord High Executioner and finds that his first intended victim is the Emperor's son, travelling incognito. This first film version of Gilbert and Sullivan's comic opera features the D'Oyly Carte Company, the same company that premiered *The Mikado* in 1885.
VHS: S05357. $39.95.
Stuart Burge, Great Britain, 1939, 93 mins.

Mozart on Tour: Volume 1 (London—The First Journey)
The first part of this documentary/performance series hosted by Andre Previn starts with this childhood visit to the British capital, where Mozart and his family were idolized by the royal court. The London influence was later felt in works like Piano Concerto No. 23, performed here by Vladimir Ashkenazy and the Royal Philharmonic Orchestra. A trip to Paris in 1778 resulted in the Symphony No. 31, performed by Jeffrey Tate and the Salzburg Mozarteum Orchestra. In Hi-Fi stereo, 75 mins.
Laser: LD71448. $34.95.

Mozart on Tour: Volume 2
With an introduction by Andre Previn, this documentary/performance investigation into the history of this great artist continues over the Alps in Italy, where Mozart was introduced to the "Manzuoli style" of virtuoso singing, and to the newly developed pianoforte instrument. In Mantua, Heidrun Holtmann performs *Piano Concerto No. 1 in F* and *Piano Concert No. 4 in D*. Marc Andrae conducts the Orchestra Della in Milan through *Piano Concerto No. 5 in D*, with American pianist Malcolm Frager. In Hi-Fi Stereo, 113 mins.
Laser: LD71466. $34.95.

Mozart on Tour: Volume 3
The third installment depicts Mozart at his musical and emotional turning point, in Mannheim where he

50 Top Opera & Classical Music Videos

meets soprano Aloysia Weber (and her sister Constanze). Gianluigi Gelmetti conducts the Radio Symphony Orchestra of Stuttgart, with pianist Christian Zacharias performing Piano Concertos No. 6 and No. 8. With an introduction by Andre Previn. Hi-Fi stereo, 109 mins.
Laser: LD71515. $34.95.

Mozart on Tour: Volume 4
Set in 1778, this program details Wolfgang Amadeus Mozart's arrival in Paris, the tragic death of his mother, and his return to Salzburg. Over the next two years he works on his important opera, *Idomeneo*, until he's summoned by the Archbishop of Vienna, and commissioned for a new work.
Laser: LD71528. $34.95.

Mozart on Tour: Volume 5
This volume of the video biography of Mozart centers on one of his most creative periods, the writing of his two greatest works, *The Marriage of Figaro* and *Don Giovanni*. Hosted by Andre Previn, the conductor and soloist with the European Chamber Orchestra. 100 mins.
Laser: LD71549. $34.95.

Mussorgsky: Pictures at an Exhibition
A three-part collaboration between filmmaker Christopher Nupen and pianist/conductor Vladimir Ashkenazy. Ashkenazy conducts the Swedish Radio Symphony Orchestra in a 1922 Leo Funtek orchestration, and gives a solo performance filmed in concert at London's Barbican Centre. In Hi-fi Stereo, 96 mins.
VHS: S16510. $29.97.
Laser: LD71458. $34.97.

Novotna in The Bartered Bride and The Last Waltz
Novotna, the acclaimed singer from 1930's Europe, stars in both these operas. Smetana's music is beautifully realized in German. Then Oscar Straus' work is presented in English. 76 minutes.
VHS: S25534. $39.95.
Max Ophuls/Leo Mittler, Germany/ Czechoslovakia, 1932
Gerald Barry, Great Britain/France, 1935

Otto Klemperer's Long Journey Through His Times
A remarkable film about a legendary musician and human being; Otto Klemperer lived and made music through two world wars to become a great interpreter of Brahms, Beethoven, Bach and Wagner. Through rare archival footage and interviews, filmmaker Philo Bregstein takes the viewer on a revealing journey through eight decades and across four continents, as this extraordinary artist battled Hitler, McCarthy and personal tragedy to become one of the supreme artists of our century. German with English subtitles.
VHS: S08220. $59.95.
Philo Bregstein, Germany/Holland, 1984, 96 mins.

Parsifal
A splendid interpretation of Wagner's last opera, performed at the Bayreuth Festival Theatre.
VHS: S15735. $44.95.

Pirates of Penzance
Linda Ronstadt stars in this modern adaptation of the Gilbert and Sullivan musical, as originally produced by Joseph Papp. With Angela Lansbury, George Rose.
VHS: S04839. $19.98.
Wilford Leach, USA, 1983, 112 mins.

Richard Strauss: Arabella
Christian Thielemann has quickly gained attention as one of the world's leading Strauss conductors. In this 1994 performance of Richard Strauss' lyric romantic comedy written in the 1920s, Thielemann demonstrates his gifts as he conducts The Metropolitan Opera. With Kiri Te Kanawa as Arabella and Wolfgang Brendel as Mandryka. "As conducted by Christian Thielemann, the orchestra was also the dominant force of the opera, not supporting the singers as much as daring them to hang on for the lush exotic ride" (*New York Times*).
VHS: S31071. $34.95.
Laser: LD76146. $59.95.
1994, 30 mins.

Rigoletto at Verona
Enjoy Verdi's *Rigoletto*, presented at the ancient Roman amphitheater in Verona, Italy. This beautiful production features top-quality digital hi-fi. 115 mins.
VHS: S02467. $29.95.

Segovia at Los Olivos
Guitarist Andres Segovia looks back on his stunning career and performs some of the music with which he is most closely associated. This film by Christopher Nupen examines one of the longest performing careers of the 20th century and highlights some of the wonderful music by Andres Segovia. 57 mins.
VHS: S27196. $19.95.

Tannhauser
Wagner's grand romantic opera is given a modern interpretation by director David Alden, who stirs up the visionary, erotic and archetypal elements of Wagner's masterpiece. This acclaimed Bayerische Staatsoper performance stars Rene Kollo, Waltraud Meier and Bernd Weikl, and is conducted by Zubin Mehta. 195 mins.
VHS: S30878. $29.95.

Tosca
A newly discovered film recording of the incomparable Renata Tebaldi at the peak of her vocal and dramatic powers in a 1961 performance of Puccini's masterpiece, filmed live at the Stuttgart Staatsoper. George London portrays Scarpia and the cast also includes Eugene Tobin. Franco Patane conducts.
VHS: S19398. $39.95.

Tristan and Isolde
Wagner's great romantic opera, with Daniel Barenboim conducting the Choir and Orchestra of the Bayreuther Festspiele with solos from Schunk, Meier, Schwarz, Becht and Kollo. In Hi-Fi stereo, 245 mins.
VHS: S16046. $44.95.
Laser: LD71189. $89.95.

War and Peace
Valery Gergiev leads the Kirov Opera in this astounding performance of Prokofiev's opera. Based on Leo Tolstoy's famed work, Prokofiev captures the epic sweep of his acclaimed novel. Olga Borodina, Aleksandr Gergalov, Yelena Prokina, Gegam Grigorian and more are featured. 248 mins.
VHS: S27072. $44.95.
Laser: LD75443. $82.50.

Who's Afraid of Opera
World-famous soprano Joan Sutherland and her magical puppet friends present a series of opera highlight programs designed for the whole family. Each program highlights two operas. Joining Sutherland in these unique programs are her funny puppet friends Sir William, an elderly, erudite goat; his nephew, Little Billy; and Rudy, the boisterous lion. The puppets punctuate storylines with bits of humor which balance the tragic overtones of some of the operas and add great humor and suspense to the lighter, comical ones. Together they relate the stories in English, and the arias are sung in their original language with costumes and sets directly from the opera house. Each of the films is designed to make adults and children who are unfamiliar with opera comfortable with this area of western culture and to appreciate the stories and music of opera. Produced and conceived by Nathan Kroll; the London Symphony Orchestra is directed by Richard Bonynge, with the puppets created by Larry Berthelson. Four volumes.
VHS: S05329. $113.81.

William Tell
Rossini's final opera features Chris Merritt in the role of Arnold, produced at La Scala under the direction of Riccardo Muti. Two videocassettes. 239 min.
VHS: S18384. $49.95.

Bizet's Carmen

25 Best Jazz & Blues Videos

Abbey Lincoln:
You Gotta Pay the Band
In its 5-star review of Abbey Lincoln's album of the same name, *Down Beat* stated, "Lady Day and Pres must have revisited Earth the day this record was made." The video edition features live and studio versions of the songs on the album, as well as clips of the 1950s and 1960s movies in which Abbey starred. Also includes interviews with Stan Getz, Tony Bennett, Ruth Brown and Spike Lee. 58 mins.
VHS: S15713. $24.95.
Laser: LD70283. $19.95.

Alberta Hunter
(Smithsonian Jazz Series)
The Grand Lady of the Blues, the late Alberta Hunter, is featured in this toe-tapping concert taped at the Smithsonian Institute. Alberta's down-and-dirty blues and tender ballads are performed with her trademark sass and sensitivity.
VHS: S05421. $29.95.

America's Music: Blues 1
Utilizes interviews with the artists, stills, film clips of Bessie Smith and others, and rousing performances from Linda Hopkins (St. Louis Blues), B.B. King, Leata Galloway, Eddie Cleanhead Vinson, Erne Andrews, Vi Redd, "Pee Wee" Crayton. 60 mins.,
VHS: S05032. $19.95.

America's Music: Blues 2
Brock Peters narrates the second volume of the birth of the blues, featuring such blues greats as Joe Williams, Paula Kelly, Esther Phillips, Bobby McGee, Buddy Guy and Junior Wells, Dorothy Donigan, Joe Williams and Addie, with film clips of Mamie Smith, Count Basie and Big Joe Turner. 60 mins.
VHS: S05033. $19.95.

America's Music:
Jazz Then Dixieland 1
Al Hirt hosts this look at Dixieland, with film clips and stills, and performances by Woody Herman, Clora Bryant, Scotty Plummer, Della Reese, Al Hirt, Johnny Guarnieri. 60 mins.
VHS: S05038. $19.95.

America's Music:
Jazz Then Dixieland 2
Al Hirt continues with music by Bob Crosby, The Hessions, Scatman Crothers, Al Hirt, Teddy Buckner, Judy Carmichael, Irma Thomas. 60 mins.
VHS: S05039. $19.95.

Benny Carter
(Smithsonian Jazz Series)
The legendary composer/arranger/trumpeter/saxophonist performs jazz standards like "Misty" and "Take the A Train." Carter, 74 years young at the

Alberta Hunter

time, performs with a quintet that also features Kenny Barron on piano and George Duvivier on bass.
VHS: S05426. $29.95.

Blues Masters, Vol. 1
An encyclopedic account of the history, personalities and evolution of the American blues masters, including Son House, Leadbelly, Bessie Smith, Mamie Smith, Roy Milton and His Orchestra, Jimmy Rushing, Ethel Waters and Big Bill Broonzy. The documentary merges archival recording footage and photographs. The highlight is a raucous version of "St. Louis Blues" by Leadbelly and Bessie Smith. 51 mins.
VHS: S19163. $19.98.

Celebrating Bird:
The Triumph of Charlie Parker
The only authorized documentary on the late, great Charlie Parker, tracing his beginnings in Kansas City to his final years in New York, featuring interviews with friends, family, colleagues, as well as archival clips and historic performances of "Confirmation," "Ballade," "A Night in Tunisia," "Just Friends," and more. 58 mins.
VHS: S05401. $29.95.

Don Cherry's Multikulti
Together with Ornette Coleman, Cherry assumed a leading position in the jazz vanguard of the 1960's. His interpretations of centuries-old vocal traditions continue to glow. This video documents Cherry's work at the prestigious Days of Jazz in Stuttgart, Germany, and includes "Walk to the Mountain," "Bemsha Swing" and "Trans Love Airways," among others. 57 mins.
VHS: S24067. $19.98.

Harlem Swings Volume 1
This collection of swing greats contains performances by Eubie Blake, Don Redman, Cab Calloway, Louis Armstrong, Duke Ellington, Les Hite and the great jazz bands of the 1930s.
VHS: S21420. $29.95.

Harlem Swings Volume 2
Swing greats Nat King Cole, Lionel Hampton, Sarah Vaughan, Nipsy Russel, Count Basie, Dinah Washington and more perform their classic hits. Also included are *The Nat King Cole Story*, which charts the rise of this singular entertainer, and *Basin Street Review.*
VHS: S21421. $29.95.

Harlem Swings Volume 3
In this collection, swing greats Dusty Fletcher, Ethel Waters, Louis Jordan and comedian Stepin Fetchit perform in all-black cast musical comedy short subjects.
VHS: S21422. $29.95.

Harlem Swings Volume 4
This collection of Harlem legends features the Harlem Hotshots, Louis Armstrong, The Ebony Trio, Lena Horne, Lionel Hampton, Ruth Brown and others.
VHS: S21423. $29.95.

Harlem Swings Volume 5
The "Rock and Roll Review" in this volume features Duke Ellington, Larry Darnell, Coles and Atkins, The Clovers, Nat "King" Cole, Lionel Hampton, Martha Davis and others.
VHS: S21424. $29.95.

Jazz on a Summer's Day
The concert movie that came first—before *Woodstock, Monterey Pop, The Last Waltz* and *Gimme Shelter*—is still among the best. On a hot summer's day in Newport, Rhode Island in 1958, jazz greats Louis Armstrong, Thelonious Monk, and Anita O'Day get together with Chuck Berry, Mahalia Jackson, and Dinah Washington among others to make this glorious gem of a movie.
VHS: S12198. $29.95.
Bert Stern, USA, 1958, 85 mins.

Lady Day: The Many Faces
of Billie Holiday
Considered by many to be the greatest jazz singer of

all time, Billie was also the victim of vicious racism, personal tragedy and drug addiction. Yet she remained a fighter, as this video portrait proves in remembrances by fellow jazz stars Carmen McRae, Harry "Sweets" Edison, Milt Gabler and Mal Waldron. And there's plenty of Lady Day herself, from her own words (as read by actress Ruby Dee) to generous film clips featuring her singing her best-loved songs. 60 mins.
VHS: S13929. $29.95.

Live at the Village Vanguard Vol. 1
The hottest sounds from the coolest cats. Freddie Hubbard on trumpet. Ron Carter on bass. Cedar Walton tickles the ivories and Lenny White is on drums. Tunes include "Happy Times", "Guernica", "Little Waltz" and "Fantasy in D". Recorded live at the Village Vanguard.
VHS: S09118. $29.95.
Bruce Buschel, USA, 1982, 59 mins.

Live at the Village Vanguard Vol. 2
The Michael Petrucciani Trio performs jazz just the way you like it in this second volume in the Village Vanguard series. With Palle Danielsson on bass; Eliot Zigmund on drums and guest star Jin Hall on guitar. For your viewing and listening pleasure they play "Gitgo", "All Alone", "Firewaltz" and "Left Alone". In color and stereo. HiFi.
VHS: S09119. $29.95.
Bruce Buschel, USA, 1982, 57 mins.

Live at the Village Vanguard Vol. 3
More hot jazz sounds recorded live at the Village Vanguard. Guitarist John Abercrombie is backed up by Michael Brecker on tenor sax, Peter Erskine on drums and Marc Johnson on bass. They perform "Dreamstepper", "Blues for Sarha", "Tavia's Tune", "Max", "Juicey Brucey" and "Subconscious Lee".
VHS: S09120. $29.95.
Bruce Buschel, USA, 1986, 58 mins.

Live at the Village Vanguard Vol. 4
The Mal Waldron Quartet, featuring Mal Waldron, Woody Shaw, Charles Rouse, Reggie Workman and Ed Blackwell, performs "Git-Go," "All Alone," and other numbers. 56 mins.
VHS: S12192. $29.95.

Live at the Village Vanguard Vol. 5
Lee Konitz and Friends perform "Max", "Dreamstepper", "A Story Often Told," and other numbers. 62 mins.
VHS: S12193. $29.95.

Live at the Village Vanguard Vol. 6
The Dave Murray Quartet performs "Off Season," "Lovers," "Morning Song," and other numbers. 56 mins.
VHS: S12194. $29.65.

My First Name Is Maceo
James Brown's longtime alto sax man steps forward to blow his horn in this portrait of the musician better known as a sideman than as a star. When Brown went to prison in the late '80s, Maceo became a bandleader in his own right with funk pioneers trombonist Fred Wesley and tenor saxophonist Pee Wee Ellis. Includes 1994 concert and rehearsal footage in New York, New Orleans and on the road, as well as revealing interviews. With George Clinton and Kim Mazelle.
VHS: S32686. $19.95.
Markus Gruber, USA, 1996, 87 mins.

Straight No Chaser: Thelonious Monk
A revealing portrait of the great Monk, featuring more than 25 Monk songs, including "Round Midnight", "Ask Me Now" and "Ruby, My Dear", and featuring an amazing insight into the personal life of the troubled but extraordinary musician.
VHS: S13023. $19.98.
Charlotte Zwerin, USA, 1989, 89 mins.

25 Best Dance Videos

3 by Martha Graham
Features three original dances choreographed by and starring Martha Graham. One of the giants of American dance, Graham is the subject of a new biography and the inspiration to her company's triumphant return to Broadway. Originally aired on television, this program has been remastered for home video. "Extraordinary" (*New York Times*). USA, 87 mins.
VHS: S15397. $59.95.

The Balanchine Celebration: Part One
Darci Kistler, Nilas Martins and Kyra Nichols are featured in this video, along with Paris Opera Ballet prima ballerina Isabelle Guerin and Kirov ballet star Zhanna Ayupova. Selections from *Apollo, Vienna Waltzes, Union Jack, Theme and Variations*, and other Balanchine works, along with the complete *Scherzo a la Russe*, reveal Balanchine's Russian and European roots.
VHS: S27060. $29.98.
Matthew Diamond, USA, 1993, 86 mins.

The Balanchine Celebration: Part Two
Darcey Bussell and Lindsay Fischer dance a *pas de deux* from *Agon*. Then, American Ballet Theater prima ballerina Susan Jaffe stars with Nikolaj Hubbe in *Western Symphony*, while Damian Woetzel and Margaret Tracey lead in the patriotic *Stars and Stripes*. Finally, *Who Cares?*, featuring Jeremy Collins and Viviana Durante, brings the era of Gershwin alive.
VHS: S27059. $29.98.
Matthew Diamond, USA, 1993, 86 mins.

Choreography by Balanchine: Selections from Jewels/Stravinsky Violin Concerto
Great dancers are featured in these excerpts from Balanchine works. Suzanne Farrell and Peter Martins dance in *Diamonds*. Merrill Ashley, Bonita Borne, Gerard Ebitz, Karin von Aroldingen, Heather Watts, Daniel Duell and Sean Lavery perform the ensemble piece *Emeralds*. Then, Peter Martins, Bart Cook, Karin von Aroldingen and Kay Mazzo perform *Stravinsky Violin Concerto*, along with members of the New York City Ballet.
VHS: S27062. $29.98.
Merrill Brockway, USA, 1977, 56 mins.

Classic Kirov Performances
A rare compendium recreates some of the legendary Kirov Theatre performances, including Anna Pavlova's work as *The Dying Swan*. The program features Natalia Dudinskaya, Galina Ulanova, Vakhtang Chabukiani, Konstantin Sergeyev, Altynai Asylmuratova and Tatyana Terekhova, in performances from *Romeo and Juliet, The Nutcracker, Sleeping Beauty* and *Don Quixote*. 110 mins.
VHS: S18568. $29.95.

Dance Basics Plus Curriculum
Designed for public and academic libraries, this six-tape set with support materials, featuring instructor Tony Louis Ridgel, comprises the most comprehensive course available for teaching students to dance. Tapes include Ballroom, featuring Foxtrot, Waltz and Single & East Coast Swings; Country, featuring Two-Step, Texas/Triple-2, Waltz and Single & East Coast Swings; Latin, featuring Rumba, Cha-Cha and Mambo; Line Dance, featuring Bayou Boogie, Cotton Eyed Joe, Electric Slide, 4-Corners, Cowboy Cha-Cha and Tush-Push; Contemporary/Social, featuring Freestyle, Single & East Coast Swing and Slow Dancing; and Hip Hop, featuring more than 30 of the most popular moves.
VHS: S30873. $209.95.

Dance Theater of Harlem
The New York Times has hailed this program as "a sheer utter triumph." Now the energy, creativity and classical perfection of the Dance Theater of Harlem has been captured in dazzling performances of four signature pieces. The American classic *Fall River Legend*, choreographed by Agnes de Mille, tells the notorious story of Lizzie Borden. *Troy Game*, by Robert North, is a dynamic satire of the machismo attitudes inherent in sports. *The Beloved*, a ballet for two dancers by Lester Horton, confronts the themes of violence and fanaticism. *John Henry*, choreographed by Arthur Mitchell, is a celebration of

the strength of the human will. 117 mins.
VHS: S12215. $29.95.

Footnotes: The Classics of Ballet
This acclaimed series explains the world of ballet, utilizing historic clips and interviews with the legends of dance. These exciting programs feature the Bolshoi, Kirov and Royal Ballets as well as superstars Rudolf Nureyev, Margo Fonteyn, Natalia Makarova, Fernando Bujones, Anthony Dowell, Edward Villella, Cynthia Gregory, Darcey Russell and many others. Hosted by Frank Augustyn. 60 minutes each.
Volume 4: Don Quixote & La Bayadere.
VHS: S31373. $19.95.
Volume 5: Cinderella & Coppelia.
VHS: S31374. $19.95.
Volume 6: The Male Dancer & Gala Excerpts.
VHS: S31375. $19.95.

Invitation to the Dance
Gene Kelly wrote, directed, choreographed and performed in this three-part tribute to his fascination with movies and movement. "Circus", "Ring around the Rosy" and "Sinbad the Sailor" each incorporate Kelly's love of dance. "Sinbad" is partially animated by the Hanna-Barbera studios. With Claire Sombert, Carol Haney, Tamara Toumanova and Igor Youskevitch.
VHS: S06169. $19.98.
Gene Kelly, USA, 1956, 93 mins.

The Nutcracker
Baryshnikov and Kirkland star in the ballet extravaganza with the ever-popular music of Tchaikovsky. USA, 1984.
VHS: S01813. $19.98.

Riverdance—The Show
American dancers Michael Flatley and Jean Butler are at the center of this thrilling dance experience. It joins traditional Irish dance and music with the passion of more recent American styles. It is as if a mixture of *Dirty Dancing* with the chemistry of Torvill and Dean were added to Irish folk ways.
VHS: S27643. $24.95.

Romeo and Juliet
Margot Fonteyn and Rudolf Nureyev team with the Royal Ballet in the classic of tragic love.
VHS: S01889. $29.95.
Paul Czinner, Great Britain, 1966, 124 mins.

Russian Ballet: The Glorious Tradition, Vol. 1
An historical preservation of ground-breaking Russian ballet, including *Don Quixote*, featuring Mikhail Baryshnikov and Lyudmila Semenyaka; *Corsaire*, with Nina Ananiashvili and Andris Liepa; *La Bayadere, The Nutcracker* and *Swan Lake.*
VHS: S18721. $39.95.

Russian Ballet: The Glorious Tradition, Vol. 2
A valuable inner view of the historical and aesthetic shifts in Russian ballet, captured through rare archival materials and films never shown in the West. This two-volume retrospective showcases the form's dominant figures, from Vera Karalli's sublime interpretation of *The Dying Swan* in 1914, through

A Tribute to Alvin Ailey

40s footage of Marina Semenova and Natalia Dudinskaya, to more recent footage of Galina Ulanova, Maya Plisetskaya and Michail Gabovich. The concluding footage is the amazing *Quixote Act Three grand pas de deux*, with Ekaterina Maximova and Vladimir Vasiliev. 71 mins.
VHS: S18994. $39.95.

Russian Ballet: The Glorious Tradition, Vol. 3
As the third installment of this all-encompassing history of Russian Ballet, *The Glorious Tradition* brings more footage of the brilliant stars of the dance world. Galina Ulanova, Maya Plisetskaya, Mikhail Baryshnikov, and Yuri Soloviev are included. 67 mins.
VHS: S20693. $39.95.

Sevillanas
Seven short flamenco performances, featuring some of Spain's top performers, are collected on this documentary-like work. This film is from the maker of the wildly successful *Carmen*, a dance-laden film featuring spectacular flamenco sequences. In addition to the terrific dance found on this newer work, there is extraordinary music and singing. Spanish with English subtitles.
VHS: S27205. $39.95.
Carlos Saura, Spain, 1992, 55 mins.

Sylvie Guillem
At only 24 years of age, Sylvie Guillem has already enjoyed a most brilliant career dancing all over the world and as a choreographer in her own right. During this one-hour portrait, we discover a young woman whose personality has remained unaffected by this meteoric rise to fame. 54 mins.
VHS: S11753. $39.95.

Tango: Our Dance
The sensuality and stylized rituals popular with the residents of Buenos Aires are part of the complex art form called the tango. Director Jorge Zanada examines the unique role of this dance within Argentina's social and personal landscape, exploring issues of machismo and passion contained within the dance. With a special appearance by Robert Duvall. Spanish with English subtitles.
VHS: S20380. $29.95.
Jorge Zanada, Argentina, 1988, 71 mins.

Tchaikovsky's Swan Lake
Bourne's Olivier Award-winning production brings a bold, new twist to an old classic. Set in the modern era with an all-male cast, Bourne's creation brings great ballet to an audience it has never before reached, and for cognoscenti it offers a new view of the breadth of possibility in Tchaikovsky's well-loved score. "One of the most gripping, funny and profoundly moving dance works I've seen" (*The Guardian*).
VHS: S32967. $29.97.
Matthew Bourne, Great Britain, 1996, 117 mins.

That's Dancing
Gene Kelly, Liza Minnelli, Baryshnikov and Ray Bolger host a look at some of the great dance scenes in Hollywood musicals from Fred Astaire films through *West Side Story.*
VHS: S03365. $29.95.
Laser: LD71154. $39.98.
Jack Haley Jr., USA, 1985, 105 mins.

A Tribute to Alvin Ailey
This two-part program celebrates this dance world legend with performances of four of his works: *For Bird with Love, Witness, Memoria* and *Episodes.* Each dance is introduced by Judith Jamison, the dancer and choreographer whose career was nurtured to stardom by Ailey and who has succeeded him as director of their company. 120 mins.
VHS: S15992. $39.95.

Twist
Canadian independent filmmaker Ron Mann, who specializes in cultural documentaries (*Comic Book Confidential*), made this entertaining work about the history of the 50s dance craze. Mann interweaves archival footage and interviews with Chubby Checker, Hank Ballard, Joey Dee and various dancers to comment on the racial, social and artistic implications of the Twist. Mann argues the movement was the catalyst for American rock and roll. Cinematography by Bob Fresco.
VHS: S19732. $9.98.
Laser: LD72280. $49.95.
Ron Mann, Canada, 1992, 78 mins.

50 Top Theatre Adaptations

American Theater Conversations: The Actors Studio

Frank Cosaro, Paul Newman, Geraldine Page, Fred Stewart, Rip Torn and Michael Wager discuss The Actors Studio, its origins, its goals and the influence of "Method" acting. The conversation was filmed at the time of the first Broadway success of The Actors Studio Theater, Eugene O'Neill's *Strange Interlude*, in which Miss Page had a starring role.
VHS: $30996. $89.95.
1963, 28 mins.

Beckett Directs Beckett: Waiting for Godot

In collaboration with the San Quentin Drama Workshop, Samuel Beckett directs his existential parable about two lost souls awaiting a rendezvous that may or may not be imaginary. With Bud Thorpe, Rick Cluchey, Lawrence Held and Alan Mandell. The play has never been "more human, more accessible or more beautiful" (*Newsweek*). In two acts running 77 and 60 mins.
VHS: $18454. $39.95.

Beckett Directs Beckett Collection

The three-tape set contains *Waiting for Godot I* and *II*, *Krapp's Last Tape* and *End Game*.
VHS: $18143. $89.95.

The Belle of Amherst

Julie Harris stars as the most famous 19th century American woman poet, Emily Dickinson. In this dramatization, her life as a recluse and spinster is recreated to reveal the sources of her poetry. Dickinson was inspired by the humble everyday occurences found in rural America.
VHS: $22940. $59.95.

Camelot

The epic Broadway hit comes alive with stunning performances by Richard Harris and Vanessa Redgrave as King Arthur and Lady Guinevere. Music by Frederick Loewe, lyrics by Alan Jay Lerner, based on the novel by T.H. White. With Franco Nero, David Hemmings. Letterboxed.
VHS: $01749. $24.98.
Joshua Logan, USA, 1967, 173 mins.

Cat on a Hot Tin Roof

Paul Newman and Elizabeth Taylor star in this steamy screen version of Tennessee Williams' famous play about a rich plantation owner, dying of cancer, who finds most of his family fawning all over him for his money. Fine performances from a cast that includes Burl Ives, Madeleine Sherwood and Larry Gates.
DVD: DV60059. $24.98.
VHS: $13776. $19.98.
Richard Brooks, USA, 1958, 108 mins.

Clarence Darrow

Henry Fonda in a command performance as the famous Clarence Darrow, the legendary attorney who fought for the rights of individuals. "I urge every man, woman and child interested in justice and America to see this...As for Mr. Fonda, it would be difficult to think of praise too high...It is just plain wonderful," wrote Clive Barnes in *The New York Times*.
VHS: $06091. $39.95.
John Houseman, USA, 1980, 81 mins.

Come Back, Little Sheba

Based on the William Inge play, which paints a gripping portrait of a marriage washed up by booze and alienation. Featuring Burt Lancaster and an Oscar and Tony Award-winning, gut-wrenching performance by Shirley Booth. The title refers to Booth's despairing search for her lost dog but, of course, it's symbolic of a whole lot more than that.
VHS: $13789. $19.95.
Daniel Mann, USA, 1952, 99 mins.

Da

Hugh Leonard's autobiographical play of growing up adopted in a small seacoast town in Ireland. The film version is directed by character actor Matt Clark.

Cat on a Hot Tin Roof

My Fair Lady

Barnard Hughes is the lovable and crusty title character with whom son Martin Sheen has many mixed emotions. A ghost story. A comedy. A celebration of life. With William Hickey.
VHS: S07581. $19.95.
Matt Clark, Ireland/USA, 1988, 102 mins.

Days of Wine and Roses
Piper Laurie and Cliff Robertson star in the Playhouse 90 production of the J.P. Miller play about a couple facing alcoholism.
VHS: S05014. $24.95.
Laser: Letterboxed. **LD71200. $34.98.**
John Frankenheimer, USA, 1958, 89 mins.

Death and the Maiden
Sigourney Weaver, Ben Kingsley and Stuart Wilson are featured in this adaptation of Ariel Dorfman's acclaimed play. A woman finally has the opportunity to see justice done for the wrong she suffered. She will go to any extreme—after all, her life was destroyed. It's a knockout psychological thriller.
VHS: S25102. $19.98.
Laser: Widescreen. **LD74959. $39.99.**
Roman Polanski, France, 1995, 103 mins.

Desire Under the Elms
In Eugene O'Neill's play adapted by Irwin Shaw, a 19th century New England family is beset by greed, lust and family hatred. With Anthony Perkins, Sophia Loren, Burl Ives and Pernell Roberts.
VHS: S00322. $19.95.
Delbert Mann, USA, 1958, 114 mins.

The Entertainer
Playwright John Osborne assisted Tony Richardson in the adaptation of his play in this brilliant depiction of the moral, spiritual and professional decline of a bogus entertainer, Archie Rice. Set against the background of the noisy holiday makers pushing past the placard proclaiming the Suez crisis in which Archie's only contact with real life, his son Mick, is to die. "Richardson used large, oppressive close-ups and shock cutting to the point of technical arrogance, but he brought the audience relentlessly face to face with the failure of the sad characters of Archie and his debilitated alcoholic wife, beautifully played by Brenda de Banzie" (Roger Manvell).
VHS: S08261. $19.95.
Laser: Widescreen. **LD75918. $49.95.**
Tony Richardson, Great Britain, 1960, 97 mins.

Equus
Richard Burton and Peter Firth in the film version of Peter Shaffer's play about a part-time stableboy who has blinded six horses. Burton as the psychiatrist

discovers that the boy comes from a repressive family background.
VHS: S00411. $14.95.
Sidney Lumet, USA, 1977, 145 mins.

Funny Girl
Barbra Streisand made her Oscar-winning film debut in this epic screen biography of entertainer Fanny Brice. She sings, dances and roller-skates her way to the top of the show business ladder. There is no doubt about it, a star is born, so please don't rain on her parade. With Omar Sharif as gambler and first husband Nicky Arnstein, Anne Francis, Kay Medford, and Walter Pidgeon as Flo Ziegfeld.
VHS: S10976. $19.95.
William Wyler, USA, 1968, 155 mins.

Glengarry Glen Ross
James Foley's adaptation of David Mamet's Pulitzer prize-winning play about the confidence games and male bravado of a group of Chicago real estate salesmen. The performances are first-rate, with Al Pacino as the silver-tongued, shrewd operator, Jack Lemmon as the one-time kingpin who's fallen on hard times and Ed Harris as an anonymous, grubby loser. Alec Baldwin turns in a terrifying cameo.
VHS: S18465. $19.98.
Laser: Widescreen. **LD75198. $34.98.**
James Foley, USA, 1992, 100 mins.

Godspell and the Filming of Godspell
Taking the hit off-Broadway musical to the screen. Features on-location scenes, rehearsals and reflections by director David Greene, composer/lyricist Stephen Schwartz and writer John-Michael Tebelak. 1973, 28 mins.
VHS: S31585. $59.95.

Grease
The movie version of a play that got its start in a bus barn in Chicago stars John Travolta and Olivia Newton-John as California high schoolers addicted to being cool. A high energy, tune-filled romp that features such quasi-teens (at the time) as Stockard Channing, Jeff Conaway and Didi Conn. Eve Arden, Sid Caesar and Edd "Kookie" Byrnes play the bona fide adults. "Grease" is the word and the word is fun.
VHS: S08292. $14.95.
Randal Kleiser, USA, 1978, 110 mins.

Gypsy
Everything is coming up roses in the big screen biography of legendary entertainer Gypsy Rose Lee. Natalie Wood stars as the child vaudeville performer who finds stardom as the classiest striptease artist on the runway. Rosalind Russell plays the ultimate show

biz mom who has difficulty letting her daughters grow up. With Karl Malden, Harvey Korman and Faith Dane. Songs include "You Gotta Have a Gimmick" and "Let Me Entertain You." Music by Julie Styne. Lyrics by Stephen Sondheim. Based on the play by Arthur Laurents and the book *Gypsy: A Memoir by Gypsy Rose Lee aka Rose Louise Hovick*.
VHS: $15840. $19.98.
Mervyn Le Roy, USA, 1962, 149 mins.

Hair
The first musical about the American anti-war movement of the 1960's. Exceptional adaptation of the musical stars Treat Williams as a hippie who meets John Savage, a youth from Oklahoma bound for Vietnam. Forman moves the story beyond the bounds of the stage play to make a strong statement about war. Choreography by Twyla Tharp.
VHS: S03486. $19.98.
Laser: LD71163. $39.98.
Milos Forman, USA, 1979, 121 mins.

The Heidi Chronicles
Jamie Lee Curtis and Tom Hulce star in this screen adaptation of the highly regarded stage play. Penned by Wendy Wasserstein, this play won both the Pulitzer Prize and a Tony Award. The film is the story of Heidi Holland (Curtis), a woman determined to experience life and all its possibilities. Over the course of three decades she fights for the political goals she believes in and manages to develop a successful career. It's a success story with real feminist ideals.
VHS: $27262. $19.98.
Laser: LD75561. $39.95.
Paul Bogart, USA, 1995

The Life and Adventures of Nicholas Nickleby
Thirty-nine actors from the Royal Shakespeare Company are presented in this dramatization of Charles Dickens' masterful tale. From Wackford Squeer's Dotheboys to the itinerant theater troupe of Mr. Vincent Crummles, this set of videos offers nine hours of engrossing viewing pleasure.
VHS: $23877. $99.95.
Laser: LD75935. $149.95.

Little Murders
Elliot Gould is the meek photographer roped into marriage with the overly aggressive Marcia Rodd in this hilarious black comedy about modern relationships, urban living and sniping as a form of therapy. With Vincent Gardenia, Elizabeth Wilson, Donald Sutherland and Alan Arkin, who also makes his film debut as a director. A sure fire hit from the pen of Jules Feiffer.
VHS: S07969. $59.98.
Alan Arkin, USA, 1971, 107 mins.

Long Day's Journey into Night
Eugene O'Neill's drama of a problem-prone Tyrone family is faithfully brought to the big screen with all the vices and vitriol intact. Ralph Richardson heads a cast that includes Katharine Hepburn, Jason Robards, Jr. and Dean Stockwell.
VHS: S02576. $19.98.
Laser: LD71550. $39.98.
Sidney Lumet, USA, 1962, 170 mins.

Look Back in Anger—Kenneth Branagh
John Osborne's play has had many successful productions featuring great British actors, including Richard Burton and Malcolm McDowell. Now Kenneth Branagh and Emma Thompson are featured in a convincing production that brings alive the fury which inspired a generation of angry young men.
VHS: $24665. $29.98.
David Jones, Great Britain, 1989, 114 mins.

Marat/Sade (The Persecution and Assassination of Jean-Paul Marat as Performed by the Inmates of the Asylum of Charenton under the Direction of Marquis de Sade)
Peter Weiss' monumental play, in a mesmerizing adaptation directed by the world-famous stage director Peter Brook, in its original production by the Royal Shakespeare Company. The play features Glenda Jackson as a nutcase in the role of Charlotte Chorday, the assassin of Marat. With Ian Richardson, Patrick Magee, Ruth Baker and Freddie Jones. Terrifying and intense.
VHS: S09855. $29.95.
Laser: LD70264. $39.95.
Peter Brook, Great Britain, 1967, 115 mins.

Marc Blitzstein: The Cradle Will Rock
Excerpts from the musical work *The Cradle Will Rock* performed by a very young Jerry Orbach and Nancy Andrews, Hal Buckley, Clifford David and Micki Grant. Howard da Silva, who had been in the original 1937 cast, is director. Also, a profile of the life, work and influence of Mark Blitzstein, bringing together comrades and admirers Aaron Copeland, Arvin Brown and John Houseman. 1964/1976, 85 mins.
VHS: S32320. $89.95.

Medea
An intense rendering of Euripides' masterpiece in this famous production which features Dame Judith Anderson, reprising her role from Broadway. With Colleen Dewhurst.
VHS: S18027. $29.95.

Monster in a Box
This film version of Spalding Gray's acclaimed stage hit follows an hilarious and insightful tale about a writer with a block. Writer's block metamorphoses into a behemoth document that won't go back in the box. Gray is thus set off on an itinerary that includes stops in an Eastern haunted writer's retreat, an L.A. where screenwriters don't write, and a movie set in Nicaragua where he plays a spy.
VHS: S26337. $19.98.
Nick Broomfield, USA, 1992, 90 mins.

My Fair Lady
Alan Jay Lerner and Frederick Loewe's variation of Shaw's *Pygmalion* is turned into an intellectual comedy of manners by expert director George Cukor, who skillfully allows the byplay of co-star Stanley Holloway to co-exist with the primary storyline of Henry Higgins' schooling of Eliza Doolittle. Rex Harrison and Audrey Hepburn (songs dubbed by Marni Nixon) are the leads; Holloway's "Get Me to the Church on Time" steals the show.
VHS: S02345. $24.95.
Laser: LD71247. $59.98.
George Cukor, USA, 1964, 170 mins.

Night of the Iguana
Richard Burton, Deborah Kerr and Ava Gardner star in this adaptation of Tennessee Williams' play about a fallen, alcoholic ex-minister, who is self-exiled to Mexico, where he works as a tour guide.
VHS: S04394. $19.98.
Laser: LD72352. $39.98.
John Huston, USA, 1964, 125 mins.

Oh Calcutta!
Video taped telecast of the long-running theatrical revue spoofing modern ideas of sex and sensuality, famous primarily for its nudity.
VHS: S02556. $29.95.
G.M. Aucion, USA, 1980, 120 mins.

Oleanna
David Mamet adapted his own provocative and acclaimed stage play that brilliantly explores the issues of sexual harassment. William H. Macy stars as the college professor who is forced to confront the moral and political implications of power, blackmail and revenge on a contemporary college campus when he is accused of sexual harassment.
VHS: S24825. $19.98.
Laser: LD74958. $39.99.
David Mamet, USA, 1994, 90 mins.

Orphans
Albert Finney stars in this acclaimed film adaptation of the New York play as Harold, a slick gangster who enters the bleak world of two teenaged orphans to become their unlikely "parent" and change their lives forever. With Matthew Mordine, Kevin Anderson.
VHS: S06607. $79.95.
Alan J. Pakula, USA, 1987, 101 mins.

Our Town
Thornton Wilder's classic play about life in a small town brings Yankee simplicity to new depths. In this version Eric Stoltz, Penelope Ann Miller, Peter Maloney, Roberta Maxwell, Frances Conroy, James Reborn and Spalding Gray, the noted monologist, portray the rural characters that epitomize the best of rural America. Produced at Lincoln Center for PBS's Great Performances series.
VHS: S24020. $74.95.
Gregory Mosher, USA, 1988

Passion
The Tony award-winning musical from Stephen Sondheim and James Lapine, set in romantic 19th-

Night of the Iguana

century Italy, about one woman's overwhelming love for a handsome, young army captain. With Donna Murphy, Jere Shea and Marin Mazzie.
VHS: S32219. $19.98.
James Lapine, USA, 1994, 105 mins.

The Piano Lesson
Charles Dutton and Alfre Woodard star in this film adaptation of August Wilson's Pulitzer Prize-winning play. A brother and sister fight over differing visions of their future. If they sell a piano they could buy a farm, but this piano represents more than money. It is a link to a vibrant tradition. With Courtney Vance, Carl Gordon, Tommy Hollis and Zelda Harris.
VHS: S26143. $14.98.
Lloyd Richards, USA, 1995, 99 mins.

Play It Again, Sam
Woody Allen's first film with Diane Keaton. Allen plays Allen, a fanatical movie buff with an outrageous recurring hallucination: Humphrey Bogart offering tips on how to make it with the ladies. Eventually Allen discovers that there is one woman with whom he can be himself: his best friend's wife. The final scene is a terrific take-off on *Casablanca*, with roaring plane propellers, heavy fog, and Bogart-style trench coats.
VHS: S01037. $19.95.
Laser: LD75349. $29.98.
Herbert Ross, USA, 1972, 86 mins.

The Rose Tattoo
A happy-go-lucky trucker awakens a widow to life's joys in this flavorful adaptation of a Tennessee Williams play. Starring Burt Lancaster and the brilliant Anna Magnani. Photographed by James Wong Howe.
VHS: S13787. $19.95.
Daniel Mann, USA, 1955, 117 mins.

Six Degrees of Separation
Stockard Channing, Will Smith and Donald Sutherland star in this unusual drama. John Guare adapted his hit Broadway play about a man pretending to be Sidney Poitier's son who works his way into the lives of a pair of rich Manhattanites. It's a witty and compelling scenario brought convincingly to the screen.
VHS: S21032. $19.98.
Laser: LD72407. $34.98.
Fred Schepisi, USA, 1993, 112 mins.

Strasberg on Acting
Author/theater critic Margaret Croyden talks with Lee Strasberg, director of The Actors Studio in New York City, considered the foremost training ground for actors in the United States. The father of "Method" acting discusses his career and ideas, reminisces about actors and the craft of acting and is shown lecturing and working with actors in scenes from *Uncle Vanya* at his Lee Strasberg Acting Institute.
VHS: S30995. $89.95.
1975, 28 mins.

A Streetcar Named Desire
Tennessee Williams' notorious play was censored when adapted for the screen. Now four minutes of the originally cut material have been found and restored to this "director's cut". Marlon Brando, Kim Hunter and Vivien Leigh star in this drama of betrayal, madness and rape.
DVD: DV60067. $24.98.
VHS: S21085. $19.98.
Laser: LD70687. $39.98.
Elia Kazan, USA, 1951, 125 mins.

Strindberg's Miss Julie:
Royal Shakespeare Company
August Strindberg, "…one of the prime innovators of our time…the impact of his dramatic method reflected in his Miss Julie is probably greater and less

acknowledged than any other modern writer. Strindberg struck strongly into O'Neill, Becket and Tennessee Williams…entering the subconscious where sexual encounter has a fight to the death…" (Arthur Miller, *N.Y. Times*).
VHS: S02006. $74.95.

Suddenly Last Summer
Elizabeth Taylor and Katharine Hepburn received Oscars for their gripping performances of Tennessee Williams' play about the beautiful Catherine, committed to a mental institution, whose aunt tries to influence the young surgeon to lobotomize her.
VHS: S01277. $19.95.
Joseph L. Mankiewicz, USA, 1959, 114 mins.

Sweet Bird of Youth
Paul Newman and Geraldine Page star in this Tennessee Williams drama of ambition, lust and faded glory. When a not-so-young stud hooks up with an aging movie star, he makes the mistake of revisiting his home town. The fine cast includes Shirley Knight, Rip Torn, Mildred Dunnock and Ed Begley, who won an Oscar for his role as the unforgiving town boss.
VHS: S11221. $19.95.
Laser: LD71178. $39.98.
Richard Brooks, USA, 1962, 120 mins.

Sweet Charity
Shirley MacLaine has the title role in director Bob Fosse's debut musical about the dime-a-dance girl with the heart of gold. This uncut version is based on the Neil Simon play based on Fellini's *Nights of Cabiria*. Highlights of the Cy Coleman-Dorothy Fields score include "If My Friends Could See Me Now" and "Big Spender."
VHS: S03493. $19.95.
Laser: LD70085. $44.98.
Bob Fosse, USA, 1969, 148 mins.

Talk Radio
Oliver Stone directed this adaptation of Eric Bogosian's hit stage play, which is loosely based on the murder of Denver talk show host Alan Berg by a neo-Nazi group. Stone transplants the setting to Texas, and weaves in a more intricate subplot involving the talk show host's estranged wife.
VHS: S09456. $19.95.
Laser: LD70086. $34.98.
Oliver Stone, USA, 1988, 103 mins.

The Theatre of Tadeusz Kantor
A unique documentary on the work of a legendary genius of theatre, Tadeusz Kantor. Filmmaker Denis Bablet traces Kantor's roots as a visual artist in Poland and explores his ingenious methods of designing the props which become living sculptures in his extraordinary theatre productions. The program features rare scenes of Kantor at work with the dedicated actors in his troupe, Cricot 2. In a unique scene, Kantor is on-stage and "conducts" the actors much as a symphony conductor leads an orchestra. Extensive segments from some of Kantor's most famous works, *Wielopole, Wielopole* and *The Dead Class*, are also included. Narrated in English. 144 mins.
VHS: S14812. $59.95.

The Three Sisters
Shelley Winters, Sandy Dennis, Geraldine Page and Kevin McCarthy star in this famed Actor's Studio production of the equally famous Chekhov play.
VHS: S14677. $59.95.
Paul Bogart, USA, 1965, 167 mins.

West Side Story
An extravaganza acclaimed for its musical and choreographic expertise. Score by Leonard Bernstein, lyrics by Stephen Sondheim, choreography by Jerome Robbins, starring Natalie Wood (her songs were dubbed by Marni Nixon) and Rita Moreno.
VHS: S01444. $19.95.
Laser: CAV, widescreen. LD70485. $124.95.
Laser: CLV, widescreen. LD70486. $69.95.
Robert Wise/Jerome Robbins, USA, 1961, 152 mins.

Who's Afraid of Virginia Woolf?
Based on Edward Albee's smash hit play; Elizabeth Taylor and Richard Burton star in the story of the love-hate relationship between a middle-aged professor and his vitriolic but seductive wife.
DVD: DV60065. $24.98.
VHS: S01737. $19.98.
Laser: LD70705. $39.98.
Mike Nichols, USA, 1966, 129 mins.

25 Great Cultural Documentaries

The Amish Folk
An overview of the Amish of southeastern Pennsylvania, including their origins, church meetings, crafts, homes, farms, and schools. With Amish songs and hymns on the soundtrack. 32 mins.
VHS: $15535. $45.00.

Ancient Mysteries
Using modern technology, scientific analysis, high-tech evidence and recent archaeological developments, the films in the *Ancient Mysteries* series are on the cutting edge of discovery.
Ark of the Covenant. This real-life search for the Ark of the Covenant is based on new interpretations of the Bible. The possible whereabouts of this ancient artifact remain a mystery that must still be solved. This tape offers new answers to the age-old question: whatever became of this sacred repository? 50 mins.
VHS: $21687. $19.95.
Enigma of the Dead Sea Scrolls. In 1947, a shepherd boy found the Dead Sea Scrolls. Originally hailed as a window to the origins of Christianity, they were soon removed from public scrutiny. This is the story of the discovery, authenticity and cover-up that make these artifacts so intriguing. 50 mins.
VHS: $23106. $19.95.
Shroud of Turin. This artifact is held by many to be the burial shroud of Jesus Christ. Investigations into the history and the composition of this shroud are documented on this video. Conflicting results may well ensure that the true nature of this cloth remains a mystery. USA, 1995, 50 mins.
VHS: $26100. $19.95.
Who Wrote the Bible?: Probing the Eternal Mysteries Behind the Origins of the Holy Scriptures. Richard Kiley and Jean Simmons host this serious documentary filmed on location in the Holy Land. Leading Biblical scholars discuss the latest scientific research on the world's most widely read book and tackle questions regarding Moses, the Torah, the Dead Sea Scrolls and more. The theological insights and scientific facts on the Holy Scriptures will leave the faithful inspired and the scholarly fascinated. Two-volume set. 1994-1995, 150 mins.
VHS: $27203. $29.95.

bell hooks on Video:
Cultural Criticism & Transformation
bell hooks, distinguished professor of English, City College of New York, and author of 14 books of commentary, criticism and autobiography, makes a compelling argument for the transformative power of cultural criticism, in this extensively illustrated two-part tape. 70 mins.
VHS: $31887. $195.00.

China Rising
For 70 years the "Bamboo Curtain" protected China from the eyes of the West. Now, for the first time, Western filmmakers have been allowed inside the world's most enigmatic country to reveal its secret history. Never-before-seen archival footage—including coverage of the Cultural Revolution—and extraordinary interviews with warlords, revolutionaries and ordinary citizens offer a privileged view of "Asia's sleeping giant." Nominated for the Japan Prize, the world's most prestigious educational award. Includes three 50-minute videos.
VHS: $30151. $49.95.

Civilization
Historian Kenneth Clark explores the civilization of mankind from the Dark Ages to the 20th century, in 13 programs.
Programs 1 & 2. In *The Skin of Our Teeth*, Clark undergoes a spiritual quest of the Dark Ages, exploring the Byzantine Ravenna, the Celtic Hebrides, Norwegian Vikings and Charlemagne's chapel at Aachen. In *The Great Thaw*, the program studies the rebirth of European civilization in the 12th century.
VHS: $18733. $19.95.

Programs 3 & 4. Clark assesses the accomplishments and evolution of late Middle Ages architecture and culture in France and Italy in *Romance and Beauty*. In *Man—The Measure of All Things*, Clark examines the revitalization of classicism, exploring the Renaissance centers of Urbino and Mantua.
VHS: $18734. $19.95.
Programs 5 & 6. In the first program, *The Hero as Artist*, Clark examines the Papal Room in the 16th century and its influence on the art of Michelangelo, Raphael and da Vinci. In *Protest and Communication*, Clark considers the impact of Reformation and the various artists influenced in Germany, France and England.
VHS: $18735. $19.95.
Programs 7 & 8. In *Grandeur and Obedience*, Clark looks at Rome and the Counter-Reformation, the place of Michelangelo and Bernini, the impact and extensive influence of the Catholic Church, and the dreamy splendor of St. Peter's. In the second program, *The Light of Experience*, technological innovations such as the telescope and microscope allow for greater information and detailed interpretation.
VHS: $18736. $19.95.
Programs 9 & 10. Clark notes how rococo architecture is mirrored in the musical flow and complex symmetry of 18th century composers Bach, Handel, Haydn and Mozart in *The Pursuit of Happiness*. In the follow-up program, *The Smile of Reason*, dissention and uproar in 18th century Paris suggests the pre-revolutionary dissatisfaction with the ancien regime. Clark also studies the expansive European palaces and Jefferson's Monticello.
VHS: $18737. $19.95.
Programs 11 & 12. In *The Worship of Nature*, the belief that divinity guides nature undermined Christianity's authority and unleashed the Romantic Movement. In *The Fallacies of Hope*, Clark explores the dissolution of the French aristocracy and how the Revolution led to Napoleon and a collection of authoritarian bureaucracies. The Romantic artists reveal their disillusionment.
VHS: $18738. $19.95.
Program 13. In *Heroic Materialism*, Clark concludes the series by assessing the materialism and humanitarianism of 20th century ideas and thought, from Britain's industrial landscape to the functional skyscrapers of contemporary New York City.
VHS: $18739. $19.95.
Civilization, Complete Set.
VHS: $18740. $119.95.

Deepak Chopra: Body, Mind and Soul
Chopra's view on the nexus between these three vital elements of human existence has been read by nearly six million readers in his five best sellers. This two-tape set brings his unique teachings to an easy-to-follow video format. 120 mins.
VHS: $27759. $39.98.

Easter Island: A Vanished Culture
Its inhabitants once called it "Te Pito o te Hanua," or the Navel of the World. The gigantic stone statues, artistic temple platforms and mysterious writings have puzzled explorers and anthropologists. This program examines theories that attempt to uncover exactly who created these artifacts and what then happened to them. Information from the recently deciphered "rongo runes" is highlighted. 44 mins.
VHS: $22926. $19.95.

The Hemp Revolution
Hemp, or marijuana, is not just a mild recreational drug. Long before it became notorious for its mind-altering qualities, it was widely grown for its resilient fibers and was used for everything from industrial strength rope to fine cloth. This documentary makes the case that growing hemp is a sound ecological enterprise with very pleasant side effects.
VHS: $29800. $29.95.
Anthony Clark, USA, 1995, 72 mins.

Indians of North America, Collection II
The well-regarded book from Chelsea House Publishers inspired this video series about Native Americans. Both historical and contemporary struggles are examined by consulting historians and living tribe members. This series tackles the myths and misconceptions that have long obscured the truth about the first Americans. Each episode is 30 minutes long.
A History of Native Americans.
VHS: S23641. $39.95.
The Chinook.
VHS: S23638. $39.95.
The Creek.
VHS: S23639. $39.95.
The Crow.
VHS: S23640. $39.95.
The Huron.
VHS: S23642. $39.95.
The Lenape.
VHS: S23643. $39.95.
The Menominee.
VHS: S23644. $39.95.
The Narragansett (Enishkeetompauog).
VHS: S23645. $39.95.
The Potawatomi (Bode wad mi).
VHS: S23646. $39.95.
The Pueblo.
VHS: S23647. $39.95.
The Ten-Volume Set.
VHS: S23648. $399.50.

Jung on Film
Share a special viewing experience! This compelling film interview with Carl Gustav Jung represents a rare record of an original genius. In *Jung on Film* the pioneering psychologist tells us about his collaboration with Sigmund Freud, the insights he gained from listening to his patients' dreams, and the fascinating turns taken by his own life. Dr. Richard I. Evans, a 1989 Presidential Medal of Freedom nominee, interviews Jung, giving us a rare glimpse into the life and career of this important historical figure. 77 mins.
VHS: S13738. $29.95.

La Belle Epoque
Douglas Fairbanks Jr. narrates how the elite of London, Paris and New York society lived in that carefree age when the pursuit of beauty and romance was a way of life, aided by newsreel clips, paintings, photographs, period costumes and re-enactments. Interviews with La Belle Epoque greats Erte, Jacques-Henri Lartigue and suffragist leader Enid Goulden-Bach provide individual and often idiosyncratic memories of the age. 105 mins.
VHS: S04650. $39.95.

Many Faces of Homelessness
Homelessness is a worldwide and growing phenomenon. The problems of homeless people are poorly understood and are challenging societies and individuals in new ways. Being homeless can mean a lot more than being houseless. It is also a symptom of value breakdowns in society. Special insights from those involved with homeless people bring to life video features from Hong Kong and Bolivia. Produced by Maryknoll Media. 28 mins.
VHS: S06266. $24.95.

Mythos with Joseph Campbell
Just before he died in 1987, Joseph Campbell made a final tour of the United States. Based on this tour, this essential five-part series presents the first volume of Campbell's compelling vision of the "One Great Story" of our human nature. The first in a series entitled *The Shaping of Our Western Tradition*, *Mythos* showcases what Campbell did best—telling profound and powerful stories from the wealth of the world's great cultures. Commentary by Susan Sarandon. 5 hours on five videocassettes.
VHS: S30981. $99.95.

The Orient Express
See the rise, decline and re-birth of the Orient Express, the world's most celebrated train, in this fascinating video. Home to royalty and racketeers, stars and statesmen, courtesans and charlatans, the Orient Express linked the great capitals of Western Europe with the Danube, the Balkans and lands far beyond. Includes rare archival scenes of the golden age of rail travel, interviews with staff, and unique behind-the-scenes footage to tell how the train is run, victualled and maintained on both sides of the channel. 60 mins.
VHS: S30188. $14.95.

Power of Myth
The brilliant historian/mythologist/thinker Joseph Campbell, in a dialogue with Bill Moyers, explores the foundations of culture and our being in this incredible six-part series. Complete set.
VHS: S07590. $124.95.

The Presence of the Goddess
The development and history of the Goddess in western civilization is finally uncovered and documented in this intriguing video. Her influence has had a humanizing effect throughout successive ages. Her inspiring ways connect all people with the earth we live on. 46 mins.
VHS: S21599. $39.95.

Tantra: The Art of Conscious Loving
Charles and Caroline Muir, the foremost Western educators of this ancient Indian art form, bring the secrets of better sex and intimacy to western audiences. 70 mins.
VHS: S30764. $39.95.

Terror in the Minefields
Investigate the terror and tragedy of Cambodia's deadly legacy of mine fields. 60 mins.
VHS: S28663. $19.95.

Treehouse People: Cannibal Justice
The Korowai are an elusive people who have maintained their unique way of life for thousands of years in the rain forest. On this Smithsonian Expedition, this isolated group of people is revealed in all their mystery. They may even practice ritual cannibalism. 50 mins.
VHS: S25869. $24.95.

The West
Ken Burns' 12-1/2 hour epic saga of the personal triumphs and tragedies involved in the expansion of the U.S. West. This nine-volume set, narrated by Peter Coyote, begins before European settlement and continues into the 20th century, overturning old stereotypes and discovering new personalities. Individual episodes include *The People* (82 mins.), *Empire upon the Trails* (84 mins.), *The Speck of the Future* (84 mins.), *Death Runes Riot* (84 mins.), *The Grandest Enterprise Under God* (84 mins.), *Fight No More* (85 mins.), *The Geography of Hope* (84 mins.), *Ghost Dance* (58 mins.) and *One Sky Above Us* (62 mins.).
VHS: S28618. $149.98.
Stephen Ives, USA, 1996

Wisdom of the Dream: C.G. Jung and His Work in the World
This three-part series traces Jung's work and message throughout his life—his split with Freud, the major works published on dreams and the psychology of religion, his travels, in particular to New Mexico, and his discovery of the collective conscious. The director uses authentic visual references of Jung's home and consulting room and the film contains previously undiscovered home movies shot during Jung's travels to Africa, plus an interview recorded in 1956.
Wisdom of the Dream Vol. 1.
VHS: S10303. $29.95.
Wisdom of the Dream Vol. 2.
VHS: S10311. $29.95.
Wisdom of the Dream Vol. 3.
VHS: S10312. $29.95.

With a Silent Mind
A richly detailed biographical portrait of Krishnamurti's life and teachings produced by Evelyne Blay. The film blends Krishnamurti's own deep insights with the impressions of scientists, authors, educators, students and friends, and with extraordinary archival footage from India, England and America in the 20's and 30's. 60 mins.
VHS: S12482. $29.95.

The Hemp Revolution

150 Best
Animation Videos

Adventures of Prince Achmed
The first animated feature film—a landmark of cinema created in Weimar Germany with Lotte Reiniger's unique paper cutout silhouette technique. The stories, based on tales from *The Arabian Nights*, come wonderfully alive in this sensitive and imaginative work. A truly beautiful film that must be seen to be believed. Transferred from an original tinted and toned print. B&W.
VHS: $22881. $19.95.

Akira
Neo-Tokyo is about to explode. Filled with action and stylized violence, this animated science-fiction feature was based on an equally notorious Japanese graphic (read "comic-book") novel. A gang of motorcycle-riding teenagers, living in post-apocalyptic Neo-Tokyo, must stop one of their own who goes on a rampage after gaining telekinetic powers in a renegade government experiment. Letterboxed. Original Japanese with English subtitles.
VHS: $16691. $39.95.
Katsuhiro Otomo, Japan, 1989, 124 mins.

Alchemist of the Surreal
Five mixed-media animated stop-motion short films from the director of *Alice*: *Jabberwocky* (1971), *Dimensions of Dialogue* (1982), *The Last Trick* (1964), *Punch & Judy* (1966) and *Etcetera* (1966).
VHS: $14554. $24.95.

Alexeieff & Parker
In their Paris studio, Russian-born artist/filmmaker Alexander Alexeieff and his American wife, Claire Parker, show and explain how they create pictures on the instrument they invented, the pinscreen (l'ecran de'epingles), in *Alexeieff at the Pinboard (A Propos de Jivago)* (1960, 8 mins.). *The Nose (Le Nez)* (1963, 11 mins.) is Gogol's celebrated short story in pinscreen animation, without words, in fantastic moving pictures that capture the scene and spirit of 19th century Russia. *Night on Bald Mountain (Une Nuit sur le Mont Chauve)* (1933, 8 mins.) is the first film made on pinboard. In this reknowned illustration of Modest Moussorgsky's tone poem, goblins, skeletons and other fantastic creatures perform outlandish three-dimensional effects. Animator Norman McLaren listed the film "first and foremost" among the animated films he most admired and liked. "Above all it is the quality of Alexeieff's imagination that stirs me profoundly," McLaren said. 27 mins.
VHS: $30223. $75.00.

Alice
Jan Svankmajer, the Czech master of animation, has fulfilled a lifetime ambition in this interpretation of *Alice in Wonderland*. Svankmajer's Alice remains true to Carroll's original, but bears the stamp of his own distinctive style and obsessions. Combination of animation and live action.
VHS: $10942. $19.95.

Alice in Wonderland
One of the most faithful adaptations of Lewis Carroll's satirical daydream, this long-lost masterpiece was produced and directed by master puppetoonist Lou Bunin in England. The film starts with a live-action prologue, then enters the abstract Wonderland with incomparable puppets and Carol Marsh as Alice.
VHS: $06599. $24.95.

Allegro Non Troppo
Bruno Bozzetto's irreverent tribute to Disney's *Fantasia*. From outrageously funny satire to breathtaking lyricism, this film visualizes six popular works by Debussy, Dvorak, Ravel, Sibelius, Vivaldi and Stravinsky. Maurizio Nichetti stars in the live-action interludes between each piece, which are now subtitled.
VHS: $00035. $29.95.

Anima Mundi
This collaboration between director Godfrey Reggio (*Koyaanisqatsi*) and composer Philip Glass (*Einstein on the Beach*) is a naturalistic documentary on the relationship between humans and animals. The film uses a series of close encounters between humans and animals of varying sizes to showcase the diversity of the animal kingdom. "The proud procession of life forms has an incandescence and mystery that neither still photographs nor museum exhibitions can begin to capture" (*New York Times*).
VHS: $19593. $19.98.
Laser: CAV. LD72437. $29.99.
Godfrey Reggio, USA, 1993, 50 mins.

Animalympics
In this animated spoof of the Olympics, animals compete from all over the world. Voices of Gilda Radner, Billy Crystal, Harry Shearer and Michael Fremer.
VHS: $29598. $12.95.

Animated Commercials #1
Did you know that Winston cigarettes originally sponsored the Flintstones? Gaze in wonderment as Fred and Barney hide out behind the house puffing on cigs. A wonderful compilation of animated characters, including classic Raid commercials, Shamus Culhane's Muriel Cigars commercials, the Hamm's Bear, EZ-Pop popcorn, Maypo and Westinghouse.
VHS: $29599. $24.95.

Animated Commercials #2
Heinz Beans, Yoo Hoo soft drink, Mr. & Mrs Potato Head with Hasbro Kid, B.C. gang for Marathon, Screaming Yellow Zonkers: Celebrities, Alka Seltzer: When You and Your Stomach Disagree (voice of Gene Wilder), Schweppes Bitter Orange, Schweppes Bitter Lemon, Elsie the Cow, Old Gold Cigarettes, Good 'n Plenty, Cocoa Puffs, Hostess Choco-Diles, Chesterfield Cigarettes, Nabisco, Hydrox Cookies, Winston Cigarettes: Pixilated Matchbooks, Rinso Detergent, Chunky Chocolate, Old Nick Chocolate, Bumble Bee Tuna, Clanky Chocolate Syrup, Muriel Cigars: Fresh Tin, Puma Soft Drink, Ipana Toothpaste, FrostyOs, Trix and many, many more!
VHS: $29600. $24.95.

Animated Commercials #3
Beech Nut Fruit Stripe Gum, Cheerios Kid, Bromo Seltzer, Lustre Creme, Ideal Toys: Mr. Machine, Esso, Bab-O Cleanser, Wildroot, Band-Aid, P.F. Flyers, Mattell: Thunder Burp Machine Gun, Cheerios Kid, Ipana, Armour Star Franks, Baker's Instant Chocolate: Jiminy Cricket, Trix, Snickers, Hostess: Captain Cupcake, Frosty-O's, Lucky Charms, Twinkles, Hamms Bear: Pie Fight, Ritz Crackers, Oreos, Fig Newtons, Lorna Doones, Sugar Wafers, Chocolate Chip Pecans, Vanilla Wafers, Shredded Wheat, Peter Pan Peanut Butter: Tinkerbell, Jell-O, Log Cabin Syrup, Peter Pan Peanut Butter: P-Nuttiest, Canada Dry: Dumbo, General Mills: Pick A Pack, Matty's Funday Funnies: Casper The Ghost, and many, many more!
VHS: $29601. $24.95.

Animated Commercials #4
Ajax: Foaming Cleanser Elves, Muriel Cigars: Pick Me Up & Smoke Me Sometime (Culhane), Quaker Puffed Wheat & Rice, Playhouse 90 Opening Title,

The Aristocats

Peter Pan Peanut Butter: Tinkerbell/Shadow Pictures, Cheerios Kid, Hi Ho Crackers: Sunshine Bakers, Coca Cola, Nabisco Wheat & Rice Honeys: Buffalo Bee, Lorna Doones, Keebler Cinnamon Crisp, Beech Nut Gum: Jazz Combo, Yellow Pages, Gillette Super Speed Razor, Dixie Cup Dispenser, Campbells BBQ Beans, DX Gasoline, Star Kist: Charlie The Tuna/Studious Type, Colgate Toothpaste, Count Chocula & Frankenberry, Funny Face Drink Mix, Cheerios: Bullwinkle/Watch Where You're Going, Vaseline Hair Tonic: Talking Sink and many, many more!
VHS: $29602. $24.95.

Animated Commercials #5
Fig Newton, Salada, Bond Bread, Coke, D-Frost, Macintosh Apple, Nabisco, Cheerios, Quisp & Quake, Cocoa Puffs, Corn Bursts, Whistle Snack, Sugar Smacks, Milk Bone, Bosco, Good 'n Plenty, Zoom Cereal, Ideal Bread, RCA, Sylvania, Lucky Stripe, Vitalis and many more.
VHS: $29603. $24.95.

Animated Commercials #6
An internal sales film for Aurora's "New Generation" toy line (ca. 1967) starring Fred & Barney, an interview with Lou Gifford discussing his studio's TV commercial animation (Lestoil) and the technique of storyboarding and cel animation, Rocky & Bullwinkle for General Mills cereals, Charlie the Tuna, Frito Bandito, Cheerios Kid, Trix Rabbit, Tony Tiger, the 1969 Plymouth cars with the Roadrunner and Wile E. Coyote, Quisp & Quake, Donald Duck and Porky Pig Soaky Toys, the 1964 Falcon with Charlie Brown and Linus, Chrysler cars and much, much more!
VHS: $29604. $24.95.

Animation Celebration Vol. 2
Seventeen titles: *ASIFA Children's Film Beat Dedication* (Bob Sabiston/USA), *A Crushed World* (Boyo Kanev/Bulgaria), *Eternity* (Sheryl Sardina/USA), *Finger Wave* (Gyula Nagy/Hungary), *Goodnight Norma...Goodnight Milton* (John Schnall/USA), *Lady and the Lamp* (John Lasseter/USA), *Lazar* (Gavrilo Gnatovich/USA), *Paradisia* (Marcy Page/USA), *Pencil Dance* (Chris Casady/USA), *Propagandance* (Tom Sito/USA), *Quinoscopo #2 (Juan Padron/Cuba)*, *Salome* (Maurizio Forestieri/Italy), *A Salute to Olive Jar* (USA), *Scaredy Cat* (Paul Clarehout/USA), *Suspicious Circumstances* (Jim Blashfield/USA), *25 Ways to Quit Smoking* (Bill Plympton/USA) and *Umbabarauma* (Susan Young & Mike Smith/UK).
VHS: $25826. $29.95.

Animation Celebration Vol. 3
Twenty titles: *The Animated Star Spangled Banner* (Skip Battaglia/USA), *Bonehead* (Michael A. Kory & Peter Conn/USA), *Darkness, Light, Darkness* (Jan Svankmajer/Czechoslovakia), *Fumo* (Giorgio Guglielmetti/Italy), *Lava Jr.* (Randy Bauer/USA), *Mr. Tao* (Bruno Bozetto/Italy), *New Fangled* (George Griffin/USA), *A Nice Day in the Country* (Chris Hinton/Canada), *Personality Software* (Sylvie Fefer/Canada), *Plymptoons* (Bill Plympton/USA), *Pounse* (Mikhail Aldashin/USSR), *Prehistoric Beast* (Phil

Tippett/USA), *The Reading Room* (John Schnall/USA), *Snowie and The Seven Dorps* (Candy Kugel & Vincent Cafarelli/USA), *Still Life* (Georges Le Piouffle/France), *This Is Not Frank's Planet* (Mike Wellins & Mark Swain/USA), *War Story* (Peter Lord/UK), *Welcome* (Alexei Karaev/USSR), *Wiseman* (Bill Plympton/USA) and *Zeno Reads a Newspaper* (Ferenc Cako/Hungary).
VHS: $25825. $29.95.

Animation Celebration Vol. 4
Nineteen titles: *The Boss* (Alison Snowden & David Fine/UK), *The Button* (Robert Sakayants/Armenia), *Canfilm* (Zlatin Radev/Bulgaria), *Dancing* (Bruno Bozetto/Italy), *Fantastic Person* (Candy Guard/UK), *The Green Beret* (Stephen Hillenburg/USA), *The Hunter* (Mikhail Aldashin/USSR), *Madcap* (Phil Denslow/USA), *Office Space* (Mike Judge/USA), *Okay Tex* (Rumen Petkov/Bulgaria), *Pre-Hysterical Daze* (Gavrilo Gnatovich/USA), *Quinoscopo ³*(Juan Padron/Cuba), *RRRINGG!* (Paul de Nooijer/Netherlands), *A Smaller World 'Big Baby'* (Corky Quakenbush/USA), *The Song of Wolfgang the Intrepid* (Mikhail Tumelya/USSR), *The Tale of Nippoless Nippleby* (DNA Productions/USA), *Tarzan* (Taku Furukawa/Japan), *Unsavory Avery* (John Schnall/USA) and *Weeds* (Thomas Stellmach/Germany).
VHS: $25827. $29.95.

Animation Propaganda
Four non-theatrical animated shorts. *Easy Does It* (1946/Hugh Harman) is a moral tale promoting Stokely VanCamp foods which is distinguished by its lavish production values. As good as anything Harman did at MGM, this short contains adult sexual innuendo and lots of campy laughs. *Winky the Watchman* (1951/Hugh Harman) is another lavish production promoting good dental hygiene. *Cleanliness Brings Health* (1946/Disney) teaches our backwards South American neighbors the rudiments of sanitation and disease prevention. *The Winged Scourge* (1954/Disney) shows the Seven Dwarfs eradicating the mosquito to prevent malaria.
VHS: $09709. $17.95.

Animation Vol. 1: The Beginning
A survey of animation from 1906 to 1927, including *Humorous Phases of Funny Faces, La Rateleur, Fantasmagoria, Mobiliu Fedele, Little Nemo, Revenge of the Kinematograph Cameraman, Professor Bonehead Is Shipwrecked, Gertie the Dinosaur, Dinosaur and the Missing Link, The Sinking of The Lusitania, Bobby Bumps Puts a Beanery on the Bum, Modelling/Bubbles, Laugh-O-Grams, Puss 'n Boots, Alice on the Farm, Small Town Sheriff, Felix in Hollywood, Oswald* and *The Mechanical Cow*. B&W.
VHS: $04816. $29.95.

Animation Vol. 2
More early animation, including *Dream of a Rarebit Fiend* (1906), *Gertie* (the true 1914 McCay version), *Krazy Kat* (1916), *The Flying House* (1921), *Surprise* (1923), *Felix in Fairyland* (1925) and *Alice's Egg Plant* (1925). B&W.
VHS: $08869. $24.95.

The Aristocats
Available on home video for the first time, *The Aristocats* was the last film supervised by Walt himself. When a millionairess names Duchess and her three kittens her sole heirs, the faithful old butler plots to do away with the adorable felines. Duchess enlists the aid of a band of jazz-playing alley cats and a couple of hillbilly basset hounds to secure her inheritance. HiFi Stereo.
VHS: $27539. $26.95.
Laser: LD75843. $29.95.

Art and Jazz in America
A four volume series by Faith and John Hubley. **Art and Jazz in America: John and Faith Hubley's Of Men and Demons**. Quincy Jones composed the masterful score for this striking animated film about a simple farmer. This farmer confronts nature with a barrage of technical measures. Also included: *Of Stars and Men*, a short film about man and the universe set to music from Bach, Beethoven, Handel, Mozart and Vivaldi. 65 mins.
VHS: $24277. $29.95.
Art and Jazz in America: John and Faith Hubley's The Hole. The title film won an Academy Award. It is about two construction workers debating the fate of the world. Dizzy Gillespie and George Matthews provide the voices for these animated characters. *The Hat* is a similar short animated film featuring

Gillespie and Dudley Moore as soldiers patrolling a border. In *Dig* Quincy Jones provides the score while Maureen Stapleton and Jack Warden provide the voices for a fantasy about a boy, his dog and their unique adventure. 58 mins.
VHS: $24278. $29.95.

Art and Jazz in America: John and Faith Hubley's Voyage to Next. The title animated film was nominated for an Academy Award. It features the voices of Maureen Stapleton and Dizzy Gillespie as Mother Earth and Father Time. Gillespie also supplies the music. Five other short films are included: *Tender Game, Eggs, Urbanissmo, Harlem Wednesday* and *Adventures of an **. Music by Benny Carter, Ella Fitzgerald, Lionel Hampton and others. 51 mins.
VHS: $24279. $29.95.

Babar: The Movie
Babar must save his kingdom from certain destruction by Rataxes and his band of invading rhinos in this full-length theatrical feature. EP Speed.
VHS: $11696. $12.95.

Bambi
The classic animated Disney feature about a young deer named Bambi, who looses his mother and learns to fend for himself with other members of the forest family like rabbits, owls and skunks. May be too intense for young viewers.
VHS: $08700. $26.95.
David Hand, USA, 1942, 69 mins.

Beastly Behavior
The wild but true sexual antics and bizarre mating rituals of more than 30 animals, insects, birds and sea creatures are hilariously animated and explained. Uproariously funny, often dangerous, always fascinating. With sidesplitting narration and special insights by the British "Professor" Roger Knightly, *Beastly Behavior* will have you roaring with laughter as all the shocking, intimate details unfold.
VHS: $30481. $19.95.
Andy Wyatt, Great Britain, 1996, 45 mins.

Beavis & Butt-head Do America
In their hilarious feature film debut, Beavis and Butt-head go on a mad, mad, mad, mad journey across America in search of video stimulation after their TV set is stolen. When they try to score with a crime babe (Demi Moore) who plants top secret information on the unsuspecting Beavis, the moronic duo find themselves contending with FBI agents, overstimulation and outbursts from Beavis' alter-ego, the caffeine-induced Cornholio. A comic tour-de-farce. Featuring the voices of Mike Judge, Robert Stack, Cloris Leachman and Eric Bogosian.
VHS: $31388. $19.95.
Mike Judge, USA, 1996, 82 mins.

Best of the Simpsons
For the first time ever, *The Simpsons* is available on home video. Creator Matt Groening has hand-picked six uncut episodes from the first season, and Fox Video has tossed in an original *Simpsons* short from *The Tracey Ullman Show* on each tape.
Volume 1. *There's No Disgrace Like Home* and *Life on the Fast Lane*. Plus a short from *The Tracey Ullman Show*. 50 mins.
VHS: $32447. $9.95.
Volume 2. *Bart the General* and *Moaning Lisa*. Plus a short from *The Tracey Ullman Show*. 50 mins.
VHS: $32448. $9.95.
Volume 3. *The Crepes of Wrath* and *Krusty Gets Busted*. Plus a short from *The Tracey Ullman Show*. 50 mins.
VHS: $32449. $9.95.
Best of the Simpsons 3-Pack. Volumes 1-3 in a collector's slipcase. 150 mins.
VHS: $32446. $24.95.

Betty Boop Definitive Collection Vol. 1: The Birth of Betty
The first volume of the collection leads off with an introduction by Max Fleischer's son, Richard, followed by eight of the earliest Betty cartoons. The first few show Betty as a nameless walk-on playing to the top-billed star, Bimbo. This proto-Betty sports long dog-ears (but nothing else especially canine) that gradually become less prominent as both she and Bimbo evolve away from dogginess in later appearances. The final cartoon on the tape shows Betty as we're accustomed to seeing her, and also gives her top billing for the first time. Eight titles: *Dizzy Dishes* ('30), *Barnacle Bill* ('30), *Mysterious Mose* ('30), *The Bum Bandit* ('31), *Silly Scandals*

('31), *Bimbo's Express* ('31), *Minding the Baby* ('31) and *Mask-A-Raid* ('31).
VHS: $30344. $7.95.

Betty Boop Definitive Collection Vol. 2: Pre-Code & Jazzy Guest Stars
The first half of the tape features Betty's more racy outings from the pre-Hays Code days. Then the second half showcases the great musical cartoons, guest-starring Louis Armstrong, Cab Calloway and others. Fourteen titles. Pre-Code: *Boop-Oop-A-Doop* ('32), *S.O.S.* ('32), *Chess-Nuts* ('32), *A Hunting We Will Go* ('32), *Betty Boop's Bizzy Bee* ('32), *Betty Boop's Bamboo Isle* ('32) and *Betty Boop for President* ('32). Jazzy Guest Stars: *Minnie the Moocher* ('32), *I'll Be Glad When You're Dead You Rascal You* ('32), *Snow-White* ('33), *The Old Man of the Mountain* ('33), *Kitty from Kansas City* ('31), *Rudy Vallee Melodies* ('32) and *You Try Somebody Else* ('32).
VHS: $30345. $9.95.

Betty Boop Definitive Collection Vol. 3: Surrealism & Prime Betty
The first half of the tape highlights the trademark Fleischer surrealism with some of the wildest shorts Betty made, and the second half is packed with a variety of the choicest Boop cartoons. Sixteen titles. Surrealism: *Bimbo's Initiation* ('31), *The Robot ('32)*, *Crazy Town* ('32), *Betty Boop M.D.* ('32), *Betty Boop's Ups and Downs* ('32), *Betty Boop's May Party* ('33), *Red Hot Mamma* ('34) and *Betty Boop in Ha! Ha! Ha!* ('34). Prime Betty: *Admission Free* ('32), *Just a Gigolo* ('32), *Betty Boop's Museum* ('32), *Is My Palm Read* ('33), Betty Boop's Penthouse ('33), *Betty Boop's Birthday Party* ('33), *Betty Boop's Ker-Choo* ('33) and *Morning Noon and Night* ('33).
VHS: $30346. $9.95.

Betty Boop Definitive Collection Vol. 4: Musical Madness & Fairy Tales
This tape features eight of Betty's music-driven cartoons and seven Betty Boop-style fairy tales. Musical Madness: *Any Little Girl That's a Nice Little Girl* ('31), *The Dancing Fool* ('32), *I Heard* ('33), *Let Me Call You Sweetheart* ('32), *Oh! How I Hate to Get Up in the Morning* ('32), *Romantic Melodies* ('32), *Popular Melodies* ('33) and *Sally Swing* ('38). Fairy Tales and Fantasy: *Mother Goose Land* ('33), *Parade of the Wooden Soldiers* ('33), *Poor Cinderella* ('34), *Jack and the Beanstalk* ('31), *Dizzy Red Riding Hood* ('31), *Betty Boop's Hallowe'en Party* ('33) and *Betty in Blunderland* ('34).
VHS: $30347. $9.95.

Betty Boop Definitive Collection Vol. 5: Curtain Call & Betty and Grampy
Eight of Betty's stage show musical cartoons and eight cartoons with the crazy inventor Grampy are featured. Curtain Call: *Betty Boop's Crazy Inventions* ('33), *Stopping the Show* ('32), *The Limited* ('32), *A Language All My Own* ('35), *Keep in Style* ('34), *Making Stars* ('35), *The New Deal Show* ('37) and *A Song a Day* ('36). Betty & Grampy: *Betty Boop and Grampy* ('35), *Grampy's Indoor Outing* ('36), *Be Human* ('36), *House Cleaning Blues* ('37), *The Impractical Joker* ('37), *The Candid Candidate* ('37), *Service with a Smile* ('37) and *Zula Hula* ('37).
VHS: $30348. $9.95.

Betty Boop Definitive Collection Vol. 6: Betty's Boys & New Friends
This volume features eight cartoons with Betty's various suitors, and eight outings with various featured buddies. Betty's Boys: *Any Rags* ('32), *Betty Boop's Life Guard* ('34), *She Wronged Him Right* ('34), *No! No! A Thousand Times No!* ('35), *Betty Boop's Prize Show* ('34), *Betty Boop and The Little King* ('36), *There's Something About a Soldier* ('34) and *Wiffle Piffle in The Hot Air Salesman* ('37). New Friends: *Betty Boop's Big Boss* ('33), *Betty Boop with Henry the Funniest Living American* ('35), *Betty Boop and Little Henry* ('36), *The Foxy Hunter* ('37), *On with the New* ('38), *Betty Boop's Trial* ('34), *Judge for a Day* ('35) and *Betty Boop's Rise to Fame* ('34).
VHS: $30349. $9.95.

Betty Boop Definitive Collection Vol. 8: Betty and Pudgy & Pudgy and Pals
Eight more cartoons with Betty and Pudgy, plus six assorted Betty cartoons. Also features closing comments by Richard Fleischer. Betty & Pudgy: *You're Not Built That Way* ('36), *Happy You and Merry Me* ('36), *Training Pigeons* ('36), *Making Friends* ('36), *Pudgy Takes a Bow-Wow* ('37), *Pudgy*

Picks a Fight ('37), *Ding Dong Doggie* ('37) and *Riding the Rails* ('38). Pudgy & Pals: *Out of the Inkwell* ('38), *The Swing School* ('38), *The Watchman* ('38), *Thrills and Chills* ('38), *My Friend the Monkey* ('39) and *Baby Be Good* ('35).
VHS: S30351. $9.95.

Betty Boop

Betty Boop Definitive Collection Boxed Set
All eight tapes in a collector's slipcase. Includes a mini-booklet, *Boopliography*.
VHS: S30002. $69.95.

British Animation Invasion
Twenty-two titles: *Bluefields Express* (Charlie Fletcher Watson), *Body Beautiful* (Joanna Quinn), *Childhood of a Prophet* (David Lodge), *Creature Comforts* (Nick Park), *Dolphins* (Ian Andrew), *Door* (David Anderson), *Going Equipped* (Peter Lord), *Ident* (Richard Goleszowski), *Jollity Farm* (David Stone), *Jonathan Hodgson Showreel* (Jonathan Hodgson), *Snapper Showreel* (Matt Forest), *Mike Smith Showreel* (Mike Smith), *Moanalogue* (Candy Guard), *Next* (Barry Purves), *Night Visitors* (Richard Ollive), *Picnic* (Paul Vester), *Prophet and Loss* (Jonathan Bairstow), *Strangers in Paradise* (Andrew Staveley), *Susan Young Showreel* (Susan Young), *Them* (Bill Mather), *What About Me* (Candy Guard) and *Wishful Thinking* (Candy Guard).
VHS: S25824. $29.95.

The Brothers Quay Vol. 1
About as far from Disney as you can get—the work of these expatriate American twins, the Brothers Quay, takes puppet animation to its furthest extremes. Terrence Rafferty calls their work "the loveliest, most hypnotic, most profoundly disturbing films ever made in that particular form." Two titles: *The Street of Crocodiles* ('86) and *The Cabinet of Jan Svankmajer* ('84). EP Speed.
VHS: S14160. $19.95.
Laser: LD72097. $49.95.

The Brothers Quay Vol. 2
With their exquisitely surreal animated puppets, Stephen and Timothy Quay create innovative short films with unsurpassed skill and dark humor. Three titles: *Epic of Gilgamesh* ('81), *Rehearsals for Extinct Anatomies* ('88) and *Nocturna Artificiala* ('79).
VHS: S14146. $19.95.
Laser: LD72098. $49.95.

Bugs Bunny/Roadrunner Movie
A compilation of Chuck Jones cartoons bridged together with new animation by most of his old staff. In addition to five complete cartoons—*Hareway to the Stars* ('58), *What's Opera Doc?* ('57), *Duck Amuck* ('53), *Bully for Bugs* ('53) and *Rabbit Fire* ('51)—excerpts from eight others are shown, along with an 11-minute *Roadrunner* compilation

consisting of 31 gags from 16 cartoons.
VHS: S01781. $14.95.

Carrotblanca
1995's theatrical short *Carrotblanca* is available on home video for the first time, along with 1990's *Box Office Bunny* and four classic shorts. Six titles: *Carrotblanca* ('95), *Dripalong Daffy* ('51), *Hare Do* ('49), *You Ought to Be in Pictures* ('40, colorized version), *The Scarlet Pumpernickel* ('50) and *Box Office Bunny* ('90).
VHS: S30357. $12.95.

Cartoon Collection Vol. 3: Coal Black & De Sebben Dwarfs
Sixteen titles: Porky Pig in *Calling Dr. Porky, Ali Baba Bound, Porky's Picnic, Little Beau Porky, Porky's Phony Express, Kristopher Kolumbus, Confusions of a Nutsy Spy* and *Scalp Trouble*. Daffy Duck in *The Daffy Doc* and *Tom Turk & Daffy*. Bosko in *Hold Anything* and *Bosko the Speed King*. Merrie Melodies include *Those Beautiful Dames, Coal Black and De Sebben Dwarfs, Eating on the Cuff* and *Billboard Frolics*.
VHS: S29612. $19.95.

Cartoon Collection Vol. 5: Racial Cartoons
Sixteen titles: *Bugs Bunny Bond Rally, Sing-a-long with Popeye, Plane Dumb, Porky's Hare Hunt, Mickey's Song, Little Black Sambo, Porky's Pooch, Joe Glow the Firefly, Porky's Movie Mystery, The Lone Stranger, Japoteurs, The Ballad of John Henry, Congo Jazz, I'll Be Glad When You're Dead, You Rascal You, Snap Happy, Jungle Jive* and preview trailers and intermission trailers. B&W/Color.
VHS: S29614. $19.95.

Cartoon Madness: The Fantastic Max Fleischer Cartoons
Leonard Maltin narrates a retrospective of Fleischer animation, covering the spectrum and providing rare, behind-the-scenes footage of the 3-D tabletop system and the new Florida studio. Many clips and much intelligent commentary. Eight complete cartoons: *She Reminds Me of You* (Screen Song), *Koko's Earth Control* ('27), *Bimbo's Initiation* ('31), *Snow White, Poor Cinderella, Dancing on the Moon, Raggedy Ann & Andy* and *Betty Boop's May Party*. Unbelievably clean film prints. The show glosses over Popeye and Superman, but is nonetheless well worth watching.
VHS: S28082. $14.95.

Cartoongate
An anthology of politically themed cartoons, including Chuck Jones' *Hell-Bent for Election*, in which Roosevelt's "Win the War Special" runs against the "Defeatist Limited." Ten titles: *Cartoongate!* ('96, Greg Ford), *Hell-Bent for Election* ('44, Chuck Jones), *Eisenhower Spots* ('52-'56), *No Substitute* ('96, Russell Calabrese), *A Political Cartoon* ('74, Joe Adamson), *Popeye for President* ('56, Famous Studios), *Jimmy Who?* ('75), *Reaganocchio* ('84, Ken Kimmelman), *Now Is the Time for All Good Men* ('60) and *Political Basketball* ('92, Greg Ford).
VHS: S28506. $14.95.

Cartoons Cel-ing Commercials Vol. 1
Animated commercials: Fred and Barney sneak cigarettes and Mr. Magoo pours beer. Superman and Tennessee Tuxedo sell soap. The Cheerios Kid saves Donald Duck from sharks. And sure you'd buy a Nash from Brer Rabbit. Mickey Mouse drawn by UPA for the 55 Rambler. Talking engines, giant safety eyes, Funny Face drinks, Mr. Bubble and more.
VHS: S13799. $19.95.

Cartoons Cel-ing Commercials Vol. 2
Animated commercials: Wash Tinkerbell's Peter Pan peanut butter down with Fred Flintstone's "Yabba Dabba Dew." Bucky Beaver and Annette Funicello, Alice in Wonderland and Alvin the Chipmunk sell Jell-O. Charlie Brown sells bread while Snoopy hawks dog food. Pink Panther Flakes and a UPA-drawn Donald Duck drives a Nash Rambler.
VHS: S13800. $19.95.

Chariots of Fur
In 1995, Chuck Jones released the first new Roadrunner theatrical cartoon in over 30 years. *Chariots of Fur* is now on home video for the first time, along with five classic shorts: *Beep Beep* ('52); *Operation: Rabbit* ('52, with Bugs); *Hook, Line and Stinker* ('58); *Ready, Woolen and Able* ('60, Ralph Wolf and Sam Sheepdog) and *Zip 'n Snort* ('61).
VHS: S30358. $12.95.

Chuck Amuck: The Movie

The man behind the madness! Warner Bros. animation legend Chuck Jones takes you on a fun-filled and cartoon-packed tour of his fascinating career. Chuck talks about the Warner characters and the studio personnel, and he draws Bugs, Porky and others while he talks about their construction and personalities. In addition to his many other talents, Jones is a thoughtful and articulate speaker.
VHS: $14619. $14.95.

Classic Cereal Commercials from the '50s & '60s

Tony the Tiger introduces George Reeves and the Superman gang hawking Sugar Smacks at the Daily Planet. Trix are for kids. Do you remember the flying Twinkles elephant with the storybook package? You'll find it a tasty treat watching rare spots from Lucky Charms, Pebbles, Rice & Wheat Honeys with Buffalo Bee, Quisp & Quake and much more.
VHS: $21334. $24.95.

Classic Shorts Compilation #12: Winsor McCay

A collection of six short animated films by Winsor McCay, a pioneer in the world of animation. McCay's early style involved delicate line drawings against a plain background; seen today, they still have considerable beauty and charm. This compilation includes *Gertie the Dinosaur* (1911), *Dream* (1922), *Bug Vaudeville* (1912), *Little Nemo* (1911), *The Pet* (1913) and *The Sinking of the Lusitania* (1919).
VHS: $15062. $29.95.
Winsor McCay, 1911-1922, 60 mins.

Columbia Cartoon Classics Vol. 3: Gerald McBoing Boing

Four titles: *Gerald McBoing Boing* ('51, Oscar winner), *Gerald McBoing Boing on the Planet Moo* ('56, Oscar nominee), *Gerald McBoing Boing's Symphony* ('53) and *How Now McBoing Boing* ('54).
VHS: $00490. $12.95.

Columbia Cartoon Classics Vol. 9: UPA Classics

Eight titles: *The Tell-Tale Heart* ('53), *Gerald McBoing Boing* ('51, Oscar winner), *Unicorn in the Garden* ('53), *Ragtime Bear* ('49, first Magoo), *Rooty Toot Toot* ('52, Oscar nominee), *Madeline* ('52, Oscar nominee), *Magoo's Puddle Jumper* ('56, Oscar winner) and *Robin Hoodlum* ('48, Oscar nominee).
VHS: $28110. $12.95.

Computer Animation Festival

From the producers of The Mind's Eye comes a new showcase of 20 cutting-edge computer-animated shorts. Each short from around the globe is shown in its entirety. Also includes Iwerks Entertainment TurboRide footage.
VHS: $29835. $14.95.
Laser: LD76050. $24.95.

Computer Animation Festival Vol. 1.0

21 award-winning computer animation shorts, including PDI's *Locomotion*, MIT's *Grinning Evil Death* and Todd Rundgren's music video *Change Myself*.
VHS: $18589. $9.95.
Laser: LD75618. $29.95.

Coonskin

One of the most controversial films ever made, *Coonskin* is an angry, violent portrayal of Harlem street life and the black condition of the 1970s. Live action and animation, starring Barry White, Scatman Crothers and Philip Michael Thomas. Original, uncut version. ADULTS ONLY.
VHS: $29624. $29.95.

Creature Comforts

Academy Award-winning animated fun from the creators of *Wallace & Gromit*. In this collection of four claymation shorts, the animals step up to the mic and talk about life on the other side of the cage in *Creature Comforts*. The Oscar-nominated *Wat's Pig* is the tale of two brothers—one raised as royalty, the other by a kindly pig. The darkly hilarious *Not Without My Handbag* shows one dear, deceased Auntie refusing to stay in Hell without a proper purse. The story of *Adam* is a whimsical "in-the-beginning" tale about a little clay and a lot of imagination.
VHS: $32415. $14.95.

Daria

Blazing new trails for teenage misfits everywhere, Daria Morgendorffer, the sarcastic classmate of MTV's *Beavis and Butt-head*, uses her intelligence and dry wit to survive the daily assaults against her sanity that constitute high school life in Lawndale. Episodes include *Esteemsters, The Invitation* and *College Bored*. 70 mins.
VHS: $32232. $12.95.

Disney Canta con Nosotros

Jiminy Cricket hosts this series of memorable Disney movie songs with on-screen lyric titles in Spanish. Students will be able to confidently sing along and reinforce their listening, reading and speaking skills. *Snow White, Peter Pan, The Little Mermaid* and *Beauty and the Beast* are covered in four volumes. Spanish narration, 30 mins.
VHS: $24785. $148.25.

Disney's Sing-Along Songs Vol. 7: Disneyland Fun

A musical day at Disneyland with Mr. Owl. See Mickey & Minnie bustle behind the scenes at the park, ride Star Tours, Splash Mountain and the Matterhorn as you sing along to 12 Disney tunes.
VHS: $28165. $12.95.

Donald in Mathmagic Land

Donald stars as a kind of modern Alice in Wonderland as he explores the mysterious world of math. A very popular educational short directed by Hamilton Luske.
VHS: $06593. $12.95.

Dragon Pink

Set in the world of swordplay and sorcery, this comic animated feature from Ito Yoko follows a slave girl who is transformed by a magical pair of panties into a veritable pussycat. Not everyone is pleased however, and together with her master Santa, she must outwit their wretched foes. Japanese with English subtitles. 35 mins. ADULTS ONLY.
VHS: $21144. $29.95.

Fantastic Planet

A French/Czech full-length animated fantasy which won a Gran Prix at the 1973 Cannes Film Festival. Animated and scored in an avant-garde style, the film tells the story of the revolt of the Oms—descendants of survivors of Earth who are kept as pets by the Draags. LP Speed.
VHS: $00432. $9.95.

Faust

Jan Svankmajer's long-awaited follow-up to his acclaimed *Alice* is an equally bizarre version of the myth of Dr. Faustus. Combining live action and stop-motion animation, Svankmajer has created an unsettling universe presided over by diabolic life-size marionettes and haunted by skulking human messengers from hell.
VHS: $29877. $79.95.

Fritz the Cat

The infamous Ralph Bakshi feature that made his reputation was the first animated film to receive an X rating (now re-classified as R). Based on R. Crumb's underground comic character, Fritz is a college-age feline wandering the hippie-era streets of New York in search of political, sexual and chemical experiences. This video version does not use the best film print in the world, but it's uncut, and still deserving of the R rating. ADULTS ONLY.
VHS: $29637. $29.95.

Golden Age of Looney Tunes Vol. 3

Five-disc boxed laserdisc set. Seventy titles. SIDE ONE: Harman-Ising: *One More Time, Red-Headed Baby, Pagan Moon, A Great Big Bunch of You, The Shanty Where Santy Claus Lives, One Step Ahead of My Shadow, The Dish Ran Away with the Spoon.* SIDE TWO: Bugs Bunny: *Wackiki Wabbit, Hare Force, Super Rabbit, Herr Meets Hare, Bugs Bunny and the Three Bears, Stage Door Cartoon, Easter Yeggs.* SIDE THREE: Chuck Jones: *The Squawkin' Hawk, Inki and the Minah Bird, From Hand to Mouse, Fin 'n Catty, Fresh Airedale, The Eager Beaver, House Hunting Mice.* SIDE FOUR: Friz Freleng: *Pigs Is Pigs, The Cat's Tale, Lights Fantastic, Ding Dog Daddy, The Wacky Worm, Peck Up Your Troubles, Racketeer Rabbit.* SIDE FIVE: Early Years: *I Wanna Be a Sailor, Circus Today, Aviation Vacation, Aloha Hooey, Holiday Highlights, Crazy Cruise, The Cagey Canary.* SIDE SIX: Tashlin/Clampett: *Little Pancho Vanilla, Booby Hatched, I Got Plenty of Mutton, Farm Frolics, Falling Hare, Birdy and the Beast, Russian Rhapsody.* SIDE SEVEN: Sports: *Freddy the Freshman, Boulevardier*

from the Bronx, Along Flirtation Walk, Sport Chumpions, Greetings Bait, Screwball Football, Baseball Bugs. SIDE EIGHT: The Evolution of Egghead: *Egghead Rides Again, Count Me Out, Johnny Smith and Poker Huntas, A Day at the Zoo, Believe It or Else, A Feud There Was, Confederate Honey.* SIDE NINE: Porky and Daffy: *Daffy Duck and the Dinosaur, Slightly Daffy, Ain't That Ducky, Wagon Heels, Along Came Daffy, Nothing But the Tooth, The Up-Standing Sitter.* SIDE TEN: Politically Incorrect: *Wake Up the Gypsy in Me, He Was Her Man, Sioux Me, The Mighty Hunters, A Feather in His Hare, The Early Worm Gets the Bird, Inki and the Lion.*
Laser: LD71817. $99.95.

Golden Age of Looney Tunes Vol. 4

Five-disc boxed laserdisc set. Seventy-two titles.
SIDE ONE: Bugs Bunny: *The Wabbit Who Came to Supper, The Hare-Brained Hypnotist, The Case of the Missing Hare, Hare Conditioned, Buccaneer Bunny, Rhapsody Rabbit, Any Bonds Today, A Wild Hare.* SIDE TWO: Early Chuck Jones: *The Good Egg, Ghost Wanted, Snow Time for Comedy, The Bird Came C.O.D., Dog Tired, Fox Pop, The Weakly Reporter.* SIDE THREE: Friz Freleng: *Trial of Mr. Wolf, Double Chaser, The Sheepish Wolf, Hiss and Make Up, Holiday for Shoestrings, The Gay Anties, Of Thee I Sting.* SIDE FOUR: Cartoon All-Stars: *Tom Turk and Daffy, I Taw a Puddy Tat, Two Gophers from Texas, Conrad the Sailor, Doggone Cats, A Horsefly Fleas, Hobo Bobo.* SIDE FIVE: Radio Daze: *Crosby Columbo and Vallee, The Woods Are Full of Cuckoos, Let It Be Me, Little Blabbermouse, Malibu Beach Party, Quentin Quail, Hush My Mouse.* SIDE SIX: The Frantic Forties: *Hop Skip and a Chump, A Hick a Slick and a Chick, Meatless Flyday, The Foxy Duckling, Bone Sweet Bone, The Rattled Rooster, The Shell-Shocked Egg.* SIDE SEVEN: Wacky Blackouts: *Land of the Midnight Fun, Wacky Wildlife, Ceiling Hero, Fresh Fish, Saddle Silly, Foney Fables, Bug Parade.* SIDE EIGHT: Ben Hardaway & Cal Dalton: *Love & Curses, Gold Rush Daze, Bars & Stripes Forever, Hobo Gadget Band, Fagin's Freshmen, Busy Bakers, Snafuperman, Spies.* SIDE NINE: Sniffles: *Naughty But Mice, Little Brother Rat, Sniffles & The Bookworm, The Egg Collector, Sniffles Bells the Cat, Toy Trouble, Brave Little Bat.* SIDE TEN: Merrie Melodies: *The Queen Was in the Parlor, I Love a Parade, The Organ Grinder, Billboard Frolics, Flowers for Madame, September in the Rain, You're an Education.*
Laser: LD75674. $99.95.

Golden Age of Looney Tunes Vol. 5

Four-disc boxed laserdisc set. Forty-nine more cartoons. SIDE ONE: Black & White Classics: *It's Got Me Again, Moonlight for Two, A Great Big Bunch of You, You're Too Careless with Your Kisses, I Wish I Had Wings, Young and Healthy, I LIke Mountain Music.* SIDE TWO: Early Avery: *Don't Look Now, I Only Have Eyes for You, Ain't We Got Fun, A Sunbonnet Blue, The Sneezing Weasel, Mice Will Play, Detouring America.* SIDE THREE: Freleng Follies: *She Was an Acrobat's Daughter, Sweet Sioux, The Lyin' Mouse, My Little Buckaroo, The Fighting 69th-1/2, Rookie Revue, Fifth Column Mouse.* SIDE FOUR: Musical Madness: *Merry Old Soul, Mr. and Mrs. Is the Name, Into Your Dance, The Country Mouse, Bingo Crosbyana, The Fella with the Fiddle, Now That Summer Is Gone.* SIDE FIVE: Pesky Pets: *The Cat Came Back, The Country Boy, Dog Daze, Doggone Modern, Curious Puppy, Stage Fright, Snowman's Land.* SIDE SIX: Objects d'Art: *Those Beautiful Dames, Little Dutch Plate, I'd Love to Take Orders from You, Toytown Hall, My Green Fedora, Streamline Greta Green, Shop Look and Listen.* SIDE SEVEN: Animal Antics: *Pop Goes Your Heart, I Wanna Play House, I'm a Big Shot Now, When I Yoo Hoo, At Your Service Madame, A Star Is Hatched, Plenty of Money and You.*
Laser: LD75861. $99.95.

Gulliver's Travels

This is the film the Fleischers moved to Miami to make. Issued as an answer to Disney's *Snow White*, this Fleischer animated feature recounts Swift's story of Gulliver and the Lilliputians.
VHS: S18185. $19.95.
Laser: LD75675. $29.95.

The Hobbit

All the enchantment, warmth and excitement of J.R.R. Tolkien's classic in this TV special. Bilbo Baggins leads a quest through Middle Earth to recover stolen treasure from the dragon Smaug and

finds a magical ring. Voices of John Huston, Orson Bean and Hans Conreid.
VHS: S03846. $14.95.

International Tournee of Animation Volume 1

[19th Tournee] Fourteen titles: *Anijam* (Marv Newland, Canada), *Bottom's Dream* (John Canemaker, USA), *Bitz Butz* (Gil Alkabetz, Israel), *Tony De Peltrie* (NFB, Canada), *Sigmund* (Bruno Bozetto, Italy), *Skywhales* (Austin/Hayes, UK), *Moa Moa* (Bruno Bozetto, Italy), *Romeo & Juliet* (Dujan Petricic, Yugoslavia), *Jumping* (Osamu Tezuka, Japan), *Conversation Pieces: Early Bird* (Lord/Sproxton, UK), *Incubus* (Guido Manuli, Italy), *Luncheon* (Csaba Varga, Hungary), *Anna & Bella* (Borge Rin, Holland, 1985 Oscar Winner) and *Charade* (Jon Minnis, Canada, '84 Oscar Winner).
VHS: S17045. $29.95.

International Tournee of Animation Volume 2

[20th Tournee] Sixteen titles: *The Frog, The Dog & The Devil* (Bob Stenhouse, New Zealand), *Set in Motion* (Jane Aaron, USA), *Success* (Zoltan Lehotay, Hungary), *Garbage In, Garbage Out* (Terry Wozniak, USA), *Carnival* (Susan Young, UK), *Baeus* (Bruno Bozetto, Italy), *Academy Leader Variations* (various), *Greek Tragedy* (N. Van Goethem, Belgium), *Plus One, Minus One* (G. Manuli, Italy), *Your Face* (Plympton, USA), *Break* (G. Bardin, USSR), *Gravity* (F. Rofusz, Hungary), *Augusta Feeds Her Child* (Csaba Varga, Hungary), *Girl's Night Out* (J. Quinn, UK), *Drawing on My Mind* (Bob Kurtz, USA) and *Snookles* (Juliet Stroud, USA).
VHS: S17046. $29.95.

International Tournee of Animation Volume 3

[21st Tournee] Ten titles: *Arnold Escapes from the Church* (USA), *Lights Before Dawn* (Sandor Bekesi), *Pas a Deux* (Van Dijk/Renault, Holland), *78 Tours* (George Schwizgebel), *When Bats Are Quiet* (Fabio Lignini, Italy), *Augusta Kneading* (Csaba Varga, Hungary), *Living in a Mobile Home* (Neville Astley, England), *Quinoscopo* (Juan Padron, Cuba), *Technological Threat* (Bill Kroyer, USA, 1988 Oscar Nominee) and *The Writer* (Paul Driessen, Holland).
VHS: S17047. $29.95.
Laser: LD75898. $39.95.

International Tournee of Animation Volume 4

[22nd Tournee] Eighteen titles: *All My Relations* (Joanna Priestly, USA), *Animated Self Portraits* (various), *The Arnold Waltz* (Craig Bartlett, USA), *Balance* (C. & W. Lauenstein, Germany, '89 Oscar Winner), *The Bedroom* (Maarten Koopman, Holland), *Cat and Rat* (James Richardson, USA), *The Cow* (Alexander Petrov, USSR, '89 Oscar Nominee), *Gisele Kerozene* (E. Cayo & J. Kounen, France), *Kakania* (Karen Aqua, USA), *Pictures from Memory* (Nedjeljko Dragic, Yugoslavia), *Plymptoons* (Bill Plympton, USA), *Sand Dance* (Richard Quade, USA), *Shadrach* (Chris Casady, USA), *A Touch of Deceit* (Michael Gagne, Canada), *Train Gang* (Paul Driessen, Holland), *A Very Very Long Time Ago* (Bill Jarcho & M. Manning, USA), *Vykrutasy* (Garri Bardin, USSR) and *A Warm Reception in L.A.* (Vincent Cafarelli & Candy Kugel, USA).
VHS: S17042. $29.95.

International Tournee of Animation Volume 5

[23rd Tournee] Sixteen titles: *At One View* (Paul De Noojier, Netherlands), *The Big Bang* (Bruno Bozetto, Italy), *Breakdown* (Klaus Geoggi, Germany), *Capital P* (Stephen Barnes, Canada), *Fast Food Matador* (Vincent Cafarelli & Candy Kugel, USA), *Getting There* (Paul Driessen, Canada), *Grey Wolf & Little Riding Hood* (Garri Bardin, USSR), *I Should See* (Paul De Noojier, Netherlands), *Les Daisons Quatre a Quatre* (Daniel Suter, Switzerland), *The Lift* (Alexander Tatarsky, USSR), *Ode to GI Joe* (Gregory Grant, USA), *Oral Hygiene* (David Fain, USA), *Photocopy Cha Cha* (Chel White, USA), *Potato Hunter* (Timothy Hittle, USA), *Push Comes to Shove* (Bill Plympton, USA) and *The Wrong Type* (Candy Guard, UK).
VHS: S25823. $29.95.
Laser: CAV. LD75679. $49.95.

International Tournee of Animation Volume 6

[24th Tournee] Fourteen titles: *Get a Haircut* (Mike Smith), *The Stain* (Marjut Rimminen), *We Love It*

(Vince Cafarelli & Candy Kugel), *The Ride to the Abyss* (Georges Schwizgebel), *The Square of Light* (Claude Luyet), *Prehistoric Beast* [excerpt] (Phil Tippett), *The Man Who Yelled* (Mo Willems), *I Think I Was an Alcoholic* (John Callahan), *Gahan Wilson's Diner* (Gahan Wilson), *The Billy Nayer Show* (Cory McAbee & Bobby Lurie), *Little Wolf* (An Vrombaut), *The Sandman* (Paul Berry), *Words Words Words* (Michaela Pavlatova) and *Mr. Resistor* (Will Vinton Studio).

VHS: $25818. $29.95.

James and The Giant Peach

Henry Selick's latest feature combines live action and stop-motion animation to bring to life Roald Dahl's famous children's story. Every bit as state-of-the-art as *Nightmare Before Christmas*, this film also has the same sort of scary-but-safe atmosphere. James boards a magical giant peach filled with anthropomorphized insects and embarks on a fantastic odyssey. Music by Randy Newman.

VHS: $28523. $22.95.

Kimba the Lion Prince

Osamu Tezuka's TV series was extremely popular in America when a translated version was broadcast in 1966 as *Kimba the White Lion*. That version has never been released on home video, but a new English-language version was assembled in 1993. The new production uses all the original Japanese footage, but the music, voices and script are all new. This is not the Fred Ladd version you may remember from your childhood, but if you want to see Tezuka's original animation, you'll appreciate this series.
Kimba: Legend of the Claw. Two episodes: *Legend of the Claw* is the episode that started it all as Kimba follows in his father's paw prints to become the pride of the jungle. In *The Wind in the Desert*, Kimba is rescued from hunters by his human friend Jonathan. 1966-67, 45 mins. Dubbed.

VHS: $29565. $12.95.
Kimba: River Battle. Two episodes: In *River Battle*, Kimba battles a giant python but must still prove he's

as wise and strong as his father. In *Human Friend*, Jonathan shows that not all humans are hunters. 1966-67, 45 mins. Dubbed.

VHS: $29566. $12.95.
Kimba: Jungle Thief. Two episodes: In *Jungle Thief*, the animals look to Kimba to solve a drought and stop a thief who's stealing emergency supplies. In *A Friend Indeed*, Bongo the leopard cub and Kimba start out as enemies, but find friendship. 1966-67, 45 mins. Dubbed.

VHS: $29567. $12.95.
Kimba: Insect Invasion. Two episodes: In *Insect Invasion*, Kimba must stop millions of locusts from eating all the animals' food. In *Troublemaker*, Kimba's evil uncle BooBoo is plotting to turn the animals against each other. With lioness cub Lea, he sets a trap to catch BooBoo and the hyenas. 1966-67, 45 mins. Dubbed.

VHS: $29568. $12.95.

Ladislas Starevitch

Ladislas Starevitch is one of the most admired pioneers of stop-motion puppet animation. He began his career in Russia in 1909, but soon moved to France, where he worked through the 1950s. This tape contains three of his sound classics. *The Mascot* ('34) is a nightmarish vision in which the dustbins of Paris disgorge skeletal demons who gather for midnight Saturnalia. *Nose to the Wind* ('56) is the story of a bear who escapes school to join a fox and a rabbit as a traveling minstrel. *Winter Carousel* ('58) is a winter adventure with a bear, rabbit, fox and scarecrow-turned snowman.

VHS: $14527. $29.95.

The Last Unicorn

The voice talents of Mia Farrow, Jeff Bridges and Angela Lansbury bring to life this animated theatrical feature tale of a lonely unicorn who sets out on an extraordinary quest. Based on the novel by Peter S. Beagle.

VHS: $04605. $14.95.

Creature Comforts

Faust

The Looney Looney Looney Bugs Bunny Movie

This Friz Freleng compilation is in three acts: first Yosemite Sam raises hell with the devil in a remake of *Devil's Feud Cake* ('63); then Bugs outwits Rocky and Mugsy who are holding Tweety hostage; and finally Bugs acts as host for a parody of Hollywood award ceremonies. Classic cartoons shown include *Knighty Knight Bugs, Sahara Hare, Roman Legion Hare, High Diving Hare, Hare Trimmed, Wild and Wooly Hare, Catty Cornered, Golden Yeggs, The Unmentionables, Three Little Bops* and *Show Biz Bugs.*
VHS: S14618. $14.95.

Lotte Reiniger Compilation

Lotte Reiniger pioneered the cut-out silhouette technique of animation in Potsdam, Germany, during the 1920s, and is credited with making the first feature-length animated film, *The Adventures of Prince Achmed.* In the 1950s, she and her husband established Primrose Productions in England and continued making silhouette films. This tape includes *Cinderella, The Frog Prince* ('55), *Hansel and Gretel* ('55), *The Little Chimney Sweep* ('54) and *The Three Wishes* ('55). Also included is *The Art of Lotte Reiniger,* a documentary of the filmmaker in which she takes us through the creation of a film step by step.
VHS: S15063. $29.95.

Marvelous Melies

A collection of great films by the great pioneer magician of the cinema, Georges Melies: *A Trip to the Moon, Paris to Monte Carlo, The Doctor's Secret, Kingdom of the Fairies, The Enchanted Well* and *The Conquest of the Pole.*
VHS: S05789. $29.95.
Georges Melies, France, 60 mins.

Masters of Animation Vol. 1: USA & Canada

USA: Interviews: Chuck Jones, Bill Littlejohn and others. Film Excerpts: *Steamboat Willie, Rooty Toot Toot, The Great Cognito* and others. NATIONAL FILM BOARD OF CANADA: Interviews: Norman McLaren and others. Film Excerpts: *Hen Hop, Blinkety Blank, The Street, Every Child* and others. CBC-RADIO CANADA/INDEPENDENTS: Interviews: Frederic Back and others. Film Excerpts: *Crac, George & The Star, Hooray for Sandbox Land* and others.
VHS: S07613. $29.95.

Masters of Animation Vol. 2: Great Britain, Italy & France

GREAT BRITAIN: Interviews: John Halas, Joy Batchelor and others. Film Excerpts: *Animal Farm, Yellow Submarine* and others. ITALY: Interviews: Emanuele Luzzatti, Guilio Gianini and Bruno Bozzetto. Film Excerpts: *Labyrinth, Allegro Non Troppo* and others. FRANCE: Interviews: Yannick Piel. Film Excerpts: *Drame Chez Les Fantoches, The Nose, Asterix in Britain* and others.
VHS: S07614. $29.95.

Masters of Animation Vol. 3: USSR, Poland, Yugoslavia & Hungary

USSR: Film Excerpts: *The Snow Queen, Nutcracker Suite, The Tale of Tales* and others. YUGOSLAVIA: Interviews: Dusan Vukotic, Nedeljko Dragic and others. Film Excerpts: *Mask of the Red Death, Per Aspera ad Astra, Second Class Traveler* and others. POLAND: Film Excerpts: *Little Black Riding Hood, The Red & The Black* and others. HUNGARY: Film Excerpts: *Story of a Beatle, Kidnapping of the Sun & Moon* and others.
VHS: S07615. $29.95.

Masters of Animation Vol. 4: Japan & Computer Animation

JAPAN: Interviews: Osamu Tezuka. Film Excerpts: *House of Flame and Dojoji Temple, Broken Down Film, Jumping* and others. COMPUTER ANIMATION PART 1: Interviews: Bob Abel, John Whitney Jr. and Charles Csuri. Artists: Charles Csuri, Carl Rosendahl and others. COMPUTER ANIMATION PART 2: Artists: Bob Abel, Art

Durinski, Eihachiro Nakamae and others.
VHS: S07616. $29.95.

Meet the Feebles
An adult fantasy film, *Meet the Feebles* relates the events that led up to the infamous "Feebles Variety Massacre," the day that rocked the puppet world. The film, directed by Peter Jackson (*Dead Alive, Heavenly Creatures*), who describes it as "a kind of *Roger Rabbit* meets *Brazil*," is set in a contemporary world like ours, with one major difference: there are no human beings. The Feebles' world is entirely populated by puppets—living, breathing, eating puppets with larger-than-life human characteristics and weaknesses...*Meet the Feebles* is a darkly comic satire on greed, lust and jealousy...part satire/soap opera/ musical that is a wildly original feature" (Charles Coleman).
VHS: S26868. $89.95.
Peter Jackson, New Zealand, 1988, 97 mins.

MGM Cartoon Classics: Happy Harmonies
In the 1930s and '40s, Hugh Harman and Rudy Ising created a series of cartoons for MGM known as *Happy Harmonies*. Here are many of their best, along with other works done for MGM, in a four-disc laserdisc boxed set. Forty-two titles: 1934: *Tale of the Vienna Woods, Toyland Broadcast*; 1935: *The Chinese Nightingale, Honeyland, The Old Plantation, Hey Hey Fever, The Calico Dragon, Barnyard Babies, Poor Little Me*; 1936: *To Spring, Bottles, Little Cheezer, Two Little Pups*; 1937: *Little Buck Cheezer, Swing Wedding, Bosko's Easter Eggs*; 1938: *Pipe Dreams*; 1939: *Goldilocks and the Three Bears, The Bear That Couldn't Sleep, Peace on Earth, The Bookworm, The Little Goldfish, Art Gallery, The Mad Maestro, The Blue Danube*; 1940: *The Fieldmouse, Mrs. Ladybug, Home on the Range, The Fishing Bear, The Milky Way, Romeo in Rhythm, The Lonesome Stranger, Tom Turkey and His Harmonica Humdingers*; 1941: *The Alley Cat, The Flying Bear, The Little Mole, Dance of the Weed, Abdul the Bulbul Ameer*; 1942: *Barney Bear's Victory Garden, The Bear and the Beavers*; 1943: *The Boy and the Wolf, The Uninvited Pest*.
Laser: LD75691. $99.95.

Mickey Mouse: The Black & White Years
Five-disc CAV laserdisc boxed set of the black-and-white Mickey Mouse cartoons. This collection contains 34 newly restored and remastered vintage shorts, many unseen in over 60 years. In addition, bonus supplemental materials include animator's story sketches, rare B&W pencil tests, and Mickey's first appearance in color—a recently rediscovered short specially made for the 1932 Academy Awards, unseen for 60 years. Thirty-three titles: 1928: *Steamboat Willie*. 1929: *Gallopin' Gaucho, Plane Crazy, Mickey's Follies*. 1930: *Fire Fighters, The Chain Gang, Gorilla Mystery, Pioneer Days*. 1931: *Birthday Party, Mickey Steps Out, Blue Rhythm, Mickey Cuts Up, Mickey's Orphans*. 1932: *Duck Hunt, Mickey's Revue, Mickey's Nightmare, The Whoopee Party, Touchdown Mickey, The Klondike Kid*. 1933: *Building a Building, The Mad Doctor, Ye Olden Days, The Mail Pilot, Mickey's Gala Premiere, Puppy Love, The Pet Store, Giant Land*. 1934: *Camping Out, Gulliver Mickey, Orphan's Benefit, The Dog Napper, Two Gun Mickey*. 1935: *Mickey's Service Station*.
Laser: LD75693. $124.95.

NFBC: Leonard Maltin's Animation Favorites from the National Film Board of Canada
Maltin selects some of his favorite cartoons in this A&E documentary special. Nine titles: *Begone Dull Care* (Norman McLaren), *Mindscape* (Jacques Drouin), *Log Driver's Waltz* (John Weldon), *The Cat Came Back* (Cordell Barker), *Getting Started* (Richard Condie), *The Sweater* (Sheldon Cohen), *The Street* (Caroline Leaf), *Pas de Deux* (Norman McLaren) and *Anniversary* (Aubry & Hebert).
VHS: S25821. $29.95.

NFBC: The Sweater
The Sweater is a charming tale of the trauma a young boy suffers when a mail-order mixup delivers him the wrong hockey sweater. Also includes *The Ride* and *Getting Started*.
VHS: S15791. $14.95.

The Nightmare Before Christmas
Tim Burton's original story is brilliantly realized through stop-motion puppet animation of a technical level never before seen. Jack Skellington, the Pumpkin King of Halloween Town, discovers the joys of Christmas Town and attempts to fill Santa's shoes. Animation is directed by Henry Selick and musical score is contributed by Danny Elfman.
VHS: S21295. $14.95.
Laser: LD75699. $29.95.

Oliver & Company
Loosely based on the themes of *Oliver Twist*, this feature marked the beginning of Disney's one-per-year animated feature film output, and just under 11 minutes contain computer-assisted animation. Cute little kitten Oliver makes friends with the street-mutt Dodger and his gang of scavengers. Their heartless human master, Fagin, orchestrates a ransom scheme involving a rich girl, but all turns out for the best eventually. Voices of Billy Joel, Cheech Marin and Bette Midler.
VHS: S29886. $26.95.

On the Comet
Jules Verne's science fiction adventure is brought to life by Czech animator Karel Zeman. Since the early 1950's Zeman has been directing highly imaginative films that combine animation and live action and are marked by their fantastic trick effects. A film for the whole family! English dialog.
VHS: S00958. $24.95.
Karel Zeman, Czechoslovakia, 76 mins.

Opera Imaginaire
Twelve popular arias are brought to life through the interpretations of some of Europe's most talented animators. All styles of animation are represented, including computer animation. Films by Ken Lidster, Monique Renault, Pascal Roulin, Jonathan Hills, Jimmy Murakami, Raimund Krumme, Stephen Palmer, Hilary Audus, Guionne Leroy and Jose Abel.
VHS: S23751. $14.95.
Laser: LD74931. $29.95.

Outrageous Animation Vol. 1
Twelve titles: *An Inside Job* (Aidan Hickey/Ireland), *Haploid Affair* (Kaminski & Lidster/Canada), *One of Those Days* (Bill Plympton/USA), *The Four Wishes* (Michel Ocelot/France), *Instant Sex* (Bob Godfrey/England), *Rondino* (Csaba Szorda/Hungary), *Full of Grace* (Nicole Van Goethem/Belgium), *Lupo the Butcher* (Danny Antonucci/Canada), *Striptease* (Bruno Bozzetto/Italy), *Great British Moments* (Peter Mudie/UK), *Love at First Sight* (Pavel Koutsky/Czechoslovakia) and *Vice Versa* (Aleksander Sroczynski/Poland).
VHS: S17043. $29.95.

Outrageous Animation Vol. 2
Eighteen titles: *Adam* (J. Ananiades/Greece), *Another Great Moment* (P. Mudie/UK), *The Club* (G. Griffin/USA), *Dialog* (D. Vunak/Yugoslavia), *Eldorado* (B. Bozzetto/Italy), *Erection* (G. Manuli/Italy), *Jac Mac & Rad Boy...Go!* (W. Archer/USA), *The Jump* (N. Astley & J. Newitt/UK), *Maxi Cat's Lunch* (Z. Grgic/Yugoslavia), *Mr. Gloom* (B. Kopp/USA), *Observational Hazard* (B. Kopp/USA), *The Prayer* (R. Gvozdanovic/Yugoslavia), *Quod Libet* (G. Van Dijk/Holland), *Royal Flush* (J. McIntyre/USA), *Sweet Dreams Luv* (D. Dames/Holland), *Toilet Bowl* (M. Jone/USA), *You Can't Teach an Old Dog New Tricks* (J. Foray/USA) and *Zwisch* (T. Sivertsen/Norway).
VHS: S17048. $29.95.
Laser: LD72086. $39.95.

Plymptoons: The Complete Works of Bill Plympton
Twenty-one titles: *Self Portrait* ('88), *The Turn On* ('68), *Lucas—The Ear of Corn* ('77), *Boomtown* ('85), *Drawing Lesson #2* ('87), *Your Face* ('87), *Love in the Fast Lane* ('87), *One of Those Days* ('88), *How to Kiss* ('89), *25 Ways to Quit Smoking* ('89), *245 Days* ('89), *Noodle Ear* ('89), *Human Rights* ('89), *Acid Rain* ('89), *Trivial Pursuit* ('90), *Sugar Delight* ('91), *Previous Lives* ('91) and *Plymptoons* ('90).
VHS: S16931. $29.95.
Laser: LD72092. $34.95.

The Point
Harry Nilsson wrote the songs (including the hit "Me and My Arrow") and script for this thought-provoking TV special. Ringo Starr narrates the tale of a child who must leave his homeland because his round head makes him a freak among his countrymen, the cone-heads.
VHS: S25004. $14.95.

Popeye the Sailor

Here are the three two-reel Technicolor special Popeyes made during the 1930's. The first two feature some of Max's dazzling 3-D backgrounds. *Popeye Meets Sinbad* ('36), *Popeye Meets Ali Baba's Forty Thieves* ('37) and *Popeye in Aladdin and His Wonderful Lamp* ('39).
VHS: S29028. $19.95.

Rime of the Ancient Mariner

A fully animated film narrated by Orson Welles. Using the classic engravings of Gustave Dore as a cut-out style of animation, the film follows Samuel Taylor Coleridge's long dream of an old mariner who kills an albatross and suffers the pains of the damned for it.
VHS: S09418. $59.95.

Roger Rabbit—The Best of

The three stand-alone Roger Rabbit theatrical shorts (*What's Cookin'* is incorporated into the *Who Framed Roger Rabbit?* feature) are collected at last on one tape. In *Tummy Trouble*, Roger takes Baby Herman to the hospital after he swallows his rattle; in *Roller Coaster Rabbit*, Roger takes Baby Herman to a fair; and in *Trail Mix-Up*, the pair go hiking in the woods. All three cartoons are brilliant homages to the Tex Avery and Bob Clampett school of 1940s Hollywood cartoons, but done with lush production values only Disney could bankroll. Laserdisc is CAV.
VHS: S29697. $12.95.
Laser: LD75879. $19.95.

Scenes from the Surreal

Three short films: In *Darkness Light Darkness*, a fragmented man emerges out of the darkness to construct his physical self. In *Manly Games*, a soccer match is interpreted by Svankmajer with balls banging off coffins. In *Death of Stalinism*, Svankmajer examines the myth and downfall of Czech communist doctrine. Also on this tape is *The Animator of Prague*, a BBC documentary by James Marsh. In addition to a look at Svankmajer's works, we join him at work on his latest creation and witness many of his trademark techniques.
VHS: S17912. $29.95.

Secret Adventures of Tom Thumb

In this highly acclaimed stop-motion animated feature, the classic tale of Tom Thumb takes a dark and sinister turn more evocative of science fiction and horror films. Through pixelation and clay animation, a world of seedy slums and sinister laboratories emerges. When Tom is stolen from his parents for experimentation, he meets other small, oppressed creatures and fights with them against the tyranny of the "giants." NOT SUITABLE FOR CHILDREN.
VHS: S26444. $29.95.
Laser: LD75881. $29.95.

Sextoons:
An Erotic Animation Festival

Sexually explicit animation ranging from tenderly erotic to laughably crude to outright disturbing. Featuring the sought-after Buried Treasure featuring Eveready Harton—reputed to be an after-hours project of a major animation studio of the '20s. Sixteen titles: *Boobs a Lot* (Bernard Ellis, sing along), *Armchair Inventions* (Gary Moore), *Little Genitalia* (Barry Brilliant), *A Child's Alphabet* (Thomas Spence), *The Further Adventures of Super Screw* (B&W), *Jack in the Fox* (Karl Krogstad), *Hearts and Arrows* (Roy Fridge), *Snow White & The Seven Dwarfs* (German, ca. 1930's), *Buried Treasure* (B&W, ca. 1924), *Out of Order (B&W, ca. 1920's, with Krazy Kat look-alike), Crocus* (Suzan Pitt Kraning), *Little Ms. Muffet* (Mark Seiderburg, 1974), *Seed Reel - (Mary Beems, 1975), L'Ombre de la Pomme* (Lapoujade), *Show Biz* (Algas Nakis) and *Boobs a Lot* (photo montage). ADULTS ONLY.
VHS: S17689. $29.95.

Short Animations by Larry Jordan

Eight titles: *Duo Concertantes, Patricia Gives Birth to a Dream by the Doorway, Gymnopedies, Our Lady of the Spheres, Moonlight Sonata, Once upon a Time, Carabosse* and *Masquerade*.
VHS: S09420. $59.95.

The Snowman

Based on the book by Raymond Briggs, this is the story of a young boy who builds a snowman that comes to life on Christmas Eve. Academy Award nominee.
VHS: S01222. $14.95.

Spike & Mike's Festival of Animation Vol. 1

Twelve titles: *How to Kiss* (Bill Plympton), *Snookles* (Juliet Stroud), *Primiti Too Taa* (Ed Akerman), *Thing What Lurked in the Tub* (David Wasson), *A Story* (Andrew Stanton), *Particle Dreams* (Karl Sims), *Charade* (John Minnus, Oscar Winner), *Western* (Gabor Hamolya), *Feet of Song* (Erica Russell), *Winter* (Pete Doctor), *Lea Press on Limbs* (Chris Miller) and *Bambi Meets Godzilla* (Marv Newland).
VHS: S15237. $29.95.

Spike & Mike's Festival of Animation Vol. 2

Eighteen titles: *Jean Jean and the Evil Cat* (Walter Santucci/USA), *License to Kill* (Teresa Lang/Canada), *La Pista* (G. Toccafundo/Italy), *Adam* (Peter Lord/UK), *Negative Man* (Cathy Joritz/USA), *Singing Ding a Lings* (Lance Kramer/USA), *The Log* (S. Kushnevrov/Russia), *Next Door* (Pete Docter/USA), *Creature Comforts at Home* (Nick Park/UK), *Street Sweeper* (Serge Elissalde/France), *Visions from the Amazon* (Nancy Kato/Brazil), *Amore Baciami* (Oliver Harrison/UK), *Grasshoppers* (Bruno Bozzetto/Italy),*Manipulation* (Daniel Greaves/UK, Oscar Winner), *Panspermia* (Karl Sims/USA), *Big Fat World of Science* (Mike Wellins/USA), *Dinko's Day* (Mike Cachuela/USA) and *Creature Comforts* (Nick Park/UK, Oscar winner).
VHS: S27549. $39.95.

Spike & Mike's Festival of Animation Vol. 3

A new collection of eight short animated films from the Spike & Mike touring revue: *Screenplay* (Barry J.C. Purves/UK, 10:50): Oscar-nominated puppet animation of a tragic Japanese love story; *Frannies Christmas* (Mike Mitchell/USA, 2:00): A poetic story of Frannie learning there's no Santa; *Streetsweeper* (Serge Elissalde/France, 6:20): The tragicomic story of a Chaplin-esque streetsweeper, rendered in pencil; *Dirdy Birdy* (John R. Dilworth/USA, 7:00): A longtime festival favorite—a starcrossed attraction taken to a hilarious Avery-esque extreme; *Blindscape* (Stephen Palmer/UK, 8:00): The animator takes us into the world of a blind man via colored pencil renderings; *The Monk and the Fish* (Michael Dudok De Wit/France/Holland, 6:00): Oscar-nominated watercolor animation of an obsessed fisherman monk; *Iddy Biddy Beat Boy* (Mo Willems/USA, 4:30): A comic tale of censure that fans of beat poetry will love; *Britannia* (Joanna Quinn/UK, 7:30): Oscar-nominated satire as a bulldog teaches us the history of Mother England.
VHS: S28625. $29.95.

Spike & Mike's Sick & Twisted Festival of Animation Vol. 1

The first two years of Mike & Spike's infamous collection of cult animated shorts: they may be gross, they may be outrageous, they may even be pornographic, but they certainly do get your attention! Fourteen titles: *How Much Is That Window in the Doggie?* (John Callahan), *Pink Komkommer* (Driessen/Newland), *Bladder Trouble* (Webster Colcord), *Discoveries* (Dan Smith), *Thanks for the Mammaries* (Cindy Banks), *Dog Pile* (Miles Thompson), *Beavus and Butthead in Peace Love & Understanding* (Mike Judge), *One Man's Instrument* (Max Bannah), *Nana and Lil' Puss Puss in Downbeat Dowager* (DNA Prod.), *Lullaby* (Ken Bruce), *Bulimiator* (Newton/Kellman), *Deadsy* (David Anderson), *Performance Art Starring Chainsaw Bob* (Brandon McKinney) and *Lupo the Butcher* (Danny Antonucci). ADULTS ONLY.
VHS: S27550. $29.95.

Spike & Mike's Sick & Twisted Festival of Animation Vol. 2

A second volume of the most sarcastic and disgusting animated short films around. Twenty titles: *Horndog* (Sean Mullen), *Brian's Brain* (Miles Thompson), *Woeful Willie* (Chris Louden), *The Cat, Cow and Beautiful Fish* (Walter Santucci), *Finger Food* (Cindy Banks), *Slaughter Day* (Webster Colcord), *Petey's Wake* (Walt Dohrn), *Mutilator II* (Eric Fogel), *Dog Pile II* (DNA Productions), *Oh Crappy Day* (Sean Mullen), *Big Top* (Zac Mayo/Fernella Boggs), *Triassic Parking Lot* (Mike Wellins), *Spaghetti Snot* (Miles Thompson), *Chainsaw Bob in a Cult Classic* (Brandon McKinney), *Tennis* (Peter Hixson), *Poetic Jaundice* (Tom Lamb/Dan Brisson), *Stubbs* (Miles Thompson), *A Hole in One* (Dave Smith), *Lloyd's Lunchbox* (Greg Ecklund) and *Wrong Hole* (Mark Oftedal). ADULTS ONLY.
VHS: S27551. $29.95.

Spike & Mike's Sick & Twisted Festival of Animation Vol. 3

Fifteen new, totally disturbed animated shorts: *Puke a Pound* (Cindy Banks/Dave Smith), *No Neck Joe* (Craig McCracken), *Gun, Zipper, Snot* (Miles Thompson), *Empty Roll* (Miles Thompson), *Hut Sluts* (Spike & Mike), *Rick the Dick in Hospital Hell* (Zac Mayo/Fernella Bogs), *Wastes Away* (Anthony Loi), *Phull Phrontal Phingers* (Mike Wellins), *The Birth of Brian* (Miles Thompson), *Dirty Birdy* (John R. Dilworth), *I Never Ho'd for My Father* (Tony Nitolli), *Adam's Other Rib* (Eric Schneider), *Phuk Yew* (Bob McAfee), *Home, Honey, I'm High* (Kevin Kalliher) and *Lloyd Loses His Lunch* (Gregory Eckland). ADULTS ONLY.
VHS: $28626. $29.95.

Tex Avery's Screwball Classics 1

Eight titles: *Little Tinker, Swing Shift Cinderella, Magical Maestro, Bad Luck Blackie, Lucky Ducky, The Cat That Hated People, Symphony in Slang* and *Who Killed Who*.
VHS: S07967. $14.95.

Tex Avery: The Compleat Tex Avery

Every single cartoon directed by Tex Avery while at MGM—collected here in a five-disc (ten sides) boxed laserdisc set—presented in chronological order. 1942: *The Blitz Wolf, The Early Bird Dood It.* 1943: *Dumb Hounded, Red Hot Riding Hood, Who Killed Who?, One Ham's Family, What's Buzzin' Buzzard?* 1944: *Screwball Squirrel, Batty Baseball, Happy-Go-Nutty, Big Heel-Watha.* 1945: *The Screwy Truant, The Shooting of Dan McGoo, Jerky Turkey, Swing Shift Cinderella, Wild and Woolfy.* 1946: *Lonesome Lenny, The Hick Chick, Northwest Hounded Police, Henpecked Hoboes.* 1947: *Hound Hunters, Red Hot Rangers, Uncle Tom's Cabana, Slap Happy Lion, King-Size Canary.* 1948: *What Price Fleadom, Little Tinker, Half-Pint Pygmy, Lucky Ducky, The Cat That Hated People.* 1949: *Bad Luck Blackie, Senor Droopy, The House of Tomorrow, Doggone Tired, Wags to Riches, Little Rural Riding Hood, Outfoxed, Counterfeit Cat.* 1950: *Ventriloquist Cat, The Cuckoo Clock, Garden Gopher, The Chump Champ, The Peachy Cobbler.* 1951: Cock-A-Doodle Dog, Daredevil Droopy, Droopy's Good Deed, Symphony in Slang, Car of Tomorrow, Droopy's Double

Trouble. 1952: *Magical Maestro, One Cab's Family, Rock-A-Bye Bear.* 1953: *Little Johnny Jet, TV of Tomorrow, The Three Little Pups.* 1954: *Drag-Along Droopy, Billy Boy, Homesteader Droopy, Farm of Tomorrow, The Flea Circus, Dixieland Droopy.* 1955: *Field and Scream, The First Bad Man, Deputy Droopy, Cellbound.* 1956: *Millionaire Droopy (Cinemascope).* 1957: *Cat's Meow* (Cinemascope).
Laser: LD71656. $99.95.

Three Caballeros/Saludos Amigos

This special Archive Edition CAV laserdisc set also includes the *Saludos Amigos* feature that has never before been released on home video.
Laser: LD75886. $99.95.

Three Little Pigs

On this latest compilation are found the Oscar-winning *Three Little Pigs* and two "sequels" from the Silly Symphonies series. All three cartoons were mastered from the original United Artists prints. In *Three Little Pigs* ('33, Oscar Winner) the Big Bad Wolf is only thwarted by the hardworking pig's house of bricks. In *The Big Bad Wolf* ('34, Silly Symphony) Little Red Riding Hood is rescued not by the woodsman, but by our well-prepared third pig. In *Three Little Wolves* ('36, Silly Symphony) the two silly pigs stand in for The Boy Who Cried Wolf and must once again be rescued by the earnest third pig.
VHS: S30490. $12.95.
Laser: LD76014. $24.95.

Twice upon a Time

Heroes Ralph and Mum search for the Magic Mainspring among the strange Rushers of Din. Filmed in Lumage—a new technique enabling depth, translucent colors and textures impossible to achieve in cel animation. Co-directed by Sesame Street animator John Korty.
VHS: S13442. $14.95.
Laser: LD75892. $34.95.

Twisted Toons: The Warped Animation of Bill Plympton

This documentary reveals the true story behind the one-of-a-kind animator. Working alone in his New York City loft, Plympton has created scores of animated shorts, MTV IDs and television

James and the Giant Peach

commercials, and even two full-length features. We talk to and watch the animator at work in his studio, and see clips of many of his films, especially his one-man feature *The Tune*.
VHS: $27852. $59.95.

Urotsukidoji: Birth of the Overfiend
The story concerns the search for the monstrous Overfiend's origins, as two demons who penetrate Myojin University track down the mysterious force. "*Urotsukidoji* is exemplary of the darkest and most disturbing side of Japanese animation" (*The Village Voice*). Japanese with English subtitles.
VHS: $19488. $99.95.

Urotsukidoji: Legend of the Overfiend
The Overfiend, or Chojin, attempts to remake the current world by merging three warring dimensions—the human world, the man beast world and the world of the monster demons. The feature length work was culled from three episodes of Takayama's video series *The Wandering Kid*. The first animated work to receive an NC-17 rating. Dubbed in English.
VHS: $18441. $29.95.
Laser: LD74517. $49.95.
Hideki Takayama, Japan, 1991, 108 mins.

Urotsukidoji IV: Inferno Road, Episode 1
The final, apocalyptic chapter in the Overfiend saga. It is the early 21st century, and the civilization of mankind is gone. Powerful, supernatural forces have sculpted our world into something more…suitable. Now, flesh-hungry demons and half-demons rule the Earth—raping and slaughtering thousands of human beings. This is the age of the Overfield. But if Himi can be brought to Osaka, then the world can be made whole once more. Buju and Himi are interrupted in their quest by a pair of refugees—fleeing from a metropolis of pure evil. Together, they discover a city where innocence masks deadly psionic powers, and where others serve as slaves, or worse. Graphic violence and explicit sexual situations. ADULTS ONLY. Dubbed.
VHS: $28466. $29.95.
Toshio Maeda, Japan, 1994, 45 mins.

Urotsukidoji IV: Inferno Road, Episode 2
In a city ruled by powerful, psionic beings, obedience is the only law. Escape is punishable by rape, torture, or worse. Trapped in the City of Evil once again, Yumi is tortured as an example for the other slaves—The Masters must be obeyed. But these beings have made a horrifying discovery—by drinking Himi's living blood, they can become immortal, retaining their incredible powers forever. Will the half-demon Amano Jyaku be able to rescue Himi from their sadistic clutches? Graphic violence and explicit sexual situations. ADULTS ONLY. Dubbed.
VHS: $28467. $29.95.
Toshio Maeda, Japan, 1994, 45 mins.

Urotsukidoji IV: Inferno Road, Episode 3
The unbelievable finale to the *Urotsukidoji* series. Desperate for the power to destroy Amano Jyaku, Yoenhime turns to the Overfiend's old nemesis—The Mad Regent Munhihausen! Under the Mad Regent's power, she is reborn as Munhihausen's newest and deadliest pawn—the demonic Yoenki. Now begins the final battle for the fate of the Earth, as Yoenki and her monstrous minions stand against Amano and his allies—and this time, the winner will reshape the planet to their liking! Graphic violence and explicit sexual situations. ADULTS ONLY. Dubbed.
VHS: $28468. $29.95.
Toshio Maeda, Japan, 1994, 45 mins.

Urotsukidoji IV: Inferno Road, 3-Pack
All three tapes in a money-saving 3-pack. Graphic violence and explicit sexual situations. ADULTS ONLY. Dubbed.
VHS: $30274. $79.95.
Toshio Maeda, Japan, 1994, 135 mins.

Wallace & Gromit Collection
Three short claymation films featuring Wallace, an eccentric English inventor, and his trusty, bookworm dog, Gromit, are joined in this set. In addition to the Academy Award-winning *The Wrong Trousers* (1994, 30 mins.) and *A Close Shave* (1995, 30 mins.), here is the Academy Award-nominated *A Grand Day Out* (1994, 30 mins.). Once you've experienced the terror of the mastermind penguin, you will understand how the *Wallace & Gromit* phenomenon started.
VHS: $29999. $24.95.
Nick Park, Great Britain, 1994/1995, 90 mins.

Wallace & Gromit: A Close Shave
Nick Park's latest Wallace and Gromit featurette won the 1995 Academy Award for animated short film. The inimitable pair return in a new adventure every bit as hilarious as their previous shorts.
VHS: $29926. $9.95.

Wallace & Gromit: A Grand Day Out
Nick Park's charming clay animation brings to life the comically pedestrian Englishman Wallace and his dog Gromit. In this Academy Award-nominated featurette, when the pair run out of cheese for their tea-time biscuits, they build a spaceship in the basement in order to fly to the moon. Once there, they meet a truly outlandish moon creature that takes exception to their cheese-harvesting mission.
VHS: $26395. $9.95.

Watership Down
The odyssey that a small group of rabbits undertakes after one of them has a vision of evil things coming to destroy their homes. This project was years in the works, originally begun and then abandoned by John Hubley. Laserdisc is widescreen.
VHS: $01605. $14.95.
Laser: LD72398. $34.95.

Who Framed Roger Rabbit?
1988's smash theatrical hit about a rabbit framed for the murder of R.K. Maroon—owner of Toontown. This live-action and animation movie was so successful and so influential that many credit it for a resurgent interest in animation in general. Down and out Private Eye Eddie Valiant is hired to clear cartoon star Roger Rabbit of murder charges. Stars Bob Hoskins and Christopher Lloyd, with voices of Kathleen Turner and Charles Fleischer.
VHS: $10337. $22.95.
Laser: LD75895. $29.95.

The Wind in the Willows
Vanessa Redgrave narrates this animated film adaptation of Kenneth Grahame's classic children's story about a wise Badger, a clever Rat, and a sensible Mole, who do their best to control the excesses of Toad when they embark on an unpredictable journey. This satire of Victorian society features the voices of Michael Palin (*Monty Python's Flying Circus*), Alan Bennett, Rik Mayall (*The Young Ones*) and Michael Gambon (*Two Deaths*). Top-notch animation from the crew who produced the Beatles' *Yellow Submarine* and *Heavy Metal*. Winner of the Gold Special Jury Award for Best Family Film at Worldfest Houston.
VHS: $30241. $14.95.
Dave Unwin, Great Britain, 1996, 74 mins.

Winsor McCay: Animation Legend
Winsor McCay was one of the most influential artists in the history of animation. This exclusive collection contains every surviving film made by McCay, transferred from beautiful 35mm Cinematheque Quebecoise archival prints. The highlight of the collection is a stunning, hand-colored copy of *Little Nemo* (1911), taken directly from the only known 35mm print in existence. Also included are *How a Mosquito Operates*, *Gertie the Dinosaur*, *The Sinking of The Lusitania*, *Gertie on Tour*, *The Centaurs* and *Flip's Circus*. The collection also features extensive liner notes by John Canemaker, an article for the Cinematheque's curator, Louise Beaudet, and comments from producer Albert Miller regarding the film-to-tape transfer. In addition to a newly composed score by R.J. Miller, all films were digitally recorded at the proper speed, and letterboxed in the original 1.33:1 aspect ratio. Color & B&W.
VHS: $19675. $39.95.
Laser: LD72098. $69.95.

The World's Greatest Animation
Sixteen independent animated short films, including 11 Oscar winners and five Oscar nominees: *Creature Comforts* ('90), *Balance* ('89), *Technological Threat* ('88), *The Cat Came Back* ('88), *Your Face* ('87), *A Greek Tragedy* ('86), *Anna and Bella* ('85), *The Big Snit* ('85), *Charade* ('84), *Sundae in New York* ('83), *The Great Cognito* ('82), *Tango* ('82), *Crac* ('81), *The Fly* ('80), *Every Child* ('79) and *Special Delivery* ('78). Laserdisc includes 15 minutes of supplemental materials.
VHS: $25652. $29.95.
Laser: LD75462. $99.95.

Top 25 Anime

Advancer Tina

A newer entry in the explicit erotic horror genre. Thirty centuries have passed since the Earth was consumed by toxic pollutants, forcing mankind to flee into the galaxy in search of life-sustaining planets. To unite these worlds, the Allied Earth Government was formed. Enter Advancers, reckless explorers employed by the new government, who risk their lives to explore new uncharted worlds for humans to colonize. Warning: this title contains scenes of rape and graphic violence. Subtitled. 45 mins.

VHS: S33406. $29.95.
VHS (Directors Cut)**: S33407. $29.95.**

Akira

One of the few anime films deserving of the label masterpiece, Akira remains a cornerstone of any anime film library. When Katsuhiro Otomo's theatrical feature was first released on home video, the Japanese animation craze in America shifted from first gear into overdrive. In 21st-century Neo-Tokyo, an outcast biker named Tetsuo is selected by the army for experiments to enhance his unusual mental aura. As in Carrie, his newly awakened power grows out of control and his lifetime worth of resentment lashes out with shattering results. 124 mins.

VHS (Dubbed)**: S15233. $19.95.**
VHS (Dubbed, letterboxed)**: S29087. $29.95.**
VHS (Subtitled, letterboxed)**: S16691. $39.95.**
Laser (CLV)**: LD75717. $59.95.**
Laser (CAV)**: LD71555. $124.95.**

Armitage III: Polymatrix

The popular four-part OVA series has been condensed into a 90-minute feature with voice work contributed by Elizabeth Barkley and Kiefer Sutherland. In a rather obvious borrowing from *Blade Runner*, humanoid androids serve their masters on a futuristic Mars. The Harrison Ford cop protagonist is partnered with a Martian android, Armitage, in order to solve a string of murders carried out by a killer who is systematically destroying the next stage of android development. This next stage involves the "thirds"—androids so lifelike they can pass for human. The film noir atmosphere and imaginative background designs lend a distinctive feel to the proceedings. Nudity and Violence. English dialog. 90 mins.

VHS: S33408. $19.95.
DVD: DV60201. $29.95.
Laser: LD76765. $34.95.

Battle Angel

When cybernetic doctor Ido finds the remains of a petite cyborg in a junk heap, he takes her home, fits her with a new, indestructible body, and renames her Gally. Savage, frenetic battles and unique art design make this dark future especially eye-catching, and the story is genuinely touching. While a somewhat older video title at this point, *Battle Angel*'s classic status continues to appeal to both new and experienced fans. Nudity. 70 mins.

VHS (Dubbed)**: S30402. $19.95.**
VHS (Subtitled)**: S19413. $24.95.**
Laser: LD75724. $39.95.

Ghost in the Shell

Battle Arena Toshinden

Based on the computer video game, *Battle Arena Toshinden* was a top-selling title 1997. Master Swordsman Eiji Shinjo has spent a year haunted by the memory of his battle with the renegade champion Gaia. Now someone is hunting down the champions of the Battle Arena, and that someone might be Eiji's long-lost brother, Sho. Lots of martial arts action, as you would expect. Violence and brief nudity. Dubbed. 60 mins.

VHS (Edited): **$30925. $19.95.**
VHS (Uncut): **$30924. $19.95.**
DVD (Uncut): **DV60202. $29.95.**

Big Wars

This one has it all: tons of high-tech hardware, big battles, mind control, nymphomaniacs…what more could an anime fan ask for? In the near future, an alien race known as The Gods decide that humanity must be stopped from expanding beyond their Martian colonies. In addition to the aliens' awesome weapons of war, mankind must also face their insidious mind-control plague that turns the most loyal soldiers into dangerous subversives. Humanity's last hope rests with Captain Akuh's secret mission…but his girlfriend is showing signs of nymphomania, the first symptom of alien subversion. Contains nudity, sexual situations and graphic violence. Dubbed. 75 mins.

VHS: $30928. $19.95.

Bio Hunter

A very popular entry in the erotic horror genre from Yoshiaki Kawajiri, director of *Ninja Scroll* and *Wicked City*. A strange virus attacks the human genetic code and transforms people into monsters with demonic powers. A famed psychic holds the secret to the identity of one such monster who is stalking the streets of Tokyo, ripping open young women and devouring their livers. Two molecular biologists try to reach the psychic and his beautiful daughter before it's too late. A dark, explicit exercise in suspense, horror and eroticism that's definitely not for kids. 58 mins.

VHS (Dubbed): **$32245. $19.95.**
VHS (Subtitled): **$32246. $29.95.**

Dragon Ball Z

Continuing the story begun in the 100-plus episode *Dragon Ball* TV series, *Dragon Ball Z*'s focus on martial arts action and superhero-like battles between alien races gave the show excellent ratings on American TV. The hero, Goku, is revealed to be an alien being called a Saiyan, sent to Earth as a baby in a spaceship almost an exact replica of the Superman origin story. Unlike Superman, though, Goku is also super-violent, having been sent to Earth to destroy all life and clear the way for alien colonization. But an early head injury scrambled his programming so that he grew up to be a good-natured innocent and defender of his adopted world. The first four episodes of the series are on the first volume, *Dragonball Z: Arrival*. Dubbed. 80 mins.

VHS: $33411. $14.95.

Final Fantasy

Vibrant colors and innovative character design distinguish this title based on the best-selling Japanese role-playing game. Planet R's existence is maintained by four magical crystals that each control an essential element: Earth, Water, Fire and Wind. Long ago, dark forces stole the crystals and ancient heroes fought desperately to recover them. Two hundred years later, three crystals have again been stolen. The young descendants of the ancient heroes, Linaly and Prettz, are all that remain to protect the Crystal of Wind from the evil forces. Directed by the

acclaimed Rin Taro (*Dagger of Kamui*). 60 mins.
VHS (Dubbed): **$32776. $19.95.**
VHS (Subtitled): **$32778. $29.95.**

Ghost in the Shell

This big-budget theatrical feature was the #1-selling anime title of 1996 and has now settled into the category of classic. It's the story of a cyborg intelligence officer hunting a bodiless super-hacker with links to her own government. Director Mamoru Oshii laces the film with biblical epigrams, dreamlike cityscapes and realistically spooky character designs. Sophisticated computer graphics and brilliant background designs evoke a futuristic city somewhere between *Blade Runner* and *Akira*. 82 mins.

VHS (Dubbed): **$28057. $19.95.**
VHS (Subtitled): **$28056. $29.95.**
Laser (CLV): **LD76017. $34.95.**
Laser (CAV): **LD76018. $49.95.**

Grappler Baki

Straight-ahead martial arts action is the appeal of this popular title. Grappler Baki is a mysterious fighter who seems to know everything about all the Karate stars, while nobody knows anything about him. Now, for the first time, Baki must face an opponent he knows nothing about—Kosho Shinogi, who has the ability to penetrate his opponents' skin, grab their cord-like nerves, and rip them out, leaving the victim paralyzed or dead. Contains graphic violence (of course). Dubbed. 45 mins.

VHS: $31321. $19.95.

The Irresponsible Captain Tylor

This 26-episode TV series has been at the top of anime fans' must-see list for years. In the distant future, the Raalgon Empire has declared war on the over-extended UPSF defense force. Knowing they're desperate for recruits, the complacent, bumbling Justy Tylor manages to charm his way into command of a UPSF starship. Disliked and distrusted even by his own crew, the new Captain Tylor takes his ship out in search of the enemy in defense of the homeland. Serendipity triumphs over incompetence as the bumbling Tylor manages to luck into enough success to acquire an unearned reputation as a brilliant tactician. Comedy and battle action combine to make this a very popular comic space-opera. Subtitled. 100 mins.

VHS: $32355. $19.95.

La Blue Girl

This six-volume OAV series continues as a mainstay of the adult sexy horror category. It features the sexploits of teenaged Miko, descendant of a ninja clan which possesses a secret signet case with the power to control oversexed demons. Explicit in terms of graphic violence and human (and inhuman) anatomy, the series showcases all manner of demonic perverts, sexual sorcery, and naughty tentacles. Absolutely not for sale or rental to minors. 45 mins.

VHS (Dubbed): **$29557. $29.95.**
VHS (Subtitled): **$25025. $29.95.**

Macross Plus: The Movie

In 2040 A.D., on the colonial planet Eden, the Ministry of Defense is testing an advanced new transforming aircraft. Isamu Dyson is an outgoing fighter pilot in competiton with his old rival, Guld, for the Super Nova project. Myung, a mutual ex-girlfriend, adds tension to the conflict. From Shoji Kawamori, director of the legendary *Macross* TV series, this action-packed, visually arresting film is the *Top Gun* of anime. Nudity and adult language. Subtitled. 180 mins.

VHS: $31322. $29.95.

MD Geist

A classic example of the mecha genre of Japanese animation. Using advanced bio-technology, one race has perfected the Most Dangerous Soldier. MD Geist, the second and deadliest of the MDS, awakens from a forced sleep on an orbiting satellite and finds his way back to his homeworld. He joins a biker gang to seek revenge on those who marooned him in space, but learns that he must instead cooperate with them if he is to save his world from a ravaging Death Program. Action galore and standard-setting mechanical designs help MD Geist remain a staple title in any anime library. Nudity and violence. 45 mins.

VHS (Dubbed): **$29570. $19.95.**
VHS (Subtitled): **$16703. $14.95.**
Laser: LD74511. $34.95.

Neon Genesis Evangelion

Credited with helping to revive the current anime

industry in Japan, *Evangelion* is the first smash-hit anime TV show since *Sailor Moon* in the early '90s. It starts with the oldest premise in the giant-robot book—a son called to pilot the robot that his father built—but quickly shows its real interest to be the dysfunctional relationships between its three generations of main characters. The 26-episode *Evangelion* series offers an *X-Files*-like investigatory feel as well as fantastic scenes of combat between the advanced robots of Earth and the alien, invading Angels. Bizarre, brutal, surrealistic and shocking scenes caused much controversy and even calls for a boycott of the show.

VHS (Dubbed): **S29578. $24.95.**
VHS (Subtitled): **S29575. $29.95.**

Patlabor 2

This theatrical feature is Mamoru Oshii's (*Ghost in the Shell*) masterpiece, and widely regarded as one of the best anime films ever made. Fantastic yet believable, *Patlabor 2* is comparable to the works of Tom Clancy in its portrayal of modern, Desert Storm-era military hardware and tactics. More than that, its also a visually stunning film, set in a winter Tokyo with a dreamlike narrative. Speculations on Japan's distorted place in the world of nations provide much food for thought, and the film eerily predicts the sort of urban terrorism that was realized only two years later in the Tokyo subway gas attack. 108 mins.

VHS (Dubbed): **S29196. $19.95.**
VHS (Subtitled): **S26765. $24.95.**

Peacock King

One of the latest hit titles in the supernatural/horror genre. Neo-Nazi Siegfried von Mittgard plans to pick up where Hitler left off. Utilizing an ancient, occult ceremony, he plans to sacrifice young mystic Tomoko and crown himself the Regent of Darkness. Opposing him are four heroes: a Chinese martial warrior, a warlock, a Buddhist exorcist and his apprentice.The struggle for the pivotal Dragon Orb leads from San Francisco's Chinatown to Mount Koya and finally to the Neo-Nazi fortress in Germany. Some nudity and lots of graphic violence. Dubbed. 49 mins.

VHS: S32268. $19.95.

Ranma 1/2 Hard Battle

This long-running TV and OAV series has been extremely popular with all stripes of anime fans since it first came out on home video in 1994. The video releases are currently well into the third TV season, known as *Hard Battle*.The premise is that Furinkan High School student Ranma falls into an enchanted Chinese spring and thereafter changes gender from male to female and back again whenever drenched in the appropriate temperature of water. Equal parts of martial arts comedy, gender-bending hijinks, and teenaged romance create a wildly successful and long-running animated series. The first two episodes are on the tape *Ranma 1/2 Hard Battle: Ukyo Can Cook*. Dubbed. 52 mins.

VHS: S27456. $24.95.

Sailor Moon

This animated series is about a gaggle of leggy schoolgirls who just happen to have been magical princesses in former lives. Each girl transforms into her superhero outfit via a stock nude transformation sequence (retouched for US broadcast) and rallies to defend Earth from the usual assortment of bad guys. The episodic superhero action is supplemented by angst-ridden teen romance and female camaraderie. The first volume is a good place to start: *Sailor Moon: A Moon Star Is Born*. Dubbed. 44 mins.

VHS: S33409. $12.95.

The Slayers

Sword-swinging comedic fantasy fare with a red-haired sorceress named Lina Inverse accompanied by a blonde male sidekick who robs from the rich to give to himself. This 26-episode TV series is first and foremost a slapstick comedy, although frequent, heated battles with otherworldly monsters and fantasy role-playing game overtones add some breadth. The balance of episodes will be released during 1998. 100 mins.

VHS (Dubbed): **S29334. $19.95.**
VHS (Subtitled): **S27683. $19.95.**

Streetfighter II Vol. 1

The *Streetfighter II* theatrical feature was a big seller when it was released on home video in 1996. Now the TV series (never aired in America) follows with 29 episodes of kung-fu fightin' action. Based on the Capcom video game, martial arts masters Ken and Ryu return to the screen as they reunite in America. Their adventures begin when Ryu loses a fight with

an Air Force officer named Guile—teaching Ryu the shortcomings of his early training. The first volume contains episodes 1 through 3 of the series. 90 mins.

VHS (Dubbed): **S30902. $19.95.**
VHS (Subtitled): **S30902. $24.95.**

Tenchi Universe

Tenchi Universe is the follow-up TV series to the extremely popular OAV series *Tenchi Muyo*. A typical Japanese schoolboy's life is turned upside down as he slowly tumbles to the fact that he's descended from alien royalty, while being thrust into the middle of a subtle galactic power struggle. Add a collection of extraordinary females all vying for his attention, and you have an adolescent's dream come true. 100 mins.

VHS (Dubbed): **S30491. $24.95.**
VHS (Subtitled): **S30492. $29.95.**
Laser: LD76021. $44.95.

Venus 5

Venus 5 is a currently popular example of the erotic violence category for which anime is so well-known. From the darkness of the past, Necros and the lords of her perverted Inma Empire have been reborn. She plans to revive the god Apollo from his 10,000-year slumber and receive his near-infinite power. But five sexy warriors stand ready to oppose her: the Venus 5—the holy warriors of Venus and the servants of the goddess Aphrodite. Featuring sexy teenage girls, lots of nudity, perversion, sex, violence, and naughty tentacles! Absolutely not for rental or sale to minors. Dubbed. 48 mins.

VHS: S30926. $29.95.

Voltage Fighter Gowcaizer

Based on the hit video game, this new OAV series features all the action you'd expect, along with plenty of busty babes. Its the dawn of the 21st Century, and the planet has been rocked by a series of natural catastrophes—the handiwork of Shizuru Ozaki. Ozaki aspires to something greater than mere mortality, even if it means destroying the Earth. But one young man has the power to stop him: the armored hero Gowcaizer. From the director of the very successful *Battle Arena Toshinden*, *Gowcaizer* delivers all the nudity and violence young anime fans demand. Dubbed. 45 mins.

VHS: S33410. $19.95.

"Funny, isn't it?
One minute you're
standing in the wings.
Next minute, you're
wearing them."

George C. Scott, *Baxter's Beauties of 1933*
segment from Movie, *Movie.*

Pill poppin' finales
Judy Garland
Marilyn Monroe
Margaret Sullavan
Lupe Valez
Montgomery Clift

Public viewing of the
body of silent screen star
Rudolph Valentino,
attended by "tens of
thousands" of viewers is
cut short due to "mass
hysteria"

Prize for worst way to check out
Actor Albert Dekker *(Dr. Cyclops)*
is found dead in his bathroom,
handcuffs hanging on one wrist,
rope around his neck, obscenities
written on his body and hypoder-
mic needle marks on his skin.
Cause of death ruled "accidental."

Director **Pier Paolo
Pasolini** is stabbed and
then run over
by a car by person
or persons unknown.

Death by Diving

Peg Endwistle
(off the Hollywood sign)
Juzo Itami
(off the 12th floor)

Felled by the Elements
Linda Darnell (fire)
Natalie Wood (water)
Carole Lombard (air)
Sonny Bono (earth)

Great Death Scenes
Brando in *The Godfather*
Garbo in *Camille*
Oddjob in *Goldfinger*
Dunaway & Beatty in *Bonnie & Clyde*
Peter Finch in *Network*
Robert Shaw in *Jaws*
Janet Leigh in *Psycho*
Nicole Kidman in *To Die For*
Orson Welles in *Citizen Kane*
Carole Laure in *Sweet Movie*
Millena Dravic *WR: Mysteries of the Organism*
Little Girl in *Frankenstein*
Anna Magnani in *Open City*
Vanessa Redgrave in *Isadora*
Tommy's mother in *Kiss of Death*
Cagney in *White Heat*

Murder

William Desmond Taylor,
Paramount's leading director
of the early 1920's, dies of
gunshot wounds. Suspect
#1? Starlet **Mary Miles
Minter's** mother.

The movies first star,
Florence Lawrence aka
The Biograph Girl, dies
of ingesting
ant poison.

Lana Turner's boyfriend,
Johnny Stampanato,
is stabbed to death by
Lana's daughter,
Cheryl Crane.

The Godfather

Oil tycoon and part-
time Hollywood
investor **John Smith**,
in a grand but fatal
attempt to prove his
love and devotion to
a 14 year old girl
PLUMMETS TO HIS
DEATH while attempt-
ing to cross Niagara
Falls in a barrel.

25 Top Nature Films

Audubon Society Videoguides to the Birds of North America

Combines bird sights and sounds for simple and accurate identification of 505 North American species. Moving and still pictures show each bird's distinctive markings and behavior, with computer-animated range maps showing breeding and wintering areas for each species. Bird calls and sounds from the Cornell Laboratory of Ornithology complement the narration and visuals.
Volume 1: 116 species of loons, grebes, pelicans and their allies, swans, geese and ducks, hawks, vultures and falcons, and the chicken-like birds (pheasants, grouse, quails, ptarmigans). 94 mins.
   VHS: S03211. $29.95.
   Laser: LD70847. $39.95.
Volume 2: 105 species of water birds, including herons and egrets, cranes, shorebirds, gulls, terns and alcids. 78 mins.
   VHS: S03123. $29.95.
   Laser: LD72223. $35.95.
Volume 4: 98 species of songbirds: flycatchers, larks, swallows, crows and jays, titmice and chickadees, nuthatches, creepers, wrens, thrushes, waxwings, shrikes, thrashers and vireos. 75 mins.
   VHS: S05966. $29.95.
   Laser: LD72225. $35.95.

Canary of the Ocean: America's Troubled Reef

Produced by award-winning filmmakers, this engaging film mixes first-person accounts of the Florida reefs before their decline with a look at the variety of human activities found to be causing their ill health. It portrays the stunning beauty of America's fragile undersea kingdom, investigates the serious threats to its health, and profiles some of the concerned people working to preserve it for future generations. Grade 8 to adult. 56 mins.
   VHS: S31911. $89.00.

Carlsbad Caverns & Guadalupe Mountains National Parks

An entirely new video program featuring the Carlsbad Caverns, New Cave and nearby Guadalupe Mountains National Park, exploring how caverns are formed, with detailed closeups of formations, bat flight.
   VHS: S06665. $29.95.

Eruption of Mt. St. Helens

Witness the explosive eruption of Mt. St. Helens and its devastating aftermath as photographed by men who narrowly escaped the Mountain's wrath. Enter the devastated area only hours after the eruption and witness the incredible destruction. 30 mins.
   VHS: S05736. $29.95.

Galapagos: Beyond Darwin

Charles Darwin's historic voyage to the Galapagos islands forever changed our view of the world, but he only scratched the surface. Climb into a state-of-the-art submersible and plunge 3,000 feet beneath the surface as history's first deep-diving expedition to the Galapagos probes where no camera has gone before. Be part of the expedition scientists will be writing about for years as you share the discovery of over two dozen new species and capture creatures never before seen or even named.
   VHS: S30591. $19.95.
   David Clarke/Al Giddings, USA, 1996, 100 mins.

Gardens of the World

Audrey Hepburn hosts this six-part series that looks at more than 50 gardens for their historical, cultural and aesthetic principals. With narration by Hepburn and Michael York.
Country Gardens. This program studies the pleasures of country gardens, with their pungent sense of smell, taste and touch. Audrey Hepburn looks at imposing gardens such as the Giardino del Ninfa, cottage gardens in England and farmhouse gardens connected to Chilcombe House in Dorset (UK). Commentary by garden designers John Brookes and Ryan Gainey. 27 mins.
   VHS: S20325. $24.95.
Flower Gardens. Claude Monet's garden at Giverny showcases the proper display of flowers. The color schemes beautifully contrast with the grace and elegance of the borders specific to the Tintinhull House in Somerset, England. The program also studies the native flora of America's Southwest. With special commentary by Penelope Hobhouse. 27 mins.
   VHS: S20324. $24.95.
Formal Gardens. Audrey Hepburn shows the evolution of formal design, visiting the luscious gardens of Renaissance-period Italy, the luminous 17th-century gardens of France, and England's elaborate 20th-century gardens. With guest commentary by garden authority Penelope Hobhouse. 27 mins.
   VHS: S20323. $24.95.
Public Gardens and Trees. Audrey Hepburn travels to the elegantly restored gardens at Mt. Vernon, formerly owned by George Washington. Hepburn also discusses the diversity and vast number of public gardens in Paris, including the "pocket parks," the grand royal gardens. 27 mins.
   VHS: S20326. $24.95.
Roses and Rose Gardens. Audrey Hepburn studies the historical importance of the rose, which has a deep symbolic meaning relevant to legend, romance and beauty. With a lecture by author Graham Stuart Thomas. 27 mins.
   VHS: S20321. $24.95.
Tulips and Spring Bulbs. Audrey Hepburn reveals the vast history of bulbs and their connection to the history of Holland. The program shows the bulb's transformation from sleeping bulb to full bloom. 27 mins.
   VHS: S20322. $24.95.
Gardens of the World, Set. The complete set of six programs is a collector's edition preserved in a beautiful box set.
   VHS: S20327. $139.95.

Post-Apocalyptic Visions

12 Monkeys
VHS: S28391. $19.98.
Laser: LD75702. $49.95.

Black Rain
VHS: S14068. $19.98.

A Boy and His Dog
VHS: S25715. $29.95.
Laser: LD75446. $49.95.

The Day the Earth Caught Fire
VHS: S29950. $9.98.

Kerouac
VHS: S00671. $29.95.

La Jetee
VHS: S18956. $19.95.

Le Dernier Combat
Out of print. For rental only.

Lord of the Flies
VHS: S18755. $29.95.
Laser: LD72099. $49.95.

On the Beach
VHS: S02557. $19.98.

Planet of the Apes
VHS: S12171. $19.98.

Road Warrior
DVD: DV60054. $24.98.
VHS: S01801. $14.95.
Laser: LD70739. $29.98.

Silent Running
VHS: S01200. $19.95.
Laser: LD70079. $34.95.

The Terminator
VHS: S05716. $19.99.

Testament
VHS: S01312. $14.95.
Laser: LD75338. $29.95.

In the Wild: Dolphins with Robin Williams

Robin Williams hosts this intimate portrait of creatures many believe to be highly intelligent and affectionate. Plenty of information about dolphins is provided by experts, but the most intriguing aspect of this video is the personal rapport Williams cultivates with them. 60 mins.
VHS: S27775. $19.98.

Lewis & Clark

This latest installment in Ken Burns' prolific American Lives series is the definitive work on Lewis & Clark, presented from a "you-are-there" perspective as the explorers search for a water route from east to west on their journey with the Corps of Discovery. Two-tape set.
VHS: S32367. $29.98.
Ken Burns, USA, 1997, 240 mins.

Maneaters of Tsavo

This documentary revisits Colonel John Patterson's spine-chilling account of the two lions responsible for the deaths of nearly 200 railway workers in Southern Kenya. Travel to Africa and uncover the incredible facts behind the hit film *The Ghost & The Darkness*, based on the same story. Features interviews with the film's stars, Michael Douglas and Val Kilmer, as well as director Stephen Hopkins.
VHS: S31178. $19.98.

National Geographic Video—Beauty and the Beasts: A Leopard's Story

Follow the fascinating lives of a great cat and a curious warthog, intertwined since birth, against the dramatic backdrop of the South African wilderness. 60 mins.
VHS: S32507. $19.98.

Out of the Way Cafe

A fictional film for adults that explores serious questions about the changing American landscape with a light and poignant touch. With imagery that critics have compared to the paintings of Edward Hopper, *Out of the Way Cafe* has been honored by the Uppsala Short Film Festival in Sweden and broadcast on national Swedish television and PBS. High school to adult. 1995, 51 mins.
VHS: S31914. $69.95.

Reader's Digest: Great Splendors of the World

Three-volume collectors edition as seen on The Disney Channel. "Splendors of Nature" follows the course of the seasons to explore five of nature's greatest events. "Ancient Splendors" explores four of the most magnificent sites in human antiquity: Egypt's temples at Thebes, The Acropolis in Athens, Guatemala's temple-pyramids at Tikal and Cambodia's Angkor Wat. "Imperial Splendors" tells the stories of great empires and their rulers and the secret world hidden behind palace doors.
VHS: S30459. $59.95.

The Snow Wolves

Narrated by Joseph Campanella, this powerful film features rare and intimate footage of nature's most mysterious canines in the wild at Yellowstone and Denali National Parks and the Canadian Arctic. 60 mins.
VHS: S32407. $14.95.

Thor Heyerdahl: Explorer and Scientist

A portrait of the colorful 82-year-old Norwegian explorer and scientist who became world famous with his Kon-Tiki expedition in 1947 when, with a crew of five, he drifted 8000 kilometers on a balsa raft from Peru to Polynesia. 52 mins.
VHS: S32387. $24.95.

Tornado! Hurricane! Flood! Wonders of Weather

Every year thousands of American lives are uprooted and lost to our most violent storm systems. Join professional storm chasers and charge into the eye of the storm to witness nature's brute force firsthand. Through unforgettable footage you'll experience a category 5 hurricane, see twisters spinning up to 300 miles per hour, watch deadly lightening bolts ignite the sky and hear one survivor's story, and track devastating flash floods from the first raindrop until people are clinging to treetops as their cars and homes float away.
VHS: S30592. $19.95.
Yavar Abbas/Richard Burke/Martin Gorse, USA, 1996, 90 mins.

Tropical Rainforest

This IMAX documentary film explores the incredible diversity of life found in the world's rain forests, as well as the problems faced by these fragile ecosystems. 90% of the world's species are found here and yet many of these may become extinct before they are even discovered. Filmed in Australia, Central and South America, and Asia. 40 mins.
VHS: S22666. $29.95.
Laser: LD74550. $39.95.

100 Super Kids Movies

101 Dalmatians
Glenn Close chews the scenery as the flamboyantly wicked Cruella DeVil, along with 101 black-and-white canines, in this live-action Disney hit based on the Disney animated classic. With Jeff Daniels, Joan Plowright and Joely Richardson. Produced and written by John Hughes.
VHS: $31391. $26.99.
Laser: THX. **LD76378. $29.99.**
Stephen Herek, 1996, USA, 103 mins.

Adventures of Milo and Otis
A live action children's adventure story about the exploits of Milo the dog and Otis the cat, narrated by Dudley Moore. Called "delightfully pure and fresh" by the *L.A. Times*. See for yourself how much mischief one canine and one feline can get into in the Land of the Rising Sun.
VHS: $11483. $19.95.
Masanori Hata, Japan/USA, 1989, 89 mins.

Alef...Bet...Blast-Off!
This award-winning series will help families discover how traditional Jewish values apply to modern life and fill a child's heart with the pride and joy of being Jewish, as the intrepid Jewish explorer Mitvah Mouse whisks David and Rachel back in time to meet some of the most important people in Jewish history.
Alef...Bet...Blast-Off!: A Whale of a New Year. David and Rachel meet a talented young Russian immigrant, Talli, who tries to teach the kids about freedom. It's hard for the kids to understand how important freedom is until an unexpected twist causes David, Rachel, Talli and Mitzvah Mouse to become personal slaves to the Pharoah (Dom DeLuise). 30 mins.
VHS: $32307. $14.95.
Alef...Bet...Blast-Off!: Lights of Freedom. David is always losing things. Though he tries to improve himself for Rosh Hashana (Jewish New Year), he still manages to lose his sister Rachel's beloved goldfish. Rachel is so upset that she can't forgive David. But thanks to Mitvah Mouse, a trip to a whale's belly, and a heart-to-heart with Jonah himself (Avery Schreiber), David learns to accept responsibility. 30 mins.
VHS: $32306. $14.95.

Alexander and the Terrible, Horrible, No Good, Very Bad Day
Everything goes wrong for Alexander in this animated version of Judith Viorst's delightful book. From gum in his hair to bullies in the yard, the world seems to conspire against Alexander until he decides to move to Australia. 30 mins.
VHS: $23276. $12.95.

Alphabet Soup
Artist William Wegman's dog Fay and her offspring, Batty, Chundo and Crooky, teach kids the about the alphabet. They do everything to make these lessons memorable, from balancing a boat on Fay's head to making alphabet soup. Don't forget the apples and zucchini! Ages 3 and up.
VHS: $26141. $12.95.
William Wegman, USA, 1995, 30 mins.

Anne of Avonlea
The critically-acclaimed sequel to the award-winning *Anne of Green Gables*, with Colleen Dewhurst, Wendy Hiller and Megan Follows as Anne Shirley. "Destined to tug at hearts, young and old, for decades to come" (*San Francisco Chronicle*).
VHS: $11443. $29.95.
Laser: LD70838. $39.99.
Kevin Sullivan, Canada, 1987, 224 mins.

Anne of Green Gables
A tender and humorous coming-of-age tale starring Anne Shirley and Tom Brown.
Laser: LD70839. $39.99.
George Nicholls, USA, 1934, 79 mins.

Annie
Aileen Quinn, Carol Burnett and Albert Finney star in this adaptation of the Broadway hit based on the comic strip. With Tim Curry and Bernadette Peters.
VHS: $01884. $12.95.
John Huston, USA, 1981, 128 mins.

Arthur's Eyes
The popular animated PBS series based on Marc Brown's award-winning books. Follow the imaginative adventures of eight-year-old Arthur, his little sister, D.W., and their friends and family. Contains two episodes. 30 mins.
VHS: $31440. $12.99.

Babar: The Movie
A feature-length, animated adventure. The kingdom is threatened by an invasion of very mean rhinos and it is up to young Babar to save the day. With the help of his friends in the animal kingdom, he attempts to use a positive mental attitude and a little cunning to beat the evil rhino horde.
VHS: $11696. $12.95.
Alan Bunce, USA, 1988, 79 mins.

Babe
Wonderful special effects make this film a magical and captivating experience that kids and adults can both enjoy. Babe, a pig, arrives on a farm where all the animals have a purpose. Through his ambitions, he makes friends among all the animals and changes forever the utilitarian view that would have destined him for the dinner table. George Miller (*Mad Max*) co-produced this wonderful barnyard fable.
VHS: $27088. $14.98.
Laser: LD75448. $34.98.
Chris Noonan, USA, 1995, 92 mins.

Bach and Broccoli
A truly wonderful film for children—and family—from Andre Melancon, the director of *The Dog Who Stopped the War*, winner of the Best Film prize at the 1987 Chicago International Festival of Children's Films. In *Bach and Broccoli*, 11-year-old Fanny meets her uncle Jonathan for the first time. They are strong-willed, independent people who are worlds apart. Fanny's best friend, Broccoli, her pet skunk, adds to the hilarity in this humorous tale of the odd couple as they learn to love and need each other. Produced by Rock Demers.
VHS: $06616. $14.95.
Andre Melancon, Canada, 1987, 96 mins.

Balto
Balto is a part husky and part wolf and, as a result, an outcast among canines. Fortunately, his other animal friends cherish him for his noble spirit. This side of Balto comes to the foreground when a blizzard cuts off his village and the local children desperately need medicine. This animated feature stars the voices of Kevin Bacon, Bridget Fonda, Bob Hoskins and Phil Collins.
VHS: $27430. $19.95.
Laser: LD75503. $34.95.
Simon Wells, USA, 1995, 78 mins.

Bambi
The classic animated Disney feature about a young deer named Bambi, who looses his mother and learns to fend for himself with other members of the forest family like rabbits, owls and skunks. May be too

intense for young viewers.
VHS: S08700. $26.95.
David Hand, USA, 1942, 69 mins.

Beethoven's 2nd
Charles Grodin stars in this story of dog family life. Beethoven the St. Bernard meets Missy, and the result is a houseful of puppies. Sadly Missy is the pawn in a human divorce. Debi Mazar plays the cruel kidnapper who jeopardizes this young canine family. It's a perfect film for kids.
VHS: S21865. $24.98.
Laser: Letterboxed. LD74933. $24.98.
Rod Daniel, USA, 1993, 88 mins.

Beneath the Ghost Moon
Jane Yolone narrates this video presentation of her Halloween tale of a courageous mouse. She convinces her friends that their home is worth fighting for and reminds them of the importance of forgiveness, especially after the mean-hearted creepy-crawlies destroy the mice's costumes designed for the upcoming Ghost Eve Ball. For grades K-3.
VHS: S31441. $44.99.

Benji
America's most lovable mutt, in his first feature film. Benji saves two kids from kidnappers and wins a home and a place in everyone's heart.
VHS: S04866. $19.99.
Joe Camp, USA, 1974, 86 mins.

Benji Takes a Dive at Marineland
America's huggable hero takes on Marineland, and comes up swimming.
VHS: S06342. $19.98.
Joe Camp, USA, 60 mins.

Black Beauty
A superb British cast, including Sean Bean, David Thewlis and Andrew Knott, is featured in this most faithful film version of Anna Sewell's delightful novel. Children have always loved this story of an indomitable black horse who personifies freedom. Everyone who came into contact with this magnificent animal was touched by his spirit.
VHS: S22412. $19.98.
Laser: LD74605. $34.98.
Caroline Thompson, USA, 1994, 88 mins.

Babe

The Black Stallion
An exciting viewing experience for all ages, *The Black Stallion* follows the adventures of a young boy and his magnificent Arabian horse. With Teri Garr, Hoyt Axton and Mickey Rooney, presented by Francis F. Coppola.
DVD: DV60103. $24.98.
VHS: S00140. $19.95.
Laser: LD70527. $34.98.
Carroll Ballard, USA, 1979, 118 mins.

The Black Stallion Returns
A sequel to the popular *Black Stallion* in which Kelly Reno loses his horse in Morocco and only gets him back after a series of hair-raising adventures.
VHS: S12428. $19.98.
Laser: LD76194. $39.98.
Robert Dalva, USA, 1983, 93 mins.

The Borrowers
Based on the best selling classic by Mary Norton, this wonderful children's film follows the adventures of a wee family who live under the floorboards of an English house until they decide to leave for the great outdoors. Starring Ian Holm and Sian Phillips, and hosted by Richard Lewis.
VHS: S21055. $14.98.
Laser: LD74461. $49.99.
John Henderson, Great Britain, 1993, 199 mins.

The Brave Little Toaster
Five electrical appliances in a country cottage suddenly feel dumped when their young owner mysteriously disappears. Together they set off for the big city in search of their beloved master, their quest becoming an unforgettable journey. "A family film in the truest sense of the term: one that adults can enjoy as well as children!" (LA Times).
VHS: S14257. $22.95.
Jerry Rees, USA, 1984, 90 mins.

Brer Rabbit and the Wonderful Tar Baby
The comic adventures of that original American troublemaker, Brer Rabbit—Bugs Bunny's great grandfather—are among the funniest and most cherished stories of our culture. The classic and hilarious tale of how he outsmarts his wily nemesis, Brer Fox, with a clever contraption he calls a "tar baby", in the story read by Danny Glover.
VHS: S12475. $9.95.

Bridge to Terabithia
Katherine Paterson's powerful story about a poor boy and an imaginative girl who share a secret hiding place they call Terabithia. But their friendship is severed when she is accidentally killed. 33 mins.
VHS: S13235. $14.95.

Caddie Woodlawn
This fanciful story is based on the Newbery Award-winning book by Carol Ryrie Brink. A high-spirited frontier girl actively opposes warlike frontiersmen who try to ambush a Native American tribe. Ages 8 and up, 120 mins.
VHS: S24275. $19.95.

Cats Don't Dance
Disney's full-length animated musical about Danny, a cool cat from Kokomo, Indiana, who dreams of making it big in Hollywood. Along the way, Danny meets a band of fun-loving animal actors. Featuring the vocal talents of Scott Bakula, Jasmine Guy, Don Knotts, George Kennedy and Kathy Najimy, original songs by Randy Newman performed by Natalie Cole, and dance sequence choreography by Gene Kelly.
VHS: S31640. $22.95.
Laser: LD76249. $34.95.
Mark Dindal, USA, 1996, 77 mins.

Charlie Brown Christmas
The Peanuts gang discovers the true meaning of Christmas in this modern holiday classic. Animated. 30 mins.
VHS: S09513. $12.95.

Charlotte's Web
One of the enduring children's films, this is a story of friendship and salvation, with Charlotte the spider trying to save her friend Wilbur the pig from the bacon factory. Wonderful animation, and with the voices of Debbie Reynolds, Paul Lunde and Agnes Moorehead.
VHS: S00230. $14.95.
Charles A. Nichols, USA, 1979, 94 mins.

Chess Kids

Chess Kids

With humor and sensitivity, this award-winning documentary goes behind the scenes of the largest World Youth Chess Tournament ever held in the United States, capturing the intensity and excitement of competitive chess. Meet Josh Waitzkin, the real-life subject of *Searching for Bobby Fischer*, and 12-year-old Judit Polgar, the best female player of all time. Featured at the 1996 Chicago International Children's Film Festival. "Chess aficionados and people who simply enjoy a well-made documentary with fascinating interviewees will appreciate this fun film" (R. Pitman, *Video Librarian*).
VHS: $30660. $29.95.
Lynn Hamrick, USA, 1996, 51 mins.

Chitty Chitty Bang Bang

Dick Van Dyke is a slightly offbeat inventor in this modern fairy tale about a magical car. Charming songs, whimsical humor, wonderful special effects and enough suspense to make this a treat for the

whole family.
VHS: $00236. $19.98.
Laser: Letterboxed, chapter search. Includes
original theatrical trailer. **LD71647. $39.98.**
Ken Hughes, USA, 1968, 143 mins.

The Chronicles of Narnia
This video collection features the magical land of
Narnia, with its mythical creatures, menacing villains
and marvelous heroes. Based on the wonderful series
of books by C.S. Lewis. Set of three 2-tape volumes.
VHS: $19403. $79.95.

Cinderella (1950)
Walt Disney's animated classic feature based on the
Charles Perrault fairy tale tells the magical tale of an
abused young woman with the only foot in the
kingdom to fit a certain glass slipper. With the help of
her fairy godmother and a few small animals she
dazzles the prince on her night off from household
drudgery. With the voices of Ilene Woods, Eleanor
Audley, William Phipps and Verna Felton as the
magic wand waver.
VHS: $07785. $26.95.
**Wilfred Jackson/Clyde Geronimi/Hamilton Luske,
USA, 1950, 74 min.**

Cinderella (1997)
Disney's new presentation of sibling rivalry, love at
first sight and beauty within. Featuring the voices of
Whitney Houston as the fairy godmother, Brandy as
Cinderella, Whoopi Goldberg, Jason Alexander and
Bernadette Peters and the music of Rogers and
Hammerstein.
VHS: $32932. $19.99.

Curious George
Based on the books by Margaret and H.A. Rey
featuring the adventures of the mischievous little
monkey George, this is a puppet animation version.
Ages 2-6. **1986.**
VHS: $24771. $12.95.

Ellis Island
This "lovingly assembled" (*People Magazine*) three-
tape program uses hundreds of interviews,
photographs, films and recreations from the Ellis
Island Oral History Project to tell the incredible
stories of immigration to America through the
"golden door," whose entrance, for over half a
century, meant an opportunity for a new life. Narrated
by Mandy Patinkin. Three 50-min. tapes.
VHS: $31296. $49.95.
Lisa Bourgoujian, USA, 1997, 150 mins.

Fearless Frida and the Secret Spies
Frida (Annette Brandt) is a curious little girl who
always leads her friends into mischief. Armed with a
camcorder, Frida and her friends accidentally
discover truly illicit activity. Once they have the tape
to prove it, these kids are under the gun to outwit the
criminals. If they succeed they could become heroes.
Dubbed in English.
VHS: $27166. $59.95.
Soren Ole Christensen, Denmark, 1995, 71 mins.

Fly Away Home
One of the most critically acclaimed films of the year,
Fly Away Home is the adventure of a teenage girl and
her estranged father, who learn about family when
they take in a flock of orphaned geese and find that
they must teach them how to fly. Starring Academy
Award-winner Anna Paquin (*The Piano*) and Jeff
Daniels. "Soaring! A hymn to the human spirit!"
(Richard Schickel, *Time*).
DVD: DV60025. $24.95.
VHS: $30576. $24.99.
Laser: LD76073. $34.95.
Carroll Ballard, USA, 1996, 107 mins.

Forever Fairytales—
Hans Christian Andersen
This two-volume gift set features four lesser-known
gems from the beloved storyteller's vast collection.
The heroines in both Andersen's *The Wild Swans* and
The Brave Duckling must overcome great adversity to
restore happiness in their lives. *The Woodcutter's
Wish* and *The Amazing Gift* are two tales in which
heroes are given a gift of magic. 128 mins.
VHS: $32423. $19.98.

Fun in a Box #1: Ben's Dream
This award-winning film promotes positive values
and offers ideas for fun and games. From acclaimed
author Chris Van Allsburg. Also includes *Fish* and
The Red Ball Express. 30 mins.
VHS: $16309. $14.95.

Gay Purr-ee
The voice of the great Judy Garland highlights this
colorful, feature-length cartoon about a country cat
who finds amour—and danger—in turn-of-the-
century Paris. Other celebrity voices include: Robert
Goulet, Red Buttons, Hermione Gingold (*Gigi*) and
the late Mel Blanc. Co-written by animation great
Chuck Jones.
VHS: $13441. $14.95.
Laser: LD70580. $34.95.
Abe Levitow, USA, 1962, 85 mins.

A Girl of the Limberlost
A poetic adaptation of Gene Stratton Porter's
sensitive study about a young girl's maturity in the
rural countryside of the Midwest at the turn of the
century. With Joanna Cassidy and Annette O'Toole.
111 mins.
VHS: $13239. $19.95.

Gulliver's Travels
Max Fleischer's evocation of Jonathan Swift's classic
fantasy of the sailor Gulliver, shipwrecked on the
shores of Lilliput, is one of the high achievements of
Hollywood animation. The Lilliputians are only
thumb-high, but they're as cantankerous and perhaps
more determined than humans. A delight.
VHS: $18185. $19.95.
Max Fleischer, USA, 1939, 71 mins.

Handel's Last Chance
Set in 18th-century Dublin, this enchanting film for
kids—the last in the award-winning Composers'
Specials series—tells the captivating story of Jamie, a
boy with a golden voice who is down on his luck, and
Handel, the great composer, whose career is failing.
Given one last chance to prove themselves, Jamie and
Handel learn to trust each other and believe in their
own talents. Joining forces, the two make the first
performances of *The Messiah* a resounding success.
50 mins.
VHS: $30652. $19.98.

Happily Ever After Fairy Tales:
Beauty and the Beast
Gregory Hines, Vanessa Williams (Beauty) and
Debbie Allen provide the voices for this animated,
multicultural version of the favorite children's story.
The African theme is just one element that makes this
video so different. It also features terrific Broadway-
style music and singing. 30 mins.
VHS: $29845. $9.98.

The Hardly Boys in Hardly Gold
In William Wegman's first feature film, doggy
detectives the Hardly Boys, have returned to
Rangeley Lake for another relaxing summer at the
Hardly Inn with their friend, Chip Mason. But soon
the boys find themselves enmeshed in a perplexing
mystery that puts their sleuthing kills and secret dog
powers to the test.
VHS: $33003. $19.95.
William Wegman, USA, 1997, 30 mins.

Harold and the Purple Crayon
and Other Harold Stories
Gene Deitch, the world's foremost animator of classic
children's books, explains how he learned from
Crockett Johnson. *Harold and the Purple Crayon*,
Harold's Fairy Tale and *A Picture for Harold's Room*
are animated shorts that make this video a delight for
children. 30 mins.
VHS: $22166. $14.95.

Harriet the Spy
Louise Fitzhugh's classic children's story about 11-
year-old Harriet (Michele Trachtenberg), who dreams
of being a writer. Harriet's nanny and best friend
Golly (Rosie O'Donnell) tells Harriet to start by
writing down everything she sees. But soon Harriet
gets into trouble with her friends when they find her
secret spy notebook. Featured at the 1996 Chicago
International Children's Film Festival. "One of the
top ten family films of all time" (Ted Baehr, *Movie
Guide*).
VHS: $30462. $19.95.
Laser: LD76171. $39.98.
Bronwen Hughes, USA, 1996, 102 mins.

Heidi
A family classic that should be part of every
childhood, featuring curly-haired Shirley Temple as
the orphaned girl who goes to live with her
grandfather on a Swiss mountaintop.
VHS: $00560. $19.98.
Allan Dwan, USA, 1937, 88 mins.

Curious George

The Indian in the Cupboard

A young boy experiences a series of unexpected adventures when one of his toys, an Indian figure, miraculously comes alive. There is also a diminutive cowboy action figure that shares the fun. Together they experience conflicts and humorous situations in a plot that is sure to delight kids.
VHS: S26661. $19.95.
Frank Oz, USA, 1995, 97 mins.

Jacob Have I Loved

Based on the popular novel by Katherine Paterson. Bridget Fonda stars in this thoughtful study in sibling rivalry. Louise (Fonda) has always felt that her sister was the favored child and so sets out to find her own special place in her small world. Produced by KCET-TV. 60 mins.
VHS: S12396. $19.95.

James and the Giant Peach

Hailed as "one of the most magical films of the decade" (KNX Radio, Los Angeles), this Walt Disney stop-motion animated feature based on the Roald Dahl book tells the story of a boy named James and his quest to reach New York City, a place where, he believes, dreams come true. Traveling with James are human-sized, talking insect friends, led by Academy Award winners Susan Sarandon as Miss Spider and Richard Dreyfuss as the Centipede. The all-star vocal cast also features Jane Leeves (*Frasier*), Joanna Lumley (*Absolutely Fabulous*) and Simon Callow (*Four Weddings and a Funeral*). From the director of *Nightmare Before Christmas*, with a score by Grammy award-winner Randy Newman.
VHS: S28523. $22.95.
Henry Selick, USA, 1995, 79 mins.

Land Before Time

An animated feature directed by Don Bluth (*An American Tail*) about cute and cuddly baby dinosaurs. Presented by George Lucas and Steven Spielberg, five young dinos take a perilous journey to find their parents and a legendary valley with lots of food. A tiny brontosaurus named Little Foot is the hero. A cranky tyrannosaurus is the relentless villain.
Laser: CAV. LD74945. $49.95.
Don Bluth, USA, 1988, 70 mins.

Lassie

The canine hero of all times is back in this full-length adventure film. When the Turner family moves to Virginia, they encounter a number of problems, both financial and domestic. Fortunately the relationship between a boy and his dog can weather even the most insurmountable troubles.
VHS: S22889. $95.95.
Daniel Petrie, USA, 1994, 95 mins.

The Leopard Son

This beautifully photographed, award-winning film is the story of a leopard cub's passage from innocent

infant to skilled, proud adult. Narrated by Sir John Gielgud. "Breathtaking…beautiful…a real life *Lion King* (Philip Murphy, *L.A. Parent Magazine*).
VHS: S31144. $14.98.
Hugo van Lawick, USA, 1996, 84 mins.

Linnea in Monet's Garden

The delightful best-selling children's book is now an animated feature. Linnea and her friend Bloom travel from Sweden to Monet's garden. While they are enjoying this magical and inspirational place, it comes to life.
VHS: S22181. $19.95.
Lena Anderson/Christina Bjork, Sweden, 1993, 30 mins.

Liszt's Rhapsody

Franz Liszt craved the creative outlet of musical composition and was acclaimed for his skills as a pianist. In this story, a young Gypsy violinist appears who helps him achieve his greatest success. This film is perfect for children. It is the third episode from the Emmy Award-winning *The Composer's Specials* series.
VHS: S27417. $19.98.
David Devine, USA, 1995, 53 mins.

The Little Mermaid

Fully restored special edition of Disney's animated masterpiece. "Show-stopping songs accompany the best animated Disney film in at least 30 years" (Janet Maslin, *The New York Times*).
VHS: S33372. $26.95.
John Musker/Ron Clements, USA, 1989, 83 mins.

The Littlest Angel

Sixties baby-boomers may remember this delightful musical rendition of Charles Tazwell's best-selling Christmas story, which first aired on TV in 1969. A little boy, Michael (Johnny Whitaker, of TV's *Family Affair*), has a fatal fall and lands in heaven. Patience (Fred Gwynne) is assigned as his guardian angel. But the little angel cannot adjust to heavenly life and wants to return to earth to retrieve his special hand-made box of found treasures. He learns a valuable lesson about the spirit of giving. Also stars Tony Randall, Connie Stevens, Cab Calloway, and E.G Marshall as God. 77 mins.
VHS: S30187. $12.95.

Madeline in London

Madeline and the rest of the boarding school visit a friend in London. Madeline gets caught up in adventures and even receives a medal from the queen. Ages 3-12. 30 mins.
VHS: S24548. $12.95.

Mary Poppins

This beloved Disney film combines brilliant, animated sequences with a delightful story about Julie Andrews as a magical nanny who transforms the lives of the children in her care. With Dick Van Dyke, Glynis Johns, Ed Wynn.
VHS: S01589. $24.95.
Laser: LD71132. $44.95.
Robert Stevenson, USA, 1964, 140 mins.

The Maurice Sendak Library

Three great stories by Maurice Sendak. First, four little poems set to music from Sendak's *The Nutshell Library: Alligators All Around, Pierre, One Was Johnny* and *Chicken Soup with Rice*. Then, *Where the Wild Things Are*, one of Sendak's classics. Finally, *In the Night Kitchen*, a little boy dreams of a special time in the kitchen when bakers bake cake, dough airplanes fly, and everyone dances to the deliciously syncopated music. Includes *Getting to Know Maurice Sendak*, a personal talk with the author/illustrator! 35 mins.
VHS: S11229. $14.95.

Mikhail Baryshnikov's Stories from My Childhood

Based on the works of acclaimed writers, these delightful fairy tales, hand-picked by world-renowned dancer and actor Mikhail Baryshnikov from the completely restored animated archives of Russia's premier production studio, Soyuzmultfilm, will entertain all generations and cultures. The series has earned awards at the Venice, London and Moscow film festivals. A portion of the proceeds from these titles will be donated to The Audrey Hepburn Hollywood for Children Fund.
Alice and the Mystery of the Third Planet. Kirsten Dunst, Jim Belushi and Harvey Fierstein provide the voices for this adventure story which chronicles the crew of the space ship *Pegasus* as they search for

unusual and exotic animals to bring back to a zoo on earth.
VHS: S30507. $12.98.
Beauty and the Beast: A Tale of the Crimson Flower. Amy Irving, Tim Curry and Robert Loggia star in Pushkin's version of this timeless love story.
VHS: S30506. $12.98.
The Twelve Months. Lolita Davidovich and Amanda Plummer are featured in this tale of a young girl who is sent by her mean stepmother into the woods to find snow flowers for the Queen, who has promised gold to anyone who brings her these rare and beautiful flowers.
VHS: S30508. $12.98.

Miracle at Moreaux
Loretta Swit stars in this compelling drama based on a true story. In World War II occupied France, a nun and her young charges risk their lives to harbor a group of Jewish children escaping from the Nazis. 60 mins.
VHS: S12402. $14.95.

Mr. Toad's Wild Ride
Monty Python meets Walt Disney in this wonderful tale that will delight kids and adults alike. Based on the Kenneth Grahame children's novel *The Wind in the Willows*, *Mr. Toad's Wild Ride* sends Mr. Toad, Rat and Mole on an exciting journey filled with fun and misadventure. Starring Pythoners John Cleese, Eric Idle, Terry Jones and Michael Palin. 88 mins.
VHS: S32349. $14.98.
Laser: LD76353. $39.99.

My Neighbor Totoro
This charming animation features the lovable, over-sized creatures called Totoros, who possess qualities that make them children's best friends. In this enchanting fantasy they will warm your heart and delight you with their magical antics.
VHS: S21354. $19.95.
Laser: LD74635. $29.95.
Hayao Miyazaki, Japan, 1993, 76 mins.

Old Yeller—40th Anniversary Limited Edition
Disney's classic boy-and-his-dog film is presented in this special, fully restored, 40th-anniversary edition. With Chuck Connors. "Still one of the best!" (Leonard Maltin).
VHS: S32290. $19.95.
Laser: THX. LD76379. $29.99.
Robert Stevenson, USA, 1957, 84 mins.

Oliver!
The musical version of Dicken's classic *Oliver Twist* adds song and dance to the story of a brave lad trying to survive amidst wretched social conditions and dire poverty. With Mark Lester as Oliver and Jack Wild as the Artful Dodger. Ron Moody is Fagin. Also Oliver Reed, Shani Wallis and Hugh Griffith. Six Oscars.
VHS: 00952. $19.95.
Laser: LD72187. $39.95.
Carol Reed, Great Britain, 1968, 153 mins.

Panda and the Magic Serpent
An animated feature from Japan narrated in English by Marvin Miller, the man who distributed the checks on *The Millionaire*. Panda and Mimi the raccoon travel with Hsu Hsien, a young man, through the Chinese countryside and meet wizards, magic snakes and fish, and the all-powerful dragon god.
VHS: S05473. $24.95.
Kazuhiko Okabe, Japan, 1961, 74 mins.

Pee-Wee's Collector's Gift Set
Eight volumes of the award-winning *Pee-Wee's Playhouse* 1986/87 television series are presented in this gift set. Episodes include "Open House," "Pee-Wee Catches a Cold," "I Remember Curtis," "Conky's Breakdown," "Store," "Playhouse in Outer Space," "Pajama Party" and "To Tell the Tooth." Stars Paul Reubens as Pee-Wee, Laurence Fishburne as Cowboy Curtis, and Phil Hartman as Captain Carl. 224 mins.
VHS: S28485. $99.92.

Pee-Wee's Collector's Gift Set: Vols. 9-16
The secret word is fun with these 14 episodes from the Emmy Award-winning series. Each tape includes two half-hour episodes. Volume 9 includes *Dr. Pee-Wee and the Del Rubios* and *Rebarella*; Volume 10 includes *Let's Play Office* and *Mystery*; Volume 11 includes *Front Page Pee-Wee* and *Tango Time*; Volume 12 includes *Playhouse Day* and *Accidental Playhouse*; Volume 13 includes *Ice Cream Soup* and

Puppy in the Playhouse; Volume 14 includes *The Cowboy and the Countess* and *Reba Eats and Pterri Runs*; Volume 15 includes *Tons of Fun* and *School*; and Volume 16 includes *Why Wasn't I Invited?* and *Ants in Your Pants*.
VHS: S31519. $99.92.

Phantom Tollbooth
Milo drives into animated fantasyland through the phantom tollbooth into the Kingdom of Wisdom. Rescued from danger by a ticking watch dog named Tock, Milo embarks on a mission to end the terrible feud between numbers and words by rescuing Rhyme and Reason from the Castle in the Air.
VHS: S01020. $19.95.
Laser: LD76386. $29.98.
Chuck Jones, USA, 1967, 90 mins.

Pippi Longstocking
The famous children's book by Astrid Lindgren is transformed into a film. Set in a small town in Sweden, Pippi, the red-haired girl, beguiles the local children with her stories and antics, accompanied by her monkey and her horse. In this story, Pippi is brought into conflict with tramps who are after her gold, and with Miss Prusselius, the school mistress, who wants to put her into a home.
VHS: S01032. $19.95.
Olle Hellbron, Sweden, 1973, 99 mins.

The Rabbit Ears Collection: Follow the Drinking Gourd
Subtitled *A Story of the Underground Railroad*, Morgan Freeman narrates this tale, adapted from the folksong, about one family's bid for freedom, achieved through the Underground Railroad. The gritty blues score is by Taj Mahal. 30 mins.
VHS: S17888. $19.98.

Red Balloon
A classic childhood fantasy with appeal for viewers of every age. This is a story of Pascal, a French boy who befriends a red balloon which follows him everywhere. A touching allegory of the magic powers of love and friendship. No dialog.
VHS: S01098. $14.95.
Albert Lamorisse, France, 1956, 34 mins.

Red Balloon/White Mane
Albert Lamorisse's *Red Balloon* is a priceless classic about a young boy's friendship with a red balloon. 1956, 38 mins. His *White Mane* explores man's relationship to nature; it chronicles the efforts of bandits to capture a wild white stallion, and a young boy who rescues him. Winner of the International Grand Prize, Best Short Film, Cannes Film Festival. 1952, 38 mins.
VHS: S18762. $24.95.
Laser: LD70443. $29.95.

Fly Away Home

Rich Little's Christmas Carol
Snow is falling, shoppers are scurrying about, bells are ringing…Christmas time is here with a twist from the comic genius of master impressionist Rich Little. Here, Little plays the whole gang! W.C. Fields is the sourest scrooge you'll ever see. Paul Lynde is poor Bob Cratchit; Richard Nixon is Marley's Ghost.
VHS: S12476. $14.95.

Rossini's Ghost
Produced by Emmy Award-winner David Devine (*Beethoven Lives Upstairs*), *Rossini's Ghost* is the fifth program in The Composers' Specials series. Set in 1816, it is the story of a composer whose friends

Shiloh

never lose faith in him, even when everything is going wrong. With an invisible little girl as his assistant, Rossini overcomes the disastrous opening night of *The Barber of Seville* to give the world one of its most beloved operas.
VHS: S30585. $19.98.
David Devine, USA, 1994, 50 mins.

Runaway
Based on Felice Holman's novel *Slake's Limbo*, this film concerns the plight of a boy who retreats from society, living underground in the subway ducts underneath New York City's massive subway system for believing he caused the accidental death of a friend. With Charles S. Dutton, Jasmine Guy and Gavin Allen. 59 mins.
VHS: S13237. $14.95.

The Secret Garden
Agnieszka Holland's haunting adaptation of Frances Hodgson Burnett's 1909 classic about an orphaned young girl (Kate Maberly) dispatched to her uncle's remote English estate. With the help of her painfully withdrawn cousin (Heydon Prowse) and a local boy (Andrew Knott), she discovers an enchanting garden. Holland beautifully captures the painful social isolation of childhood. Maggie Smith plays the tyrannical housekeeper.
VHS: S20217. $19.98.
Laser: LD72328. $34.98.
Agnieszka Holland, USA, 1993, 102 mins.

The Secret of Roan Inish (Island of the Seals)
Magical and unforgettable, this beautiful film, shot on location in Ireland, captures the grandeur of simple lives transformed by fantasy. A young girl must find her missing brother. This simple but vital task sparks a story which brings an Irish legend to life. It involves an enchanted isle inhabited by seals.
VHS: S26620. $19.98.
Laser: LD75113. $34.95.
John Sayles, USA, 1995, 102 mins.

The Shaggy Dog
Magical words spoken from the inscription of an ancient ring turn young Wilby Daniels into a shaggy pooch leading to canine high jinks in this classic Disney shaggy dog story starring Fred MacMurray.
VHS: S32311. $19.95.
Charles T. Barton, USA, 1959, 101 mins.

Shiloh
In this "modern day *Old Yeller*," a boy learns about responsibility, commitment and friendship while trying to rescue a beagle pup from mistreatment by its owner. Adapted from the Newbery Award-winning novel. With Michael Moriarty, Rod Steiger, Scott Wilson and Blake Heron.
VHS: S31298. $19.98.
Dale Rosenbloom, USA, 1996, 94 mins.

Sleeping Beauty
Disney's 16th full-length animated masterpiece, from the cherished fairy tale, has been fully restored to its original theatrical brilliance. With commemorative booklet.
VHS: S31509. $26.95.
Laser: CAV, THX. LD72468. $99.99.
Laser: CLV, THX. LD72469. $29.99.
Clyde Geronimi, USA, 1959, 75 mins.

Sounder
Paul Winfield stars as a Black sharecropper in Louisiana who steals food in a desperate attempt to feed his family. Cicely Tyson portrays his wife, providing love and strength to keep the family together.
VHS: S01235. $14.95.
Laser: LD75336. $29.98.
Martin Ritt, USA, 1972, 105 mins.

Swiss Family Robinson
Jonathon Wyss' book of the same name is adapted for the screen in this early version of the much admired tale. A man decides to move his family to Australia, but the ship is destroyed, forcing them to make do on a deserted island. There the harshness and beauty of the landscape challenge and inspire this family to be better than they thought they could be.
VHS: S21560. $24.95.
Edward Ludwig, USA, 1940, 92 mins.

That Darn Cat
Disney redoes Disney in this remake of the classic about a teenager (Christina Ricci, *The Addams Family*) whose boredom with her sleepy hometown disappears when her tomcat D.C. (Darn Cat) delivers an important clue in a mysterious kidnapping. She teams up with a rookie FBI agent (Doug E. Doug, *Cool Runnings*), leading to goofy entanglements and misunderstandings.
VHS: S31698. $103.99.
Laser: LD76293. $39.99.
Bob Spiers, USA, 1997, 89 mins.

Thomas the Tank Engine and Friends: The Gallant Old Engine and Other Thomas Stories
Thomas and his friends, Percy, Stuart, Falcon, Duke and Henry, are all featured in this video. Whether it involves saving a stuck elephant or carrying passengers home during a dangerous storm, this collection of stories will enthrall children. 35 mins.
VHS: S29965. $12.98.

Toy Story Deluxe Edition
This exclusive collector's set includes the videocassette of the acclaimed full-length animated feature film, a bonus video providing an exclusive glimpse behind the scenes of the film, one-of-a-kind 3-D commemorative lenticular artwork showcasing the wonders of computer animation, and *The Art of Disney's Toy Story* book. *Toy Story*, the first computer-animated, feature-length film, derives

much of its appeal from engaging characters which feature the voices of Tom Hanks, Tim Allen and Don Rickles. Despite the high-tech look, this film offers an appealing story set amid the imaginary world of toys. Darker aspects of violence and neglect deepen this film's overt and beguiling innocence.
VHS: S30018. $79.95.
Laser: LD75985. $124.95.
John Lasseter, USA, 1995, 81 mins.

Voyage en Ballon
From the director of *The Red Balloon*, a marvelous adventure as Little Pascal and his grandfather take off across France in a 60-foot-tall balloon with many humorous and suspenseful adventures which ensue. Dubbed in English.
VHS: S01421. $19.95.
Albert Lamorisse, France, 1962, 82 mins.

Where the Red Fern Grows
A young boy yearns for two Red-bone coon hounds amidst the splendor of the Ozarks. But life is hard in Depression-era Oklahoma. Facing adventure and tragedy with his new canine friends, Billy ultimately learns of love and hope. With James Whitmore, Beverly Garland and Stewart Peterson.
VHS: S01447. $19.98.
Norman Tokar, USA, 1974, 108 mins.

Willa: An American Snow White
In this award-winning production, the classic tale of envy, death and redemption from the Brothers Grimm is set in the countryside of Virginia's Faulkier county, with a cast selected from Washington, D.C.'s renowned Shakespeare Theatre.
VHS: S31705. $39.95.
Tom Davenport, USA, 1997, 85 mins.

William Wegman's Mother Goose
Everyone's favorite childhood rhymes get the wry Wegman touch with his canine companions Batty, Crooky, Chundo and Chip, as Mother Goose attempts to teach her son Simon the art of rhyming with some surprising advice from Grandmother Goose.
VHS: S31642. $9.95.
William Wegman, USA, 1997, 30 mins.

Willie Wonka and the Chocolate Factory
Amusing and unconventional story based on the children's book by Roald Dahl features Gene Wilder as a madcap candy man. With Jack Albertson.
VHS: S01604. $19.98.
Laser: LD70707. $34.98.
Mel Stuart, US, 1971, 94 mins.

Willow
From master storytellers George Lucas (*Star Wars*) and Ron Howard (*Cocoon*) comes this odyssey of unlikely heroes, villains and innocent souls caught in a mysterious realm of battle, magic and comaraderie. Willow Ufgood (Warwick Davis) leaves his village to carry a special child to safety who is destined to bring everlasting peace and freedom to the land.
VHS: S30255. $14.99.
Ron Howard, USA, 1988, 130 mins.

The Wind in the Willows
Vanessa Redgrave narrates this animated film adaptation of Kenneth Grahame's classic children's story about a wise Badger, a clever Rat, and a sensible Mole, who do their best to control the excesses of Toad when they embark on an unpredictable journey. This satire of Victorian society features the voices of Michael Palin (*Monty Python's Flying Circus*), Alan Bennett, Rik Mayall (*The Young Ones*) and Michael Gambon (*Two Deaths*). Top-notch animation from the crew who produced the Beatles' *Yellow Submarine* and *Heavy Metal*. Winner of the Gold Special Jury Award for Best Family Film at Worldfest Houston.
VHS: S30241. $14.95.
Dave Unwin, Great Britain, 1996, 74 mins.

The Yearling
Twelve-year-old Jody confronts the joys and pains of growing up when the needs of his beloved pet fawn compete with those of his struggling family. Marjorie Kinnan Rawlings' novel is touchingly brought to the screen by Gregory Peck, Jane Wyman and Claude Jarman, Jr., who received an Academy Award for portraying a child enduring harsh pioneer life.
VHS: S01488. $19.95.
Laser: LD70716. $44.98.
Clarence Brown, USA, 1946, 129 mins.

The Wind in the Willows

Facets Exclusives

After the Revolution
The "hero" of this film is a middle-aged writer who ekes out an existence with his cat in a small, suburban apartment. An experimental, tongue-in-cheek feature made in the wake of the cataclysmic political changes of his native Hungary. Hungarian with English subtitles.
VHS: S15161. $59.95.
ISBN: 1-56580-003-6. UPC: 7-36899-15161-4.
Andras Szirtes, Hungary, 1990, 82 mins.

Alias, La Gringa
This powerful political drama from Peru follows the adventures and escapades of La Gringa, a charismatic criminal who cannot be incarcerated by any jail. Spanish with English subtitles.
VHS: S20383. $59.95.
ISBN: 1-56580-030-3. UPC: 7-36899-20383-2.
Alberto Durant, Peru, 1991, 92 mins.

All My Good Countrymen
One of the wonders of the Czech New Wave. Stylistically a work of great lyricism, humor and originality, the film weaves magical and funny stories about a group of characters in a small Moravian village, responding to the coming of socialization and Stalinism. Czech with English subtitles.
VHS: S05252. $59.95.
ISBN: 1-56580-114-8. UPC: 7-36899-05252-2.
Vojtech Jasny, Czechoslovakia, 1968, 115 mins.

All the Love in the World
Oscar-winning cinematographer Janusz Kaminski (*Schindler's List*) shot this beautiful story of love and murder. Eddy Wluicki is a young man who loves being in love, in a world where such romantic notions fade when confronted by the brutal realities of life. He strikes back at the innocent victims whom he blames for the death of love.
VHS: S21129. $59.95.
ISBN: 1-56580-028-1. UPC: 7-36899-21129-5.
Daniel Curan, USA, 1990, 90 mins.

Almanac of Fall
An intensely naturalistic drama set in the claustrophobic interiors of a large apartment, where a group of people congregate to reveal their darkest secrets, fears, obsessions and hostilities in a style that combines the anguish and existentialism of Bergman with the emotional intensity of Cassavetes. Hungarian with English subtitles.
VHS: S18690. $59.95.
ISBN: 1-56580-058-3. UPC: 7-36899-18690-6.
Bela Tarr, Hungary, 119 mins.

Amida (Dan Reeves Retrospective, Vol. 2)
Five works by Dan Reeves: *Amida* is a visual poem concerned with the cycles of nature and the exploration of the spiritual through landscape and image. *A Mosaic for the Kali Yuga* is a short and dense work which touches on the state of society of information overload and manipulation of image and landscape. *Arches* is an exploration of language and landscape in the Utah desert; *Body Count* is an emotionally searing tape that ironically presents youth's fascination with military glory, based on the artist's memories of his Vietnam experience. *Hey Joe* is a unique psychedelic music video, set to a Jimi Hendrix song.
VHS: S10417. $59.95.
ISBN: 1-5680-115-6. UPC: 7-36899-10417-7.
Dan Reeves, USA, 32 mins.

The Anna Akhmatova File
A moving portrait of the extraordinary Soviet poet Anna Akhmatova. Although her work was banned and went unpublished for 17 years, her poem "Requiem" became the underground anthem for the millions who suffered under Stalin. Russian with English subtitles.
VHS: S13313. $29.95.
ISBN: 1-56580-116-4. UPC: 7-36899-13313-9.
Semeon Aranovich, USSR, 1989, 65 mins.

The Art of Haiti
A powerful documentary from Chicago filmmaker Mark Mamalakis on the absorbing art movement that has emerged from the rage, poverty and passion of Third World cultures, specifically Haiti. The film includes interviews with artists Philome Obin and Rigaud Benoit and detailed retrospectives of painters Hector Hyppolite and Andre Pierre.
VHS: S03471. $39.95.
ISBN: 1-56580-117-2. UPC: 7-36899-03471-9.
Mark Mamalakis, USA, 1983, 26 mins.

Art of Memory
This experiment with political and religious forms by acclaimed video artist Woody Vasulka. Documentary images of World War II, the Spanish Civil War and the Russian Revolution appear against vistas of southwestern desert landscapes providing an authenticity that the artist believes encourages people to synthesize their own experiences.
VHS: S05398. $59.95.
ISBN: 1-56580-118-0. UPC: 7-36899-05398-7.
Woody Vasulka, 36 mins.

Autobiographical Mysteries
(The Films of James Broughton, Vol. 4)
Includes *Testament* (1974), an exquisite self-portrait in which the poet-filmmaker views his life and work with wit and charm in a rich pageantry of personal imagery, songs, anecdotes and dreams, and *Devotions* (1983), a work made with collaborator Joel Singer which envisions a world where men have abandoned rivalries in favor of comradely devotion, featuring 45 different couples who reveal the many pleasures that men can enjoy together.
VHS: S07287. $29.95.
ISBN: 1-56580-011-7. UPC: 7-36899-07287-2.
James Broughton, USA, 1974-1983, 57 mins.

The Birth of the Counter-Culture
(The Films of Scott Bartlett, Vol. 1)
Three films by Scott Bartlett: the historic *Offon* (1968), the first videographic film ever made in America, begins with a pulsating eyeball and pulls the viewer deep into a metamorphosing mindscape; *Moon 1969* portrays the Moon's magic dominion over the Earth's creatures; and *1970* juxtaposes Bartlett's personal experience as an artist in America with the ephemeral promises of the larger culture.
VHS: S05621. $59.95.
ISBN: 1-56580-199-7. UPC: 7-36899-15161-6.
Scott Bartlett, USA, 1968-1970, 55 mins.

Black & White
Lisa is a young Soviet emigré studying medicine in Manhattan. She meets Roy, an African-American man working as a building superintendent on New York's Lower East Side, and the two fall in love.
VHS: S26333. $59.95.
ISBN: 1-56580-053-2. UPC: 7-36899-26333-1.
Boris Frumin, USA/Russia, 1991, 96 mins.

Black River
Pure Garcia Marquez set in the far reaches of the Venezuelan Amazon, where absolute power corrupts absolutely.
VHS: S27737. $59.95.
ISBN: 1-56580-103-2. UPC: 7-36899-27737-6.
Athualpa Lichy, Venezuela/Spain, 1990, 116 mins.

Boris Frumin Three-Pack
Includes the films *Viva Castro!*, *Black & White* and *The Errors of Youth (Wild Oats)*, by acclaimed Russian filmmaker Boris Frumin.
VHS: S26354. $149.95.
ISBN: 1-56580-055-9. UPC: 7-36899-26354-6.
Boris Frumin, USA/Russia, 1978-1993, 265 mins.

bottom land
Voted Best First Feature at the Houston Film Festival, this is a moving tale of three simple farmers confounded by tragic circumstances. Besieged with guilt after the car accident which killed his wife, Stephen Saunders checks himself into a mental institution for four months, but inevitably, he must return to face the father and son he left behind.
VHS: S21131. $59.95.
ISBN: 1-56580-036-2. UPC: 7-36899-21131-8.
Edward Akira Radtke, USA, 1989, 75 mins.

Buccaneer Soul
One of the most creative Brazilian filmmakers, Carlos Reichenbach, directs this mesmerizing saga of two friends as their lives reflect the turbulent '60s in Brazil.
VHS: S27735. $59.95.
ISBN: 1-56580-101-6. UPC: 7-36899-27735-2.
Carlos Reichenbach, Brazil, 1993, 116 mins.

Butterfly Wings (Alas de Mariposa)
This unusual drama about a dysfunctional family registers alternately as sad, horrifying and somber. Carmen hopes her unborn child is a son in order to carry on her husband's name. Guilt and fear prevent her from telling her sensitive and shy six-year-old daughter. The birth of the child triggers a series of nightmarish events. Winner of the Best Picture at the San Sebastian Film Festival. Spanish with English subtitles.
VHS: S20382. $59.95.
ISBN: 1-56580-033-8. UPC: 7-36899-20382-5.
Juanma Bajo Ulloa, Spain, 1991, 105 mins.

Caligari's Cure
Tom Palazzolo's first feature film, a surreal comedy which draws upon *The Cabinet of Dr. Caligari*, performance art and the rituals of a Catholic upbringing.
VHS: S00207. $39.95.
ISBN: 1-56580-118-0. UPC: 7-36899-00207-7.
Tom Palazzolo, USA, 1983, 80 mins.

Charuga
The spectacular, true story of a Croatian 1920s Robin Hood, a fanatic ex-soldier and Bolshevik who tried to bring the Revolution to Yugoslavia. A visually complex, engrossing, sensual and unsettling action-adventure movie which is also a serious political drama.
VHS: S27795. $29.95.
ISBN: 1-56580-095-8. UPC: 7-36899-27795-6.
Rajko Grlic, Croatia, 1991, 108 mins.

Chicago Maternity Center Story
For more than 75 years, The Chicago Maternity Center provided safe home deliveries for Chicago mothers. But a change in attitude of modern medicine toward home birth and a decline in funding forced its closure.
VHS: S27851. $29.95.
ISBN: 1-56580-094-X. UPC: 7-36899-27851-9.
Kartemqin Films, USA, 1976, 60 mins.

Chicago Nazis
From the violent confrontations of American Nazis led by Frank Collins, these two documentaries, *Marquette Park I* and *Marquette Park II*, offer rare insights into extremism in America.
VHS: S06473. $39.95.
ISBN: 1-56580-120-2. UPC: 7-36899-06473-0.
Tom Palazzolo, USA, 1976-1978, 60 mins.

Circus
Alexandrov's daring attempt to import the American musical comedy form into the Soviet Union was conceived by its director as "an eccentric comedy...a real side splitter." Its star is an American circus artiste who has a black baby—a daring conceit for 1936! Russian with English subtitles.
VHS: S27216. $29.95.
ISBN: 1-56580-081-8. UPC: 7-36899-27216-6.

Cold Days
A film is based on the massacre of several thousand Jewish and Serbian people of Novi Sad in 1942. "The film is structured around the memories and self-justifications of four men involved in the massacre as they await trial in 1946.

Each, of course, denies his complicity or responsibility.... Many of the images in the film remain unforgettable." Hungarian with English subtitles.
VHS: S13338. $59.95.
ISBN: 1-56580-121-0. UPC: 7-36899-13338-2.
Andras Kovacs, Hungary, 1966, 102 mins.

Comment Ca Va? (How Is It Going?)
Co-directed by Anne-Marie Mieville, Jean-Luc Godard's work—combining video and film—is a fascinating dialectic on the dissemination and processing of information, both literary and visual. Two workers of a communist newspaper strike out to make a film and video about the newspaper and the printing plant. French with English subtitles.
VHS: S19232. $59.95.
ISBN: 1-56580-049-4. UPC: 7-36899-19232-7.
Jean-Luc Godard/Anne-Marie Mieville, France, 1976, 76 mins.

The Commission
Video artist Woody Vasulka's experiment with narrativity through electronic tools is presented in this new operatic work that evokes the friendship between composer Berlioz and the violinist Paganini, whose ill health, loss of voice and habit of gambling led to his death at an early age.
VHS: S05645. $59.95.
ISBN: 1-56580-122-9. UPC: 7-36899-05647-6.
Woody Vasulka, USA, 1987, 45 mins.

Confessing to Laura (Confesion a Laura)
A gut-wrenching drama from Colombia which is set during a raging civil war in the aftermath of liberal leader Jorge Elieser Gaitain in 1948. Three people are trapped in Laura's home during a riot, setting the stage for an intense, unforgettable night. Spanish with English subtitles.
VHS: S20379. $59.95.
ISBN: 1-56580-032-X. UPC: 7-36899-20379-5.
Jaime Osorio Gomez, Colombia, 1990, 90 mins.

The Coward
A school teacher and his young wife find a wounded Russian parachutist in their front yard just as the Germans occupy the village; the wife supports the anti-Nazi partisans but her husband collaborates with the Germans. Czech with English subtitles.
VHS: S27177. $29.95.
ISBN: 1-56580-076-1. UPC: 7-36899-27177-0.
Jiri Weiss, Czech Republic, 1962, 113 mins.

Crime and Punishment
Two of the greatest actors, Harry Baur and Pierre Blanchar, and the master of French poetic realism, Pierre Chenal, join in this masterful adaptation of one of the great works of literature. Hailed worldwide as one of the most imaginative adaptations of Dostoyevsky's complex, brooding novel. French with English subtitles.
VHS: S09197. $59.95.
ISBN: 1-56580-123-7. UPC: 7-36899-09197-2.
Pierre Chenal, France, 1935, 110 mins.

The Cyclist
A visually sophisticated film which deals with the themes of man's exploitation of man and the inequities between rich and poor. The cyclist is Nassim, an Afghan refugee in need of money to pay his wife's medical expenses. Gamblers, bookies and food vendors gather to watch the desperate cyclist from the sidelines, turning his suffering to their own profit.
VHS: S27790. $29.95.
ISBN: 1-56580-088-5. UPC: 7-36899-27790-1.
Mohsen Makhmalaf, Iran, 1989, 75 mins.

Alias, La Gringa

The Day You Love Me
Humor and caricature capture the dreamy year of 1935, when Caracas, Venezuela, was host to the great Tango singer Carlos Gardel.
VHS: S27739. $59.95.
ISBN: 1-56580-105-9. UPC: 7-36899-27739-0.
Sergio Dow, Colombia, 1986, 80 mins.

Diamonds of the Night
Jan Nemec's debut feature film, based on a short story by Arnost Lustig. *Diamonds of the Night* is a brilliantly visual tour-de-force, the story of two boys who escape from a Nazi concentration camp transport train—their flight, dreams, nightmares. Also includes the short film *A Bite to Eat.* Czech with English subtitles.
VHS: S04737. $59.95.
ISBN: 1-56580-124-5. UPC: 7-36899-04737-5.
Jan Nemec, Czechoslovakia, 1964, 71 mins.

Digital Speech/Pressures of the Text
Digital Speech uses a traveler's anecdote, a perverse variant of a classic Zen parable, as a vehicle for an exploration of language, thought and gesture. *Pressures of the Text* integrates direct address, invented languages, ideographic subtitles, sign language and simultaneous translation to investigate the feel and form of sense, the shifting boundaries between meaning and meaninglessness.
VHS: S09206. $59.95.
ISBN: 1-56580-124-5. UPC: 7-36899-09206-1.
Peter Rose, USA, 1984, 30 mins.

Disarmament: Public Opinion Poll
In June, 1982, there were rallies held throughout the world in support of the U.N. Conference on Disarmament. This tape features the most interesting, most humorous and most eccentric of these interviews with individuals of all races, colors and professions, offering a panorama of characters expressing their hopes, fears and concerns about the nuclear issue.
VHS: S08527. $29.95.
ISBN: 1-56580-126-1. UPC: 7-36899-08527-8.
Skip Blumberg, 1982, 30 mins.

Distance of the Outsider, Part One: India Time (The Films of Ken Feingold, Volume 3)
India Time shows the people of India in their daily work, and often in response to the fact that they are being recorded by the camera. It is as much about the meeting of cultures, and the imposition of Feingold's own perspective on Indian culture, as it is about Indian culture itself.
VHS: S15648. $59.95.
ISBN: 1-56580-023-0. UPC: 7-36899-15648-0.
Ken Feingold, 1985-1988, 46 mins.

Dita Saxova
The moving—and beautifully told—story of an 18-year-old girl, living in Prague, who seems beautiful and strong to everyone around her until, a year later, she commits suicide by jumping off a cliff. Czech with English subtitles.
VHS: S04739. $59.95.
ISBN: 1-56580-127-X. UPC: 7-36899-04739-9.
Antonin Moskalyk, Czechoslovakia, 1967, 98 mins.

Dreamwood
A spiritual odyssey into the landscape of the dream in which its poet hero set forth to rescue the bride of his soul and bring about his own rebirth.
VHS: S01575. $29.95.
ISBN: 1-56580-013-3. UPC: 7-36899-01575-6.
James Broughton, USA, 1972, 45 mins.

Erotic Celebrations (The Films of James Broughton, Vol. 1)
Contains Broughton's 1968 masterpiece *The Bed*—a lyrically erotic celebration of just about everything that could happen on a bed—with an all-nude cast, among them some of San Francisco's best-known artists, and *Erogeny* (1976), an intimate exploration of the landscape of the human body. *Hermes Bird* (1979) and *Song of the Godbody* (1977) continue Broughton's sly attacks on sexual taboos and celebrate the ecstasy of physical awareness with close-up camerawork that caresses the body parts it explores.
VHS: S07284. $29.95.
ISBN: 1-56580-008-7. UPC: 7-36899-07284-1.
James Broughton, USA, 1968-1979, 47 mins.

The Errors of Youth (Wild Oats)
The Errors of Youth is the story of Dmitri (Stanislav Zhdanko), a former conscript in the Red Army (now a highly-paid construction worker in Siberia), who finds his love affair disintegrating over the question of children. Disillusioned, he moves to Leningrad and falls into a life of black marketeers, and enters into a marriage of expediency. Russian with English subtitles.
VHS: S26332. $59.95.
ISBN: 1-56580-052-4. UPC: 7-36899-26332-4.
Boris Frumin, USSR, 1978-1989, 87 mins.

Far from Poland
This is a remarkable documentary about the Solidarity movement, through the personal testimonies of a woman involved in the first Gdansk shipyard strike, a censor and a mine worker.
VHS: S02656. $69.95.
ISBN: 1-56580-129-6. UPC: 7-36899-02656-1.
Jill Godmilow, USA, 1984, 106 mins.

Fictions (The Films of Ken Feingold, Volume 5)
A collection of four wide-ranging video shorts from director Ken Feingold, whose intelligent, disjointed and confrontational style has invited favorable comparisons to radical mainstream directors like Nagis Oshima and Sergei Eisenstein. Includes *The Smallest Particle* (1987, 8 mins.), *In Shadow City (A Speech)* (1985, 29 mins.) and *Un Chien Delicieux* (1991, 19 mins).
VHS: S15650. $59.95.
ISBN: 1-56580-050-8. UPC: 7-36899-15650-3.
Ken Feingold, USA, 1985-1991, 69 mins.

The Fifth Seal
A group of friends are arrested when one of them makes a casual remark that offends a commandant. From this chance event a series of daunting tasks emerges that test their commitment to their moral ideals.
VHS: S20618. $59.95.
ISBN: 1-56580-027-3. UPC: 7-36899-20618-5.
Zoltan Fabri, Hungary, 1976, 116 mins.

The Films of James Broughton: Complete Set
Spanning an artistic career of 40 years, the collected films of James Broughton represent a remarkable body of work by a leading avant-garde American filmmaker—an undisputed master of the fusion of spoken poetry with moving images. A poet and dramatist as well as a filmmaker, Broughton has transformed all three of these forms into what Stan Brakhage calls "an art of lifelong montage." Included are *Erotic Celebrations, Rituals of Play, Pleasure Garden, Autobiographical Mysteries, Parables* and *Dreamwood.* (See descriptions of individual titles.)
VHS: S07289. $149.75.
ISBN: 1-56580-014-1. UPC: 7-36899-07289-6.
James Broughton, USA/Sri Lanka/Great Britain, 1948-1983, 246 mins.

Flowers of Reverie
A former soldier named Ferenc is imprisoned for his work in the resistance, leading to a tragic outcome. Hungarian with English subtitles.
VHS: S20617. $59.95.
ISBN: 1-56580-026-5. UPC: 7-36899-20617-8.
Laszlo Lugossy, Hungary, 1984, 106 mins.

The Future of Human Mythology (The Films of Scott Bartlett, Vol. 2)
Four works by Scott Bartlett: *The Serpent* particularizes the creative-destructive force of the primal chaotic life force in mystic symbology with an amalgam of sensuously, darkly erotic images; *Sound of One* is bravura hand-held camera technique in a depiction of T'ai Chi Ch'uan; *Heavy Metal* is a graphic disintegration of paranoia, perversion and violence in Chicago; and *Medina* is a travelogue through the ancient Medinas of Morocco, an evocative journey to the inner values of the culture.
VHS: S05644. $59.95.
ISBN: 1-56580-130-X. UPC: 7-36899-05644-5.
Scott Bartlett, USA, 54 mins.

Ganapati/A Spirit in the Bush
Artist Daniel Reeves creates a haunting and impressionistic song about the relationship of men and animals, using the poetry of Lorca, Rilke, Kipling and Reeves and location footage of India, Kenya and Thailand matched with archival

footage. Reeves' "procession of charged images involves and implicates the viewer through its silently scrolling text."
VHS: S16736. $59.95.
ISBN: 1-56580-015-X. UPC: 7-36899-16736-3.
Daniel Reeves, 45 mins.

Gay for a Day
Two documentaries by Tom Palazzolo, dealing with gay issues: *Gay for a Day* is the story of the 1976 Gay Pride Parade; *Costumes on Review* is an hilarious documentary about a gay Halloween party.
VHS: S06112. $39.95.
ISBN: 1-56580-131-8. UPC: 7-36899-06112-8.
Tom Palazzolo, USA, 1976, 45 mins.

Golub
Art, politics and the media intersect in artist Leon Golub's nightmarish images of war, torture, death squads and mercenaries. The documentary follows the creation of one of his monumental canvases, White Squad X, detailing his complex and unorthodox techniques.
VHS: 27803. $29.95.
ISBN: 1-56580-092-3. UPC: 7-36899-27803-8.
Kartemquin Films, USA, 1988, 56 mins.

Grain of Sand (Le Grain de Sable)
An incisive study of a woman's attempt at independence stars Delphine Seyrig as an unemployed woman in Paris who tries to reconcile her past with her present. French with English subtitles.
VHS: S03718. $59.95.
ISBN: 1-56580-132-6. UPC: 7-36899-03718-5.
Pomme Meffre, France, 1984, 90 mins.

The Great Sadness of Zohara
Nina Menkes combines sound, image and fragments of poetry in this moving film about the journey of a young Jewish woman who is drawn to explore the world of the spirit. Her journey takes her to remote and increasingly desolate regions of the Arab lands—alienating her from the Orthodox Jewish community in Israel.
VHS: S07374. $39.95.
ISBN: 1-56580-133-4. UPC: 7-36899-07374-9.
Nina Menkes, 1983, 40 mins.

The Green Wall
The Green Wall is "a bitter and beautiful movie," in which "Godoy translates his experience into film poetry rather than flat reportage and uses the physical environment (exquisitely photographed by his cameraman brother, Mario) as a great natural mystery, idyllic but cruel, rich but unyielding to the will of a handsome young settler (Mexican star Julio Aleman, in a vibrant performance) who is determined to survive there with his family." "A masterpiece!" (Roger Ebert). Spanish with English subtitles.
VHS: S11250. $79.95.
UPC: 1-56580-134-2. UPC: 7-36899-11250-9.
Armondo Robles Godoy, Peru, 1970, 110 mins.

A Happy New Year!
A harsh, fluid, social commentary about class distinctions and social grievances related through this spirited comedy of manners. Three chemical engineers, two men and a woman, ward off the effects of a hangover. Szoreny paints a vivid portrait of urban alienation and social disruption within Hungary's professional classes. Hungarian with English subtitles.
VHS: S18688. $59.95.
ISBN: 1-56580-056-7. UPC: 7-36899-18688-3.
Reszo Szoreny, Hungary, 1979, 84 mins.

The H.D. Trilogy Film
This loving portrait of "H.D."—imagist poet Hilda Doolittle—by filmmaker Larry Jordan comprises a merging of images: Joanna McClure's reading of H.D.'s long poem, *Hermetic Definitions*, and the traditional music of the Mediterranean. Planned around the visual cues found in H.D.'s writings, *The H.D. Trilogy Film* is an intimate, subjective look at Hilda Doolittle through the life of Joanna McClure during the years 1990 through 1992.
VHS: S23210. $29.95.
ISBN: 1-56580-039-7. UPC: 7-36899-23210-8.
Larry Jordan, USA, 1990-1994, 115 mins.

Heimat I
The nine-tape boxed set, featuring the titles *The Call of Faraway Places (1919-1928)*, *The Center of the World (1928-1933)*, *The Best Christmas Ever (1935)*, *The New Road (1938)* and *Up and Away and Back (1939)*, *The Home Front*

(1943) and *Soldiers and Love (1944)*, *The American (1945-1947)*, *Little Herman (1955-1956)*, *The Proud Years (1967-1969)* and *The Feast of the Living and the Dead (1982)*, from Edgar Reitz's long-running German miniseries.
VHS: S27403. $149.95.
ISBN: 1-56580-084-2. UPC: 7-36899-27403-0.
Edgar Reitz, West Germany, 1984, 924 mins.

Heimat II
"Staggeringly rich, *The Second Heimat*, which runs 25½ hours, forms, with its predecessor, a magnificent, nearly unprecedented "film novel": a portrait of Germany in the 20th century with few equals in either film or literature...outlandishly ambitious...an often dazzling success.... The story is of Maria's son, Herrmann Simon, and his life in Munich from 1960 to 1970. There, a brilliant young modernist musician and composer, he falls in with an incandescent circle of young students, artists, rebels and lovers.... *The Second Heimat* may be the screen's finest portrayal of youth in the '60s" (Michael Wilmington, *Chicago Tribune*).
VHS: S27808. $249.95.
ISBN: 1-56580-109-1. UPC: 7-36899-27808-3.
Edgar Reitz, Germany, 1994, 1416 minutes

Heimat I and II Set
Includes *Heimat* and *Second Heimat*.
VHS: S30170. $349.95.
ISBN: 1-56580-192-X. UPC: 7-36899-30170-5.
Edgar Reitz, West Germany, 1984/1994, 2340 minutes

The House of UnAmerican Activities/ Dreams from China/Dreams Documentary
House of UnAmericanActivities (1983, 17 mins.) draws on a wealth of family archives (stills, home movies, documents and a video interview with the filmmaker's mother), as the filmmaker searches for the father he never really knew and for the meaning of a troubled era. *Dream Documentary* (1981, 5 mins.) uses footage from other films to create a surreal and foreboding societal landscape. *Dreams from China* (1989, 30 mins.), shot from 1983-1985 while working in Tianjin and Beijing, is a highly lyrical, diary-like film essay, lending perspective to the tragedy of Tiananmen Square. "Extremely sincere...presenting a paradox of Chinese politics and society" (*New York Times*).
VHS: S23209. $29.95.
ISBN: 1-56580-038-9. UPC: 7-36899-23209-2.
Frederick Marx, USA, 1981-1994, 52 mins.

Heimat II

Innocence Unprotected

Hungarian Rhapsody
Part of Jancso's proposed trilogy dealing with the relationships between the classes in pre-revolutionary Hungary. Set in 1911, the film follows Istvan, a nobleman who joins ranks with the peasants in opposition to the ruling class in general, and to his statesman brother in particular. Hungarian with English subtitles.
VHS: S12509. $59.95.
ISBN: 1-56580-135-0. UPC: 7-36899-12509-7.
Miklos Jancso, Hungary, 1983, 101 mins.

I Was Stalin's Bodyguard
Filmmaker Semeon Aranovich found the last surviving personal bodyguard of Josef Stalin, who began to work for him in the 1930s. *I Was Stalin's Bodyguard* weaves together unprecedented, first-hand testimony with rare footage, including Stalin's home movies. Russian with English subtitles.
VHS: S13312. $29.95.
ISBN: 1-56580-136-9. UPC: 7-36899-13312-2.
Semeon Aranovich, USSR, 1990, 73 mins.

I Worked for Stalin
A brilliant assembly of eyewitness testimony and rare archival photographs and materials. It records the Machiavellian power plays between Zhdanov, Andreyev, Khrushchev, Malenkov, Suslov and Molotov as they maneuvered for power and prestige to gain the inside track of becoming Stalin's successor. Russian with English subtitles.
VHS: S18686. $29.95.
ISBN: 1-56580-054-0. UPC: 7-36899-18686-9.
Semeon Aranovich, USSR, 1990, 67 mins.

Ici et Ailleurs (Here and Elsewhere)
Jean-Luc Godard initiated his radical video period with this startling film that combines videotape and film, enabling him to superimpose more than two images simultaneously. Godard, Gorin and Mieville contrast a French family ("Here") with an impressionistic portrait of Palestine ("Elsewhere") reflected and transmitted by television, books and pictures. French with English subtitles.
VHS: S19231. $59.95.
ISBN: 1-56580-048-6. UPC: 7-36899-19231-0.
Jean-Luc Godard, France/Switzerland, 1970-1976

In Between
Wade Novy's moving portrait of stillness, the study of a single woman's process of alienation and disassociation, is one of the landmark American experimental films of the '80s.
VHS: S03722. $39.95.
ISBN: 1-56580-137-7. UPC: 7-36899-03722-2.
Wade Novy, USA, 1979-1980, 30 mins.

In Motion: Amiri Baraka
Called "a brilliantly executed documentary" by *The New York*

Times, In Motion: Amiri Baraka is a fascinating exploration of the writer and political activist formerly known as LeRoi Jones. Following Baraka from his early days as a poet in New York City's Greenwich Village to his present literary and political activities, the film is a portrait of a man of singular commitment to social change.
VHS: S10909. $59.95.
ISBN: 1-56580-138-5. UPC: 7-36899-10909-7.
St. Clair Bourne, USA, 1985, 60 mins.

In the Jaws of Life
At the heart of this disarmingly funny and sexy comedy is a middle-aged woman filmmaker, a bit on the chubby side, with a rather confused personal life, who is making a soap opera titled *The Jaws of Life*, which follows the life of a chubby office clerk not unlike the filmmaker. The two stories unfold side by side until the stories begin to converge.
VHS: S27796. $29.95.
ISBN: 1-56580-096-6. UPC: 7-36899-27796-3.
Rajko Grlic, Yugoslavia, 1984, 95 mins.

India Time
See *Distance of the Outsider, Part 1.*

Innocence Unprotected
In 1942 a professional strong man named Dragoljub Aleksic directed and starred in a trite little melodrama titled *Innocence Unprotected*—the first Serbian talkie. Over 20 years later, Dusan Makavejev retrieved the film from the Archives, tinted many of the sequences by hand, and interviewed Aleksic and his coworkers in present-day Yugoslavia 1968. The resulting cinematic collage is a funny and daring (in both content and form) mix of a wide variety of film footage—including documentary, narrative, agitprop and various other bits and pieces of found footage. Serbian with English subtitles.
VHS: S15487. $59.95.
ISBN: 1-56580-004-4. UPC: 7-36899-15487-5.
Dusan Makavejev, Yugoslavia, 1968, 78 mins.

Interpretation of Dreams
Twentieth-century Russia is the less-than-willing subject of this close psychoanalytic interpretation, inspired by Freud's book of the same name. Archival and newsreel footage, together with commentary employing the psychoanalytic method, offer great insights which clarify such cataclysmic events as the rise of Stalin and the Cold War. Russian with English subtitles.
VHS: S21132. $29.95.
ISBN: 1-56580-037-0. UPC: 7-36899-21132-5.
Andrei Zagdansky, Russia, 1994, 50 mins.

Invisible Adversaries
Valie Export's controversial feature has been called a feminist *Invasion of the Body Snatchers*. Anna (Susanne Widl), a Viennese photographer, discovers that extraterrestrial beings are colonizing the minds of her fellow citizens by raising the human aggression quotient. The outer world immediately becomes disjointed, but the inner world does too, as Anna and her love (Peter Weibel) try to hang onto their deteriorating relationship. German with English subtitles.
VHS: S10414. $59.95.
ISBN: 1-56580-140-7. UPC: 7-36899-10414-6.
Valie Export, Germany, 1977, 112 mins.

Iranian Cinema Collection
Included are: *The Peddler, The Need, The Key, The Cyclist, Where Is the Friend's Home* and *Life and Nothing More*. (See descriptions of individual titles.)
VHS: 27786. $149.95.
ISBN: 1-56580-141-5. UPC: 7-36899-27786-4.

J.S. Bach
Juan Downey's beautiful documentary on J.S. Bach places the famous composer's career and his powerful music in counterpoint with the gritty reality of his life.
VHS: S08996. $39.95.
ISBN: 1-56580-144-X. UPC: 7-36899-08996-2.
Juan Downey, USA, 1986, 28 mins.

Jolly Fellows (Jazz Comedy)
The rags-to-fame story of a sheperd boy who reaches lofty heights as a jazz orchestra conductor, remarkable for the clever camera work of Vladimir Nilsen, who introduced Western camera tricks to Soviet cinema. Russian with English subtitles.
VHS: S27215. $29.95.
ISBN: 1-56580-080-X. UPC: 7-36899-27215-9.

The Journey, Vol. 1
Includes parts 1, 2 and 3: Citizens in Scotland discuss military expansion in their neighborhood. A Hiroshima survivor begins her recollection of the aftermath of the bombing....
VHS: S14296. $29.95.
ISBN: 0-9615518-2-8. UPC: 7-36899-14296-4.
Peter Watkins, 141 mins.

The Journey, Vol. 2
Includes parts 4, 5 and 6: Families from around the world respond to photographic images of Hiroshima. A Norwegian community dramatization of evacuation begins....
VHS: S14297. $29.95.
ISBN: 0-9615518-3-6. UPC: 7-36899-14297-1.
Peter Watkins, 134 mins.

The Journey, Vol. 3
Includes parts 7, 8 and 9: Recollections of the bombing of Hamburg during World War II. A woman describes her evacuation of Leningrad during the war....
VHS: S14298. $29.95.
ISBN: 0-9615518-4-4. UPC: 7-36899-14298-8.
Peter Watkins, 128 mins.

The Journey, Vol. 4
Includes parts 10, 11 and 12: Women of a Mozambique farming collective discuss the war in their country and its effects on their ability to produce food. Watkins details the amount the U.S. government pays American colleges and universities for their part in nuclear weapons design and production.
VHS: S14299. $29.95.
ISBN: 0-9615518-5-2. UPC: 7-36899-14299-5.
Peter Watkins, 136 mins.

The Journey, Vol. 5
Includes parts 13 and 14: An Australian family discusses local media coverage of the nuclear industry in Australia and the protest against it. The New York State evacuation dramatization culminates....
VHS: S14300. $29.95.
ISBN: 0-9615518-6-0. UPC: 7-36899-14300-8.
Peter Watkins, 87 mins.

The Journey, Vol. 6
Includes parts 15 and 16: A Korean man describes Japanese treatment of Koreans during World War II. A family demonstrates the personal cost of the MX missile, in bags of groceries....
VHS: S14301. $29.95.
ISBN: 0-9615518-7-9. UPC: 7-36899-14301-5.
Peter Watkins, 104 mins.

The Journey, Vol. 7
Includes parts 17, 18 and 19: The Australian community group discusses their experiences as "evacuees." The hundreds of people involved in the production of *The Journey* are acknowledges in an ingenious, entertaining, 30-minute credit sequence.
VHS: S14302. $29.95.
ISBN: 0-9615518-8-7. UPC: 7-36899-14302-2.
Peter Watkins, 138 mins.

The Journey: Complete Set
The complete seven-volume set.
VHS: S16588. $179.95.
ISBN: 1-56580-044-3. UPC: 7-36899-16588-8.
Peter Watkins, 868 mins.

Kamikaze Hearts
Juliet Bashore's dark drama boldly merges documentary and narrative storytelling in a fascinating portrait of the lesbian underground. Sharon ("Mitch") Mitchell, an actress, and Tina ("Tigr") Mennett, a producer, are lovers and junkies. They accentuate the perverse sexual nature of their relationship by making explicit pornographic films.
VHS: S19104. $59.95.
ISBN: 1-56580-065-6. UPC: 7-36899-19104-7.
Juliet Bashore, USA, 1991, 80 mins.

Kartemquin Films, Vol. 1: Inquiring Nuns
Set in Chicago in 1967, at the height of the Vietnam War, this disarming, intimate work finds two nuns moving through the city's densely populated streets, asking the question: "Are you happy?"
VHS: S18198. $29.95.
ISBN: 1-56580-017-6. UPC: 7-36899-18198-7.
Kartemquin Films Collective, USA, 1968, 66 mins.

Kartemquin Films, Vol. 2: Winnie Wright, Age 11
Three films by the Kartemquin Films Collective poignantly and honestly deal with personal and social change. In *Winnie Wright, Age 11*, Winnie is the daughter of a steelworker and school teacher watching the dramatic racial and class changes in her neighborhood. *Now We Live on Clifton* focuses on Pam and Scott Taylor, children who watch their multiracial, working-class neighborhood through an awkward though inevitable gentrification. *Parents* is an open-ended discussion about a youth group and their feelings about their parents and the "generation gap" (1968, 22 mins.).
VHS: S18199. $29.95.
ISBN: 1-56580-018-4. 7-36899-18199-4.
Kartemquin Films Collective, USA, 1968-1974, 74 mins.

Kartemquin Films, Vol. 3: Trick Bag
Three films capture the history and apocalyptic social and personal changes of the Vietnam era. *Trick Bag* (1975, 21 mins.) allows gang members, Vietnam vets and young factory workers to relate their personal experiences of racism. *What the Fuck are These Red Squares* (1970, 15 mins.) looks at striking students at The School of The Art Institute in the wake of the killing of student protestors at Kent State and Jackson State. *Hum 255* (1969, 28 mins.) traces the activities of two students and their return to the University of Chicago following their expulsion for illegally occupying the Administration building.
VHS: S18200. $29.95.
ISBN: 0-56580-019-2. UPC: 7-36899-18200-7.
Kartemquin Films Collective, USA, 1969-1975, 64 mins.

Kartemquin Films: Complete Set
Includes the *Inquiring Nuns*, *Winnie Wright, Age 11* and *Trick Bag* collections. (See descriptions of individual titles.)
VHS: S18201. $74.95.
ISBN: 1-56580-020-6. UPC: 7-36899-18201-4.
Kartemquin Films Collective, USA, 1968-1975, 204 mins.

The Key
Humor, pathos and suspense fill this story of a four-year-old and an infant left home alone while their mother runs out to do some shopping. Young Amir Mohammed has his own ideas about what he wants to do—and watching his baby brother and the meal cooking in the kitchen are not among them. Winner of the award for Best Children's Film at the Berlin Film Festival.
VHS: S27789. $29.95.
ISBN: 1-56580-087-7. UPC: 7-36899-27899-5.
Ebrahim Forouzesh, Iran, 1986, 76 mins.

Krik? Krak! Tales of a Nightmare
An unflinching, passionate, disturbing portrait of Haiti directed by Jac Avila and Vanyoska Gert: an extraordinary, clandestinely filmed story of the hidden struggle of Haitian villagers against repression. *Krik? Krak!* is at the same time a great horror film in the tradition of *Witchcraft through the Ages.*"
VHS: S27807. $29.95.
ISBN: 1-56580-110-5. UPC: 7-36899-27807-6.
Jac Avila/Vanyoska Gert, Canada/USA, 78 mins.

La Memoria del Agua
The story of Joseph Fruferman, whose memories of his childhood in Russia and his adult life in France take up the last moments of his life. The film centers on the love that makes the impossible possible through its overwhelming power. Spanish and Russian with English subtitles.
VHS: S27799. $29.95.
ISBN: 1-56580-099-0. UPC: 7-36899-27799-4.
Hector Faver, Spain, 1991, 82 mins.

Latino Cinema Collection
Included are *Alias, La Gringa; Butterfly Wings (Alas de Mariposa); Confessing to Laura (Confession a Laura); Savage Capitalism (Capitalismo Salvage); Shoot to Kill (Disparen a Matar)* and *Tango: Our Dance (Tango: Baile Nuestro).* (See descriptions of individual titles.)
VHS: S20598. $299.99.
ISBN: 1-56580-046-X. UPC: 7-36899-20598-0.

Latino Cinema Collection II
Included are *Buccaneer Soul, Black River, The Lover of Silent Films, We're all Stars, The Day You Love Me, Martin Fierro, Painted Lips* and *The Seven Madmen.* (See descriptions of individual titles.)
VHS: S27831. $349.99.
ISBN: 1-56580-143-1. UPC: 7-36899-27831-1.

Lesbian Humor

Barbara Hammer's films from the 1980s, exploring the details and issues of personal relationships with great humor and sensitivity.
VHS: S08608. $59.95.
ISBN: 1-56580-144-X. UPC: 7-36899-08608-4.
Barbara Hammer, USA, 1975-1987, 59 mins.

Lesbian Sexuality

The films in this group celebrate female energy and power, reflective of the feminist idealistic spirit of the 1970s.
VHS: S08609. $59.95.
ISBN: 1-56580-145-8. UPC: 7-36899-08609-1.
Barbara Hammer, USA, 1974-1976, 57 mins.

Life in Exile (The Films of Ken Feingold, Volume 4)

Life in Exile is Ken Feingold's ambitious two-part video examining the philosophy and political predicament of the Tibetan refugee community in India.
VHS: S15649. $59.95.
ISBN: 1-56580-024-9. UPC: 7-36899-15649-7.
Ken Feingold, USA, 1988, 90 mins.

Little Valentino

A brilliant film debut, and one of the most highly acclaimed European films of recent years, this deceptively simple black-and-white feature anticipates and stylistically surpasses Jim Jarmusch's *Stranger Than Paradise*. The film focuses on Laszlo, a 20-year-old driver's assistant, who spends his day and his money—which he has just stolen—in the aimlessness of everyday life. Hungarian with English subtitles.
VHS: S13337. $59.95.
ISBN: 1-56580-146-6. UPC: 7-36899-13337-5.
Andras Jeles, Hungary, 1979, 102 mins.

The Live Short Films of Larry Jordan

Visions of a City is a lyrical, mystical film featuring the poet Michael McClure's face reflected from, in and on the surfaces of car windows, shop windows, bottles and mirrors of San Francisco in 1957, with a musical score by William Moraldo. Also includes *Magenta Geryon* and *Cornell, 1956*, a personal, sensitive homage to Joseph Cornell, Jordan's mentor, in a warm and affectionate view of the great artist/filmmaker. This is the only known film footage of Cornell.
VHS: S09419. $59.95.
ISBN: 1-56580-147-4. UPC: 7-36899-09419-5.
Larry Jordan, USA, 1956-1957, 35 mins.

Lover of Silent Films

Ralph De Palma had a brief encounter with fame as a Latin lover in silent Hollywood films. Now he recreates his past glories in a bizarre ritual in a funeral home in Argentina.
VHS: S27736. $59.95.
ISBN: 1-56580-102-4. UPC: 7-36899-27736-9.

Love Affair: Or, The Case of the Missing Switchboard Operator

The story of a young switchboard operator who falls in love with a sanitary worker until she allows herself to be seduced by a younger, more glamorous man. Serbian with English subtitles.
VHS: S02653. $59.95.
ISBN: 1-56580-148-2. UPC:7-36899-02653-0.
Dusan Makavejev, Yugoslavia, 1967, 70 mins.

Magdalena Viraga

This mysterious and imaginative experimental feature film concerns the inner life of a prostitute who is arrested as a murder suspect. Filmed in the bars, dance halls and churches of East L.A., it is a compelling portrayal of the young woman's psychological journey from passivity to awareness.
VHS: S07376. $49.95.
ISBN: 1-56580-149-0. UPC: 7-36899-07376-3.
Nina Menkes, USA, 1986, 90 mins.

Maidsplay and Dreiske Discipline Lecture Demonstration

An original theater piece inspired by Jean Genet's *The Maids of Budapest*, the production utilizes actual information about the two sisters whose extraordinary crime inspired Genet to write *The Maids* and highlights the themes of violence, sex, drugs, jealousy and incest in the story of the two sisters.
VHS: S03474. $60.00.
ISBN: 1-56580-150-4. UPC: 7-36899-03474-0.
Ildiko Szabo, Hungary, 1983, 80 mins.

Mama Florence and Papa Cock

Alan Leder's moving portrait of an elderly Jamaican couple in transition is a sensitive, lyrical evocation of two individuals and a study of Jamaica in transition, set against a pulsating reggae score.
VHS: S01955. $45.00.
ISBN: 1-56580-151-2. UPC: 7-36899-01955-6.
Alan Leder, Jamaica

The Man from Nowhere

Pierre Blanchar is the henpecked husband who unexpectedly gets a chance to start a new life. A colorful supporting cast, pungent dialog and Chenal's ironic direction combine in a film which mixes melodrama with satire. French with English subtitles.
VHS: S09198. $59.95.
ISBN: 1-56580-152-0. UPC: 7-36899-09198-9.
Pierre Chenal, France, 1937, 98 mins.

Man Is Not a Bird

A work of genius which takes place in a mining town in eastern Serbia. The central characters are an engineer in one of the factories and a young hairdresser with whom he has an affair; the film "blends actuality with fiction in a manner so unselfconscious as to seem almost natural. The film is not just the chronicle of four personalities, meetings and interchangings. It discusses, via the lovers' entanglements, the needs, aspirations, and realities of communist life..." (*International Film Guide*). Serbian with English subtitles.
VHS: S08265. $59.95.
ISBN: 1-56580-153-9. UPC: 7-36899-08265-9.
Dusan Makavejev, Yugoslavia, 1966, 80 mins.

The Man Who Could Not See Far Enough

A powerful work of independent American experimental cinema, *The Man Who Could Not See Far Enough* uses literary, structural, autobiographical and performance metaphors to construct a series of tableaux that evoke the act of vision, the limits of perception and the rapture of space.
VHS: S09207. $59.95.
ISBN: 1-56580-154-7. UPC: 7-36899-09207-8.
Peter Rose, USA, 1981, 33 mins.

Maria's Day

Maria's Day is set 17 years after the failed revolution of 1848. An aristocratic family gathers at the home of Ignac Czendrey to celebrate his youngest daughter's Name Day. In the course of the one day, the unusual past and present of the Czendrey family are unfolded. A powerful and moving film. Hungarian with English subtitles.
VHS: S11289. $59.95.
ISBN: 1-56580-155-5. UPC: 7-36899-11289-9.
Judit Elek, Hungary, 1985, 113 mins.

Martin Fierro

The legendary director Leopoldo Torre Nilsson depicts the saga of a man who abandons his family to fight the Indians and then is forced to hide among his former enemies when he commits a murder in self defense.
VHS: S27740. $59.95.
ISBN: 1-56580-106-7. UPC: 7-36899-27740-6.
Leopoldo Torre Nilsson, Argentina, 1968, 135 mins.

Maxwell Street Blues

From the street of urban legend, where ethnic groups mingle and a great Blues music continues to be born and reborn on the urban street corners, comes this unique documentary tracing the historical background of the street with the present-day story of its unique Blues musicians.
VHS: S03587. $39.95.
ISBN: 1-56580-200-4. UPC: 7-36899-03587-7.
Linda Williams/Raul Zaritsky, USA, 1981, 60 mins.

Melody Haunts My Reverie (You Only Love Once)

Voted the third best Yugoslav film ever made, and an Official Selection at Cannes, this daring film is the story of an idealistic, young, partisan war hero who becomes a leader in the emerging socialist society of a small Croat village, and finds adjustment to the "new Yugoslavia" extremely difficult.
VHS: S27797. $29.95.
ISBN: 1-56580-097-4. UPC: 7-36899-27797-0.
Rajko Grlic, Yugoslavia, 1981, 103 mins.

Menschenfrauen

Valie Export's daring film about relationships, *Menschenfrauen* (loosely translated, "human-women"), focuses on Franz S., a journalist, and his relationship with four women: the kindergarten nurse Petra, the teacher

Menschenfrauen

Gertrude, barmaid Elisabeth and his wife Anna. Franz "doles out honorary pieces of himself to the 'human women' in his seraglio, whispering the same assurances. Eventually, everyone catches on and makes some effort toward independence" (Gary Indiana, *East Village Eye*). German with English subtitles.
VHS: S10416. $59.95.
ISBN: 1-56580-156-3. UPC: 7-36899-10416-0.
Valie Export, Austria, 1980, 100 mins.

Murder Czech Style (The Crime)

Jiri Weiss' *Murder Czech Style* features an endearing performance by Rudolf Hrusinsky as a contented, chubby and slightly clumsy office clerk who gets a shot at true love only to eventually discover that his wife is having a torrid affair with the manager of her husband's company. Czech with English subtitles.
VHS: S27178. $29.95.
ISBN: 1-56580-077-X. UPC: 7-36899-27178-7.
Jiri Weiss, Czech Republic, 1966, 90 mins.

Names in Search of a Body
(The Films of Ken Feingold, Volume 2)

A kaleidoscopic pair of videos from director Ken Feingold: *5 dim/MIND* (1983, 29 mins.) and *The Double* (1984, 29 mins.). These collected images are from around the world, culled from various films and broadcasts as well as original footage by the artist. The surreal suppression of conventional continuity, achieved through Feingold's freewheeling, associative editing style, creates a series of signs and symbols which appeal directly to the intellect—personally involving viewers in its philosophical meditations on the world as we know it or, rather, should know it.
VHS: S15647. $59.95.
ISBN: 1-56580-022-2. UPC: 7-36899-15647-3.
Ken Feingold, USA, 1983-84, 58 mins.

The Need

Two boys are poised between childhood and manhood. Both are poor. The boy through whose eyes we experience the drama has lost his father in the war and seems to have only the bleakest of prospects, until a relative finds him a choice apprentice's position in a print shop. But there is a catch: another boy coveting the spot has also been taken on, with the better of the two getting the permanent job after a trial period.
VHS: S27788. $29.95.
ISBN: 1-56580-086-9. UPC: 7-36899-27788-8.
Alireza Davudneshad, Iran, 1991, 28 mins.

The Nice Neighbor

Laszlo Szabo stars as a clever but cruel occupant of a Budapest boarding house, one who exercises his exploitative skills to the hilt when the building is torn down and the tenants are allotted new living space.
VHS: S12510. $59.95.
ISBN: 1-56580-157-1. UPC: 7-36899-12510-3.
Zsolt Kezdi-Kovacs, Hungary, 1979, 90 mins.

Notorious Nobodies (Illustres Inconnus)

Winner of the Camera Award, *Notorious Nobodies* comprises eight individual stories taking place on the same day in far-flung corners of the globe, *Notorious Nobodies* is "a chronicle of emotions and images of an era, with horror made banal, abrasive humor, and above all, hope dotted throughout. *Notorious Nobodies* is a report both impartial and exhilarating, a film which is humble and ambitious."
VHS: S07822. $59.95.
ISBN: 1-56580-158-X. UPC: 7-36899-07822-5.
Stanislav Stanojevic, France, 1986, 102 mins.

Numero Deux (Number Two)

Jean-Luc Godard brilliantly mixes video and film, set in the director's Grenoble studio. The action unfolds on two television monitors. The elusive plot essentially concerns the marital discord—set off by the wife's infidelity—between a young working-class couple (Sandrine Battistella and Pierre Oudrey) who live in a claustrophobic, high-rise apartment complex. French with English subtitles.
VHS: S19233. $59.95.
ISBN: 1-56580-050-8. UPC: 7-36899-19233-4.
Jean-Luc Godard, France/Switzerland, 1976, 88 mins.

Optical Nerves

Parisian Blinds and *Tourist*, both films by Barbara Hammer, "investigate the nature of spectator perception in an unfamiliar environment." *Optic Nerves* is a powerful personal exploration of family and aging. *Place Mattes* explores the space between reaching and touching with animation and optical printing used to create travelling mattes for places. *Endangered*, Hammer's most recent work, has light, life and film as endangered in this exquisite film etched with acid.
VHS: S08611. $59.95.
ISBN: 1-56580-159-8. UPC: 7-36899-08611-4.
Barbara Hammer, USA, 1984-88, 44 mins.

Oratorio for Prague

One of the most powerful documentaries ever made and a unique document of the Soviet invasion of Czechoslovakia in 1968, *Oratorio for Prague* "is a film so moving that one is near tears from the first moment after the credits appear. The movie was begun as a documentary about the liberalization of Czechoslovakia and then simply continued when the Russian tanks moved in," wrote Renata Adler in *The New York Times*. Narrated in English.
VHS: S11991. $19.95.
ISBN: 1-56580-006-0. UPC: 7-36899-11991-1.
Jan Nemec, Czechoslovakia/France, 1968, 26 mins.

Oriane

A taut, gothic, Latin-American romance, winner of the Camera d'Or at the Cannes Film Festival. Marie returns to a rundown Venezuelan house in the jungle where she spent summers as a child. Her return ignites memories of a summer when her adolescent sexual curiosity led to a surprising encounter. Spanish with English subtitles.
VHS: S27801. $29.95.
ISBN: 1-56580-111-3. UPC: 7-36899-27801-4.
Fina Torres, Venezuela, 1991, 92 mins.

Orlova Three-Pack

Includes the titles *Circus*, *Jolly Fellows (Jazz Comedy)* and *Volga-Volga*.
VHS: S27217. $79.95.
ISBN: 1-56580-082-6. UPC: 7-36899-27217-3.

Other Prisoners

A unique documentary looking at prison life from a completely original perspective—that of a guard. Winner of awards as both documentary and as art, *Other Prisoners* observes human character and circumstance with irony and dark funny humor.
VHS: S10931. $59.95.
ISBN: 1-56580-161-X. UPC: 7-36899-10931-8.
Stephen Roszell, USA, 1987, 58 mins.

Otto Klemperer's Long Journey
Through His Times

A remarkable film about a legendary musician and human

being: Otto Klemperer lived and made music through two World Wars to become a great interpreter of Brahms, Beethoven, Bach and Wagner. This extraordinary artist battled Hitler, McCarthy and personal tragedy to become one of the supreme artists of our century. German with English subtitles.
VHS: S08220. $59.95.
ISBN: 1-56560-162-8. UPC: 7-36899-08220-8.
Philo Bregstein, Germany/Netherlands, 1984, 96 mins.

Palazzolo's Chicago, Vol. 1
Four "classic" short documentaries by one of America's premiere documentary filmmakers, Tom Palazzolo, which capture people, events and rituals at their oddest—and funniest—moments. Included are *Your Astronauts*, which follows the Apollo 11 parade; *Jerry's*, a classic documentary on a deli owner who prods his customers through blatant terror tactics; *Tattooed Lady of Riverview*, a Diane Arbus-like foray into the freak show carnival as spectacle; and *Enjoy Yourself: It's Later Than You Think*, a panoramic view of a senior citizen's picnic.
VHS: S02655. $39.95.
ISBN: 1-56580-163-6. UPC: 7-36899-02655-4.
Tom Palazzolo, USA, 60 mins.

Palazzolo's Chicago, Vol. 2
Two priceless gems from filmmaker Tom Palazzolo: *At Maxwell Street* (40 mins.) explores the sounds and textures of the legendary Chicago street where street peddlers mingle with blues musicians. *Labor Day—East Chicago* is a hilarious document of a beauty contest in East Chicago, Indiana, a steeltown event which offers wonderful insights into hometown rituals.
VHS: S06471. $39.95.
ISBN: 1-56580-164-4. UPC: 7-36899-06471-6.
Tom Palazzolo, USA, 65 mins.

The Popovich Brothers of South Chicago

Palazzolo's Films from the Sixties
The Bride Stripped Bare is an ironic film about the ritual which surrounds the unveiling of the large Picasso outdoor sculpture in Chicago called "The Woman" (1967, 14 min.). *Campaign* is a disturbing political account of the events surrounding the 1968 Democratic Convention (1968, 14 mins.). *Love It, Leave It* develops themes of freedom and openness in shots of a southern nudist camp (1970, 14 mins.). *Venus Adonis* is a sarcastic view of modernism in a black-and-white satire of the bridges, beaches and skyline of Chicago.
VHS: S13701. $39.95.
ISBN: 1-56580-165-2. UPC: 7-36899-13701-4.
Tom Palazzolo, USA

Parables of Wonder
(The Films of James Broughton, Vol. 5)
Five important works by James Broughton from the decade of the '70s. *High Kukus* (1973) is a visualization of a Zen teaching accompanied by 14 of Broughton's cuckoo haikus, while *Golden Positions* (1978) is a series of tableaux vivants that follow the form of a liturgical service and glorify the naked human body. *This Is It* (1971) is a playful, pseudo-Zen creation myth shot in a home-movie style with a two-year-old Adam in a backyard Eden. *The Gardener of Eden* (1981) is an

intense poetic work that celebrates the sexual dance of all creation, set in Sri Lanka. The tape concludes with *Water Circle* (1975), an homage to Lao-Tzu in a joyful poem read by the filmmaker and set to music by Corelli.
VHS: S07288. $29.95.
ISBN: 1-56580-012-5. UPC: 7-36899-07288-9.
James Broughton, USA/Sri Lanka, 1971-1981, 56 mins.

The Paul Glabicki Animation Tape
A collection of four fascinating, intricately constructed shorts from independent filmmaker Paul Glabicki—an artist whose extraordinarily complex recent works are founded on a distinctive graphic style: intricate, hand-drawn, geometric animation which is so exact that it looks computer-generated. Includes *Diagram Film* (1978), *Five Improvisations* (1980), *Film-Wipe-Film* (1984) and *Object Conversation* (1985).
VHS: S15645. $29.95.
ISBN: 1-56580-007-9. UPC: 7-36899-15645-9.
Paul Glabicki, USA, 1978-1991, 55 mins.

The Peddler
Three short tales set among the poor of contemporary Tehran. The first episode follows a kindly but naive couple who want someone to adopt their newborn daughter. The second, an astonishing mix of absurdist comedy and the supernatural, concerns a mentally unstable man who lives with his mother in a ramshackle apartment. The final section draws on the American gangster film to show the last hours of a peddler suspected of betraying his friends.
VHS: S27787. $29.95.
ISBN: 1-56580-085-0. UPC: 7-36899-27787-1.
Mohsen Makhmalbaf, Iran, 1986, 95 mins.

The People vs. Paul Crump
William Friedkin's debut film is an impassioned plea for mercy and justice, based on the true story of Paul Crump, a man who is still in Illinois prisons, sentenced to die in the electric chair.
VHS: S06320. $39.95.
ISBN: 1-56580-166-0. UPC: 7-36899-06320-7.
William Friedkin, USA, 52 mins.

People's Gala Concert
In his landmark documentary about paranoia, fear, ambition and cover up, director Semeon Aranovich explores the roots of Russian anti-Semitism during the bloody and destructive reign of Stalin's final years. Russian with English subtitles.
VHS: S15824. $79.95.
ISBN: 1-56580-005-2. UPC: 7-36899-15824-8.
Semeon Aranovich, Russia, 1991, 143 mins.

Perceptual Landscapes
Four works that explore personal landscapes: *Pools*, made with Barbara Klutinis, is an exploration above and under water of two of the first swimming pools, designed by the first woman architect in the U.S.; *Pond and Waterfall* is an exploration of verdant pond growth as well as dynamic light and water reflections; *Stone Circles* is a celebration of ancient, pre-patriarchal standing mounds and circles, including Stonehenge and Asbury; and *Bent Time* is one of Hammer's most ambitious films, in "which she attempts to render visually the scientific theory that time, like rays, curves at the outer edges of the universe" (*L.A. Times*).
VHS: S08610. $59.95.
ISBN: 1-56580-167-9. UPC: 7-36899-08610-7.
Barbara Hammer, USA, 1981-1983, 54 mins.

The Personal Life of Anna Akhmatova
See *The Anna Akhmatova File*.

Peter Thompson Films
Three extremely moving documentaries: *Two Portraits*, a diptych film about the filmmaker's father and mother; *Universal Hotel*, a record of the filmmaker's search for historical, graphic evidence on medical experiments in deep cold by Nazi doctors; and *Universal Citizen*, detailing an encounter with a former inmate at Dachau, now a smuggler in the Guatemalan jungle.
VHS: S05650. $59.95.
ISBN: 1-56580-168-7. UPC: 7-36899-05650-6.
Peter Thompson, USA, 63 mins.

The Pleasure Garden
(The Films of James Broughton, Vol. 3)
A comic fantasy with songs that celebrate the triumph of love and liberty over the forces of restriction. Filmed with a professional cast in the ruined gardens of the Crystal Palace in London, the satiric fairy tale won a prize for poetic fantasy

at the Cannes Film Festival of 1954.
VHS: S07286. $29.95.
ISBN: 1-56580-010-9. UPC: 7-36899-07286-5.
James Broughton, Great Britain, 1954, 38 mins.

The Popovich Brothers of South Chicago
Focuses on a musical group that has been keeping traditional Serbian music alive and well within Chicago's ethnic Serbian community for over 50 years.
VHS: S21130. $29.95.
ISBN: 1-56580-029-X. UPC: 7-36899-21130-1.
Jill Godmilow, USA, 1978, 60 mins.

The Practice of Love
"A dazzling cinematic tour-de-force, combining a thriller narrative with experimental images to tell the story of Judith, a journalist, whose investigation of a murder implicates her two male lovers (an arms dealer and a psychiatrist). Through these relationships, Judith discovers that in a world of male power struggles, love is complicit, marginal or impossible.
VHS: S10415. $59.95.
ISBN: 1-56580-169-5. UPC: 7-36899-10415-3.
Valie Export, Austria, 1984, 90 mins.

Prayer for Katarina Horovitzova
Awarded the top prize at the Monte Carlo Film and Television Festival and the winner of eight other international prizes, it is the story of a beautiful Polish singer and her passion for life, set against the backdrop of the cruel game of trading Jewish lives for those of Nazi officers imprisoned in American jails. Czech with English subtitles.
VHS: S13695. $59.95.
ISBN: 1-56580-170-9. UPC: 7-36899-13695-6.
Czechoslovakia, 1969-1991, 60 mins.

A Priceless Day
From the director of *Time Stands Still*, this is a thoughtful, ironic rumination on desire and sexual awakening. A 30-year-old kindergarten teacher visits her lover's wife and the two enter a pact to rid themselves of their men. Hungarian with English subtitles.
VHS: S18689. $59.95.
ISBN: 1-56580-057-5. UPC: 7-36899-18689-0.
Lajos Koltai, Hungary, 1980, 87 mins.

Process of Creation in Media Arts (The Films of Scott Bartlett, Vol. 3)
Two films, *Making Offon* and *Making Serpent*, provide a unique insight into the film and videomaking process. *Making Offon* is based on the 1980 re-creation of Scott Bartlett's electrovideographic event that became the classic experimental work *Offon*. *Making Serpent* describes the creative process behind the award-winning short film, teaching how film techniques can be used to structure non-verbal narrative.
VHS: S05643. $59.95.
ISBN: 1-56580-171-7. UPC: 7-36899-05643-8.
Scott Bartlett, USA, 1967-1980, 40 mins.

Queen of Diamonds
Tinka Menkes plays a Vegas blackjack dealer abandoned by her husband. Her life is irrevocably altered by her friendship and caring for a dying old man.
VHS: S18685. $59.95.
ISBN: 1-56580-053-2. UPC: 7-36899-18685-2.
Nina Menkes, USA, 1991, 77 mins.

Red Earth
A frenetic, freewheeling village comedy and shrewd satire about totalitarian regimes. A bauxite mixer discovers his pigs have unearthed high quality bauxite from his back yard. The troubles start when the village bureaucrats and bauxite prospectors insist the discovery was the result of careful, methodical planning. Hungarian with English subtitles.
VHS: S18687. $59.95.
ISBN: 1-56580-055-9. UPC: 7-36899-18687-6.
Laszlo Vitezy, Hungary, 105 mins.

A Report on the Party and the Guests
Banned "forever" in its native Czechoslovakia, Jan Nemec's Kafka-esque masterpiece is a searing satire on conformity and the willingness of individuals to give up their personal liberty. Voted one of the best films of the decade by *The New York Times*, it is "an extraordinary allegory... evocative of Kafka or Dostoyevsky. Czech with English subtitles.
VHS: S05654. $59.95.
ISBN: 1-56580-172-5. UPC: 7-36899-05654-4.
Jan Nemec, Czechoslovakia, 1966, 71 mins.

Rime of the Ancient Mariner
Using the cut-out style of animation for which he is well-known, Larry Jordan marries the classic engravings of Gustave Dore to the classic poem by Samuel Taylor Coleridge. Orson Welles narrates this long opium dream of the old mariner who wantonly killed the albatross and suffered the pains of the damned for it.
VHS: S09418. $59.95.
ISBN: 1-56580-173-3. UPC: 7-36899-09418-8.
Larry Jordan, USA, 1977, 42 mins.

Rituals of Play (The Films of James Broughton, Vol. 2)
Three important black-and-white films by James Broughton, including the classic *Mother's Day* (1948), an ironic recollection of childhood games in the nostalgic style of a cluttered family album, enacted by adults; *Four in the Afternoon* (1951), with four poetic variations on the search for love from a girl of 10 to a man of 40; and the comedy *Loony Tom* (1951), picturing the amorous progress of an amiable tramp who makes love to every woman he meets.
VHS: S07285. $29.95.
ISBN: 1-56580-009-5. UPC: 7-36899-07285-8.
James Broughton, USA, 1948-1951, 48 mins.

Romeo, Juliet and Darkness (Sweet Light in a Dark Room)
Pavel, a student, hides Hana, a young Jewish girl, in the attic of his apartment building. He is her only link to the outside world, and their growing trust develops into love, until the two are discovered by Pavel's mother. Weiss' double tragedy of young love and the moral question of responsibility to the Jews during the Nazi occupation is treated with poetic restraint. Czech with English subtitles.
VHS: S27179. $29.95.
ISBN: 1-56580-078-8. UPC: 7-36899-27179-4.
Jiri Weiss, Czech Republic, 1959, 96 mins.

The Russian Language
A collaboration between two Russian linguists and the St. Petersburg's Documentary Film Studio, this program provides extensive lessons in learning, applying and use of the Russian language, conveyed through the circumstances and events of a fictional American businessman and his various encounters in Russian locations. The video includes an illustrated and colorful textbook and audio cassette of the soundtrack portion to aid the listener and viewer.
VHS: S18446. $99.95.
ISBN: 1-56580-052-4. UPC: 7-36899-18446-9.

Sabda (The Dan Reeves Retrospective, Vol. 3)
Inspired by the works of the mystical poets, this lyrical video poem blends ancient words with contemporary sights and sounds of India. *Sombra and Sombra*, also on this tape, is an elegy of remembrance and meditation on the architecture of the abandoned as evoked in the writing of Peruvian poet Cesar Vallejo.
VHS: S06303. $59.95.
ISBN: 1-56580-175-X. UPC: 7-36899-06303-0.
Daniel Reeves, India/Spain, 32 mins.

The Sacred Art of Tibet/ The Visible Compendium
An exciting and evocative pair of short films from independent filmmaker Larry Jordan. *The Sacred Art of Tibet* (1972, 28 mins.) was inspired by a gallery showing of unique Tibetan thankas, religious scroll paintings, rupas and other sacred images and artifacts. *The Visible Compendium* (1990, 17 mins.) is an animated film that takes the viewer on a trip through idyllic lands where plants smile, an image of a tiger appears in the sun, and nude women wander about comfortably within an enchanted landscape.
VHS: S14552. $59.95.
ISBN: 1-56580-000-1. UPC: 7-36899-14552-1.
Larry Jordan, USA, 1972-1990, 45 mins.

Savage Capitalism (Capitalismo Salvaje)
Brazil's outrageously dramatic tele-novelas inspired this tale of marital infidelity, national betrayal, public scandal, long lost orphans and, of course, forbidden love. When a reporter uncovers the truth behind a company's plans to mine in the interior of Brazil, it sets in motion a complex tale. Portugese with English subtitles.
VHS: S21133. $59.95.
ISBN: 1-56580-035-4. UPC: 7-36899-21133-2.
Andre Klotzel, Brazil, 1993, 86 mins.

Second Heimat

The second section of Edgar Reitz's "film novel" focuses on a young classical musician and composer and his journey from a small village to Munich to start a new life. "Anyone who sees this great, overflowing film novel will enter into a whole breathing, pulsing world: rich, teeming and unforgettable, the movie experience of a lifetime" (Michael Wilmington). 13 tapes.
VHS: S27898. $249.95.
ISBN: 1-56580-109-1. UPC: 7-36899-27808-3.
Edgar Reitz, Germany, 1994, 25 hrs.

Seeing Red

A powerful documentary by Julia Reichert and Jim Klein that assesses the cultural, political, social and personal evolution of members of the American Communist Party. The film moves from the idealistic fervor and radical intensity of '30s Depression-era humanism to the harsh persecution of ideas during McCarthyism and the onset of the Cold War.
VHS: S19234. $29.95.
ISBN: 1-56580-069-9. UPC: 7-36899-19234-1.
Julia Reichert/Jim Klein, USA, 1983, 100 mins.

The Seven Madmen

Based on two novels by Robert Arlt, this is the tension-filled story of a young inventor who becomes involved with a terrorist group, in a metaphysical film with an unforgettable, apocalypticending.
VHS: S27742. $59.95.
ISBN: 1-56580-108-3. UPC: 7-36899-27742-0.
Leopoldo Torre Nilsson, Argentina, 1973, 121 mins.

Shoot to Kill (Disparen a Matar)

A mother seeks to clear the damaged reputation of her son when he is murdered during a routine police round-up and condemned as a criminal. Spanish with English subtitles.
VHS: S20381. $59.95.
ISBN: 1-56580-031-1. UPC: 7-36899-20381-8.
Carlos Azpurua, Venezuela, 1990, 90 mins.

Short Animations by Larry Jordan

A major collection of the animations by this premiere American animator: *Duo Concertantes* (*The Centennial Exposition* and *Patricia Gives Birth to a Dream by the Doorway*), *Gymnopedies* (music by Satie in an intricate slight-of-mind game), *Our Lady of the Sphere* (an animated film-dream journey that juxtaposes 19th-century engravings with space-age symbols), *Orb* (full-color cut-out animation depicting the eternal round shape), *Once upon a Time* (a cobweb castle, filled with the haunting doubts of a young protagonist), *Moonlight Sonata* (moon and moonlight are the "guiding lights," set to music by Satie), *Carabosse* (a jewel-like opera on black space) and *Masquerade* (animation of hand-painted, engraved cut-outs on a full color background).
VHS: S09420. $59.95.
ISBN: 1-56580-177-6. UPC: 7-36899-09420-1.
Larry Jordan, USA, 1964-1985, 56 mins.

Sideburns

Yuri Mamin's bitter, dark satire about the rise of fascism and reactionary elements in Russia concerns the Pushkin Club, a right wing movement, enlisted by the Party to orchestrate "a social cleaning service" charged with eliminating "the scum of Western influence." Russian with English subtitles.
VHS: S16737. $59.95.
ISBN: 1-56580-016-8. UPC: 7-36899-16737-0.
Yuri Mamin, Russia, 1991, 110 mins.

Simultaneous: The Works of Scott Rankin

Ten individual works by the important video artist Scott Rankin, demonstrating his concerns with narrative, language

Shoot to Kill

and perception. Included are *This and That* (1987), Rankin's most recent work, a tape about naming and categories in language and perception; *Fugue* (1985); *LA84*, which was commissioned for the LA Olympics; *Synchronicity*, a self-conscious love story; *Simultaneous* (1981); and works from 1979 and 1980: *French Performance, Magic, Swedish Two, Swedish One* and *Carousel*.
VHS: S08612. $59.95.
ISBN: 1-56580-178-4. UPC: 7-36899-08612-1.
Scott Rankin, USA, 1980-1988, 77 mins.

Smothering Dreams (Dan Reeves Retrospective, Vol. 1)

Dan Reeves' powerful, autobiographical reflections on the Vietnam War. He presents a collage of images in the form of childhood dreams and adult nightmares that represent his personal visions of the atrocities of violence and war.
VHS: S01221. $59.95.
ISBN: 1-56580-179-2. UPC: 7-36899-01221-2.
Daniel Reeves, USA, 45 mins.

Sneakin' and Peekin'

Sneakin' and Peekin' is a funny, revealing trip to a famous nudist camp for its annual Mr. and Mrs. Nude America contest; *I Was a Contestant at Mother's Wet T-Shirt Contest* is a documentary on the Chicago landmark contest at Mother's Bar; *Hot and Nasty* is a very funny look inside the comings and goings of a massage parlor. Americana by Tom Palazzolo at its very best (and most hilarious).
VHS: S06111. $39.95.
ISBN: 1-56580-180-6. UPC: 7-36899-06111-1.
Tom Palazzolo, USA, 55 mins.

Sophie's Place

The masterpiece of Larry Jordan's full, hand-painted, cut-out animation and the result of five years of work. The film begins in a garden resembling paradise and proceeds to the interior of the Mosque of St. Sophia, then develops into episodes centering around the forms of Sophia—an early Greek and Gnostic embodiment of spiritual wisdom.
VHS: S09421. $59.95.
ISBN: 1-56580-201-2. UPC: 7-36899-09421-8.
Larry Jordan, USA, 1986, 90 mins.

Stalin by Those Who Knew Him Three-Pack

Includes *Anna Akhmatova File*, *I Was Stalin's Bodyguard* and *I Worked for Stalin*.
VHS: S31724. $79.95.
ISBN: 1-56580-112-1. UPC: 7-36899-31724-9.
Semeon Aranovich, USSR, 1989-1990

Sunday Daughters

Juli, a 16-year-old inmate, seems to be moving toward delinquency, and after repeated rejections from her family, escapes. After a close call with death, she survives and her life brightens when an older woman takes her in, but these hopes are smashed when Juli becomes involved with the woman's son. Hungarian with English subtitles.
VHS: S11288. $59.95.
ISBN: 1-56580-181-4. UPC: 7-36899-11288-2.
Janosz Rozsa, Hungary, 1980, 100 mins.

Sweet Movie

This modern cult classic is a hilarious comedy with elements of thriller and horror, "an experience to defy criticism...one of the most challenging, shocking and provocative films of recent years" (Roger Ebert). This daring and totally original film from Dusan Makavejev (*WR: Mysteries of the Organism, Montenegro, The Coca-Cola Kid*) skillfully blends two independent stories with often shocking newsreel footage into a "movie we can't be passive about." In English and other languages with English subtitles.
VHS: S10575. $79.95.
ISBN: 1-56580-182-2. UPC: 7-36899-10575-4.
Dusan Makavejev, Canada/France, 1975, 97 mins.

Tango: Baile Nuestro (Tango: Our Dance)

The sensuality and stylized rituals popular with the residents of Buenos Aires are part of the complex art form called the tango. Director Jorge Zanada examines the unique role of this dance with Argentina's social and personal landscape, exploring issues of machismo and passion contained within the dance. Spanish with English subtitles.
VHS: S20380. $29.95.
ISBN: 1-56580-034-6. UPC: 7-36899-20380-1.
Jorge Zanada, Argentina, 1988, 71 mins.

The Theatre of Tadeusz Kantor

A unique documentary on the work of a legendary genius of theater, Tadeusz Kantor. Filmmaker Denis Bablet traces Kantor's roots as a visual artist in Poland and explores his ingenious methods of designing the props which become living sculptures in his extraordinary theater productions. Narrated in English.

VHS: S14812. $59.95.
ISBN: 1-56580-183-0. UPC: 7-36899-14812-6.
Denis Bablet, 165 mins.

Top Dog

A merciless satire with a dynamic performance from Jerzy Stuhr as an emcee who will do anything—and sacrifice anyone—to get to the top, a moral investigation of an ambitious individual who rushes into a tangled web of favor-trading, bribery and slander to eliminate his rivals. Polish with English subtitles.

VHS: S02657. $69.95.
ISBN: 1-56580-184-9. UPC: 7-36899-02657-8.
Feliks Falk, Poland, 1978, 115 mins.

The Track of the Ants

"Halfway between *Koyannisqatsi* and *Brazil*.... Dispensing with story and words, Venezuelan filmmaker Rafael MarzianoTinoco looks at the life of Caracas much as a disenchanted god might survey an ant hill gone awry" (*Village Voice*). Best documentary, Philadelphia Film Festival. No dialog.

VHS: S27798. $29.95.
ISBN: 1-56580-098-2. UPC: 7-36899-27798-7.
Rafael Marziano-Tinoco, Venezuela/Poland, 1993, 54 min.

Transport from Paradise

An intense psychological drama set in the Terezin ghetto, based on a novel by Arnost Lustig. The film is remarkable not only for its visual dynamism, but also for the humanization of its characters, which makes it all the more haunting. B&W. Czech with English subtitles.

VHS: S04738. $59.95.
ISBN: 1-56580-185-7. UPC: 7-36899-04738-2.
Zybnek Brynych, Czechoslovakia, 1965, 83 mins.

The Unquiet Death of Julius and Ethel Rosenberg

This award-winning documentary by Alvin Goldstein delves deeply into the facets and procedures of the Rosenberg case, creating a moving drama which asks the ultimate question—whether justice was truly served in the era of Cold War hysteria.

VHS: S04736. $59.95.
ISBN: 1-56580-186-5. UPC: 7-36899-04736-8.
Alvin Goldstein, USA, 1974, 83 mins.

Viva Castro!

Young Kolya's father flees from his home and his family after stealing some coins from a museum; Kolya's mother is sent to a labor camp as punishment for her husband's crime. Russian with English subtitles.

VHS: S26331. $59.95.
ISBN: 1-56580-054-0. UPC: 7-36899-26331-7.
Boris Frumin, Russia, 1993, 82 mins.

Volga-Volga

An unseen miracle of 1930s Soviet cinema; a classic musical comedy set on a giant steamboat making its way up the Volga River. On board is a motley collection of amateur singers and dancers travelling to Moscow to take part in a musical contest. At their center is Lyubov Orlova. Russian with English subtitles.

VHS: S27214. $29.95.
ISBN: 1-56580-079-6. UPC: 7-36899-27214-2.
Grigori Alexandrov, USSR, 1937, 90 mins.

Ward Six

One of the most powerful stories by Anton Chekhov receives a masterful film adaptation. The story, set at the turn of the century in a provincial Russian town, concerns a doctor who oversees a grotesque mental ward. The only person he meets with any comprehension of life is one of the inmates. The doctor is reported to the authorities by one of the inmates, is judged mad, and the story's two most humane and intelligent men are locked together in Ward No. 6. Serbian with English subtitles.

VHS: S10009. $59.95.
ISBN: 1-56580-202-0. UPC: 7-36899-10009-4.
Lucian Pintilie, Yugoslavia, 1976, 93 mins.

Water Falling from One World to Another (The Films of Ken Feingold, Volume 1)

A moody and suggestive pair of short works from highly acclaimed video artist Ken Feingold. This collection, which includes *Water Falling from One World to Another* (1980, 34 mins.) and *Purely Human Sleep* (1980, 28 mins.), contemplates the endless, human pursuit of the invisible, especially as it confronts the limits of the body—limitations which often manage to imprison us, reining in our perceptions of the world around us.

VHS: S15646. $59.95.
ISBN: 1-56580-021-4. UPC: 7-36899-15646-6.
Ken Feingold, USA, 1980, 62 mins.

Water Is Wet

A very special children's film, produced by the Erikson Institute for Early Childhood Education, which was made to engage the imagination and learning spirit of the youngest children. *Water Is Wet* is a visual and auditory exploration of simple elements, always striving to engage the child's imagination and sense of discovery in learning more.

VHS: S03490. $39.95.
ISBN: 1-56580-187-3. UPC: 7-36899-03490-0.
Gordon Weisenborn, USA, 1968, 65 mins.

We're All Stars

A wonderful comedy of errors from Peru: the Humbachano family dreams of winning fame and fortune on the TV game show *We're All Stars*. But they're far from the "perfect" family the show wants.

VHS: S27738. $59.95.
ISBN: 1-56580-104-0. UPC: 7-36899-27737-6.
Felipe De Gregori, Peru, 1993, 80 mins.

What Do Those Old Films Mean?: Vol. 1: Great Britain 1900-1912: Along the Great Divide

Using extremely rare films, newly scored music and a lively commentary, film historian Noel Burch explores the contradictions in early British cinema between the "gentlemen inventors of the cinema" and film as an entertainment for the poor.

VHS: S08682. $29.95.
ISBN: 1-56580-193-8. UPC: 7-36899-08682-4.
26 mins.

What Do Those Old Films Mean?: Vol. 2: USA 1902-1914: Tomorrow the World

Film historian Noel Burch examines early filmmaking in America against the social background of the immigrant masses streaming into the slums, factories and sweat-shops of an industrialized America.

VHS: S08683. $29.95.
ISBN: 1-56580-194-6. UPC: 7-36899-08683-1.
26 mins.

What Do Those Old Films Mean?: Vol. 3: Denmark 1902-1914: She!

Why was Copenhagen the undisputed birthplace of the mature cinema, of psychological realism on the screen, at a time when French or American films were no more than rudimentary melodramas? Film historian Noel Burch examines the Danish silent film phenomenon both from the standpoint of its key figures, and from the social perspective of a Denmark in which women had an advanced position for the time, where feminism was prominent and attitudes towards sexuality liberal.

VHS: S08684. $29.95.
ISBN: 1-56580-195-4. UPC: 7-36899-08684-8.
26 mins.

What Do Those Old Films Mean?: Vol. 4: France 1904-1912: The Enemy Below

A fascinating program covering the early years of cinema in France, film historian and critic Noel Burch follows the thesis that the appeal of the silent French cinema was to the working class.

VHS: S08685. $29.95.
ISBN: 1-56580-196-2. UPC: 7-36899-08685-5.
26 mins.

What Do Those Old Films Mean?: Vol. 5: USSR 1926-1930: Born Yesterday

Amid general poverty, social disorder, an exodus from the rural areas, and the sudden arrival of women in industry, post-Revolutionary Russia was also a period of extraordinary

Volga-Volga

social and cultural experiment. Using rare films which are virtually unknown in the West, Burch provides a unique perspective on this great era of cinema in a climate of virulent change.
VHS: S08686. $29.95.
ISBN: 1-56580-197-0. UPC: 7-36899-08686-2.
26 mins.

What Do Those Old Films Mean?: Vol. 6: Germany 1926-1932: Under Two Flags
This volume of *What Do Those Old Films Mean?* focuses on films produced in Germany in the '20s, rarely shown or discussed today. Influenced by the achievements of the young Soviet cinema, the German social workers' movements created the *German Workers' Film*. But it was ultimately replaced by the more palatable—and cheerful—films of Billy Wilder and Robert Siodmak, and, ultimately, by the victory of Nazism.
VHS: S08687. $29.95.
ISBN: 1-56580-198-9. UPC: 7-36899-08687-9.
26 mins.

What Do Those Old Films Mean?: Complete Set
The complete six-volume set.
VHS: S08688. $149.75.
ISBN: 1-56580-047-8. UPC: 7-36899-08688-6.
156 mins.

Where Is the Friend's Home?
A lyrical tale about a traveller searching for his friend's home, who finds himself on an excursion through places and moments of great beauty and wonder.
VHS: S27791. $29.95.
ISBN: 1-56580-089-3. UPC: 7-36899-27791-8.
Abbas Kiarostami, Iran, 1989, 90 mins.

Whoever Says the Truth Shall Die: A Film on Pier Paolo Pasolini
Philo Bregstein's remarkable documentary features Alberto Moravia, Bernardo Bertolucci, clips from Pasolini's films and rare footage in a portrait of this great filmmaker, as well as an investigation into his death. English, Italian and Dutch with English subtitles.
VHS: S02654. $59.95.
ISBN: 1-56580-189-X. UPC: 7-36899-02654-7.
Philo Bregstein, Netherlands, 1981, 90 mins.

Wolf Trap
Wolf Trap is set in a small town in Moravia and focuses on a marital triangle. The town veterinarian is married to an older, domineering, yet insecure and needful wife. They adopt an orphaned teenage girl. As the veterinarian gradually falls in love with his adopted daughter, director Jiri Weiss brilliantly constructs a psychological prison of middle class life from which there is no escape. Czech with English subtitles.
VHS: S27176. $29.95.
ISBN: 1-56580-075-3. UPC: 7-36899-27176-3.
Jiri Weiss, Czech Republic, 1957, 95 mins.

The Works of Ken Feingold: The Complete Set
Includes ten films made between 1980 and 1991, ranging from 8 to 90 minutes.
VHS: S18808. $249.95.
ISBN: 1-56580-203-9. UPC: 7-36899-18808-5.
Ken Feingold, USA, 1980-1991, 325 min.

WR: Mysteries of the Organism
WR: Mysteries of the Organism is a unique blend of fact and fiction, and Makavejev's landmark film. It deftly juxtaposes the story of the sexual encounter between the beautiful, liberated Milena and a repressed Soviet figure-skating champion with an exploration of the life and theories of psychoanalyst Wilhelm Reich. In English and Serbian with English subtitles.
VHS: S11290. $79.95.
ISBN: 1-56580-190-3. UPC: 7-36899-11290-5.
Dusan Makavejev, Yugoslavia/USA, 1971, 84 mins.

Writing in Water/Admiral Bataille & The S.S. Esoterica
Writing in Water, by Stephen R. Roszell, is a simply wonderful work about the recollections of a rural Kentucky family of a harrowing event in their past, steeped in the Southern story-telling tradition. *Admiral Bataille & The S.S. Esoterica*, by Jim Newberry, is an experimental documentary about an enigmatic human being, Kris Bataille.
VHS: S05367. $49.95.
ISBN: 1-56580-191-1. UPC: 7-36899-05367-3.
Stephen R. Roszell/Jim Newberry, USA, 43 mins.

Zuppa di Pesce
Set between the 1950s and late '70s against the beauty of the Tuscany seaside, *Fish Soup* offers, in Chekovian detail, small sketches of family behavior and psychology, from gatherings to complicated relationships, with a light but indelible touch. "A family-size *Amarcord* set of recollections" (*L'Avvenire*). Starring Macha Meril, Andrea Prodan, Renzo Montagnani and Fausto Fiorentini.
VHS: S32622. $29.95.
ISBN: 1-56580-113-X. UPC: 7-36899-32622-7.
Fiorella Infacselli, Italy/France, 107 mins.

Index of Titles

D

Free catalogs from Facets® Multi-Media

Keep up with all the new releases on video by staying in touch! If you would like to receive any of our *free* catalogs, just fill out the following form and we will be happy to send you copies!

To: **Facets® Video**, 1517 West Fullerton, Chicago, IL 60614 or fax 773-929-5437 or e-mail: sales@facets.org

Name_____

Address_____

City_____State___Zip _____

fax:_____

e-mail:_____

For Reference

Not to be taken from this room